Lab Safety

Safety symbol	What it means	What to do in the event of an accident
Eye protection	Wear safety goggles anytime there is the slightest chance that your eyes could be harmed.	If anything gets into your eyes, notify your teacher immediately and flush your eyes with running water for 15 minutes.
Hand safety	Wear appropriate protective gloves when working with an open flame, chemicals, or plants. Your teacher will provide the type of gloves necessary for a given activity.	If any chemical gets on your hands, rinse it off immediately with water for at least 5 minutes while calling to your teacher. Report any burn of the hands to your teacher no matter how minor it seems. Wash your hands with soap and hot water at the end of every lab.
Clothing protection	Wear your apron whenever you are working with chemicals or whenever you are instructed to do so.	If you spill a corrosive chemical onto your clothing, rinse it off immediately by using a faucet or the safety shower and remove the affected clothing while calling to your teacher.
Sharp/pointed object safety	Use knives and other sharp objects with extreme care. Place objects on a suitable work surface for cutting.	Notify your teacher immediately in the event of a cut or puncture no matter how minor it seems.
Heating safety	Wear safety goggles when using a heating device or flame. Wear heat-resistant gloves whenever instructed to do so. When heating materials in a test tube, angle the test tube away from yourself and others.	Notify your teacher immediately in the event of a burn or fire no matter how minor it seems.
Electrical safety	Do not place electrical cords where they could trip someone or cause equipment to fall. Do not use equipment with damaged cords. Do not use electrical equipment near water or when your clothing or hands are wet. Make sure that electrical equipment is in the "off" position before plugging it in. Turn off and unplug electrical equipment when you have finished using it.	Notify your teacher immediately if you notice any abnormal or potentially dangerous equipment. In the event of an electric shock, notify your teacher no matter how minor it seems.
Chemical safety	Wear safety goggles, an apron, and gloves whenever working with chemicals.	If a chemical spills onto your skin, rinse it off immediately by using the faucet or safety shower for at least 5 minutes while calling to your teacher.
Animal safety	Handle animals only as your teacher directs. Treat animals carefully and respectfully. Wash your hands thoroughly after handling any animal.	Notify your teacher immediately if you injure yourself or any live specimen no matter how minor the injury seems.
Plant safety	Do not eat any part of a plant or plant seed used in the laboratory. When in nature, do not pick any wild plants unless your teacher instructs you to do so. Wash your hands thoroughly after handling any part of a plant.	Notify your teacher immediately if any potentially dangerous plant material comes into contact with your skin or if any plant matter is inhaled or ingested no matter how minor the event seems.

Common Words with Multiple Meanings

Word	Common meaning	Scientific meaning
area	a region (for example, a rural area)	a measure of the size of a surface or a region
cell	a small, confining room	the smallest structural and functional unit of all living organisms
class	a group of students who are taught together at regular meetings	a taxonomic category below the phylum and above the order
condensation	the droplets of liquid on the outside of a glass or window	the change of state from a gas to a liquid
consumer	someone who purchases goods or services	an organism that eats other organisms or organic matter
date	an engagement to go out socially	to measure the age of an event or object
daughter	one's female child	the offspring of cell division; not dependent on gender
egg	a thin-shelled product from a bird used in cooking	a sex cell produced by a female
family	all of the members of a household	the taxonomic category below the order and above the genus
host	to serve as the entertainer or receiver of guests	an organism from which a parasite takes food or shelter
instrument	a device used for making music (for example, a trumpet)	a piece of equipment used during experimentation (for example, a scalpel)
kingdom	a region ruled by a king or queen	the taxonomic category below the domain and above the phylum
law	a rule of conduct established by the government	a descriptive statement or equation that reliably predicts events under certain conditions
legend	a romanticized story or myth	a list of map symbols and their meanings
mass	a quantity of material that has an unspecified shape	a measure of the amount of matter in an object
matter	a subject of concern or topic of discussion	anything that has mass and takes up space
medium	an intermediate measurement between small and large	a physical environment in which phenomena occur
model	a person who poses (for example, a fashion model)	a pattern, plan, representation, or description designed to show the structure or workings of an object, system, or concept
order	a command	the taxonomic category below the class and above the family
organ	a musical instrument similar to a piano	a collection of tissues that carry out a specialized function of the body
reaction	a response to a stimulus	the process by which one or more substances change to produce one or more different substances
resolution	an expression of intent (for example, a New Year's resolution)	in microscopes, the ability to form images in fine detail
theory	an assumption based on limited knowledge	a system of ideas that explains many related observations and is supported by a large body of evidence acquired through scientific investigation
tissue	a soft, absorbent piece of paper	a group of similar cells that perform a common function

HOLT CALIFORNIA

Life Science

Teacher's Edition WALK-THROUGH

Student Edition CONTENTS IN BRIEF

HOLT, RINEHART AND WINSTON

A Harcourt Education Company

Orlando • **Austin** • New York • San Diego • London

Master the California Science Standards with *Holt California Science*

Holt California Science provides the support you need to help your students master the California Science Standards. *Holt California Life, Physical,* and *Earth Science* align with the California Science Standards provided in the California Science Framework.

Reading support helps students unlock the California Science Standards

- **Unpacking the Standards,** found at the beginning of every chapter, breaks down the **California Science Standards** covered in the chapter by defining the academic vocabulary and restating the standards as simply as possible.
- **Graphic Organizers** provided throughout the chapter help students organize information and improve their reading comprehension and retention.
- **The Big Idea** prepares students for learning by introducing the student to the chapter's main topic.
- **Key Concept** at the beginning of each section introduces students to the section's main idea.
- **Wordwise** helps students understand the meaning of scientific vocabulary by desconstructing the word into prefixes, roots, and suffixes and defining each part's meaning.
- **Section** and **Chapter Summaries,** and **Super Summaries** review and reinforce what the students learned.

Activities reinforce students' understanding of the California Science Standards

- Every chapter begins with an **Explore Activity** that motivates students and introduces students to one or more **California Science Standards.**
- **Quick Labs** in every section focus on a standard covered in the section.
- **Chapter Lab** at the end of each chapter reinforces the Big Idea for that chapter.
- **Science Skills Activities** develop a particular skill described in the **Investigation and Experimentation Standards.** Within the program these skills include process skills related to scientific methods, graphing skills, data analysis, and mapping skills.

Assessments monitor students' mastery of the California Science Standards

- **Standards Checks** found frequently throughout each section monitor students' comprehension as they read the chapter.

- **Section** and **Chapter Reviews** assess students' progress in mastering the **California Science Standards** covered in the chapter. **Also available in Spanish.**

- **Standards Assessment** at the end of the chapter provides two pages of additional practice questions that focus on the **California Science Standards** covered in the chapter. **Also available in Spanish.**

- **Standards Review Workbook** provides a review of **California Science Standards,** and additional practice to assess student's mastery of the standard. **Also available in Spanish.**

- **Standards Review Transparencies** are transparencies of the **Standards Review Workbook.**

Differentiated instruction provides universal access for all students

- **Strategies** on almost every spread of the Teacher's Edition adapt instruction for students with identified special needs, including **English Learners, struggling readers, advanced learners/ GATE, basic learners,** and **special education students.**

- **Differentiated datasheets** for **Explore Activities, Chapter Labs** and **Quick Labs** make inquiry accessible to all students. **Also available in Spanish.**

- **Interactive Reader and Study Guide** makes the content from the Student Edition accessible to struggling readers and English Learners.

- **Differentiated Directed Reading Worksheets** and **Vocabulary & Section Summary Worksheets** help students of varying ability levels access chapter content. **Directed Reading Worksheet A and Vocabulary & Section Summary Worksheet A are also available in Spanish.**

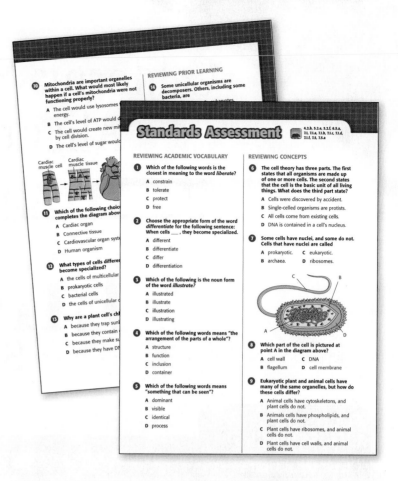

Universal Access · Differentiated Instruction

English Learners

Hypothesis, Theory, and Law Make sure students understand the relationship between scientific hypothesis, theory, and law. Ask them to write a definition for each term and then to orally use the two of the terms in one sentence in English. (Sample answer: Definitions–hypothesis: possible explanation/answer to a question; theory– explanation tying together many related facts, observations, and tested hypotheses; law–a statement that makes predictions under certain conditions; Sentences–After the hypothesis was supported by many experiments, it became recognized as a theory. A theory describes why something happens and a law states what will happen.) **LS Verbal**

California Standards Alignment

HOLT CALIFORNIA Life Science

CELL BIOLOGY

7.1 All living organisms are composed of cells, from just one to many trillions, whose details usually are visible only through a microscope.

Standard		Page
7.1.a	Students know cells function similarly in all living organisms.	SE 51, 52, 53, 54, 55, 56, 57, 58, 59, 60, 61, 66, 67, 68, 69, 113, 114, 115, 116, 117, 118, 119, 120, 121, 122, 123, 124, 125, 126, 127, 138, 139, 140, 212, 213, 214, 215, 216, 217, 222, 223, 224, 225, 339, 340, 342, 343, 348, 349, 351
7.1.b	Students know the characteristics that distinguish plant cells from animal cells, including chloroplasts and cell walls.	SE 120, 121, 122, 124, 126, 127, 134, 135, 138, 139, 140, 141, 148, 149, 150, 151, 154, 155, 157, 162, 163, 164, 165, 360, 361, 363, 386, 387, 389, 396, 410, 411, 415, 416
7.1.c	Students know the nucleus is the repository for genetic information in plant and animal cells.	SE 117, 118, 119, 122, 126, 127, 134, 135, 138, 139, 140
7.1.d	Students know that mitochondria liberate energy for the work that cells do and that chloroplasts capture sunlight energy for photosynthesis.	SE 124, 126, 127, 138, 139, 140, 141, 147, 145, 148, 149, 150, 151, 162, 163, 164, 165, 327, 360, 363, 386, 387, 388, 396, 397, 398, 399, 410, 411, 414, 415, 416
7.1.e	Students know cells divide to increase their numbers through a process of mitosis, which results in two daughter cells with identical sets of chromosomes.	SE 152, 153, 154, 155, 156, 157, 158, 159, 162, 163, 164
7.1.f	Students know that as multicellular organisms develop, their cells differentiate.	SE 128, 129, 130, 131, 132, 133, 138, 139, 140 ,141, 395, 404, 407, 409, 414, 415, 416, 425, 427, 429, 448, 449, 455, 456, 457, 467, 471, 487, 488, 489, 563, 564, 565, 567, 572, 574

GENETICS

7.2 **A typical cell of any organism contains genetic instructions that specify its traits. Those traits may be modified by environmental influences.**

Standard		Page
7.2.a	Students know the differences between the life cycles and reproduction methods of sexual and asexual organisms.	**SE** 54, 55, 62, 63, 66, 67, 68, 69, 364, 365, 366, 367, 368, 369, 371, 372, 373, 386, 387, 388, 400, 402, 403, 414, 415, 416, 417, 427, 429, 442, 443, 448, 449, 454, 455, 456, 457
7.2.b	Students know sexual reproduction produces offspring that inherit half their genes from each parent.	**SE** 189, 190, 191, 193, 194, 195, 198, 199, 200, 555, 558, 559, 561, 573, 574, 575
7.2.c	Students know an inherited trait can be determined by one or more genes.	**SE** 184, 185, 187, 198, 199, 200, 201
7.2.d	Students know plant and animal cells contain many thousands of different genes and typically have two copies of every gene. The two copies (or alleles) of the gene may or may not be identical, and one may be dominant in determining the phenotype while the other is recessive.	**SE** 173, 174, 176, 177, 178, 179, 180, 181, 182, 183, 186, 187, 194, 195, 198, 199, 200, 201
7.2.e	Students know DNA (deoxyribonucleic acid) is the genetic material of living organisms and is located in the chromosomes of each cell.	**SE** 152, 153, 155, 157, 158, 159, 162, 163, 164, 165, 188, 189, 193, 199, 201, 207, 208, 210, 211, 212, 213, 217, 218, 219, 222, 223, 224, 225

EVOLUTION

7.3 **Biological evolution accounts for the diversity of species developed through gradual processes over many generations.**

Standard		Page
7.3.a	Students know both genetic variation and environmental factors are causes of evolution and diversity of organisms.	**SE** 297, 312, 313, 317, 318, 319, 320, 322, 323, 325
7.3.b	Students know the reasoning used by Charles Darwin in reaching his conclusion that natural selection is the mechanism of evolution.	**SE** 306, 307, 308, 309, 310, 311, 322, 323, 325
7.3.c	Students know how independent lines of evidence from geology, fossils, and comparative anatomy provide the bases for the theory of evolution.	**SE** 239, 240, 241, 245, 246, 247, 248, 249, 254, 256, 263, 264, 265, 266, 267, 268, 269, 288, 289, 299, 300, 301, 302, 303, 304, 305, 322, 323, 325
7.3.d	Students know how to construct a simple branching diagram to classify living groups of organisms by shared derived characteristics and how to expand the diagram to include fossil organisms.	**SE** 301, 305, 323, 324, 331, 332, 333, 334, 335, 336, 337, 338, 339, 340, 341, 342, 343, 344, 345, 348, 349, 350, 351
7.3.e	Students know that extinction of a species occurs when the environment changes and the adaptive characteristics of a species are insufficient for its survival.	**SE** 313, 316, 317, 322

EARTH AND LIFE HISTORY (EARTH SCIENCES)

7.4   Evidence from rocks allows us to understand the evolution of life on Earth.

Standard		Page
7.4.a	Students know Earth processes today are similar to those that occurred in the past and slow geologic processes have large cumulative effects over long periods of time.	**SE** 234, 235, 236, 237, 254, 255, 256, 270, 271, 272, 273, 274, 275, 288, 289, 290, 291
7.4.b	Students know the history of life on Earth has been disrupted by major catastrophic events, such as major volcanic eruptions or the impacts of asteroids.	**SE** 233, 235, 236, 237, 254, 255, 256, 512, 513
7.4.c	Students know that the rock cycle includes the formation of new sediment and rocks and that rocks are often found in layers, with the oldest generally on the bottom.	**SE** 238, 239, 240, 241, 242, 243, 244, 245, 254, 255, 256, 257, 263, 264, 265, 266, 267, 268, 269, 288, 289, 290
7.4.d	Students know that evidence from geologic layers and radioactive dating indicates Earth is approximately 4.6 billion years old and that life on this planet has existed for more than 3 billion years.	**SE** 246, 247, 248, 249, 250, 251, 254, 255, 256, 257, 277, 278, 279, 280, 281, 282, 283, 288, 290, 291, 464, 465
7.4.e	Students know fossils provide evidence of how life and environmental conditions have changed.	**SE** 237, 254, 255, 264, 265, 266, 267, 268, 269, 272, 273, 274, 275, 277, 278, 279, 280, 281, 282, 283, 284, 285, 288, 289, 290, 291, 512, 513
7.4.f	Students know how movements of Earth's continental and oceanic plates through time, with associated changes in climate and geographic connections, have affected the past and present distribution of organisms.	**SE** 270, 271, 272, 273, 274, 275, 288, 289, 290, 291, 314, 315, 317, 323, 324
7.4.g	Students know how to explain significant developments and extinctions of plant and animal life on the geologic time scale.	**SE** 276, 277, 278, 279, 280, 281, 282, 283, 288, 289, 290, 291, 464, 465

STRUCTURE AND FUNCTION IN LIVING SYSTEMS

7.5   The anatomy and physiology of plants and animals illustrate the complementary nature of structure and function.

Standard		Page
7.5.a	Students know plants and animals have levels of organization for structure and function, including cells, tissues, organs, organ systems, and the whole organism.	**SE** 128, 130, 131, 132, 133, 138, 139, 140, 141, 359, 362, 363, 364, 365, 367, 374, 375, 376, 377, 378, 379, 381, 382, 383, 386, 387, 388, 389, 395, 405, 406, 409, 414, 415, 417, 423, 425, 426, 428, 429, 431, 432, 433, 434, 435, 436, 437, 438, 439, 443, 444, 448, 449, 450, 454, 455, 456, 457, 466, 467, 468, 469, 470, 471, 472, 473, 475, 476, 480, 481, 486, 496, 497, 498, 499, 500, 501, 502, 503, 504, 505, 506, 507, 508, 509, 510, 511, 512, 513, 516, 517, 518, 519, 526, 527, 530, 532, 533, 534, 535, 536, 540, 541, 546, 547, 548, 556, 557, 558, 561, 572, 574, 575
7.5.b	Students know organ systems function because of the contributions of individual organs, tissues, and cells. The failure of any part can affect the entire system.	**SE** 327, 425, 429, 440, 441, 443, 445, 446, 447, 449, 454, 455, 456, 468, 470, 471, 486, 487, 488, 496, 497, 498, 499, 500, 501, 502, 503, 504, 506, 507, 508, 509, 510, 511, 512, 513, 516, 517, 518, 519, 525, 526, 527, 528, 529, 530, 531, 532, 533, 534, 535, 540, 541, 546, 547, 548
7.5.c	Students know how bones and muscles work together to provide a structural framework for movement.	**SE** 428, 429, 445, 449, 450, 455, 457, 465, 473, 474, 475, 477, 481, 486, 487, 488, 489
7.5.d	Students know how the reproductive organs of the human female and male generate eggs and sperm and how sexual activity may lead to fertilization and pregnancy.	**SE** 556, 557, 558, 559, 561, 562, 566, 567, 572, 573, 574, 575
7.5.e	Students know the function of the umbilicus and placenta during pregnancy.	**SE** 563, 564, 567, 568, 569, 572, 573, 574
7.5.f	Students know the structures and processes by which flowering plants generate pollen, ovules, seeds, and fruit.	**SE** 368, 369, 372, 373, 379, 380, 381, 382, 383, 386, 387, 389, 400, 401, 402, 403, 414, 415, 416, 417
7.5.g	Students know how to relate the structures of the eye and ear to their functions.	**SE** 441, 443, 447, 449, 455, 456, 457, 536, 537, 538, 539, 541, 542, 543, 546, 547, 548, 549

PHYSICAL PRINCIPLES IN LIVING SYSTEMS (PHYSICAL SCIENCES)

7.6 Physical principles underlie biological structures and functions.

Standard		Page
7.6.a	Students know visible light is a small band within a very broad electromagnetic spectrum.	**SE** 77, 78, 80, 81, 103, 104
7.6.b	Students know that for an object to be seen, light emitted by or scattered from it must be detected by the eye.	**SE** 84, 85, 87, 89, 102, 103, 104, 536, 537, 541, 547, 548, 549
7.6.c	Students know light travels in straight lines if the medium it travels through does not change.	**SE** 82, 83, 86, 89, 90, 91, 92, 97, 102, 103, 105
7.6.d	Students know how simple lenses are used in a magnifying glass, the eye, a camera, a telescope, and a microscope.	**SE** 93, 94, 95, 96, 97, 98, 102, 105
7.6.e	Students know that white light is a mixture of many wavelengths (colors) and that retinal cells react differently to different wavelengths.	**SE** 30, 75, 79, 80, 81, 86, 87, 88, 89, 91, 97, 102, 103, 104, 105
7.6.f	Students know light can be reflected, refracted, transmitted, and absorbed by matter.	**SE** 82, 83, 84, 85, 86, 87, 88, 89, 90, 91, 92, 93, 94, 95, 96, 97, 98, 102, 103, 104, 105
7.6.g	Students know the angle of reflection of a light beam is equal to the angle of incidence.	**SE** 82, 83, 89, 102, 105, 537
7.6.h	Students know how to compare joints in the body (wrist, shoulder, thigh) with structures used in machines and simple devices (hinge, ball-and-socket, and sliding joints).	**SE** 465, 474, 475, 486, 487, 488
7.6.i	Students know how levers confer mechanical advantage and how the application of this principle applies to the musculoskeletal system.	**SE** 478, 479, 481, 482, 483, 486, 487, 488
7.6.j	Students know that contractions of the heart generate blood pressure and that heart valves prevent backflow of blood in the circulatory system.	**SE** 495, 496, 497, 498, 500, 501, 504, 507, 516, 517, 518, 519

INVESTIGATION AND EXPERIMENTATION

7.7 Scientific progress is made by asking meaningful questions and conducting careful investigations. As a basis for understanding this concept and addressing the content in the other three strands, students should develop their own questions and perform investigations.

Standard		Page
7.7.a	Select and use appropriate tools and technology (including calculators, computers, balances, spring scales, microscopes, and binoculars) to perform tests, collect data, and display data.	**SE** 20, 21, 22, 23, 24, 25, 33, 35, 37, 38, 39, 42, 44, 64, 100, 113, 134, 135, 187, 412, 423, 542, 543, 544
7.7.b	Use a variety of print and electronic resources (including the World Wide Web) to collect information and evidence as part of a research project.	**SE** 9, 11, 20, 25, 40, 42, 43, 44, 187, 514, 570
7.7.c	Communicate the logical connection among hypotheses, science concepts, tests conducted, data collected, and conclusions drawn from the scientific evidence.	**SE** 7, 8, 10, 11, 12, 13, 14, 15, 16, 17, 18, 19, 29, 30, 31, 42, 43, 44, 51, 59, 62, 63, 160, 182, 194, 195, 207, 220, 250, 251, 256, 297, 313, 318, 319, 320, 359, 365, 369, 379, 398, 402, 410, 411, 450, 473, 484, 512, 513, 568, 569
7.7.d	Construct scale models, maps, and appropriately labeled diagrams to communicate scientific knowledge (e.g., motion of Earth's plates and cell structure).	**SE** 28, 31, 42, 43, 45, 115, 121, 134, 135, 136, 155, 158, 159, 181, 194, 195, 210, 252, 284, 285, 286, 331, 333, 342, 344, 382, 383, 384, 452, 465, 470, 482, 483, 495, 504, 532, 539, 564, 568, 569
7.7.e	Communicate the steps and results from an investigation in written reports and oral presentations.	**SE** 18, 19, 42, 43, 45, 196, 318, 319, 320, 346

Reading support helps students unlock the California Science Standards

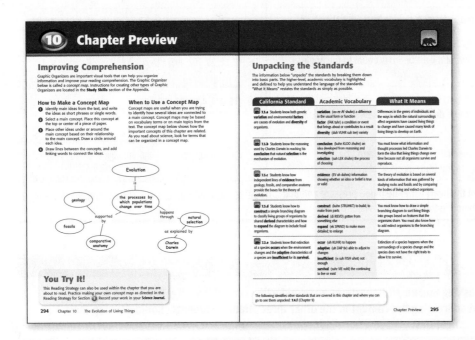

Chapter Preview

- **Improving Comprehension** helps students organize information and improve their reading comprehension through the use of graphic organizers.

- **Unpacking the Standards** breaks down the **California Science Standards** covered in the chapter by defining the academic vocabulary and restating the standards as simply as possible.

Chapter Opener

- **The Big Idea** highlights the chapter's main topic and makes it relevant to students through an engaging photo and short narrative.

- Students can preview the **California Standards** that are covered in the chapter.

- **Organize** helps students create their own interactive study guide.

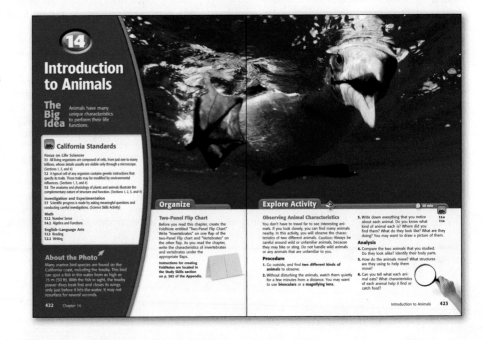

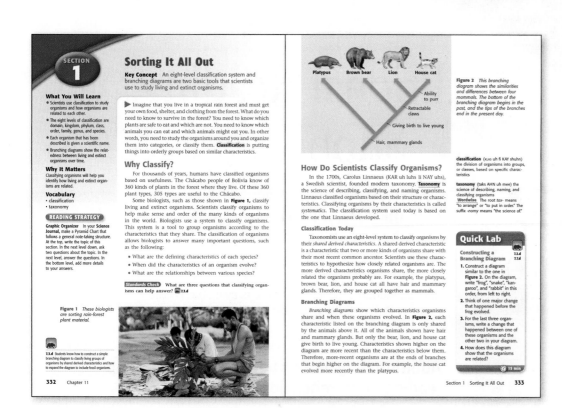

Section Opener

- **Key Concept** highlights the main idea of the section.

- **What You Will Learn** previews the main concepts.

- **Why It Matters** explains why the content is relevant to students.

- **Vocabulary** lists the important terms covered in the section. Terms are highlighted in the text and defined at point of use.

- **Reading Strategy** helps students better understand what they read.

- The **California Science Standards** that are covered in the section are previewed in the margin.

- **Wordwise** helps students understand the meaning of scientific vocabulary by deconstructing complex words and defining prefixes, roots, and suffixes.

Section and Chapter Summaries

- **Section Summary** reviews the section's main concepts.

- **Chapter Summary** uses both text and visuals to connect the **Key Concepts** to **The Big Idea**.

- **Super Summary** provides additional online help in reviewing the content of each chapter.

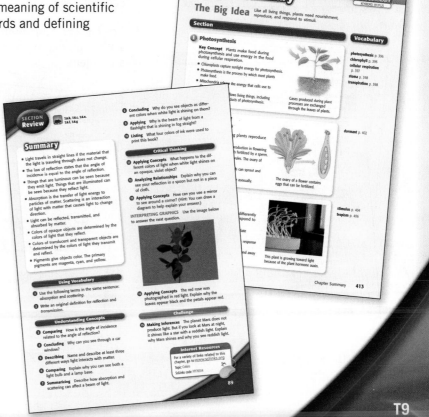

Additional Reading Support

Live Ink® Reading Help is proven to raise test scores

Live Ink Reading Help, a scientifically-researched tool for improving students' reading comprehension, is proven to raise students' scores. Live Ink is available on the **Premier Online Edition** of **Holt California Science.**

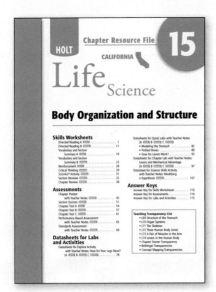

Additional resources help students develop reading comprehension skills

Chapter Resource Files

- **Directed Reading Worksheets** guide students through each section and focus their attention on key elements. These worksheets are available in two levels: **BASIC** (A) and **GENERAL** (B). The **BASIC** worksheet is also available in Spanish.

- **Vocabulary and Section Summary Worksheets** help students review vocabulary words and provide a bulleted list of main topics from each section. These worksheets are available in two levels: **BASIC** (A) and **GENERAL** (B). The **BASIC** worksheet is also available in Spanish.

- **Reinforcement Worksheets** make reviewing and reinforcing chapter content easy.

- **Critical Thinking Worksheets** allow students to demonstrate their understanding of the content by applying their knowledge to solve a problem.

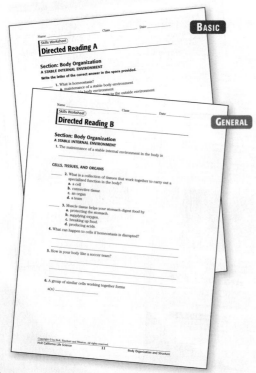

Study Guides

- **Study Guide A** contains **BASIC** worksheets for Directed Reading and Vocabulary & Section Summary.

- **Study Guide B** contains **GENERAL** worksheets for Directed Reading and Vocabulary & Section Summary.

Interactive Reader and Study Guide makes the content from the Student Edition accessible to struggling readers and English Learners. Reading strategies and directed reading questions are also provided to help develop students' reading skills.

Guided Reading Audio CD Program is a direct reading of the student text. This program is helpful to students who benefit from different teaching styles. **Also available in Spanish.**

Student Edition CD-ROM contains the **Student Edition,** the **Interactive Reader and Study Guide,** and workbooks that improve students reading comprehension and reinforces students' understanding of the **California Science Standards.** These workbooks include **Section Reviews and Chapter Reviews, Study Guide A, Study Guide B, Standards Review Workbook,** and the **Multilingual Glossary.**

Holt Science Skills Workshop: Reading in the Content Area targets the reading skills specific to the comprehension of science texts. Using these activities and exercises, students learn to analyze test structures, recognize patterns, and organize information in ways that help them construct meaning.

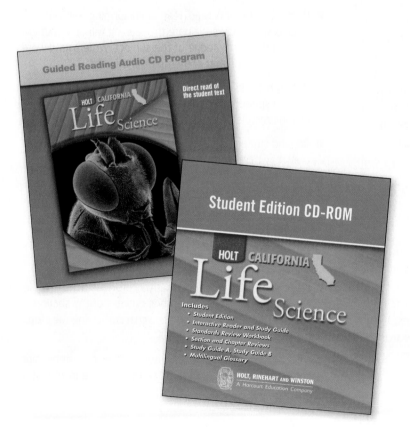

Teaching English Learners in the Science Classroom

by Dr. Robin Scarcella

Dr. Robin Scarcella, Ph.D., is a professor and the director of the Academic English and English as a Second Language Program at the University of California at Irvine. Dr. Scarcella has taught English Learners at the elementary, junior high, and high school levels. In addition, she has written more than 30 articles and several books about ESL teaching and secondary language acquisition, contributed to several other books, and edited numerous ESL instruction texts. Dr. Scarcella has lectured at more than 50 universities.

Teaching English Learners in the Science Classroom

The content of fact-packed scientific writing is often intimidating to English Learners (ELs). Many new words are introduced in a small amount of text, and the grammar is complex. Fortunately, a variety of motivating and effective means are available to teach reading in science classrooms. These means help not only your EL students but also many of your monolingual English-speaking students. You can incorporate a deliberate focus on reading comprehension by using a combination of reading comprehension strategies and language instruction.

Reading Comprehension

Reading comprehension strategies are conscious plans or sets of specific steps that enable students to make sense of and remember concepts. These strategies help students identify and "fix" their reading comprehension difficulties. Teach these strategies explicitly, explaining why the strategies are useful and when and how to use them. Take time to demonstrate the ways you use the strategies. When appropriate, provide students with useful lists of words and expressions for which they might need to use a strategy. Then give students guided and independent practice.

Some Reading Comprehension Strategies

- Before students read, assess their knowledge to discover what they already know and what they need to know.

- Before EL students read, lead brainstorming sessions to discuss what they anticipate the reading will be about and to build their knowledge of the subject. Write useful words and expressions that come up on the board.

- During reading, tell students to ask questions, adjust their reading speed to fit the difficulty of the text, and read the text in reasonable sections.

- Remind students that science text is difficult and that they may have to read and outline sections many times to understand it.

- Encourage students to look ahead and backwards in the text to identify and address their comprehension difficulties.

- Help students use graphic organizers to identify and understand critical science concepts. Have them use a list of specific expressions that you provide to make tables comparing one topic to another, outlines of the section using section headings, and flowcharts showing the steps of specific processes.

- After reading, help students improve their comprehension with summarization. Students can summarize in writing or orally with a partner.

Language Instruction

To further improve the reading skills of EL students, provide these students with language instruction focused on types of writing, grammar, and vocabulary.

Types of Writing Teaching the various types of writing that science textbooks use demystifies science passages. The most commonly occurring writing is *factual*. You can help EL students understand this kind of writing by teaching them language for introducing major points and examples, illustrations, facts, and statistics. Also familiarize students with the predictable language patterns found in tests. Doing so will do much to build their confidence and reading proficiency.

Grammar You do not need to know the correct grammatical terminology to teach grammar. Simply writing sentences on the board and calling attention to patterns and punctuation will help students learn grammatical features. For instance, before making a reading assignment, write sentences from the textbook containing complex grammatical structures on the board. Prompt students to break the sentences into smaller sentences with the same meaning. Adjectives and adverbial forms such as *almost, probably, never, exactly, least,* and *higher* modify the meanings of sentences and words. Point out these words to students, and discuss their meanings. Write sentences that contain these words on the board, and ask students to identify the word or words they modify.

Similarly, help students understand that pronouns represent nouns by writing sentences on the board and asking students to identify the nouns that the pronouns represent.

Vocabulary To read with comprehension, students need to understand many words. These words include the following:

- **Everyday Vocabulary with Specialized Meanings in Science** Many words used in science have different everyday meanings in English. Examples include *fault, reflection, power, force, active,* and *plate.*

- **Academic Vocabulary** Academic words are different from the technical or content terms used in science. They are words used across all academic disciplines (e.g., *accommodate, inhibit,* and *deviate*).

- **Content Words** Content words such as *germinate, piston,* and *stamen* are discipline-specific words.

Teach vocabulary systematically by encouraging students to read words and use words in a variety of contexts. Provide direct, structured instruction, scaffolding, group and pair learning, and word learning strategies through the four language skills—reading, writing, speaking, and listening.

Ask students to repeat words after you several times to give students the opportunity to hear and practice the words. Incorporate an explicit focus on word use into your instruction, teaching students about words whenever the occasion arises by discussing related words and word families (e.g., *stabile, stabilize,* and *stabilization*), playing synonym/antonym guessing games, and teaching word connotations. Point out the vocabulary that signals relationships such as cause and effect (e.g., *as a result, when,* and *because*), comparison and contrast (e.g., *as, like, in contrast,* and *differ*), and generalization (e.g., *in general* and *to conclude*). In addition, point out collocations, fixed words, and expressions that go together (e.g., *associated with, depend on, valid assumption,* and *kinetic energy*) to characterize specific science text.

Learning by Doing

Encourage students to *use* the language they are learning in their speech and writing. Provide them with many opportunities to talk about their reading. Scaffold the oral communication of your EL students by providing them with lists of useful words they can use when summarizing passages in pairs, when brainstorming, and when discussing their reading. Get students to write about their reading to reinforce concepts and clarify misconceptions. Again, scaffold the students' writing by providing assignments that require using the words in the textbook, teaching students how to structure their writing as well as teaching them the specific words you want them to use.

For students whose first exposure to English begins in secondary school, time is perhaps the biggest challenge to teaching them to read science materials. Provide English Learners additional instructional time—before class, during class, and after class.

Standard English Learners

Language Acquisition as a Scaffold to Science Curricula

by Dr. Noma LeMoine

Dr. Noma LeMoine, Ph.D., is the director of the Los Angeles Unified School District's Academic English Mastery Program (AEMP). Dr. LeMoine also served three years as principal and director of operations of the NASA-funded Saturday Academy for Student Advancement in Math, Science and Communications. She has written and spoken extensively on academic English mastery and is a highly sought-after consultant to colleges, universities, and school districts nationwide. Dr. LeMoine is also the author of *English for Your Success: A Language Development Program for African-American Students.*

Who Are Standard English Learners?

Standard English Learner (SEL) students are students for whom standard English is not native or students whose home language—the language acquired between infancy and five years of age—structurally does not match the language of school academics. Standard English Learners include African American, Hawaiian American, Mexican American, and Native American students who have in common a linguistic history grounded in languages other than English. Prior to coming in contact with English, their ancestors spoke African languages, Hawaiian languages, Latin American Spanish, or American Indian languages.

In each case these "involuntary minorities"—people who were enslaved, colonized, conquered, or otherwise subordinated in the context of America—combined English vocabulary with their native language and fashioned new ways of communicating in their new environments. These language forms, which include African American Language (often referred to as Black English), Hawaiian American Language (referred to as Hawaiian Pidgin English), Mexican American Language (referred to as Chicano English), and Native American Language (sometimes referred to as Red English), incorporate English vocabulary but differ in structure and form from standard American English. Standard English Learners arrive at school in kindergarten as competent users of the language of their home but demonstrate limited proficiency in the language of school, i.e., Standard American English. They are generally classified as "English Only" on school language surveys even though many of the rules that govern their home language are based in languages other than English. Because they are designated as "English Only," their need for structured programs that support their acquisition of Standard and academic English is often overlooked.

Language Variation and Learning in SEL Students

If culturally and linguistically diverse Standard English Learners are to succeed academically, they must acquire the language, culture, and literacies of school. They must become literate in the forms of English that appear in newspapers, magazines, science textbooks, voting materials, and consumer contracts. How best to facilitate this learning in Standard English Learners has proven elusive for most American public educational institutions. Minimal emphasis has been placed on identifying instructional methodologies that scaffold SEL students' access to core curricula.

Learning is viewed as a social phenomenon, and knowledge is recognized as a social construction that is influenced by the cultural and linguistic experiences, perspectives, and frames of reference that both students and teachers bring to the learning environment. For Standard English Learners this learning process suggests that an instructional model that validates and builds on prior knowledge, experiences, language, and culture while supporting the acquisition of school language through content learning is an appropriate pedagogy.

Engaging Standard English Learners

A good science curriculum uses scientific inquiry as a means for investigating the natural world. The curriculum should therefore provide opportunities for students to think, write, speak, and act as scientists. For Standard English Learners, whose language and learning styles often do not match mainstream expectations, engaging them in applied learning activities that emphasize critical thinking, problem solving, writing, and speaking is essential to their success in mastering core curricula. As teachers assist Standard English Learners and other students in developing scientific skills such as hypothesizing, experimenting, making observations, collecting data, and drawing conclusions, students can also be provided with opportunities to develop their skills as speakers, readers, and writers.

The acquisition of school language and literacy in Standard English Learners is not optional. The ability to speak, read, and write using Standard English forms is critical to success in school. SEL students must have opportunities to engage in and see school language and literacy practices modeled and must be able to utilize that knowledge in the context of disciplinary learning if they are to compete successfully with their more mainstream peers. Limited familiarity with Standard American English syntax may impair SEL students' ability to identify important syntactic relationships in Standard English, and limited Standard English vocabulary may cause difficulty in using semantic cues for making predictions and comprehending what is read. In order for SELs to experience greater success in accessing core science curricula, teachers will need to construct learning environments that are authentic and culturally responsive and that support oral and written language development.

SEL Instructional Support Strategies

- Emphasize and teach deductive reasoning through relevant science activities.

- Incorporate appropriate second-language acquisition methodologies and strategies into instruction. Strategies include using visuals, manipulatives, graphic organizers, media, and other tools to explain scientific concepts.

- Provide continuous and varied opportunities for students to use language to interact with each other and the science content through instructional conversations.

- Establish culturally relevant classroom libraries. Include literature that makes connections to students' experiences and conveys knowledge about historical and contemporary achievers of color in science.

- Encourage student/classroom development of a thesaurus of conceptually coded words to support the acquisition of the academic vocabulary of science.

- Target the development of listening, speaking, reading, and writing skills in Standard English in the context of the science instruction.

- Make connections to students' prior knowledge, experiences, and cultural funds of knowledge to support learning and retention of learned scientific concepts.

- Incorporate contrastive analysis strategies (linguistic, contextual, situational, and elicited) into the daily instruction of SEL students to facilitate mastery of academic language.

- Support cooperative learning communities that engage teachers in a review of the literature on the culture and language of SEL students.

Teaching Scientific Inquiry

What is **scientific inquiry?** Scientific inquiry is the process by which scientists ask questions, develop and carry out investigations, make predictions, gather evidence, and propose explanations. Inquiry is often associated with "hands-on" learning or activity-based instruction. Research shows that this type of instruction has been effective in fostering scientific literacy and the understanding of scientific processes. Furthermore, inquiry-based instruction has been reported to improve students' analytical skills.

As students practice inquiry, they develop process skills and behaviors used by scientists and thus begin thinking like a scientist. The development of these process skills involves the student being in a situation in which he or she has to think like a scientist. Process skills can be developed through simple activities but students need to be continually exposed to these activities. Listed below are process skills that students develop while doing inquiry.

- Observation
- Experimentation
- Data Collection
- Measuring
- Sorting, Classifying, and Comparing
- Analysis
- Communication

Inquiry in Holt California Science

Listed below are three different approaches to teaching scientific inquiry. **Holt California Science** provides a variety of activities and labs throughout their program that introduce the student to each of these approaches and thus to a different learning situation. The different types of labs and activities provide flexibility to accommodate any classroom and any teaching situation. By using **Holt California Science** students actively learn by incorporating key science concepts through hands-on activity. This reinforces science concepts, improving science literacy and developing science skills.

- **Structured Inquiry** Students follow teacher's instructions to perform an activity but are not provided with the expected outcome.
- **Guided Inquiry** Students develop a procedure to investigate a problem selected by the teacher.
- **Open Inquiry** Students develop a problem to investigate and design their own investigation.

Scientific Inquiry in Holt California Science

Student Edition	Teacher's Edition	Lab Generator	Additional Technology
Inquiry Lab	Group ACTIVITY	LONG-TERM PROJECTS & RESEARCH IDEAS	Lab Videos
Model-Making Lab	ACTIVITY	ECOLABS & FIELD ACTIVITIES	
Skills Practice Lab		LABS YOU CAN EAT	Earth Science Virtual Investigations CD-ROM
SCHOOL to HOME	Demonstration	WHIZ-BANG DEMONSTRATIONS	
Explore Activity		CALCULATOR-BASED LABS	
Quick Lab		Explore Activity	Life Science Virtual Investigations CD-ROM
Science Skills Activity		Quick Lab	
		Science Skills Activity	Physical Science Virtual Investigations CD-ROM
		Inquiry Lab	
		Model-Making Lab	
		Skills Practice Lab	

Activities reinforce students' understanding of the California Science Standards

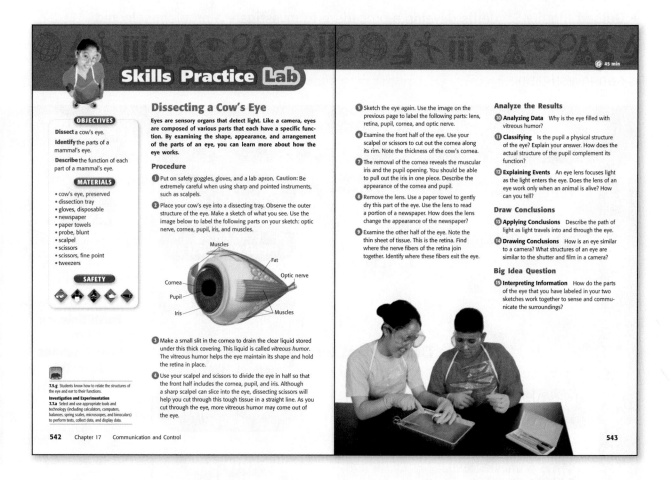

Holt California Science provides investigations and experiments that reinforce and are integral to learning the **California Science Standards.** Students develop investigative and experimental skills in the context of content standards.

Chapter Labs—Inquiry Labs, Skills Practice Labs, and Model-Making Labs—include clear procedures and explanations, demonstrate scientific concepts covered in the **California Science Standards,** and help develop students' understanding of scientific methods. All labs have been classroom tested and reviewed for reliability, safety, and efficiency. Labs are rated in the Teacher's Edition, making it easy to select labs that are appropriate for your classroom.

Datasheets for all Explore Activities, Quick Labs, Science Skills Activities, and Chapter Labs are available in each **Chapter Resource File** and on the **Lab Generator.** In addition, datasheets are differentiated— **BASIC**, **GENERAL**, and **ADVANCED** —to help you reach the different ability levels in your classroom. **Datasheets are also available in Spanish on the Lab Generator.**

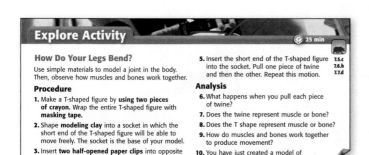

Explore Activity is a short, but engaging activity at the beginning of the chapter that motivates students to learn.

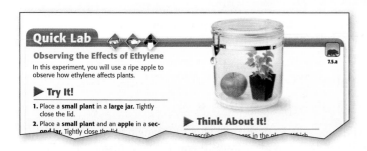

Quick Lab reinforces a standard or standards covered in a particular section, is easy to execute, and requires minimal time and materials. These labs are great for an in-class activity, teacher demonstration, or group presentation.

Science Skills Activity develops a particular skill described in the **Investigation and Experimentation Standards.** These skills include process skills related to scientific methods, graphing skills, data analysis, and mapping skills.

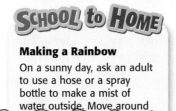

School-to-Home Activity provides an opportunity for parents and guardians to get involved with student learning. These activities require little or no equipment and do not require safety precautions.

Internet Activity sends students online for a variety of projects, such as creating scientist biographies and writing science articles.

You can also integrate additional activities from the Teacher's Edition, such as **Activity, Group Activity, Connection Activity, Demonstration,** and **Homework,** into your lessons.

Technology makes planning labs easier

Holt California Science provides technology that makes planning labs easier and makes doing labs more cost effective.

Lab Generator CD-ROM features all labs from Holt California Science plus additional labs

Differentiated datasheets in both English and Spanish are available for all the labs found in the Student Edition. Also available are datasheets for the additional labs. These additional labs include:

- **Calculator-Based Labs** integrate calculator use into science labs, providing a link to help students develop mathematics skills.

- **Labs You Can Eat** spark student interest, while explaining important scientific concepts.

- **Inquiry Labs** introduce students to the world of science inquiry and foster the skills necessary to develop hands-on science literacy.

- **EcoLabs & Field Activities** provide students with ideas for exploring the world of science outside the classroom.

- **Long-Term Projects & Research Ideas** help students think about science as a long-term process. Students are encouraged to study topics they find intriguing and to construct their own types of investigation.

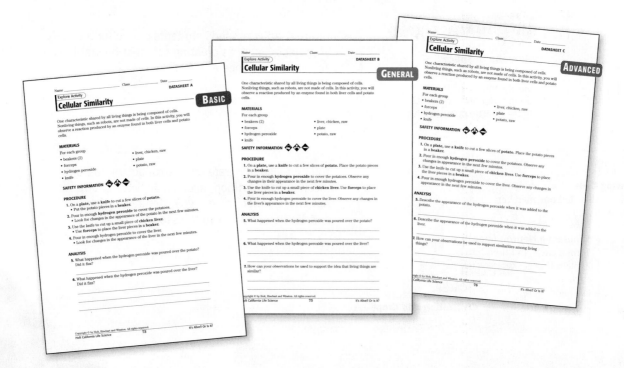

Lab Generator CD-ROM is a time-saving resource that allows you to

- **Search** for labs by topic, difficulty level, lab duration, or **California Science Standard.**
- **Edit** labs to fit classroom needs.
- **Develop** new labs from our easy-to-use formatted template.
- **Save time** ordering materials using the **Lab Materials QuickList Software.**

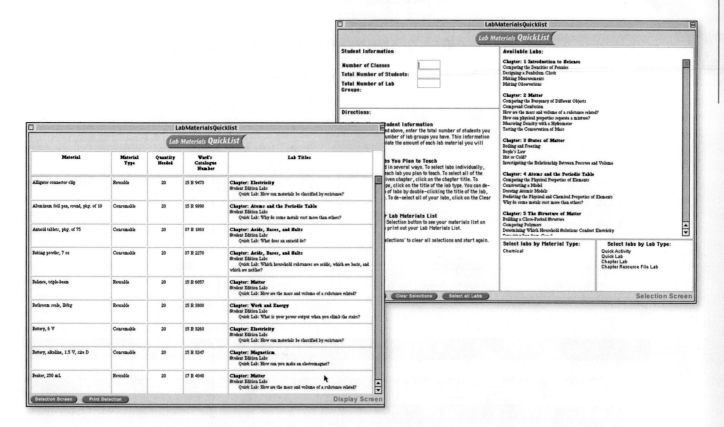

Lab Videos make it easier to integrate more experiments into your lessons without the preparation time and costs of a traditional laboratory set-up. These videos demonstrate the end-of-chapter labs and are available on DVD and VHS.

Virtual Investigations CD-ROMs make it easy for students to practice science skills without the expense. Students perform lab activities in a safe, simulated environment.

California Standards Alignment to Labs and Activities

The following table shows a detailed correlation of the labs and activities to the **California Science Standards** for each chapter of *Holt California Life Science*. In addition, the table also provides pacing information that compares the instructional time for the labs and activities to the total instruction time for each chapter.

Chapter 1 The Nature of Life Science

Lab or Activity	Standard	Page	Time to Teach
Explore Activity Identifying Unknown Objects	7.7.c	7	15 min
Quick Lab Asking Questions	7.7.b	9	15 min
Quick Lab Investigating and Experimenting with Yeast	7.7.c	18	30 min
Quick Lab Measure Up!	7.7.a	24	25 min
Quick Lab Constructing Scale Diagrams	7.7.d	28	20 min
Quick Lab Preparing for an Experiment	7.7.a	35	20 min
Skills Practice Lab Collecting and Displaying Data	7.7.a	38	45 min
Science Skills Activity Using Internet Resources for Research	7.7.b	40	45 min
	Total Time for Labs and Activities		215 min (5 days)
	Total Instructional Time		540 min (12 days)
Percent of Instructional Time			**40%**

Chapter 2 It's Alive!! Or Is it?

Lab or Activity	Standard	Page	Time to Teach
Explore Activity Cellular Similarity	7.1.a, 7.7.c	51	20 min
Quick Lab The Role of Cells	7.1.a	53	10 min
Quick Lab Observing Enzymes in Pineapples	7.1.a, 7.7.c	59	30 min
Skills Practice Lab Comparing Methods of Reproduction	7.2.a, 7.7.c	62	45 min
Science Skills Activity Selecting Tools to Collect Data	7.7.a	64	45 min
	Total Time for Labs and Activities		150 min (3 days)
	Total Instructional Time		360 min (8 days)
Percent of Instructional Time			**42%**

Chapter 3 Light and Living Things

Lab or Activity	Standard	Page	Time to Teach
Explore Activity Seeing Colors of Light	7.6.e	75	20 min
Quick Lab Refraction Rainbow	7.6.e	80	15 min
Quick Lab Reflecting Mirrors	7.6.c, 7.6.g	83	30 min
Quick Lab Refracting Water	7.6.c, 7.6.f	92	10 min
Skills Practice Lab Images from Convex Lenses	7.6.d, 7.6.f	98	45 min
Science Skills Activity Using a Microscope to Collect Data	7.7.a	100	30 min
	Total Time for Labs and Activities		150 min (3 days)
	Total Instructional Time		495 min (11 days)
Percent of Instructional Time			**30%**

Chapter 4 Cells: The Basic Units of Life

Lab or Activity	Standard	Page	Time to Teach
Explore Activity What are Plants Made Of?	**7.1.a, 7.7.a**	113	20 min
Quick Lab Observing Cells	**7.1.a, 7.7.d**	115	20 min
Quick Lab Cell Diagrams	**7.1.b, 7.7.d**	121	20 min
Quick Lab A Division of Labor	**7.1.f**	129	15 min
Skills Practice Lab Cells Alive!	**7.1.b, 7.1.c, 7.7.a, 7.7.d**	134	45 min
Science Skills Activity Constructing Scale Diagrams	**7.7.d**	136	35 min
	Total Time for Labs and Activities		155 min (3 days)
	Total Instructional Time		450 min (10 days)
	Percent of Instructional Time		**34%**

Chapter 5 The Cell in Action

Lab or Activity	Standard	Page	Time to Teach
Explore Activity The Purpose of Pigment	**7.1.d**	147	15 min
Quick Lab Currency of the Cell	**7.1.d**	149	10 min
Quick Lab The Mitosis Flip Book	**7.1.e, 7.7.d**	155	30 min
Skills Practice Lab Phases of Mitosis	**7.1.e, 7.2.e, 7.7.d**	158	45 min
Science Skills Activity Drawing Conclusions from Data	**7.7.c**	160	25 min
	Total Time for Labs and Activities		125 min (3 days)
	Total Instructional Time		315 min (7 days)
	Percent of Instructional Time		**40%**

Chapter 6 Heredity

Lab or Activity	Standard	Page	Time to Teach
Explore Activity Modeling Traits	**7.2.d**	173	15 min
Quick Lab Flower Cross	**7.2.d**	177	15 min
Quick Lab Completing a Punnett Square	**7.2.d, 7.7.d**	181	15 min
Quick Lab Exploring Probability	**7.2.d, 7.7.c**	182	15 min
Quick Lab Meiosis Skit	**7.2.b**	191	20 min
Model-Making Lab Modeling Space Bug Genetics	**7.2.b, 7.2.c, 7.7.c, 7.7.d**	194	45 min
Science Skills Activity Giving Oral Presentations	**7.7.e**	196	40 min
	Total Time for Labs and Activities		165 min (4 days)
	Total Instructional Time		450 min (10 days)
	Percent of Instructional Time		**37%**

Chapter 7 Genes and DNA

Lab or Activity	Standard	Page	Time to Teach
Explore Activity Fingerprint Identification	**7.2.e, 7.7.c**	207	20 min
Quick Lab Making a Model of DNA	**7.2.e, 7.7.d**	210	25 min
Quick Lab Cracking the Code	**7.1.a**	216	15 min
Skills Practice Lab Extracting DNA	**7.2.e**	218	45 min
Science Skills Activity Connecting Scientific Methods	**7.7.c**	220	30 min
	Total Time for Labs and Activities		135 min (3 days)
	Total Instructional Time		405 min (9 days)
Percent of Instructional Time			**33%**

Chapter 8 Studying Earth's Past

Lab or Activity	Standard	Page	Time to Teach
Explore Activity Model Craters	**7.4.b**	233	20 min
Quick Lab Geology Flip Book	**7.4.a, 7.4.b**	236	25 min
Quick Lab Solve a Rock-Layer Puzzle!	**7.4.c**	244	20 min
Quick Lab Radioactive Decay	**7.4.d**	248	10 min
Skills Practice Lab The Half-Life of Pennies	**7.4.d, 7.7.c**	250	45 min
Science Skills Activity Constructing Labeled Diagrams	**7.7.d**	252	35 min
	Total Time for Labs and Activities		155 min (3 days)
	Total Instructional Time		450 min (10 days)
Percent of Instructional Time			**34%**

Chapter 9 The History of Life on Earth

Lab or Activity	Standard	Page	Time to Teach
Explore Activity Making Fossils	**7.3.c, 7.4.c**	263	20 min
Quick Lab Connecting Fossils to Climates	**7.4.e**	267	15 min
Quick Lab Climate Changes	**7.4.f**	275	20 min
Quick Lab Timeline of Earth's History	**7.4.d, 7.4.g**	278	30 min
Skills Practice Lab Interpreting Fossil Finds	**7.4.e, 7.7.d**	284	45 min
Science Skills Activity Constructing Models	**7.7.d**	286	30 min
	Total Time for Labs and Activities		160 min (4 days)
	Total Instructional Time		450 min (10 days)
Percent of Instructional Time			**36%**

Chapter 10 The Evolution of Living Things

Lab or Activity	Standard	Page	Time to Teach
Explore Activity Modeling Successful Traits	**7.3.a, 7.7.c**	297	15 min
Quick Lab Similarities in Anatomy	**7.3.c**	304	15 min
Quick Lab Population Growth Vs. Food Supply	**7.3.b**	309	15 min
Quick Lab Adaptations of Bird Beaks	**7.3.a, 7.3.e, 7.7.c**	313	20 min
Inquiry Lab Survival of the Chocolates	**7.3.a, 7.7.c, 7.7.e**	318	45 min
Science Skills Activity Scientific Methods: Testing Hypotheses	**7.7.c**	320	45 min
	Total Time for Labs and Activities		155 min (3 days)
	Total Instructional Time		450 min (10 days)
	Percent of Instructional Time		**34%**

Chapter 11 Classification

Lab or Activity	Standard	Page	Time to Teach
Explore Activity Analyzing a Branching Diagram	**7.3.d, 7.7.d**	331	15 min
Quick Lab Constructing a Branching Diagram	**7.3.d, 7.7.d**	333	15 min
Quick Lab Fossils and Branching Diagrams	**7.3.d, 7.7.d**	342	15 min
Skills Practice Lab Grouping Life-Forms by Their Characteristics	**7.3.d, 7.7.d**	344	45 min
Science Skills Activity Communicating Through Written Reports	**7.7.e**	346	40 min
	Total Time for Labs and Activities		130 min (3 days)
	Total Instructional Time		405 min (9 days)
	Percent of Instructional Time		**32%**

Chapter 12 Introduction to Plants

Lab or Activity	Standard	Page	Time to Teach
Explore Activity Observing Plant Growth	**7.5.a, 7.7.c**	359	20 min
Quick Lab Cell Walls and Wilting	**7.1.b**	361	15 min
Quick Lab Moss Mass	**7.2.a, 7.7.c**	365	20 min
Quick Lab Dissecting Seeds	**7.5.f, 7.7.c**	369	15 min
Quick Lab How Do the Parts of a Plant Work Together?	**7.5.a, 7.7.c**	379	20 min
Model-Making Lab Build a Flower	**7.5.a, 7.5.f, 7.7.d**	382	45 min
Science Skills Activity Constructing Scale Diagrams	**7.7.d**	384	35 min
	Total Time for Labs and Activities		170 min (4 days)
	Total Instructional Time		495 min (11 days)
	Percent of Instructional Time		**34%**

Chapter 13 Plant Processes

Lab or Activity	Standard	Page	Time to Teach
Explore Activity Observing Structure and Function in Plants	**7.1.f, 7.5.a**	395	10 min
Quick Lab Measuring Gas Exchange in Plants	**7.1.d, 7.7.c**	398	15 min
Quick Lab Plant Cuttings	**7.2.a, 7.7.c**	402	15 min
Quick Lab Observing the Effects of Ethylene	**7.5.a**	405	60 min
Skills Practice Lab Food Factory Waste	**7.1.b, 7.1.d, 7.7.c**	410	45 min
Science Skills Activity Selecting Tools to Display Data	**7.7.a**	412	30 min
	Total Time for Labs and Activities		175 min (4 days)
	Total Instructional Time		405 min (9 days)
	Percent of Instructional Time		**43%**

Chapter 14 Introduction to Animals

Lab or Activity	Standard	Page	Time to Teach
Explore Activity Observing Animal Characteristics	**7.5.a, 7.7.a**	423	20 min
Quick Lab Differentiating Blood Cells	**7.1.f**	427	20 min
Quick Lab Grouping Organisms by Characteristics	**7.5.a**	431	15 min
Quick Lab Seeing Like an Insect	**7.5.g**	441	20 min
Quick Lab Amplifying Sound	**7.5.g**	447	15 min
Skills Practice Lab Structure and Function of Bone	**7.5.a, 7.5.c, 7.7.a**	450	45 min
Science Skills Activity Constructing Distribution Maps	**7.7.d**	452	30 min
	Total Time for Labs and Activities		165 min (4 days)
	Total Instructional Time		585 min (13 days)
	Percent of Instructional Time		**28%**

Chapter 15 Body Organization and Structure

Lab or Activity	Standard	Page	Time to Teach
Explore Activity How Do Your Legs Bend?	**7.5.c, 7.6.h, 7.7.d**	465	25 min
Quick Lab Modeling the Stomach	**7.5.a, 7.5.b, 7.7.d**	470	25 min
Quick Lab Pickled Bones	**7.5.a, 7.7.c**	474	15 min
Quick Lab How Do Levers Work?	**7.6.i,**	479	25 min
Skills Practice Lab Levers and Mechanical Advantage	**7.6.i, 7.7.d**	482	45 min
Science Skills Activity Modifying a Hypothesis	**7.7.c**	484	30 min
	Total Time for Labs and Activities		165 min (4 days)
	Total Instructional Time		405 min (9 days)
	Percent of Instructional Time		**41%**

Chapter 16 Circulation and Respiration

Lab or Activity	Standard	Page	Time to Teach
Explore Activity Modeling a Valve	7.6.j, 7.7.d	495	15 min
Quick Lab Vessel Blockage	7.5.b	500	10 min
Quick Lab Modeling Blood Pressure	7.6.j, 7.7.d	504	10 min
Quick Lab Replicate Respiration	7.5.a	510	15 min
Skills Practice Lab Carbon Dioxide in Respiration	7.5.a, 7.5.b, 7.7.c	512	45 min
Science Skills Activity Evaluating Resources for Research	7.7.b	514	40 min
		Total Time for Labs and Activities	135 min (3 days)
		Total Instructional Time	405 min (9 days)
		Percent of Instructional Time	**33%**

Chapter 17 Communication and Control

Lab or Activity	Standard	Page	Time to Teach
Explore Activity Measuring Reaction Time	7.5.b	525	15 min
Quick Lab Building a Neuron	7.5.a, 7.7.d	532	20 min
Quick Lab What Does the Ear Drum Do?	7.5.g, 7.7.d	539	30 min
Skills Practice Lab Dissecting a Cow's Eye	7.5.g, 7.7.a	542	45 min
Science Skills Activity Selecting Tools to Perform Tests	7.7.a	544	25 min
		Total Time for Labs and Activities	135 min (3 days)
		Total Instructional Time	405 min (9 days)
		Percent of Instructional Time	**33%**

Chapter 18 Reproduction and Development

Lab or Activity	Standard	Page	Time to Teach
Explore Activity Dance of the Chromosomes	7.2.b	555	20 min
Quick Lab Modeling Inheritance	7.2.b	559	20 min
Quick Lab Development Timeline	7.1.f, 7.5.e, 7.7.d	564	15 min
Skills Practice Lab It's a Comfy, Safe World!	7.5.e, 7.7.c, 7.7.d	568	90 min
Science Skills Activity Using Print Resources for Research	7.7.b	570	40 min
		Total Time for Labs and Activities	185 min (4 days)
		Total Instructional Time	450 min (10 days)
		Percent of Instructional Time	**41%**

Program Totals

Program Total for Labs and Activities	51 days
Program Total Instructional Time	176 days
Percent of Total Program Time as Hands-On	**30%**

Safety in your laboratory
Risk Assessment

Making your laboratory a safe place to work and learn

Concern for safety must begin before any activity in the classroom and before students enter the lab. A careful review of the facilities should be a basic part of preparation for each school term. You should investigate the physical environment, identify any safety risks, and inspect your work areas for compliance with safety regulations.

The review of the lab should be thorough, and all safety issues must be addressed immediately. Keep a file of your review, and add to the list each year. This will allow you to continue to raise the standard of safety in your lab and classroom.

Many classroom experiments, demonstrations, and other activities are classics that have been used for years. This familiarity may lead to a comfort that can obscure inherent safety concerns. Review all experiments, demonstrations, and activities for safety concerns before presenting them to the class. Identify and eliminate potential safety hazards.

1. Identify the Risks

Before introducing any activity, demonstration, or experiment to the class, analyze it and consider what could possibly go wrong. Carefully review the list of materials to make sure they are safe. Inspect the equipment in your lab or classroom to make sure it is in good working order. Read the procedures to make sure they are safe. Record any hazards or concerns you identify.

2. Evaluate the Risks

Minimize the risks you identified in the last step without sacrificing learning. Remember that no activity you perform in the lab or classroom is worth risking injury. Thus, extremely hazardous activities, or those that violate your school's policies, must be eliminated. For activities that present smaller risks, analyze each risk carefully to determine its likelihood. If the pedagogical value of the activity does not outweigh the risks, the activity must be eliminated.

3. Select Controls to Address Risks

Even low-risk activities require controls to eliminate or minimize the risks. Make sure that in devising controls you do not substitute an equally or more hazardous alternative. Some control methods include the following:

- Explicit verbal and written warnings may be added or posted.
- Equipment may be rebuilt or relocated, parts may be replaced, or equipment be replaced entirely by safer alternatives.
- Risky procedures may be eliminated.
- Activities may be changed from student activities to teacher demonstrations.

4. Implement and Review Selected Controls

Controls do not help if they are forgotten or not enforced. The implementation and review of controls should be as systematic and thorough as the initial analysis of safety concerns in the lab and laboratory activities.

Some Safety Risks and Preventative Controls

The following list describes several possible safety hazards and controls that can be implemented to resolve them. This list is not complete, but it can be used as a starting point to identify hazards in your laboratory.

Identified risk	Preventative control
Facilities and equipment	
Lab tables are in disrepair, room is poorly lighted and ventilated, faucets and electrical outlets do not work or are difficult to use because of their location.	Work surfaces should be level and stable. There should be adequate lighting and ventilation. Water supplies, drains, and electrical outlets should be in good working order. Any equipment in a dangerous location should not be used; it should be relocated or rendered inoperable.
Wiring, plumbing, and air circulation systems do not work or do not meet current specifications.	Specifications should be kept on file. Conduct a periodic review of all equipment, and document compliance. Damaged fixtures must be labeled as such and must be repaired as soon as possible.
Eyewash fountains and safety showers are present, but no one knows anything about their specifications.	Ensure that eyewash fountains and safety showers meet the requirements of the ANSI standard (Z358.1).
Eyewash fountains are checked and cleaned once at the beginning of each school year. No records are kept of routine checks and maintenance on the safety showers and eyewash fountains.	Flush eyewash fountains for 5 min. every month to remove any bacteria or other organisms from pipes. Test safety showers (measure flow in gallons per min.) and eyewash fountains every 6 months and keep records of the test results.
Labs are conducted in multipurpose rooms, and equipment from other courses remains accessible.	Only the items necessary for a given activity should be available to students. All equipment should be locked away when not in use.
Students are permitted to enter or work in the lab without teacher supervision.	Lock all laboratory rooms whenever a teacher is not present. Supervising teachers must be trained in lab safety and emergency procedures.
Safety equipment and emergency procedures	
Fire and other emergency drills are infrequent, and no records or measurements are made of the results of the drills.	Always carry out critical reviews of fire or other emergency drills. Be sure that plans include alternate routes. Don't wait until an emergency to find the flaws in your plans.
Emergency evacuation plans do not include instructions for securing the lab in the event of an evacuation during a lab activity.	Plan actions in case of emergency: establish what devices should be turned off, which escape route to use, and where to meet outside the building.
Fire extinguishers are in out-of-the-way locations, not on the escape route.	Place fire extinguishers near escape routes so that they will be of use during an emergency.
Fire extinguishers are not maintained. Teachers are not trained to use them.	Document regular maintenance of fire extinguishers. Train supervisory personnel in the proper use of extinguishers. Instruct students not to use an extinguisher but to call for a teacher.

Identified risk	Preventative control
Safety equipment and emergency procedures, *continued*	
Teachers in labs and neighboring classrooms are not trained in CPR or first aid.	Teachers should receive training. The American Red Cross and other groups offer training. Certifications should be kept current with frequent refresher courses.
Teachers are not aware of their legal responsibilities in case of an injury or accident.	Review your faculty handbook for your responsibilities regarding safety in the classroom and laboratory. Contact the legal counsel for your school district to find out the extent of their support and any rules, regulations, or procedures you must follow.
Emergency procedures are not posted. Emergency numbers are kept only at the switchboard or main office. Instructions are given verbally only at the beginning of the year.	Emergency procedures should be posted at all exits and near all safety equipment. Emergency numbers should be posted at all phones, and a script should be provided for the caller to use. Emergency procedures must be reviewed periodically, and students should be reminded of them at the beginning of each activity.
Spills are handled on a case-by-case basis and are cleaned up with whatever materials happen to be on hand.	Have the appropriate equipment and materials available for cleaning up; replace them before expiration dates. Make sure students know to alert you to spilled chemicals, blood, and broken glass.
Work habits and environment	
Safety wear is only used for activities involving chemicals or hot plates.	Aprons and goggles should be worn in the lab at all times. Long hair, loose clothing, and loose jewelry should be secured.
There is no dress code established for the laboratory; students are allowed to wear sandals or open-toed shoes.	Open-toed shoes should never be worn in the laboratory. Do not allow any footwear in the lab that does not cover feet completely.
Students are required to wear safety gear, but teachers and visitors are not.	Always wear safety gear in the lab. Keep extra equipment on hand for visitors.
Safety is emphasized at the beginning of the term but is not mentioned later in the year.	Safety must be the first priority in all lab work. Students should be warned of risks and instructed in emergency procedures for each activity.
There is no assessment of students' knowledge and attitudes regarding safety.	Conduct frequent safety quizzes. Only students with perfect scores should be allowed to work in the lab.
You work alone during your preparation period to organize the day's labs.	Never work alone in a science laboratory or a storage area.
Safety inspections are conducted irregularly and are not documented. Teachers and administrators are unaware of what documentation will be necessary in case of a lawsuit.	Safety reviews should be frequent and regular. All reviews should be documented, and improvements must be implemented immediately. Contact legal counsel for your district to make sure your procedures will protect you in case of a lawsuit.

Identified risk	Preventative control
Purchasing, storing, and using chemicals	
The storeroom is too crowded, so you decide to keep some equipment on the lab benches.	Do not store reagents or equipment on lab benches and keep shelves organized. Never place reactive chemicals (in bottles, beakers, flasks, wash bottles, etc.) near the edges of a lab bench.
You prepare solutions from concentrated stock to save money.	Reduce risks by ordering diluted instead of concentrated substances.
You purchase plenty of chemicals to be sure that you won't run out or to save money.	Purchase chemicals in class-size quantities. Do not purchase or have on hand more than one year's supply of each chemical.
You don't generally read labels on chemicals when preparing solutions for a lab because you already know about a chemical.	Read each label to be sure it states the hazards and describes the precautions and first aid procedures (when appropriate) that apply to the contents in case someone else has to deal with that chemical in an emergency.
You never read the Material Safety Data Sheets (MSDSs) that come with your chemicals.	Always read the Material Safety Data Sheet (MSDS) for a chemical before using it and follow the precautions described. File and organize MSDSs for all chemicals where they can be found easily in case of an emergency.
The main stockroom contains chemicals that haven't been used for years.	Do not leave bottles of chemicals unused on the shelves of the lab for more than one week or unused in the main stockroom for more than one year. Dispose of or use up any leftover chemicals.
No extra precautions are taken when flammable liquids are dispensed from their containers.	When transferring flammable liquids from bulk containers, ground the container, and before transferring to a smaller metal container, ground both containers.
Students are told to put their broken glass and solid chemical wastes in the trash can.	Have separate containers for trash, for broken glass, and for different categories of hazardous chemical wastes.
You store chemicals alphabetically instead of by hazard class. Chemicals are stored without consideration of possible emergencies (fire, earthquake, flood, etc.), which could compound the hazard.	Use MSDSs to determine which chemicals are incompatible. Store chemicals by the hazard class indicated on the MSDS. Store chemicals that are incompatible with common fire-fighting media like water (such as alkali metals) or carbon dioxide (such as alkali and alkaline-earth metals) under conditions that eliminate the possibility of a reaction with water or carbon dioxide if it is necessary to fight a fire in the storage area.
Corrosives are kept above eye level, out of reach from anyone who is not authorized to be in the storeroom.	Always store corrosive chemicals on shelves below eye level. Remember, fumes from many corrosives can destroy metal cabinets and shelving.
Chemicals are kept on the stockroom floor on the days that they will be used so that they are easy to find.	Never store chemicals or other materials on floors or in the aisles of the laboratory or storeroom, even for a few minutes.

Assessments monitor students' mastery of the California Science Standards

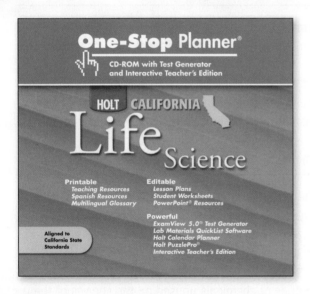

The ExamView® 5.0 Test Generator gives you the power to customize your own assessments.

With the ExamView® 5.0 Test Generator on the **One-Stop Planner®** you can do the following:

- Customize assessments by selecting from a bank of questions that are organized by chapter and are correlated to the **California Science Standards.**

- Post tests to **Holt Online Assessment.** The system automatically grades tests so that you can diagnose student mastery of **California Science Standards** and track student progress.

- Develop multiple reports that track students' progress and mastery of the **California Science Standards.**

Section Assessment

Standards Checks are found throughout each section. Students are encouraged to check their understanding of standards content by answering standards check questions found throughout the chapter.

Section Review assesses students' understanding of standards content covered in the section. Blackline masters of Section Reviews are provided in the **Chapter Resource Files** and in a separate workbook titled **Section and Chapter Reviews. Also available in Spanish.**

Standards Focus at the close of every section provides a quick way to **assess, reteach,** and **re-assess** one or more standards-based concepts in each section.

Standards Check What would happen to the shark if its heart failed? **7.5.b**

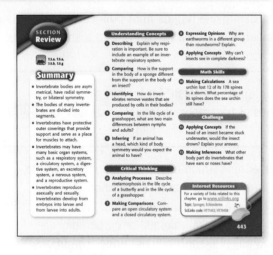

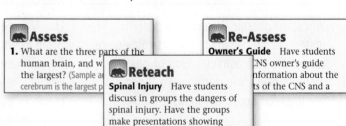

Assess
1. What are the three parts of the human brain, and w[...] the largest? (Sample a[...] cerebrum is the largest p[...]

Reteach
Spinal Injury Have students discuss in groups the dangers of spinal injury. Have the groups make presentations showing

Re-Assess
Owner's Guide Have students [...] CNS owner's guide [...] nformation about the [...]ts of the CNS and a

Section Review Standards Guide			
	Supporting	Mastering	Exceeding
7.2.a	4, 6, 8		12
7.5.a			2, 5
7.5.b	7	1, 3, 11	
7.5.g		9	

The **Section Review Standards Guide** in the Teacher's Edition lets you see which review questions correlate with a specific standard.

Supporting items assess prior knowledge that students need to know before they can master the standard.

Mastering items assess whether students fully understand the standard or a specific part of the standard.

Exceeding items require students to extend their understanding of the standard or to apply this understanding to another scientific concept.

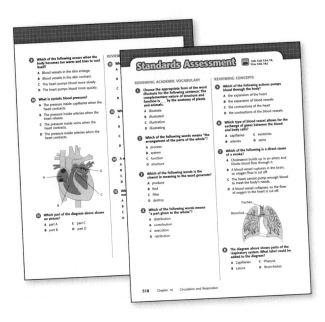

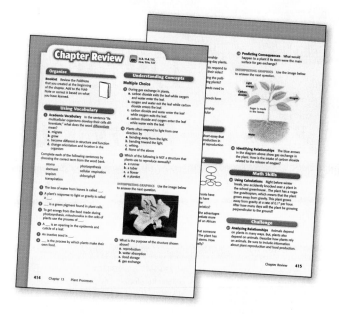

Chapter Assessment

Chapter Review checks students' understanding of all **California Science Standards** covered in the chapter. This review includes a variety of question types and a range of thinking levels. Blackline masters of Chapter Reviews are provided in the **Chapter Resource Files** and in a separate workbook titled **Section and Chapter Reviews. Also available in Spanish.**

Standards Assessment helps students review the **California Science Standards** and prepare for testing. Each two-page assessment includes a review of academic vocabulary and concepts related to the **California Science Standards** covered in the chapter and a connection to prior learning. **Assessment Doctor** in the Teacher's Edition helps you diagnose why a student answered a question incorrectly.

Standards Review Workbook provides a review of **California Science Standards,** and additional practice to assess student's mastery of the standard. **Also available in Spanish.**

Chapter Resource Files include a **Pretest,** a **Performance-Based Assessment** plus three levels of **Chapter Tests**— **BASIC**, **GENERAL**, and **ADVANCED**—to meet the needs of your classroom. The **GENERAL** test is also available in Spanish.

Brain Food Video Quizzes (on DVD and VHS) are game show-style quizzes that assess students' progress and help them prepare for tests.

The **Chapter Review Standards Guide** in the Teacher's Edition lets you see which review questions correlate with a specific standard.

Chapter Review Standards Guide

	Supporting	Mastering	Exceeding
7.1.b	27		
7.1.d	4, 8, 27	5, 18	20, 24–25
7.1.f	10, 13–14	22	
7.2.a		11, 23	19
7.5.a	6, 9		21, 24
7.5.f		12, 15, 17	16, 27

Standards Review Workbook

HOLT CALIFORNIA

Life Science

HOLT, RINEHART AND WINSTON

ASSESSMENT DOCTOR

Question 1: The correct answer is B. The past participle of *illustrate* is *illustrated.* To *illustrate* something is to make clear or to show the subject.

Question 2: The correct answer is D. The *structure* of something is the way it is built or constructed. The structure of an object is closely related to the function that object performs.

Differentiated instruction provides universal access for all students

English Learners

Mapping Photosynthesis To help students understand both the terms and the process of photosynthesis, ask them to create a flow chart showing the steps of photosynthesis. Have them work in pairs and use as many of the following words as they can: *photosynthesis, pigments, light energy, chlorophyll, carbon dioxide, water, food, glucose, stored energy,* and *oxygen.* **LS** Visual Co-op Learning

Advanced Learners/GATE

Cellular Respiration Ask students who can benefit from more in-depth studies to work together to prepare an overhead presentation using words and pictures to show the difference between a person breathing and the cellular respiration that takes place within a person's cells. Allow time for the students to share the project with the whole class. **LS** Visual/Interpersonal

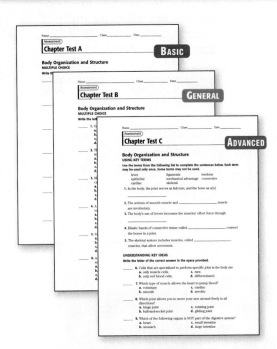

Universal Access/Differentiated Instruction

Additional strategies for English Learners, struggling readers, advanced learners/GATE students, basic learners, and special education students are included in the Teacher's Edition.

Differentiated Worksheets

Holt California Science provides leveled worksheets for the following resources:

- Chapter Tests— **BASIC** , **GENERAL** , and **ADVANCED**
- Datasheets for **Explore Activities, Quick Labs,** and **Chapter Labs**— **BASIC** , **GENERAL** , and **ADVANCED**
- Directed Reading Worksheets— **BASIC** and **GENERAL**
- Vocabulary and Section Summary Worksheets— **BASIC** and **GENERAL**

Differentiated Workbooks

Study Guide A for **BASIC** students includes:

- Directed Reading Worksheets A
- Vocabulary and Section Summary Worksheets A

Study Guide B for **GENERAL** students includes:

- Directed Reading Worksheets B
- Vocabulary and Section Summary Worksheets B

Interactive Reader and Study Guide makes the content from the Student Edition accessible to struggling readers and English Learners. Reading strategies and directed reading questions are also provided to help develop students' reading skills.

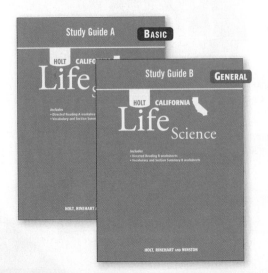

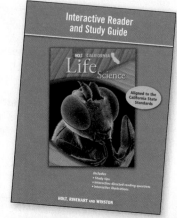

Resources for English Learners

Open the door for students who are frequently locked out. EL resources and translations help you make science accessible to your EL students.

- **Student Edition** in Spanish
- **Interactive Reader and Study Guide**
- **Spanish Glossary** in both the English and Spanish Student Edition
- **Study Guide A** in Spanish
- **Section and Chapter Reviews Workbook** in Spanish
- **Assessments** in Spanish
- **Standards Review Workbook** in Spanish
- **Guided Audio Reading CD-Program** in Spanish
- **Lab Datasheets** available on the **Lab Generator**® in Spanish
- **Strategies for English Learners**
- **Multilingual Glossary for Science** provides simple definitions of key science terms in multiple languages.

All of the resources for Universal Access that are listed on these pages are available on the One Stop Planner®.

Meeting Individual Needs

Students have a wide range of abilities and learning exceptionalities. These pages show you how *Holt California Science* provides resources and strategies to help you tailor your instruction to engage every student in your classroom.

Learning Exceptionality	Resources and Activities for Differentiating Instruction	
Visual Impairments Students who are blind or who have difficulty seeing	• Universal Access resources labeled *Special Education Students* • Activities labeled **LS Auditory**	• Activities labeled *Co-op Learning* • Assessments that use oral presentations
Struggling Readers Students who have dyslexia or dysgraphia, and students reading below grade level	• Universal Access resources labeled *Struggling Readers* • Activities labeled **BASIC** • *Reteach*	• Activities labeled **LS Visual**, **LS Kinesthetic**, or **LS Auditory** • *Reading Strategies* • *Graphic Organizers*
Hearing Impairments Students who are deaf or who have difficulty hearing	• Universal Access resources labeled *Special Education Students* • Activities labeled **LS Visual**	• Activities labeled *Co-op Learning* • Assessments that use written presentations
Developmental Delays Students who are functioning far below grade level because of mental retardation, autism, or brain injury	• Universal Access resources labeled *Special Education Students* or *Basic Learners*	• Activities labeled **BASIC** • *Reteach* • *Reinforcement worksheets*
Behavior Control Issues Students learning to manage their behavior	• Universal Access resources labeled *Special Education Students* • Activities labeled **BASIC**	• Assignments that actively involve students and help students develop confidence and improved behaviors
Basic Learners Students having difficulty understanding abstract or complex concepts, and slow learners	• Universal Access resources labeled *Basic Learners* • Activities labeled **BASIC** • *Reteach* • Hands-on activities or projects	• Activities labeled **LS Visual**, **LS Kinesthetic**, or **LS Auditory** • *Graphic Organizers* • *Reinforcement worksheets*
Attention Deficit Disorders Students experiencing difficulty completing a task that has many steps, difficulty handling long assignments, or difficulty concentrating without sensory input from physical activity	• Universal Access resources labeled *Special Education Students* or *Basic Learners* • Activities labeled **BASIC** • *Reteach* • Activities labeled *Co-op Learning*	• Activities labeled **LS Visual**, **LS Kinesthetic**, or **LS Auditory** • Activities that break concepts into small chunks • Oral presentations instead of written tests or assignments
English Learners Students learning English	• Universal Access resources labeled *English Learners* • *Multilingual Glossary*	• *Reteach* • Activities labeled **LS Visual**
Advanced Learners / Gifted and Talented (GATE) Students who are performing above grade level	• Universal Access resources labeled *Advanced Learners/GATE* • Activities labeled **ADVANCED**	• Activities that involve multiple tasks, a strong degree of independence, and student initiative

Learning Styles The following are descriptions of the learning styles found in the *Teacher's Edition:*

LS Visual learning through pictures, colors, and shapes

LS Verbal learning through words

LS Logical learning through patterns, reason, or numbers

LS Kinesthetic learning through physical activity and touch

LS Auditory learning through sound

LS Interpersonal learning through interactions with others

LS Intrapersonal learning through independent work and reflection

General inclusion Strategies

The following strategies can help you modify instruction to help students who struggle with common classroom difficulties.

A student experiencing difficulty with...	May benefit if you...	
Beginning assignments	• Assign work in small amounts • Have the student use cooperative or paired learning • Provide varied and interesting activities	• Allow choice in assignments or projects • Reinforce participation • Seat the student closer to you
Following directions	• Gain the student's attention before giving directions • Break up the task into small steps • Give written directions rather than oral directions • Use short, simple phrases	• Stand near the student when you are giving directions • Have the student repeat directions to you • Prepare the student for changes in activity • Give visual cues by posting general routines • Reinforce improvement in or approximation of following directions
Keeping track of assignments	• Have the student use folders for assignments • Have the student use assignment notebooks	• Have the student keep a checklist of assignments and highlight assignments when they are turned in
Reading the textbook	• Provide outlines of the textbook content • Reduce the length of required reading • Allow extra time for reading • Have the students read aloud in small groups	• Have the student use peer or mentor readers • Have the student use books on tape or CD • Discuss the content of the textbook in class after reading
Staying on task	• Reduce distracting elements in the classroom • Provide a task-completion checklist • Seat the student near you	• Provide alternative ways to complete assignments, such as oral projects taped with a buddy
Behavioral or social skills	• Model the appropriate behaviors • Establish class rules, and reiterate them often • Reinforce positive behavior • Assign a mentor as a positive role model to the student • Contract with the student for expected behaviors • Reinforce the desired behaviors or any steps toward improvement	• Separate the student from any peer who stimulates the inappropriate behavior • Provide a "cooling off" period before talking with the student • Address academic/instructional problems that may contribute to disruptive behaviors • Include parents in the problem-solving process through conferences, home visits, and frequent communication
Attendance	• Recognize and reinforce attendance by giving incentives or verbal praise • Emphasize the importance of attendance by letting the student know that he or she was missed when he or she was absent	• Encourage the student's desire to be in school by planning activities that are likely to be enjoyable, giving the student a preferred responsibility to be performed in class, and involving the student in extracurricular activities • Schedule problem-solving meeting with parents, faculty, or both
Taking Tests	• Prepare the student for testing by teaching ways to study in pairs, such as using flashcards, practice tests, and study guides, and by promoting adequate sleep, nourishment, and exercise • Decrease visual distraction by improving the visual design of the test through use of larger type, spacing, consistent layout, and shorter sentences	• During testing, allow the student to respond orally on tape or to respond using a computer; to use notes; to take breaks; to take the test in another location; to work without time constraints; or to take the test in several short sessions

Align your lessons with the California Science Standards

15 Standards Course of Study

The elements listed in the Standards Course of Study provide a base for presenting, supporting, and assessing the California Grade 7 Science Standards. Use this Standards Course of Study as a base for planning your lessons.

Why Teach
Body Organization and Structure

This chapter was designed to cover the California Grade 7 Science Standards about structure and function and how structure and function apply to the human body (7.1.f, 7.5.a, 7.5.b, 7.5.c, 7.6.h, and 7.6.i). This chapter describes the levels of organization in the human body as well as the relationship between structure and function in human body parts with an emphasis on bones and muscles. This chapter also details the important relationship of bones and muscles in the human body.

After they have completed this chapter, students will begin a chapter about the human circulatory system.

California Standards

Focus on Life Sciences

7.1.f Students know that as multicellular organisms develop, their cells differentiate.

7.5.a Students know plants and animals have levels of organization for structure and function, including cells, tissues, organs, organ systems, and the whole organism.

7.5.b Students know organ systems function because of the contributions of individual organs, tissues, and cells. The failure of any part can affect the entire system.

7.5.c Students know how bones and muscles work together to provide a structural framework for movement.

7.6.h Students know how to compare joints in the body (wrist, shoulder, thigh) with structures used in machines and simple devices (hinge, ball-and-socket, and sliding joints).

7.6.i Students know how levers confer mechanical advantage and how the application of this principle applies to the musculoskeletal system.

Investigation and Experimentation

7.7.c Communicate the logical connection among hypotheses, science concepts, tests conducted, data collected, and conclusions drawn from the scientific evidence.

7.7.d Construct scale models, maps, and appropriately labeled diagrams to communicate scientific knowledge (e.g., motion of Earth's plates and cell structure).

Chapter Pacing

Getting Started — 45 min, pp. 464–465
The Big Idea The human body is composed of major systems that have differing functions, but all of the systems work together to maintain homeostasis.
7.5.c, 7.6.h, 7.7.d

Section 1 Body Organization — 60 min, pp. 466–471
Key Concept The human body functions because of the contributions of cells, tissues, organs, and organ systems.
7.1.f, 7.5.a, 7.5.b, 7.7.d

Section 2 The Skeletal System — 60 min, pp. 472–475
Key Concept The skeletal system is an organ system. The functions of the skeletal system include support, protection, movement, and the production of blood cells.
7.5.a, 7.5.c, 7.6.h, 7.7.c

Section 3 The Muscular System — 60 min, pp. 476–481
Key Concept The muscular system is an organ system. The skeletal and muscular systems work together to provide a structural framework for movement.
7.5.a, 7.5.c, 7.6.i

Wrapping Up — 180 min, pp. 482–491
7.6.j, 7.7.c, 7.7.d

Basic Learners
- TE Key Term Review, p. 469
- TE Modifying a Hypothesis as a Class, p. 484
- Reinforcement Worksheet
- Chapter Test A
- Differentiated Datasheets A for Labs and Activities ■
- Study Guide A

Advanced Learners/GATE
- TE Skeletal System Dysfunction, p. 475
- TE Classifying Exercises, p. 480
- TE Additional Hypotheses, p. 484
- Critical Thinking Worksheet
- Chapter Test C
- Differentiated Datasheets C for Labs and Activities ■

461A Chapter 15 • Body Organization and Structure

General Learners BASIC Most students fall into this category. These students often need extra help mastering abstract ideas and concepts and also need help in synthesizing ideas.

Basic Learners GENERAL Students at this level can only manage core assignments. These students have difficulty understanding abstract or complex concepts and may be limited in their ability to learn.

Advanced Learners / GATE ADVANCED Students at this level are capable of solving hypothetical problems and applying deductive logic. They can readily master the challenge of critical-thinking and synthesis activities.

Pacing Each **Standards Course of Study** breaks down the chapter into instructional blocks. The **Standards Course of Study** lists the activities, labs, and resources that provide complete instruction on the **California Science Content Standards** covered in the chapter. The **Standards Course of Study** is the curriculum recommended for **GENERAL** students.

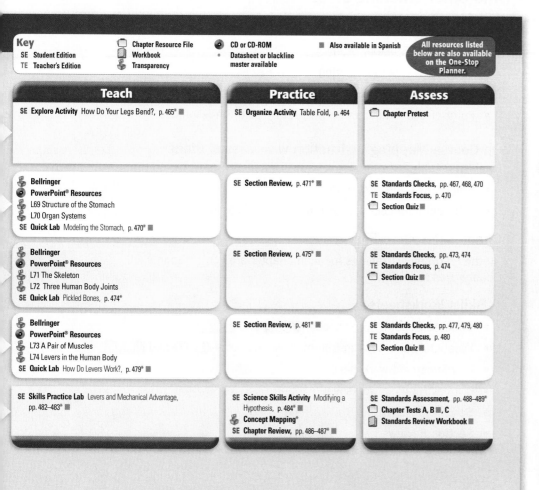

Key

SE Student Edition	☐ Chapter Resource File
TE Teacher's Edition	☐ Workbook
	☐ Transparency

◉ CD or CD-ROM
* Datasheet or blackline master available

■ Also available in Spanish

All resources listed below are also available on the One-Stop Planner.

Teach

SE **Explore Activity** How Do Your Legs Bend?, p. 465* ■

🔔 **Bellringer**
◉ **PowerPoint® Resources**
☐ L69 Structure of the Stomach
☐ L70 Organ Systems
SE **Quick Lab** Modeling the Stomach, p. 470* ■

🔔 **Bellringer**
◉ **PowerPoint® Resources**
☐ L71 The Skeleton
☐ L72 Three Human Body Joints
SE **Quick Lab** Pickled Bones, p. 474*

🔔 **Bellringer**
◉ **PowerPoint® Resources**
☐ L73 A Pair of Muscles
☐ L74 Levers in the Human Body
SE **Quick Lab** How Do Levers Work?, p. 479* ■

SE **Skills Practice Lab** Levers and Mechanical Advantage, pp. 482–483* ■

Practice

SE **Organize Activity** Table Fold, p. 464

SE **Section Review**, p. 471* ■

SE **Section Review**, p. 475* ■

SE **Section Review**, p. 481* ■

SE **Science Skills Activity** Modifying a Hypothesis, p. 484* ■
☐ **Concept Mapping***
SE **Chapter Review**, pp. 486–487* ■

Assess

☐ **Chapter Pretest**

SE **Standards Checks**, pp. 467, 468, 470
TE **Standards Focus**, p. 470
☐ **Section Quiz** ■

SE **Standards Checks**, pp. 473, 474
TE **Standards Focus**, p. 474
☐ **Section Quiz** ■

SE **Standards Checks**, pp. 477, 479, 480
TE **Standards Focus**, p. 480
☐ **Section Quiz** ■

SE **Standards Assessment**, pp. 488–489*
☐ **Chapter Tests A, B** ■, **C**
☐ **Standards Review Workbook** ■

Universal Access Differentiated resources are listed under **Resources for Universal Access/ Differentiated Instruction.** Lesson plans that focus on differentiated instruction can be found in the teacher resource titled **On Course Mapping Instruction with Lesson Plans for Universal Access.**

Resources for Universal Access · Differentiated Instruction

English Learners
TE Demonstration, pp. 473, 477, 478
TE Using the Figure, p. 473
TE Visualizing Joints, p. 475
TE Group Activity, p. 476
☐ Vocabulary and Section Summary A ■, B

☐ Section Quizzes ■
☐ Chapter Tests A, B ■
☐ Differentiated Datasheets A, B, and C for Labs and Activities ■
☐ Study Guide A ■
☐ Multilingual Glossary

Struggling Readers
TE Reading Strategy, pp. 467, 478
TE Visual Aids for Levers, p. 478

Special Education Students
TE Body Tissue Clues, p. 466
TE Body System Cooperation, p. 468
TE Finding Bones in the Body, p. 472
TE Muscle Pairs, p. 476
TE Demonstration, p. 484

To help plan your lessons, refer to the On Course Mapping Instruction booklet.

Standards Course of Study   461B

English Learners Students at this level are learning English. These students may be at various learning levels.

Struggling Readers Students at this level have difficulty understanding text and recalling or retaining information from text that they have read.

Special Education Students Students at this level have learning disabilities including visual impairments, hearing impairments, behavioral issues, or delayed development.

Instruction and Planning

Where do I locate lesson plans, additional resources, and other teaching aids?

Teacher's Edition

- Standards Course of Study
- Standards-based instruction and strategies
- Universal Access/Differentiated Instruction
- Point-of-use reminders for integrating program resources

On Course Mapping Instruction with Lesson Plans for Universal Access

- Standards Course of Study
- Differentiated Lesson Plans for a diverse classroom

Chapter Resource File

All the following worksheets for each chapter are contained in each Chapter Resource File.

Skills Worksheets

- Directed Reading worksheets— **BASIC** and **GENERAL**
- Vocabulary and Section Summary worksheets— **BASIC** and **GENERAL**
- Reinforcement worksheet
- Critical Thinking worksheet
- SciLinks® Activity
- Section Reviews
- Chapter Review

Assessments

- Chapter Pretest with Teacher Notes
- Section Quizzes
- Chapter Tests— **BASIC**, **GENERAL**, and **ADVANCED**
- Performance-Based Assessment with Teacher Notes
- Standards Assessment

Datasheets for Labs and Activities

- Datasheets for Explore Activity— **BASIC**, **GENERAL**, and **ADVANCED**
- Datasheets for Quick Labs— **BASIC**, **GENERAL**, and **ADVANCED**
- Datasheets for Chapter Lab— **BASIC**, **GENERAL**, and **ADVANCED**
- Datasheet for Science Skills Activity

Transparencies

- Teaching Transparencies
- Chapter Starter Transparency
- Bellringer Transparencies
- Concept Mapping Transparencies
- Standards Review Transparencies

One-Stop Planner®

- Holt Calendar Planner
- Editable Lesson Plans
- All reproducible ancillaries
- ExamView® 5.0 Test Generator (**Also available in Spanish**)
- Holt PuzzlePro
- PowerPoint® Resources
- Interactive Teacher's Edition

Lab Generator

- Editable labs (**Also available in Spanish**)
- Formatted templates to develop new labs
- Lab Materials QuickList Software
- All labs correlated to the California Science Standards

What resources are available to ensure that Advanced Learners/GATE master the standards?

Teacher's Edition Activities

- Universal Access/Differentiated Instruction for Advanced Learners/GATE
- Connection Activities

Chapter Resource Files

- Critical Thinking Worksheet
- Chapter Test C
- Datasheets C for Explore Activity, Quick Labs, and Chapter Lab

What resources are available to ensure that English Learners master the standards?

Teacher's Edition Activities

- Universal Access/Differentiated Instruction for English Learners
- Group Activities, Demonstrations, Wordwise

Resources for English Learners

- Student Edition in Spanish
- Spanish Glossary in both the English and Spanish Student Edition
- Study Guide A in Spanish
- Section and Chapter Reviews in Spanish
- Assessments in Spanish
- Guided Audio Reading CD Program in Spanish
- Lab Datasheets available in Spanish on the Lab Generator
- Strategies for English Learners
- Multilingual Glossary
- Standards Review Workbook in Spanish

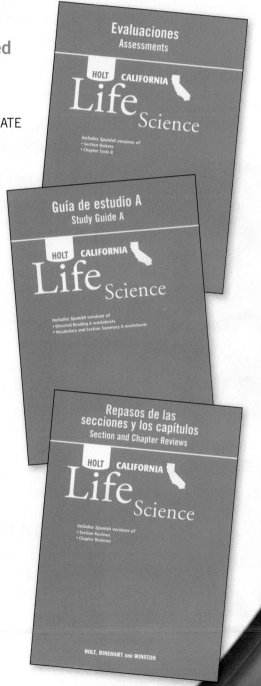

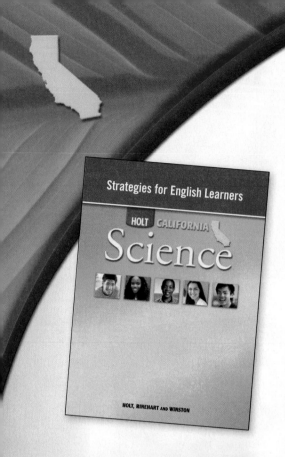

What modified materials are available for students who are struggling?

Teacher's Edition Activities

- Universal Access/Differentiated Instruction for Basic Learners, Struggling Readers, and Special Education Students
- Reading Strategies
- Activities and Group Activities
- Demonstrations

Chapter Resource Files

- Directed Reading Worksheet A
- Vocabulary and Section Summary Worksheet A
- Reinforcement Worksheet
- Chapter Test A
- Datasheets A for Explore Activity, Quick Labs, and Chapter Lab

Interactive Reader and Study Guide

What resources can I use to determine if my students are making progress in mastering the standards?

Student Edition

- Standards Checks
- Section Reviews
- Chapter Review

Teacher's Edition Activities

- Standards Focus, with Assess, Reteach, Re-Assess

Chapter Resource Files

- Section Reviews
- Chapter Review
- Chapter Pretest with Teacher Notes
- Standards Assessment with Assessment Doctors and Diagnostic Teaching Tips
- Section Quizzes
- Chapter Tests—**BASIC**, **GENERAL**, and **ADVANCED**
- One-Stop Planner® ExamView® 5.0 Test Generator
- Online Edition Holt Online Assessment

What teacher training resources are available to help me grow professionally?

- In-service and staff development as part of your **Holt California Science** product purchase.
- Holt Science Professional Reference for Teachers
- Strategies for English Learners
- Holt Science Skills Workshop: Reading in the Content Area, Teacher's Edition

HOLT CALIFORNIA
Life Science

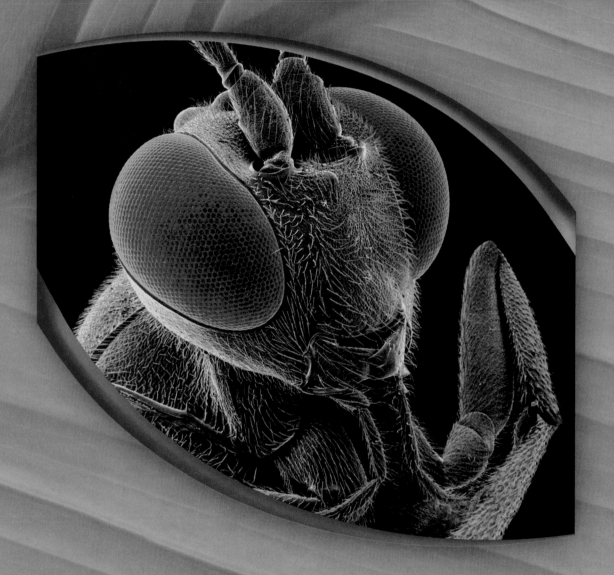

HOLT, RINEHART AND WINSTON

A Harcourt Education Company

Orlando • **Austin** • New York • San Diego • London

Acknowledgments

Contributing Authors

Katy Z. Allen
Science Writer
Wayland, Massachusetts

Linda Ruth Berg, Ph.D.
Adjunct Professor of Natural Sciences
St. Petersburg College
St. Petersburg, Florida

Barbara Christopher
Science Writer and Editor
Austin, Texas

Richard Cowen
Senior Lecturer Emeritus
Department of Geology
University of California, Davis
Davis, California

Leila Dumas, MA
Former Physics Teacher
Lago Vista, Texas

Jennie Dusheck
Science Writer
Santa Cruz, California

Robert H. Fronk, Ph.D.
Professor
Science and Mathematics Education
    Department
The University of Texas at Austin
Austin, Texas

Gregory K. Pregill, Ph.D.
Professor
Department of Biology
University of San Diego
San Diego, California

Anne Stephens, MA
Science Teacher
Marsh Junior High School
Co-Director, Hands-on Science Lab
College of Natural Sciences
California State University, Chico
Chico, California

Lee Summerlin, Ph.D.
Professor of Chemistry (retired)
University of Alabama
Birmingham, Alabama

Mark F. Taylor, Ph.D.
Associate Professor of Biology
Biology Department
Baylor University
Waco, Texas

Consultants

Ellen McPeek Glisan
Special Needs Consultant
San Antonio, Texas

Belinda Dunnick Karge, Ph.D.
Chair, Department of Special Education
California State University, Fullerton
Fullerton, California

Robin Scarcella, Ph.D.
*Director, Academic English and English as a
    Second Language Program*
University of California, Irvine
Irvine, California

Safety Reviewer

Jim Adams
Science Education Technician (retired)
Las Positas College
Livermore, California

Jack Gerlovich, Ph.D.
Associate Professor
School of Education
Drake University
Des Moines, Iowa

Senior Advisors

Susana E. Deustua, Ph.D.
Director of Educational Activities
American Astronomical Society
Washington, D.C.

Frances Marie Gipson, MA
*Director of the UCLA and District 3
    LAUSD Partnership*
Department of Secondary Literacy
University of California, Los Angeles; Center X
Los Angeles, California

Ron Hage
Science Partner
University of California, Los Angeles;
    Los Angeles Unified School District
Los Angeles, California

James E. Marshall, Ph.D.
Professor of Science Education
Department of Curriculum
    and Instruction
California State University, Fresno
Fresno, California

Richard D. McCallum, Ph.D.
Research Specialist
Graduate School of Education
University of California, Berkeley
Berkeley, California

Acknowledgments
continued on p. 667

ISBN 0-03-046459-5

1 2 3 4 5 6 7   048   10 09 08 07 06

Contents in Brief

Contents

CHAPTER

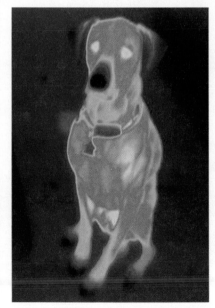

Contents   **v**

UNIT 2 Cells

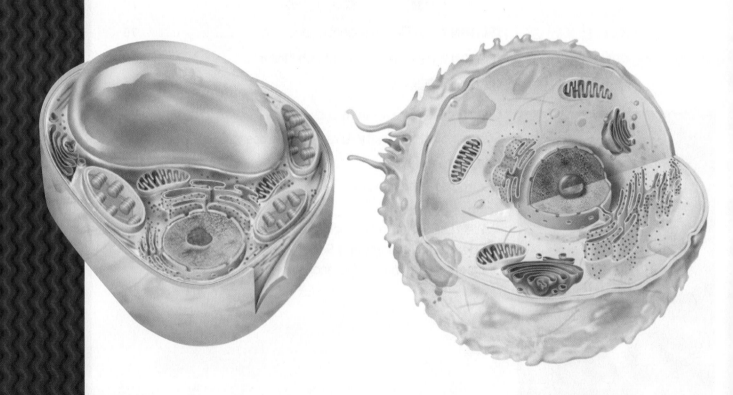

UNIT 3 Heredity and Genes

UNIT 4 Earth and Life History

CHAPTER

11

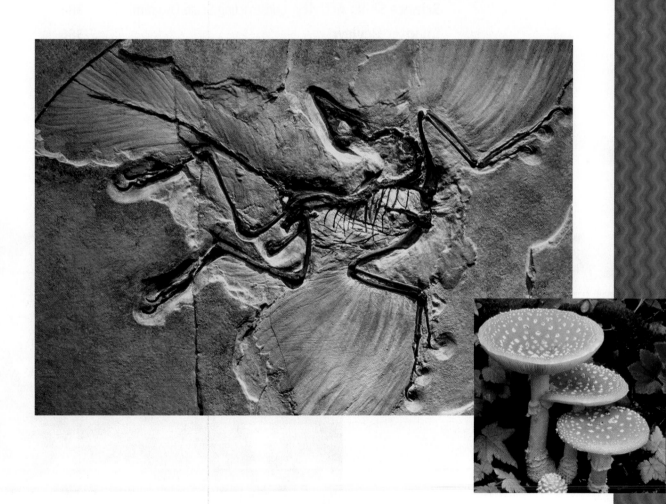

UNIT 5 Structure and Function in Plants and Animals

CHAPTER

12

UNIT 6 Human Body Systems

CHAPTER

15

CHAPTER 18

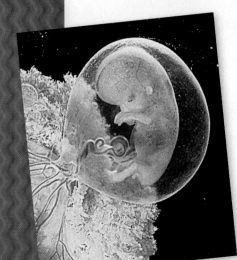

Chapter Previews

Improving Comprehension

Jump-start your learning!

Each chapter starts with a **Chapter Preview** that does two things. The Chapter Preview describes how to make a **Graphic Organizer** to improve your comprehension. And it helps you "unpack" the **California Science Standards,** which will help you better understand what the standards say and mean.

Unpacking the California Standards

Standard 🐻

Organize Activities

Reading Strategies

There are ways to make reading easier.

Reading Strategies at the beginning of each section will help you remember and organize information as you read the chapter.

Math Practice

Math Focus

Quick Labs

The more labs, the better!

Take a minute to browse the variety of exciting labs in this textbook. All **labs** are designed to help you experience science firsthand. But please don't forget to be safe. Read the Safety First! section before starting any of the labs.

Chapter Labs

Labs and Activities

Explore Activities

Start your engines with an activity!

Get motivated to learn by doing an activity at the beginning of each chapter. The **Explore Activity** helps you gain scientific understanding of the chapter material through hands-on experience.

Internet Activities

Get caught in the Web!

Go to **go.hrw.com** for **Internet Activities** related to each chapter. To find the Internet Activity for a particular chapter, just type in the keyword.

Labs and Activities

School-to-Home Activities

Science is not just for the classroom!

Bring science into your home by doing **School-to-Home Activities** with a family member or another adult in your household.

Science Skills Activities

Learn and practice the skills of a scientist!

The **Science Skills Activity** in each chapter helps you build investigation and experimentation skills. These skills are essential to learning science.

Science in Action

Science moves beyond the classroom!

Read **Science in Action** articles to learn more about science in the real world. These articles will give you an idea of how interesting, strange, helpful, and action-packed science is. And if your thirst is still not quenched, go to **go.hrw.com** for details about each article.

How to Use Your Textbook

Your textbook may seem confusing at first. But with a little introduction, you'll realize that your science textbook can be a big help. In the next few pages, you'll learn how this textbook can help you become a successful science student. You will also learn how interesting and exciting science can be.

Jump-Start Your Learning

The Chapter Preview helps you brush up on your learning skills and helps you focus on what is important.

Each chapter starts with instructions on how to make a **Graphic Organizer,** a tool for organizing the information that you read. A sample Graphic Organizer gives you a sneak preview of the major concepts in the chapter.

California has important **Science Standards** that guide your learning. Use this page to get to know the standards better. The chart contains **Academic Vocabulary** found in the standards. Also, **What It Means** describes each standard in basic terms.

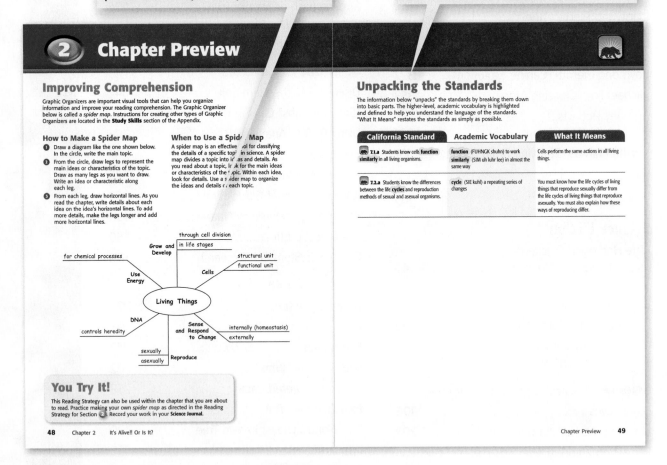

2 Chapter Preview

Improving Comprehension

Graphic Organizers are important visual tools that can help you organize information and improve your reading comprehension. The Graphic Organizer below is called a *spider map*. Instructions for creating other types of Graphic Organizers are located in the **Study Skills** section of the Appendix.

How to Make a Spider Map

1. Draw a diagram like the one shown below. In the circle, write the main topic.
2. From the circle, draw legs to represent the main ideas or characteristics of the topic. Draw as many legs as you want to draw. Write an idea or characteristic along each leg.
3. From each leg, draw horizontal lines. As you read the chapter, write details about each idea on the idea's horizontal lines. To add more details, make the legs longer and add more horizontal lines.

When to Use a Spider Map

A spider map is an effective tool for classifying the details of a specific topic in science. A spider map divides a topic into ideas and details. As you read about a topic, look for the main ideas or characteristics of the topic. Within each idea, look for details. Use a spider map to organize the ideas and details of each topic.

You Try It!

This Reading Strategy can also be used within the chapter that you are about to read. Practice making your own *spider map* as directed in the Reading Strategy for Section ②. Record your work in your **Science Journal.**

48   Chapter 2   It's Alive!! Or Is It?

Unpacking the Standards

The information below "unpacks" the standards by breaking them down into basic parts. The higher-level, academic vocabulary is highlighted and defined to help you understand the language of the standards. "What It Means" restates the standards as simply as possible.

California Standard	Academic Vocabulary	What It Means
7.1.a Students know cells **function similarly** in all living organisms.	**function** (FUHNGK shuhn) to work **similarly** (SIM uh luhr lee) in almost the same way	Cells perform the same actions in all living things.
7.2.a Students know the differences between the life **cycles** and reproduction methods of sexual and asexual organisms.	**cycle** (SIE kuhl) a repeating series of changes	You must know how the life cycles of living things that reproduce sexually differ from the life cycles of living things that reproduce asexually. You must also explain how these ways of reproducing differ.

Chapter Preview   49

Step into Science

The beginning of each chapter is designed to get you involved with science. You will immediately see that science is cool!

Check out the **Big Idea** to see the focus of the chapter. The entire chapter supports this Big Idea.

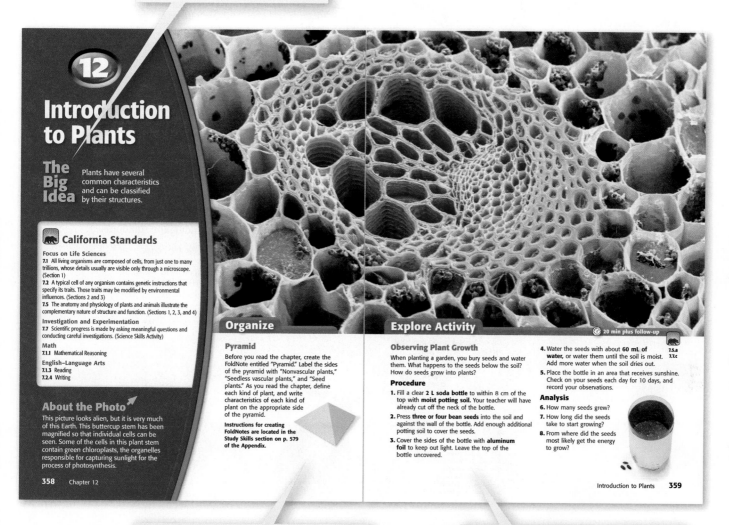

12

Introduction to Plants

The Big Idea
Plants have several common characteristics and can be classified by their structures.

California Standards

Focus on Life Sciences
7.1 All living organisms are composed of cells, from just one to many trillions, whose details usually are visible only through a microscope. (Section 1)
7.2 A typical cell of any organism contains genetic instructions that specify its traits. Those traits may be modified by environmental influences. (Sections 2 and 3)
7.5 The anatomy and physiology of plants and animals illustrate the complementary nature of structure and function. (Sections 1, 2, 3, and 4)

Investigation and Experimentation
7.7 Scientific progress is made by asking meaningful questions and conducting careful investigations. (Science Skills Activity)

Math
7.1.1 Mathematical Reasoning

English–Language Arts
7.1.3 Reading
7.2.4 Writing

About the Photo
This picture looks alien, but it is very much of this Earth. This buttercup stem has been magnified so that individual cells can be seen. Some of the cells in this plant stem contain green chloroplasts, the organelles responsible for capturing sunlight for the process of photosynthesis.

358 Chapter 12

Organize

Pyramid
Before you read the chapter, create the FoldNote entitled "Pyramid." Label the sides of the pyramid with "Nonvascular plants," "Seedless vascular plants," and "Seed plants." As you read the chapter, define each kind of plant, and write characteristics of each kind of plant on the appropriate side of the pyramid.

Instructions for creating FoldNotes are located in the Study Skills section on p. 579 of the Appendix.

Explore Activity

Observing Plant Growth
When planting a garden, you bury seeds and water them. What happens to the seeds below the soil? How do seeds grow into plants?

Procedure
1. Fill a clear **2 L soda bottle** to within 8 cm of the top with **moist potting soil.** Your teacher will have already cut off the neck of the bottle.
2. Press **three or four bean seeds** into the soil and against the wall of the bottle. Add enough additional potting soil to cover the seeds.
3. Cover the sides of the bottle with **aluminum foil** to keep out light. Leave the top of the bottle uncovered.
4. Water the seeds with about **60 mL of water,** or water them until the soil is moist. Add more water when the soil dries out.
5. Place the bottle in an area that receives sunshine. Check on your seeds each day for 10 days, and record your observations.

Analysis
6. How many seeds grew?
7. How long did the seeds take to start growing?
8. From where did the seeds most likely get the energy to grow?

🕐 20 min plus follow-up

Introduction to Plants **359**

You can't be organized enough when learning science. The **FoldNote** provided here gives you note-taking options. These FoldNotes are fun to make and help you understand and remember what you have learned.

It is never too early for exploration in science. The **Explore Activity** gives you a chance to get some hands-on experience right away. Each activity is a lot of fun and introduces you to one or more California Science Standards from the chapter.

Read for Meaning

You want to get the most out of your reading. One way to do so is to take a minute to learn how the sections are organized.

Be sure to start each section by reading the information in the margin. This information tells you **What You Will Learn** and **Why It Matters.** Believe it or not, knowing these things will improve your learning.

Don't skip the **Reading Strategy.** Each strategy provides tips on how to take better notes and how to read for better understanding.

The **Key Concept** sets the stage for your understanding of the section. Read it carefully, and notice how it relates to the chapter's Big Idea. Together, the Big Idea and the Key Concepts give you an excellent overview of the chapter.

SECTION 1

What You Will Learn
- In plant cells, chloroplasts capture energy from the sun in order to make food during photosynthesis.
- Cells release energy from food through either cellular respiration or fermentation.

Why It Matters
Understanding the differences in how plants and animals obtain energy is an important part of cell biology.

Vocabulary
- photosynthesis
- cellular respiration
- fermentation

READING STRATEGY

Graphic Organizer In your **Science Journal,** create a Cause-and-Effect Map about fermentation.

photosynthesis
(FOHT oh SIN thuh sis) the process by which plants, algae, and some bacteria use sunlight, carbon dioxide, and water to make food
Wordwise The root *phot-* means "light."

Wordwise chloroplast
The root *chlor-* means "green." The root *plast-* means "to form."

7.1.b Students know the characteristics that distinguish plant cells from animal cells, including chloroplasts and cell walls.
7.1.d Students know that mitochondria liberate energy for the work that cells do and that chloroplasts capture sunlight energy for photosynthesis.

148 Chapter 5   The Cell in Action

Cell Energy

Key Concept   All cells need energy to carry out cell functions. However, cells may obtain and process energy in different ways.

▶ Why do you get hungry? Feeling hungry is your body's way of telling you that your cells need energy. All cells need energy to live, grow, and reproduce. Plant cells get their energy from the sun. Many animal cells get their energy from food.

From Sun to Cell
Nearly all of the energy that fuels life comes from the sun. Plants absorb energy from the sun and change the energy into food through a process that plants make gives them a source of energy for the org

Photosynthesis
Plant cells have molecule molecules are called *pigme* the main pigment used in ph green color. Chlorophyll s fo

Plants cannot use energy directly from the sun to perform life processes. Instead they use the sun's energy to change carbon dioxide and water into food. The food is in the form of the simple sugar glucose. Glucose can be stored and used by the plant's cells. Photosynthesis also produces oxygen. The chemical equation for photosynthesis is shown in **Figure 1.**

Standards Check   What kind of cell has chloroplasts? **7.1.b**

Do you understand what you are reading? Don't wait until test time to find out. The **Standards Checks** help you see if you are understanding the standards.

Figure 1 Photosynthesis takes place in chloroplasts. Chloroplasts are found inside plant cells.

Photosynthesis

$$6CO_2 + 6H_2O + \text{light energy} \rightarrow C_6H_{12}O_6 + 6O_2$$

Carbon dioxide   Water   Glucose   Oxygen

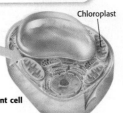

Chloroplast

Plant cell

Notice how vocabulary is treated in the margins. All vocabulary terms are defined in the margins for quick reference. Also look for **Wordwise** items, which help you understand how prefixes and suffixes are used in scientific words.

Keep an Eye on the Headings

Notice how the headings in the textbook are different sizes and different colors. The headings help you organize your reading and form a simple outline, as shown below.

Blue: section title

Red: major subheads

Light blue: minor subheads

One good way to study is to write down the headings in outline form in your notes. Reviewing this outline will give you a good idea of the main concepts in the chapter and will show you how they are related.

Science Is Doing

You get many opportunities throughout the textbook to actually do science.

Each section has at least one **Quick Lab** to help you get real experience doing science. Also look for **School-to-Home Activities** for cool activities that you can do at home.

Quick Lab

7.6.j
7.7.d

Modeling Blood Pressure

In this activity, you will demonstrate systolic and diastolic blood pressure. You will use a pipet bulb to represent the heart.

1. Fill a **pipet bulb** with **water**. Stretch the mouth of a **long balloon** around the end of the pipet bulb. Secure with **tape**.
2. Carefully squeeze the pipet bulb in one hand. Describe the pressure in the balloon.
3. Release your squeeze on the pipet bulb. Describe the pressure in the balloon now.
4. If the pipet bulb represents the heart, what does the balloon represent?
5. Which state, bulb squeezed or not squeezed, is similar to systolic pressure? Explain.
6. What is your blood pressure if your diastolic pressure is 60 mm Hg and your systolic pressure is 95 mm Hg?

10 min

The **Chapter Lab** at the end of each chapter helps you build your understanding of scientific methods. These labs reinforce the California Science Standards with a hands-on activity.

Science Skills Activity

Scientific Methods | Research | Data Analysis | Models, Maps & Diagrams

Investigation and Experimentation
7.7.a Select and use appropriate tools and technology (including calculators, computers, balances, spring scales, microscopes, and binoculars) to perform tests, collect data, and display data.

Using a Microscope to Collect Data

► **Tutorial**

A microscope is a tool often used by life scientists to collect data. Follow these instructions when you use a light microscope.

1. Turn on the light source of your microscope, and select the low-power objective lens.
2. Light from the light source passes through a small hole in the stage. Place a prepared slide over this hole. Secure the slide with the stage clips.
3. Look at the stage from eye level. Slowly turn the adjustment knob to lower the objective lens until the lens almost touches the slide.
4. Look through the ocular lens. Turn the adjustment knob to raise the objective lens until the image is in focus.
5. Make sure that the image is exactly in the center of your field of vision. Then, switch to the high-power objective. If necessary, use the adjustment knob to focus.

Ocular lens

Objective lens
Adjustment knob

Stage clip
Stage
Light

► **You Try It!**

Procedure

6. Obtain a **light microscope**, and id...
parts. Learn how the various parts...
you are familiar with how the micr...
works, ask your teacher for a prep...
7. Follow the steps described above t...
slide. Be sure to view the slide by...
least two different objective lenses...

Analysis

8. **Collecting Data** Draw a diagram...
image that you saw when you...
objective lens.
9. **Identifying Relationships** How d...
ent objective lenses change what y...

100   Chapter 3   Light and...

Each chapter has one **Science Skills Activity,** which gives you an opportunity to develop your science skills. Scientific methods, doing research, analyzing data, and making graphs are highlighted here. The step-by-step instructions make learning these skills easy.

Using Scientific Methods

Skills Practice Lab

Images from Convex Lenses

OBJECTIVES

Use a convex lens to form images.

Determine the characteristics of real images formed by convex lenses.

MATERIALS

• candle
• card, index, 4 × 6 in. or larger
• clay, modeling
• convex lens
• jar lid
• matches
• meterstick

SAFETY

A convex lens is thicker in the center than at the edges. Parallel light rays passing through a convex lens come together at a focal point. Under certain conditions, a convex lens will create a real image of an object. The characteristics of this image depend on the distance between the object and the lens. In this experiment, you will determine the characteristics of real images created by a convex lens—the kind of lens that is used as a magnifying lens.

Ask a Question

1. What are the characteristics of real images created by a convex lens? For example, are the images upright or inverted (upside down)? Are the images larger or smaller than the object?

Form a Hypothesis

2. Write a hypothesis that is a possible answer to the questions above. Explain your reasoning.

Test the Hypothesis

3. Copy the table below.

Data Collection

Image	Orientation (upright/ inverted)	Size (larger/ smaller)	Image distance (cm)	Object distance (cm)
1				
2	DO NOT WRITE IN BOOK			
3				

4. Use modeling clay to make a base for the lens. Place the lens and base in the middle of the table.
5. Stand the index card upright in some modeling clay on one side of the lens.
6. Place the candle in the jar lid, and anchor it with some modeling clay. Place the candle on the table so that the lens is halfway between the candle and the card. Light the candle. **Caution:** Use extreme care around an open flame.
7. In a darkened room, slowly move the card and the candle away from the lens while keeping the lens exactly halfway between the card and the candle. Continue until you see a clear image of the candle flame on the card. This image is image 1.
8. Measure and record the distance between the lens and the card (image distance) and the distance between the lens and the candle (object distance).
9. Is the image upright or inverted? Is it larger or smaller than the candle? Record this information in the table.
10. Move the lens toward the candle. The new object distance should be less than half the object distance measured in step 8. Move the card back-and-forth until you find a sharp image (image 2) of the candle on the card.
11. Repeat steps 8 and 9 for image 2.
12. Leave the card and candle in place, and move the lens toward the card to get the third image (image 3).
13. Repeat steps 8 and 9 for image 3.

Analyze the Results

1. **Recognizing Patterns** Describe the... between image distance and image s...
2. **Examining Data** What are the simi... between the real images that are for... convex lenses?

Draw Conclusions

3. **Making Predictions** The lens of y... convex lens. Use the information tha... lected to describe the image projecte... back of your eye when you look at an...

Big Idea Question

4. **Making Predictions** Light can inter... matter in many different ways. Descri... different ways that light from the can... have interacted with matter in the ro...

Applying Your Data

Convex lenses are used in film projec... Explain why your favorite movie stars... truly "larger than life" on the screen i... of image distance and object distance...

7.6.d Students know how simple lenses are used in a magnifying glass, the eye, a camera, a telescope, and a microscope.
7.6.f Students know how light can be reflected, refracted, transmitted, and absorbed by matter.

98   Chapter 3   Light and Living Things

99

Review What You Have Learned

You can't review too much when you are learning science. To help you review, a **Section Review** appears at the end of every section and a **Chapter Summary** and **Chapter Review** appear at the end of every chapter. These reviews not only help you study for tests but also help further your understanding of the content.

Just a few clicks away, each **Super Summary** gives you even more ways to review and study for tests.

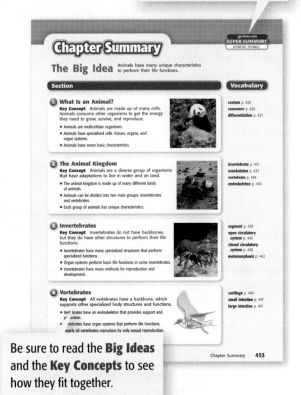

Internet Resources let you link to interesting topics and activities related to the section's content.

Be sure to read the **Big Ideas** and the **Key Concepts** to see how they fit together.

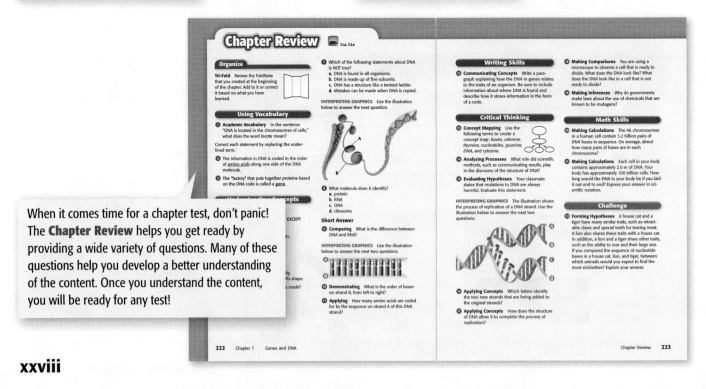

When it comes time for a chapter test, don't panic! The **Chapter Review** helps you get ready by providing a wide variety of questions. Many of these questions help you develop a better understanding of the content. Once you understand the content, you will be ready for any test!

Review the Standards

Mastering the California Science Standards takes practice and more practice! The **Standards Assessment** helps you review the California Science Standards covered in the chapter. The multiple-choice questions also give you some additional practice with standardized tests.

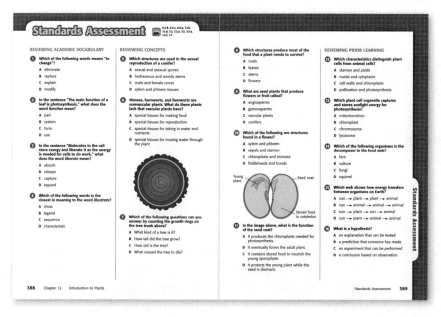

Test-Drive Your Understanding

How well can you use the book now? Use Chapter 1 to answer the questions below and to find out!

1. Which type of Graphic Organizer is used in the Chapter Preview?
2. Which California Science Standards are covered in Chapter 1?
3. What is the Big Idea of this chapter?
4. What will you be doing in the Explore Activity?
5. What is the Key Concept of Section 2?
6. What is the Reading Strategy for Section 1?
7. What new vocabulary terms are introduced in Section 3?
8. How many Standards Checks are in Section 1?
9. What is the name of the Quick Lab in Section 4?
10. On what page does the Chapter Summary appear?
11. How many Standards Assessment questions are there?
12. What is the Super Summary code for Chapter 1?

⇗ Be Resourceful—Use the Web!

Internet Resources for Each Section

A box on the Section Review page for each section takes you to resources that you can use for science projects, reports, and research papers. To find information on a topic, go to **scilinks.org** and type in the code provided.

Current Events in Science

Check out the online magazine articles and other materials that go with your textbook at **go.hrw.com.** Click on the textbook icon and the Table of Contents to see all of the resources for each chapter.

Your Online Textbook

If your teacher gives you a special password to log onto the **Holt Online Learning** site, you'll find your complete textbook on the Web. In addition, you'll find some great learning tools and practice quizzes. You'll be able to see how well you know the material from your textbook.

SAFETY FIRST!

Exploring, inventing, and investigating are essential to the study of science. However, these activities can also be dangerous. To make sure that your experiments and explorations are safe, you must be aware of a variety of safety guidelines. You have probably heard of the saying "It is better to be safe than sorry." This is particularly true in a science classroom where experiments and explorations are being performed. Being uninformed and careless can result in serious injuries. Don't take chances with your own safety or with anyone else's.

The following pages describe important guidelines for staying safe in the science classroom. Your teacher may also have safety guidelines and tips that are specific to your classroom and laboratory. Take the time to be safe.

Safety Rules!

Start Out Right

Always get your teacher's permission before attempting any laboratory exploration. Read the procedures carefully, and pay particular attention to safety information and caution statements. If you are unsure about what a safety symbol means, look it up or ask your teacher. You cannot be too careful when it comes to safety. If an accident does occur, inform your teacher immediately no matter how minor the event seems.

Safety Symbols

All of the experiments and investigations in this book and their related worksheets include important safety symbols to alert you to particular safety concerns. Become familiar with these symbols so that when you see them, you will know what they mean and what to do. It is important that you read this entire safety section to learn about specific dangers in the laboratory.

If you are instructed to note the odor of a substance, wave the fumes toward your nose with your hand. Never put your nose close to the source.

 Eye protection

 Clothing protection

 Hand safety

 Heating safety

 Electric safety

 Chemical safety

 Animal safety

 Sharp object

 Plant safety

Eye Safety

Wear safety goggles when working around chemicals, acids, bases, or any type of flame or heating device. Wear safety goggles anytime there is the slightest chance that your eyes could be harmed. If anything gets into your eyes, notify your teacher immediately and flush your eyes with running water for at least 15 minutes. Treat any unknown chemical as if it were a dangerous chemical. Never look directly into the sun. Doing so could cause permanent blindness.

Avoid wearing contact lenses in a laboratory situation. Even if you are wearing safety goggles, chemicals can get between the contact lenses and your eyes. If your doctor requires that you wear contact lenses instead of glasses, wear eye-cup safety goggles in the lab.

Safety Equipment

Know the locations of the nearest fire alarms and any other safety equipment, such as fire blankets and eyewash fountains, as identified by your teacher. And know the procedures for using the equipment.

Neatness

Keep your work area free of all unnecessary books and papers. Tie back long hair, and secure loose sleeves or other loose articles of clothing, such as ties and bows. Remove dangling jewelry. Don't wear open-toed shoes or sandals in the laboratory. Never eat, drink, or apply cosmetics in a laboratory setting. Food, drink, and cosmetics can easily become contaminated with dangerous materials.

Certain hair products (such as aerosol hair spray) are flammable and should not be worn while working near an open flame. Avoid wearing hair spray or hair gel on lab days.

Sharp/Pointed Objects

Use knives and other sharp instruments with extreme care. Never cut objects while holding them in your hands. Place objects on a suitable work surface for cutting.

Be extra careful when using any glassware. When adding a heavy object to a graduated cylinder, tilt the cylinder so that the object slides slowly to the bottom.

Chemicals

Wear safety goggles when handling any potentially dangerous chemicals. Wear an apron and protective gloves when you work with chemicals or whenever you are told to do so. If a spill gets on your skin or clothing, rinse it off immediately with water for at least 5 minutes while calling to your teacher. If you spill a corrosive chemical onto your clothing, rinse it off immediately by using a faucet or the safety shower and remove the affected clothing while calling to your teacher.

Never mix chemicals unless your teacher tells you to do so. Never taste, touch, or smell chemicals unless you are specifically directed to do so. Before working with a flammable liquid or gas, check for the presence of any source of flame, spark, or heat.

Heat

Wear safety goggles when using a heating device or a flame. Whenever possible, use an electric hot plate as a heat source instead of using an open flame. When heating materials in a test tube, angle the test tube away from yourself and others. To avoid burns, wear heat-resistant gloves whenever instructed to do so.

Electricity

Be careful with electrical cords. When using a microscope with a lamp, do not place the cord where it could trip someone. Do not let cords hang over a table edge in a way that could cause equipment to fall if the cord is accidentally pulled. Do not use equipment with damaged cords. Do not use electrical equipment near water or when your clothing or hands are wet. Make sure that electrical equipment is in the "off" position before plugging it in. Turn off and unplug electrical equipment when you have finished using it.

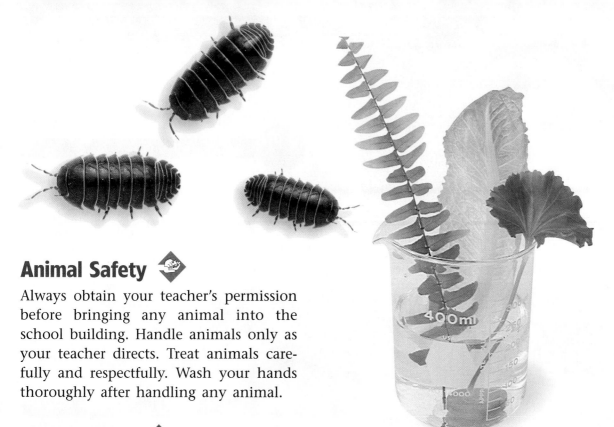

Animal Safety

Always obtain your teacher's permission before bringing any animal into the school building. Handle animals only as your teacher directs. Treat animals carefully and respectfully. Wash your hands thoroughly after handling any animal.

Plant Safety

Do not eat any part of a plant or plant seed used in the laboratory. Wash your hands thoroughly after handling any part of a plant. When in nature, do not pick any wild plants unless your teacher instructs you to do so.

Glassware

Examine all glassware before use. Be sure that glassware is clean and free of chips and cracks. Report damaged glassware to your teacher. Glass containers used for heating should be made of heat-resistant glass.

UNIT 1

TIMELINE

The Study of Living Things

Life science is the study of living things—from the tiniest bacterium to the largest tree! In this unit, you will discover the similarities of all living things. You will learn about the tools that life scientists use, and you'll learn to ask your own questions about the living world around you.

People have always searched for answers about life. This timeline includes a few of the many people who have studied living things and a few events that have shaped the history of life science. And there's always more to be learned, so keep your eyes open.

Around 2700 BCE

Si Ling-Chi, empress of China, observes silkworms in her garden and develops a process to cultivate them and make silk.

1931

The first electron microscope is developed.

1934

Dorothy Crowfoot Hodgkin uses X-ray techniques to determine the protein structure of insulin.

1970

Floppy disks for computer data storage are introduced.

1983

Dian Fossey writes *Gorillas in the Mist*, a book about her research on mountain gorillas in Africa and her efforts to save them from poachers.

Around 1000

Arab mathematician and physicist Ibn al Haytham discovers that vision is caused by the reflection of light from objects into the eye.

1684

Improvements to microscopes allow the first observation of red blood cells.

1914

His studies on agriculture and soil conservation lead George Washington Carver to perform research on peanuts.

1944

Oswald T. Avery demonstrates that DNA is the material that carries genetic properties in living organisms.

1946

ENIAC, the first entirely electronic computer, is built. It weighs 30 tons.

1967

Dr. Christiaan Barnard performs the first successful human heart transplant.

1984

A process known as DNA fingerprinting is developed by Alec Jeffreys.

1998

In China, scientists discover a fossil of a dinosaur that had feathers.

2001

A team of scientists led by Philippa Uwins announces that tiny nanobes that are 20 to 150 nanometers wide have been found in Australia. Scientists debate whether these particles are living.

The elements listed in the Standards Course of Study provide a base for presenting, supporting, and assessing the California Grade 7 Science Standards. Use this Standards Course of Study as a base for planning your lessons.

Why Teach

The Nature of Life Science

This chapter was designed to cover the California Grade 7 Science Standards about investigation and experimentation (7.7.a, 7.7.b, 7.7.c, 7.7.d, and 7.7.e) and the California science framework requirements regarding safety. This is the first chapter in the *Holt California Life Science book* because it increases students' mastery of the skills and processes of science. In each of the subsequent chapters, students will benefit from an understanding of the nature of science and experimentation.

After they have completed this chapter, students will begin a chapter about the shared characteristics of all living things.

 California Standards

Investigation and Experimentation

7.7.a Select and use appropriate tools and technology (including calculators, computers, balances, spring scales, microscopes, and binoculars) to perform tests, collect data, and display data.

7.7.b Use a variety of print and electronic resources (including the World Wide Web) to collect information and evidence as part of a research project.

7.7.c Communicate the logical connection among hypotheses, science concepts, tests conducted, data collected, and conclusions drawn from the scientific evidence.

7.7.d Construct scale models, maps, and appropriately labeled diagrams to communicate scientific knowledge (e.g., motion of Earth's plates and cell structure).

7.7.e Communicate the steps and results from an investigation in written reports and oral presentations.

Chapter Pacing

Getting Started **45 min** pp. 6–7
The Big Idea Scientists use scientific processes to study the patterns of natural events and to solve problems. **7.7.c**

Section 1 Asking About Life **45 min** pp. 8–11
Key Concept Asking questions is the first step in a scientific investigation. **7.7.b**

Section 2 Scientific Methods **90 min** pp. 12–19
Key Concept Scientific methods are used to investigate questions and to solve problems. **7.7.c, 7.7.e**

Section 3 Tools and Measurement **90 min** pp. 20–25
Key Concept Scientists select and use tools and technology to perform tests and collect data.  **7.7.a**

Section 4 Scientific Models and Knowledge **45 min** pp. 26–31
Key Concept Models are used to study living things, test hypotheses, explain observations, and communicate knowledge. **7.7.c, 7.7.d**

Section 5 Safety in Science **45 min** pp. 32–37
Key Concept Following safety rules during scientific investigations will help prevent accidents and injury. **7.7.a**

Wrapping Up **180 min** pp. 38–47

7.7.a, 7.7.b

Basic Learners

TE Frog Calls, p. 14
TE Testing Hypotheses, p. 15
TE Mathematical Models, p. 27
TE Finding Keywords, p. 40
Reinforcement Worksheet
Chapter Test A
Differentiated Datasheets A for Labs and Activities ■
Study Guide A ■

Advanced Learners/GATE

TE Understanding Diseases, p. 10
TE Temperature Scales, p. 25
Critical Thinking Worksheet
Chapter Test C
Differentiated Datasheets C for Labs and Activities ■

Teach

SE **Explore Activity** Identifying Unknown Objects, p. 7* ■

📊 **Bellringer**
💿 **PowerPoint® Resources**
SE **Quick Lab** Asking Questions, p. 9* ■

📊 **Bellringer**
💿 **PowerPoint® Resources**
📊 L1 Scientific Methods
SE **Quick Lab** Investigating and Experimenting with Yeast, p. 18* ■

📊 **Bellringer**
💿 **PowerPoint® Resources**
📊 L2 Common SI Units and Conversions
SE **Quick Lab** Measure Up!, p. 24* ■

📊 **Bellringer**
💿 **PowerPoint® Resources**
SE **Quick Lab** Constructing Scale Diagrams, p. 28* ■
📊 L3 Scales in Maps

📊 **Bellringer**
💿 **PowerPoint® Resources**
SE **Quick Lab** Preparing for an Experiment, p. 35* ■

SE **Skills Practice Lab** Collecting and Displaying Data, pp. 38–39* ■

Practice

SE **Organize Activity** Layered Book, p. 6

SE **Section Review,** p. 11* ■

SE **Section Review,** p. 19* ■

SE **Section Review,** p. 25* ■

SE **Section Review,** p. 31* ■

SE **Section Review,** p. 37* ■

SE **Science Skills Activity** Using Internet Resources for Research, p. 40* ■
📊 **Concept Mapping***
SE **Chapter Review,** pp. 42–43* ■

Assess

📁 **Chapter Pretest**

SE **Standards Check,** p. 9
TE **Standards Focus,** p. 10
📁 **Section Quiz** ■

SE **Standards Checks,** pp. 12, 15, 18
TE **Standards Focus,** p. 18
📁 **Section Quiz** ■

SE **Standards Checks,** pp. 21, 23
TE **Standards Focus,** p. 24
📁 **Section Quiz** ■

SE **Standards Checks,** pp. 28, 31
TE **Standards Focus,** p. 30
📁 **Section Quiz** ■

SE **Standards Checks,** pp. 32, 35
TE **Standards Focus,** p. 36
📁 **Section Quiz** ■

SE **Standards Assessment,** pp. 44–45*
📁 **Chapter Tests A, B** ■**, C**
📁 **Standards Review Workbook** ■

Resources for Universal Access • Differentiated Instruction

English Learners

TE Group Activity, pp. 9, 21, 27, 32, 35
TE Connection To Social Studies, p. 13
TE Parts of Speech, p. 16
TE Using the Figure, pp. 17, 28, 33
TE Demonstration, pp. 20, 23, 34, 35
TE Hypothesis, Theory, and Law p. 29

TE Safety Symbols, p. 33
📁 Vocabulary and Section Summary A ■, B
📁 Section Quizzes ■
📁 Chapter Tests A, B ■
📁 Differentiated Datasheets A, B, and C for Labs and Activities ■
📓 Study Guide A ■
📓 Multilingual Glossary

Struggling Readers

TE Picturing Life Science, p. 8
TE Reading Strategy, pp. 13, 27, 33
TE Tools and Measurement Vocabulary, p. 20
TE First Aid, p. 36

Special Education Students

TE Reading Disconnect, p. 13
TE Factors and Variables, p. 17
TE Physical Information, p. 22
TE Hand Dinosaurs, p. 30
TE Dry–Run Experiment, p. 34

To help plan your lessons, refer to the On Course Mapping Instruction booklet.

Visual Resources

CHAPTER STARTER TRANSPARENCY

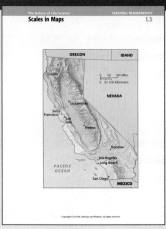

BELLRINGER TRANSPARENCIES

TEACHING TRANSPARENCIES

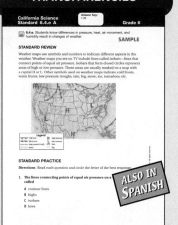
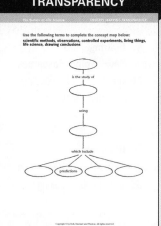

TEACHING TRANSPARENCIES

STANDARDS REVIEW TRANSPARENCIES

CONCEPT MAPPING TRANSPARENCY

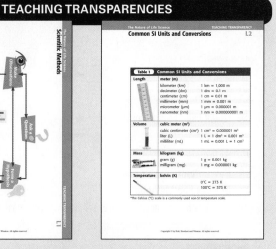

Planning Resources

PARENT LETTER

TEST ITEM LISTING

One-Stop Planner® CD-ROM

This CD-ROM package includes all of the resources shown here and the following time-saving tools:

- **Lab Materials QuickList Software**

- **Customizable Lesson Plans** Correlated to the California Science Standards

- **Holt Calendar Planner**

- **PowerPoint® Resources**

- **Printable Worksheets**

- **ExamView® Test Generator** Correlated to the California Science Standards

- **Holt PuzzlePro®**

- **Interactive Teacher's Edition**

Meeting Individual Needs

DIRECTED READING A

BASIC
ALSO IN SPANISH

DIRECTED READING B
GENERAL

VOCABULARY AND SECTION SUMMARY A
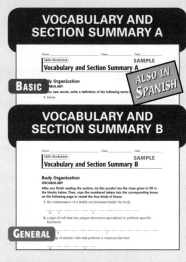
BASIC
ALSO IN SPANISH

VOCABULARY AND SECTION SUMMARY B
GENERAL

REINFORCEMENT
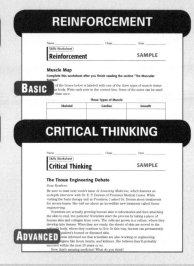
BASIC

CRITICAL THINKING
ADVANCED

INTERACTIVE READER AND STUDY GUIDE

MULTILINGUAL GLOSSARY

Labs and Activities

DIFFERENTIATED DATASHEETS FOR EXPLORE ACTIVITY, QUICK LABS, AND CHAPTER LAB
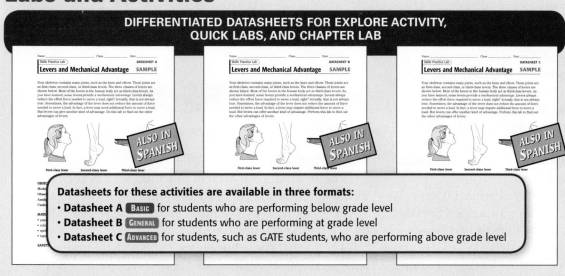
ALSO IN SPANISH

Datasheets for these activities are available in three formats:
- **Datasheet A** **BASIC** for students who are performing below grade level
- **Datasheet B** **GENERAL** for students who are performing at grade level
- **Datasheet C** **ADVANCED** for students, such as GATE students, who are performing above grade level

DATASHEET FOR SCIENCE SKILLS ACTIVITY
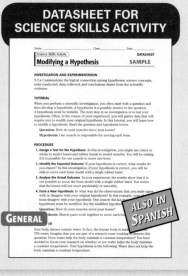
GENERAL
ALSO IN SPANISH

Reviews and Assessments

SECTION REVIEWS
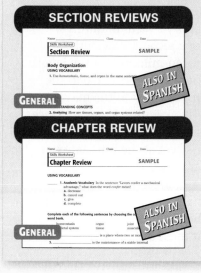
GENERAL
ALSO IN SPANISH

CHAPTER REVIEW
GENERAL
ALSO IN SPANISH

CHAPTER PRETEST
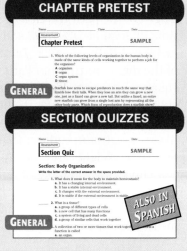
GENERAL

SECTION QUIZZES
GENERAL
ALSO IN SPANISH

CHAPTER TEST A
BASIC

CHAPTER TEST B
GENERAL
ALSO IN SPANISH

CHAPTER TEST C
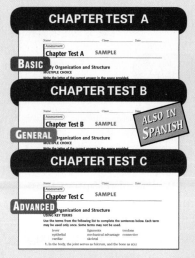
ADVANCED
ALSO IN SPANISH

STANDARDS ASSESSMENT
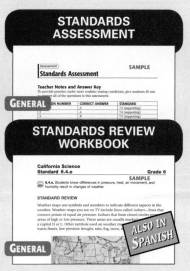
GENERAL

STANDARDS REVIEW WORKBOOK
GENERAL
ALSO IN SPANISH

This Teacher Background explains science concepts, principles, and theories that appear in the chapter. Use the information on these pages to refresh or enhance your understanding of the topics covered.

Section 1

Asking About Life

Understanding Science

Science is a process of people gathering and organizing information so that it can be useful. Because scientists are always challenging and questioning, they are continually using scientific methods to formulate new theories. Scientists even disprove or change previously accepted theories if new technology reveals new data or mistakes in previous testing. For example, Hippocrates proposed that the bodies of cheerful, active people had a high percentage of blood content and the bodies of sad, brooding people had a high percentage of black bile. Though this theory sounds silly today and was proved wrong long ago with further research on blood, theories like this were important because they led to research and experimentation.

Mathematics is an essential partner with science, especially because scientific methods often use mathematical models. Although all areas of math can apply to science, statistics and calculus are the mathematics fields that are most closely linked to science.

Sometimes scientists set out to solve problems for people, and sometimes they discover unintended applications of their work that improve the lives of people. For example, Dr. Ron Ho from Cornell University and Dr. Ron Miles of State University of New York began studying the physiology of the eardrums of flies. Their research led to their current project of developing a hearing aid that will help people with hearing problems determine the sources of sounds they hear.

Section 2

Scientific Methods

What Are Scientific Methods?

Observation, communication, scientific inquiry, and experimental design are tools people use to study life. Collecting information from a variety of resources is an important part of scientific inquiry. The skills needed to search out and recognize accurate and useful resources are complex and generally require significant knowledge

of the topic. The tools scientists use for this process are known as scientific methods and include steps that may be completed in varying orders as shown in **Figure A** below. Use this figure to point out to students that there are loops within the steps. Analyzing the results of an experiment may not end the process but instead may lead to the formation of a new hypothesis.

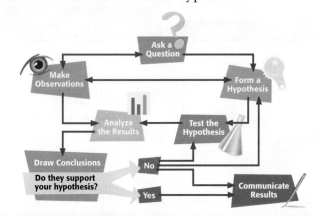

Figure A *Scientific methods flow in a logical, sometimes varying sequence.*

Section 3

Tools and Measurement

Measurement

The International System of Units (SI) was conceived in the late 1700s to form a global measurement system. This system, used by scientists around the world, is based on the metric system.

The general conference on Weights and Measure (CGPM, Conférence Générale des Poids et Mesures) is the organization responsible for maintaining the SI. The CGPM, which represents 50 countries, updates the units as warranted by advances in science and technology. For example, in 1983 the definition of a meter was changed to equal the length of the path traveled by light in vacuum during a time interval of 1/299,792,458 of a second. Previously, a meter was defined as 10^{-7} or one ten-millionth of the length of the meridian through Paris from the North Pole to the equator. The mass of a kilogram was equal to the mass of a cubic decimeter of water in the 18th century. However, since 1889, the mass of a kilogram has been based on a prototype made of platinum-iridium that is kept at the International Bureau of Weights and Measures.

The following table of length, area, and volume measuring units shows how the U.S. measurement units relate to the SI units. Metric units are the universal measurement standard used in most of the world.

Characteristic	U.S. measurement	Metric
Length	in, ft, yd, mi	mm, cm, dm, m, km
Area	in², ft², yards², mi²	cm², m², km²
Volume	ounces, cups, pints, quarts, and gallons	milliliters, liters, mm³, cm³, m³

Temperature is measured with two systems: Fahrenheit and Celsius. The Fahrenheit scale, named after Gabriel Daniel Fahrenheit (1686–1736), a German-born physicist, measures freezing water at 32°F and boiling water at 212°F. The Celsius system was named after Anders Celsius, a Swedish astronomer. A degree Celsius is equal in magnitude to a Kelvin. A comparison of the Fahrenheit and Celsius temperature scales is shown in **Figure B.** You can point out to students that a rise or fall of one degree on the Celsius scale is a larger change in temperature than a rise or fall of one degree on the Fahrenheit scale.

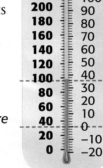

Figure B *The range in temperature between which water freezes and boils is defined as the points 180°F but only 100°C.*

Section 4

Scientific Models and Knowledge

Types of Scientific Models

In science, models are representations used to approximate information in an effort to clarify details about an object, system, or situation that might be too large, too small, too complicated, or not available to study. Scientists strive to create concrete and theoretical models that are technically representative enough to be useful in making observations and accurately communicating scientific knowledge. Types of models include physical models (example: model airplane), mathematical models (example: Punnett square), conceptual models (example: representation of an idea).

Scientific Theory Vs. Scientific Law

Theories, which are constantly developing, combine related facts, observations, and hypotheses into current scientific understandings that help explain how nature works. On the other hand, scientific law, such as a law of motion, describes what happens in a specific example. Scientific law is established only after many experiments and observations agree in support of the law.

Section 5

Safety in Science

Proper Procedures

Safety guides for classroom science programs have been produced by the Council of State Science Supervisors (CSSS) with support from the American Chemical Society, the Eisenhower National Clearinghouse for Mathematics and Science Education, the National Aeronautics and Space Administration, Dupont Corporation, Intel Corporation, American Chemical Society, and the National Institutes of Health. Currently, these guides can be found on the Web site for the CSSS.

Many life scientists and even healthcare professionals work with infectious diseases, microorganisms, laboratory animals, or other potentially hazardous biological substances. To ensure the safety of individuals working in these environments as well as safety for the environment and the community, four biosafety levels have been designated. Biosafety Level 1 is suitable for work involving well-characterized agents not known to cause disease in healthy adult humans and of minimal potential hazard to laboratory personnel and the environment. Biosafety Level 2 is suitable for work involving agents of moderate potential hazard to personnel and the environment. Biosafety Level 3 is applicable to clinical, diagnostic, teaching, research, or production facilities in which work is done with indigenous or exotic agents that may cause serious or potentially lethal disease as a result of exposure by inhalation. Biosafety Level 4 is required for work with dangerous and exotic agents that pose a high individual risk of aerosol-transmitted laboratory infections and life-threatening diseases.

Internet Resources

SciLinks is maintained by the National Science Teachers Association to provide you and your students with interesting, up-to-date links that will enrich your classroom presentation of the chapter.

Visit **www.scilinks.org** and enter the SciLinks code for more information about the topic listed.

Topic: Careers in Life Science **SciLinks code:** HY70224	**Topic:** SI Units **SciLinks code:** HY71390
Topic: Deformed Frogs **SciLinks code:** HY70383	**Topic:** Using Models **SciLinks code:** HY71588
Topic: Scientific Methods **SciLinks code:** HY71359	**Topic:** Safety **SciLinks code:** HY71339
Topic: Tools of Life Science **SciLinks code:** HY71535	

1 Chapter Preview

📋 **Chapter Pretest**
Use the Chapter Pretest in the Chapter Resource File to determine the prior knowledge of your students. The Test Doctors and diagnostic teaching tips in the Teacher Notes pages will help you tailor your instruction to your students' specific needs.

Improving Comprehension

Use the Graphic Organizer on this page of the Student Edition to introduce the topics that are covered in this chapter, to summarize the chapter material, or to show students how to build an idea wheel.

Teaching Tips

• Explain to students that an idea wheel is most useful when the categories contain details that are not analogous or when the details require more space than other classification organizers permit.

• Explain to students that an idea wheel is useful for organizing topics that include figurative details, such as sketches, equations, and graphs.

LS Logical

Improving Comprehension

Graphic Organizers are important visual tools that can help you organize information and improve your reading comprehension. The Graphic Organizer below is called an *idea wheel*. Instructions for creating other types of Graphic Organizers are located in the **Study Skills** section of the Appendix.

How to Make an Idea Wheel

❶ Draw a circle. Draw a larger circle around the first circle. Divide the ring between the circles into sections by drawing lines from one circle to the other across the ring. Divide the ring into as many sections as you want.

❷ Write a main idea or topic in the smaller circle. Label each section in the ring with a category or characteristic of the main idea.

❸ In each section of the ring, include details that are unique to the topic.

When to Use an Idea Wheel

An idea wheel is an effective type of visual organization in which ideas in science can be divided into categories or parts. It is also a useful way to illustrate characteristics of a main idea or topic. As you read, look for topics that are divided into ideas or categories, that can be organized around an idea wheel.

Idea wheel — The Nature of Life Science

Questioning
• ask a question
• make observations
• form a hypothesis
• test the hypothesis
• analyze the results
• draw conclusions
• communicate results

Scientific Methods
• Asking a question is the first step in scientific investigation.
• Answers to questions in life science affect you and your community.

Tools and Models
• Scientists choose and use tools of measurement to test hypotheses, and to collect, store, and analyze data.
• Scientific models are tools that help explain how something works or is structured.

Safety
• Following directions is the most important safety rule.
• Safety symbols can help identify potential dangers.
• Using safety equipment can protect you from injury.

You Try It!

This Reading Strategy can also be used within the chapter that you are about to read. Practice making your own *idea wheel* as directed in the Reading Strategies for Section ❹ and Section ❺. Record your work in your **Science Journal.**

Using Other Graphic Organizers

Students can practice using a variety of Graphic Organizers while reading this chapter. The following Graphic Organizers may also be useful in this chapter.

A **process chart** can be used to diagram scientific methods, described in Section 2.

A **comparison table** can be used to compare SI units, described in Section 3. A **comparison table** also can be used to compare the various types of models described in Section 4.

Combination notes can be used to describe safety symbols and their applications, introduced in Section 5.

Instructions for creating these Graphic Organizers are located on pp. 583–591 of the Appendix.

Unpacking the Standards

The information below "unpacks" the standards by breaking them down into basic parts. The higher-level, academic vocabulary is highlighted and defined to help you understand the language of the standards. "What It Means" restates the standards as simply as possible.

Unpacking the Standards

Use the following information with the *What It Means* in the Student Edition to help students understand why studying each standard is important.

California Standard	Academic Vocabulary	What It Means	Why It Matters
7.7.a **Select** and use **appropriate** tools and **technology** (including calculators, **computers,** balances, spring scales, microscopes, and binoculars) to perform tests, collect data, and **display** data.	**select** (suh LEKT) to choose, to pick up **appropriate** (uh PROH pree it) correct for the use; proper **technology** (tek NAHL uh jee) tools, including electronic products **computer** (kuhm PYOOT uhr) an electronic device that stores, retrieves, and calculates data **display** (di SPLAY) to show	Choose the correct tools and technology (including calculators, computers, balances, spring scales, microscopes, and binoculars) to perform an experiment. Use these tools and technology to collect facts and figures, and show your research findings.	Scientific research depends on the collection of accurate and precise data. Scientists must choose the correct tools and technology to get reliable, accurate results.
7.7.b Use a variety of print and electronic **resources** (including the World Wide Web) to collect information and evidence as part of a **research project.**	**resource** (REE sawrs) anything that can be used to take care of a need **research** (REE suhrch) a careful search for and study of information **project** (PRAH jekt) a special task done to use, explain, or add information to classroom lessons	Do research by using both print sources (such as newspapers and books) and electronic sources (such as websites and databases) to collect information, facts, and figures as part of a research project.	One must know how to find and evaluate information on the Internet to gather up-to-date information.
7.7.c **Communicate** the **logical** connection among hypotheses, science **concepts,** tests **conducted,** data collected, and conclusions drawn from the scientific evidence.	**communicate** (kuh MYOO ni kayt) to make known, to tell **logical** (LAHJ i kuhl) reasoned, well thought out **concept** (KAHN sept) an idea or thought **conduct** (kuhn DUHKT) to carry out; to do	Tell others how possible explanations for observations, ideas, experiments, facts and figures, and results and conclusions are related.	Communication skills are critical for processing and relaying information in all disciplines.
7.7.d **Construct** scale models, maps, and **appropriately labeled** diagrams to communicate scientific knowledge (e.g., motion of Earth's plates and cell structure).	**construct** (kuhn STRUHKT) to build; to make from parts **appropriately** (uh PROH pree it lee) in a correct or proper way **labeled** (LAY buhld) marked with a name or description	Build models, maps, and diagrams that are proportional to what they represent in the real world and that have correct and useful labels to explain scientific information. For example, build a model or make a diagram that shows the motion of Earth's plates or the structure of a cell.	Models simplify and help one understand complex concepts or structures. A model suggests how something works or might work.
7.7.e Communicate the steps and results from an **investigation** in written reports and oral presentations.	**investigation** (in ves tuh GAY shuhn) a detailed search for answers	Clearly explain the steps and the results of an experiment by using written reports and oral presentations.	Scientists share the results of their research with other scientists. To be an effective scientist, one must be able to write clearly and to speak to people effectively.

Using the Unpacked Standards

Students may benefit from "unpacking" the standards themselves. Ask students to use the *Academic Vocabulary* and the *What It Means* from the Student Edition to identify what *facts* and *words* they must know, what *concepts* they must understand, and what *skills* they must acquire to master each standard. Students should record this information in a "Know, Understand, Do" table in their

Science Journal. By making and using their tables as guides, students become more accountable for mastering the standards. **LS** Intrapersonal

Know	facts and words
Understand	concepts
Do	skills

Chapter Overview

Tell students that this chapter will introduce them to the nature of life science—including plants, animals, bacteria, mushrooms, health, disease, and anything else related to living organisms. Explain that they will see that science is about asking questions and using scientific methods to find answers and build knowledge. Add that science is also about using models and tools to investigate questions and share answers.

The Nature of Life Science

The Big Idea

Scientists use scientific processes to study the patterns of natural events and to solve problems.

California Standards

Investigation and Experimentation
7.7 Scientific progress is made by asking meaningful questions and conducting careful investigations. (Sections 1, 2, 3, 4, and 5 and Science Skills Activity)

Math
7.1.2 Number Sense

English–Language Arts
7.1.3 Reading
7.2.5 Writing

About the Photo

What happened to the legs of these frogs? Life science can help answer this question. Deformed frogs, such as the ones in this photo, have been found in the northern United States and southern Canada. Sometimes, frogs are injured by predators. But other frogs develop deformities while they are growing. Scientists and students like you have been using life science to investigate why frogs develop deformities.

Organize

Layered Book

Before you read this chapter, create the FoldNote entitled "Layered Book." Label each tab of the layered book with "Scientific methods," "Tools and measurement," "Scientific models," and "Safety." As you read the chapter, write information that you learn about each category on the appropriate tab.

Instructions for creating FoldNotes are located in the Study Skills section on p. 580 of the Appendix.

California Standards Alignment

Investigation and Experimentation

7.7.a Select and use appropriate tools and technology (including calculators, computers, balances, spring scales, microscopes, and binoculars) to perform tests, collect data, and display data. **pp. 20–25, 33, 35, 37–39**

7.7.b Use a variety of print and electronic resources (including the World Wide Web) to collect information and evidence as part of a research project. **pp. 9, 11, 20, 25, 40, 42–44**

7.7.c Communicate the logical connection among hypotheses, science concepts, tests conducted, data collected, and conclusions drawn from the scientific evidence. **pp. 7–8, 10–19, 29–31, 42–44**

7.7.d Construct scale models, maps, and appropriately labeled diagrams to communicate scientific knowledge (e.g., motion of Earth's plates and cell structure). **pp. 28, 31, 42–43, 45**

7.7.e Communicate the steps and results from an investigation in written reports and oral presentations. **pp. 18–19, 42–43, 45**

Math Standards

Number Sense 7.1.2 Add, subtract, multiply, and divide rational numbers (integers, fractions, and terminating decimals) and take positive rational numbers to whole-number powers. **pp. 23, 25**

Measurement and Geometry 7.1.2 Construct and read drawings and models made to scale. **pp. 28, 31, 43**

Explore Activity

 15 min

Identifying Unknown Objects

In this activity, you will find out that you can learn about the unknown without having to see it.

Procedure

1. Your teacher will give you a **coffee can** to which a **sock** has been attached. Do not look into the can.

2. Reach through the opening in the sock. You will feel **several objects** inside the can.

3. Record observations you make about the objects by feeling the objects, shaking the can, and so on.

4. What do you think is in the can? List your guesses. State some reasons for your guesses.

5. Pour the contents of the can onto your desk. Compare your list with what was in the can.

Analysis

6. Did you guess the contents of the can correctly? What might have caused you to guess wrongly?

7. What observations did you make about each of the objects while the objects were in the can? Which of your senses did you use?

7.7.c

English–Language Arts Standards

Reading 6.2.4 Clarify understanding of texts by creating outlines, logical notes, summaries, or reports. **pp. 26, 32**

Writing 7.2.5 Write summaries of reading materials: (a) Include the main ideas and most significant details; (b) Use the student's own words, except for quotations; (c) Reflect underlying meaning, not just the superficial details. **p. 43**

Chapter Starter Transparency
Use this transparency to help students begin thinking about the nature of life science and scientific methods.

Preteach

Reviewing Prior Knowledge

Ask students to compare an eagle, a chicken, and a turkey. (Sample answer: An eagle has bigger wings and a smaller head in relation to its body than either a chicken or a turkey does. Chickens and turkeys have similar shapes.) Ask students how the bodies of the animals relate to how the animals live. (Sample answer: Eagles can fly higher and longer; chickens and turkeys move quickly on the ground.) Discuss that comparing eagles, turkeys, and chickens is an example of making a basic scientific observation.

 **Bellringer**

Have students focus on standard 7.7.b by asking them to list all the different resources they could use to find answers to questions about the natural world. (Sample answer: books, newspapers, magazines, interviews, World Wide Web, Documentaries.)

📦 Bellringer Transparency

Motivate

Discussion

Asking Questions Have students look at the questions the girl in **Figure 1** is asking. Then, have students ask some science questions of their own. **LS** Verbal

---

What You Will Learn

● Questions lead to learning about science.

● Print or electronic resources can be used to find information.

● Your everyday life is affected by life scientists in many ways.

Why It Matters

Asking questions and performing scientific investigations help you learn about the world around you.

Vocabulary

• life science

READING STRATEGY

Prediction Guide Before reading this section, write each heading from this section in your **Science Journal.** Below each heading, write what you think you will learn.

Figure 1 *Part of science is asking questions about the world around you.*

Why do leaves change color in the fall?

How do birds know where to go when they migrate?

How are a frog and a lizard different?

Asking About Life

Key Concept Asking questions is the first step in a scientific investigation.

▶ Imagine that it's summer. You are lying in the grass at the park, casually looking around. Three dogs are playing on your left. A few bumblebees are visiting nearby flowers. And an ant is carrying a crumb away from your sandwich.

Suddenly, a question pops into your head: How do ants find food? Then, you think of another question: Why do the bees visit the yellow flowers but not the red ones? Congratulations! You have just taken the first steps toward becoming a life scientist. How did you do it? You observed the living world around you. You were curious, and you asked questions about your observations. Once you have a question, you can start thinking about ways to find answers. Those steps are what science is all about. **Life science** is the study of living things.

Starting with a Question

The world around you is full of an amazing diversity of life. Single-celled algae, giant redwood trees, and 40-ton whales are living things. For every living thing, or organism, you could ask questions such as: (1) How does the organism get its food? (2) Where does it live? and (3) Why does it behave in a particular way?

In Your Own Backyard

Questions are easy to think of. Take a look around your room, your home, and your neighborhood. What questions about life science come to mind? The student in **Figure 1** has questions about some very familiar organisms. Do you know the answer to any of her questions?

Touring the World

The questions you can ask about your neighborhood are examples of the questions you could ask about the world. The world is made up of many different types of places, such as deserts, forests, coral reefs, and tide pools. Just about anywhere you go, you will find some kind of living organism. If you observe this organism, you can easily think of questions to ask about it.

Universal Access · Differentiated Instruction

Struggling Readers

Picturing Life Science Tell students that one way to make the information they are reading easier to remember is to stop reading for a few seconds and picture descriptions in their heads. Use the following script to model reading the first paragraph:

I read the first sentence and stopped. The first sentence says, "Imagine it's summer." In my head, I picture something I

like about summer, such as sitting under a shade tree eating watermelon. Then, I read the second sentence, "You are lying in the grass at the park, casually looking around." I picture myself on soft grass at a park. I can feel the softness and coolness of the grass. I look around.

Continue modeling the entire paragraph in this fashion. **LS** Visual/Auditory

---

Investigation: The Search for Answers

Once you ask a question, it's time to look for an answer. But how do you start your investigation? There are several methods that you can use.

Research

You can find answers to some of your questions by doing research, as **Figure 2** shows. You can ask someone who knows a lot about the subject of your questions. You can look up information in print resources, such as textbooks, encyclopedias, and magazines. You can also use electronic resources, such as the World Wide Web. The World Wide Web is a computer network that allows people all over the world to share information. You may learn more about your subject if you find the report of an experiment that someone has done. But be sure to think about the source of the information that you find. Scientists use information only from reliable sources.

Standards Check What is an example of an electronic resource that you can use to do research? 7.7.b

Observation

You can also find answers to questions by making careful observations. For example, if you want to know which birds live around you, you can go for a walk and look for them. Or you can hang a bird feeder outside your window and observe the birds that use it.

Experimentation

You can even answer some of your questions by doing an experiment, as **Figure 3** shows. An experiment should be carefully designed to answer a specific question. Making good observations and analyzing data are some of the other important parts of doing experiments.

Figure 3 *This student is doing an experiment to find the hardness of a mineral.*

life science (LIEF SIE uhns) the study of living things

Figure 2 *At a library, you will find many print and electronic resources.*

Quick Lab

Asking Questions 7.7.b

1. With your group, pick a living thing. Print the name of the living thing in the middle of a large piece of **paper.**

2. Use **markers** to write questions about the living thing on the paper.

3. Choose one of the questions. On the back of the paper, list all of the possible ways that you could find an answer to that question.

⏱ 15 min

Investigation and Experimentation
7.7.b Use a variety of print and electronic resources (including the World Wide Web) to collect information and evidence as part of a research project.

Quick Lab

⏱ 15 min

Teacher Notes

This activity has students practice thinking about the types of resources they can use to do research (covers standard 7.7.b). To assure variety, have groups call out the living things they are planning to use. Encourage students to write questions to which they do not already know the answers.

Materials for Each Group
• marker, water-based (at least one)
• paper, large (one piece)

2. Sample answers: How does the organism get energy? How does it reproduce?

3. Sample answers: Interviews with biologists, zookeepers, or gardeners; books; the Internet

📋 Differentiated Datasheets
A **BASIC**, B **GENERAL**, C **ADVANCED**

Also editable on the
Holt Lab Generator
CD-ROM

Teach

Discussion
Why Ask Why? Ask students to write a paragraph that explains the benefit of studying how the human body responds to space travel. Invite students to read their papers, and as they do, write a list of the benefits on the board. **LS** Verbal/Interpersonal

Group ACTIVITY

Wildfire Safari Arrange a visit to a local zoo or wildlife area and encourage students to compile a list of questions in advance that they can ask the caretakers. During the visit, guide students in a fact-finding mission about the kinds of animals in the facility. When you return to class, discuss your fact-finding mission. **LS** Kinesthetic Co-op Learning

MISCONCEPTION ALERT

Need for Scientists Some students might think modern-day humans know so much about the world that the need for life scientists is not as great as it used to be. To combat this misconception, ask students to think of one medical problem that is not solved (Sample answer: diabetes), one agricultural problem (Sample answer: blight ruins tomato crop), and one diet question. (Sample answer: How can fast food be made healthier?) Discuss that the need for life scientists will probably always exist.

Answer to Standards Check

An example of an electronic resource is the World Wide Web. **7.7.b** (mastering)

Standards Focus

This **Standards Focus** provides you with a quick way to **assess, reteach,** and **re-assess** one or more concepts in the section.

Assess

1. What are some print resources and some electronic resources that can be used to collect information? (Sample answer: Books and magazines are examples of print resources. The World Wide Web is an electronic resource.) **7.7.b**

Reteach

Library Research   Take the class to the school's resource center. Ask students a question and challenge them to find the answer in as many different types of resources as they can. **LS** Logical **7.7.b**

Re-Assess

Disease Prevalence   Ask students to research formerly common diseases. Students should find out when and why the disease became less common, and if it is less common worldwide or just in the U.S. and other countries with similar health care standards. (Sample diseases to research: diphtheria, tuberculosis, polio, mumps, whooping cough, typhoid fever, cholera, hepatitis, leprosy, plague, rabies, malaria) **LS** Logical **7.7.b**

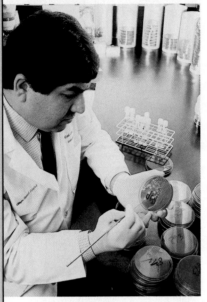

Figure 4 *Scientists hope to find a cure for AIDS by studying the virus that causes the disease.*

Why Ask Questions?

What is the point of asking all of these questions? Life scientists may find some interesting answers, but do any of the answers matter? Will the answers affect *your* life? Absolutely! As you study life science, you will see how the investigations of life science affect you and all living things around you.

Fighting Diseases

Polio is a disease that causes paralysis by affecting the brain and nerves. Do you know anyone who has had polio? Probably not. The polio virus has been eliminated from most of the world. But at one time, it was much more common. In 1952, before life scientists discovered ways to prevent the spread of the polio virus, it infected 58,000 Americans.

Today, life scientists continue to search for ways to fight diseases. Acquired immune deficiency syndrome (AIDS) is a disease that kills millions of people every year. The scientist in **Figure 4** is trying to learn more about AIDS. Life scientists have discovered how the virus that causes AIDS is carried from one person to another. Scientists have also learned about how the virus affects the body. By learning more about the virus, scientists may find a cure for this deadly disease.

Researching Food Sources

How can enough food be produced to feed everyone? How can we make sure that food is safe to eat? Many scientists do research to find answers to these types of questions. The scientist in **Figure 5** is studying a plant that was grown in a lab. Some scientists do experiments to see if they can make plants grow faster or larger. Other scientists research ways to preserve food so that it lasts longer.

Figure 5 *Scientists study plants to find better ways to produce food.*

Protecting the Environment

Life scientists also study environmental problems on Earth. Many environmental problems are caused by the misuse of natural resources. Understanding how we affect the world around us is the first step in finding solutions to problems such as pollution and the extinction of wildlife.

Why should we try to decrease pollution? Pollution can harm our health and the health of other organisms. Water pollution may be a cause of frog deformities seen in parts of the world. Pollution in oceans kills marine mammals, birds, and fish. The scientists in **Figure 6** are monitoring water quality to determine if the water is polluted.

The actions of humans affect many living things. When we cut down trees to clear land for crops or to get lumber, we change and sometimes destroy habitats. Hunting and loss of habitat have caused many animals, including Siberian tigers, California condors, and some species of fish, to become endangered. By learning about the food and habitat needs of endangered animals, scientists hope to develop a plan that will ensure the survival of these animals.

Figure 6 *These environmental scientists are testing water quality.*

SECTION Review

 7.7.b

Summary

- Science is a process of gathering knowledge about the natural world. Science includes making observations and asking questions. Life science is the study of living things.

- To find answers to your questions, you can make observations, do experiments, or use print and electronic resources to do research.

- Life science can help find cures for diseases, can research food sources, can monitor pollution, and can help living things survive.

Using Vocabulary

❶ Write an original definition for *life science*.

Understanding Concepts

❷ **Describing** Why are questions important in life science?

❸ **Listing** Give three examples of resources that you can use to do research.

INTERPRETING GRAPHICS Use the picture below to answer the next item.

❹ **Listing** Propose five questions about the animal in this picture.

Critical Thinking

❺ **Expressing Opinions** You can find a wide variety of information on the World Wide Web. What do you think makes a source reliable?

❻ **Applying Concepts** When would a life scientist study a nonliving thing, such as a lake or a rock?

❼ **Making Comparisons** A volcanologist is a scientist who studies volcanoes. How is the work of a volcanologist similar to the work of a life scientist? How do the two jobs differ?

Internet Resources

For a variety of links related to this chapter, go to www.scilinks.org
Topic: Careers in Life Science
SciLinks code: HY70224

Homework

Critter Comics Have students create a comic book about an imaginary organism and an environment in which it lives. Students should consider what and how the organism eats, the other kinds of organisms in its environment, and how all of the organisms coexist. **LS Visual/Logical**

Section Resources

📄 Directed Reading
A **BASIC** (Also in Spanish), B **GENERAL**

📄 Interactive Reader and Study Guide

📄 Section Quiz **GENERAL** (Also in Spanish)

📄 Section Review **GENERAL** (Also in Spanish)

📄 Vocabulary and Section Summary
A **BASIC** (Also in Spanish), B **GENERAL**

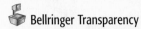

Preteach

Reviewing Prior Knowledge

Ask students the following question: Why do scientists use standard tools to make and record observations? (The observations are useful only if they are accurately made and recorded.)

🔔 Bellringer

Have students focus on standard 7.7.c and 7.7.e by asking them the following questions:

1. Describe an advertisement that cites research results. (Sample answer: Four out of five dentists recommend…)

2. Why is it important for scientists to write reports about their findings? (so other scientists can repeat the studies or consider the information)

🗄 Bellringer Transparency

Motivate

ACTIVITY

Now You See It As an exercise in observation, use an overhead projector to display a collection of assorted shapes. Allow students to look at the shapes for 15 seconds. Turn the projector off, and then have the students spend 5 minutes describing or drawing in their **Science Journals** as many of the shapes as they can.

LS Visual/Intrapersonal

What You Will Learn

- Scientists ask questions, make observations, form hypotheses, test hypotheses, analyze results, and draw conclusions.
- Scientists communicate their steps and results from investigations in written reports and oral presentations.

Why It Matters

You can use scientific methods to investigate your questions about the natural world.

Vocabulary

- scientific methods
- hypothesis
- controlled experiment
- variable

READING STRATEGY

Outlining In your **Science Journal,** create an outline of the section. Use the headings from the section in your outline.

Scientific Methods

Key Concept Scientific methods are used to investigate questions and to solve problems.

▶ Imagine that your class is on a field trip to a wildlife refuge. You discover several deformed frogs. You wonder what is causing the deformities.

A group of students from Le Sueur, Minnesota, actually made this discovery! By making observations and asking questions about the observations, the students used scientific methods.

What Are Scientific Methods?

When scientists observe the natural world, they often think of questions or problems. But scientists don't guess the answers. They use scientific methods. **Scientific methods** are the ways in which scientists follow steps to answer questions and solve problems. The steps used for all investigations are the same. But the order in which the steps are followed may vary, as **Figure 1** shows. Scientists may use all of the steps or just some of the steps during an investigation. They may even repeat some of the steps. The order depends on what will work best to answer their questions. No matter where they work or what questions they try to answer, all life scientists have two things in common. They are curious about the natural world, and they use similar methods to investigate it.

Standards Check What are scientific methods? 🐻 **7.7.c**

Figure 1 *Scientific methods often include the same steps, but the steps are not always used in the same order.*

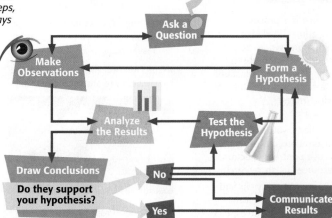

Investigation and Experimentation
7.7.c Communicate the logical connection among hypotheses, science concepts, tests conducted, data collected, and conclusions drawn from the scientific evidence.
7.7.e Communicate the steps and results from an investigation in written reports and oral presentations.

Answer to Standards Check

Scientific methods are the steps scientists follow to answer questions and solve problems. **7.7.c** (mastering)

Imagination Albert Einstein said, "Imagination is more important than knowledge. Knowledge is limited. Imagination encircles the world." He also said, "Logic will get you from A to B. Imagination will take you everywhere."

Ask a Question

Have you ever observed something that was out of the ordinary or difficult to explain? Such an observation usually raises questions. For example, you might ask, "Could something in the water be causing the frogs' deformities?" Looking for answers may include making more observations.

Make Observations

After the students from Minnesota realized something was wrong with the frogs, they decided to make additional, careful observations. They counted the number of deformed frogs and the number of normal frogs that they caught. The students also photographed the frogs, took measurements, and wrote a detailed description of each frog.

In addition, the students collected data on other organisms living in the pond. They also conducted many tests on the pond water, measuring things such as the level of acidity. The students carefully recorded their data and observations. Observations are only useful if they are accurately made and recorded.

Types of Observations

Any information gathered through the senses is an observation. Observations can take many forms. They may be measurements of length, volume, time, speed, or loudness. They may describe the color or shape of an organism. Or they may describe the behavior of organisms. Scientists use many standard tools and methods to make and record observations. Examples of these tools are shown in **Figure 2.**

INTERNET ACTIVITY

Careers in Life Science
Would you like to be a life scientist? Write an essay on your investigation of an interesting career. Go to **go.hrw.com** and type in the keyword HY7LIVW.

scientific methods
(SIE uhn TIF ik METH uhds) a series of steps followed to solve problems

Figure 2 *Microscopes, rulers, and thermometers are some of the tools that scientists use to collect information. Scientists record their observations carefully.*

Teach

📖 READING STRATEGY

Mnemonics Have students develop a mnemonic device that will remind them of the six steps of scientific methods: **A**sk a question, **F**orm a hypothesis, **T**est the hypothesis, **A**nalyze the results, **D**raw conclusions, and **C**ommunicate results. An example is: "**A**nne **F**ound **T**wenty **A**dorable **D**ogs and **C**ats."

LS Verbal

Connection To *Social Studies*

A Lifetime of Discoveries
To help students become aware of how science and technology affect their lives, have them work together to develop a timeline of discoveries that have occurred during their lifetime. Divide the class into small groups and assign each group a year. Have them use library resources or the Internet to research their year. Have each student prepare a note card for each event and illustrate at least one of the events. Tell them the cards should include the year, the discovery, and a few descriptive sentences about its significance. Have several volunteers assemble the timeline on a bulletin board.

LS Visual/Kinesthetic Co-op Learning

Teaching Transparency:
L1 Scientific Methods

Universal Access · Differentiated Instruction

Special Education Students

Reading Disconnect Some students have a disconnect when they read text that references a point made on a previous page. Direct students' attention to the first sentence under the subheading "Make Observations." Ask students "What students from Minnesota does this sentence refer to?" Some students will probably not remember reading in the first paragraph on page 12 about the students from Minnesota. Tell students to skim the previous paragraph looking for the word "Minnesota" and to keep backing up one paragraph at a time until they see the word. Make sure students find the word "Minnesota" in the second paragraph on page 12. Then, redirect students' attention back to the first sentence under the subheading "Make Observations." Again, ask students "What students from Minnesota does this sentence refer to?" (Sample answer: The students who found the deformed frogs.) **LS** Visual

Historic Disease Researcher
Share this information with students: Shibasaburo Kitasato was an important Japanese life scientist in the late 1800s and early 1900s. Using scientific methods, Kitasato was one of the first scientists to discover the bacteria for tetanus, diphtheria, and the bubonic plague, and he also developed a procedure to grow pure tetanus bacteria. This success led him to develop treatments for tetanus infections and to discover new ways to fight diphtheria and plague. Ask students if they have had shots or treatments for these diseases. (Diphtheria and plague have been almost eradicated, but most students have been vaccinated for diphtheria. Some may have been vaccinated or treated for tetanus.)

Wordwise

The Prefix *Hypo-* Review the definition of *hypothesis,* and point out that the prefix *hypo-* means "under" and the root *thesis* means "proposition." Then, ask students what the terms *hypodermic, hypothermia, hypoallergenic,* and *hypothyroidism* mean. (hypodermic: relating to the layer of skin just under the epidermis; hypothermia: abnormally low body temperature (under the normal temperature); hypoallergenic: decreased tendency to cause an allergic reaction (under the normal level for causing allergic reactions); hypothyroidism: lower than normal production of thyroid hormones) **LS Logical**

hypothesis (hi poth es is) a testable idea or explanation that leads to scientific investigation
Wordwise The prefix *hypo-* means "under." The root *thesis* means "proposition." Other examples are *hypodermic* and *hypoallergenic.*

Form a Hypothesis

After asking questions and making observations, scientists may form a hypothesis. A **hypothesis** (hie PAHTH uh sis) is a possible explanation or answer to a question. A good hypothesis is based on observations and can be tested. When scientists form hypotheses, they think logically and creatively and consider what they already know.

Scientists thought about the different things that could be affecting the frogs. Some chemicals can be dangerous to living things. Maybe chemicals used in agriculture and industry had been washed into ponds. Some parasites can cause diseases that produce deformities. Maybe small parasites in the water were attacking the frogs. Large amounts of ultraviolet (UV) light can cause damage in living things. Maybe human activity had damaged the ozone layer, which was letting in more UV light from the sun. Chemical pollutants, parasites, or UV light were possible explanations for the deformities seen in frogs.

Scientists used their observations and reasoning to form the hypotheses in **Figure 3.** Were any of these explanations correct? To find out, scientists had to test each hypothesis.

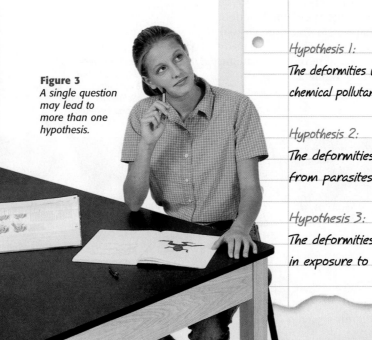

Figure 3
A single question may lead to more than one hypothesis.

Hypothesis 1:
The deformities were caused by one or more chemical pollutants in the water.

Hypothesis 2:
The deformities were caused by attacks from parasites or other frogs.

Hypothesis 3:
The deformities were caused by an increase in exposure to ultraviolet light from the sun.

Basic Learners

Frog Calls Tell students that scientists who study frogs often locate the frogs by their calls. Explain that the northern leopard frog, which inhabits the pond that the Minnesota students studied, has quite a peculiar call—a mixture of grunts, snores, and squeaks that sounds like a wet palm being rubbed across an inflated balloon. Ask a volunteer to use a balloon to demonstrate the frog's call for the class.
LS Kinesthetic/Auditory

Predictions

Before scientists can test a hypothesis, they must first make predictions. A prediction is a statement of cause and effect that can be used to set up a test for a hypothesis. Predictions are usually stated in an if-then format, as shown in **Figure 4.**

More than one prediction may be made for each hypothesis. For the hypotheses on the previous page, the predictions in **Figure 4** were made. A prediction for hypothesis 3 is as follows: If an increase in exposure to UV light is causing the deformities, then frog eggs exposed to more ultraviolet light in a laboratory will be more likely to develop into deformed frogs than frog eggs that are exposed to less UV light will.

Scientists can conduct experiments to see whether the results match the predictions of the hypothesis. Sometimes, the results clearly match the predictions of one hypothesis. At other times, the results may not have been predicted by any of the hypotheses. In these cases, new hypotheses and new tests are needed.

Standards Check What is the connection between hypotheses and the tests that are conducted in an investigation? 🐻 **7.7.c**

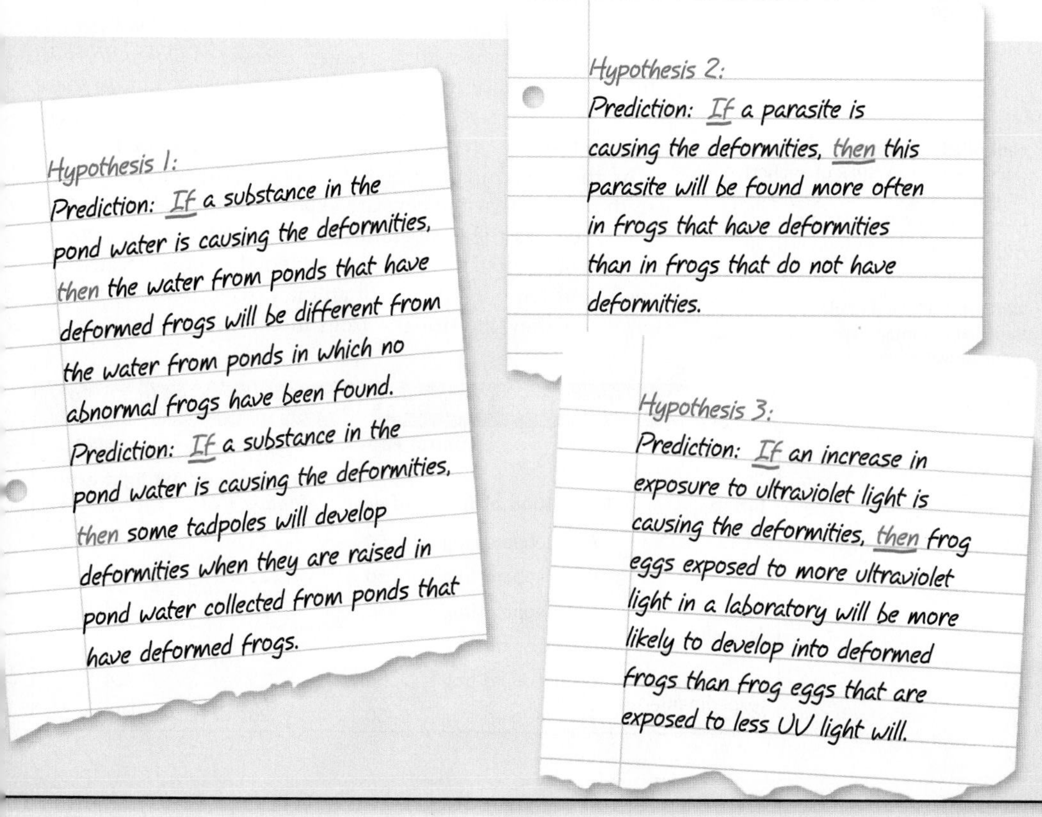

Figure 4 *A single hypothesis may lead to more than one prediciton.*

Hypothesis 1:
Prediction: If a substance in the pond water is causing the deformities, then the water from ponds that have deformed frogs will be different from the water from ponds in which no abnormal frogs have been found.
Prediction: If a substance in the pond water is causing the deformities, then some tadpoles will develop deformities when they are raised in pond water collected from ponds that have deformed frogs.

Hypothesis 2:
Prediction: If a parasite is causing the deformities, then this parasite will be found more often in frogs that have deformities than in frogs that do not have deformities.

Hypothesis 3:
Prediction: If an increase in exposure to ultraviolet light is causing the deformities, then frog eggs exposed to more ultraviolet light in a laboratory will be more likely to develop into deformed frogs than frog eggs that are exposed to less UV light will.

Answer to Standards Check

The tests that are conducted during an experiment are designed to test the predictions made by that hypothesis.
7.7.c (mastering)

Universal Access · Differentiated Instruction

Basic Learners

Testing Hypotheses Help students understand the concept of a "testable hypothesis." Have them discuss and decide which of the following hypotheses are testable.

1. Kyle is too tall. (no, "too tall" cannot be supported or disproved)

2. Kyle is taller than 95% of the students in school. (yes)

3. Red is the favorite color of students in this school. (yes)

4. Red is prettier than blue. (no, "prettier" cannot be supported or disproved)

LS Verbal

Discussion

Are We Next? At the forefront of the deformed-frog situation are these concerns:

Is human health at risk? Do the deformed frogs signal a widespread environmental problem?

Discuss these concerns with students and pose this question: "What steps can scientists take to find out whether humans are also at risk?" **LS** Verbal/Logical

Using the Table

Experimental Factors Ask students the following questions about the table on this page:

What is the only factor that differs between the control group and the experimental group? (the variable, which is exposure time to UV light)

What would happen if the temperature varied for each of the groups? (The experiment would not be controlled, because there would be more than one variable.)

How should the experiment be altered if we wanted to test the effect of temperature? (Have a different temperature of water for each group, but do not expose any of the frogs to UV light. Leave the other factors the same.)

MISCONCEPTION ALERT

Exciting Experiments
Students often assume that worthwhile experiments should be dazzling—something must explode or change color. Explain that, as the frog-egg example shows, many good experiments are not so dramatic and take a long time to yield results. Ask students to work in groups of three or four to think of meaningful, but non-glamorous experiments.

Figure 5 *Many factors affect this tadpole in the wild. These factors include chemicals, light, temperature, and parasites.*

controlled experiment
(kuhn TROLD ek SPER uh muhnt) an experiment that tests only one factor at a time by using a comparison of a control group with an experimental group

variable (VER ee uh buhl) a factor that changes in an experiment in order to test a hypothesis

---

Test the Hypothesis

Scientists try to design experiments that will show whether a particular factor caused an observed outcome. A *factor* is anything in an experiment that can influence the experiment's outcome. Factors can be anything from temperature to the type of organism being studied. Many factors affect the development of frogs in the wild, as **Figure 5** shows.

To study the effect of each factor, scientists perform controlled experiments. A **controlled experiment** tests only one factor at a time and consists of a control group and one or more experimental groups. All of the factors for the control group and the experimental groups are the same except for one. The one factor that differs is called the **variable.** Because the only difference between the control group and the experimental groups is the variable, any differences observed in the outcome of the experiment are probably caused by the variable.

Designing an Experiment

Every factor must be considered when designing an experiment. Scientists must also use ethics guidelines when designing and conducting an experiment. Examine the prediction for Hypothesis 3: *If an increase in exposure to ultraviolet light is causing the deformities, then frog eggs exposed to more ultraviolet light in a laboratory will be more likely to develop into deformed frogs than frog eggs that are exposed to less UV will.* An experiment to test this hypothesis is summarized in **Table 1.**

In the experiment shown in **Table 1,** the variable is the length of time that the eggs are exposed to UV light. All other factors, such as the temperature of the water, are the same in the control group and in the experimental groups. Because the experiment requires the use of animals, scientists use compassion when they care for the frogs in the experiment.

Table 1	Experiment to Test Effect of UV Light on Frogs				
	Control Factors				**Variable**
Group	**Tank**	**Kind of frog**	**Number of eggs**	**Temperature of water (°C)**	**UV light exposure (days)**
#1 (control)	A	leopard frog	50	25	0
	B	leopard frog	50	25	0
#2 (experimental)	C	leopard frog	50	25	15
	D	leopard frog	50	25	15
#3 (experimental)	E	leopard frog	50	25	24
	F	leopard frog	50	25	24

Universal Access • Differentiated Instruction

English Learners

Parts of Speech Point out that some words in the English language can be used as different parts of speech, such as nouns, verbs, and adjectives. On the board, write these words from the text under the subheading "Test the Hypothesis": *experiment, wild, tests.* Ask students to find each word in the text and identify whether it is a noun, verb, or adjective. Then, ask them for an example of each word used as a different part of speech. (Sample answers: Second sentence—experiment/noun, Verb: I am going to experiment to find out if olives freeze.; Fourth sentence—wild/noun, Adjective: The wild raccoon did not make a good pet.; Sixth sentence—tests/verb, Noun: We studied for our tests in science and history.) **LS** Verbal

Figure 6 UV Light Experiment

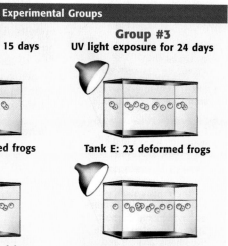
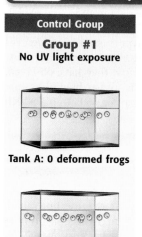

Control Group

Group #1
No UV light exposure

Tank A: 0 deformed frogs

Tank B: 0 deformed frogs

Experimental Groups

Group #2
UV light exposure for 15 days

Tank C: 0 deformed frogs

Tank D: 0 deformed frogs

Group #3
UV light exposure for 24 days

Tank E: 23 deformed frogs

Tank F: 24 deformed frogs

Collecting Data

As **Table 1** shows, each group in the experiment contains 100 eggs. Scientists always try to test many individuals. The greater the number of organisms that they test, the more certain they can be of the data. They want to be certain that differences between control and experimental groups are caused by differences in the variable, not by differences between individuals. To support their conclusions, scientists repeat their experiments. If an experiment produces the same results again and again, they can be more certain about the effect of the variable on the outcome of the experiment. The experimental setup to test Hypothesis 3 and the results are shown in **Figure 6.**

Analyze the Results

A scientist's work does not end when an experiment is finished. After scientists finish their tests, they must analyze the results. They organize the data so that the data can be analyzed. For example, scientists may organize the data in a table or a graph. The data collected from the UV light experiment are shown in the bar graph in **Figure 7.** Analyzing results helps scientists explain and focus on the effect of the variable. For example, the bar graph shows that the length of UV exposure has an effect on the development of deformities in frogs.

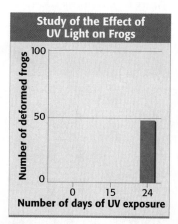

Study of the Effect of UV Light on Frogs

Number of deformed frogs

Number of days of UV exposure

Figure 7 This graph shows that 24 days of UV exposure had an effect on deformities in frogs. Shorter exposure had no effect.

Special Education Students

Factors and Variables Some students will better understand the meaning of "factors" and "variables" if they practice identifying them. Tell students to imagine they are going to do an experiment to determine if backpacks are too heavy for students to carry. Divide the class into groups of three to five students. Ask each group to act out something that could affect whether backpacks are too heavy for students to carry. (Sample answers: student size, student health, weight distribution of backpack style, distance backpack must be carried) Explain that anything affecting whether the backpack is too heavy is a factor that could be used as a variable. **LS** Logical/Kinesthetic

Using the Figure

Control Group Have students carefully examine the experimental setup depicted in **Figure 6.** Be sure that they observe how the setup matches the information in **Table 1.** Ask them the following questions:

1. Which of the aquariums shown are part of the control group, and which are experimental? (The control group includes tanks A and B; the experimental groups are tanks C, D, E, and F.)

2. If it were not labeled, how could you tell which group was the control group? (It is the group that does not have any exposure to UV light. The other groups have differing amounts of this variable.)

3. Other than the variable, what differences are there between the groups? (The only difference is the level of UV light exposure; all other factors are the same. Group #3 is the only group with different results.) **LS** Verbal/Logical

Discussion

Experimental Setup Discuss the conditions within each of the aquariums in the experiment in **Figure 6.** Ask students to think about any factors that should be considered before the experiment begins. (Sample answer: The condition, size, and filtration of each tank should be the same.) You may want to discuss how this example of an experiment has been simplified. Ask students to explain why most scientists would want to use many more tanks than shown in **Figure 6.** (Repeating an experiment many times helps to ensure that the variable being tested, and not another factor, is responsible for the results.) Ask students what special considerations must be examined for experiments involving animals. (Sample answer: First, scientists must prove that the experiment is likely to yield new knowledge. Second, scientists must show compassion when they are working with living things in experiments.) **LS** Verbal

Standards Focus

This **Standards Focus** provides you with a quick way to **assess, reteach,** and **re-assess** one or more concepts in the section.

Assess

1. Why is it important to have a control group when doing an experiment? (Data from the experimental groups are compared with data from the control group to see the effect caused by changes to the variable.) **7.7.c**

2. Why should a hypothesis be testable? (If a hypothesis is not testable, there is no way to support it or to show that it is wrong.) **7.7.c**

Reteach

Experimental Setup Have students propose other experiments that scientists could use to test the effect of UV light on frogs. Discuss how such an experiment might be set up. **LS** Logical **7.7.c**

Re-Assess

Using Scientific Methods Have students use scientific methods to answer a simple, everyday question. Ask students to set up experiments, keep careful records, summarize their results, and then present them to the class.
LS Logical/Verbal **7.7.e**

Answer to Standards Check

Scientists communicate the results of scientific investigations so that the investigations can be repeated. When scientists communicate their results, other scientists learn new information. **7.7.e** (mastering)

Quick Lab

Investigating and Experimenting with Yeast

7.7.c

1. Mix **1/2 tsp of yeast** with **warm water** and **sugar.**

2. Make observations. Compose a list of questions about the factors that influence yeast to activate.

3. Use scientific methods to investigate yeast activation. For this investigation, you will need to form a hypothesis, design and conduct an experiment to test the hypothesis, analyze and collect data, and state the conclusions.

4. Did your results support your hypothesis?

⏱ **30 min**

Figure 8 *This student scientist is communicating the results of his investigation at a science fair.*

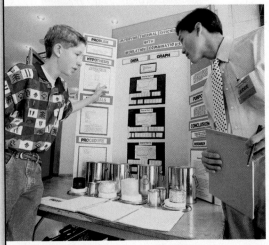

Draw Conclusions

After scientists have analyzed the data from several experiments, they can draw conclusions. They decide whether the results of the experiments support a hypothesis. When scientists find that a hypothesis is not supported by the tests, they must try to find another explanation for what they have observed. Proving that a hypothesis is wrong is just as helpful as supporting it. Why? The scientist have learned something, which is the purpose of using scientific methods.

What Is the Answer?

The UV light experiment supports the hypothesis that the deformities in frog can be caused by exposure to UV light. Does the experiment prove that UV light caused the frogs living in the Minnesota wetland to be deformed? No, the only thing this experiment shows is that UV light may cause deformities in frog. Results of tests performed in a laboratory may differ from results of tests performed in the wild. In addition, the experiment did not investigate the effects of parasites or other substances on the frogs. In fact, more than one factor could be causing the deformities.

Puzzles as complex as the deformed-frog mystery are rarely solved with a single experiment. The quest for a solution may continue for years. Finding an answer doesn't always end an investigation. Often, that answer begins another investigation. In this way, scientists continue to build knowledge.

Communicate Results

After they complete an investigation, scientists communicate their steps and results. Written reports and oral presentations are two ways in which scientists share information. **Figure 8** shows a student explaining a science project.

There are several reasons that scientists regularly share their results. First, other scientists may repeat the experiments to see if they get the same results. Second, the information can be considered by other scientists with similar interests. The scientists can then compare hypotheses and form consistent explanations. New data may strengthen existing hypotheses or show that the hypotheses need to be altered. After learning about an experiment, a scientist might have questions and decide to preform his or her own investigation.

Standards Check Why do scientists communicate the results of their investigations? **7.7.e**

Quick Lab

⏱ **30 min**

Teacher Notes

This activity has students practice using scientific methods (covers standard 7.7.c). The yeast needs to be fairly fresh so that when it emerges from dormancy, it will begin to metabolize the sugar for energy.

Materials for Each Group
• sugar
• yeast, ½ teaspoon
• water, warm

Safety Caution

Remind students to review all safety cautions and icons before beginning this lab.

Answers

4. Depending on the hypotheses chosen, the results may or may not support the students' hypotheses.

📁 **Differentiated Datasheets**
A **BASIC**, B **GENERAL**, C **ADVANCED**

Also editable on the **Holt Lab Generator CD-ROM**

SECTION Review

7.7.c, 7.7.e

Summary

- Scientific methods are the ways in which scientists follow steps to answer questions and solve problems.

- Any information gathered through the senses is an observation. Observations often lead to the formation of questions and hypotheses.

- A hypothesis is a possible explanation or answer to a question. A well-formed hypothesis may be tested by experiments.

- A controlled experiment tests only one factor at a time and consists of a control group and one or more experimental groups.

- After testing a hypothesis, scientists analyze the results and draw conclusions about whether the hypothesis is supported.

- Communicating results allows others to check the results, add to their knowledge, and design new experiments.

Using Vocabulary

1 Use *hypothesis, controlled experiment,* and *variable* in the same sentence.

Understanding Concepts

2 Describing The steps of scientific methods are not always used in the same order in every investigation. Support or argue this statement.

3 Describing What are the essential parts of a controlled experiment?

4 Listing What are two ways in which scientists share results?

5 Classifying A team of scientists wants to study the size of Anaconda snakes in the wild. After capturing a snake, the team measures and records the length of each snake. After the snakes are released, the team finds the average length of the captured snakes. Which scientific methods have the scientists used?

Critical Thinking

6 Analyzing Methods Why was UV light chosen to be the variable in the frog experiment?

7 Analyzing Processes Why do scientists repeat the examples of other scientists?

8 Making Inferences Why might two scientists working on the same problem draw different conclusions?

INTERPRETING GRAPHICS The table below shows how long one bacterium takes to divide and become two bacteria. Use the table below to answer the next question.

Temperature (°C)	Time to double (min)
10	130
20	60
25	40
30	29
37	17
40	19
45	32
50	no growth

9 Evaluating Data Plot this information on a graph. Put temperature on the x-axis and the time to double on the y-axis. Do not graph values for which there is no growth. What temperature allows the bacteria to multiply most quickly?

Challenge

10 Predicting Consequences You are doing an experiment and get surprising results. However, you realize that two factors were changed at the same time. How does this fact affect your ability to draw conclusions?

Internet Resources

For a variety of links related to this chapter, go to www.scilinks.org

Topic: Scientific Methods; Deformed Frogs

SciLinks code: HY71359; HY70383

---

7. Sample answer: Scientists repeat experiments done by other scientists to see if they get similar results. If the scientists get similar results, it means that the results are probably accurate. **7.7.e** (exceeding)

8. Sample answer: In addition to the variable being tested, other factors for the control group and the experimental group may not be the same. **7.7.c** (exceeding)

9. See sample graph below. The temperature that allows bacteria to multiply most quickly is 37°C. **7.7.c** (mastering)

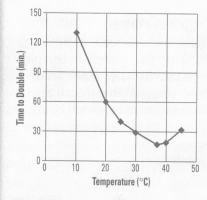

10. Sample answer: If two factors were changed at the same time, you will not be able to draw conclusions. And therefore, you will not be able to tell which factors influenced the results. **7.7.c** (exceeding)

Section Review Standards Guide	Supporting	Mastering	Exceeding
7.7.c		1–2, 5, 9	3, 6, 8, 10
7.7.e		4	7

Answers to Section Review

1. Sample answer: A good controlled experiment will test a single hypothesis and a single variable at a time. **7.7.c** (mastering)

2. The steps of scientific methods are not always used in the same order. For example, an investigation may start with asking a question, making an observation, or at the point of drawing conclusions in a previous investigation. **7.7.c** (mastering)

3. The essential parts of a controlled experiment are a control group and one or more experimental groups that differ by only one factor—the variable. **7.7.c** (exceeding)

4. Scientists share results though oral presentations and written reports. **7.7.e** (mastering)

5. The scientists used the following scientific methods: ask a question, make observations, and analyze the results. **7.7.c** (mastering)

6. UV light was chosen to be the variable because the scientists were trying to test the hypothesis: UV light causes deformities. UV light was the factor that needed to be varied—the variable. **7.7.c** (exceeding)

Section Resources

- Directed Reading A **BASIC** (Also in Spanish), B **GENERAL**

- Interactive Reader and Study Guide

- Section Quiz **GENERAL** (Also in Spanish)

- Section Review **GENERAL** (Also in Spanish)

- Vocabulary and Section Summary A **BASIC** (Also in Spanish), B **GENERAL**

Preteach

Reviewing Prior Knowledge

Point out that scientists' observations are important to the advancement of science. Ask students what scientists do with their results. (Sample answer: Scientists analyze and share their results.)

Bellringer

Have students focus on standard 7.7.a by asking them to complete this activity: Give examples of how common items, such as calculators and computers, are used as tools in science. (Sample answer: Calculators and computers can both be used to quickly make calculations and to improve the accuracy of results. In addition, computers can be used to gather information)

Ask students to share their answers with the class and briefly discuss their responses.

Bellringer Transparency

Motivate

Demonstration

Tools for Seeing Assemble a collection of images of ordinary objects viewed variously with light and electron microscopes, X rays, MRIs, and CAT scans. Display the images on an overhead projector. Challenge students to identify the objects.

What You Will Learn

- Scientists use technology, such as computers and microscopes, to perform tests and collect information.
- The International System of Units enables scientists to compare information and to convert between units.
- Measurements such as length, area, volume, temperature, and mass can be obtained with the right tools.

Why It Matters

Selecting and using the right tools and technology will help you conduct your own scientific investigations.

Vocabulary

- technology
- compound light microscope
- electron microscope
- area
- volume
- mass
- weight
- temperature

READING STRATEGY

Clarifying Concepts Take turns reading this section out loud with a partner. Stop to discuss ideas that seem confusing.

technology (tek NAHL uh jee) the application of science for practical purposes; the use of tools, machines, materials, and processes to meet human needs

Tools and Measurement

Key Concept Scientists select and use tools and technology to perform tests and collect data.

▶ Would you use a knife to mix cake batter? You probably would not. To be successful in many tasks, you need the correct tools.

Life scientists use various tools to make observations and to collect, store, and analyze information. Selecting and using tools properly are important parts of scientific work.

Technology in Science

The application of science for practical purposes is called **technology.** By using technology, life scientists are able to find information and solve problems in new ways. New technology allows scientists to get information that was not available previously.

Calculators and Computers

Calculators and computers are two types of technology that are frequently used in science. Scientists frequently collect large amounts of data. Calculators and computers can be used to quickly and accurately make calculations of data. Some calculators and computers can be programed to create graphs and to solve complex equations. Computers also help scientists share data and ideas with each other and publish reports about their research.

Binoculars

Imagine that you are studying eagles that nest in tall trees. You need to make observations. But it is not always easy or safe to get close to what you are studying. Binoculars can help you make observations from a distance. **Figure 1** shows a scientist using binoculars to make observations.

Figure 1 Binoculars help scientists make observations when they cannot get close to their subject.

Universal Access · Differentiated Instruction

Struggling Readers

Tools and Measurement Vocabulary

Some students benefit from organized vocabulary activities before they start reading, especially when there are many vocabulary words to learn. Ask students to fold a piece of paper lengthwise so that 1/3 of the page is to the left of the fold and 2/3 is to the right. Skipping three lines between each word, have students write the vocabulary words in the smaller left column. Then, as a group, discuss the definitions of the words and have students write the definitions on the right side. Finally, divide the students into teams of four to six students. Call out the definitions (repeatedly, in random order) and have the teams compete to see which team can supply the quickest correct answers. **LS** Verbal/Auditory

---

Figure 2   Types of Microscopes

Compound Light Microscope
Light passes through the specimen and produces a flat image.

Transmission Electron Microscope   Electrons pass through the specimen and produce a flat image.

Scanning Electron Microscope
Electrons bounce off the surface of the specimen and produce a three-dimensional (3-D) image.

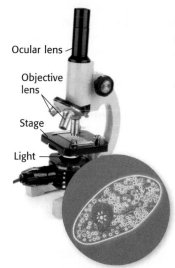

Ocular lens

Objective lens

Stage

Light

Compound Light Microscope

The compound light microscope is a common tool in a life science laboratory. A **compound light microscope** is an instrument that magnifies small objects so that they can be seen easily. It has three main parts—a tube with two or more lenses, a stage, and a light. Items may be colored with special dyes to make them more visible. Items are placed on the stage so that the light passes through them. The lenses at each end of the tube magnify the image.

Electron Microscopes

Not all microscopes use light. In **electron microscopes,** tiny particles called *electrons* are used to produce magnified images. The images produced are clearer and more detailed than those made by light microscopes. However, living things cannot be viewed with electron microscopes because the preparation process kills them. The two kinds of electron microscopes used in life science are the transmission electron microscope (TEM) and the scanning electron microscope (SEM). **Figure 2** shows three kinds of microscopes and an example of the images that each kind can produce.

Standards Check   Which type of technology would you use to observe the movement of a small living thing? **7.7.a**

compound light microscope
(kahm POWND   LIET   MIE kruh SKOHP) an instrument that magnifies small objects so that they can be seen easily by using two or more lenses

Wordwise   The root *micro-* means "small." The root *-scope* means "an instrument for seeing or observing."

electron microscope
(ee LEK trahn   MIE kruh SKOHP) a microscope that focuses a beam of electrons to magnify objects

Investigation and Experimentation
7.7.a   Select and use appropriate tools and technology (including calculators, computers, balances, spring scales, microscopes, and binoculars) to perform tests, collect data, and display data.

Answer to Standards Check

a compound light microscope **7.7.a** (mastering)

Teach

It All Adds Up!   Devices that assist in calculations have been around for a long time. Many cultures have used variations of the calculator, including the "pebble computer" and the abacus. Have students research and prepare presentations about some of these early tools and the ways in which they work. **LS** Verbal

ACTIVITY

Using a Microscope   Help students become familiar with the parts of a compound microscope and its functions by using a microscope to look at pond water. Encourage students to ask questions if they are confused. Prepare a wet-mount slide with a drop of pond water. Allow each student to view the slide through the microscope and turn the adjustment knob (or knobs) to view the water at different depths of focus. Discuss what the students observed. **LS** Visual

Group ACTIVITY

X Rays   Tell students that when Wilhelm Roentgen discovered the X ray in 1895, his discovery amused people, but they really didn't know what to do with the technology. Organize students into small groups. Have them imagine that they are Roentgen's assistants and that they have been instructed to develop a list of applications for this new discovery. Have students name at least five uses, either real or imagined. **LS** Interpersonal

Debate

SI in United States Explain to students that the United States does not use SI to the extent that most other countries do. Have students debate the issue of whether the government should force U.S. citizens to use SI for all types of measurement. Suggest that students support their arguments with examples from the history of the English system and SI. **LS** Verbal/Interpersonal

Connection To
Math

SI Conversions

To help students understand SI conversions, have them answer the following questions:

1. How many meters are in 2.5 km? (2500 m)

2. How many centimeters are in 3.1 m? (310 cm)

3. What is 20 km in millimeters? (20,000,000 mm)

Using the Table

Check Your SI Knowledge

To check their familiarity with SI units, ask students to read **Table 1** and count the terms with which they are familiar. Discuss that in the 1950s, most U.S. students were not familiar with more than one or two of the terms, if any. **LS** Verbal

 Teaching Transparency: L2 Common SI Units and Conversions

Answers to School-to-Home Activity

Measurements may vary depending on the standard of measurement chosen. Some units might include hand width, hand length, or pencil length. By comparing their units and measurements with others, students should recognize that scientists need a common standard of measurement to be able to communicate data and be understood.

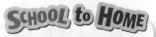

How You Measure Matters

Measure the length and width of a desk or table, but do not use a ruler. Pick a common object as your unit of measurement. It could be a pencil, your hand, or anything else. Use that unit to determine the area of the desk or table.

To calculate the area of a rectangle, first measure the length and width. Then, use the following equation:

area = length × width

Ask your parent or guardian to do this activity on his or her own. When he or she is finished, compare your area calculations.

area (ER ee uh) a measure of the size of a surface or a region

volume (VAHL yoom) a measure of the size of a body or region in three-dimensional space

---

Table 1	Common SI Units and Conversions	
Length	**meter (m)**	
	kilometer (km)	1 km = 1,000 m
	decimeter (dm)	1 dm = 0.1 m
	centimeter (cm)	1 cm = 0.01 m
	millimeter (mm)	1 mm = 0.001 m
	micrometer (μm)	1 μm = 0.000001 m
	nanometer (nm)	1 nm = 0.000000001 m
Volume	**cubic meter (m³)**	
	cubic centimeter (cm³)	1 cm³ = 0.000001 m³
	liter (L)	1 L = 1 dm³ = 0.001 m³
	milliliter (mL)	1 mL = 0.001 L = 1 cm³
Mass	**kilogram (kg)**	
	gram (g)	1 g = 0.001 kg
	milligram (mg)	1 mg = 0.000001 kg
Temperature	**kelvin (K)**	
		0°C = 273 K
		100°C = 373 K

*The Celcius (°C) scale is a commonly used non-SI temperature scale.

Measurement

The ability to make reliable measurements is an important skill in science. But different standards of measurement have developed throughout the world. Ancient measurement units were based on parts of the body, such as the foot, or on objects, such as grains of wheat. Such systems were not very reliable. Even as better standards were developed, they varied from country to country.

The International System of Units

In the late 1700s, the French Academy of Sciences began to form a global measurement system now known as the *International System of Units*. (The system is also called *SI*, or *Système International d'Unités*). Today, most scientists and almost all countries use this system. One advantage of using SI measurements is that scientists can share and compare their observations and results.

Another advantage is that almost all SI units are based on the number 10, which makes conversions from one unit to another easy. **Table 1** contains SI units for length, volume, mass, and temperature. Notice how the prefix of each SI unit relates to a base unit.

Universal Access · Differentiated Instruction

Special Education Students

Physical Information Many students can best understand information when it is presented in physical ways. Use this activity to help students understand *irregular shape*. Gather items with regular and irregular shapes, for example:

- Regular: textbook, large cardboard box, cylindrical container, shoe box, round ball
- Irregular: shoe, phone, watch, coffee mug, chair, backpack, stapler

Place the items on a desk or table. Ask students to separate the items into regular and irregular shapes. **LS** Visual/Kinesthetic

---

Length

How long is an ant? A life scientist would probably use millimeters (mm) to describe an ant's length. If you divide 1 m into 1,000 parts, each part equals 1 mm. Although millimeters seem like a small unit, some living things and structures are so tiny that even smaller units—micrometers (μm) or nanometers (nm)—must be used.

Area

How much paper would you need to cover the top of your desk? To answer this question, you must find the area of the desk. **Area** is a measure of how much surface an object has. Area can be calculated from measurements such as length and width. Area is stated in square units, such as square meters (m²), square centimeters (cm²), and square kilometers (km²).

Volume

How many books will fit into a bag? The answer depends on the volume of the bag and the volume of each book. **Volume** is a measure of the size of something in three-dimensional space.

The volume of a liquid is most often described in liters (L). Liters are based on the meter. A cubic meter (1 m³) is equal to 1,000 L. So, 1,000 L will fit into a box measuring 1 m on each side. A milliliter (mL) will fit into a box that is 1 cm on each side. So, 1 mL = 1 cm³. Graduated cylinders are used to measure the volume of liquids, as **Figure 3** shows.

The volume of a solid object is given in cubic units, such as cubic meters (m³), cubic centimeters (cm³), or cubic millimeters (mm³). To find the volume of a box-shaped object, multiply the object's length by its width and height. As **Figure 3** shows, the volume of an irregularly shaped object can be found by measuring the amount of liquid that the object displaces.

Standards Check What tool would you select to measure the volume of a liquid? **7.7.a**

Figure 3 Adding a rock to a graduated cylinder raised the level of water from the 70 mL mark to the 80 mL mark. Because the rock displaced 10 mL of water and 1 mL = 1 cm³, the volume of the rock is 10 cm³.

70 mL

80 mL

Close

Standards Focus

This **Standards Focus** provides you with a quick way to **assess, reteach,** and **re-assess** one or more concepts in the section.

 Assess

1. What is the SI unit for length? for mass? for temperature? (meter; kilogram; Kelvin) **7.7.a**

2. What is the area of the front of a compact disc case with sides measuring 14 cm and 12.5 cm? (14 cm × 12.5 cm = 175 cm²) **7.7.a**

3. How could you find the volume of an irregularly shaped pebble? (Use a graduated cylinder to measure the amount of water that the pebble displaces.) **7.7.a**

Reteach

SI Estimation Display or name various objects one at a time. For each object, call on a different student to identify an SI unit that could be used for a measurement of the object and then to estimate the measurement in SI units. Have another student verify each measurement.

LS Verbal/Kinesthetic **7.7.a**

Re-Assess

Section Dictionary Have students each create an illustrated dictionary of the vocabulary words used in the section. Students can share their dictionaries with the rest of the class.

LS Visual **7.7.a**

Figure 4 Tools Used to Measure Mass and Weight

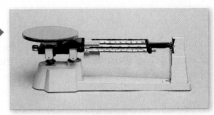

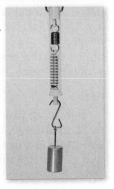

You can use a **spring scale** to measure weight. ▶

You can use a **balance** ▶ to measure mass.

mass (MAS) a measure of the amount of matter in an object

weight (WAYT) a measure of the gravitational force exerted on an object; its value can change with the location of the object in the universe

temperature (TEM puhr uh chuhr) a measure of how hot (or cold) something is; specifically, a measure of the average kinetic energy of the particles in an object

Mass and Weight

A measure of the amount of matter in an object is called **mass.** The mass of an object is constant anywhere in the universe because the amount of matter stays the same. The kilogram (kg) is the base unit for mass. The mass of a small object may be described in grams (g). Mass can be measured by using a balance, as **Figure 4** shows. Weight and mass are sometimes confused, but they are different. **Weight** is a measure of the force of gravity on an object and is expressed in newtons (N). The force of gravity changes depending on where the object is in the universe. So, the weight of an object on Earth differs from the weight of the object on the moon. Weight is measured by using a spring scale, as **Figure 4** shows.

Quick Lab

7.7.a

Measure Up!

1. Your teacher will provide you with a variety of tools, such as a **graduated cylinder, balance, spring scale, thermometer,** and **meterstick**.

2. Make a table similar to the table at right.

3. Select a tool to take the measurement of each object listed in the table. Record each tool in your table.

4. Take each measurement and record it in your table.

Measuring Objects			
Object	Measurement needed	Tools needed	Measurement (with units)
Water in a cup	volume	graduated cylinder	350 mL
Classroom	area		
Bolt	volume		
Chalk board	length		
Shoe	weight		
Outside air	temperature		
Pencil	mass		

DO NOT WRITE IN BOOK

🕐 **25 min**

Quick Lab

🕐 **25 min**

Teacher Notes

Students will practice selecting and using the appropriate tools to measure various objects (covers 7.7.a).

Materials

Measurable items, such as the following:
- air
- bolt
- chalk board or white board
- classroom
- pencil
- shoe box
- water in a cup

Safety Caution

Remind students to review all safety cautions before beginning this lab activity. Non-mercury thermometers and plastic graduated cylinders are recommended.

Answers

Make sure students choose appropriate measuring tools and use the tools correctly.

 Differentiated Datasheets
A **BASIC**, B **GENERAL**, C **ADVANCED**

Also editable on the Holt Lab Generator CD-ROM

Temperature

How much should food be heated to kill any bacteria in the food? To answer this question, a life scientist would measure the temperature at which bacteria die. **Temperature** is a measure of how hot or cold something is. Temperature is actually an indication of the amount of energy within matter. You are probably used to describing temperature in degrees Fahrenheit (°F). Although the kelvin (K) is the official SI base unit for temperature, scientists commonly use degrees Celsius (°C). You will use degrees Celsius in this book. The thermometer in **Figure 5** shows how the Fahrenheit and Celsius scales compare.

Figure 5 *This thermometer shows the relationship between degrees Fahrenheit and degrees Celsius.*

7.7.a

SECTION Review

Summary

- Life scientists use tools to collect, store, organize, analyze, and share data.
- Scientists use technology such as calculators, computers, binoculars, and microscopes.
- The International System of Units (SI) is a simple and reliable system of measurement that is used by most scientists.
- Graduated cylinders measure the volume of liquids, rulers measure length, thermometers measure temperature, and balances measure mass.
- You can calculate the area and volume of box-shaped solids by using measurements taken with a ruler.

Using Vocabulary

Use a term from the section to complete each sentence below.

1. The measure of the surface of an object is called ___.

2. Life scientists use kilograms when measuring an object's ___.

3. The ___ of a liquid is usually described in liters.

Understanding Concepts

4. **Describing** Why do scientists use SI units when making measurements?

5. **Describing** How are computers used in scientific investigations?

6. **Identifying** Which tool would you select to measure the mass of an object?

Math Skills

7. **Making Calculations** Convert 3.0 L into cubic centimeters.

8. **Making Calculations** Calculate the volume of a textbook that is 28.5 cm long, 22 cm wide, and 3.5 cm thick.

Critical Thinking

9. **Predicting Consequences** What problems could occur if some scientists measured objects by using SI units and other scientists measured objects by using other units, such as inches?

INTERPRETING GRAPHICS Use the picture of a mite below to answer the next question.

10. **Making Inferences** The mite shown above is about 500 μm long in real life. What tool was probably used to produce this image? How can you tell?

Internet Resources

For a variety of links related to this chapter, go to www.scilinks.org
Topic: Tools of Life Science; SI Units
SciLinks code: HY71535; HY71390

Answers to Section Review

1. area **7.7.a** (supporting)

2. mass **7.7.a** (supporting)

3. volume **7.7.a** (supporting)

4. Since all scientists use SI units, they can easily share information. Also, SI units can easily be converted from one unit to another because they are based on the number 10. **7.7.a** (supporting)

5. Computers are used to make calculations, create graphs, and share data. **7.7.a** (mastering)

6. A balance is used to measure mass. **7.7.a** (mastering)

7. 3.0 L × 1,000 mL/L = 3,000 mL; 3,000 mL × 1 cm³/mL = 3,000 cm³

8. (28.5 × 22 × 3.5) = 2,194.5 cm³; or about 2195 cm³

9. If scientists used different units of measurement, it would be difficult for them to compare results and to communicate knowledge. **7.7.a** (exceeding)

10. The image is a SEM; you can tell by the magnification and by the visible three-dimensional features. **7.7.a** (exceeding)

Section Review Standards Guide		
	Supporting	Mastering	Exceeding
7.7.a	1, 2, 3, 4	5, 6	9, 10

Preteach

Reviewing Prior Knowledge

Write "cm" and "km" on the board to serve as the headings for two columns. Underline both abbreviations. Divide students into small groups. Ask each group to think of two things to add to each list that would logically be measured with the unit at the top.

 Bellringer

Have students focus on standard 7.7.d by having them write the answers to the following questions in their **Science Journals:**

1. What is a model? (Sample answer: A model is a representation of an object or system.)

2. Name several types of models. (physical, mathematical, conceptual)

Bellringer Transparency

Motivate

Discussion

Toys as Models Children's toys are often physical models of everyday objects. Have students pass around a variety of toys, such as cars, dolls, and stuffed animals. Discuss how the toys are similar to the objects they represent and how they are different. Discuss the limitations of the toys. (The toys may look similar to the objects they represent but may be smaller and have simpler features. The limitations of toys as models may be good or bad—the models may be safer, easier to handle, or more durable, but not as useful as the real thing.)

LS Logical/Kinesthetic

What You Will Learn

- Physical models, mathematical models, and conceptual models are all representations of ways to study objects or systems.
- Scientific theories are conceptual models that organize scientific thinking and explain why things happen.
- Scientific laws tell you what will happen in a specific situation.

Why It Matters

Learning about models and theories will give you a better understanding of how science works.

Vocabulary
- model
- scale
- theory
- law

Graphic Organizer In your **Science Journal,** create an Idea Wheel about the types of scientific models.

model (MAHD' l) a pattern, plan, representation, or description designed to show the structure or workings of an object, system, or concept

Scientific Models and Knowledge

Key Concept Models are used to study living things, test hypotheses, explain observations, and communicate knowledge.

▶ Your body is made up of trillions of cells. You need a microscope to see inside most cells. But how do you learn about the parts of a cell if you don't have a microscope? Models are useful tools for sharing information, such as the structure of cells.

Types of Scientific Models

A **model** is a representation of an object or a system. Models are used in science to help explain how something works or is structured. Models can also be used to make predictions or to explain observations. However, models have limitations. A model is never exactly like the real thing. If it were, it would not be a model. There are many kinds of scientific models. Some examples are physical models, mathematical models, and conceptual models.

Physical Models

A toy rocket and a plastic skeleton are examples of physical models. Many physical models, such as the model of a human body in **Figure 1,** look like the thing that they model. A limitation of the model of a body is that the model is not alive and doesn't act exactly like a human body. Yet the model is useful for understanding how the body works. Other physical models may look and act more like or less like what they represent than the model in **Figure 1** does. Scientists often use the model that is simplest to use but that is still helpful.

Figure 1 This physical model looks a lot like a real human body. But it is easier to see inside this model than to see inside a real human body.

Mathematical Models

A mathematical model may be made up of numbers, equations, or other forms of data. Some mathematical models are simple and can be used easily. The graph in **Figure 2** is a model of life expectancy—a measure of how long, on average, people live. This model was created by collecting information in different areas of the world over many years. Then, the information was used to predict life expectancy in the future. For example, if the life expectancy in an area increased by 5 years in the last 10 years, one might hypothesize that the life expectancy will continue to increase at a similar rate.

Computers are very useful for creating and manipulating mathematical models. They make fewer mistakes than humans do and can keep track of more variables than humans can. But a computer model can be incorrect in many ways. The more complex a model is, the more carefully scientists must build the model.

Conceptual Models

Conceptual models are diagrams, drawings, or verbal descriptions of how something works or is put together. The conceptual model in **Figure 3** describes how mercury released from burning coal could travel through the environment and affect humans. Scientists create such diagrams to show how the parts of a system affect one another.

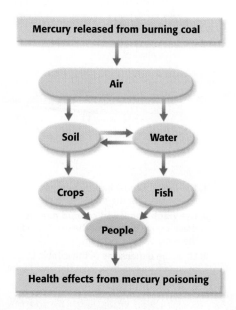

Figure 2 This mathematical model shows average life expectancy in the past. This information is used to predict what the life expectancy will be in the future.

Figure 3 This conceptual model shows how mercury released from burning coal could end up affecting humans.

Investigation and Experimentation
7.7.c Communicate the logical connection among hypotheses, science concepts, tests conducted, data collected, and conclusions drawn from the scientific evidence.
7.7.d Construct scale models, maps, and appropriately labeled diagrams to communicate scientific knowledge (e.g., motion of Earth's plates and cell structure).

Teach

READING STRATEGY

Paired Reading Pair each student with a partner. Have each student read the "Types of Scientific Models" section silently and note any confusing passages. After students finish reading, ask one student of each pair to summarize the section and the second student to add any ideas that were omitted. Both readers should help each other with any parts that either person did not understand. Have the student pairs prepare a list of questions (with answers) to ask the class.
LS Verbal/Interpersonal Co-op Learning

Group ACTIVITY

Classifying Tell students that over the past two centuries, biologists have developed a system for classifying all living things. This classification system is a conceptual model. Organize the class into two groups. Provide each group with assorted objects or pictures of objects such as buttons, paper clips, screws, rubber bands, and pencils. Have each group develop a classification scheme for the items. Ask each group to use a visual organizer to illustrate its classification system.
LS Visual/Interpersonal Co-op Learning

Connection To Real Life

Bridge Breakup Explain to students that in 1940 the Tacoma Narrows Bridge in Washington broke apart and crashed into the river below. Add that because the bridge was destroyed, scientists had to use complex mathematical models and scale models of the bridge to determine the cause of the accident. Explain that both physicists and engineers studied the bridge extensively, and that their work led to better construction guidelines and safer bridges.

Universal Access • Differentiated Instruction

Basic Learners

Mathematical Models Some students may benefit from learning how a mathematical model is made. For example, tell students that because of new housing being built near a school, the population of the school is increasing. Two years ago the school had 400 students enrolled. Last year, the school had 422 students enrolled. This year, 440 students are enrolled. Ask students to calculate the average increase in students per year. (20 students per year)

Tell students that the number of students is expected to increase at the same rate for the next few years. Ask them to predict the number of enrolled students for the next year and in two years. (460 students next year; 480 students in two years) Ask students what could affect the accuracy of this model. (Sample answer: The model cannot predict if people will continue to move into the area. Also, eventually the school would be overcrowded, so additional students would not be able to enroll.) **LS** Verbal/Logical

Quick Lab 20 min

Teacher Notes

This activity has students construct scale diagrams (covers 7.7.d).

Materials for Each Group
• colored pencils
• graph paper

Answers

Answers may vary. The total area of the exhibit should be 250 m², and should include a pond, five individual shelters, and play places such as trees and tires. The diagram should be to scale and include dimensions.

 Differentiated Datasheets
A **BASIC**, B **GENERAL**, C **ADVANCED**

Also editable on the Holt Lab Generator CD-ROM

Using the Figure

Using Scale Maps Ask students to use a meter ruler to measure the distance from San Francisco to Los Angeles in **Figure 4.** (5.15 cm) Write this math problem on the board: 1 cm/100 km = 5.15 cm/x km. Ask students to solve the problem. ($x = 5.15 \times 100 = 515$ kilometers) Explain that kilometers can be converted to miles by multiplying the kilometers by 0.62. Ask students to convert the km to mi. (515 km × 0.62 = 319 mi)

LS Logical

 Teaching Transparency:
L3 Scales in Maps

Answer to Standards Check

Scale is the relationship between the measurement of a model and actual measurement of a real object.

7.7.d (mastering)

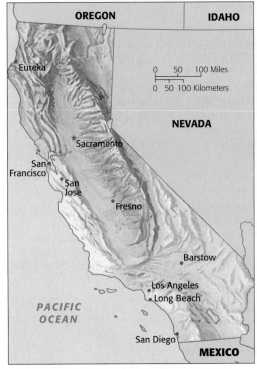

Figure 4 *This map of California is drawn to a scale of 1 cm:100 km.* **How far is San Francisco from Los Angeles?**

Using Scale in Models

Imagine that you see a model of your school with a new addition for a swimming pool. In the model, the new addition is the size of the cafeteria. You expect that a large pool will be built. But when the addition is finished, the pool is only as large as the principal's office. What happened?

The model that you saw was not drawn to scale. **Scale** is the relationship between the measurement of a model and the actual measurement of the real object. Measurements in a scale model are proportionally smaller or larger than the real object. In a scale model of your school, the new pool would be the size of the principal's office, not as big as the cafeteria.

Maps and diagrams can also be drawn to scale. For example, **Figure 4** shows a map of California. The scale of the map is 1 cm: 100 km. This ratio means that 1 cm on the map represents 100 km in California. Because the proportions of a map, model, or diagram match the proportions of the real object, scale models, maps, and diagrams can accurately communicate scientific knowledge.

Standards Check What is scale? 🐻 **7.7.d**

Quick Lab

Constructing Scale Diagrams

You have been hired to design a monkey exhibit for a zoo. You are required to submit a scale diagram of the exhibit. The zoo has given you the following requirements for the new monkey exhibit.

1. The exhibit will house five adult monkeys. Each animal needs at least 50 m² of space.
2. The exhibit should include a pond. The pond should cover 10 m².
3. The exhibit should include a shelter for each animal. Each shelter should enclose an area of 1 m².

4. The exhibit should include trees, tires, and other places for the monkeys to play.
5. Use **graph paper** and **colored pencils** to draw a scale diagram of the exhibit. Indicate the scale on your diagram.
6. Label the dimensions of the exhibit. Indicate in square meters how large the area of the exhibit is.

 20 min

```
MISCONCEPTION
ALERT
```

Scale Toys Show students several toy cars. Ask students if the toys are to scale. Some students may think that most toys are to scale. Have students measure the diameter of both the tires and the steering wheels of the toys and compute ratios. Then, have them measure or research the same measurements on the actual cars and compute ratios. Have them compare the ratios to determine if the toys are scale models. Ask students for examples of items that would likely be scale models. (Sample answers: an architect's drawing; model airplanes that are labeled "to scale")

Benefits of Models

Models are often used to represent things that are very small or very large. Models may also represent things that are very complicated or things that no longer exist. For example, **Figure 5** is a computer model of a dinosaur. Such computer models have been used for many things, including to make movies about prehistoric life on Earth. Models are used, of course, because filming a real dinosaur in action is impossible. But in building models, scientists may discover things that they hadn't thought of before.

A model can be a kind of hypothesis and can be tested. To build a model of an organism, scientists must gather information collected from fossils and other observations. Then, they can test whether their model fits with their ideas about how an organism moved or what the organism ate.

Building Scientific Knowledge

Sometimes, scientists may draw different conclusions from the same data. Other times, new results show that old conclusions are wrong. Sometimes, more information is needed. Life scientists are always asking new questions or looking at old questions from a new angle. As they find new answers, scientific knowledge continues to grow and change.

Scientific Theories

For every hypothesis, more than one prediction can be made. Each time the results of an investigation match a prediction, the hypothesis gains more support. Over time, scientists try to tie together all that they have learned. An explanation that ties together many related facts, observations, and tested hypotheses is called a **theory.** Theories are conceptual models that help organize scientific thinking. Theories are used to explain observations and to predict what might happen in the future.

Scientific Laws

The one kind of scientific idea that rarely changes is called a *scientific law*. In science, a **law** is a summary of many experimental results and observations. Unlike traffic laws, scientific laws are not based on what people may want to happen. Instead, scientific laws are statements of what *will* happen in a specific situation. And unlike theories, scientific laws tell you what happens, not why it happens.

Figure 5 *This computer-generated model doesn't just look like a dinosaur. This model includes the movement of bones and muscles.*

scale (SKAYL) the relationship between the measurements on a model, map, or diagram and the actual measurement or distance

theory (THEE uh ree) a system of ideas that explains many related observations and is supported by a large body of evidence acquired through scientific investigation

law (LAW) a descriptive statement or equation that reliably predicts events under certain conditions

Close

Standards Focus

This **Standards Focus** provides you with a quick way to **assess, reteach,** and **re-assess** one or more concepts in the section.

Assess

1. How is a scientific theory different from a scientific law? (A theory is an explanation for a range of information, and a law is a summary of many results and observations.) **7.7.d**

2. What kind of model is a globe, and what are some of its limitations? (A globe is a physical model of Earth. Its limitations include that it does not support life, and that it may not have varying geographic features like those of Earth.) **7.7.d**

Reteach

Human Models Hold up a wooden body model used in art classes. Ask students what kind of a model it is and what some of its limitations are. (Sample answers: physical model; limitations include size proportions, inability to talk or move, and absence of internal body systems) Ask if the model is a scale model. (no) Ask students to name features that are not to scale. (Sample answers: waist is too small, legs are too small) Ask students for an example of a time when a wooden model would be an acceptable model and a time when it would not be acceptable. (The model could serve as an example when drawing a human figure; Would not work as a model to determine styles of clothes that look good on an actual person.) **LS** **Logical/Verbal 7.7.d**

Re-Assess

Ask students to create a poster with three sections describing physical models, mathematical models, and conceptual models. **LS** **Visual 7.7.d**

Combining Scientific Ideas

Scientific laws are at work around you every day. For example, the law of gravity is at work when you see a leaf fall to the ground. The law of gravity tells us that objects fall toward the center of Earth. Many laws of chemistry are at work inside your cells. However, living organisms are very complex. So, there are very few laws within life science. But some theories are very important in life science and are widely accepted. An example is the theory that all living things are made up of cells.

Scientific Change

Scientific ideas can change. For example, scientists used to think that the dinosaur *Apatosaurus* (uh PA tuh SAWR uhs) used its long neck to reach leaves high in trees, as **Figure 6** shows. To test this idea, scientists took measurements of the vertebrae, or neck bones, of fossils from the dinosaur. Then, they entered this information into computer models to study how the bones fit together. The models showed that an *Apatosaurus* could not have held its head up straight. Now, many scientists think that an *Apatosaurus* held its head horizontally, as **Figure 6** shows. The models show that the neck muscles and bones would have worked better in a horizontal position.

Figure 6 **An Example of Scientific Change**

Scientists used to think that an *Apatosaurus* used its long neck to reach leaves high in trees.

Computer models show that *Apatosaurus* could not have held its head high. An *Apatosaurus* probably held its head out horizontally.

Universal Access · Differentiated Instruction

Special Education Students

Hand Dinosaurs Help a student with visual impairments understand the information given in **Figure 6.** Ask the student to make a fist with his or her right hand and rest it on the desk. Next, ask him or her to keep the fist, but point the right index finger upwards. Explain that the fist is like a dinosaur body and the index finger is how scientists initially thought *Apatosaurus* used its neck to eat leaves from trees. Then, tell the student you are going to gently push his or her finger down into the position that scientists now think *Apatosaurus* held its neck. Push the finger down so that it is outstretched beside the fist and touching the desk. Ask the student what the dinosaur would be able to eat with its neck in that position. (Sample answer: vegetation close to the ground) **LS** **Kinesthetic**

Evaluating Scientific Ideas

When a scientist proposes a theory, other scientists examine the evidence and decide if the evidence supports the theory. Scientists use scientific methods to test the new theory. If the theory and evidence are contradictory, scientists revise the theory or propose alternative theories. The theory that provides the best explanation and has the most evidence supporting it becomes the theory that most scientists accept.

Scientists should be open to new ideas, but they should always test those ideas with scientific methods. The process of building scientific knowledge never ends.

Standards Check How can new evidence change scientific theories?
🐻 **7.7.c**

SECTION Review

🐻 **7.7.c, 7.7.d**

Summary

- A model is a representation of an object or system. Models often use familiar things to represent unfamiliar things. Three main types of models are physical, mathematical, and conceptual models.

- Scale models, maps, or diagrams match the proportions of the objects they represent.

- Scientific knowledge is built as scientists form and revise scientific hypotheses, models, theories, and laws.

Using Vocabulary

Use a term from the section to complete each sentence below.

1 A ___ is an explanation that matches many hypotheses but that may change.

2 A ___ tells you exactly what to expect in certain situations.

Understanding Concepts

3 Describing What is a limitation of a model?

4 Listing What are three types of models? Give an example of each type.

5 Comparing Compare how scientists use theories with how they use laws.

Critical Thinking

6 Applying Concepts You are making a three-dimensional model of an extinct plant. Describe some of the potential uses for your model. What are some limitations of your model?

7 Analyzing Processes How do scientists evaluate theories?

Math Skills

8 Making Calculations If Jerry is 2.1 m tall, how tall is a scale model of Jerry that has a scale of 10 cm:1 m?

Challenge

9 Analyzing Processes Most doctors give advice to their patients about their diet. Imagine that an organization announces that it has discovered that a high-fat diet is the healthiest diet. What should happen before doctors start to recommend that their patients eat a high-fat diet?

Internet Resources

For a variety of links related to this chapter, go to www.scilinks.org
Topic: Using Models
SciLinks code: HY71588

---

6. Sample answer: The plant model could be used to determine if a certain prehistoric animal was tall enough to reach the leaves of the plant or to show what the environment of a certain prehistoric area looked like. A limitation of the model is that it might not smell or taste like the real plant did. **7.7.d** (exceeding)

7. Scientists use scientific methods to obtain evidence to evaluate theories. If the evidence supports a theory, the theory gains acceptance. If a theory is not supported by the evidence, the theory is modified or abandoned for a different theory. **7.7.c** (exceeding)

8. $(2.1 \text{ m} \div 10) = 0.21 \text{ m}$; or 21 cm **7.7.d** (mastering)

9. Doctors would want to see if these results of the high-fat diet were replicated in other experiments. Other scientists should do experiments comparing high-fat diets to other types of diets. If enough evidence was found, doctors would recommend that their patients eat a high-fat diet. **7.7.c** (exceeding)

Section Review Standards Guide

	Supporting	Mastering	Exceeding
7.7.c			1–2, 5, 7, 9
7.7.d	4	8	3, 6

Answer to Standards Check

If new evidence contradicts an existing theory, then the theory may be revised or a new theory may be proposed. **7.7.c** (exceeding)

Answers to Section Review

1. A theory is an explanation that matches many hypotheses but that may change. **7.7.c** (exceeding)

2. A law tells you exactly what to expect in certain situations. **7.7.c** (exceeding)

3. One limitation of models is that they do not act exactly like the things that they represent. **7.7.d** (exceeding)

4. Sample answer: physical model: a plastic human body; mathematical model: an equation to predict population changes; conceptual model: a flow chart about how mercury moves through the environment. **7.7.d** (supporting)

5. Sample answer: Scientists use laws to predict what will happen under specific conditions but not to explain why. Scientists use theories to make general predictions and explain why they think something happens. **7.7.c** (exceeding)

Section Resources

📁 **Directed Reading** A ⬛ BASIC (Also in Spanish), B ⬛ GENERAL

📁 **Interactive Reader and Study Guide**

📁 **Section Quiz** GENERAL (Also in Spanish)

📁 **Section Review** GENERAL (Also in Spanish)

📁 **Vocabulary and Section Summary** A ⬛ BASIC (Also in Spanish), B ⬛ GENERAL

Preteach

Reviewing Prior Knowledge

Ask students to read the red and blue headings in the section. Then, ask students what they think the section is about. Finally, ask students what they already know about safety in science.

🔊 Bellringer

Have students focus on standard 7.7.a by asking them to complete the following tasks:

1. List some safety rules for science classes. (Sample answer: always walk, not run, when in the classroom; wear safety glasses during experiments; make sure all chemicals are labeled)

2. Explain the purpose of each rule you listed. (Sample answer: if people move quickly in the classroom they are more likely to trip or cause an accident; wearing safety glasses may prevent eye injuries; many chemicals look alike and using misidentified chemicals can lead to dangerous reactions)

📋 Bellringer Transparency

Motivate

Group ACTIVITY

How to Be Safe As a group, brainstorm five possible lab scenarios and list them on the board. Ask students to write pertinent safety risks next to each scenario. Then, discuss safety precautions that can protect against each risk.

SECTION

5

What You Will Learn

- The elements of safety include following safety symbols, following directions, being neat, using proper safety equipment, and using proper cleanup procedures.

- Following the proper procedure for accidents can help reduce the effects of an accident.

Why It Matters

Serious injuries can occur if safety rules are not followed.

Vocabulary
- first aid

READING STRATEGY

Graphic Organizer In your **Science Journal,** create an Idea Wheel that describes elements of safety in science.

Investigation and Experimentation
7.7.a Select and use appropriate tools and technology (including calculators, computers, balances, spring scales, microscopes, and binoculars) to perform tests, collect data, and display data.

Safety in Science

Key Concept Following safety rules during scientific investigations will help prevent accidents and injury.

▶ While walking by a construction site, you notice a sign on the fence: "Hard Hat Area." When you look through the fence, you see that all of the construction workers are wearing heavy plastic helmets.

Construction workers wear hard hats to prevent injury if an accident happens. Likewise, you take precautions to be safe at home and in school. You also take special care when you learn science, as **Figure 1** shows.

The Importance of Safety Rules

Safety is the state of being free of danger or injury. To be safe while doing science, you must learn some safety rules. Perhaps the most important safety rule is to follow the directions given by your teacher. Following directions will make your work easier, and will help you get better results. And, you will be safer!

Standards Check **What is safety?**

Preventing Accidents

Following rules may not seem like fun. But following rules is better than getting hurt! The most important reason for obeying safety rules is to prevent accidents. Your teacher will remind you of safety rules, but it's your job to follow them. Accidents are less likely to happen when safety rules are followed.

Preventing Injury

Unfortunately, accidents can happen even when all safety rules are obeyed. When an accident does happen, you or someone nearby could get hurt. Following safety rules can help you avoid or reduce injury. For example, wearing gloves will help protect your skin if you accidentally spill a chemical on your hands.

Figure 1 *Wearing safety equipment and following your teacher's directions will keep you safe in the science lab.*

Answer to Standards Check

Safety is the state of being free of danger or injury.
(CA Science Framework)

Figure 2 Safety Symbols

Eye protection

Clothing protection

Hand safety

Heating safety

Electrical safety

Chemical safety

Animal safety

Sharp objects

Plant safety

For more safety tips, read the Safety First! section at the front of your book.

Elements of Safety

There are many parts to safety. Recognizing safety symbols can alert you to potential dangers. Reading directions and being neat can prevent accidents. Safety equipment keeps you safe during experiments, and proper cleanup procedures keep your classroom safe after an experiment is over.

Safety Symbols

Most road signs have specific meanings. For example, a stop sign means that cars must stop moving. A one-way sign means that cars must travel only in a certain direction. Signs and symbols that have specific meanings are also used in science. **Figure 2** shows the safety symbols that are used in this book. For example, if you see the symbol for goggles listed on an activity, you should wear eye protection during that activity. Learning the meaning of and obeying these symbols can help prevent injury or an accident.

In some experiments, such as the one shown in **Figure 3,** you must work with live animals. When you do an experiment with animals, you will see the symbol for animal safety. This symbol tells you to be careful when handling animals. For example, you should never squeeze or frighten animals. You should follow your teacher's directions on how to pick up animals and how to dispose of animal waste. You should handle only the animals provided by your teacher and should never bring wild animals into the classroom. And after working with animals, you should wash your hands thoroughly with soap and water.

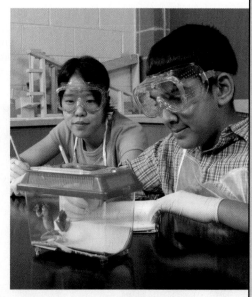

Figure 3 *You should wear protective gloves when handling animals during an experiment.*

Teach

Using the Figure
Interpreting the Safety Symbols
Organize the class into nine teams. Ask each team to create a poster explaining the meaning of one of the safety symbols in **Figure 2.** Ask them to divide the posters into two sections: a drawing or picture of the sign on one side and a list of related safety points on the other side.
LS Visual/Kinesthetic Co-op Learning

READING STRATEGY

Paired Summarizing Have students write a summary describing the safe and proper way to work with an animal in a laboratory. Tell them to include how to meet an animal's requirements for food and water, clean and safe shelter, and appropriate attention, as well as how to handle the animal. Then, have students pair up and check each other's summaries for thoroughness.
LS Interpersonal Co-op Learning

Research
Industrial Safety Encourage interested students to research and write a report on safety procedures in an industry they find interesting. Possible industries of interest include airplane manufacturing, pharmaceuticals, computer-chip manufacturing, and solar-panel manufacturing. **LS** Verbal

Universal Access · Differentiated Instruction

English Learners

Safety Symbols It is imperative that all students understand the safety symbols. Point out that safety symbols are designed without words so that people of all languages can understand them. Add that symbols without words work well once students learn them. Ask students to write a complete sentence explaining the meaning of each symbol in **Figure 2.** Tell them to write each explanatory sentence twice: once in their first language and once in English. Tell them to thumb through the book and look for experiments that use the symbols. Ask them to find at least one experiment that uses each symbol and write the page number next to the definition of the symbol. **LS** Verbal/Logical

Chemical-Safety Brochure Ask students to create a pamphlet illustrating proper lab procedures when working with chemicals. Encourage students to illustrate the pamphlet and use a creative design. **LS Visual/Kinesthetic**

Answers to School-to-Home Activity

Answers may vary. Sample answer: Turn all pan handles away from the edge of the stove. Wipe up all spills. Keep cloth and paper away from the stove. Turn off the stove and oven when they are not in use. Use a step stool to reach high shelves.

Demonstration

Safety Stations in the Lab

To make sure that each student knows the location of all safety stations in the lab, lead a tour of those stations. Have all students learn how to operate the eye-wash, ask them to look at the items in the first-aid kit, and have them identify where proper disposal containers are for sharp objects and broken glassware. **LS Visual**

MISCONCEPTION ALERT

Everyday Safety Students may forget that everyday activities can be unsafe if people are not careful. Point out that riding a bike can be unsafe if riders don't wear helmets, use hand signals, and stay alert to people and vehicles around them. Call out the following everyday activities and ask volunteers to act out or describe related safety precautions:

riding in a car (wear seatbelts, go the speed limit, stay alert)

crossing the street (wait for a walk sign, pay attention to cars, walk quickly across)

taking a shower (have a slip-free floor, adjust the water slowly)

Kitchen Safety Rules

If you aren't careful, you can be hurt when working in a kitchen. With a parent or guardian, discuss some accidents that could happen in your kitchen. In your **Science Journal,** write at least five kitchen safety rules that will help you avoid the accidents that you discussed.

Reading and Following Directions

If you want to bake a cake successfully, you will probably use a recipe. The recipe tells you the ingredients to use and the proper procedure to follow. When scientists work in the laboratory, they also follow directions. Likewise, when you work in the laboratory, you must follow directions given by your teacher and the lab procedure.

Before starting a science experiment, you should read all of the instructions. Reading the directions before you start will help you get better results and will reduce the chance of having an accident. If you don't understand the instructions in a lab procedure, you should ask your teacher to explain the directions in a different way.

When you do an experiment, you should leave your book open to the page that shows the instructions. You will be able to find the instructions quickly if you need to reread them.

Neatness Counts!

Before starting any science activity, you should clear your work area of books, backpacks, and any other unneeded objects. These objects can get in the way and may cause you to trip or spill your materials. Also, you should prepare data tables and gather necessary safety equipment, as **Figure 4** shows.

Neatness also counts when you are doing an experiment. You should arrange the lab materials on the desk or table so that you can find them easily. And you should label all chemicals so that they won't be mixed up. And you should record your findings carefully in a notebook or data table so that you and others can read them.

Figure 4 *Proper preparation before an experiment will help keep you safe in the laboratory.*

Universal Access • Differentiated Instruction

Special Education Students

Dry–Run Experiment For some students, it is helpful to have a "dry–run" experiment before doing an actual experiment. Give students a list of "general experiment steps," such as the following:

1. Read all the steps.
2. Arrange your book (or direction sheet) so that you can reread the directions.
3. Make sure you understand the safety symbols.
4. Clear your work area.
5. Gather necessary safety equipment.
6. Gather these items carefully: scissors, four pieces of paper, and a ruler.
7. Arrange the lab materials neatly.
8. Clean up your work area. Put all things away and wipe your desk with a wet paper towel.
9. Wash your hands with soap and water. **LS Kinesthetic**

Figure 5 *These students are wearing protective gloves when they work with chemicals. But they put on heat-resistant gloves before lifting the beakers off the hot plates.*

Using Proper Safety Equipment

Safety equipment can protect you from injury. Safety goggles, gloves, and aprons are some examples of lab safety equipment. The safety symbols shown next to laboratory instructions indicate what kind of safety equipment to use. For example, when you see the eye protection symbol, you must put on your safety goggles. Goggles should fit comfortably but snugly.

If you see the symbol for hand protection, you need to wear gloves. If you are using chemicals or animals, you must wear protective gloves. But if you are handling warm objects, using a hot plate, or using an open flame, you must wear heat-resistant gloves. Both kinds of gloves are shown in **Figure 5.**

Standards Check Why is it important to select the appropriate safety equipment when you perform a scientific investigation? **7.7.a**

Proper Cleanup Procedures

After finishing a science experiment, you should clean up your work area. You should place caps on bottles, and return everything to its proper place. If you have used burners, you must be sure to turn off the gas. Wash all of your glassware, and check for chips and cracks. You must give any damaged glassware to your teacher. You should dispose of any extra or waste chemicals as your teacher directs. Once your desk or table is clear, you should wipe it with a wet paper towel. Finally, you should wash your hands thoroughly with soap and water.

Quick Lab

Preparing for an Experiment   7.7.a

1. Select an animal. Think of a question about that animal's behavior.

2. Design an experiment to investigate the behavior of the animal.

3. Compile a list of all of the tools and technology needed for the experiment.

4. Create a second list of all of the safety materials and safety procedures that you would need to follow during the experiment.

🕐 **20 min**

Quick Lab   🕐 **15 min**

Teacher Notes

This activity has students practice selecting the tools and the safety procedures for an investigation (covers 7.7.a and CA Science Framework)

Materials for Each Group

• paper
• pencil

Answers

3. Answers may include binoculars, balances, spring scales, metersticks, computers, or other tools.

4. Answers may include eye protection, gloves, clothing protection or other safety equipment; and maintaining a safe distance, limiting handling of animals, or following other safety procedures.

📋 Differentiated Datasheets
A **Basic**, B **General**, C **Advanced**

Also editable on the Holt Lab Generator CD-ROM

Standards Focus

This **Standards Focus** provides you with a quick way to **assess, reteach,** and **re-assess** one or more concepts in the section.

Assess

1. What is the first thing you should do before starting any science activity? (read all the instructions very carefully) **CA Science Framework**

2. How can you find out if you need to wear goggles or an apron during an experiment? (look at the safety symbols on the instructions) **7.7.a**

3. What should you do with waste chemicals after you finish an activity? (follow the teacher's instructions for chemical disposal) **CA Science Framework**

Reteach

Reading Safety Symbols
Choose three labs in the book and ask students to turn to those page numbers, look at the safety symbols for each lab, and identify the required safety precautions that the symbols represent. Discuss the importance of completely understanding the symbols before starting to do the labs. **LS Visual CA Science Framework**

Re-Assess

Reading Safety Signals Choose three different labs in the book than those used for the reteaching activity above. Tell students what activities are involved in the labs. Then, ask students to think about what safety symbols would be most important for each lab. After discussing this, students can look up these labs and see which symbols are included for each lab.
LS Kinesthetic CA Science Framework

Figure 6 Emergency Equipment

▼ A **first-aid kit** contains many things for treating injury, including things to clean and cover wounds.

A **fire extinguisher** ▶ is a safe and effective tool for putting out fires.

An **eyewash** is ▶ used to remove chemicals or small particles from the eye.

Proper Accident Procedures

Sometimes, accidents do happen. After any accident, you should the follow the four steps below in order.

- Remain calm, and assess the situation. Look around, and do your best to determine what happened.
- Secure the area around the accident. Make sure that you are safe and that no one else is in danger.
- Tell your teacher, or call for help. Always tell your teacher if an accident happens, even if the accident seems minor.
- Assist your teacher with cleaning up or giving aid. Do exactly what your teacher tells you to do.

After an accident, your teacher may need you to get emergency equipment. The emergency equipment shown in **Figure 6** is often found in labs. You should learn how to use the emergency equipment and you should know where it is kept in your classroom.

Table 1	Simple First-Aid Procedures
Injury	**First-aid procedure**
Minor heat-related burn	Hold affected area under cold, running water for at least 15 min.
Small cuts	Clean the area, cover it with a clean cloth or gauze pad, and apply pressure.
Chemicals on skin	Rinse area with running water.
Chemical in eye	Rinse eye with running water or in an eyewash.

Universal Access · Differentiated Instruction

Struggling Readers

First Aid It is critical that students understand the first-aid procedures. Make no assumptions about what students read and/or understood. Read the "Simple First-Aid Procedures" in **Table 1** as a group. Discuss each procedure, and have a student go to the required location and/or get the required items and demonstrate. Make sure students understand the concepts of using the water temperature called for, applying pressure, and rinsing thoroughly. Make sure students know where to find clean cloths, gauze, and eyewash.
LS Verbal/Kinesthetic

Proper First-Aid Procedures

If an accident results in an injury, it is important that you know what to do. Fortunately, almost all laboratory injuries are minor and are treated easily. When treating an injury in the lab, your teacher will use first aid. **First aid** is emergency medical care for someone who has been hurt.

You should not perform first aid unless you are properly trained. If first aid is not done properly, a victim can be more seriously injured. However, you may do a few simple first-aid procedures that you can do without training. These procedures are listed in **Table 1**. Because first aid is only temporary care, an injured person should see a doctor for more treatment.

first aid (FUHRST AYD) emergency medical care for someone who has been hurt or who is sick

---

 7.7.a

Summary

- Following safety rules helps prevent accidents and helps reduce injury.
- Five elements of safety are recognizing safety symbols, following directions, being neat, using proper safety equipment, and using proper cleanup procedures.
- Animals used in scientific research require special care.
- When an accident happens, you should assess the situation, secure the area, tell your teacher, and help your teacher with cleanup or first aid.
- First aid is emergency medical care. Some first-aid procedures can be done without training.

Using Vocabulary

1. Write an original definition for *first aid*.

Understanding Concepts

2. **Describing** Why are safety rules important?

3. **Describing** What are five elements of safety?

4. **Listing** List the four steps that you should take after an accident happens.

5. **Applying** What should you do if you spill a chemical on your skin?

Critical Thinking

6. **Making Inferences** Suppose that you are doing research to determine how quickly a mouse can learn to run a maze. Explain how you would care for and handle the mouse.

7. **Applying Concepts** Imagine that your lab partner dropped a glass beaker and cut his finger on the broken glass. Describe what you should do next.

8. **Applying Concepts** Rabies is a viral disease that is often transmitted through the bite of an animal that is infected by the rabies virus. People who get the rabies virus suffer from a variety of symptoms and will die if not treated in time. Many types of animals including bats, dogs, and raccoons can carry rabies. What precautions should scientists who are studying bats take?

INTERPRETING GRAPHICS Use the symbols below to answer the next question.

9. **Applying Concepts** The symbols above appear on an activity. What precautions should you take before you begin this activity?

Internet Resources

For a variety of links related to this chapter, go to www.scilinks.org
Topic: Safety
SciLinks code: HY71339

---

7. Sample answer: First, I would look around to understand what happened. Second, to make sure no one else is in danger, I would tell others to avoid the broken glass. Third, I would tell the teacher and help get bandaging materials for my partner. Finally, I would help the teacher clean up the glass by putting the glass in a broken glassware box. (CA Science Framework)

8. Scientists who are studying bats should not handle the animals if possible. If they must handle bats, they should be careful and wear protective clothing such as gloves. (CA Science Framework)

9. This activity calls for clothing protection and hand safety. An apron and gloves should be worn. (CA Science Framework)

Section Review Standards Guide	Supporting	Mastering	Exceeding
7.7.a		6, 7, 8, 9	

Answers to Section Review

1. Sample answer: First aid is emergency medical care. (CA Science Framework)

2. Safety rules can help to prevent accidents and injuries. (CA Science Framework)

3. Safety symbols tell you what to do to prevent injury or accidents. Reading and following directions include following the teacher's directions and asking questions when directions are not clear. Neatness includes keeping your work area clear and labeling chemicals. Safety equipment includes gloves, aprons, and goggles. Proper clean-up procedures include checking for damaged glassware, disposing of extra materials properly, and washing hands. (CA Science Framework)

4. Remain calm and assess the situation. Secure the area around the accident. Tell the teacher, or call for help. Assist the teacher with cleanup or first aid. (CA Science Framework)

5. If you spill chemicals on your skin, you should rinse the area with running water. (CA Science Framework)

6. Sample answer: I would provide clean shelter for the mouse and give it plenty of food and water. Before I pick up the mouse, I would put on protective gloves and goggles. I would handle the mouse gently to avoid hurting or scaring it. (CA Science Framework)

Section Resources

Directed Reading A **BASIC** (Also in Spanish), B **GENERAL**

Interactive Reader and Study Guide

Section Quiz **GENERAL** (Also in Spanish)

Section Review **GENERAL** (Also in Spanish)

Vocabulary and Section Summary A **BASIC** (Also in Spanish), B **GENERAL**

Teacher Notes

This lab has students collect and display data (covers standard 7.7.a).

Time Required

One 45-minute class period

Lab Ratings

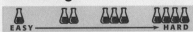

EASY ——————→ HARD

Teacher Prep
Student Set-Up
Concept Level
Clean Up

Materials

The materials listed on the student page are enough for a group of three students.

Safety Caution

Remind students to review all safety cautions and icons before beginning this lab activity. Caution students to handle thermometers with care.

Skills Practice Lab

Collecting and Displaying Data

When performing an experiment, you usually need to collect data. To understand the data, you can often organize the data into a graph. Graphs can show trends and patterns that you may not notice in a table or list. In this exercise, you will practice collecting data and organizing the data into a graph.

OBJECTIVES

Collect data during an experiment.

Create a graph to display the data.

MATERIALS

- beaker, 500 mL
- clock (or watch) with a second hand
- gloves, heat-resistant
- hot plate
- ice
- paper, graph
- thermometer, Celsius, with a thermometer holder
- water (200 mL)

SAFETY

Investigation and Experimentation
7.7.a Select and use appropriate tools and technology (including calculators, computers, balances, spring scales, microscopes, and binoculars) to perform tests, collect data, and display data.

Procedure

1. Make a table like the one below. Leave space to continue recording for more than 20 min.

Water Temperature	
Time (min)	**Temperature (°C)**
0	
1	
2	
3	

DO NOT WRITE IN BOOK

2. Pour 200 mL of water into a 500 mL beaker. Add ice to the beaker until the waterline is at the 400 mL mark.

3. Place a Celsius thermometer into the beaker. Use a thermometer holder to prevent the thermometer from touching the bottom of the beaker.

4. Place the beaker and thermometer on a hot plate. Record the temperature of the ice water. The initial temperature is recorded as "0 min" because the water has been heated for 0 minutes.

Lab Resources

 Differentiated Datasheets
A **BASIC**, B **GENERAL**, C **ADVANCED**

 Classroom Lab Video/DVD

Holt Lab Generator CD-ROM

Search for any lab by topic, standard, difficulty level, or time. Edit any lab to fit your needs, or create your own labs. Use the Lab Materials QuickList software to customize your lab materials list.

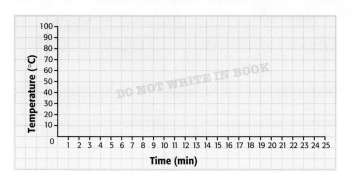

Temperature (°C): 100, 90, 80, 70, 60, 50, 40, 30, 20, 10, 0
Time (min): 1 2 3 4 5 6 7 8 9 10 11 12 13 14 15 16 17 18 19 20 21 22 23 24 25

DO NOT WRITE IN BOOK

5 Turn the hot plate on medium heat. After 1 min Record the temperature every minute until the water temperature reaches 100°C.

6 Using heat-resistant gloves, remove the beaker from the hot plate. Continue to record the temperature of the water each minute for 10 more min. **Caution:** Don't forget to turn off the hot plate.

7 On a piece of graph paper, create a graph similar to the one above Label the horizontal axis (the *x*-axis) "Time (min)," and mark the axis in increments of 1 min. Label the vertical axis (the *y*-axis) "Temperature (°C)," and mark the axis in increments of 10°.

8 Find the 0 min mark on the *x*-axis, and move up the graph to the temperature that you recorded at 0 min. Place a dot on the graph at that point. Plot each temperature in the same way. When you have plotted all of your data, connect the dots with a smooth line.

Analyze the Results

9 **Examining Data** Examine your graph. Do you think that the water heated faster than it cooled? Explain.

10 **Analyzing Results** Estimate what the temperature of the water was 2.5 min after you placed the beaker on the hot plate. Explain how you can make a good estimate of temperature.

Draw Conclusions

11 **Evaluating Methods** Explain how a graph may give more information than the same data in a table does.

Big Idea Question

12 **Evaluating Methods** Why is it important to collect and display data from a scientific investigation?

Analyze the Results

9. Answers may vary according to several factors, including altitude.

10. Answers may vary. To make the estimate, students should find 2.5 minutes on the *x*-axis of the graph and find where 2.5 intersects the graph. The estimate is the *y*-axis value at the intersection point.

Draw Conclusions

11. A table is organized information. It is often helpful to put collected data into one of these forms before graphing. Because a graph is like a picture, it can often help scientists see what is happening better than numbers can. A graph can show a trend or a pattern that may not be easily seen in a table.

Big Idea Question

12. Scientists collect data to record what happened in an investigation. Results from the data collected can be analyzed and conclusions can be drawn. Displaying data is important because it can show trends that are difficult to see in tables. Also, displaying data helps other people understand the details and results of an investigation.

TEACHER TESTED & APPROVED

Carol Lindstrom
Leonard Herman
Intermediate School
San Jose, CA

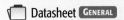
Science Skills Activity

Scientific Methods	Research	Data Analysis	Models, Maps & Diagrams

Investigation and Experimentation
7.7.b Use a variety of print and electronic resources (including the World Wide Web) to collect information and evidence as part of a research project.

Using Internet Resources for Research

▶ Tutorial

Because the Internet contains a great deal of information, it can be a useful tool for doing research. But you may find that the Internet contains too much information or that most of the information is not *reliable*. Reliable information is information that is likely to be correct because it is based on observations or research. In this tutorial, you will learn tips for using the Internet to do research.

Procedure

1 **Use Keywords** Choose keywords for the topic that you are researching.
- Use multiple keywords to narrow your search.
- Use quotation marks around keywords to find exact matches. For example, if you are researching a person, put quotation marks around the person's full name to exclude other people who share part of the person's full name.
- Enter the keywords into a search engine.

2 **Find Reliable Information** A search may return many sites that contain information about the topic. You need to determine which sites contain reliable information. Only use reliable information in your investigation.

- Reliable information usually comes from reliable sources. Look for information from government agencies, museums, and newspapers.
- Be careful when reviewing personal Web sites. They may contain more opinions than facts.
- Watch for biased sources. A *biased source* contains incomplete or misleading information. If you suspect that a source is biased, find other sources to check the information.

3 **Cite Sources** If you use information from the Internet in a report, you must cite that source in a bibliography. Your teacher will tell you the information that you should include and the format in which the information should be listed. The following information is often included:
- author of the material
- specific page of the site
- name of the Web site
- date the page was created
- address of the Web site
- date the Web site was viewed

▶ You Try It!

In this activity, you will practice finding and using sources on the Internet. The question that you are researching is the following: How many Siberian tigers are left in the wild?

Procedure

1 **Use Keywords** Determine the keywords that you will use for your search. Enter different combinations of keywords into a search engine and record the number of Web sites that each combination returns. Which keyword search returned the most Web sites that contain information on your topic?

2 **Find Reliable Information** Find at least three sources that contain reliable information. What makes this information reliable? Read the sources, and write a paragraph describing what you learned.

3 **Cite Sources** Create a bibliography that shows the sources that you used. When you cite a source, be sure to include all the important information for that source.

Universal Access · Differentiated Instruction

Basic Learners

Finding Keywords Some students may need help finalizing their Internet search keywords. Ask students to write five questions they would like to answer about the topic. Then, tell them to circle the most important words in their sentences. Finally, have them list the circled words in order of importance on a separate piece of paper. **LS** Logical

Chapter Summary

The Big Idea Scientists use scientific processes to study the patterns of natural events and to solve problems.

Section

Vocabulary

1 Asking About Life

Key Concept Asking questions is the first step in a scientific investigation.

- Questions lead to learning about science.
- Print or electronic resources can be used to find information.
- Your everyday life is affected by life scientists in many ways.

life science p. 8

2 Scientific Methods

Key Concept Scientific methods are used to investigate questions and to solve problems.

- Scientists ask questions, make observations, form hypotheses, test hypotheses, analyze results, and draw conclusions.
- Scientists communicate their steps and results from investigations in written reports and oral presentations.

Test the Hypothesis

scientific methods p. 12
hypothesis p. 14
controlled experiment p. 16
variable p. 16

3 Tools and Measurement

Key Concept Scientists select and use tools and technology to perform tests and collect data.

- Scientists use technology, such as computers and microscopes, to perform tests and collect information.
- The International System of Units enables scientists to compare information and to convert between units.
- Measurements such as length, area, volume, temperature, and mass can be obtained with the right tools.

technology p. 20
compound light microscope p. 21
electron microscope p. 21
area p. 23
volume p. 23
mass p. 24
weight p. 24
temperature p. 25

4 Scientific Models and Knowledge

Key Concept Models are used to study living things, test hypotheses, explain observations, and communicate knowledge.

- Physical models, mathematical models, and conceptual models are representations of ways to study objects or systems.
- Scientific theories are conceptual models that organize scientific thinking and explain why things happen.
- Scientific laws tell you what will happen in a specific situation.

model p. 26
scale p. 28
theory p. 29
law p. 29

5 Safety in Science

Key Concept Following safety rules during scientific investigations will help prevent accidents and injuries.

- The elements of safety include following safety symbols, following directions, being neat, using proper safety equipment, and using proper cleanup procedures.
- Following the proper procedure for accidents can help reduce the effects of an accident.

first aid p. 37

Review Resources

- 📁 Reinforcement Worksheet **BASIC**
- 📁 Critical Thinking Worksheet **ADVANCED**
- 📁 Chapter Review **GENERAL** (Also in Spanish)
- 📘 Standards Review Workbook (Also in Spanish)
- 📘 Study Guide A **BASIC** (Also in Spanish), B **GENERAL**

Assessment Resources

- 📁 Chapter Tests A **BASIC**, B **GENERAL** (Also in Spanish), C **ADVANCED**
- 📁 Standards Assessment **GENERAL**

Chapter Summary

SUPER SUMMARY

Have students connect the major concepts in this chapter through an interactive Super Summary. Visit go.hrw.com and type in the keyword HY7LIVS to access the Super Summary for this chapter.

Identifying Word Parts

Science Bingo Create a 5 column, 7 row grid on a computer. The column heads should be B-I-N-G-O. Place the word "Free" in the center square. To fill the other 34 squares, randomly add the 18 vocabulary words from the chapter. Then, copy the whole page, paste it onto a new page, and re-scramble the words and definitions. Repeat to create as many different bingo sheets as needed. Make copies of the bingo sheets for your students, pass out beans for markers, and play Science bingo. (Call out clues for each word chosen, such as the definition of the word or its root, prefix, or suffix.) **LS** Visual/Verbal

Focus on Speaking

Explaining the Standards
Organize the class into small groups and assign a different standard covered in this chapter to each group. Ask each group to give an oral presentation that explains the standard, explains how the standard relates to the material in the chapter, and give examples of the standard if applicable. Every student in the group should have a chance to speak. After each presentation, invite the class to ask the presenting group questions. **LS** Verbal/Interpersonal

Chapter Review

 7.7.a, 7.7.b, 7.7.c, 7.7.d, 7.7.e

Assignment Guide

Section	Questions
1	1, 11, 17
2	2, 6, 12, 16, 18–20, 22
3	4–5, 7, 9–10, 14
4	3, 13, 15, 21
5	8

Answers

Using Vocabulary

1. c

2. Sample answer: In a controlled experiment, all factors are kept the same except the variable. **7.7.c** (exceeding)

3. A hypothesis is a testable explanation that leads to research. A theory is an explanation based on research. **7.7.c** (mastering)

4. A compound light microscope uses light to create an image of an object. An electron microscope uses electrons to create an image of an object. **7.7.a** (exceeding)

5. Area is a measure of a surface. Volume is a measure of space or size in three dimensions.

Understanding Concepts

6. c **7.7.c** (mastering)

7. b **7.7.a** (mastering)

8. d **7.7.a** (supporting)

9. d **7.7.a** (supporting)

10. a; (200 mL − 125 mL = 75 mL = 75 cm³) **7.7.a** (mastering)

11. Sample answer: books, magazines, the World Wide Web **7.7.b** (mastering)

12. oral presentations and written reports **7.7.e** (mastering)

13. Some advantages of models are that they are useful for sharing information and they can simplify complicated material. Some limitations of models are that they do not behave exactly like the real thing and are sometimes not created to scale. **7.7.d** (supporting)

14. The SI units used to describe volume are liters (L), units based on the liter, and units based on the cubic meter (m³, cm³, mm³). **7.7.a** (supporting)

Organize

Layered Book Review the Fold-Note that you created at the beginning of the chapter. Add to or correct the FoldNote based on what you have learned.

Using Vocabulary

1 **Academic Vocabulary** In the sentence "They used a variety of print resources in their research project," what does the word *resources* mean?
a. materials used to make products
b. materials containing information
c. materials used to gather information
d. materials about science

2 Use *controlled experiment* and *variable* in the same sentence.

For each pair of terms, explain how the meanings of the terms differ.

3 *theory* and *hypothesis*

4 *compound light microscope* and *electron microscope*

5 *area* and *volume*

Understanding Concepts

Multiple Choice

6 The steps of scientific methods
a. must all be used in every scientific investigation.
b. must always be used in the same order.
c. often start with a question.
d. always result in the development of a theory.

7 Which of the following tools is best for measuring 100 mL of water?
a. 10 mL graduated cylinder
b. 150 mL graduated cylinder
c. 250 mL graduated cylinder
d. 500 mL graduated cylinder

INTERPRETING GRAPHICS Use the symbols below to answer the next question.

8 The directions for a lab include the safety icons shown above. These icons mean that
a. you should be careful.
b. you are going into the laboratory.
c. you should wash your hands first.
d. you should wear safety goggles, a lab apron, and gloves during the lab.

INTERPRETING GRAPHICS The pictures below show how an egg can be measured by using a beaker and water. Use the pictures below to answer the next two questions.

Before: 125 mL   After: 200 mL

9 What kind of measurement is being taken?
a. area
b. length
c. mass
d. volume

10 Which of the following is an accurate measurement of the egg in the picture?
a. 75 cm³
b. 125 cm³
c. 125 mL
d. 200 mL

Short Answer

11 **Listing** What are three examples of resources scientists might use to collect information as part of a research project?

12 **Listing** List two ways that scientists communicate the steps and results of investigations.

13 **Describing** What are some advantages and limitations of models?

14 **Identifying** Which SI units can be used to describe an object's volume?

22. Sample answer: no; Madison's experiment did not test her hypothesis. The hypothesis was "Plants grow better with fertilizer than without it," so the variable should have been fertilizer. In the experiment, the variable was the amount of water. The experiment did not give any information about whether or not fertilizer affected the growth of the plants.

7.7.c (exceeding)

Chapter Review Standards Guide	Supporting	Mastering	Exceeding
7.7.a	8–9, 14	7, 10	4
7.7.b		11	17
7.7.c		3, 6, 16, 20	2, 19, 22
7.7.d	13	21	
7.7.e		12	18

Writing Skills

15. **Communicating Concepts** Write a paragraph explaining how scientific explanations change. Include information about why scientists propose new theories. Also, describe how scientists evaluate new theories.

Critical Thinking

16. **Concept Mapping** Use the following terms to create a concept map: *observations, predictions, questions, controlled experiments, variable,* and *hypothesis.*

17. **Expressing Opinions** Your classmate says that all information on the Internet is reliable. Do you agree with this statement? Explain your answer.

18. **Analyzing Methods** Why is it important for scientists to write reports about the scientific investigations that they perform?

INTERPRETING GRAPHICS Use the table below to answer the next question.

Number of Frogs		
Year	Normal	Deformed
1999	25	0
2000	21	0
2001	19	1
2002	20	2
2003	17	3
2004	20	5

19. **Expressing Opinions** A group of citizens wants the local government to ban the use of a new chemical pesticide. The group proposes that since 1999, when the pesticide was first used, the number of deformed frogs has increased. To support the proposal, the group submits the table above. Do you think that the pesticide should be banned, or is more information needed? Explain your answer.

20. **Forming Hypotheses** A scientist who studies mice observes that on the day the mice are fed vitamins with their meals, they perform better in mazes. What hypothesis would you form to explain this phenomenon? Write a testable prediction based on your hypothesis.

Math Skills

INTERPRETING GRAPHICS Use the scale map below to answer the next question.

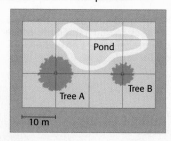

21. **Making Calculations** If the scale of this map is 1 square:10 m, what is the distance between the center of Tree A and the center of Tree B?

Challenge

22. **Analyzing Methods** Madison wants to test the following hypothesis: "Plants grow better with plant fertilizer than without it." So, she plants seeds in pots and places the plants in a window so that all the plants get the same amount of sunlight. Then, she divides the plants into two groups: Group A and Group B. Group A plants get 50 mL of water each day, and Group B plants get 100 mL of water each day. Once a week, she mixes fertilizer into the water. After three weeks, Madison measures the plants and finds that all of the plants are the same height. She concludes that fertilizer does not make plants grow better. Did Madison's experiment test her hypothesis? Explain your answer.

Writing Skills

15. Answers may vary but should cover all requirements stated in the question. Responses should emphasize that scientific methods are used to obtain information and to evaluate theories.

Critical Thinking

16. The answer to this exercise can be found at the end of this book. **7.7.c** (mastering)

17. Sample answer: no; Not all of the information on the Internet is reliable. Some of it is biased or not based on research. Reliable information comes from reliable sources. **7.7.b** (exceeding)

18. Scientists write reports about their research so that other scientists can learn about it. Learning about research gives scientists new ideas. **7.7.e** (exceeding)

19. Answers may vary. **7.7.c** (exceeding)

20. Sample answer: Hypothesis: Vitamins help the mice move faster. Prediction: If the mice are fed vitamins, then they will run at a faster rate. **7.7.c** (mastering)

Math Skills

21. The centers of Tree A and Tree B are 20 m apart. **7.7.d** (mastering)

Standards Assessment

Teacher Notes

To provide practice under more realistic testing conditions, give students 20 min to answer all of the questions in this assessment.

Answer Key

Question Number	Correct Answer
1	B
2	B
3	D
4	C
5	C
6	B
7	A
8	D
9	D
10	D
11	B
12	A
13	B
14	B
15	D

Standards Guide

	Supporting	Mastering	Exceeding
6.7.b		14	13
6.7.d	15		
7.7.a		4, 7	
7.7.b		5–6	
7.7.c		1–2, 9	
7.7.d	10	3, 11	
7.7.e		12	

Standards Assessment **GENERAL**

Teacher Notes for Standards Assessment contain a longer Assessment Doctor and Diagnostic Teaching Tips.

REVIEWING ACADEMIC VOCABULARY

1 In the sentence "After conducting the science experiment, we recorded and analyzed the results," what does the word *conducting* mean?

- **A** directing
- **B** doing
- **C** researching
- **D** constructing

2 In the sentence "A two-year-old child is too young to understand the concept of cooperation," what does the word *concept* mean?

- **A** act
- **B** idea
- **C** reward
- **D** process

3 Choose the appropriate form of the word *construct* for the following sentence: I have _____ a model of Earth's layers.

- **A** construct
- **B** will construct
- **C** are constructing
- **D** constructed

4 Which of the following words is the closest in meaning to the word *appropriate*?

- **A** regular
- **B** formal
- **C** proper
- **D** common

REVIEWING CONCEPTS

5 Which of the following is a print resource that is useful for researching a topic?

- **A** television
- **B** computer
- **C** newspaper
- **D** typewriter

6 What is the name of the computer network that allows scientists from all over the world to share information?

- **A** The Punnett Square
- **B** World Wide Web
- **C** International System of Units
- **D** Public Broadcasting System

7 Which of the following is a tool for measuring the volume of a liquid?

- **A** graduated cylinder
- **B** cubic centimeter
- **C** spring balance
- **D** meterstick

8 It is important to know proper first-aid procedures when conducting laboratory experiments. What is the proper treatment for a minor burn?

- **A** to apply firm pressure to the burn
- **B** to apply first-aid cream to the burn
- **C** to cover the burn with a clean cloth
- **D** to rinse the burn under cold water

9 The steps in a scientific investigation must

- **A** include laboratory experiments.
- **B** begin with a good hypothesis.
- **C** include the development of a theory.
- **D** be performed in a logical sequence.

ASSESSMENT DOCTOR

Question 1: The correct answer is B. *Doing* and *conducting* are interchangeable in the context of conducting experiments.

Question 2: The correct answer is B. A concept is a general idea.

Question 3: The correct answer is D. *Constructed* completes the sentence correctly. The auxiliary *have* tells you that the sentence is in the present perfect tense and needs a past participle.

Question 4: The correct answer is C. *Proper* and *appropriate* are similar in meaning.

Question 5: The correct answer is C. A newspaper is an example of a print resource that is useful for researching a topic.

Question 6: The correct answer is B. The World Wide Web is an electronic resource that scientists use to access information and to share information with other scientists.

Question 7: The correct answer is A. A graduated cylinder is used to measure the volume of liquids.

212°F Water boils — 100°C Water boils

98.6°F Normal body temperature — 37°C Normal body temperature

32°F Water freezes — 0°C Water freezes

10 The conversion table above shows Fahrenheit and Celsius temperature scales. According to the conversion chart, which of the following sentences is true?

A You can swim in water that is 100°C.

B You can boil eggs in water that is 150°F.

C You can skate on water that is 10°C.

D Your body temperature is about 37°C.

11 In which type of model are the measurements of the model proportional to the measurements of the real object?

A a conceptual model

B a scale model

C a simple model

D a mathematical model

12 Written reports and oral presentations are part of which step of scientific methods?

A communicating results

B asking questions

C performing tests

D analyzing results

REVIEWING PRIOR LEARNING

Experiment to Test Effect of UV Light on Frogs

Group	Control factors			Variable
	Kind of frog	Number of eggs	Temperature of water (°C)	UV light exposure (days)
#1 (control)	leopard frog	100	25	0
#2 (experimental)	leopard frog	100	25	15
#3 (experimental)	leopard frog	100	25	24

13 The data in the table above were collected during an experiment to test the effects of UV light on frogs. What is the variable in the experiment?

A water temperature

B length of exposure to UV light

C number of eggs

D kind of frog

14 What is a hypothesis?

A an accurate prediction

B a possible explanation that can be tested

C a sentence that states statistical data

D a factor that may cause a certain result

15 What is the purpose of scientific investigation?

A to demonstrate how scientific methods work

B to learn about discoveries

C to perform experiments

D to answer questions about the natural world

Standards Assessment

Question 8: The correct answer is D. Rinsing the area with cold water helps cool the burn area and reduce pain. (CA Science Framework)

Question 9: The correct answer is D. The steps in a scientific method may vary, but their sequence must be logical.

Question 10: The correct answer is D. Your body temperature is 37°C.

Question 11: The correct answer is B. The measurements of a scale model are proportional to the measurements of the object the model represents. If one structure in a model is five times as large as that particular structure in the real object, than all of the other structures in the model will also be five times as large as the structures they represent.

Question 12: The correct answer is A. Scientists communicate their results through written reports and oral presentations.

Question 13: The correct answer is B. The length of exposure is the only factor that differs from group to group, so it is the variable.

Question 14: The correct answer is B. A hypothesis is a possible explanation that can be tested.

Question 15: The correct answer is D. The main purpose of performing scientific investigations is to learn about the world around us and how it works.

Scientific Debate

Background

There are three main ingredients of a fire: oxygen, heat, and fuel. Firefighters call this the *fire triangle*, and their goal is to eliminate at least one ingredient. Two groups of firefighters are sent into a forest fire: *hotshots* and *smokejumpers*. Hotshots build a *firebreak* in order to stop the spread of the fire. They clear an area of land of anything that could become fuel for fire, such as trees, bushes, and grass. The smokejumpers jump from airplanes into remote places to fight small blazes or to start *backfires* in order to eliminate fuel from an oncoming fire.

Science Fiction

ACTiViTY

Further Reading   If students liked this story, recommend other stories by Edward D. Hoch, such as the following:

- *The Monkey's Clue*
- *The Stolen Sapphire*
- *The Night, My Friend: Stories of Crime & Suspense*

Science in Action

Scientific Debate

Should We Stop All Forest Fires?

Each year in California, forest fires endanger lives and damage homes and timber. Since 1972, the policy of the National Park Service has been to manage the national parks as naturally as possible. Most fires caused by lightning are allowed to burn. The only lightning-caused fires that are put out are those that threaten lives, property, uniquely scenic areas, or endangered species. All human-caused fires are put out. However, this policy has caused some controversy. Some people want this policy followed in all public forests and even grasslands. Others think that all fires should be put out.

Social Studies ACTiViTY

Research a location where there is a debate about controlling forest fires. You might look into national forests or parks. Record your research in your **Science Journal**. Write a newspaper article about the issue. Be sure to present all sides of the debate.

Science Fiction

"The Homesick Chicken" by Edward D. Hoch

Why did the chicken cross the road? You think you know the answer to this old riddle, don't you? But "The Homesick Chicken," by Edward D. Hoch, may surprise you. That old chicken may not be exactly what it seems.

One of the chickens at the high-tech Tangaway Research Farms has escaped. Then, it was found in a vacant lot across the highway from Tangaway, pecking away contentedly. Why did it bother to escape? Barnabus Rex, a specialist in solving scientific riddles, is called in to work on this mystery. As he investigates, he finds clues and forms a hypothesis. Read the story, and see if you can explain the mystery before Mr. Rex does.

Language Arts ACTiViTY

In your **Science Journal,** write your own short story about a chicken crossing a road for a mysterious reason. Give the reader clues (evidence) about the mysterious reason but do not reveal the truth until the end of the story. Be sure that the story makes sense scientifically.

Answers to Social Studies Activity
Student articles should reflect objective, journalistic style and present more than one perspective on the issue. Encourage students to research areas that are close to where they live.

Answers to Language Arts Activity
Student stories should include logical clues and have a logical ending. Encourage students to read each other's stories and give each other feedback on the use of scientific reasoning in the story.

Yvonne Cagle

Flight Surgeon and Astronaut   Most doctors practice medicine with both feet on the ground. But Dr. Yvonne Cagle found a way to fly with her medical career. Cagle became a flight surgeon for the U. S. Air Force and an astronaut for the National Aeronautics and Space Administration (NASA).

Cagle's interest in both medicine and space flight began early. As a little girl, Cagle spent hours staring at X rays in her father's medical library. Those images sparked an early interest in science. Cagle also remembers watching Neil Armstrong walk on the moon when she was five years old. As she tried to imagine the view of Earth from space, Cagle decided that she wanted to see it for herself.

Becoming a flight surgeon in the U. S. Air Force was a good first step toward becoming an astronaut. As a flight surgeon, Cagle learned about the special medical challenges that humans face when they are launched high above Earth. Being a flight surgeon also allowed Cage to work with some of the best pilots and to fly in the latest jets.

It wasn't long before Cagle worked as an occupational physician for NASA at the Johnson Space Center. Two years later, she was chosen to begin astronaut training. Cagle completed two years of training and is now qualified for flight assignment as a mission specialist. Through hard work and dedication, Cagle has achieved many of her childhood goals.

Math ACTiViTY

In spaceflight, astronauts experience changes in gravity that affect their bodies in several ways. Because of gravity, a person who has a mass of 50 kg weighs 110 lb on Earth. But on the moon, the same person weighs about 17% of his or her weight on Earth. How much does the person weigh on the moon? Show your work in your **Science Journal.**

Internet Resources

- To learn more about careers in science, visit **www.scilinks.org** and enter the SciLinks code HY70225.
- To learn more about these Science in Action topics, visit **go.hrw.com** and type in the keyword HY7LIVF.
- Check out articles related to this chapter by visiting **go.hrw.com**. Just type in the keyword HY7LIVC.

Answers to Math Activity
18.7 lb; 0.17 × 110 lb = 18.7 lb

Flight Risks   Flight surgeons work to prevent illness in the abnormal environment of flight. Arrange students into groups and have them use the Internet to research the medical risks of flight. Have them focus on environmental conditions that can cause problems and ways to prevent those problems. Have each group organize its findings on a poster. (Sample answers: Low oxygen, decreased pressure, high acceleration, extreme heat or cold, high noise levels, and bright sun can cause medical problems during or after flight. These problems can be prevented with oxygen masks, a pressurized cabin, pressurized suits, and protective masks and clothing.)

MISCONCEPTION ALERT

Mass Confusion   Students may confuse density with mass or weight. Ask students the question "Which has more mass: 1 kg of feathers or 1 kg of lead?" (They both have the same mass.) Remind students that the kilogram is a unit of mass, so the masses are the same. Also, remind students that density involves both mass and volume. Point out that, because feathers have a much lower density than lead, 1 kg of feathers would have a much larger volume than 1 kg of lead. Ask students: In space, if you threw 1 kg of feathers and 1 kg of lead with the same force at the same time, which would move farther or faster?" (Again, note that the two objects have the same mass and were moved with the same force. Thus, according to Newton's laws, the two objects would move at the same speed and keep going until they bump into something or another force acts upon them.)

Standards Course of Study

The elements listed in the Standards Course of Study provide a base for presenting, supporting, and assessing the California Grade 7 Science Standards. Use this Standards Course of Study as a base for planning your lessons.

Why Teach

It's Alive!! Or Is It?

This chapter was designed to introduce the California Grade 7 Science Standards about cells and the methods of reproduction (7.1.a and 7.2.a). It follows a chapter about scientific methods. After completing this chapter, students will have an understanding of the basic characteristics of living things. Also, students will have the background needed to begin an in-depth exploration of cells and organisms.

After they have completed this chapter, students will begin a chapter about the ways in which living things use and rely on light energy.

Chapter Pacing

Getting Started — 45 min, pp. 50–51
The Big Idea All living things share characteristics and needs.
7.1.a, 7.7.c

Section 1 Characteristics of Living Things — 45 min, pp. 52–55
Key Concept Living things have six characteristics in common.
7.1.a, 7.2.a

Section 2 The Necessities of Life — 90 min, pp. 56–61
Key Concept Every living thing needs water, a place to live, and food in order to survive.
7.1.a, 7.7.c

Wrapping Up — 180 min, pp. 62–71
7.2.a, 7.7.a, 7.7.c

California Standards

Focus on Life Sciences
7.1.a Students know cells function similarly in all living organisms.
7.2.a Students know the differences between the life cycles and reproduction methods of sexual and asexual organisms.

Investigation and Experimentation
7.7.a Select and use appropriate tools and technology (including calculators, computers, balances, spring scales, microscopes, and binoculars) to perform tests, collect data, and display data.
7.7.c Communicate the logical connection among hypotheses, science concepts, tests conducted, data collected, and conclusions drawn from the scientific evidence.

Basic Learners
TE Paired Summarizing, p. 53
TE Food Choices, p. 59
📄 Reinforcement Worksheet
📄 Chapter Test A
📄 Differentiated Datasheets A for Labs and Activities ■
📄 Study Guide A ■

Advanced Learners/GATE
TE DNA, p. 54
TE Adaptations, p. 57
TE Carbohydrates, p. 59
TE Explorer Equipment, p. 64
📄 Critical Thinking Worksheet
📄 Chapter Test C
📄 Differentiated Datasheets C for Labs and Activities ■

Teach

SE Explore Activity Cellular Similarity, p. 51* ■

📠 **Bellringer**
💿 **PowerPoint® Resources**
SE Quick Lab The Role of Cells, p. 53* ■
📠 L4 A Budding Hydra

📠 **Bellringer**
💿 **PowerPoint® Resources**
SE Quick Lab Observing Enzymes in Pineapples, p. 59* ■
📠 L5 Phospholipid Molecule and Cell Membrane

SE Skills Practice Lab Comparing Methods of Reproduction, pp. 62–63* ■

Practice

SE Organize Activity Double Door, p. 50

SE Section Review, p. 55* ■

SE Section Review, p. 61* ■

SE Science Skills Activity Selecting Tools to Collect Data, p. 64* ■
📠 **Concept Mapping***
SE Chapter Review, pp. 66–67* ■

Assess

📁 **Chapter Pretest**

SE Standards Checks, pp. 52, 54
TE Standards Focus, p. 54
📁 **Section Quiz** ■

SE Standards Checks, pp. 56, 58, 60
TE Standards Focus, p. 60
📁 **Section Quiz** ■

SE Standards Assessment, pp. 68–69*
📁 **Chapter Tests A, B** ■**, C**
📓 **Standards Review Workbook** ■

Resources for Universal Access • Differentiated Instruction

English Learners

TE Naked Eye Vision, p. 52
TE Using the Figure, p. 54
TE Science Pronunciation, p. 54
TE Demonstration, p. 56
TE Understanding Slang and Idioms, p. 64
📁 Vocabulary and Section Summary A ■, B

📁 Section Quizzes ■
📁 Chapter Tests A, B ■
📁 Differentiated Datasheets A, B, and C for Labs and Activities ■
📓 Study Guide A ■
📓 Multilingual Glossary

Struggling Readers

TE Section Summary, p. 55
TE Consumers or Decomposers?, p. 56
TE Reading Strategy, p. 58

Special Education Students

TE Sensing and Responding, p. 53
TE Playing a Phospholipid, p. 60

To help plan your lessons, refer to the On Course Mapping Instruction booklet.

2 Chapter Resources

Visual Resources

CHAPTER STARTER TRANSPARENCY

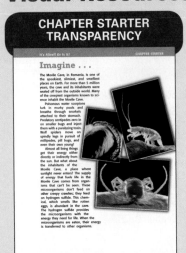

Imagine . . .

The Movile Cave, in Romania, is one of the spookiest, slimiest, and smelliest places on Earth. For more than 5 million years, the cave and its inhabitants were sealed off from the outside world. Many of the creepiest organisms known to science inhabit the Movile Cave.

Poisonous water scorpions lurk in murky pools and breathe through snorkels attached to their stomach. Predatory centipedes zero in on smaller bugs and inject them with a paralyzing toxin. Wolf spiders move on spindly legs in pursuit of millipedes, pill bugs, and even their own young!

Almost all living things get their energy either directly or indirectly from the sun. But what about the inhabitants of the Movile Cave, a place where sunlight never enters? The supply of energy that fuels life in the Movile Cave comes from organisms that can't be seen. These microorganisms don't feed on other creepy crawlies; they feed on hydrogen sulfide. This chemical, which smells like rotten eggs, is abundant in the cave. The hydrogen sulfide provides the microorganisms with the energy they need for life. When the microorganisms are eaten, their energy is transferred to other organisms.

BELLRINGER TRANSPARENCIES

Section: Characteristics of Living Things
Brainstorm characteristics of living things.

Write your answers in your **science journal.**

Section: The Necessities of Life
Most cells are made up of about 70% water. What would your mass be if there was no water in your body?

Write your answer in your **science journal.**

TEACHING TRANSPARENCIES

A Budding Hydra   L4

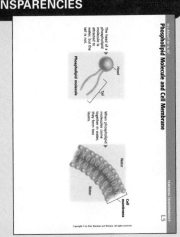

Phospholipid Molecule and Cell Membrane   L5

TEACHING TRANSPARENCIES

Complex Carbohydrates

LINK TO PHYSICAL SCIENCE

STANDARDS REVIEW TRANSPARENCIES

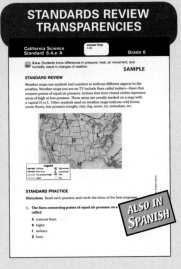

California Science Standard 6.4.e A   Grade 6

6.4.e. Students know differences in pressure, heat, air movement, and humidity result in changes of weather.

SAMPLE

STANDARD REVIEW

Weather maps use symbols and numbers to indicate different aspects in the weather. Weather maps you see on TV include lines called isobars—lines that connect points of equal air pressure. Isobars that form closed circles represent areas of high or low pressure. These areas are usually marked on a map with a capital H or L. Other symbols used on weather maps indicate cold fronts, warm fronts, low pressure troughs, rain, fog, snow, ice, tornadoes, etc.

STANDARD PRACTICE

Directions Read each question and circle the letter of the best response.

1. The lines connecting points of equal air pressure on a
   called

   A contour lines
   B highs
   C isobars
   D lows

ALSO IN SPANISH

CONCEPT MAPPING TRANSPARENCY

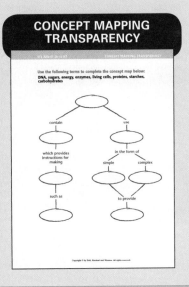

Use the following terms to complete the concept map below: DNA, sugars, energy, enzymes, living cells, proteins, starches, carbohydrates

Planning Resources

PARENT LETTER

SAMPLE

Dear Parent,

Your son's or daughter's science class will soon begin exploring the chapter entitled "The Nature of Physical Science." In this chapter, students will learn about how the scientific method applies to the world of physical science and the role of physical science in the world. By the end of the chapter, students should demonstrate a clear understanding of the chapter's main ideas and be able to discuss the following topics:

1. the role of questions in the process of investigation (Section 1)
2. how applying science saves lives and benefits the environment (Section 1)
3. careers that rely on science (Section 1)
4. the steps used in scientific methods (Section 2)
5. how scientific methods are used to answer questions and solve problems (Section 2)
6. the importance of safety precautions in the laboratory (Section 3)
7. examples of safety equipment and when to use them (Section 3)
8. how safety symbols are used to make laboratories safer (Section 3)

Questions to Ask Along the Way

You can help your child learn about these topics by asking interesting questions as he or she progresses through the chapter. For example, you may wish to ask your son or daughter the following questions:

What are some surprising careers that use science?

What is a characteristic of a good hypothesis?

What is the first step to take if an accident happens?

ALSO IN SPANISH

TEST ITEM LISTING

SAMPLE

Holt California Physical Science

Chapter 6 Introduction to Atoms
Test Item Listing
Multiple choice

1. The smallest particle into which an element can be divided and still have the properties of that element is called a(n)
   a. nucleus.   c. atom.
   b. electron.   d. neutron.
   ANS: C   DIF: 1   REF: 1   OBJ: 2   STO: 8.3.a   KEY: atom
          MSC: SQ.1.1

2. What particle did J. J. Thomson discover?
   a. neutron   c. atom
   b. electron   d. proton
   ANS: B   DIF: 1   REF: 1   OBJ: 2   STO: 8.3.a   KEY: electron   MSC: SQ.1.2

3. How would you describe the nucleus?
   a. dense, positively charged
   b. mostly empty space, positively charged
   c. tiny, negatively charged
   d. dense, negatively charged
   ANS: A   DIF: 1   REF: 1   OBJ: 2   STO: 8.3.a   KEY: nucleus   MSC: SQ.1.3

4. Where are electrons likely to be found?
   a. in the nucleus
   b. in electron clouds
   c. mixed throughout the atom
   d. in definite paths
   ANS: B   DIF: 1   REF: 1   OBJ: 2   STO: 8.3.a   KEY: electron   MSC: SQ.1.4

5. Dalton believed that
   a. atoms of the same element are exactly alike.
   b. most, but not all, substances are made of atoms.
   c. atoms of different elements are the same.
   d. atoms can be divided.
   ANS: A   DIF: 1   REF: 1   OBJ: 2   STO: 8.3.a   KEY: atom

6. Every atom of a given element has the same number of
   a. protons.
   b. neutrons.
   c. electrons
   d. isotopes.
   ANS: A   DIF: 1   REF: 1   OBJ: 2   STO: 8.3.a

ALSO IN SPANISH

One-Stop Planner® CD-ROM

This CD-ROM package includes all of the resources shown here and the following time-saving tools:

- **Lab Materials QuickList Software**
- **Customizable Lesson Plans** Correlated to the California Science Standards
- **Holt Calendar Planner**
- **PowerPoint® Resources**
- **Printable Worksheets**
- **ExamView® Test Generator** Correlated to the California Science Standards
- **Holt PuzzlePro®**
- **Interactive Teacher's Edition**

Meeting Individual Needs

DIRECTED READING A
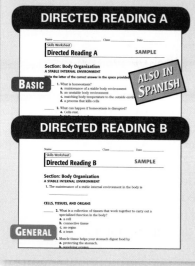

Skills Worksheet
Directed Reading A SAMPLE

Section: Body Organization
A STABLE INTERNAL ENVIRONMENT
Write the letter of the correct answer in the space provided.

BASIC

ALSO IN SPANISH

DIRECTED READING B

Skills Worksheet
Directed Reading B SAMPLE

Section: Body Organization
A STABLE INTERNAL ENVIRONMENT

1. The maintenance of a stable internal environment in the body is

CELLS, TISSUES, AND ORGANS

GENERAL

VOCABULARY AND SECTION SUMMARY A
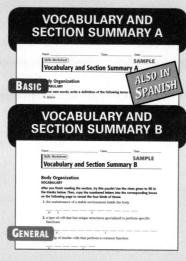

Skills Worksheet
Vocabulary and Section Summary A SAMPLE

BASIC

ALSO IN SPANISH

VOCABULARY AND SECTION SUMMARY B

Skills Worksheet
Vocabulary and Section Summary B SAMPLE

Body Organization
VOCABULARY

GENERAL

REINFORCEMENT

Skills Worksheet
Reinforcement SAMPLE

Muscle Map
Complete this worksheet after you finish reading the section "The Muscular System."

Three Types of Muscle

Skeletal	Cardiac	Smooth

BASIC

CRITICAL THINKING

Skills Worksheet
Critical Thinking SAMPLE

The Tissue Engineering Debate
Dear Readers:

ADVANCED

INTERACTIVE READER AND STUDY GUIDE
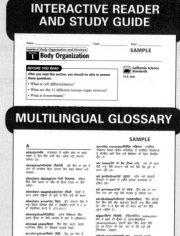

Body Organization SAMPLE

BEFORE YOU READ
After you read this section, you should be able to answer these questions:

California Science Standards

MULTILINGUAL GLOSSARY

SAMPLE

Labs and Activities

DIFFERENTIATED DATASHEETS FOR EXPLORE ACTIVITY, QUICK LABS, AND CHAPTER LAB
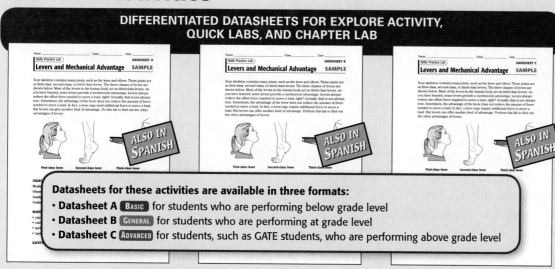

Skills Practice Lab
Levers and Mechanical Advantage DATASHEET A SAMPLE

Skills Practice Lab
Levers and Mechanical Advantage DATASHEET B SAMPLE

Skills Practice Lab
Levers and Mechanical Advantage DATASHEET C SAMPLE

ALSO IN SPANISH

First-class lever   Second-class lever   Third-class lever

Datasheets for these activities are available in three formats:
- **Datasheet A** BASIC for students who are performing below grade level
- **Datasheet B** GENERAL for students who are performing at grade level
- **Datasheet C** ADVANCED for students, such as GATE students, who are performing above grade level

DATASHEET FOR SCIENCE SKILLS ACTIVITY
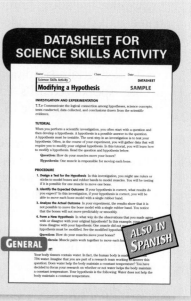

Science Skills Activity
Modifying a Hypothesis DATASHEET SAMPLE

INVESTIGATION AND EXPERIMENTATION

TUTORIAL

GENERAL

ALSO IN SPANISH

Reviews and Assessments

SECTION REVIEWS
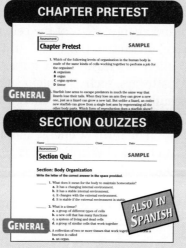

Skills Worksheet
Section Review SAMPLE

Body Organization
USING VOCABULARY

GENERAL

ALSO IN SPANISH

CHAPTER REVIEW

Skills Worksheet
Chapter Review SAMPLE

USING VOCABULARY

GENERAL

ALSO IN SPANISH

CHAPTER PRETEST
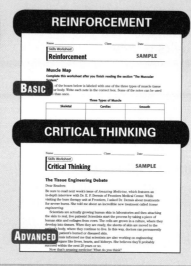

Assessment
Chapter Pretest SAMPLE

GENERAL

SECTION QUIZZES

Assessment
Section Quiz SAMPLE

Section: Body Organization
Write the letter of the correct answer in the space provided.

GENERAL

ALSO IN SPANISH

CHAPTER TEST A
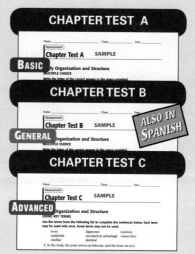

Assessment
Chapter Test A SAMPLE

Body Organization and Structure
MULTIPLE CHOICE

BASIC

CHAPTER TEST B

Assessment
Chapter Test B SAMPLE

Body Organization and Structure
MULTIPLE CHOICE

GENERAL

ALSO IN SPANISH

CHAPTER TEST C

Assessment
Chapter Test C SAMPLE

Body Organization and Structure

ADVANCED

STANDARDS ASSESSMENT
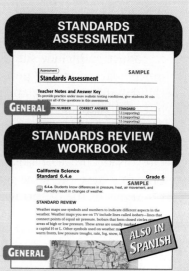

Assessment
Standards Assessment SAMPLE

Teacher Notes and Answer Key

GENERAL

STANDARDS REVIEW WORKBOOK

California Science Standard 6.4.e   Grade 6

SAMPLE

6.4.e. Students know differences in pressure, heat, air movement, and humidity result in changes of weather.

STANDARD REVIEW

GENERAL

ALSO IN SPANISH

This Teacher Background explains science concepts, principles, and theories that appear in the chapter. Use the information on these pages to refresh or enhance your understanding of the topics covered.

Section 1

Characteristics of Living Things

Similar Cell Structures, Similar Cell Functions

Specialized cells have varying structures and functions. However, these structures and functions are similar in most organisms. For example, muscle cells in humans have structures that are similar to muscle cells in most mammals, such as horses.

Stem cells are unique cells found in many multicellular organisms, including humans. Stem cells are undifferentiated cells that can divide many times. In humans, stem cells are found both in embryos and adults. Adult stem cells are less adaptable than embryonic stem cells.

Under certain conditions, stem cells can be induced to become specialized cells. For this reason, scientists think that stem cells might be used to treat otherwise irreversible diseases, such as Parkinson's disease, a neurological disorder characterized by the progressive deterioration of neurons. Understanding how cell proliferation among stem cells is controlled also has implications for understanding uncontrolled cell division in cancer.

Stem cells are quite similar between species. For example, human stem cells have been injected into mice, where they subsequently developed into specialized cardiac cells.

Reproduction

Organisms reproduce asexually, sexually, or both. Asexual reproduction requires no fertilization event. Instead, a single parent produces offspring that are genetically identical to the parent. Methods of asexual reproduction include simple mitotic division (as in unicellular eukaryotic protists), budding (as in the multicellular animal *hydra*), and propagation from cuttings (as in *Coleus* plants).

One advantage of asexual reproduction is the ability to reproduce without the assistance of another organism. One disadvantage of asexual reproduction is that the offspring have the same genome as the parent, which often means the offspring are less likely to survive a significant environmental change.

During sexual reproduction, sex cells from two parents combine to form offspring that are genetically similar to each parent but are not genetically identical to either parent. In some cases, a single organism may supply both sex cells. When this occurs in flowering plants, the process is called *self-pollination*.

Sexual reproduction results in offspring that have a genome that varies from the parents. This is a potential advantage if the environment changes, as more offspring are likely to survive. However, sexual reproduction is disadvantageous because it requires two parents and often results in fewer offspring than asexual reproduction does.

Figure A shows the offspring of sexual reproduction. Images such as this can be used to help students recognize that the offspring resulting from sexual reproduction are very similar to, but are not identical to, the parents.

Figure A *Bears reproduce sexually, which increases the chances that their offspring will survive environmental changes.*

Metabolism

All of the chemical reactions that take place within an organism make up the organism's metabolism. Metabolism encompasses thousands of chemical reactions, most of which occur along specific metabolic pathways. These pathways are controlled through the activity of enzymes, which speed up the rate of metabolic reactions.

Metabolism is primarily concerned with the material and energy needs of the cell. Catabolic pathways, such as cellular respiration, result in the breakdown of molecules, often to release energy for use by the cell. Anabolic pathways, such as protein synthesis, consume energy to build molecules. The energy and materials released by catabolic pathways are used by the anabolic pathways.

The form of energy employed by metabolic processes is chemical energy, and is sometimes called chemical potential energy. The energy in molecules is stored in the bonds between the atoms in the molecules. When these bonds are broken, the chemical energy is converted to kinetic energy and some energy is lost as heat energy.

HOLT SCIENCE
Professional Reference for Teachers

For background information about teaching strategies and issues, refer to the
Professional Reference for Teachers.

Section 2

The Necessities of Life

Water

The cells of all living organisms are made up mostly of water. Water plays an important role in metabolic reactions, both as a component of the medium in which these reactions take place and as a reactant in some metabolic reactions. For example, water is combined with carbon dioxide to produce carbohydrates during photosynthesis.

Air

Air consists of a mixture of gases, including oxygen, nitrogen, and carbon dioxide, that enable organisms to perform vital life functions. Nearly all food chains on Earth depend on photosynthetic organisms. These organisms require carbon dioxide for photosynthesis. Without air, plants cannot produce the nutrients on which they and other organisms depend. In turn, most animals need the oxygen in air to break down food molecules for energy.

Food

Food provides organisms with energy and the materials for building proteins and replacing or repairing cells. The materials in foods that are most important to organisms include carbohydrates, proteins, fats, vitamins, and minerals.

Cells use carbohydrates to produce energy and to build proteins. Monosaccharides are the simplest carbohydrates. Monosaccharides are used most frequently for energy and as a carbon source. The most commonly used monosaccharide, glucose ($C_6H_{12}O_6$), is comprised of a six-carbon ring that has a carbonyl group and five hydroxyl groups. Glucose and other six-carbon monosaccharides are often called hexoses.

Monosaccharides are often combined into polymers, such as disaccharides (two monosaccharides) and polysaccharides (three or more monosaccharides). Polysaccharides are typically storage molecules, such as starch and glycogen. Some polysaccharides, such as cellulose (in plant cells) and chitin (in arthropods), are used as structural components in cells. All polysaccharides must be broken down into their component monosaccharides before the cell can use them for energy.

Proteins have many functions throughout an organism. Some proteins facilitate metabolic reactions, and others move materials across the cell membrane. Humans make use of tens of thousands of proteins, many of which are similar to proteins used by other organisms.

Lipids are hydrophobic molecules. Lipids include phospholipids, which make up cell membranes; steroids, such as cholesterol and hormones; and fats. Fats are molecules comprised of glycerol and three fatty acids. Glycerol is a three-carbon alcohol in which each carbon atom binds to one hydroxyl group. Fatty acids are long carbon chains that include a carboxyl group. These fats are also known as triacylglycerols. The primary function of fats is energy storage.

Figure B shows the basic structure of a phospholipid and a phospholipid membrane. The hydrophobic tails point toward the center of the double layer and the hydrophilic heads point outward. You can use this image to guide students through a model-building activity in which the students construct a lipid bilayer membrane. Challenge students to predict other forms that phospholipids might produce. Some students may recognize that lipids can form droplets, in which several lipids form a small, single-layered sphere.

Figure B *Phospholipids are the primary component of semi-permeable cellular membranes.*

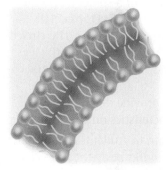

Nucleic Acids

DNA and RNA are two types of nucleic acids. A nucleic acid is a polymer of nucleotides, which are made up of three components: a nitrogenous base, a pentose sugar, and a phosphate group. The nitrogenous base is a pyrimidine, such as cytosine, thymine, and uracil, or a purine, such as adenine or guanine. Each gene is a unique sequence of nucleotides. The order of these nucleotides determines which amino acids are strung together to form proteins.

Internet Resources

SciLinks is maintained by the National Science Teachers Association to provide you and your students with interesting, up-to-date links that will enrich your classroom presentation of the chapter.

Visit www.scilinks.org and enter the SciLinks code for more information about the topic listed.

Topic: Characteristics of Living Things
SciLinks code: HY70258

Topic: The Necessities of Life
SciLinks code: HY71018

Chapter Preview

Chapter Pretest
Use the Chapter Pretest in the Chapter Resource File to determine the prior knowledge of your students. The Test Doctors and diagnostic teaching tips in the Teacher Notes pages will help you tailor your instruction to your students' specific needs.

Improving Comprehension

Use the Graphic Organizer on this page of the Student Edition to introduce the topics that are covered in this chapter, to summarize the chapter material, or to show students how to make a spider map.

Teaching Tips

• Point out to students that the structure of a spider map visually suggests levels of detail within a main topic. The circled idea is the main topic, the legs provide characteristics of the circled idea, and the horizontal lines provide details about the characteristics on the legs.

• Explain to students that a spider map works best when the characteristics of the main topic are analogous and the details about the characteristics can be written concisely.

LS Logical

Improving Comprehension

Graphic Organizers are important visual tools that can help you organize information and improve your reading comprehension. The Graphic Organizer below is called a *spider map*. Instructions for creating other types of Graphic Organizers are located in the **Study Skills** section of the Appendix.

How to Make a Spider Map

❶ Draw a diagram like the one shown below. In the circle, write the main topic.

❷ From the circle, draw legs to represent the main ideas or characteristics of the topic. Draw as many legs as you want to draw. Write an idea or characteristic along each leg.

❸ From each leg, draw horizontal lines. As you read the chapter, write details about each idea on the idea's horizontal lines. To add more details, make the legs longer and add more horizontal lines.

When to Use a Spider Map

A spider map is an effective tool for classifying the details of a specific topic in science. A spider map divides a topic into ideas and details. As you read about a topic, look for the main ideas or characteristics of the topic. Within each idea, look for details. Use a spider map to organize the ideas and details of each topic.

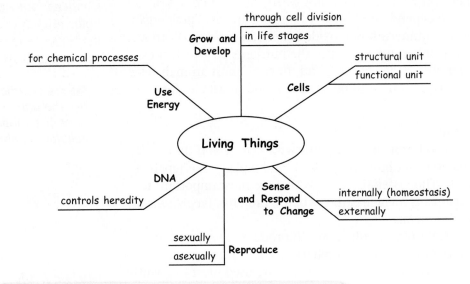

You Try It!

This Reading Strategy can also be used within the chapter that you are about to read. Practice making your own *spider map* as directed in the Reading Strategy for Section ❷. Record your work in your **Science Journal**.

Using Other Graphic Organizers

Students can practice using a variety of Graphic Organizers while reading this chapter. The following Graphic Organizers may also be useful in this chapter:

A **cause-and-effect map** can be used to describe how an organism responds to external change, explained in Section 1.

An **idea wheel** can be used to organize details about the groups in which organisms are divided based on how they get food, discussed in Section 2.

Instructions for creating these Graphic Organizers are located on pp. 583–591 of the Appendix.

Unpacking the Standards

The information below "unpacks" the standards by breaking them down into basic parts. The higher-level, academic vocabulary is highlighted and defined to help you understand the language of the standards. "What It Means" restates the standards as simply as possible.

California Standard	Academic Vocabulary	What It Means
7.1.a Students know cells **function similarly** in all living organisms.	**function** (FUHNGK shuhn) to work **similarly** (SIM uh luhr lee) in almost the same way	Cells perform the same actions in all living things.
7.2.a Students know the differences between the life **cycles** and reproduction methods of sexual and asexual organisms.	**cycle** (SIE kuhl) a repeating series of changes	You must know how the life cycles of living things that reproduce sexually differ from the life cycles of living things that reproduce asexually. You must also explain how these ways of reproducing differ.

Unpacking the Standards

Use the following information with the *What It Means* in the Student Edition to help students understand why studying each standard is important.

Why It Matters
At the cellular level, all living organisms share common traits. Understanding this idea allows one to understand the nature of life on Earth.
Students should be aware of the variety of ways in which organisms reproduce.

Words with Multiple Meanings

Words that have both common and scientific meanings can be confusing to students. The following table identifies some of those words that are used in this chapter.

Term	Common meaning	Scientific meaning
cell	a small, confining room	the smallest structural and functional unit of all living organisms
consumer	someone who purchases goods or services	an organism that eats other organisms or organic matter

Practice Have students complete the sentences below to help them understand how the scientific and common meanings of the word *cell* can differ.

a. Each prisoner's ___ had only a bed and a small ceiling light. (cell)

b. Some living things have many ___, while others only have one. (cell)

Chapter Overview

This chapter discusses the characteristics and necessities of living things. The chapter examines molecules that are important for life including nutrients and cellular building blocks.

It's Alive!! Or Is It?

The Big Idea
All living things share characteristics and needs.

California Standards

Focus on Life Sciences
7.1 All living organisms are composed of cells, from just one to many trillions, whose details usually are visible only through a microscope. (Sections 1 and 2)
7.2 A typical cell of any organism contains genetic instructions that specify its traits. Those traits may be modified by environmental influences. (Section 1)

Investigation and Experimentation
7.7 Scientific progress is made by asking meaningful questions and conducting careful investigations. (Science Skills Activity)

Math
7.1.1 Mathematical Reasoning
7.1.1 Algebra and Functions

English–Language Arts
7.1.3 Reading
7.2.1 Writing

About the Photo

What does it mean to say that something is alive? To be alive, an organism must have all of the characteristics of living things. Machines have some but not all of the characteristics of living things. This amazing robotic insect can respond to changes in its environment. It can walk over obstacles. It can perform some tasks. But it is not alive. How is it like and unlike a living insect?

Organize

Double Door

Before you read this chapter, create the FoldNote entitled "Double Door." Write "Characteristics" on one flap of the double door and "Needs" on the other flap. As you read the chapter, compare the two topics, and write characteristics of each topic on the inside of the appropriate flap.

Instructions for creating FoldNotes are located in the Study Skills section on p. 579 of the Appendix.

California Standards Alignment

Focus on Life Sciences

7.1.a Students know cells function similarly in all living organisms. **pp. 51–61, 66–69**

7.2.a Students know the differences between the life cycles and reproduction methods of sexual and asexual organisms. **pp. 54–55, 62–63, 66–69**

Investigation and Experimentation

7.7.a Select and use appropriate tools and technology (including calculators, computers, balances, spring scales, microscopes, and binoculars) to perform tests, collect data, and display data. **p. 64**

7.7.c Communicate the logical connection among hypotheses, science concepts, tests conducted, data collected, and conclusions drawn from the scientific evidence. **pp. 51, 59, 62–63**

Math Standards

Algebra and Functions 7.1.1 Use variables and appropriate operations to write an expression, an equation, an inequality, or a system of equations or inequalities that represents a verbal description (e.g., three less than a number, half as large as area A). **pp. 55, 61, 67**

Mathematical Reasoning 7.1.1 Analyze problems by identifying relationships, distinguishing relevant from irrelevant information, identifying missing information, sequencing and prioritizing information, and observing patterns. **p. 58**

Teacher Notes

Students It will observe the same chemical reaction in cells of a plant and an animal (covers standards 7.1.a and 7.7.c). Catalase is an enzyme found in both the cells of a potato and of a chicken liver. When mixed with hydrogen peroxide, catalase accelerates the decomposition of hydrogen peroxide into water and oxygen. The bubbles that result from the reaction contain oxygen gas.

Materials for Each Group

- beakers (2)
- forceps
- gloves, protective
- hydrogen peroxide
- knife
- liver, chicken, raw
- plate
- potato, raw
- safety goggles

Safety Caution

Remind students to review all safety cautions and icons before beginning this activity. You might wish to recommend disposable gloves to students for handling the liver. Remind students to take care when using the knife to cut the potato and liver, and to wash their hands after completion of the activity. Dispose of raw meat properly.

Answers

5. Sample answer: Eventually, the hydrogen peroxide began to fizz after I added it to the potato.

6. Sample answer: The hydrogen peroxide began to fizz right away when I added it to the liver.

7. The hydrogen peroxide fizzed when it came into contact with the potato and the liver, so the same enzyme must be found in the cells of both organisms.

📋 Differentiated Datasheets
A **BASIC**, B **GENERAL**, C **ADVANCED**

Also editable on the Holt Lab Generator CD-ROM

Explore Activity 🥽 ◆ ◆ ⏱ 20 min

Cellular Similarity

One characteristic shared by all living things is being composed of cells. Nonliving things, such as robots, are not made of cells. In this activity, you will observe a reaction produced by an enzyme found in both liver cells and potato cells.

Procedure

1. On a **plate,** use a **knife** to cut a few slices of **potato.** Place the potato pieces in a **beaker.**

2. Pour in enough **hydrogen peroxide** to cover the potatoes. Observe any changes in their appearance in the next few minutes.

3. Use the knife to cut up a small piece of **chicken liver.** Use **forceps** to place the liver pieces in a **beaker.**

4. Pour in enough hydrogen peroxide to cover the liver. Observe any changes in the liver's appearance in the next few minutes.

7.1.a
7.7.c

Analysis

5. What happened when the hydrogen peroxide was poured over the potato?

6. What happened when the hydrogen peroxide was poured over the liver?

7. How can your observations be used to support the idea that living things are similar?

English–Language Arts Standards

Reading 7.1.3 Clarify word meaning through the use of definition, example, restatement, or contrast. **p. 56**

Writing 7.2.1 Write fictional or autobiographical narratives: (a) Develop a standard plot line (having a beginning, conflict, rising action, climax, and denouement) and point of view; (b) Develop complex major and minor characters and a definite setting; (c) Use a range of appropriate strategies (e.g. dialogue; suspense; naming of specific narrative action, including movement, gestures, and expressions). **p. 67**

Chapter Starter Transparency
Use this transparency to help students begin thinking about the characteristics of all living things.

Preteach

Reviewing Prior Knowledge

Ask student volunteers to read the red and blue heads in the section aloud. Then, ask students to describe what they think the section is about. Finally, ask students to relate what they already know about living things.

Bellringer

Have students focus on standard 7.1.a by asking them to brainstorm the characteristics of living things. (Sample answers: All living things have one or more cells, sense and respond to change, reproduce, have DNA, use energy, and grow and develop.)

Bellringer Transparency

Motivate

Discussion

Homeostasis Ask students to describe what they do when they go outside on a cold day. Tell students that cold air is a stimulus, and their reaction to cold air is a response that helps them maintain homeostasis. **LS** Auditory

---

MISCONCEPTION ALERT

Growing Crystals Students may think that everything that grows is alive. To help students overcome this misconception, make rock candy. Rock candy appears to "grow," but when they compare the other characteristics of living things to the rock candy, they will conclude that the rock candy is not actually alive.

Answer to Standards Check

All living things are made up of cells.
7.1.a (supporting)

What You Will Learn

- Living things are composed of one or more cells.
- Living things sense and respond to changes in their environment.
- Living things produce offspring through sexual reproduction or asexual reproduction.
- The cells of living things contain DNA.
- Living things use energy.
- Living things grow and develop.

Why It Matters

Learning about the characteristics that all living things share helps you understand life science.

Vocabulary

- cell
- homeostasis
- sexual reproduction
- asexual reproduction
- metabolism

READING STRATEGY

Summarizing Read this section silently. In pairs, take turns summarizing the material. Stop to discuss ideas and words that seem confusing.

7.1.a Students know cells function similarly in all living organisms.
7.2.a Students know the differences between the life cycles and reproduction methods of sexual and asexual organisms.

Characteristics of Living Things

Key Concept Living things have six characteristics in common.

▶ While outside one day, you notice something strange in the grass. It is slimy and bright yellow and is about the size of a dime. You have no idea what it is. Is it alive? How can you tell? An amazing variety of *organisms,* or living things, exist on Earth. All living things are alike in several ways. What does a dog have in common with a bacterium? And what do *you* have in common with a slimy, yellow blob known as a *slime mold?* Read on to find out about the six characteristics that all organisms share.

Living Things Have Cells

All living things, such as those in **Figure 1,** are composed of one or more cells. A **cell** is the structural and functional unit of life. It is the smallest unit that can carry out the activities of life. All cells are surrounded by a *cell membrane,* which separates the contents of the cell from the cell's environment. Most cells are too small to be seen with the naked eye.

In an organism made up of only one cell, different parts of the cell perform different functions. For example, a one-celled protist needs to eat. So, some parts of the cell take in food. Other parts of the cell break down the food. Still other parts of the cell excrete wastes.

Some living things are made up of trillions of cells. In an organism with many cells, different kinds of cells perform specialized functions. For example, your nerve cells transport signals, and your muscle cells are specialized for movement.

Standards Check What are all living things made of? 📖 **7.1.a**

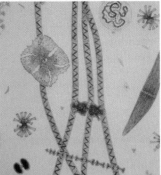

Figure 1 *Some organisms, such as the California quail on the left, are made up of trillions of cells. The protists on the right are made up of one cell or a few cells. They are so small that they can be seen only with a microscope.*

Universal Access · Differentiated Instruction

English Learners

Naked Eye Vision Many students new to English and scientific terminology may be confused by unexpected phrases. For these learners, a term such as "naked eye" is not meaningful. Choose a slide with a microscopic item on it. Ask students to look at the slide and describe what they see. (Sample answer: I see a colored blob.) Explain that there is something on the slide, but they cannot see it because it is too small for the human eye to see without help. Explain that the phrase *naked eye* means "without magnification." Let students look at the slide with magnification. Ask them if they can see anything that they were not able to see with their naked eyes. (Sample answer: yes; I can see cells.) 📖 **Verbal**

Figure 2 *The touch of an insect triggers the Venus' flytrap to close its leaves quickly.*

Living Things Sense and Respond to Change

All living things are able to sense change in their environment and to respond to that change. When your pupils are exposed to light, they respond by becoming smaller. A change that affects the activity of an organism is called a *stimulus* (plural, *stimuli*).

Stimuli can be chemicals, gravity, light, sounds, hunger, or anything that causes organisms to respond in some way. A gentle touch causes a response in the plant shown in **Figure 2.**

Homeostasis

Even though an organism's outside environment may change, conditions inside its body must stay the same. Many chemical reactions keep an organism alive. These reactions can take place only when conditions are exactly right. An organism must maintain stable internal conditions to survive. The maintenance of a stable internal environment is called **homeostasis.**

Responding to External Changes

Your body maintains a temperature of about 37°C. When you get hot, your body responds by sweating. When you get cold, your muscles twitch in an attempt to warm you up. This twitching is called *shivering*. Whether you are sweating or shivering, your body is trying to return itself to normal.

Other organisms also need to have stable internal conditions. But many cannot respond the way you do. Some living things control their body temperature by moving from one environment to another. If they get warm, they move to the shade. If they get cool, they move into the sunlight. For example, turtles often can be seen sunning themselves on rocks. When they get too warm, the turtles slide into the water.

cell (SEL) the smallest functional and structural unit of all living organisms

homeostasis (HOH mee OH STAY sis) the maintenance of a constant internal state in a changing environment

Quick Lab

The Role of Cells 7.1.a

1. Gather **20 to 30 small marshmallows.**
2. Use **toothpicks** to connect your marshmallows into any shape that you like.
3. Compare your marshmallow arrangements with your classmates'. What do they have in common?
4. If your arrangement represents an organism, describe how the marshmallows represent cells.

⏱ 10 min

Standards Focus

This **Standards Focus** provides you with a quick way to **assess, reteach,** and **re-assess** one or more concepts in the section.

 **Assess**

1. What structure is common to all living things? (the cell) **7.1.a**

 **Reteach**

Writing Quizzes Ask students to write a quiz that reviews the characteristics of living things. Students should exchange and complete each other's quizzes.

LS Intrapersonal **7.1.a, 7.2.a**

Re-Assess

Predicting Offspring Show students pictures of several different animals. Tell students that most animals can only reproduce with animals of the same species. Ask students to select two of the animals that you showed them, regardless of species, and have them draw a picture of what their offspring would look like if they were able to reproduce sexually. (Drawings should show a combination of traits.) LS Visual/Logical **7.2.a**

Using the Figure

Asexual Reproduction Ask students to examine the figure of the hydra on this page. Have students identify the structures that will become new hydras. (Two buds are forming near the base of the hydra.) Ask students to identify other organisms that reproduce asexually. (Students may note that most unicellular organisms reproduce asexually.) Answer to question in caption: The new buds will be identical to the parent. LS Visual

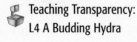 Teaching Transparency:
L4 A Budding Hydra

Figure 3 *Like most animals, bears produce offspring by sexual reproduction.*

Figure 4 *The hydra can reproduce asexually by forming buds that break off and grow into new individuals.* **How will the new buds compare to the original organism?**

sexual reproduction (SEK shoo uhl REE pruh DUHK shuhn) reproduction in which the sex cells from two parents unite to produce offspring that share traits from both parents

asexual reproduction (ay SEK shoo uhl REE pruh DUHK shuhn) reproduction that does not involve the union of sex cells and in which one parent produces offspring that are genetically identical to the parent

metabolism (muh TAB uh LIZ uhm) the sum of all chemical processes that occur in an organism

Living Things Reproduce

Living things make offspring like themselves by either sexual reproduction or asexual reproduction. In **sexual reproduction,** two parents produce offspring that share characteristics of both parents. Most plants and animals, such as the bears in **Figure 3,** reproduce sexually. In **asexual reproduction,** a single parent produces offspring that are identical to the parent. Most single-celled organisms and many multicellular organisms reproduce asexually. **Figure 4** shows a hydra, a multicellular animal that reproduces asexually.

Standards Check Describe asexual reproduction. **7.2.a**

Living Things Have DNA

The cells of all living things contain the molecule **d**eoxyribo**n**ucleic **a**cid (dee AHK see RIE boh noo KLEE ik AS id), or DNA. DNA carries instructions for the organism's traits. When organisms reproduce, they pass copies of their DNA to their offspring. Passing DNA ensures that the traits of parents are passed to the offspring. This passing of traits is called *heredity.*

Living Things Use Energy

Living things use energy to carry out the chemical activities of life. Some of these activities are changing energy into food, breaking down food, moving materials into and out of cells, growing, and building cells. An organism's **metabolism** is the sum of all of the activities that the organism performs.

Universal Access · Differentiated Instruction

Advanced Learners/GATE

DNA Have students investigate DNA. Students should identify the percentage by which DNA differs between parents and offspring in humans. Then, students should identify the percentage by which DNA differs between humans and chimpanzees, between humans and a reptile, and between humans and a bacterium. Students should predict why these differences might exist. Have students give an oral presentation on their findings. LS Verbal

English Learners

Science Pronunciation Direct students' attention to the word *deoxyribonucleic* under "Living Things Have DNA." Have them note the pronunciation provided in parentheses. Point out that the pronunciations in parentheses and in the margins in this book will help them learn new words correctly. Say the word and show them that capitalized syllables are stressed syllables. Have students practice pronouncing this word and other words in the margins. LS Verbal/Auditory

Living Things Grow and Develop

All living things grow during parts of their lives. In a single-celled organism, the cell gets larger and divides, which makes other organisms. In a multicellular organism, the number of cells increases, and the organism gets bigger. As living things grow, they also may develop and change. Like the organisms in **Figure 5,** you will pass through different stages in your life as you develop into an adult.

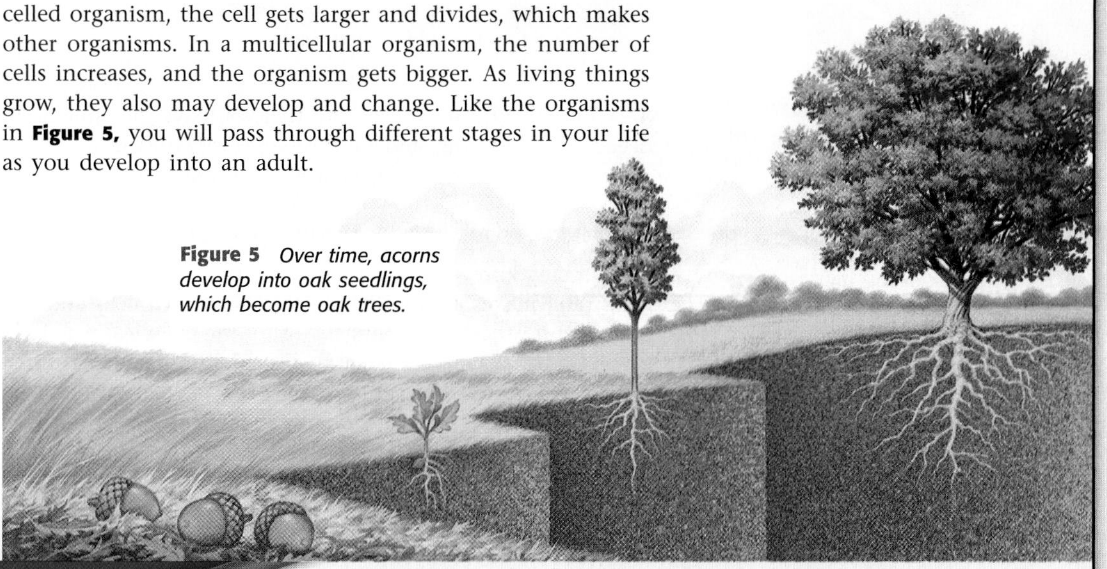

Figure 5 *Over time, acorns develop into oak seedlings, which become oak trees.*

SECTION Review

7.1.a, 7.2.a

Summary

- Organisms are made up of one or more cells.
- Organisms detect and respond to stimuli.
- Organisms reproduce through sexual or asexual reproduction.
- Organisms have DNA.
- Organisms use energy to carry out their activities.
- Organisms grow and develop.

Using Vocabulary

Complete each of the following sentences by choosing the correct term from the word bank.

cells, stimulus, homeostasis, metabolism

1. Sunlight can be a ___.
2. Living things are made of ___.

Understanding Concepts

3. **Describing** Describe the six characteristics of living things.
4. **Comparing** Explain the two types of reproduction.

Critical Thinking

5. **Applying Concepts** How are traits of parents passed to offspring? What traits might be passed to offspring if both parents are California quails?
6. **Identifying Relationships** How is the fur coat of a bear related to homeostasis?

Math Skills

7. **Using Equations** Bacteria double every generation. If one bacterium is in the first generation, how many bacteria will be in the sixth generation?

Challenge

8. **Making Inferences** Sexual reproduction produces offspring that share characteristics from two parents. What is an advantage of sexual reproduction?

Internet Resources

For a variety of links related to this chapter, go to www.scilinks.org
Topic: Characteristics of Living Things
SciLinks code: HY70258

Universal Access • Differentiated Instruction

Struggling Readers

Section Summary Point out to students that the Summary at the beginning of the Section Review can be quite helpful in making sure they understand the section. Have students work in pairs. Ask each pair of students to read and discuss each bullet under the summary. Tell them to look back at the text as needed. **LS Verbal/ Auditory**

Answer to Standards Check

Asexual reproduction involves only one parent and produces offspring that are identical to a single parent. **7.2.a** (mastering)

Answers to Section Review

1. stimulus **7.1.a** (supporting)
2. cells **7.1.a** (supporting)
3. Sample answer: All living organisms are made up of structural and functional units called cells. Organisms sense stimuli, such as temperature, and respond accordingly. Living things produce offspring sexually or asexually. The cells of living things contain DNA that is passed from parents. Living things need energy to survive and perform life functions. Last, living things grow and change throughout their lives. **7.1.a** (mastering), **7.2.a** (supporting)
4. Sample answer: Asexual reproduction involves one parent, and offspring are identical to the parent. Sexual reproduction involves two parents, and offspring share characteristics of both parents. **7.2.a** (mastering)
5. Traits of parents are passed on through DNA. The offspring of a pair of California quails may have similar feathers, nesting habits, and calls. **7.2.a** (mastering)
6. Sample answer: A bear's fur keeps the bear warm when temperatures are cold, which helps to maintain the bear's internal environment, or homeostasis. **7.1.a** (supporting)
7. 32 bacteria; The population doubles every generation, so $2^5 = 32$ (first generation = 1 bacterium, second generation = 2 bacteria, third generation = 4 bacteria, fourth generation = 8 bacteria, fifth generation = 16 bacteria, and sixth generation = 32 bacteria).
8. Sample answer: The offspring aren't exactly like either parent, which is an advantage if a parent has an undesirable trait. The offspring may not inherit the undesirable trait. **7.2.a** (exceeding)

Section Review Standards Guide

	Supporting	Mastering	Exceeding
7.1.a	1–2, 6	3	
7.2.a	3	4–5	8

Section Resources

- Directed Reading A BASIC (Also in Spanish), B GENERAL
- Interactive Reader and Study Guide
- Section Quiz GENERAL (Also in Spanish)
- Section Review GENERAL (Also in Spanish)
- Vocabulary and Section Summary A BASIC (Also in Spanish), B GENERAL

Preteach

Reviewing Prior Knowledge

Review standard 7.1.a with your students. Ask students to summarize the standard in their own words. Then, ask students to predict how that standard may apply to this section.

 **Bellringer**

Have students focus on standard 7.1.a by reminding them that most cells are made of about 70% water. Then, ask students: "What would your mass be if there was no water in your body?" (Sample answer for a 40 kg student: 40 kg × 0.7 = 28 kg. The student's mass without water would be 40 kg − 28 kg = 12 kg.)

 Bellringer Transparency

Motivate

Demonstration

Fire and Life Demonstrate that some nonliving things can exhibit characteristics of living things by showing the class a burning candle. Ask students if they can think of any similarities between the candle and a human. Then, tell students that both a human and a burning candle use oxygen and fuel (food and wax, respectively), and they both give off carbon dioxide and energy (in the form of heat). Now ask students to explain how a candle is different from a living thing. **LS** Visual/Verbal

Answer to Standards Check

Most of the chemical reactions involved in metabolism involve water.

7.1.a (supporting)

What You Will Learn

- The cells of every living thing need water and food in order to function properly.
- Proteins, carbohydrates, lipids, ATP, and nucleic acids are molecules that support the functions of cells.

Why It Matters

Understanding the needs of living things will help you recognize how humans are similar to other organisms.

Vocabulary

- producer
- consumer
- decomposer
- protein
- carbohydrate
- lipid
- phospholipid
- ATP
- nucleic acid

READING STRATEGY

Graphic Organizer In your **Science Journal**, make a Spider Map that shows proteins, carbohydrates, lipids, ATP, and nucleic acids as nutrients that living things need.

7.1.a Students know cells function similarly in all living organisms.

SCIENCE HUMOR

Q: How does a cell wrap a sandwich?

A: In cell-ophane, of course!

The Necessities of Life

Key Concept Every living thing needs water, a place to live, and food in order to survive.

▶ Would it surprise you to learn that you have the same basic needs as a tree, a frog, and a fly? Almost every organism has the same basic needs: water, air, a place to live, and food.

Water

You may know that your body is made mostly of water. In fact, water makes up approximately 70% of your cells and the cells of almost all living things. Most of the chemical reactions involved in metabolism require water. But organisms differ greatly in terms of how much water they need and how they get it. You could survive for only about three days without water. You get water from the fluids you drink and the food you eat. The desert-dwelling kangaroo rat never drinks. It gets all of its water from food.

Standards Check Why do cells require water? **7.1.a**

Air

Air is a mixture of several gases, including oxygen, nitrogen, and carbon dioxide. Most living things use oxygen in the chemical process that releases energy from food. Oxygen may come from the air or may be dissolved in water. The European diving spider in **Figure 1** goes to great lengths to get oxygen. Green plants, algae, and some bacteria need carbon dioxide as well as oxygen. They use oxygen and carbon dioxide to produce food and oxygen through the process of photosynthesis (FOHT oh SIN thuh sis).

Although most living things need air, some do not. Organisms that can live without air are *anaerobic*. A kind of bacterium that causes sickness in humans, *Clostridium botulinum*, is anaerobic. It will not grow in the presence of air.

Figure 1 *This spider surrounds itself with an air bubble that provides the spider with a source of oxygen underwater.*

Universal Access · Differentiated Instruction

Struggling Readers

Consumers or Decomposers? Many students understand written information more easily when they can tie it directly to their personal experiences. As you discuss consumers and decomposers, ask students to relate what they have seen animals eat, and have students indicate whether the animals were consumers or decomposers. (Sample answer: A deer was eating live shrubs in my backyard. The deer is a consumer.) **LS** Verbal

---

A Place to Live

All living things need a place to live that has all of the things that they need to survive. Some organisms, such as elephants, must have a large amount of space. Other organisms may live their entire life in one small area.

Space on Earth is limited. Often, organisms must compete with each other for food, water, and other necessities. Many animals, including the warbler in **Figure 2,** will claim a particular space. After claiming a space, they try to keep other animals away.

Food

All living things need food. Food gives organisms energy and the raw materials needed to carry out life processes. Organisms use nutrients from food to make cells and build body parts. But not all organisms get food in the same way. In fact, every kind of organism can be placed into one of three groups based on how it gets food.

Making Food

Some organisms, such as plants, are producers. **Producers** make their own food through photosynthesis. Like most producers, plants use the sun's energy to make food from water and carbon dioxide. Some producers get energy and food from the chemicals in their environment.

Taking Food

Other organisms are consumers. **Consumers** must eat (consume) other organisms, such as plants or animals, to get food. The frog in **Figure 3** is a consumer. It gets the energy that it needs by eating insects and other organisms.

Some consumers get their food by breaking down the nutrients in dead organisms or in animal wastes. These organisms are **decomposers.** Decomposers are consumers because they must eat their food. The mushroom in **Figure 3** is a decomposer.

Figure 2 *A warbler's song is more than just a pretty tune. The warbler is protecting its home by telling other warblers to stay out of its territory.*

producer (proh DOOS uhr) an organism that can make its own food by using energy from its surroundings

consumer (kuhn SOOM uhr) an organism that eats other organisms or organic matter

decomposer (DEE kuhm POHZ uhr) an organism that gets energy by breaking down the remains of dead organisms or animal wastes and consuming or absorbing the nutrients

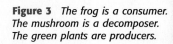
Figure 3 *The frog is a consumer. The mushroom is a decomposer. The green plants are producers.*

READING STRATEGY

Anticipation Guide Before students read this spread, ask them to identify where they have heard the terms *protein, carbohydrate,* and *fat.* (Answers may vary. Students may relate that they have heard the terms associated with specific diets.) Ask students to predict the function of each molecule in living things. Have students evaluate their answers after they read the spread. **LS** Logical

---

MISCONCEPTION //// ALERT \\\\

Simple Versus Complex
Students may not differentiate between simple and complex sugars. Show students molecular models of glucose and starch. Point out that complex carbohydrates, such as starch, are made up of many simple carbohydrate molecules, such as glucose. To help students recognize that complex carbohydrates are often long chains of simple sugars, provide students with string and beads. Tell students that each bead represents a simple carbohydrate and stringing the beads into chains makes a complex carbohydrate. Students should make bead chains of varying lengths. Ask students to describe the relationship in size between a simple carbohydrate and a complex carbohydrate. (Students should recognize that simple carbohydrates are much smaller than complex carbohydrates.)

Oxygen Molecule Count
Each red blood cell carries about 250 million molecules of hemoglobin. If every hemoglobin molecule were attached to four oxygen molecules, how many molecules of oxygen could a single red blood cell deliver throughout the body? Record your work in your **Science Journal.**

protein (PROH TEEN) a molecule that is made up of amino acids and that is needed to build and repair body structures and to regulate processes in the body

carbohydrate (CAHR boh HIE drayt) a class of molecules that includes sugars, starches, and fiber

Figure 4 *Spider webs, hair, horns, and feathers are made from proteins.*

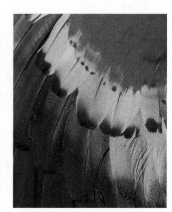

Putting It All Together

Some living things make their own food. Some get food from eating other organisms. But all organisms need to break down their food in order to use the nutrients in it.

Nutrients are made up of molecules. A *molecule* is a substance made when two or more atoms join together. Molecules made of different kinds of atoms are *compounds.* Molecules found in living things are most often combinations of six elements: carbon, hydrogen, nitrogen, oxygen, phosphorus, and sulfur. These elements join together to form proteins, carbohydrates, lipids, ATP, and nucleic acids.

Proteins

Almost all life processes of a cell involve proteins. **Proteins** are large molecules that are made up of smaller molecules called *amino acids.* Living things break down proteins in food to supply their cells with amino acids. These amino acids then join together to form new proteins. Some proteins are made up of only a few amino acids. Others have more than 10,000 amino acids.

Proteins in Action

Proteins have many functions. Some proteins form structures that are easy to see, such as the examples in **Figure 4.** Other proteins are very small and help cells do their jobs. Inside red blood cells, the protein hemoglobin (HEE moh GLOH bin) binds oxygen and delivers it throughout the body. Some proteins protect cells. Other proteins, called *enzymes* (EN ZIEMZ), start or speed up chemical reactions in cells.

Standards Check What function do enzymes in cells serve? **7.1.a**

Fireflies Fireflies produce their flashing light through a chemical reaction. The enzyme luciferase acts on the chemical luciferin in the presence of ATP to produce light.

Answer to Standards Check

Enzymes start or speed up chemical reactions within cells. **7.1.a** (supporting)

Quick Lab

Observing Enzymes in Pineapples

The enzymes in pineapple break down other proteins, such as the proteins in gelatin. In this activity, you will observe how altering an enzyme affects its function.

7.1.a
7.7.c

▶ Try It!

1. Gather **two small cups of gelatin,** a **piece of prepared pineapple,** and a **piece of fresh pineapple.** The pieces of pineapple should be similar in size.

2. Use a **marker** to label one cup "Prepared" and the other cup "Fresh."

3. Place the piece of prepared pineapple on top of the gelatin in the cup labeled "Prepared." Place the piece of fresh pineapple on top of the gelatin in the cup labeled "Fresh."

4. After 20 min, record your observations.

▶ Think About It!

5. Did the enzymes in the fresh pineapple break down the proteins in the gelatin? Explain your answer.

6. Did the enzymes in the prepared pineapple break down the proteins in the gelatin? Explain your answer.

7. The prepared pineapple was heated to denature its enzymes. To *denature* something is to remove the natural qualities of an object, such as its shape. Denaturing an enzyme makes it unable to perform its function. What might happen to a cell if all of its enzymes were denatured?

⏱ **30 min**

Carbohydrates

Molecules made of sugars are called **carbohydrates.** Carbohydrates provide and store energy for cells. A living thing's cells break down carbohydrates to free the energy that carbohydrates store. There are two kinds of carbohydrates: simple carbohydrates and complex carbohydrates.

Simple Carbohydrates

Simple carbohydrates are made up of one sugar molecule or a few sugar molecules. Table sugar and the sugar in fruits are examples of simple carbohydrates. The simple carbohydrate *glucose* is the most common source of energy for cells.

Complex Carbohydrates

When an organism has more sugar than it needs, its extra sugar may be stored as complex carbohydrates. *Complex carbohydrates* are made up of hundreds of sugar molecules linked together. Plants, such as the potato plant in **Figure 5,** store extra sugar as starch. When you eat mashed potatoes, you are eating the stored starch of the potato plant. Your body then breaks down this complex carbohydrate to free the energy stored in the potato.

Figure 5 *The extra sugar in a potato plant is stored in the potato as starch, a complex carbohydrate.*

Figure 6 Phospholipid Membranes

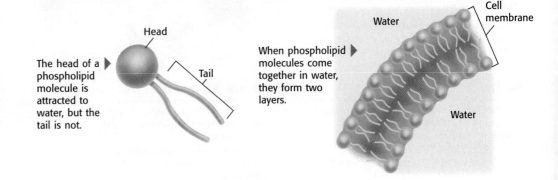

The head of a phospholipid molecule is attracted to water, but the tail is not.

Head

Tail

When phospholipid molecules come together in water, they form two layers.

Water

Cell membrane

Water

Standards Focus

This **Standards Focus** provides you with a quick way to **assess**, **reteach**, and **re-assess** one or more concepts in the section.

Assess

1. What two molecules store energy for cell processes? (carbohydrates and lipids) **7.1.a**

2. What nutrient is involved in nearly all of the life processes within cells? (protein) **7.1.a**

Reteach

Making Tables Have students make tables describing the characteristics of proteins, carbohydrates, lipids, and nucleic acids. Students should express how each type of molecule is important to the survival of cells. **LS** **Logical 7.1.a**

Re-Assess

Job Description Have students write a job description for each of the four basic chemical building blocks of cells and ATP. Tell students to describe job responsibilities, the expected workload, and whether the molecule works independently or with other cell components. **LS** **Intrapersonal 7.1.a**

Wordwise

Phospholipid Relate to students that the root *phospho-* comes from the Greek word *phos* meaning "light." Ask students to look up the definition of *phosphorus*. (Students should note that phosphorus is an element that changes color when exposed to light.) Ask students to write *phospholipid* in their **Science Journal.** Next, students should write a list of all the information that is presented in the term. **LS** **Verbal**

📦 Teaching Transparency: L5 Phospholipid Molecule and Cell Membrane

lipid (LIP id) a fat molecule or a molecule that has similar properties

phospholipid (FAHS foh LIP id) a lipid that contains phosphorus and that is a structural component in cell membranes
Wordwise The root *phospho-* means "containing phosphorus." The root *lip-* means "fat."

ATP (AY TEE PEE) adenosine triphosphate, a molecule that acts as the main energy source for cell processes

nucleic acid (noo KLEE ik AS id) a molecule made up of subunits called *nucleotides*

Pen a Menu
With an adult, write a menu for a favorite meal. Using Nutrition Facts labels, find out which items on your menu include proteins, carbohydrates, and fats.

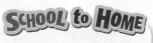

Lipids

Lipids are molecules that cannot mix with water. Lipids have many jobs in the cell. Like carbohydrates, some lipids store energy. Other lipids form the membranes of cells.

Phospholipids

All cells are surrounded by a *cell membrane*. The cell membrane helps protect the cell and maintain homeostasis. **Phospholipids** are molecules that form much of the cell membrane. The head of a phospholipid molecule is attracted to water. The tail is not. When phospholipids are in water, the tails come together and the heads face out into the water. As **Figure 6** shows, the phospholipids form a two-layer membrane. This membrane protects the cell by making it difficult for materials to move into or out of the cell.

Standards Check List two functions of cell membranes. **7.1.a**

Fats and Oils

Fats and oils are lipids that store energy. When an organism has used up most of its carbohydrates, it can get energy from these lipids. Fats and oils are almost the same in structure, but at room temperature, most fats are solid, and most oils are liquid. Most of the lipids stored in plants are oils. Most of the lipids stored in animals are fats.

ATP

Adenosine **tri**phosphate (uh DEN uh SEEN trie FAHS FAYT), or ATP, is another important molecule. **ATP** is the major energy-carrying molecule of cells. The energy in carbohydrates and lipids is transferred to ATP to provide fuel for cellular activities.

Universal Access · Differentiated Instruction

Special Education Students

Playing a Phospholipid Kinesthetic or physical learning gives students with ADD a chance to constructively get out of their seats. Also, physical learning tends to result in long-term retention. Ask all students to stand. Divide the class into two groups. Ask each group to form a line, and place the two lines facing each other. Tell students to pretend they are phospholipids; their arms are phospholipid tails and their heads are phospholipid heads. Explain that they are in water and ask them to react as phospholipids would react. (Response: Students should extend their arms towards the other line and extend their heads away from the other line.) **LS** **Kinesthetic**

Nucleic Acids

Nucleic acids are molecules that carry the directions for how to make proteins. Nucleic acids are made up of smaller molecules called *nucleotides* (NOO klee oh TIEDZ). A nucleic acid may have thousands of nucleotides. The nucleotide sequence stores information.

DNA is a nucleic acid. A DNA molecule is like a cookbook called *How to Make Proteins*. When a cell needs to make a certain protein, the cell gets directions from the sequence of the nucleotides in DNA. The sequence of nucleotides tells the cell the order in which the amino acids must be linked together to make the protein.

Newfound Pet

What kind of information would help you properly care for a new pet? Write a short story about living with an unusual pet. Go to **go.hrw.com,** and type in the keyword HY7ALVW.

SECTION Review

7.1.a

Summary

- The cells of living things need water to function.
- The cells of some living things need gases, such as oxygen, to release the energy contained in food.
- Living things must have a place to live.
- Cells store energy in carbohydrates, which are made up of sugars.
- Proteins are made up of amino acids. Some proteins are enzymes.
- Lipids store energy and make up cell membranes.
- Cells use molecules of ATP to fuel their activities.
- Nucleic acids, such as DNA, are made up of nucleotides.

Understanding Concepts

1. **Summarizing** Summarize the way plants store extra sugar.
2. **Listing** List four things that all organisms need to survive.
3. **Describing** Describe the chemical building blocks of cells.
4. **Analyzing** How is water related to how a cell functions?
5. **Applying** What are the functions of the cell membrane?

Critical Thinking

6. **Making Inferences** Could life as we know it exist on Earth if air contained only oxygen? Explain.
7. **Predicting Consequences** What would happen to the supply of ATP in your cells if you ate too few carbohydrates? How would your cells be affected?
8. **Applying Concepts** Which resource do you think is most important to your survival: water, air, a place to live, or food? Explain your answer.

INTERPRETING GRAPHICS Use the figure below to answer the next question.

9. **Forming Hypotheses** Which end of the phospholipid is not attracted to water? How might this fact affect the arrangement of phospholipids in a cell membrane?

Math Skills

10. **Using Equations** Protein A is a chain of 660 amino acids. Protein B is a chain of 11 amino acids. How many times as many amino acids does protein A have than protein B?

Internet Resources

For a variety of links related to this chapter, go to www.scilinks.org
Topic: The Necessities of Life
SciLinks code: HY71018

Section Resources

- Directed Reading A **BASIC** (Also in Spanish), B **GENERAL**
- Interactive Reader and Study Guide
- Section Quiz **GENERAL** (Also in Spanish)
- Section Review **GENERAL** (Also in Spanish)
- Vocabulary and Section Summary A **BASIC** (Also in Spanish), B **GENERAL**

Teacher Notes

Students will compare sexual and asexual reproduction methods of plants and draw conclusions about the reproduction methods of other plants (covers standards 7.2.a and 7.7.c). If cared for properly, the plants propagated in steps 6 and 8 will grow. The Petri dishes should be kept in a warm location that is out of direct sunlight. Keep soil moist.

Time Required

One 45-minute class period

Lab Ratings

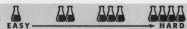

Teacher Prep 🧪🧪
Student Set-Up 🧪
Concept Level 🧪🧪🧪
Clean Up 🧪🧪

Materials

The materials listed on the student page are enough for 1 or 2 students. Remind students that they are handling living things, which they should treat with respect. The soil used in this lab should be sterilized potting soil.

Safety Caution

Remind students to review all safety cautions and icons before beginning this lab activity. Ask students if they are allergic to any of the materials used in this lab, such as flower pollen. Allergic students should be excused from the activity. These students can do their own research in the library or on the Internet to investigate sexual and asexual reproduction in plants.

Preparation Notes

For this activity, use perfect flowers (flowers that have both male and female reproductive structures) with reproductive structures that are easily identified. Hibiscus, lily, and tulip flowers are perfect flowers that have

Skills Practice Lab

OBJECTIVES

Simulate methods of plant reproduction.

Compare sexual and asexual reproduction in plants.

MATERIALS

• *Coleus* (whole plant)
• flower, complete
• flower seeds
• magnifying lens
• Petri dishes (2)
• pipe cleaner
• potting soil (1 cup)
• scissors

SAFETY

7.2.a Students know the differences between the life cycles and reproduction methods of sexual and asexual organisms.

Investigation and Experimentation
7.7.c Communicate the logical connection among hypotheses, science concepts, tests conducted, data collected, and conclusions drawn from the scientific evidence.

Comparing Methods of Reproduction

All types of organisms reproduce. Living things reproduce either by sexual reproduction or by asexual reproduction. In sexual reproduction, offspring are produced by two parents. As a result of this process, the offspring share traits from both parents. During asexual reproduction, a new individual is produced from one parent. This individual is an exact copy of the parent.

Plants can reproduce sexually or asexually. Some plants can use both methods to reproduce. During sexual reproduction, seeds are produced in the flower. Seed formation requires *pollination,* the transfer of pollen from the anther to the stigma. Although some plants can self-pollinate, pollination typically requires help from the wind, birds, and insects. Asexual methods of reproduction include planting runners, cuttings, and specialized plant parts from grown plants.

Part A: Sexual Reproduction

Procedure

❶ Use the image of the flower below to identify the anthers and stigma of your flower. Observe them with your magnifying lens.

❷ Gently brush the anthers with the pipe cleaner. Anthers are part of the male reproductive structure of a flower. Observe the pipe cleaner through the magnifying lens. You should see grains of pollen. Pollen contains male genetic information.

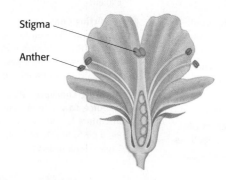

Stigma

Anther

easily differentiated reproductive structures. Flowers can be obtained from a florist or you can use live plants. Seeds and plants can be obtained from a nursery or from gardening mail-order catalogs.

As an extension of this exercise, you can use plants that produce plantlets or runners for further examples of asexual vegetative propagation in plants. You may also choose to place a *Coleus* cutting into a jar of water for several days before the experiment. Students will be able to see the formation and initial growth of roots on the cutting.

Lab Resources

📁 Differentiated Datasheets
A **BASIC**, B **GENERAL**, C **ADVANCED**

📀 Classroom Lab Video/DVD

💿 Holt Lab Generator CD-ROM

Search for any lab by topic, standard, difficulty level, or time. Edit any lab to fit your needs, or create your own labs. Use the Lab Materials QuickList software to customize your lab materials list.

③ Trade flowers with another group of students. Identify the stigma. The stigma is part of the female reproductive structure of a flower. The female reproductive structure contains the female genetic information.

④ Gently brush the same pipe cleaner on the stigma. You have now pollinated the flower.

⑤ Use your magnifying lens to study the flower seeds. These seeds are similar to those that your flower might have produced. The genetic information stored in seeds is a combination of the male and female genetic information.

⑥ Place one or two flower seeds in a Petri dish filled with moist potting soil.

Part B: Asexual Reproduction

Procedure

⑦ Snip off a tip from an actively growing *Coleus* stem. The cutting should be about 6 cm in length. Remove leaves from the bottom third of the cutting.

⑧ Place the cutting in a dish filled with moist potting soil.

Analyze the Results

⑨ **Explaining Events** How did you simulate asexual plant reproduction in this lab? How did you simulate sexual plant reproduction?

⑩ **Recognizing Patterns** Predict what the offspring will look like from each method of reproduction. Explain your predictions.

Draw Conclusions

⑪ **Interpreting Information** Examine the image above that shows an assortment of *Coleus* plants. Do you think that these plants were cuttings from the same parent plant? Explain.

⑫ **Drawing Conclusions** Can all organisms reproduce both sexually and asexually?

⑬ **Evaluating Methods** Compare sexual and asexual reproduction.

Big Idea Question

⑭ **Applying Conclusions** What is an advantage of sexual reproduction? What is an advantage of asexual reproduction?

Analyze the Results

9. Sample answer: When I took a cutting from the *Coleus* stem and put it in soil, I simulated asexual reproduction. I simulated sexual reproduction when I brushed pollen from one flower onto the stigma of the second flower.

10. Sample answer: The offspring of asexual reproduction will be identical to the parent because the genetic information comes from only one parent source. The offspring of sexual reproduction will have characteristics of two parents because each parent contributes genetic information to the offspring.

Draw Conclusions

11. Sample answer: no; The plants have different traits, so they could not have been cuttings of the same parent plant. If they had come from the same parent, they would all look exactly like the parent plant and each other.

12. Sample answer: no; Some organisms, such as humans, must have two parents to produce offspring.

13. Sample answer: Both types of reproduction result in offspring. Asexual reproduction involves one parent and produces genetically identical offspring. Sexual reproduction involves two parents and produces offspring that have traits of both parents.

Big Idea Question

14. Sample answer: Sexual reproduction produces offspring that are genetically different, so some of the offspring may be better able to survive environmental changes. Asexual reproduction requires one parent, and therefore offspring can be produced even when there is only one member of a species in an area.

Catherine Haynes
El Segundo Middle School
El Segundo, California

Teacher Notes

In this activity, students are asked to apply scientific methods to a scenario so that they can determine the correct tools to use for an investigation (covers standard 7.7.a). To help students recall scientific methods, ask them to diagram the steps of scientific methods.

Answers to You Try It!

1. Answers may vary. Students' hypotheses should reflect their understanding of the characteristics that define living things.

2. Answers may vary. Students should state that they are examining the yellow blobs to see if they have cells, if they sense and respond to stimuli, if they reproduce, if they have DNA, if they use energy, and if they grow and develop.

3. Sample answers: I will need a microscope, slides, cover slips, materials that might be used for food, goggles, gloves, and equipment to detect DNA.

4. Sample answer: A microscope will help me determine if the blob has cells. I can magnify the blob with the microscope to see if it has cells. A balance will tell me the mass of the blob, but even nonliving things have mass. The binoculars can see objects that are far away, but cannot see objects that are very small.

5. Answers may vary. Students should demonstrate an understanding that inappropriate tools will keep them from accurately testing their hypotheses and that safety equipment is necessary to prevent injury.

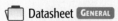 Datasheet GENERAL

**Also editable on the
Holt Lab Generator
CD-ROM**

Science Skills Activity

| Scientific Methods | Research | Data Analysis | Models, Maps & Diagrams |

Investigation and Experimentation
7.7.a Select and use appropriate tools and technology (including calculators, computers, balances, spring scales, microscopes, and binoculars) to perform tests, collect data, and display data.

Selecting Tools to Collect Data

▶ Tutorial

Scientists ask many questions about the natural world, so they conduct experiments to find answers. To perform an experiment and communicate the results, scientists must choose the correct equipment and tools. It is very important to select these tools before beginning the experiment so that data are not lost.

Procedure

1. Write a question on a subject that you want to investigate. Then, write a hypothesis to explain your question. The hypothesis must be testable. If the hypothesis is not testable, revise it.

2. List all of the different things, or factors, that could influence the experiment's outcome. Choose one factor that you will test.

3. Write a list of all of the materials needed to perform your experiment. This list should include safety equipment.

4. Determine the scientific equipment and tools that you will need for observing, measuring, recording, analyzing, and communicating data.

① Question: Does ice exist at room temperature?
Hypothesis: Ice melts at room temperature.

② Factors:
— temperature
— purity of water
— time

③ Materials:
— water
— ice cubes
— cups

④ Scientific Equipment Tools:
— calculator   — thermometers
— binoculars   — graph paper

▶ You Try It!

Procedure

You are a scientist on the *Intergalactic Beagle Starship Explorer.* When your starship discovers a new planet, your job is to determine if there are any lifeforms on the planet. On one mission, you find many small, yellow blobs. Use the steps above to plan the experiment(s) and to select the appropriate equipment and tools to determine if the blobs are alive.

Analysis

① **Forming a Hypothesis** What question are you asking? How does your hypothesis offer an explanation to your question?

② **Analyzing Ideas** List the factors that you will be testing. How will you experiment for each factor?

③ **Analyzing Methods** What equipment and tools will you need for each experiment?

④ **Making Comparisons** Which of the following tools is best for determining whether your blob is made up of cells: a balance, a microscope, or binoculars? Explain your answer.

⑤ **Predicting Consequences** What might happen if you select inappropriate tools for your experiment? What might happen if you do not have the correct safety equipment?

Universal Access · Differentiated Instruction

Advanced Learners/GATE

Explorer Equipment Have students make a list of the types of experimental equipment they think the *Intergalactic Beagle Starship Explorer* would have onboard. The list should also include a brief explanation of what the equipment measures or tests. Encourage students to combine creativity, realism, and logic. **LS** Verbal/Logical

English Learners

Understanding Slang and Idioms
Idioms and slang words may present problems to English Learners. Write the word *blob* on the board. Tell students that *blob* is an example of American slang. Ask the class to brainstorm possible synonyms for the word *blob.* (Sample answers: clump, pile, chunk, and mass) Have students start a page in their **Science Journals** for slang words with *blob* recorded as the first entry.
LS Verbal

The Big Idea
All living things share characteristics and needs.

Section | Vocabulary

① Characteristics of Living Things

Key Concept Living things have six characteristics in common.

- Living things are composed of one or more cells.
- Living things sense and respond to changes in their environment.
- Living things produce offspring through sexual reproduction or asexual reproduction.
- The cells of living things contain DNA.
- Living things use energy.
- Living things grow and develop.

An acorn develops into an oak tree.

cell p. 52
homeostasis p. 53
sexual reproduction p. 54
asexual reproduction p. 54
metabolism p. 54

② The Necessities of Life

Key Concept Every living thing needs water, a place to live, and food in order to survive.

- The cells of every living thing need water and food in order to function properly.
- Proteins, carbohydrates, lipids, ATP, and nucleic acids are molecules that support the functions of cells.

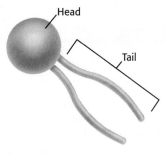

Head
Tail

A phospholipid is the type of lipid found in cell membranes.

producer p. 57
consumer p. 57
decomposer p. 57
protein p. 58
carbohydrate p. 59
lipid p. 60
phospholipid p. 60
ATP p. 60
nucleic acid p. 61

Chapter Summary

SUPER SUMMARY

Have students connect the major concepts in this chapter through an interactive Super Summary. Visit go.hrw.com and type in the keyword HY7ALVS to access the Super Summary for this chapter.

Identifying Word Parts

Crossword Puzzle Ask students to work in small groups to create a crossword puzzle that reviews the vocabulary words from this chapter. Students should identify and use the definitions of the word parts for each term as clues in their crossword puzzles. In addition to standard dictionaries, students can use the glossary and "Understanding Word Parts" pages in the Appendix of this book when searching for word parts. After students complete their puzzles, ask them to trade with another group and have that group complete the new crossword puzzle. **LS Verbal**

Focus on Reading

Illustrating Concepts Ask students to read each bulleted point in the summary. For each bulleted point, have students make an illustration that describes the bulleted point. **LS Verbal/Visual**

Review Resources

- Reinforcement Worksheet **BASIC**
- Critical Thinking Worksheet **ADVANCED**
- Chapter Review **GENERAL** (Also in Spanish)
- Standards Review Workbook (Also in Spanish)
- Study Guide A **BASIC** (Also in Spanish), B **GENERAL**

Assessment Resources

- Chapter Tests A **BASIC**, B **GENERAL** (Also in Spanish), C **ADVANCED**
- Standards Assessment **GENERAL**

Chapter Review
 7.1.a, 7.2.a

Assignment Guide

Section	Questions
1	2, 6, 12, 15–17, 20–21, 24–25, 27
2	3–5, 7–11, 13–14, 18–19, 22–23

Answers

Using Vocabulary

1. c

2. metabolism **7.1.a** (supporting)

3. consumer **7.1.a** (supporting)

4. carbohydrate **7.1.a** (supporting)

5. lipid **7.1.a** (supporting)

Understanding Concepts

6. d **7.1.a** (mastering)

7. b **7.1.a** (mastering)

8. a **7.1.a** (supporting)

9. c **7.1.a** (supporting)

10. c **7.1.a** (mastering)

11. a **7.1.a** (supporting)

12. Asexual reproduction occurs with a single parent, and offspring are identical to the parent. Sexual reproduction requires two parents, and offspring share characteristics of both parents. **7.2.a** (mastering)

13. Sample answer: Most of the chemical reactions involved in metabolism involve water. **7.1.a** (mastering)

14. Sample answer: ATP is an energy-storage molecule within the cell. It provides fuel for cellular activities. **7.1.a** (mastering)

15. Organism C **7.2.a** (mastering)

16. Organism D will be similar or slightly different than its parents, but not identical. **7.2.a** (mastering)

Organize

Double Door Review the FoldNote that you created at the beginning of the chapter. Add to or correct the FoldNote based on what you have learned.

Using Vocabulary

1. **Academic Vocabulary** Choose the appropriate form of the word *similar* for the following sentence: "Cells function ___ in all organisms."
   a. similarity
   b. similar
   c. similarly
   d. dissimilar

Complete each of the following sentences by choosing the correct terms from the word bank.

lipid	carbohydrate
consumer	metabolism
homeostasis	producer

2. All of the chemical activities of an organism are the organism's ___.

3. A ___ obtains food by eating other organisms.

4. Starch is a ___ and is made up of sugars.

5. Fat is a ___ that stores energy for an organism.

Understanding Concepts

Multiple Choice

6. Which of the following statements about cells is true?
   a. Cells are the smallest structural unit of life.
   b. All organisms are made up of cells.
   c. Sometimes, cells are specialized for particular functions.
   d. All of the above

7. Which of the following statements about all living things is true?
   a. All living things reproduce sexually.
   b. All living things have one or more cells.
   c. All living things must make their own food.
   d. All living things reproduce asexually.

8. Organisms must have food because
   a. food is a source of energy.
   b. food supplies cells with oxygen.
   c. organisms never make their own food.
   d. All of the above

9. Organisms store energy in
   a. nucleic acids.   c. lipids.
   b. phospholipids.   d. water.

10. The molecule that contains the information about how to make proteins is
    a. ATP.   c. DNA.
    b. a carbohydrate.   d. a phospholipid.

11. The subunits of nucleic acids are
    a. nucleotides.
    b. oils.
    c. sugars.
    d. amino acids.

Short Answer

12. **Comparing** What is the difference between asexual reproduction and sexual reproduction?

13. **Summarizing** In one or two sentences, explain why living things must have water.

14. **Identifying** What is ATP, and why is it important to a cell?

INTERPRETING GRAPHICS Use the table below to answer the next two questions.

Characteristics of Three Living Organisms

Organism	A	B	C
Comparison to parent(s)	slightly different	similar	identical

15. **Applying** Juan is studying three different organisms so that he can classify them according to how much each organism is like its parent. The table shows the characteristics of the three different organisms. Which of the organisms that Juan studied could have been produced from a single parent?

16. **Comparing** Juan adds organism D to the table. The organism has been produced through sexual reproduction. How will organism D compare to its parent(s)?

Writing Skills

17 **Creative Writing** You find a strange creature while walking on the beach one day. In a short story, describe the creature, including how it displays the six characteristics of living things.

Critical Thinking

18 **Concept Mapping** Use the following terms to create a concept map: *cell, carbohydrates, protein, enzymes, DNA, sugars, lipids, nucleotides, amino acids,* and *nucleic acid.*

19 **Applying Concepts** Using what you know about carbohydrates, lipids, and proteins, explain why a balanced diet is important?

20 **Evaluating Hypotheses** Your friend tells you that the stimulus of music makes his goldfish swim faster. How would you design a controlled experiment to test your friend's claim?

21 **Analyzing Ideas** A flame can move, grow larger, and give off heat. Is a flame alive? Explain.

INTERPRETING GRAPHICS Use the diagram below to answer the next two questions.

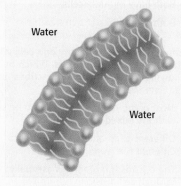

Water

Water

22 **Evaluating Data** What part of the cell does this image show?

23 **Analyzing Relationships** What is the function of this part of the cell?

INTERPRETING GRAPHICS The pictures below show the same plant over a period of three days. Use the pictures below to answer the next two questions.

Day 1

Day 2

Day 3

24 **Evaluating Data** What is the plant doing?

25 **Applying Concepts** What characteristic(s) of living things is the plant exhibiting?

Math Skills

26 **Using Equations** A young tree grows 6 cm per year. Use the equation *height* = 6 cm × *number of years* to find how many years the tree would take to grow 1 m.

Challenge

27 **Making Comparisons** Some reptiles are able to grow a new tail if their original tail has been damaged or lost. Does this ability fit the description of asexual reproduction? Why or why not?

---

21. Sample answer: A flame is not alive. A flame can move, grow, and give off heat, but it is not made up of cells, nor does it have DNA. **7.1.a** (exceeding)

22. cell membrane **7.1.a** (mastering)

23. Cell membranes protect the cell and keep the internal conditions of the cell stable. **7.1.a** (mastering)

24. The plant is bending toward the light coming through the window.

25. Sample answer: The plant is sensing a stimulus, the light, and responding to it. **7.1.a** (supporting)

Math Skills

26. n = number of years; 1 m = 6 cm/y × ny, so n = 1 m ÷ 6 cm/y = 100 cm ÷ 6 cm/y = 16 2/3 y

Challenge

27. Sample answer: This does not fit the description of asexual reproduction because the growth of a new tail does not result in the production of a new organism. **7.2.a** (exceeding)

Chapter Review Standards Guide		
	Supporting	Mastering	Exceeding
7.1.a	2–5, 8–9, 11, 20, 25	6–7, 10, 13–14, 17–18, 22–23	19, 21
7.2.a		12, 15–16	27

Writing Skills

17. Answers may vary. Students should demonstrate an understanding of the characteristics of living things. **7.1.a** (mastering)

Critical Thinking

18. An answer to this exercise can be found at the end of the book. **7.1.a** (mastering)

19. Sample answer: The raw materials that the body needs—carbohydrates, lipids, and proteins—come from the foods that people eat. Carbohydrates and lipids provide energy, and proteins provide amino acids for building other proteins. A shortage of any of these substances will keep cells from working properly. **7.1.a** (exceeding)

20. Sample answer: A controlled experiment would include goldfish in a control group and goldfish in an experimental group. The goldfish in the control group would not be exposed to music, but the goldfish in the experimental group would be exposed to music. The goldfish in each group would need to be the same species and age. They would have to live in the same type of environment and eat the same type and amount of food. **7.1.a** (supporting)

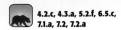
Teacher Notes

To provide practice under more realistic testing conditions, give students 20 min to answer all of the questions in this assessment.

Answer Key

Question Number	Correct Answer
1	C
2	D
3	A
4	D
5	C
6	B
7	D
8	D
9	A
10	A
11	A
12	D
13	C
14	C
15	A

Standards Guide

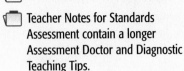

	Supporting	Mastering	Exceeding
4.2.c		14	
4.3.a		15	
5.2.f		13	
6.5.c		12	
7.1.a	1–2, 5	7–9	10
7.2	3–4		
7.2.a		6	11

📁 Standards Assessment **GENERAL**

📁 Teacher Notes for Standards Assessment contain a longer Assessment Doctor and Diagnostic Teaching Tips.

REVIEWING ACADEMIC VOCABULARY

1 Which of the following words is closest in meaning to the word *function*?

  A control

  B standard

  C use

  D rate

2 In the sentence "The cell membranes of all cells work similarly," what does the word *similarly* mean?

  A from the start

  B by cell division

  C without interest

  D in almost the same way

3 Which of the following words means "to define or describe in detail"?

  A specify

  B stimulate

  C personalize

  D associate

4 Which of the following words best completes the following sentence: The cell membrane of a one-celled animal protects the animal from ___ dangers.

  A pivotal

  B insignificant

  C harmful

  D environmental

REVIEWING CONCEPTS

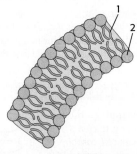

5 Which part of the phospholipid membrane is found at point 1 in the diagram above?

  A water–loving tail

  B water–loving head

  C water–hating tail

  D water–hating head

6 New organisms are created either by sexual or asexual reproduction. How are offspring produced sexually and offspring produced asexually similar?

  A Both are identical to one parent.

  B Both have DNA.

  C Both have multiple cells.

  D Both share traits of two parents.

7 Some organisms have only one cell, while others have trillions of cells. Which of the following statements best describes an organism that has many cells?

  A Most of the organism's cells can be seen with the naked eye.

  B Different parts of each cell perform different functions.

  C The organism reproduces asexually through cell division.

  D Different kinds of cells perform specialized functions.

➕ **ASSESSMENT DOCTOR**

Question 1: The correct answer is C. *Use* and *function* are similar in meaning; a cell part's *function* is its use within the cell or the work it does.

Question 2: The correct answer is D. *Similar* means "almost the same." Its adverb form, *similarly,* means "in almost the same way."

Question 3: The correct answer is A. A typical cell of any organism contains genetic instructions that *specify* its traits.

Question 4: The correct answer is D. *Environmental* means "the surrounding natural conditions that affect an organism." Environmental dangers might include chemicals and pathogens.

Question 5: The correct answer is C. Hydrophobic phospholipid tails are found inside the bilayer. Hydrophilic phospholipid heads are found on the outside of the bilayer.

Question 6: The correct answer is B. Offspring produced from both sexual and asexual reproduction have DNA. All living organisms have DNA.

8 You may think that humans do not have anything in common with a bacterium, but they do! Which of the following sentences best describes what bacteria and humans have in common?

A Both are multicellular organisms.

B Both reproduce sexually.

C Both are warmblooded.

D Both have DNA.

9 Proteins play a role in most cell processes. What do cells make proteins from?

A amino acids

B lipids

C nucleic acids

D carbohydrates

10 Which of the following sentences best describes how DNA affects heredity?

A DNA ensures that traits of the parent are passed to the offspring.

B The order of DNA nucleotides tells a cell how to make proteins.

C DNA controls the structure and function of cells in all organisms.

D Nucleic acids such as DNA are sometimes called the "blueprints of life."

11 Which of the following functions can be performed by a hydra but cannot be performed by a California quail?

A A hydra can reproduce without a partner.

B A hydra can divide cells through mitosis.

C A hydra can maintain homeostasis in cells.

D A hydra can pass traits to offspring.

REVIEWING PRIOR LEARNING

12 Which term best describes the rabbit in the food chain pictured above?

A omnivore

B top-level predator

C carnivore

D primary consumer

13 Plants make food through photosynthesis. What waste product do plants excrete as a result of this chemical process?

A carbon dioxide

B nitrogen

C oxygen

D sugar

14 Which group of organisms completes the food chain by returning nutrients to the soil?

A primary consumers

B secondary consumers

C decomposers

D producers

15 The nonliving components of an ecosystem are called

A abiotic components.

B rock cycles.

C natural disasters.

D organisms.

Standards Assessment

Question 11: The correct answer is A. A hydra reproduces asexually, and a California quail reproduces sexually. Asexual reproduction requires only one parent and produces offspring that are genetically identical to the parent. Sexual reproduction requires two parents and produces offspring that have a combination of genetic material.

Question 12: The correct answer is D. Rabbits are primary consumers, which means that they eat producers, as shown in the food chain. The clover is a producer, and the coyote is a carnivore and a top-level predator.

Question 13: The correct answer is C. Plants use sunlight to convert water and carbon dioxide into sugar molecules during the process of photosynthesis. Oxygen is the waste product of this process.

Question 14: The correct answer is C. Decomposers are organisms that consume dead organisms or animal wastes.

Question 15: The correct answer is A. An ecosystem is made up of biotic and abiotic factors. Abiotic factors include weather conditions and soil type.

Question 7: The correct answer is D. In multicellular organisms, the cells are specialized, meaning different types of cells perform different functions, such as taking in food, breaking it down, and excreting waste.

Question 8: The correct answer is D. Both a paramecium and a human have DNA in their cells. All living organisms have DNA, which passes the characteristics of the parent along to the offspring.

Question 9: The correct answer is A. Cells use amino acids to make proteins. When an organism takes in protein as food, cells break it down into amino acids, which are used to form new proteins. DNA directs cells on how to make these new proteins.

Question 10: The correct answer is A. When organisms reproduce, either sexually or asexually, they pass copies of their DNA to their offspring. Because DNA determines an organism's traits, offspring share their parents' traits. This passing of traits from parent to offspring is called heredity.

Weird Science

Teaching Strategy

Students may not realize that arsenic is a very dangerous substance. Ask students to identify how arsenic affects living organisms. Then, ask students to research how SLAS-1 can survive in such deadly conditions. Finally, ask students to identify other organisms that can survive in conditions that seem unsuitable for life. **LS Verbal**

Science Fiction

Background

Terry Bisson has written comic books, short stories, novels, plays, how-to articles about writing, and news editorials. In 1991, Bisson's short story "Bears Discover Fire" received two of the most prestigious science fiction literature awards—the Nebula Award and the Hugo Award.

Science in Action

Weird Science

Breathing Arsenic

Searles Lake in the Mojave Desert of California isn't like most lakes. It's mostly salt-crusted ooze that smells like a combination of rotten eggs, dead fish, and old cheese. To top things off, Searles Lake contains extreme levels of deadly arsenic.

Scientists never expected to find organisms living in Searles Lake. Incredibly, one organism thrives in the poisonous lake. This organism, a bacterium named *SLAS-1*, is an extremophile. Extremophiles can exist in extreme environments where most other living things cannot. For example, most organisms need oxygen, but there is no oxygen in the ooze at Searles Lake. Instead, SLAS-1 uses arsenic for its cellular activities.

Math ACTIVITY

Searles Lake contains levels of arsenic that are 29,000 times as high as the levels in drinking water! If there are 0.01 mg of arsenic in 1 L of drinking water, how many grams of arsenic are in half of that volume at Searles Lake? Record your work in your **Science Journal.**

Science Fiction

"They're Made Out of Meat" by Terry Bisson

Two space explorers millions of light-years from home are visiting an uncharted sector of the universe to find signs of life. Their mission is to contact, welcome, and log any and all beings in this part of the universe.

During their mission, the explorers encounter a life-form quite unlike anything that they have ever seen before. It looks strange and disgusting. The explorers have very strong doubts about adding this new organism to the log. But their official duty is to contact and welcome all life-forms no matter how ugly they are. Can the explorers bring themselves to perform their duty?

You'll find out by reading "They're Made Out of Meat," a short story by Terry Bisson. This story is in the *Holt Anthology of Science Fiction.*

Language Arts ACTIVITY

Write a story about what happens when the explorers meet new creatures on a distant planet. Record your work in your **Science Journal.**

Answer to Math Activity

0.01 mg/L × 29,000 = 290 mg/L = 0.290 g/L;
0.290 g/L ÷ 2 = 0.145 g per 0.5 L water

Answer to Language Arts Activity

Answers may vary. Students should creatively demonstrate their understanding of the characteristics of life.

Careers

Janis Davis-Street

NASA Nutritionist Do astronauts eat shrimp cocktail in space? Yes, they do! Shrimp cocktail is nutritious and tastes so good that it is one of the most popular foods in the space program. And having a proper diet helps astronauts stay healthy while they are in space.

But who figures out what astronauts need to eat? Janis Davis-Street is a nutritionist and laboratory supervisor for the Nutritional Biochemistry Laboratory at the Johnson Space Center in Houston, Texas. She was born in Georgetown, Guyana, on the northeastern coast of South America. She was educated in Canada.

Davis-Street is part of a team whose members use their knowledge of nutrition, biology, and chemistry to figure out the nutritional requirements for spaceflight. For example, they determine how many Calories and other nutrients each astronaut needs per day during spaceflight.

The Nutritional Biochemistry Laboratory's work on the space shuttle missions and *Mir* space station developed into tests that allow NASA to help ensure the health of astronauts before, during, and after flight. These tests are important for understanding how the human body adapts to long space missions. They also help determine whether treatments for preventing bone and muscle loss during spaceflight are working.

Social Studies ACTiViTY

Scientists from more than 30 countries have been on space missions. Research which countries have provided astronauts or cosmonauts for space missions. On a map, place self-stick notes on countries that have provided scientists for space missions. Write the names of the appropriate scientists on the self-stick notes.

Internet Resources

- To learn more about careers in science, visit **www.scilinks.org** and enter the SciLinks code HY70225.
- To learn more about these Science in Action topics, visit **go.hrw.com** and type in the keyword HY7ALVF.
- Check out articles related to this chapter by visiting **go.hrw.com**. Just type in the keyword HY7ALVC.

Careers

Background

One of the reasons to conduct nutritional studies in space is to determine if there are benefits for disease research and medicine on Earth. One of Davis-Street's projects is Experiment E381, "Calcium Kinetics During Space Flight." This experiment addresses bone health and bone loss during space missions. Calcium may be lost from bones during space flight, in part as a result of insufficient levels of vitamin D. Vitamin D is synthesized during exposure to sunlight and ultraviolet radiation, and spaceships are heavily shielded from ultraviolet light. Calcium kinetics tracks the movement of calcium tracers throughout an astronaut's body, from absorption from food to the formation and breakdown of bones. If the rate of bone loss during flight and the recovery rate on the ground are constant, scientists predict it will take 2.5 times the length of the mission to recover lost bone mass. Understanding bone and calcium dynamics in accelerated contexts, such as space, might help people better understand bone diseases, such as osteoporosis, on Earth.

Answer to Social Studies Activity

Answers may vary. Some of the countries from which astronauts or cosmonauts have come include the United States, Russia, Israel, India, Japan, Canada, Brazil, Germany, Italy, Switzerland, France, Sweden, and China.

Standards Course of Study

The elements listed in the Standards Course of Study provide a base for presenting, supporting, and assessing the California Grade 7 Science Standards. Use this Standards Course of Study as a base for planning your lessons.

Why Teach
Light and Living Things

This chapter was designed to cover the California Grade 7 Science Standards about physical principles in living things but with an emphasis on light (7.6.a, 7.6.b, 7.6.c, 7.6.d, 7.6.e, 7.6.f, and 7.6.g). It follows a chapter that introduced the basic characteristics of living things. Students will have learned that living things use energy. This chapter will explain where that energy comes from and how living things use light energy.

After they have completed this chapter, students will begin a chapter about cells, which make up all living things.

 ## California Standards

Focus on Life Sciences
7.6.a Students know visible light is a small band within a very broad electromagnetic spectrum.

7.6.b Students know that for an object to be seen, light emitted by or scattered from it must be detected by the eye.

7.6.c Students know light travels in straight lines if the medium it travels through does not change.

7.6.d Students know how simple lenses are used in a magnifying glass, the eye, a camera, a telescope, and a microscope.

7.6.e Students know that white light is a mixture of many wavelengths (colors) and that retinal cells react differently to different wavelengths.

7.6.f Students know light can be reflected, refracted, transmitted, and absorbed by matter.

7.6.g Students know the angle of reflection of a light beam is equal to the angle of incidence.

Investigation and Experimentation
7.7.a Select and use appropriate tools and technology (including calculators, computers, balances, spring scales, microscopes, and binoculars) to perform tests, collect data, and display data.

Chapter Pacing

Getting Started **45 min** pp. 74–75
The Big Idea Light is an electromagnetic wave that interacts with matter in many different ways.
 7.6.e

Section ❶ The Electromagnetic Spectrum **90 min** pp. 76–81
Key Concept Visible light, infrared waves, and ultraviolet light are small parts of a large electromagnetic spectrum.
7.6.a, 7.6.e

Section ❷ Interactions of Light with Matter **90 min** pp. 82–89
Key Concept Light interacts with matter during reflection, absorption, scattering, and transmission.
7.6.b, 7.6.c, 7.6.e, 7.6.f, 7.6.g

Section ❸ Refraction **90 min** pp. 90–97
Key Concept Light can be bent, or refracted, by matter. Lenses refract light to form images.
7.6.c, 7.6.d, 7.6.e, 7.6.f

Wrapping Up **180 min** pp. 98–107
7.6.d, 7.6.f, 7.7.a

Basic Learners
- TE Exponents, p. 77
- TE Absorption and Scattering, p. 84
- TE Mnemonics, p. 88
- TE Redrawing Figures, p. 91
- TE Partners in Sight, p. 100
- 📄 Reinforcement Worksheet
- 📄 Chapter Test A
- 📄 Differentiated Datasheets A for Labs and Activities ■
- 📄 Study Guide A ■

Advanced Learners/GATE
- TE The Structure of EM Waves, p. 76
- TE Color of Light, p. 79
- TE Seeing in Color, p. 87
- TE Sight Correction, p. 93
- TE Animal Eyes, p. 94
- 📄 Critical Thinking Worksheet
- 📄 Chapter Test C
- 📄 Differentiated Datasheets C for Labs and Activities ■

Key

SE Student Edition
TE Teacher's Edition

📁 Chapter Resource File
📄 Workbook
📊 Transparency

💿 CD or CD-ROM
* Datasheet or blackline master available

■ Also available in Spanish

All resources listed below are also available on the One-Stop Planner.

Teach

SE **Explore Activity** Seeing Colors of Light, p. 75* ■

📊 **Bellringer**
💿 **PowerPoint® Resources**
📊 L6 The Electromagnetic Spectrum
SE **Quick Lab** Refraction Rainbow, p. 80* ■

📊 **Bellringer**
💿 **PowerPoint® Resources**
SE **Quick Lab** Reflecting Mirrors, p. 83* ■
📊 L7 The Law of Reflection; Regular Reflection Versus Diffuse Reflection

---

📊 **Bellringer**
💿 **PowerPoint® Resources**
SE **Quick Lab** Refracting Water, p. 92* ■
📊 L8 Parts of the Human Eye; How a Camera Works
📊 L9 How a Refracting Telescope Works; How a Light Microscope Works

---

SE **Skills Practice Lab** Images from Convex Lenses, pp. 98–99* ■

Practice

SE **Organize Activity** Key-Term Fold, p. 74

SE **Section Review,** p. 81* ■

SE **Section Review,** p. 89* ■

SE **Section Review,** p. 97* ■

SE **Science Skills Activity** Using a Microscope to Collect Data, p. 100* ■
📊 **Concept Mapping***
SE **Chapter Review,** pp. 102–103* ■

Assess

📁 **Chapter Pretest**

SE **Standards Checks,** pp. 77, 78, 79, 80
TE **Standards Focus,** p. 80
📁 **Section Quiz** ■

SE **Standards Checks,** pp. 82, 84, 85, 86, 87, 88
TE **Standards Focus,** p. 88
📁 **Section Quiz** ■

SE **Standards Checks,** pp. 90, 91, 93, 94, 95, 96
TE **Standards Focus,** p. 96
📁 **Section Quiz** ■

SE **Standards Assessment,** pp. 104–105*
📁 **Chapter Tests A, B** ■**, C**
📄 **Standards Review Workbook** ■

Resources for Universal Access • Differentiated Instruction

English Learners

TE Connection Activity, p. 77
TE Group Activity, pp. 82, 87, 93, 95
TE Clarifying a Perpendicular, p. 82
TE Using the Figure, p. 85
TE Demonstration, pp. 86, 90
TE Recognizing Cognates, p. 95
TE Microscope Parts, p. 100
📁 Vocabulary and Section Summary A ■, B

📁 Section Quizzes ■
📁 Chapter Tests A, B ■
📁 Differentiated Datasheets A, B, and C for Labs and Activities ■
📄 Study Guide A ■
📄 Multilingual Glossary

Struggling Readers

TE Using Figures, p. 78
TE Paired Summarizing, p. 90
TE Mental Memory Cues, p. 92

Special Education Students

TE Units, p. 81
TE Seeing Through, p. 86
TE Reviewing Words, p. 96

To help plan your lessons, refer to the **On Course Mapping Instruction** booklet.

Visual Resources

CHAPTER STARTER TRANSPARENCY

Strange but True!

BELLRINGER TRANSPARENCIES

Section: The Electromagnetic Spectrum
Describe the weather conditions necessary to produce a rainbow.

Why do you think rainbows form?

Write your responses in your **science journal.**

Section: Interactions of Light with Matter
How do mirrors work?

What do mirrors do to light waves?

Write your answers in your **science journal.**

TEACHING TRANSPARENCIES

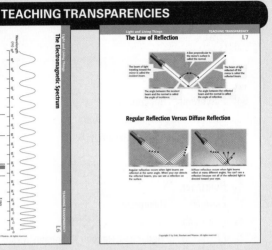

The Electromagnetic Spectrum

The Law of Reflection

Regular Reflection Versus Diffuse Reflection

TEACHING TRANSPARENCIES

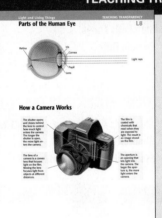

Parts of the Human Eye

How a Camera Works

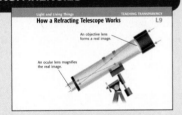

How a Refracting Telescope Works

An objective lens forms a real image.

An ocular lens magnifies the real image.

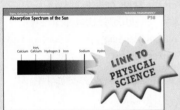

Absorption Spectrum of the Sun

LINK TO PHYSICAL SCIENCE

STANDARDS REVIEW TRANSPARENCIES

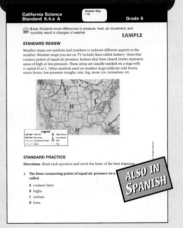

California Science Standard 6.4.e A — Grade 6

STANDARD REVIEW

STANDARD PRACTICE

ALSO IN SPANISH

CONCEPT MAPPING TRANSPARENCY

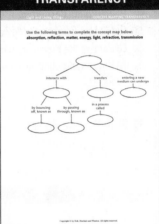

Use the following terms to complete the concept map below: absorption, reflection, matter, energy, light, refraction, transmission

Planning Resources

PARENT LETTER

SAMPLE

Dear Parent,

Your son's or daughter's science class will soon begin exploring the chapter entitled "The Nature of Physical Science." In this chapter, students will learn about how the scientific method applies to the world of physical science and the role of physical science in the world. By the end of the chapter, students should demonstrate a clear understanding of the chapter's main ideas and be able to discuss the following topics:

1. the role of questions in the process of investigation (Section 1)
2. how applying science saves lives and benefits the environment (Section 1)
3. careers that rely on science (Section 1)
4. the steps used in scientific methods (Section 2)
5. how scientific methods are used to answer questions and solve problems (Section 2)
6. the importance of safety precautions in the laboratory (Section 3)
7. examples of safety equipment and when to use them (Section 3)
8. how safety symbols are used to make laboratories safer (Section 3)

Questions to Ask Along the Way

You can help your child learn about these topics by asking interesting questions as he or she progresses through the chapter. For example, you may wish to ask your son or daughter the following questions:

What are some surprising careers that use science?

What is a characteristic of a good hypothesis?

What is the first step to take if an accident happens?

ALSO IN SPANISH

TEST ITEM LISTING

SAMPLE

Holt California Physical Science
Chapter 6 Introduction to Atoms
Test Item Listing
Multiple choice

ALSO IN SPANISH

One-Stop Planner® CD-ROM

This CD-ROM package includes all of the resources shown here and the following time-saving tools:

- **Lab Materials QuickList Software**
- **Customizable Lesson Plans** Correlated to the California Science Standards
- **Holt Calendar Planner**
- **PowerPoint® Resources**

- **Printable Worksheets**
- **ExamView® Test Generator** Correlated to the California Science Standards
- **Holt PuzzlePro®**
- **Interactive Teacher's Edition**

Meeting Individual Needs

DIRECTED READING A
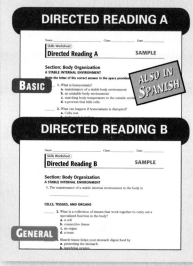
BASIC

VOCABULARY AND SECTION SUMMARY A
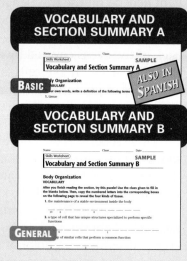
BASIC

REINFORCEMENT
BASIC

INTERACTIVE READER AND STUDY GUIDE
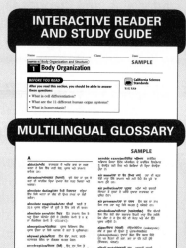

DIRECTED READING B
GENERAL

VOCABULARY AND SECTION SUMMARY B
GENERAL

CRITICAL THINKING
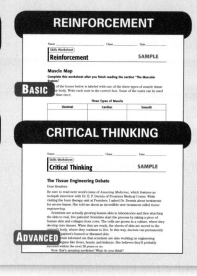
ADVANCED

MULTILINGUAL GLOSSARY

Labs and Activities

DIFFERENTIATED DATASHEETS FOR EXPLORE ACTIVITY, QUICK LABS, AND CHAPTER LAB

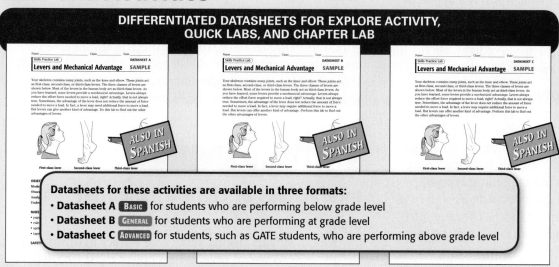

DATASHEET FOR SCIENCE SKILLS ACTIVITY

GENERAL

Datasheets for these activities are available in three formats:
- **Datasheet A** BASIC for students who are performing below grade level
- **Datasheet B** GENERAL for students who are performing at grade level
- **Datasheet C** ADVANCED for students, such as GATE students, who are performing above grade level

Reviews and Assessments

SECTION REVIEWS
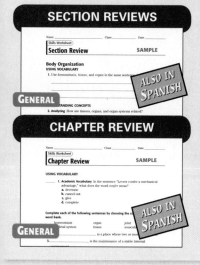
GENERAL

CHAPTER PRETEST
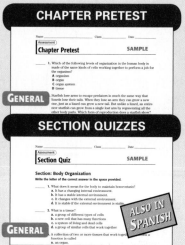
GENERAL

CHAPTER TEST A
BASIC

STANDARDS ASSESSMENT
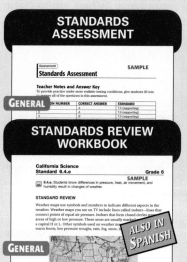
GENERAL

CHAPTER REVIEW
GENERAL

SECTION QUIZZES
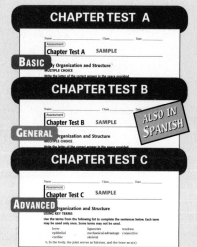
GENERAL

CHAPTER TEST B
GENERAL

CHAPTER TEST C
ADVANCED

STANDARDS REVIEW WORKBOOK
GENERAL

This Teacher Background explains science concepts, principles, and theories that appear in the chapter. Use the information on these pages to refresh or enhance your understanding of the topics covered.

Section 1

The Electromagnetic Spectrum

The Discovery of Electromagnetic Waves

The concept of electromagnetic waves was first proposed in 1861 by James Clerk Maxwell. Maxwell's idea was precipitated by the need to define a situation in which a wave alternating between an electric current and a magnetic field could travel through empty space. He knew that copper wire can carry an electric current that in turn generates a magnetic field. Because empty space obviously does not form a finite loop of copper wire, it was not apparent how electric current could be transmitted across that space. So, Maxwell proposed that it was possible for such a wave to travel through empty space at the speed of light. He further determined that such a wave was actually light.

Characteristics of Light Waves

Like all waves, electromagnetic waves have amplitude, wavelength, speed, and frequency. Wavelength in the electromagnetic spectrum varies from 10^5 m (radio waves) to 10^{-13} m (gamma rays). Visible light makes up a very small portion of the electromagnetic spectrum, with wavelengths between 400 nm and 700 nm, as shown in **Figure A.** The waves that have the shortest wavelengths—ultraviolet light, X rays, and gamma rays—are the most dangerous to living organisms.

Color Vision

White light is a mixture of several wavelengths of visible light. When white light is split into the visible spectrum, it forms a continuous band of color. However, the visible spectrum is described as being composed of red, orange, yellow, green, blue, and violet light. The colors of light depend on the wavelengths of the visible light waves.

Light passes through the cornea and the lens of the eye, which focus the light on the back of the eye. The back of the eye is covered by a layer of nerve cells, called the *retina*. These nerve cells are photoreceptors. There are two types of photoreceptors: rods and cones. Rods help people see in low light. Cones detect color. Cones are localized in an area of the retina called the *fovea*.

Three subclasses of cones are red, green, and blue cones, so-named because each type of cone best absorbs light of the given color. These cones are also called, respectively, *rho*, *gamma*, and *beta*. The subclasses of cones are excited by specific wavelengths. The combination of cones that are excited by light stimulus and the number of each subclass excited determine the color of light seen. For example, when red and green cones are excited, a person may see yellow or orange, but the color perceived depends on the relative number of each type of cone excited by the stimulus.

Sometimes, light receptors do not function properly. Color deficiency, or color blindness, is a condition in which individuals have trouble differentiating between certain colors, most commonly red and green. The condition is caused by an inadequate number of properly working rho and gamma cones.

Section 2

Interactions of Light with Matter

Sight

An object can absorb, reflect, or refract light. In order for our eyes to see an object, that object must first reflect or emit light. Some objects emit their own light, as does a television screen or a light bulb. After being reflected or emitted by an object, light enters the eye and is converted into electric impulses through a series of interactions in the eye. The brain then interprets those electric

Figure A *Visible light occupies a small band at about the two-thirds point of the electromagnetic spectrum. Light waves on the electromagnetic spectrum to the right of and shorter than visible light are the most dangerous to living organisms.*

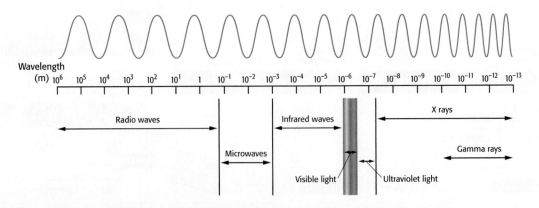

impulses. Thus, the wavelengths of light that reach the eye and their subsequent interpretation by the brain determine what a person sees.

Reflection

The angle of reflection is always equal to the angle of incidence. There are two types of reflection: regular reflection, sometimes called *specular reflection,* and diffuse reflection. Regular reflection is exhibited by smooth, flat surfaces, such as a mirror. In regular reflection, all incident light rays run parallel to each other and remain parallel after reflection on a surface. So, all the rays have the same angle of incidence and angle of reflection. Diffuse reflection is reflection off any rough surface, even minutely rough surfaces such as paper. Diffuse reflection happens when incident light rays are parallel to each other but reflected light rays are not parallel. Irregularities in the surface of the object change the angle of incidence for individual incident light rays, so the light rays reflect in several different planes.

Section 3

Refraction

Refraction and Media

Light travels in a straight line when the medium through which it is traveling does not change. However, when light travels at an angle from one medium to another, it is refracted, or bent at the boundary between the media. An example of refraction is shown in **Figure B.** Light travels in a straight line through the air, bends where air meets the edge of a prism, travels in a straight line through the prism, and bends again as it exits the prism.

A medium has an index of refraction. A medium's index of refraction is the ratio between the speed of light in a vacuum and the speed of light in the medium. The ratio between the wavelength of light in a vacuum and the wavelength in a medium is also equal to the medium's index of refraction. Air has an index of refraction of 1.0003, whereas water and glass each have an index of refraction of 1.52. The index of refraction of each medium through which light travels determines how much the light bends.

Lenses

Lenses are transparent objects that refract light. Lenses are often made of glass, crystal, or plastic. Two types of lenses are the double convex lens, or convex lens, and the double concave lens, or concave lens. When parallel light waves pass through a convex lens, they converge on a focal point on the principal axis that lies

past the lens. For this reason, convex lenses are called *converging lenses.* The focal length, or the distance between the lens and the focal point, of a converging lens is always positive. When parallel light waves pass through a concave lens, however, they diverge as though they originated from a focal point on the principal axis that lies in front of the lens. Concave lenses are diverging lenses, which always have a negative focal length.

The lens of the human eye is a convex lens. Human-made convex lenses are often used to magnify objects. The simplest example of this is the magnifying glass. Convex lenses are also used to correct the sight of near-sighted people. A concave lens makes images look smaller than they actually are. Concave lenses are used to correct the sight of people who are farsighted.

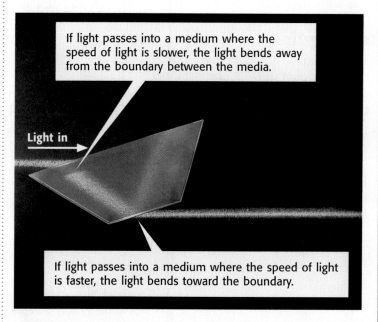

If light passes into a medium where the speed of light is slower, the light bends away from the boundary between the media.

Light in

If light passes into a medium where the speed of light is faster, the light bends toward the boundary.

Figure B *Refraction occurs because light changes speed and wavelength as it enters another medium. Speed is decreased as light exits the air and enters a denser medium, such as glass. Wavelength also decreases.*

Internet Resources

SciLinks is maintained by the National Science Teachers Association to provide you and your students with interesting, up-to-date links that will enrich your classroom presentation of the chapter.

Visit **www.scilinks.org** and enter the SciLinks code for more information about the topic listed.

Topic: Electromagnetic Spectrum
SciLinks code: HY70482

Topic: Colors
SciLinks code: HY70314

Topic: Lenses
SciLinks code: HY70868

Chapter Preview

📁 Chapter Pretest

Use the Chapter Pretest in the Chapter Resource File to determine the prior knowledge of your students. The Test Doctors and diagnostic teaching tips in the Teacher Notes pages will help you tailor your instruction to your students' specific needs.

Improving Comprehension

Use the Graphic Organizer on this page of the Student Edition to introduce the topics that are covered in this chapter, to summarize the chapter material, or to show students how to make a cause-and-effect map.

Teaching Tips

• Remind students that a cause-and-effect map shows a process; it describes how, when, or why one event causes another event.

• Remind students that there can be multiple causes and effects in one cause-and-effect map. Explain that one cause may have several effects and one effect may have several causes.

LS Logical

Improving Comprehension

Graphic Organizers are important visual tools that can help you organize information and improve your reading comprehension. The Graphic Organizer below is called a *cause-and-effect map*. Instructions for creating other types of Graphic Organizers are located in the **Study Skills** section of the Appendix.

How to Make a Cause-and-Effect Map

1 Draw a box, and write a cause in the box. You can have as many cause boxes as you want. The diagram shown here is one example of a cause-and-effect map.

2 Draw another box to the right of the cause box to represent an effect. You can have as many effect boxes as you want. Draw arrows from each cause box to the appropriate effect boxes.

3 In the cause boxes, explain the process that makes up the cause. In the effect boxes, write a description of the effect or details about the effect.

When to Use a Cause-and-Effect Map

A cause-and-effect map is a useful tool for illustrating a specific type of scientific process. Use a cause-and-effect map when you want to describe how, when, or why one event causes another event. As you read, look for events that are either causes or results of other events, and draw a cause-and-effect map that shows the relationships between the events.

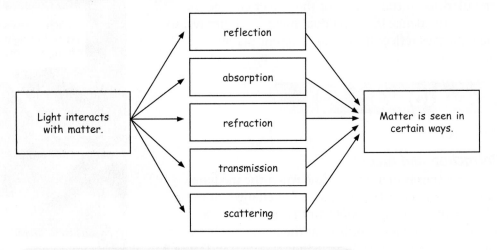

You Try It!

This Reading Strategy can also be used within the chapter that you are about to read. Practice making your own *cause-and-effect map* as directed in the Reading Strategy for Section **1**. Record your work in your **Science Journal.**

Using Other Graphic Organizers

Students can practice using a variety of Graphic Organizers while reading this chapter. The following Graphic Organizers may also be useful in this chapter.

An **idea wheel** can be used to organize details about infrared, visible, and ultraviolet light, discussed in Section 1.

Combination notes can be used to explain various kinds of reflection, discussed in Section 2. **Combination notes** also can be used to explain the types of lenses, discussed in Section 3.

Instructions for creating these Graphic Organizers are located on pp. 583–591 of the Appendix.

Unpacking the Standards

The information below "unpacks" the standards by breaking them down into basic parts. The higher-level, academic vocabulary is highlighted and defined to help you understand the language of the standards. "What It Means" restates the standards as simply as possible.

Unpacking the Standards

Use the following information with the *What It Means* in the Student Edition to help students understand why studying each standard is important.

California Standard	Academic Vocabulary	What It Means	Why It Matters
7.6.a Students know **visible** light is a small band within a very broad electromagnetic spectrum.	**visible** (VIZ uh buhl) that can be seen	The light you are able to see is just a small part of the range of radiation that surrounds you.	Infrared radiation, microwaves, X rays, and other wavelengths of the electromagnetic spectrum are as important as visible light.
7.6.b Students know that for an object to be seen, light emitted by or scattered from it must be **detected** by the eye.	**detect** (dee TEKT) to notice	For you to see an object, the light that is given off by an object or that bounces off an object must enter your eye.	Before one receives visual stimuli from an object, light must be emitted or scattered by the object.
7.6.c Students know light travels in straight lines if the **medium** it travels through does not change.	**medium** (MEE dee uhm) a substance through which something else is sent or carried	Light moves in a straight line if the light passes through only one kind of material.	The physical properties of light are constants that help us understand how we are able to perceive the world.
7.6.d Students know how simple lenses are used in a magnifying glass, the eye, a camera, a telescope, and a microscope.		You must know how simple lenses are used in a magnifying glass, the eye, a camera, a telescope, and a microscope.	The lens of an eye and lenses that are manufactured are similar in structure and function.
7.6.e Students know that white light is a mixture of many wavelengths (colors) and that retinal cells **react** differently to different wavelengths.	**react** (ree AKT) to act in return; to respond	White light consists of many wavelengths of radiation, or colors. Cells in the back of human eyes respond to these different wavelengths in different ways.	Human eyes can detect only a narrow band of wavelengths of the electromagnetic spectrum. Other wavelengths (such as microwaves, X rays, and infrared light) are also useful to humans.
7.6.f Students know light can be reflected, refracted, **transmitted,** and absorbed by matter.	**transmit** (trans MIT) to send or cause to go from one thing to another	Light can be reflected, bent (refracted), transmitted, and absorbed by matter.	Matter interacts with light. When a human sees an object, he or she is seeing reflected light. Some matter refracts or transmits light. Most objects absorb some wavelengths of light.
7.6.g Students know the angle of reflection of a light beam is equal to the angle of **incidence.**	**incidence** (IN suh duhns) the point at which a line or something moving in a straight line, such as a ray of light, meets a surface	The angle at which light will bounce off of a mirror is the same angle at which the light hits the mirror's surface.	Understanding the relationship between the angle of reflection and the angle of incidence is important for understanding how mirrors and lenses work in optics.

Academic Vocabulary

Standards that are covered in this chapter may contain academic terms that are unfamiliar to students. The following table identifies some of the academic terms used in this chapter and their meanings.

Term	Definition
incidence	the point at which a line or something moving in a straight line, such as a ray of light, meets a surface
medium	a substance through which something else is sent or carried
visible	that can be seen

Practice From the chapter, give each student a term and its meanings. Have students make a list of three clues that would help other students guess the term. Clues do not have to be related to the scientific meaning of the term. Have students work in groups to guess the terms by using the clues. Make sure that no students in a group have the same term. (Students may give clues by creating sentences with blanks that prompt classmates to fill in the blanks and by providing synonyms and antonyms.)

Chapter Overview

This chapter introduces students to electromagnetic waves, focusing on visible light. Students will learn about the divisions of the electromagnetic spectrum. Students will also learn about how light interacts with matter by reflection, refraction, transmission, and absorption.

Light and Living Things

The Big Idea

Light is an electromagnetic wave that interacts with matter in many different ways.

California Standards

Focus on Life Sciences
7.6 Physical principles underlie biological structures and functions. (Sections 1, 2, and 3)

Investigation and Experimentation
7.7 Scientific progress is made by asking meaningful questions and conducting careful investigations. (Science Skills Activity)

Math
6.2.1 Algebra and Functions

English–Language Arts
7.1.3, 7.2.3 Reading
7.2.5 Writing

About the Photo

What kind of alien life is this? Actually, these glowing blobs are animals that live off the coast of California. These jellyfish are bioluminescent, which means that they produce their own light. Many bioluminescent animals live in the oceans, but others, such as fireflies, live on land.

Organize

Key-Term Fold

Before you read the chapter, create the FoldNote entitled "Key-Term Fold." Write a key term from the chapter on each tab of the key-term fold. As you read the chapter, write the definition of each key term under the appropriate tab.

Instructions for creating FoldNotes are located in the Study Skills section on p. 581 of the Appendix.

California Standards Alignment

Focus on Life Sciences

7.6.a Students know visible light is a small band within a very broad electromagnetic spectrum. **pp. 77–78, 80–81, 103–104**

7.6.b Students know that for an object to be seen, light emitted by or scattered from it must be detected by the eye. **pp. 84–85, 87, 89, 102–104**

7.6.c Students know that light travels in straight lines if the medium it travels through does not change. **pp. 82–83, 86, 89–92, 97, 102–103, 105**

7.6.d Students know how simple lenses are used in a magnifying glass, the eye, a camera, a telescope, and a microscope. **pp. 93–99, 102, 105**

7.6.e Students know that white light is a mixture of many wavelengths (colors) and that retinal cells react differently to different wavelengths. **pp. 75, 79–81, 86–89, 91, 97, 102–105**

7.6.f Students know that light can be reflected, refracted, transmitted, and absorbed by matter. **pp. 82–99, 102–105**

7.6.g Students know that the angle of reflection of a light beam is equal to the angle of incidence. **pp. 82–83, 89, 102, 105**

Investigation and Experimentation

7.7.a Select and use appropriate tools and technology (including calculators, computers, balances, spring scales, microscopes, and binoculars) to perform tests, collect data, and display data. **pp. 100, 105**

Teacher Notes

Students will use a spectroscope to separate white light into different colors of light (covers standard 7.6.e). To make a spectroscope, follow these instructions:

1. Cut a slit in the center of a piece of black construction paper. Tape the paper to one end of a paper-towel tube so that the paper covers the tube's opening. Make sure that the slit is wide enough for light to pass through.

2. Hold a diffraction grating against the open end of the tube. Look at a light bulb through the grating. Keep the slit in the paper vertical.

3. Rotate the diffraction grating until you see colors inside the tube to the left and right sides of the slit. Tape the diffraction grating to the tube in this position.

Materials for Each Group

- light bulb, fluorescent
- light bulb, incandescent
- spectroscope

Safety Caution

Remind all students to review all safety cautions and icons before beginning this activity.

Answers

4. Incandescent light: continuous band of colors that have the same brightness. Fluorescent light: separate bands of colors that have different brightnesses.

5. White light is made up of different colors of light.

6. Sample answer: I think I will see several colors of light.

Differentiated Datasheets
A **BASIC**, B **GENERAL**, C **ADVANCED**

Also editable on the
**Holt Lab Generator
CD-ROM**

Explore Activity

20 min

7.6.e

Seeing Colors of Light

Is white light really white? In this activity, you will use a spectroscope to answer that question. A spectroscope is a device that separates light into different colors.

Procedure

1. Your teacher will give you a **spectroscope** or instructions for making one.

2. Turn on an **incandescent light bulb.** Look at the light bulb through your spectroscope. Write a description of what you see.

3. Repeat step 2 by using a **fluorescent light.** Again, describe what you see.

Analysis

4. Compare what you saw by using the incandescent light bulb with what you saw by using the fluorescent light bulb.

5. Both kinds of bulbs produce white light. What did you learn about white light by using the spectroscope?

6. Light from a flame is yellowish but is similar to white light. What do you think you would see if you used a spectroscope to look at light from a flame?

Math Standards

Algebra and Functions 6.2.1 Convert one unit of measurement to another (e.g., from feet to miles, from centimeters to inches). **p. 103**

English–Language Arts Standards

Reading 7.1.3 Clarify word meanings through the use of definition, example, restatement, or contrast. **p. 90**

Reading 7.2.3 Analyze text that uses the cause-and-effect organizational pattern. **pp. 76, 82**

Writing 7.2.5 Write persuasive compositions: (a) State a clear position on a proposition or proposal; (b) Support the position with organized and relevant evidence; and (c) Anticipate and address reader concerns and counterarguments. **p. 103**

Strange but True!

Chapter Starter Transparency
Use this transparency to help students begin thinking about light.

Preteach

Reviewing Prior Knowledge

Lead a discussion about the colors of visible light and the electromagnetic spectrum. Ask students to name some colors of visible light. (red, orange, yellow, green, blue, and violet) If students have trouble answering the question, tell them to think about a rainbow. Then, ask students to name different kinds of light that they cannot see. (Sample answer: Infrared light and ultraviolet light are kinds of light that I cannot see.)

 **Bellringer**

Have students focus on standard 7.6.e by asking them to describe the weather conditions necessary to produce a rainbow. (It must be raining and the sun must be shining.) Then, ask students why they think rainbows form. (Some students may recognize that rainbows form when white light passes through raindrops, which separate the colors of light.)

 Bellringer Transparency

Motivate

ACTIVITY

Wavelengths Discuss with students the various lengths of EM waves. Explain that FM radio waves are about 3 m long. Have students use a meterstick to draw an FM radio wave on the board. Then, tell students that the wavelength produced by a typical microwave oven is 12 cm. Ask students to draw this wave. Challenge students to imagine the length of a visible light wave, which is between 400 nm (0.0000004 m) and 700 nm (0.0000007 m).
LS Visual

What You Will Learn

- Light is an electromagnetic wave.
- Visible light is a small part of a very broad electromagnetic spectrum.
- White light is a mixture of many wavelengths of visible light.
- Infrared waves and ultraviolet light affect living things.

Why It Matters

The electromagnetic waves that make up the electromagnetic spectrum affect living things.

Vocabulary

- electromagnetic wave
- electromagnetic spectrum

READING STRATEGY

Graphic Organizer In your **Science Journal,** show the bad and good effects of ultraviolet light in a Cause-and-Effect Map.

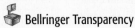

7.6.a Students know visible light is a small band within a very broad electromagnetic spectrum.
7.6.e Students know that white light is a mixture of many wavelengths (colors) and that retinal cells react differently to different wavelengths.

The Electromagnetic Spectrum

Key Concept Visible light, infrared waves, and ultraviolet light are small parts of a large electromagnetic spectrum.

▶ When you look around, you can see things that reflect light to your eyes. But a bee might see the same things differently, as **Figure 1** shows. Bees can see a kind of light—called *ultraviolet light*—that you can't see!

It might seem odd to label something that you can't see with the term *light.* The light that you are most familiar with is called *visible light.* Ultraviolet light is similar to visible light. Both are forms of energy that travel as a certain kind of wave.

Light: An Electromagnetic Wave

Some kinds of waves, such as water waves, must travel through *matter,* which is anything that has mass and takes up space. All light waves can also travel through matter. But light does not need matter through which to travel. Light is an electromagnetic wave (EM wave). An **electromagnetic wave** is a wave that consists of changing electric and magnetic fields. EM waves can travel through empty space or matter.

Fields exist around certain objects and can exert a force on another object without touching that object. The electric field in an EM wave is similar to the electric fields around charged particles. And the magnetic field in an EM wave is similar to the magnetic fields around magnets. But keep in mind that these fields, like all fields, are not made of matter.

Figure 1 *The petals of the flower on the right look solid yellow to you. But a bee looking at the same flower can see the ultraviolet markings, which are shown in the flower on the left. These markings direct the bee to the center of the flower.*

Universal Access • Differentiated Instruction

Advanced Learners/GATE

The Structure of EM Waves Ask students to investigate the electric and magnetic fields of electromagnetic waves. Students should use what they learn to diagram the relationship between the electric and magnetic fields of the wave.
LS Visual

Figure 2 **The Electromagnetic Spectrum**

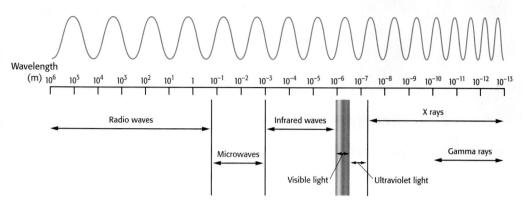

A Spectrum of Waves

Visible light waves and ultraviolet light waves are both kinds of electromagnetic waves. Other kinds of EM waves include radio waves, infrared waves, and X rays. Visible light, ultraviolet light, and infrared waves are important to living things.

The entire range of electromagnetic waves is called the **electromagnetic spectrum.** The electromagnetic spectrum is shown in **Figure 2.** As you can see, visible light is only a small band within the broad electromagnetic spectrum. There is no sharp division between one kind of wave and the next. Some kinds even have overlapping ranges.

Standards Check What is the electromagnetic spectrum? **7.6.a**

Wavelength and the EM Spectrum

You probably know how different kinds of EM waves are used. For example, microwaves are used to cook food in microwave ovens. Radio waves are used to send TV and radio signals. And X rays are used in X-ray machines to make images of tissues and bones. How is one kind of EM wave different from other kinds of EM waves? An important difference between kinds of EM waves is their wavelength.

A *wavelength* is the distance from any point on a wave to an identical point on the next wave. **Figure 3** shows how wavelength can be measured on a wave. Notice that the wavelength of the wave is the same no matter where it is measured. You can see the range of wavelengths for the different kinds of EM waves in **Figure 2.**

electromagnetic wave
(ee LEK troh mag NET ik WAYV) a wave that consists of electric and magnetic fields that vibrate at right angles to each other

electromagnetic spectrum
(ee LEK troh mag NET ik SPEK truhm) all of the frequencies or wavelengths of electromagnetic radiation

Figure 3 *Wavelength can be measured between any two corresponding points on adjacent waves.*

Universal Access · Differentiated Instruction

Basic Learners

Exponents Some students will not understand the meaning of the exponential numbers in **Figure 2.** Show students how to calculate a number with an exponent by using the numbers 10^6 and 10^{-6} as examples. Tell students that 10^6 is calculated in the following way: $10 \times 10 \times 10 \times 10 \times 10 \times 10 = 1,000,000$. Also tell students that 10^{-6} is calculated in the following way: $1 \div 10 \div 10 \div 10 \div 10 \div 10 \div 10 = 0.000001$. Divide the class into 11 teams and ask each team to write out the calculation for exponents from 10^1 to 10^5 and from 10^{-7} to 10^{-13}. Then, have a member of each team write the team's calculation on the board. **LS** Logical/Interpersonal

Infrared Film By using infrared film, scientists can detect mineral deposits, diseased vegetation, and a variety of other things. For example, rocks and minerals vary in color on infrared film because they have slightly different temperatures. For this reason, geologists can chart mineral content of soil from the air. Ask students to identify other ways that scientists use infrared film. Students should write a short report about their findings. **LS** Verbal

ACTiViTY

Pit Vipers and Infrared Light

More than 140 species belong to the family of snakes commonly known as pit vipers. Rattlesnakes, cottonmouths, and copperheads are common North American pit vipers. Bushmasters and fer-de-lance are Central and South American pit vipers. Pit vipers have a pair of pits between the eyes and nostrils. These organs are very sensitive to infrared radiation from a source that is as far away as 20 cm. A pit viper's brain interprets nerve impulses from the pits as a picture. This function allows pit vipers to see at night. Have each student research one species of pit viper and then present his or her findings to the class. **LS** Verbal

---

Answer to Standards Check

Humans can see the range of wavelengths between 400 nm and 700 nm.
7.6.a (mastering)

Teaching Transparency: **LINK TO**
PHYSICAL SCIENCE P58 Absorption
Spectrum of the Sun

Figure 4 *In this photograph, brighter colors indicate higher temperatures. The dark color of the nose shows that this dog has a cold nose!*

Infrared Waves

Infrared waves are EM waves that have wavelengths between 700 nanometers and 1 mm. A nanometer (nm) is equal to 0.000000001 m. The size of an atom is about 0.1 nm.

Infrared waves are important to living things. On a sunny day, you may be warmed by infrared waves from the sun. The sun also warms other things on Earth and even warms Earth itself! In fact, infrared waves from the sun keep the temperatures on Earth suitable for life.

All things, including buildings, trees, animals, and you, give off infrared waves. The amount of infrared waves an object gives off depends on the object's temperature and the properties of the object's surface. Warmer objects give off more infrared waves than cooler objects do. You can see the temperature differences on the surface of a dog in **Figure 4.** This photo was taken with film that is sensitive to infrared waves.

Visible Light

Visible light is the very narrow range of wavelengths in the electromagnetic spectrum that humans can see. Visible light waves have wavelengths between 400 nm and 700 nm.

Visible light energy is changed into chemical energy by green plants during photosynthesis, as shown in **Figure 5.** The chemical energy can be stored in food that you can eat.

Standards Check What range of wavelengths can humans see?
7.6.a

Figure 5 **From Light Energy to Chemical Energy**

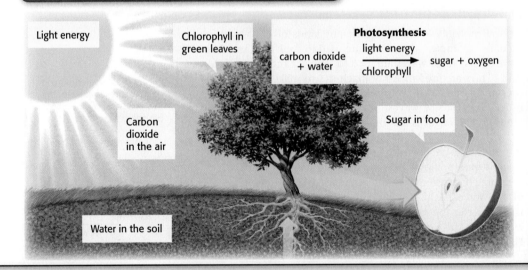

Light energy

Chlorophyll in green leaves

Photosynthesis

carbon dioxide + water →[light energy / chlorophyll] sugar + oxygen

Carbon dioxide in the air

Sugar in food

Water in the soil

Universal Access • Differentiated Instruction

Struggling Readers

Using Figures Direct students' attention to the boldface "**Figure 4**" in the body text on this page. Model studying the figure before reading the text by saying, "When I look at the section under the heading "Infrared Waves," I immediately notice **Figure 4** in boldface type in the third paragraph. So, I read the first two paragraphs. Then, before reading the third paragraph, I look at **Figure 4.** I see that the caption says brighter colors show higher temperatures. I can see that the dog's nose is dark in the picture, so I understand that the dog has a cold nose. After I know what the figure is explaining, I read the third paragraph, and I understand what an infrared photo looks like." Ask students to follow the same procedure for **Figure 5** and for the other figures throughout the text. **LS** Visual/Verbal

Figure 6 Water droplets can separate white light into visible light of different wavelengths. As a result, you see the colors of visible light in a rainbow.

Visible Light from the Sun

Some of the energy that reaches Earth from the sun is visible light. The visible light from the sun is white light. *White light* is visible light of all wavelengths combined. Light from lamps in your home as well as from the fluorescent bulbs in your school is also white light.

Standards Check What is white light? 🐾 **7.6.e**

Colors of Light

Cells in the human eye react differently to different wavelengths of light. As a result, humans see the different wavelengths of visible light as different colors, as shown in **Figure 6.** The longest wavelengths are seen as red light. The shortest wavelengths are seen as violet light.

The range of colors is called the *visible spectrum,* which is shown in **Figure 7.** To help you remember the colors, you can use the name *ROY G. BiV.* The capital letters in Roy's name represent the first letter of each color of visible light: **r**ed, **o**range, **y**ellow, **g**reen, **b**lue, and **v**iolet. You can think of *i* in Roy's last name as standing for the color indigo. Indigo is a dark blue color. Though the colors are given separate names, the visible spectrum is a continuous band of colors.

SCHOOL to HOME

Making a Rainbow
On a sunny day, ask an adult to use a hose or a spray bottle to make a mist of water outside. Move around until you see a rainbow in the water mist. In your **Science Journal,** draw a diagram that shows the positions of the water mist, the sun, the rainbow, and yourself.

ACTIVITY

Figure 7 The visible spectrum contains all colors of light.

R O Y G B V

Standards Focus

This **Standards Focus** provides you with a quick way to **assess, reteach,** and **re-assess** one or more concepts in the section.

1. Visible light makes up what portion of the electromagnetic spectrum? (Sample answer: It makes up a very narrow range of the electromagnetic spectrum near the middle of the spectrum.) **7.6.a**

2. What is the range of colors that make up white light called? (visible spectrum) **7.6.e**

Making Tables Ask students to make a table comparing visible light, infrared light, and ultraviolet light. For each group of EM waves, students should write the relative wavelengths, the proportion of the EM spectrum it makes up, and its importance to humans. **LS** Logical **7.6.a, 7.6.e**

Re-Assess

Short Story Ask students to write a creative short story in which the characters are affected by a group of EM waves. For example, students could explore how ultraviolet light affects people or what would happen if white light disappeared. **LS** Verbal **7.6.a, 7.6.e**

Answer to Standards Check

Ultraviolet waves have shorter wavelengths than visible light waves have. **7.6.a** (exceeding)

Quick Lab

Refraction Rainbow

1. Tape a **piece of construction paper** over the end of a **flashlight.** Use **scissors** to cut a slit in the paper.

2. Turn on the flashlight, and lay it on a table. Place a **prism** on end in the beam of light.

3. Slowly rotate the prism until you can see a rainbow on the surface of the table.

4. What colors do you see in your rainbow?

5. Compare the colors of the rainbow with the color of the light produced by the flashlight.

7.6.e

⏱ 15 min

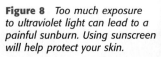

What's Your Frequency?

Create a brochure helping soon-to-propagate waves decide on a frequency that will meet their personal goals. Go to **go.hrw.com,** and type in the keyword HY7LGTW.

Ultraviolet Light

Ultraviolet light (UV light) is another kind of electromagnetic wave that affects living things. Ultraviolet waves have shorter wavelengths than visible light waves do. The wavelengths of ultraviolet light waves vary between 60 nm and 400 nm. Ultraviolet light affects your body in both bad and good ways.

Standards Check Compare ultraviolet light waves with visible light waves. **7.6.a**

Bad Effects

On the bad side, too much ultraviolet light can cause sunburn, as you can see in **Figure 8.** Too much ultraviolet light can also cause skin cancer, wrinkles, and damage to the eyes. Luckily, much of the ultraviolet light from the sun does not reach Earth's surface. But you should still protect yourself against the ultraviolet light that does reach you. To do so, you should use sunscreen that has a high SPF (**s**un **p**rotection **f**actor). You should also wear sunglasses that block out UV light to protect your eyes. Clothes, such as hats, long-sleeved shirts, and long pants, can protect you, too. You need this protection even on overcast days because UV light can travel through clouds.

Figure 8 *Too much exposure to ultraviolet light can lead to a painful sunburn. Using sunscreen will help protect your skin.*

Quick Lab

⏱ 15 min

Teacher Notes

In this activity, students will use a prism to separate white light into different colors (covers standard 7.6.e). This activity should be done in a darkened room and with powerful flashlights. Alternately, this activity can be done outside by using sunlight rather than a flashlight.

Materials for Each Group

- construction paper
- flashlight
- prism
- scissors

Safety Caution

Remind students to review all safety cautions and icons before beginning this activity.

Answers

4. Sample answer: I see red, orange, yellow, green, blue, and violet.

5. Sample answer: I see different colors in the rainbow, but I see only white light from the flashlight.

📋 Differentiated Datasheets
A **BASIC**, B **GENERAL**, C **ADVANCED**

Also editable on the Holt Lab Generator CD-ROM

Good Effects

On the good side, ultraviolet light that is produced by ultraviolet lamps is used to kill bacteria on food and surgical tools. In addition, small amounts of ultraviolet light are good for your body. When exposed to ultraviolet light, skin cells produce vitamin D. This vitamin allows the intestines to absorb calcium. Without calcium, your teeth and bones would be very weak. **Figure 9** shows a good effect of ultraviolet light.

Figure 9 *Healthy teeth need calcium. Vitamin D that is produced when your skin is exposed to ultraviolet light helps your body absorb calcium.*

SECTION Review

7.6.a, 7.6.e

Summary

- Light is an electromagnetic wave (EM wave). An EM wave can travel through matter or space.
- The entire range of EM waves is called the *electromagnetic spectrum*.
- Infrared waves from the sun warm Earth and everything on Earth.
- Visible light is the narrow range of wavelengths in the electromagnetic spectrum that humans can see.
- Humans see different wavelengths of visible light as different colors.
- Ultraviolet light is both harmful and helpful to living things.

Using Vocabulary

1. In your own words, write a definition for the term *electromagnetic spectrum*.

Understanding Concepts

2. **Comparing** Compare the size of the visible light spectrum with the size of the electromagnetic spectrum.

3. **Describing** How do the various kinds of EM waves differ from each other?

4. **Applying** Explain why ultraviolet light can be both helpful and harmful.

5. **Listing** What colors of light make up white light?

6. **Identifying** What is the visible spectrum?

Critical Thinking

7. **Applying Concepts** Describe three ways that electromagnetic waves have affected you today.

8. **Making Comparisons** Compare the wavelengths of infrared waves, ultraviolet light, and visible light.

INTERPRETING GRAPHICS Use the diagram of two EM waves below to answer the next two questions.

a

b

9. **Applying Concepts** Which wave has the longest wavelength?

10. **Analyzing Relationships** Suppose that one of the waves represents an infrared wave and that one of the waves represents a visible light wave. Which wave represents the visible light wave?

Internet Resources

For a variety of links related to this chapter, go to www.scilinks.org
Topic: Electromagnetic Spectrum
SciLinks code: HY70482

Universal Access · Differentiated Instruction

Special Education Students

Units Create a chart on the board to relate "nm" and "nanometers" to something concrete that the students can understand. Write these abbreviations on the board, one under the other: m, cm, mm, and nm. Ask volunteers to write the full words for the abbreviations. (meter, centimeter, millimeter, and nanometer) Ask a volunteer to find something in the room that measures about one meter. (Sample answer: width of a teacher's desk) Repeat with one centimeter. (Sample answer: width of a piece of tape) Point out that 1 cm is 10^{-2} m because there are 100 cm in 1 m. Write 10^{-2} m next to the word "centimeter." Ask a volunteer how to express mm as a part of 1 m. (10^{-3} m) Tell students to look at 1 mm and realize that it is 10^{-3} m and to imagine how small 10^{-9} m must be. Have students finish filling in the chart. **LS** Kinesthetic/Logical

Preteach

Reviewing Prior Knowledge

Write standard 7.6.e on the board. Ask students to summarize the standard in their own words. Then, ask students to predict how the standard may apply to this section.

Bellringer

Have students focus on standard 7.6.f by answering the following questions: "How do mirrors work? What do mirrors do to light waves?" (Accept all reasonable answers. Students should demonstrate an understanding of reflection.)

Bellringer Transparency

Motivate

Group ACTIVITY

Make a Periscope Have students work in groups of three to make a periscope. Give each group a shoebox, modeling clay, two small mirrors, and a pair of scissors. Have one student cut a 3 cm hole on the left side of one end of the box. Ask the second student to cut another hole at the other end of the box such that it is not directly opposite the first hole. Ask the third student to position the mirrors using the modeling clay so that you can look in one hole and see what is outside the other hole. Ask students to take turns testing their periscope. Have them identify the property of light that makes a periscope work. (reflection)

LS Kinesthetic/Interpersonal
Co-op Learning

SECTION 2

What You Will Learn

- Light travels in straight lines if the material that the light travels through does not change.
- The angle of reflection of a light beam is equal to the angle of incidence.
- An object can be seen if light emitted by or reflected by it is detected by the eye.
- Light can be reflected, absorbed, scattered, or transmitted by matter.

Why It Matters

The way that light interacts with matter affects what you see.

Vocabulary

- reflection • scattering
- absorption • transmission

READING STRATEGY

Clarifying Concepts Take turns reading this section out loud with a partner. Stop to discuss ideas that seem confusing.

reflection (ri FLEK shuhn) the bouncing back of a ray of light, sound, or heat when the ray hits a surface that it does not go through

Wordwise The prefix *re-* means "again" or "back." The root *flect-* means "to bend."

Interactions of Light with Matter

Key Concept Light interacts with matter during reflection, absorption, scattering, and transmission.

▶ Have you ever seen a cat's eyes glow in the dark when light shines on them? Cats have a special layer of cells in the back of their eyes that reflects light. This layer helps the cat see better by giving the eyes a second chance to detect the light. Reflection is one interaction of light waves with matter.

Reflection

Light travels in straight lines as long as the material that the light travels through doesn't change. So, a ray of light shining through air is usually straight. One way to change the direction of a light beam is by reflection. **Reflection** is the bouncing back of light rays when they hit an object. But light doesn't change directions randomly. Instead, it follows the law of reflection.

The Law of Reflection

Light is reflected by surfaces the same way that a ball bounces off the ground. If you throw the ball straight down, it will bounce straight up. If you throw the ball at an angle, it will bounce away at an angle. The *law of reflection* states that the angle of incidence is equal to the angle of reflection. *Incidence* is the arrival of a beam of light at a surface. **Figure 1** shows this law.

Standards Check When does a ray of light travel in a straight line? What is the law of reflection? **7.6.c, 7.6.g**

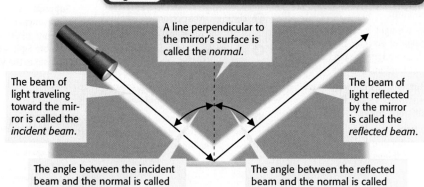

Figure 1 The Law of Reflection

A line perpendicular to the mirror's surface is called the *normal*.

The beam of light traveling toward the mirror is called the *incident beam*.

The beam of light reflected by the mirror is called the *reflected beam*.

The angle between the incident beam and the normal is called the *angle of incidence*.

The angle between the reflected beam and the normal is called the *angle of reflection*.

Universal Access • Differentiated Instruction

English Learners

Clarifying Perpendicular Make sure students understand the meaning of the word *perpendicular* in **Figure 1.** Ask students to respond to the following commands: 1. Hold your science book perpendicular to your desk. 2. Hold your science book in a way that is not perpendicular to your desk. 3. Place your body so that it is perpendicular to the floor. 4. Identify two things in the room that are perpendicular to each other. **LS** Kinesthetic

---

Answer to Standards Check

A ray of light travels in a straight line when the material that the light travels through does not change. The law of reflection states that the angle of incidence is equal to the angle of reflection.
7.6.c (mastering), **7.6.g** (mastering)

Quick Lab

Reflecting Mirrors

In this activity, you will use the law of reflection to direct a beam of light.

7.6.c
7.6.g

1. Spread a sheet of **butcher paper** on a table or on the floor.

2. Lay a **flashlight** on its side on the edge of the butcher paper so that the beam of light will shine on the paper.

3. Place a **paper cup** on the edge of the paper. You can put the cup on any edge as long as the cup is not directly across from the flashlight.

4. Turn the flashlight on, and use **three small mirrors** to direct the beam of light so that the beam of light shines on the cup. Use pieces of **modeling clay** to hold each mirror in place.

5. Carefully trace the path of the beam of light on the paper. Also, trace the locations of the flashlight, the mirrors, and the cup.

6. Describe the path of the beam of light before and after the light hits a mirror.

7. Use a **protractor** to measure the angle of incidence and the angle of reflection for one mirror. Compare the angles.

🕐 30 min

Types of Reflection

Why can you see your image in a mirror but not in a wall? The answer has to do with the differences between the two surfaces. A mirror's surface is very smooth. Thus, light beams are reflected by all points of the mirror at the same angle. This kind of reflection is called *regular reflection*. A wall's surface is slightly rough. Light beams will hit the wall's surface and reflect at many different angles. So, the light scatters as it is reflected. This kind of reflection is called *diffuse reflection*. **Figure 2** shows the difference between the two kinds of reflection.

7.6.b Students know that for an object to be seen, light emitted by or scattered from it must be detected by the eye.

7.6.c Students know light travels in straight lines if the medium it travels through does not change.

7.6.e Students know that white light is a mixture of many wavelengths (colors) and that retinal cells react differently to different wavelengths.

7.6.f Students know light can be reflected, refracted, transmitted, and absorbed by matter.

7.6.g Students know the angle of reflection of a light beam is equal to the angle of incidence.

Figure 2 Regular Reflection Vs. Diffuse Reflection

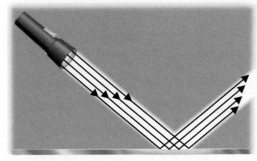

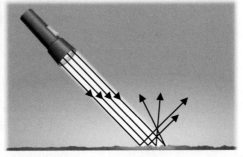

Regular reflection occurs when light beams are reflected at the same angle. When your eye detects the reflected beams, you can see a reflection on the surface.

Diffuse reflection occurs when light beams reflect at many different angles. You can't see a reflection because not all of the reflected light is directed toward your eyes.

Wordwise

Reflection Ask students to brainstorm other words that include the roots *re-* and *flect-*. Then, ask students to use what they know about the meaning of these roots to predict the definitions of the words they brainstormed. Finally, have students look up the definitions of the terms and compare them to their predictions. **LS** Verbal

Teach

Quick Lab 🕐 30 min

Teacher Notes

In this activity, students will use the law of reflection to direct a beam of light toward a target (covers standards 7.6.c and 7.6.g).

Materials for Each Group

- butcher paper
- cup, paper
- flashlight
- mirrors, small (3)
- modeling clay
- protractor

Safety Caution

Remind students to review all safety cautions and icons before beginning this activity.

Answers

6. The beam of light traveled in a straight line before and after it hit a mirror.

7. The angle of incidence is equal to the angle of reflection.

📋 Differentiated Datasheets
  A **BASIC**, B **GENERAL**, C **ADVANCED**

Also editable on the
**Holt Lab Generator
CD-ROM**

📦 Teaching Transparency:
L7 The Law of Reflection; Regular Reflection Versus Diffuse Reflection

CONNECTION ACTIVITY
History

Sight Theories Greek philosophers Hero and Ptolemy believed that the eyes emitted rays that were reflected back by objects. Abu 'Ali al-Hasan ibn al-Haytham (c. 965–1040), an Iraqi scientist, believed differently. Ask students to identify his theory of vision. Then, have students write a paragraph that describes their findings. (Students should find that Abu 'Ali al-Hasan ibn al-Haytham theorized that objects could be seen because they reflected or emitted light.) **LS** Verbal

ACTIVITY

Why Is the Sky Blue? Ask students to research why the sky is blue. Wrong answers to this question are quite common, so ask students to identify some of these wrong answers. Then, students should analyze why the answers are wrong. Students should create an informative pamphlet that describes the correct reason why the sky is blue and that debunks the myths about why the sky is blue. **LS** Verbal

Discussion

Scattering Tell students that a blue jay's feathers are not really blue and that the color they see is the result of scattering. Ask students to predict how this might be possible. (Air particles on the barbs of the blue jay's feathers scatter red and green light, which leaves only blue light to reflect to the observer's eyes.) Ask students to identify another example of scattering. (Sample answer: A flashlight beam scatters and becomes dimmer.) Ask students to identify the color that scatters most readily. (blue) **LS** Verbal

Answer to Standards Check

Sample answer: I see luminous objects when my eyes detect light emitted by the objects. I see illuminated objects when my eyes detect light that is reflected by the objects. **7.6.b** (mastering)

BRAIN FOOD

Early Mirrors The earliest human-made mirrors date back to about 6000 BCE. These mirrors, which archaeologists discovered in Turkey and Egypt, were about 90 mm in diameter and were made from flat pieces of polished obsidian, an igneous rock.

Figure 3 *You can see the tail of this firefly because it is luminous. But you see its body because it is illuminated.*

Light Source or Reflection?

If you look at a TV set in a bright room, you see the cabinet around the TV and the image on the screen. But if you look at the same TV in the dark, you see only the image on the screen. The difference is that the screen is a light source, but the cabinet around the TV is not.

You can see a light source even in the dark because light emitted by it is detected by your eyes. The tail of the firefly in **Figure 3** is a light source. Flames, light bulbs, and the sun are also light sources. Objects that emit visible light are called *luminous* (LOO muh nuhs).

Most things around you are not light sources. But you can still see them because light from light sources is reflected by the objects and then is detected by your eyes. A visible object that is not a light source is *illuminated*.

Standards Check Explain how you see luminous and illuminated objects. **7.6.b**

Absorption and Scattering

Have you noticed that when you use a flashlight, the light is dimmer the farther it travels from the flashlight? Partly because the beam spreads out and partly because of absorption and scattering, the light is weaker the farther it is from the source.

Absorption of Light

absorption (ab SAWRP shuhn) in optics, the transfer of light energy to particles of matter

The transfer of energy carried by light waves to particles of matter is called **absorption.** When a beam of light shines through the air, particles in the air absorb some of the energy from the light. As a result, the beam of light becomes dim. The farther the light travels from its source, the more the light is absorbed by particles, and the dimmer it becomes.

Universal Access · Differentiated Instruction

Basic Learners

Absorption and Scattering Have students sit in a large semicircle so that you can stand in the center and have ample space to shine a flashlight. Make the room as dark as possible. Turn the flashlight on so that it is shining toward the opening in the semicircle. Set the flashlight on a chair so that you can move about without displacing the flashlight. Ask a volunteer to stand up and show where on the beam of light he or she can tell that absorption has taken place. (Student should identify where the beam of light is clearly becoming weaker.) Ask another volunteer to stand up and show an example of light scattering from the beam of light. (Student should show how he or she can see something that is near, but not within, the beam of light.) **LS** Visual/Kinesthetic

Scattering of Light

Scattering is an interaction of light with matter that causes light to change direction. Light scatters in all directions after colliding with particles of matter or undergoing diffuse reflection. Light from the ship shown in **Figure 4** is scattered out of the beam by particles in the fog. This scattered light allows you to see things that are outside the beam. But because light is scattered out of the beam, the beam becomes dimmer.

Scattering makes the clear sky blue. Light that has shorter wavelengths is scattered more by particles of gas in the air than light that has longer wavelengths is. Sunlight is made up of many colors of light, but blue light (which has a very short wavelength) scatters more than any other color. So, when you look at the sky, you see a background of blue light.

Light and Matter

When light hits any form of matter, the light can interact with the matter in different ways. The light can be reflected, absorbed, or transmitted.

You know that reflection happens when light bounces off an object. Reflected light allows you to see things. And you know that absorption is the transfer of light energy to matter. Absorbed light can make things feel warmer. **Transmission** is the passing of light through matter. In fact, without the transmission of light, you couldn't see! All of the light that reaches your eyes is transmitted through air and several parts of your eyes. Light can interact with matter in several ways at the same time, as **Figure 5** shows.

Standards Check What are three ways that light can interact with matter? 7.6.f

Figure 4 *Partly because of scattering, a beam of light becomes dimmer the farther it is from its source.*

scattering (SKAT uhr ing) an interaction of light with matter that causes light to change its energy, direction of motion, or both

transmission (trans MISH uhn) the passing of light or other form of energy through matter.

You can see objects outside because light is transmitted through the glass.

You can see the glass and your reflection in it because light is reflected off the glass.

The glass feels warm when you touch it because some light is absorbed by the glass.

Figure 5 *Light is transmitted, reflected, and absorbed when it strikes the glass in a window.* **Describe at least two ways that light interacts with the person in this photo.**

CONNECTION ACTIVITY
Real World

Fiber Optics Fiber-optic technology has become a standard for the telecommunication industry. This technology utilizes light beams, which contain encoded information, and small, pliable glass cables through which the light beams travel. The glass, or fiber-optic, cables are composed of two types of optically conducting materials. The *core* is the glass through which light travels. The *clad*, which surrounds the core, totally reflects light internally, so that the light is contained in the core. Ask students to research the characteristics of fiber-optic cable. Then, have students build a model illustrating their findings. **LS Verbal/Kinesthetic**

Using the Figure

Light and Matter Tell students to study **Figure 5.** Then, ask students to identify the ways in which light interacts with the objects in the photo. (Answer to caption question: Light reflects off the person, which allows me to see her. Light is absorbed by the person. Light is also transmitted through the person's fingers and through parts of the person's eyes.) **LS Visual**

Answer to Standards Check

Light can be reflected, absorbed, or transmitted by matter. **7.6.f** (mastering)

MISCONCEPTION ALERT

Translucent Versus Transparent
Some students may not recognize the difference between the terms *translucent* and *transparent* because the words are so similar. Show students examples of each type of material. Then, tell students that the root *trans-* means "across" or "through," the root *-lucent* is derived from a word that means "light," and the root *-parent* is derived from a word that means "to appear." Ask students to write their own definitions for each term. Students who overcome the misconception will define the words correctly.

Cataracts Although the lens of the human eye is usually transparent, some conditions, such as cataracts, and injuries can make the lens translucent or opaque. Ask students to research and identify what might cause cataracts. (Cataracts are the result of aging or long-term exposure to ultraviolet light.) Ask students how they can prevent cataracts. (Students should note that avoiding ultraviolet light by wearing a hat or sunglasses can help prevent cataracts.) **LS** Verbal

Demonstration

Color Perception Cover the lens of a high-intensity flashlight with a red filter, and cover the lens of another high-intensity flashlight with a green filter. In a darkened room, alternate turning the lights on, shining them on a white sheet, wall, or screen. Ask students to predict what color the red and green lights will produce if they are overlapped. (Most likely, students will suggest that the light will be brown.) Then, overlap the lights. (They produce yellow.) Ask students to describe why this might happen. (Accept all reasonable answers. When red cones and green cones are simultaneously excited in the eye, the brain interprets this color as yellow.) **LS** Visual

Answer to Standards Check

Sample answer: I can't see clearly through translucent objects because light is scattered as it passes through the objects. **7.6.f** (exceeding)

Figure 6 Transparent, Translucent, and Opaque

Transparent plastic makes it easy to see what you are having for lunch.

Translucent wax paper makes it a little harder to see exactly what's for lunch.

Opaque aluminum foil makes it impossible to see your lunch without unwrapping it.

Types of Matter

Matter through which visible light is easily transmitted is said to be *transparent.* Air, glass, and water are examples of transparent matter. You can see objects clearly when you view them through transparent matter.

Sometimes, windows in bathrooms are made of frosted glass. If you look through one of these windows, you will see only blurry shapes. You can't see clearly through a frosted window because it is translucent (trans LOO suhnt). *Translucent* matter transmits light but also scatters the light as it passes through the matter. Wax paper is an example of translucent matter.

Matter that does not transmit any light is said to be *opaque* (oh PAYK). You cannot see through opaque objects. Metal, wood, and this book are opaque. You can compare transparent, translucent, and opaque matter in **Figure 6.**

Standards Check Why can't you see clearly through translucent objects? **7.6.f**

Colors of Objects

How is an object's color determined? Humans see different wavelengths of light as different colors. For example, humans see long wavelengths as red and short wavelengths as violet. And, some colors, such as pink and brown, are seen when certain combinations of wavelengths are present.

The color that something appears to be is determined by the wavelengths of light that reach your eyes. Light can reach your eyes after being reflected by an object, transmitted through an object, or emitted by an object. When your eyes receive the light, they send signals to your brain. Your brain interprets the signals as colors.

Universal Access · Differentiated Instruction

Special Education Students

Seeing Through Some students, such as students with visual impairments, have difficulty understanding complicated vocabulary. Use this touch activity to explain the meaning of the words *transparent, translucent,* and *opaque.* Place a bowl of water, a ball of modeling clay, and a piece of wood on a table. Ask students to put their fingers in the water, poke a hole in the modeling clay, and tap on the wood. Explain that *transparent* means that light passes through a material easily, as their fingers pass through the water. Point out that *translucent* means that light passes through a material less readily, as they can put their fingers through modeling clay less easily. Tell students that *opaque* means that light cannot pass through something at all, as they cannot put their fingers through the wood. **LS** Kinesthetic

Figure 7 Opaque Objects and Color

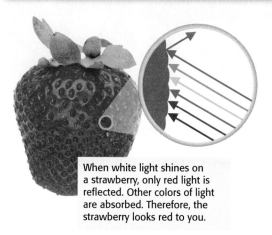

When white light shines on a strawberry, only red light is reflected. Other colors of light are absorbed. Therefore, the strawberry looks red to you.

This cow's white hair reflects all of the colors of light, but the black hair absorbs all of the colors.

Colors of Opaque Objects

When white light strikes a colored opaque object, some colors of light are absorbed, and some are reflected. Only the light that is reflected reaches your eyes and is detected. So, the colors of light that are reflected by an opaque object determine the color you see. For example, if a sweater reflects blue light and absorbs all other colors, you will see that the sweater is blue. Another example is shown on the left in **Figure 7.**

What colors of light are reflected by the cow shown on the right in **Figure 7**? Remember that white light includes all colors of light. So, white objects—such as the cow's white hair—appear white because all of the colors of light are reflected. On the other hand, black is the absence of color. When light strikes a black object, all of the colors are absorbed.

Standards Check Describe what happens to the colors in white light when the light strikes a green, opaque object?  7.6.e, 7.6.f

Colors of Transparent and Translucent Objects

The colors of transparent and translucent objects are determined differently than the colors of opaque objects. Ordinary window glass is colorless in white light because it transmits all of the colors that strike it. But some transparent or translucent objects are colored, such as the window in **Figure 8.** When you look through colored transparent or translucent objects, you see the color of light that was reflected by or transmitted through the material. The other colors were absorbed.

Figure 8 Stained glass has different colors because different colors are reflected and transmitted.

Universal Access · Differentiated Instruction

Advanced Learners/GATE

Seeing in Color Ask students to research the reactions that take place in the eye and brain that lead to the perception and interpretation of color. Students should investigate how the eye processes light and how the brain interprets it. Have students give a short oral presentation about their findings. **LS** Verbal

---

Group ACTiViTY

Color Deficiency Up to 1 in 12 men are reported to have color deficiency, or colorblindness. Colorblindness does not mean that people see in only black and white. In fact, most colorblind people can see some color, but they have difficulty distinguishing between red and green. Some colorblind people cannot distinguish between red and yellow. Based on this information, have students work in groups to design a traffic light system that would be better suited for colorblind people. **LS** Logical

Cultural Awareness

Symbolic Color Colors have symbolic meaning in many cultures. For example, red can mean danger, while green can represent safety. In the Ukraine, people color and decorate eggs to express emotions and to send messages. Egg decorators use red for love, pink for success, and black for remembrance. Ask students to study the importance of color in other cultures. Then, have students make posters that describe their findings. **LS** Verbal/Visual

Homework

Seeing Color Cone cells in the human eye react to different colors of light. Humans can detect a tremendous range of colors, tints, and shades. Ask students to make a table or chart that describes the different colors that they see at home. Have students describe as many colors as they can.
LS Visual/Intrapersonal

Answer to Standards Check

When white light strikes a green, opaque object, green light is reflected and the other colors of light are absorbed. **7.6.e** (exceeding) **7.6.f** (exceeding)

Close

Standards Focus

This **Standards Focus** provides you with a quick way to **assess, reteach,** and **re-assess** one or more concepts in the section.

Assess

1. For an object to be seen, what must happen? (Light must be emitted by or scattered from the object.) **7.6.b**

2. What is the relationship between the angle of incidence and the angle of reflection? (They are equal.) **7.6.g**

3. If the medium through which it travels does not change, how does light travel? (in straight lines) **7.6.c**

 Reteach

Learning Vocabulary Have students make flashcards to help them learn the boldface and italic terms in this section. On one side of each card, students should write a term. On the other side, student should write the definition of the term and describe a scenario that will help them remember the term.

LS Verbal **7.6.b, 7.6.f, 7.6.g**

Re-Assess

Concept Mapping Have students create a concept map that describes three ways that light interacts with matter.

LS Visual **7.6.f**

Answer to Standards Check

A pigment gives a substance its color by absorbing some colors of light and reflecting other colors. **7.6.f** (exceeding)

Figure 9 *Some leaves contain orange and yellow pigments. But you can't see these pigments if chlorophyll is present. In the fall, chlorophyll breaks down and other pigments in the leaves can be seen.*

Pigments and Color

A *pigment* is a material that gives a substance its color by absorbing some colors of light and reflecting others. Almost everything contains pigments. For example, *melanin* (MEL uh nin) is a pigment that gives your skin its color. *Chlorophyll* (KLAWR uh FIL) is the pigment that gives plants a green color. The light energy absorbed by chlorophyll is converted into chemical energy during photosynthesis. Some tree leaves have pigments other than chlorophyll, as **Figure 9** shows.

Standards Check What is a pigment? **7.6.f**

Color Subtraction

Each pigment absorbs at least one color of light. When you mix pigments together, more colors of light are absorbed or taken away. So, mixing pigments is called *color subtraction*.

The *primary pigments* are yellow, cyan, and magenta. They can be combined to make any other color. In fact, every color in this book was made by using just the primary pigments and black ink. The black ink was used to provide contrast to the images. **Figure 10** shows how the four pigments combine to produce many different colors.

Figure 10 *The picture of the balloon on the left was made by overlapping yellow ink, cyan ink, magenta ink, and black ink.*

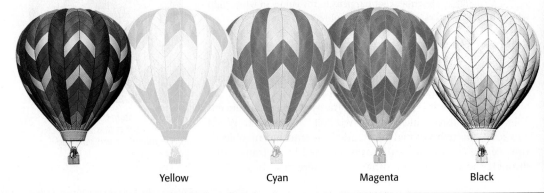

| Yellow | Cyan | Magenta | Black |

Universal Access · Differentiated Instruction

Basic Learners

Mnemonics Ask students to write mnemonics that help them remember the terms *opaque, transparent,* and *translucent.* (Sample mnemonics: opaque oak and transparent tape) Then, ask students to write mnemonics to help them remember the primary pigments. Remind students to review their mnemonics to reinforce the material.

LS Verbal

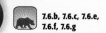
Summary

- Light travels in straight lines if the material that the light is traveling through does not change.
- The law of reflection states that the angle of incidence is equal to the angle of reflection.
- Things that are luminous can be seen because they emit light. Things that are illuminated can be seen because they reflect light.
- Absorption is the transfer of light energy to particles of matter. Scattering is an interaction of light with matter that causes light to change direction.
- Light can be reflected, transmitted, and absorbed by matter.
- Colors of opaque objects are determined by the colors of light that they reflect.
- Colors of translucent and transparent objects are determined by the colors of light they transmit and reflect.
- Pigments give objects color. The primary pigments are magenta, cyan, and yellow.

Using Vocabulary

1 Use the following terms in the same sentence: *absorption* and *scattering*.

2 Write an original definition for *reflection* and *transmission*.

Understanding Concepts

3 **Comparing** How is the angle of incidence related to the angle of reflection?

4 **Concluding** Why can you see through a car window?

5 **Describing** Name and describe at least three different ways light interacts with matter.

6 **Comparing** Explain why you can see both a light bulb and a lamp base.

7 **Summarizing** Describe how absorption and scattering can affect a beam of light.

8 **Concluding** Why do you see objects as different colors when white light is shining on them?

9 **Applying** Why is the beam of light from a flashlight that is shining in fog straight?

10 **Listing** What four colors of ink were used to print this book?

Critical Thinking

11 **Applying Concepts** What happens to the different colors of light when white light shines on an opaque, violet object?

12 **Analyzing Relationships** Explain why you can see your reflection in a spoon but not in a piece of cloth.

13 **Applying Concepts** How can you use a mirror to see around a corner? (Hint: You can draw a diagram to help explain your answer.)

INTERPRETING GRAPHICS Use the image below to answer the next question.

14 **Applying Concepts** The red rose was photographed in red light. Explain why the leaves appear black and the petals appear red.

Challenge

15 **Making Inferences** The planet Mars does not produce light. But if you look at Mars at night, it shines like a star with a reddish light. Explain why Mars shines and why you see reddish light.

Internet Resources

For a variety of links related to this chapter, go to www.scilinks.org
Topic: Colors
SciLinks code: HY70314

10. Yellow, cyan, magenta, and black were the colors of ink used to print this book.

11. When white light shines on an opaque violet object, violet light is reflected. All other colors of light are absorbed. **7.6.e** (exceeding), **7.6.f** (exceeding)

12. Light reflects off a spoon by regular reflection, so I can see my image in the spoon. But light reflects off a piece of cloth by diffuse reflection. So, I can see the cloth but not my image. **7.6.b** (supporting), **7.6.f** (exceeding)

13. Sample answer: If I place a mirror at a 45° angle near the corner of a building, light from the other side of the corner will hit the mirror and be reflected toward me on my side of the corner. (Note: Students may draw a diagram for their answer. Their diagrams should illustrate the use of the law of reflection to see around a corner.) **7.6.g** (exceeding)

14. The petals of the rose look red because the red light shining on them is reflected. The leaves of the rose look black because the leaves absorb red light and there is no green light for the leaves to reflect. **7.6.f** (exceeding)

15. Mars shines because light from the sun reflects off the planet. Mars looks reddish because Mars reflects mostly red light. Other colors of light are absorbed by the surface of the planet. **7.6.f** (exceeding)

Section Review Standards Guide			
	Supporting	**Mastering**	**Exceeding**
7.6.b	12	6	
7.6.c		9	
7.6.e		8	11
7.6.f	1, 2	4–5	7–8, 11–12, 14–15
7.6.g		3	13

Answers to Section Review

1. Sample answer: When light hits matter, the light can undergo absorption and scattering. **7.6.f** (supporting)

2. Sample answer: Reflection is the bouncing back of a ray of light. Transmission is the passing of light through matter. **7.6.f** (supporting)

3. The angle of incidence is equal to the angle of reflection. **7.6.g** (mastering)

4. I can see through a car window because light is transmitted through the window. **7.6.f** (exceeding)

5. Answers may vary. Students may describe reflection, absorption, scattering, and transmission. **7.6.f** (mastering)

6. Sample answer: I can see a light bulb because it emits light. I can see the lamp base because light reflects off the base. **7.6.b** (mastering)

7. Particles in the air absorb some energy from light traveling through air. Scattering causes light to change direction and move out of the beam of light. So, absorption and scattering can make a beam of light dimmer. **7.6.f** (exceeding)

8. White light is a mixture of different colors. When white light strikes an object, some colors of light are reflected and some are absorbed. The reflected colors determine the color of the object. **7.6.e** (mastering), **7.6.f** (exceeding)

9. The beam of light from a flashlight is straight in fog because the material through which the light is shining does not change. **7.6.c** (mastering)

Section Resources

- Directed Reading A **BASIC** (Also in Spanish), B **GENERAL**
- Interactive Reader and Study Guide
- Section Quiz **GENERAL** (Also in Spanish)
- Section Review **GENERAL** (Also in Spanish)
- Vocabulary and Section Summary A **BASIC** (Also in Spanish), B **GENERAL**

Preteach

Reviewing Prior Knowledge

Tell students that this section discusses lenses. Ask students to describe uses for lenses.

 Bellringer

Have students focus on standard 7.6.f by answering the following questions:

• Can light bend? (Yes, when it passes into another medium at an angle.)

• What happens when light passes through water? (It can bend.)

Bellringer Transparency

Motivate

Demonstration

Prisms   Show students how prisms bend light. Explain to students that light travels more slowly in the prism than it does in air, so it refracts. Point out to students that light refracts when it enters the prism and again when it leaves the prism. Help students recognize that light bends away from the boundary when it enters a denser medium and bends toward the boundary when it enters a less dense medium. **LS** Visual

Answer to Standards Check

Light undergoes refraction when it passes from one medium to another at an angle. **7.6.c** (supporting) **7.6.f** (supporting)

Q: Why did the light beam get angry at the prism?

A: The light was all bent out of shape!

What You Will Learn

• Light is refracted when the medium it travels in changes.
• Convex and concave lenses refract light to form images.
• Human eyes, magnifying glasses, cameras, telescopes, and microscopes have lenses that form images.

Why It Matters

Refraction by the cornea and lens of the eye allows you to see.

Vocabulary

• refraction   • convex lens
• lens   • concave lens

READING STRATEGY

Summarizing   Read this section silently. In pairs, take turns summarizing the material. Stop to discuss ideas and words that seem confusing.

Figure 1   *Light travels more slowly through glass than it does through air. So, light refracts as it passes at an angle from air to glass or from glass to air.*

7.6.c Students know light travels in straight lines if the medium it travels through does not change.
7.6.d Students know how simple lenses are used in a magnifying glass, the eye, a camera, a telescope, and a microscope.
7.6.e Students know that white light is a mixture of many wavelengths (colors) and that retinal cells react differently to different wavelengths.
7.6.f Students know light can be reflected, refracted, transmitted, and absorbed by matter.

Refraction

Key Concept   Light can be bent, or refracted, by matter. Lenses refract light to form images.

▶ Imagine that you and a friend are at a lake. Your friend wades into the water. You look at her, and her feet appear to have separated from her legs! You know her feet did not fall off, so how can you explain what you see? The answer has to do with refraction.

Refraction and Media

Light often travels through a medium, such as air, glass, or water. A *medium* is a substance through which a wave can travel. The plural of *medium* is *media*. If the medium through which light is travelling does not change, the light travels in a straight line. But if the medium changes, refraction can happen. **Refraction** is the bending of a wave as it passes at an angle from one medium to another. Refraction, shown in **Figure 1,** is one way that light interacts with matter.

Refraction can also happen when the density of a medium varies. For example, on sunny days, the air above a paved road has a higher temperature than the air around it has. So, the air above the road has a lower density than the surrounding air has. If you look over the pavement, the objects in the distance may seem to shimmer or wobble because of refraction.

Standards Check   When does light undergo refraction?   **7.6.c, 7.6.f**

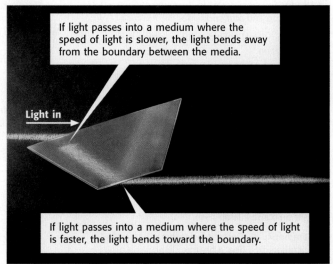

If light passes into a medium where the speed of light is slower, the light bends away from the boundary between the media.

Light in

If light passes into a medium where the speed of light is faster, the light bends toward the boundary.

Universal Access · Differentiated Instruction

Struggling Readers

Paired Summarizing   Group students into pairs, and have them read silently about refraction and media. Then, have one student summarize the main points of refraction and media. The other student should listen to the retelling and should point out any inaccuracies or ideas that were left out. Allow students to refer to the text as needed. **LS** Verbal

---

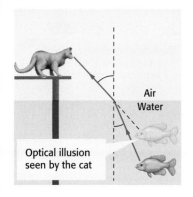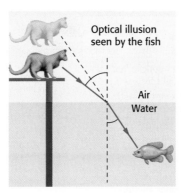

Optical illusion
seen by the fish

Air
Water

Air
Water

Optical illusion
seen by the cat

Figure 2 *Because of refraction, the cat and the fish see optical illusions. To the cat, the fish appears closer than it really is. To the fish, the cat appears farther away than it actually is.*

Refraction and Optical Illusions

Usually, when you look at an object, the light reflected by the object travels in a straight line from the object to your eye. Your brain always interprets light as traveling in straight lines. But when you look at something that is underwater, the light reflected by it does not travel in a straight line. Instead, it refracts. **Figure 2** shows how refraction creates an optical illusion. A similar kind of illusion causes a person's feet to appear separated from his or her legs when the person is wading.

Refraction and Color Separation

White light is made up of all of the wavelengths, or colors, of visible light. When white light is refracted, the amount that the light bends depends on its wavelength. Waves that have short wavelengths bend more than waves that have long wavelengths do. As **Figure 3** shows, white light can be separated into different colors during refraction. Color separation by refraction is responsible for rainbows. Rainbows form when sunlight is refracted by water drops.

Standards Check How do rainbows form? 🐾 **7.6.e, 7.6.f**

refraction (ri FRAK shuhn) the bending of a wavefront as the wavefront passes between two substances in which the speed of the wave differs

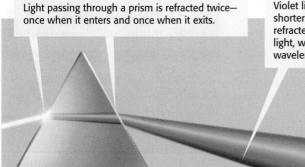

Light passing through a prism is refracted twice—once when it enters and once when it exits.

Violet light, which has a shorter wavelength, is refracted more than red light, which has a longer wavelength.

Figure 3 *A prism is a piece of glass that separates white light into the colors of visible light by refraction.*

Quick Lab 10 min

Teacher Notes

In this activity, students will see how refraction causes an optical illusion (covers standards 7.6.c and 7.6.f).

Materials for Each Group
- beaker, 250 mL, or cup, clear plastic
- pencil
- water

Safety Caution

Remind students to review all safety cautions and icons before beginning this activity.

Answers

2. Sample answer: The pencil is whole and is resting on the side of the container. It looks the same from all angles.

5. Sample answer: I have to look at an angle through the side of the glass and down through the top of the water's surface to see a broken pencil.

6. Sample answer: I have to look straight down through the top of the glass to see the pencil in one piece.

7. Sample answer: Changing the angle at which I look at the pencil changes the path the light that reflects off the pencil takes to reach my eye. If I look from some angles, the light is refracted before it reaches my eyes, and the pencil appears broken. If I look from other angles, the light is not refracted and the pencil appears in one piece.

Differentiated Datasheets
A BASIC, B GENERAL, C ADVANCED

Also editable on the
Holt Lab Generator
CD-ROM

Quick Lab

Refracting Water

In this activity, you will see an optical illusion created by the refraction of light by water.

1. Place a **pencil** in a **clear, empty plastic cup** or an empty **250 mL beaker.** The pencil should be leaning against the side of the container.

2. Study the pencil from all angles. Write a description of what you see.

3. Watch the pencil from the side as you slowly pour **water** into the container. Fill the container half full with water.

4. Study the pencil from all angles again.

5. The pencil should look different when viewed from different angles. Describe how to look at the pencil to make it appear to be broken.

6. How do you have to look at the pencil to see it in one piece?

7. Why does changing the angle at which you look at the pencil change what you see?

 7.6.c 7.6.f

⏱ 10 min

lens (LENZ) a transparent object that refracts light waves such that they converge or diverge to create an image

Lenses and Refraction of Light

What do cameras, telescopes, and the human eye have in common? They all use lenses to form images. A **lens** is a transparent object that forms an image by refracting, or bending, light. Two kinds of lenses, convex and concave, are shown in **Figure 4.** The yellow beams in **Figure 4** show that light rays that pass through the center of any lens are not refracted. The point at which beams of light cross after going through a lens is called the *focal point*. The distance between the lens and the focal point is called a *focal length*.

Figure 4 How Lenses Refract Light

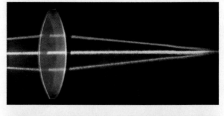

When light rays pass through a convex lens, the rays are refracted toward each other.

When light rays pass through a concave lens, the rays are refracted away from each other.

Universal Access · Differentiated Instruction

Struggling Readers

Mental Memory Cues Tell students that one way to remember details that you are reading is to make a mental memory cue while reading. Ask students to share a mental memory cue that they could use to help them remember the differences between concave and convex lenses. (Sample answer: a conCAVE lens is thinner in the middle, so it looks like the entrance to a CAVE, while a conveX lens is eXtra thick in the middle, so it bulges out.) **LS** Logical/Intrapersonal

Figure 5 How Convex Lenses Form Images

If an object is less than 1 focal length away from a convex lens, a virtual image is formed. The image is larger than the object.

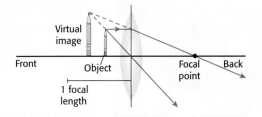

If an object is more than 2 focal lengths away from the lens, a real image is formed. The image is inverted and is smaller than the object.

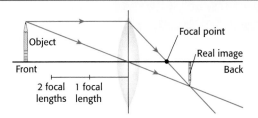

Convex Lenses

A lens that is thicker in the middle than at the edges is a **convex lens.** Convex lenses can form real images and virtual images. A *real image* can be projected onto a screen because light passes through the image. A *virtual image* cannot be projected because light doesn't travel through the image.

A magnifying glass has a convex lens. A magnifying glass can form images of an object that are larger or smaller than the object is. **Figure 5** shows how a convex lens, such as the lens in a magnifying glass, forms two kinds of images.

The lens of the human eye is also a convex lens. This lens refracts light and focuses the light on the back surface, or retina, of the eye, as shown in **Figure 6.** The muscles that hold the lens of the eye can change the shape of the lens to help it focus images. The cornea of the eye also refracts light.

convex lens (kahn VEKS LENZ) a lens that is thicker in the middle than at the edges

Standards Check How are lenses used in a magnifying glass and in the eye? 🐛 **7.6.d**

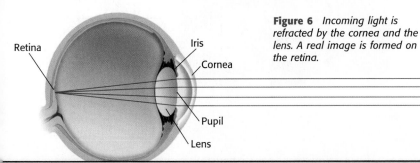

Retina

Iris

Cornea

Pupil

Lens

Figure 6 *Incoming light is refracted by the cornea and the lens. A real image is formed on the retina.*

Light rays

Homework

Corrective Lenses Have students research how lenses are used to correct vision. Students should understand the physiological characteristics of the sight disorder and how lenses are used to help a person see clearly. Have students write a short story in which lenses are used to correct a character's vision. Remind students that their stories should show sensitivity to people who use corrective lenses and that students should show sensitivity to such people in everyday life.
LS Verbal

CONNECTION ACTIVITY
Art

Photography Photography is a combination of art and science. A photographer must understand the processes that enable film, light, and lenses to work together to produce an image. Invite a photographer to speak to your class. Before the photographer arrives, have students prepare interview questions. Students should learn how a photographer understands and uses light and lenses to his or her advantage.
LS Verbal/Interpersonal

Answer to Standards Check

When light travels through a concave lens, light rays are refracted and bent away from each other. **7.6.f** (exceeding)

Figure 7 *The four-eyed fish has eyes specially adapted to see above and below water at the same time.*

concave lens (kahn CAYV LENZ) a lens that is thinner in the middle than at the edges

Animal Eyes

Many animal eyes also contain convex lenses. The lenses of animal eyes focus light in a way similar to the way that the lenses of human eyes focus light. However, some animal eyes are very different from human eyes.

For example, dragonflies have compound eyes. Compound eyes are made of thousands of lens-like facets that each form a separate image. The dragonfly's brain uses these images to form a composite image.

Another animal that has interesting eyes is a fish called the *four-eyed fish*. This fish, shown in **Figure 7,** does not actually have four eyes. Each of the fish's two eyes are divided into two regions. The upper and lower regions of the eyes are shaped differently and have separate retinas. When the fish swims on the surface of the water, part of each eye is above water and part is below. The differences in the two regions allow the fish to see above water and below water at the same time.

Concave Lenses

A **concave lens** is a lens that is thinner in the middle than at the edges. Light rays entering a concave lens are refracted and bend away from each other. For a distant object, the refracted rays appear to come from a focal point in front of the lens. But the rays never actually meet. So, concave lenses do not form a real image. Instead, they form virtual images, as shown in **Figure 8.**

Standards Check What happens to light when it travels through a concave lens? **7.6.f**

Figure 4 **How a Concave Lens Forms an Image**

 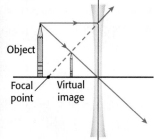

Concave lenses can form only virtual images. The image formed is always smaller than the object.

Advanced Learners/GATE

Animal Eyes Ask students to investigate how different animals see, the spectrum their eyes interpret, and how the eye is specialized to help the animal survive. Some of the adaptations that students may want to investigate are binocular vision, compound eyes, and the ability to see other than visible light. Students should study the structure of the eye and its adaptive advantages. Then, have students prepare a multimedia presentation for the class. **LS** Visual

Optical Instruments and Refraction

Optical instruments are things that help people make observations. Many optical instruments contain convex and concave lenses that refract light to form images.

Some optical instruments help you see things that are very far away. Others help you see things that are very small. Some optical instruments record images. The optical instrument that you are probably most familiar with is the camera.

Cameras

Cameras are used to record images as photos. The way a camera works is similar to the way your eye works. Like your eye, a camera has a lens that focuses light to form an image. But unlike your eye, the lens of a camera is moved back-and-forth to focus light. The image formed by a camera lens is focused on the film. The image is then recorded on the film. **Figure 9** shows the parts of a 35 mm camera and explains how a camera works.

A digital camera has a lens, a shutter, and an aperture (AP uhr chuhr) like a 35 mm camera has. But instead of using film, a digital camera uses light sensors to record images. The sensors send an electrical signal to a computer in the camera. This signal carries data about the image that are stored in the computer and then on a memory stick, card, or disk.

Standards Check What does the lens of a camera do? 7.6.d

Figure 9 How a Camera Works

The shutter opens and closes behind the lens to control how much light enters the camera. The longer the shutter is open, the more light enters the camera.

The lens of a camera is a convex lens that focuses light on the film. Moving the lens focuses light from objects at different distances.

The film is coated with chemicals that react when they are exposed to light. The result is an image stored on the film.

The aperture is an opening that lets light into the camera. The larger the aperture is, the more light enters the camera.

Standards Focus

This **Standards Focus** provides you with a quick way to **assess, reteach,** and **re-assess** one or more concepts in the section.

Assess

1. Which optical instrument allows people to see things that are far away? (telescope) **7.6.d**

2. What are three items that contain lenses? (Sample answer: magnifying glass, microscope, and telescope) **7.6.d**

Reteach

Illustrating Refraction Ask students to draw pictures showing three different effects of refraction. For example, students may show a rainbow, an optical illusion of a broken pencil, and a magnifying glass in use.

LS Visual **7.6.f**

Re-Assess

Making Tables Have students make tables that describe the two types of lenses, where each is found, and how each is used. Students should also identify how the lenses affect light.

LS Logical **7.6.d**

Answer to Math Practice

$(5\times) \times (20\times) = 100\times$

Answer to Standards Check

The objective lenses in telescopes and microscopes form real images. The ocular lenses magnify the real image.
7.6.d (mastering)

🖥 Teaching Transparency: L9 How a Refracting Telescope Works; How a Light Microscope Works

---

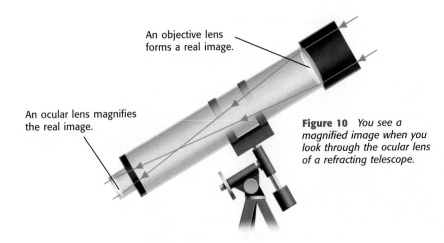

An objective lens forms a real image.

An ocular lens magnifies the real image.

Figure 10 *You see a magnified image when you look through the ocular lens of a refracting telescope.*

Telescopes

Telescopes are used to see images of large, distant objects. Astronomers use telescopes to study things in space, such as planets and stars. Telescopes that use lenses to focus light are called *refracting telescopes*. A simple refracting telescope has two convex lenses. An objective lens points toward the object being studied. An ocular lens is the lens that you look through. **Figure 10** shows how these lenses are used in a telescope.

Light Microscopes

Simple light microscopes are similar to refracting telescopes. These microscopes also have two convex lenses. Biologists use microscopes to see magnified images of tiny, nearby objects, such as cells and microscopic organisms. **Figure 11** explains how a microscope works.

Standards Check How are lenses used in telescopes and in microscopes? **7.6.d**

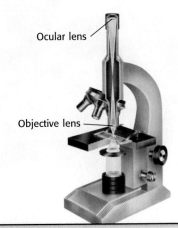

Ocular lens

Objective lens

Figure 11 *The objective lens of a microscope forms a real image. The ocular lens then produces a larger virtual image that you see when you look through the microscope.*

MATH PRACTICE

Microscope Magnification

Some microscopes use more than one lens to magnify objects. The power of each lens indicates the amount of magnification the lens gives. For example, a 10× lens magnifies objects 10 times. To find the amount of magnification given by two or more lenses used together, multiply the powers of the lenses. What is the magnification given by a 5× lens used with a 20× lens?

Universal Access · Differentiated Instruction

Special Education Students

Reviewing Words Students may have difficulty recalling terms that they have previously learned. For these students, it is helpful to review the meanings of any words that are not commonly used. Before having students read this page, write these words on the board: *lenses, focus, refraction, convex lens, cells,* and *microscopic organisms.* Ask students to read the words aloud chorally. Then, ask volunteers to use each word in a sentence. **LS** Verbal

Summary

- Light travels in straight lines if the medium through which the light travels does not change.
- Refraction is the bending of a wave, such as light, as it passes at an angle from one medium to another.
- Refraction of light can create optical illusions and can separate white light into different colors.
- Lenses form images by refracting light.
- Convex lenses produce both real images and virtual images.
- A magnifying glass and the lens of the human eye are convex lenses.
- Concave lenses produce only virtual images.
- Cameras, telescopes, and microscopes are optical instruments that use lenses to form images.

Using Vocabulary

1. Use *refraction* and *lens* in the same sentence.

2. Explain how the meanings of *convex lens* and *concave lens* differ.

Understanding Concepts

3. **Applying** Why do you not normally see refraction when you look across a room?

4. **Describing** Explain the role of lenses in a magnifying glass, a camera, a telescope, a microscope, and the human eye.

5. **Summarizing** What happens to white light when it passes at an angle through a prism?

6. **Describing** What happens when light is refracted by matter?

7. **Comparing** How are telescopes and microscopes similar? How are they different?

8. **Analyzing** What are the similarities and differences between a camera and the human eye?

Critical Thinking

9. **Forming Hypotheses** Imagine that you are toasting a piece of bread in a toaster. As you wait for your toast, you notice that the air above the toaster appears to be wiggling or shimmering. Form a hypothesis that explains what you see.

10. **Making Inferences** Teachers sometimes use overhead projectors to show transparencies on a screen. What type of lens does an overhead projector use? Explain your reasoning.

INTERPRETING GRAPHICS Use the image below to answer the next two questions.

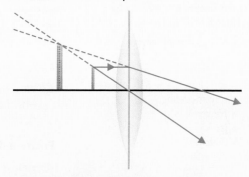

11. **Applying Concepts** What kind of lens is shown in the diagram?

12. **Making Inferences** Is the lens forming a real image or a virtual image?

Challenge

13. **Predicting Consequences** Some animals have simple eyes called *ocelli*. Ocelli have receptors that can detect light, but do not have lenses. What do you think an animal that has ocelli sees?

Internet Resources

For a variety of links related to this chapter, go to www.scilinks.org
Topic: Lenses
SciLinks code: HY70868

8. Sample answer: A camera and the eye are similar because they both contain lenses that focus light. A camera and the eye are different because the lens of a camera moves back and forth to properly focus light and the lens of the eye changes shape to properly focus light. **7.6.d** (mastering)

9. Sample answer: The toaster is heating the air above it. This heating causes the air above the toaster to have a lower density than the surrounding air. Because the air has a different density, light refracts as it passes through it, and the air appears to wiggle or shimmer. **7.6.c** (exceeding), **7.6.f** (exceeding)

10. An overhead projector has a convex lens. Convex lenses can form real images, but concave lenses cannot. Only real images can be projected onto a screen.

11. A convex lens is shown in the diagram.

12. The image formed is a virtual image.

13. Sample answer: An animal that has ocelli can probably tell the difference between light and dark and can probably see some movement. But the animal cannot see focused images because it does not have lenses that can focus light. **7.6.d** (exceeding)

Section Review Standards Guide

	Supporting	Mastering	Exceeding
7.6.c		3	9
7.6.d	1–2	4, 7–8	13
7.6.e			5
7.6.f	1	5–6	9

Answers to Section Review

1. Sample answer: A lens bends light by refraction. **7.6.d** (supporting), **7.6.f** (supporting)

2. Sample answer: A convex lens is thicker in the middle than at the edges. A concave lens is thinner in the middle than at the edges. **7.6.d** (supporting)

3. Sample answer: I don't see refraction when I look across a room because the medium through which light is traveling doesn't change. So, light travels in a straight line and does not refract. **7.6.c** (mastering)

4. Sample answer: The lenses in a magnifying glass, a camera, a telescope, a microscope, and the human eye focus light to form images. **7.6.d** (mastering)

5. When white light passes through a prism, refraction separates the light into different colors. **7.6.e** (exceeding) **7.6.f** (mastering)

6. Light is bent when it is refracted by matter. **7.6.f** (mastering)

7. Sample answer: Microscopes and telescopes are similar because they both have objective lenses and ocular lenses. They are different because telescopes are used to see images of large, distant objects and microscopes are used to see tiny, nearby objects. **7.6.d** (mastering)

Section Resources

- Directed Reading A **BASIC** (Also in Spanish), B **GENERAL**
- Interactive Reader and Study Guide
- Section Quiz **GENERAL** (Also in Spanish)
- Section Review **GENERAL** (Also in Spanish)
- Vocabulary and Section Summary A **BASIC** (Also in Spanish), B **GENERAL**

Teacher Notes

In this activity, students use a convex lens to form three different images (covers standards 7.6.d and 7.6.f).

Time Required

One 45-min class period

Lab Ratings

EASY ——————→ HARD

Teacher Prep △
Student Set-Up △
Concept Level △△△
Clean Up △

Materials

The materials listed on the student page are enough for a pair of students. Lenses with a focal length of around 25 cm work well.

Safety Caution

Remind students to review all safety cautions and icons before beginning this lab activity. Caution students about working over an open flame. Before beginning the experiment, students should tie back any loose hair or clothing. If you are concerned about having your students work with an open flame, you can do this lab as a demonstration.

Lab Notes

Image 1 forms when the distance between the candle and the card is four times the focal length of the lens. However, students do NOT need to know the focal length of the lens to complete this exercise.

Images from Convex Lenses

A convex lens is thicker in the center than at the edges. Parallel light rays passing through a convex lens come together at a focal point. Under certain conditions, a convex lens will create a real image of an object. The characteristics of this image depend on the distance between the object and the lens. In this experiment, you will determine the characteristics of real images created by a convex lens—the kind of lens that is used as a magnifying lens.

Ask a Question

1. What are the characteristics of real images created by a convex lens? For example, are the images upright or inverted (upside down)? Are the images larger or smaller than the object?

Form a Hypothesis

2. Write a hypothesis that is a possible answer to the questions above. Explain your reasoning.

Test the Hypothesis

3. Copy the table below.

	Data Collection			
Image	Orientation (upright/ inverted)	Size (larger/ smaller)	Image distance (cm)	Object distance (cm)
1				
2		DO NOT WRITE IN BOOK		
3				

OBJECTIVES

Use a convex lens to form images.

Determine the characteristics of real images formed by convex lenses.

MATERIALS

- candle
- card, index, 4 × 6 in. or larger
- clay, modeling
- convex lens
- jar lid
- matches
- meterstick

SAFETY

7.6.d Students know how simple lenses are used in a magnifying glass, the eye, a camera, a telescope, and a microscope.
7.6.f Students know how light can be reflected, refracted, transmitted, and absorbed by matter.

Lab Resources

📁 Differentiated Datasheets
A BASIC, B GENERAL, C ADVANCED

💿 Classroom Lab Video/DVD

⦿ Holt Lab Generator CD-ROM

Search for any lab by topic, standard, difficulty level, or time. Edit any lab to fit your needs, or create your own labs. Use the Lab Materials QuickList software to customize your lab materials list.

④ Use modeling clay to make a base for the lens. Place the lens and base in the middle of the table.

⑤ Stand the index card upright in some modeling clay on one side of the lens.

⑥ Place the candle in the jar lid, and anchor it with some modeling clay. Place the candle on the table so that the lens is halfway between the candle and the card. Light the candle. **Caution:** Use extreme care around an open flame.

⑦ In a darkened room, slowly move the card and the candle away from the lens while keeping the lens exactly halfway between the card and the candle. Continue until you see a clear image of the candle flame on the card. This image is image 1.

⑧ Measure and record the distance between the lens and the card (image distance) and the distance between the lens and the candle (object distance).

⑨ Is the image upright or inverted? Is it larger or smaller than the candle? Record this information in the table.

⑩ Move the lens toward the candle. The new object distance should be less than half the object distance measured in step 8. Move the card back-and-forth until you find a sharp image (image 2) of the candle on the card.

⑪ Repeat steps 8 and 9 for image 2.

⑫ Leave the card and candle in place, and move the lens toward the card to get the third image (image 3).

⑬ Repeat steps 8 and 9 for image 3.

Analyze the Results

⑭ **Recognizing Patterns** Describe the pattern between image distance and image size.

⑮ **Examining Data** What are the similarities between the real images that are formed by a convex lens?

Draw Conclusions

⑯ **Making Predictions** The lens of your eye is a convex lens. Use the information that you collected to describe the image projected on the back of your eye when you look at an object.

Big Idea Question

⑰ **Making Predictions** Light can interact with matter in many different ways. Describe four different ways that light from the candle may have interacted with matter in the room.

Applying Your Data

Convex lenses are used in film projectors. Explain why your favorite movie stars are truly "larger than life" on the screen in terms of image distance and object distance.

Analyze the Results

14. When the image distance gets larger, the image size gets larger.

15. The images are inverted.

Draw Conclusions

16. Sample answer: The image projected on the back of my eye is a real image that is inverted and is smaller than the object.

Big Idea Question

17. Sample answer: Light from the candle reflected off my shirt, which allowed me to see my shirt. Light from the candle was refracted by the lens and formed an image on the card. Light from the candle was transmitted through the air so I could see the candle from anywhere in the room. Light from the candle was absorbed by the jar lid.

Applying Your Data

The object distance (from the film to the lens) is much smaller than the image distance (from the lens to the screen). Thus, the image projected on the screen is very large compared with the size of the image on the film itself.

Joel S. Brener
Daniel Webster Middle School
Los Angeles, California

Teacher Notes

In this activity, students will learn how to use a light microscope properly (covers standard 7.7.a). Students can work on this activity in small groups. Prepared slides of organisms that have large cells work best for this activity.

Materials for Each Group
- light microscope
- prepared slide

Answers to You Try It!

3. Answers may vary. Students should have at least two drawings of the same microorganism. The drawings should show the microorganism as viewed using different objective lenses.

4. Sample answer: When I used an objective lens with a higher power, I saw an image that was larger and more detailed.

5. Sample answer: A biologist could attach a camera to a microscope to take photographs of the microscopic organisms. The photographs could then be printed and displayed for others to see.

 Datasheet **GENERAL**

Also editable on the Holt Lab Generator CD-ROM

Science Skills Activity

| Scientific Methods | Research | Data Analysis | Models, Maps & Diagrams |

Investigation and Experimentation
7.7.a Select and use appropriate tools and technology (including calculators, computers, balances, spring scales, microscopes, and binoculars) to perform tests, collect data, and display data.

Using a Microscope to Collect Data

▶ Tutorial

A microscope is a tool often used by life scientists to collect data. Follow these instructions when you use a light microscope.

1 Turn on the light source of your microscope, and select the low-power objective lens.

2 Light from the light source passes through a small hole in the stage. Place a prepared slide over this hole. Secure the slide with the stage clips.

3 Look at the stage from eye level. Slowly turn the adjustment knob to lower the objective lens until the lens almost touches the slide.

4 Look through the ocular lens. Turn the adjustment knob to raise the objective lens until the image is in focus.

5 Make sure that the image is exactly in the center of your field of vision. Then, switch to the high-power objective. If necessary, use the adjustment knob to focus.

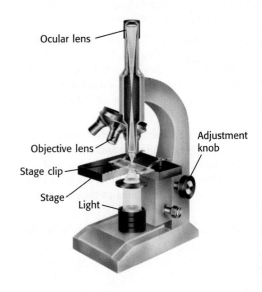

Ocular lens

Adjustment knob

Objective lens

Stage clip

Stage

Light

▶ You Try It!

Procedure

1 Obtain a **light microscope,** and identify its parts. Learn how the various parts work. When you are familiar with how the microscope works, ask your teacher for a **prepared slide.**

2 Follow the steps described above to view the slide. Be sure to view the slide by using at least two different objective lenses.

Analysis

3 **Collecting Data** Draw a diagram of the image that you saw when you used each objective lens.

4 **Identifying Relationships** How did the different objective lenses change what you saw?

5 **Making Inferences** Biologists often use microscopes to collect data about microscopic organisms. How could a biologist adapt a microscope to display data? (Hint: Think about other kinds of optical instruments.)

Universal Access · Differentiated Instruction

Basic Learners

Partners in Sight Some students learn better when in a group with learners who clearly understand the task. Pair basic learners with more advanced learners. Ask the members of each pair to take turns reading and discussing the steps to this Science Skills Activity so that they understand the activity. Make sure that partners are both participating and that they are addressing the steps in the intended order.
LS Verbal/Interpersonal

English Learners

Microscope Parts Some students need to do more than look at a labeled diagram to learn the parts of a microscope. Conduct a quick review. Ask students to close their books so that the diagram is not visible. Then, call out the following parts and ask students to point to the parts on their microscopes: *stage clip, objective lens, stage, adjustment knob, light,* and *ocular lens.* **LS Visual/Kinesthetic**

Chapter Summary

The Big Idea   Light is an electromagnetic wave that interacts with matter in many different ways.

Section

Vocabulary

1 The Electromagnetic Spectrum

Key Concept   Visible light, infrared waves, and ultraviolet light are small parts of a large electromagnetic spectrum.

- Light is an electromagnetic wave.
- Visible light is a small part of a very broad electromagnetic spectrum.
- White light is a mixture of many wavelengths of visible light.
- Infrared waves and ultraviolet light affect living things.

Exposure to ultraviolet light can cause sunburn.

electromagnetic **wave** p. 76
electromagnetic **spectrum** p. 77

2 Interactions of Light with Matter

Key Concept   Light interacts with matter during reflection, absorption, scattering, and transmission.

- Light travels in straight lines if the material that the light travels through does not change.
- The angle of reflection of a light beam is equal to the angle of incidence.
- An object can be seen if light emitted by or reflected by it is detected by the eye.
- Light can be reflected, absorbed, scattered, or transmitted by matter.

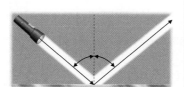

The angle of reflection is equal to the angle of incidence.

reflection p. 82
absorption p. 84
scattering p. 85
transmission p. 85

3 Refraction

Key Concept   Light can be bent, or refracted, by matter. Lenses refract light to form images.

- Light is refracted when the medium it travels in changes.
- Convex and concave lenses refract light to form images.
- Human eyes, magnifying glasses, cameras, telescopes, and microscopes have lenses that form images.

The lens of the eye refracts light and focuses the light on the retina.

refraction p. 90
lens p. 92
convex lens p. 93
concave lens p. 94

Review Resources

- 📋 Reinforcement Worksheet **BASIC**
- 📋 Critical Thinking Worksheet **ADVANCED**
- 📋 Chapter Review **GENERAL** (Also in Spanish)
- 📖 Standards Review Workbook (Also in Spanish)
- 📖 Study Guide A **BASIC** (Also in Spanish), B **GENERAL**

Assessment Resources

- 📋 Chapter Tests A **BASIC**, B **GENERAL** (Also in Spanish), C **ADVANCED**
- 📋 Standards Assessment **GENERAL**

Chapter Summary

SUPER SUMMARY

Have students connect the major concepts in this chapter through an interactive Super Summary. Visit go.hrw.com and type in the keyword HY7LOWS to access the Super Summary for this chapter.

Identifying Prefixes

Group Activity   Ask students to look over the vocabulary words from this chapter and to identify the words that have prefixes. (*electromagnetic, reflection, transmission, refraction, convex,* and *concave*) Then, have students work in small groups to determine what each prefix means. Encourage students to use their textbook and a dictionary to find their answers. (*electro-*: electricity; *re-*: again or backward; *trans-*: across; *con-*: with or together) **LS** Verbal

Focus on Reading

Paired Reading   Have students work in pairs. Have one member of each pair read an objective from the Chapter Summary (*i.e.* a bullet point on this page). The other member of the pair should find the corresponding text in a Section Summary and read it aloud. Students should take turns until all of the objectives and the Section Summaries have been read aloud. **LS** Verbal/Interpersonal

Chapter Review

Assignment Guide

Section	Questions
1	3, 5, 23, 26
2	2, 6–8, 10, 14–15, 17, 21–22, 24, 27
3	1, 4, 9, 11–13, 16, 18–20, 25

Answers

Using Vocabulary

1. c

2. Reflection **7.6.f** (supporting)

3. electromagnetic spectrum **7.6.a** (mastering)

4. Refraction **7.6.f** (supporting)

5. electromagnetic wave **7.6.a** (supportng)

6. transmission **7.6.f** (supporting)

Understanding Concepts

7. c **7.6.f** (exceeding)

8. c **7.6.b** (exceeding)

9. b **7.6.e** (exceeding), **7.6.f** (exceeding)

10. Sample answer: To see an object, my eye must detect light emitted by the object or reflected off the object. **7.6.b** (mastering)

11. Sample answer: Convex lenses are found in magnifying glasses and in the human eye. These lenses focus light to form images. **7.6.d** (mastering)

12. Sample answer: The lenses in telescopes and microscopes form enlarged images that people can see and study. People can use these images to make observations of objects that are far away or objects that are very small. **7.6.d** (mastering)

13. Sample answer: Sunlight is white light. White light is a mixture of different colors of light. So, when sunlight passes through water drops, the light is refracted and separated into colors to form a rainbow. **7.6.e** (mastering)

14. Sample answer: When light is reflected, the light waves bounce off matter. When light is refracted, the light waves bend as they enter a new medium. When light is transmitted, the light waves pass through matter. When light is absorbed, energy is transferred to matter. **7.6.f** (mastering)

15. The angle of reflection is the angle between the reflected beam and the normal. The angle of incidence is the angle between the incident beam and the normal. The angle of reflection is equal to the angle of incidence. **7.6.g** (mastering)

16. Sample answer: The large beam of light does not bend because it does not strike the boundary between the water and the air at an angle. Refraction occurs only when light waves pass from one medium to another at an angle. **7.6.c** (mastering)

17. Sample answer: The bottom light beam is reflecting off the surface of the water. **7.6.f** (mastering)

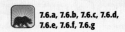
Organize

Key-Term Fold Review the FoldNote that you created at the beginning of the chapter. Add to or correct the FoldNote based on what you have learned.

Using Vocabulary

1 **Academic Vocabulary** Which of the following is the plural form of the word *medium*?
a. mediums
b. medians
c. media
d. medias

Complete each of the following sentences by choosing the correct term from the word bank.

refraction	reflection
scattering	transmission
electromagnetic	electromagnetic
wave	spectrum

2 ___ happens when light waves bounce off matter.

3 Visible light is a small part of the ___.

4 ___ happens when light waves enter a new medium at an angle.

5 Light is a kind of ___ and therefore can travel through matter and space.

6 During ___, light travels through an object.

Understanding Concepts

Multiple Choice

7 Objects that transmit light easily are
a. opaque.
b. translucent.
c. transparent.
d. colored.

8 You can see yourself in a mirror because of
a. absorption.
b. scattering.
c. regular reflection.
d. diffuse reflection.

9 Prisms produce the colors of the rainbow through
a. reflection.
b. refraction.
c. scattering.
d. absorption.

Short Answer

10 **Describing** What has to happen to light for you to see an object?

11 **Identifying** What kind of lenses are found in magnifying glasses and in the human eye? What do these lenses do?

12 **Summarizing** Describe how the lenses in telescopes and microscopes help people make observations.

13 **Concluding** Why can sunlight form a rainbow?

14 **Listing** Explain what happens to light when it is reflected, refracted, transmitted, and absorbed by matter.

15 **Comparing** What are the angle of reflection and the angle of incidence? How are they related?

INTERPRETING GRAPHICS Use the image below to answer the next two questions.

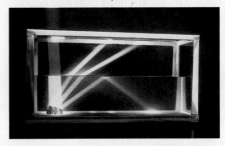

16 **Analyzing** Why doesn't the large beam of light bend like the two beams in the middle of the tank?

17 **Identifying** Which interaction of light explains what is happening to the bottom light beam?

Writing Skills

18 Communicating Key Concepts Analyze the information in one section of this chapter. Then, write a one-page paper that identifies and explains the main concepts in your own words. Be sure to use vocabulary words from the section in your paper.

Critical Thinking

19 Concept Mapping Use the following terms to create a concept map: *light, matter, reflection, absorption, refraction,* and *transmission*.

20 Applying Concepts A tern is a type of bird that dives underwater to catch fish. When a young tern begins learning to catch fish, the bird is rarely successful. The tern has to learn that when a fish appears to be in a certain place underwater, the fish is actually in a slightly different place. Why does the tern see the fish in the wrong place?

21 Evaluating Conclusions Imagine that you are teaching your brother about light. You tell him that white light is light of all of the colors of the rainbow combined. But your brother says that you are wrong because mixing different colors of paint produces black and not white. Why is your brother's conclusion wrong?

22 Making Inferences If you look around a parking lot during the summer, you might see sunshades set up in the windshields of cars. How do sunshades help keep the insides of cars cool?

23 Identifying Relationships What is the electromagnetic spectrum? How is the visible spectrum related to the electromagnetic spectrum?

24 Applying Concepts Imagine that you are at a concert. While the music is playing, beams of laser light flash through the air. The light beams travel in straight lines. What can you conclude about the medium through which the light is travelling?

INTERPRETING GRAPHICS Use the images below to answer the next question.

A

B

C

25 Analyzing Processes Each photo shows at least one interaction of light with matter. Identify the interactions shown.

Math Skills

26 Making Conversions One nanometer (1 nm) is equal to 0.000000001 m. Visible light has wavelengths between 400 nm and 750 nm. Convert this range of wavelengths to meters.

Challenge

27 Predicting Consequences The phrase "looking at the world through rose-colored glasses," is an adage that means that a person has an overly positive view of things. What would you expect to see if you actually looked at the world through rose-colored glasses?

23. The electromagnetic spectrum is the entire range of electromagnetic waves. The visible spectrum is the small part of the electromagnetic spectrum that humans can see. **7.6.a** (mastering)

24. Sample answer: The medium through which the light is traveling does not change because the beams of light are straight. Light always travels in straight lines if the medium it travels through does not change. **7.6.c** (mastering)

25. **a.** refraction
    b. absorption and scattering (also acceptable: reflection or diffuse reflection)
    c. reflection
    7.6.c (mastering), **7.6.f** (mastering)

Math Skills

26. 400 nm = 0.0000004 m and 750 nm = 0.00000075 m

Challenge

27. Sample answer: Anything that emitted or reflected red light would appear red to me. But anything that absorbed red light would look black to me. **7.6.b** (exceeding)

Chapter Review Standards Guide			
	Supporting	Mastering	Exceeding
7.6.a	5	3, 23	
7.6.b		10	8, 21, 27
7.6.c		16, 24–25	20
7.6.d		11, 12	
7.6.e		13	9, 21
7.6.f	2, 4, 6	14, 17, 19, 25	7, 9, 20, 22
7.6.g		15	

Writing Skills

18. Answers may vary. Answers should meet all the requirements stated in the question.

Critical Thinking

19. An answer to this exercise can be found at the end of this book. **7.6.f** (mastering)

20. Sample answer: The tern sees the fish in the wrong place because light refracts as it passes from the water to the air. This refraction creates an optical illusion for the tern. **7.6.c** (exceeding), **7.6.f** (exceeding)

21. Sample answer: My brother's conclusion is wrong because mixing colors of light is not the same as mixing colors of paint. Paint contains pigments that absorb light. When you mix colors of paint, you mix pigments that absorb different colors of light. When enough pigments are mixed, all colors of light are absorbed and you see black. **7.6.b** (exceeding), **7.6.e** (exceeding)

22. Sample answer: Sunshades keep the interior of the cars from getting very hot because sunshades reflect light that is transmitted through the windshield of the car. Because the light reflects back out through the window, the light cannot warm the inside of the car. **7.6.f** (exceeding)

Standards Assessment

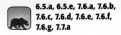 6.5.a, 6.5.e, 7.6.a, 7.6.b, 7.6.c, 7.6.d, 7.6.e, 7.6.f, 7.6.g, 7.7.a

Teacher Notes

To provide practice under more realistic testing conditions, give students 20 min to answer all of the questions in this assessment.

Answer Key

Question Number	Correct Answer
1	A
2	C
3	D
4	C
5	B
6	B
7	D
8	A
9	C
10	B
11	B
12	C
13	D
14	A

Standards Guide

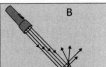

	Supporting	Mastering	Exceeding
6.5.a		14	
6.5.e		13	
7.6.a	1	5	
7.6.b	2	6	
7.6.c		9	
7.6.d		10	
7.6.e	4	9	11
7.6.f	3	7, 9, 11	
7.6.g		8	
7.7.a	12		

Standards Assessment GENERAL

Teacher Notes for Standards Assessment contain a longer Assessment Doctor and Diagnostic Teaching Tips.

REVIEWING ACADEMIC VOCABULARY

1 Which of the following words means "that can be seen"?

A visible

B audible

C palpable

D sensible

2 Which of the following sets of words best completes the following sentence: Light is _____ the eye.

A detects with

B detected for

C detected by

D detecting in

3 Which of the following sets of words best completes the following sentence: Light can be _____ matter.

A transmitted with

B transmits in

C transmits by

D transmitted through

4 Which of the following words is closest in meaning to the word *react*?

A repeat

B renovate

C respond

D remove

REVIEWING CONCEPTS

5 Which of the following best describes the relationship between infrared waves, ultraviolet light, and visible light?

A Infrared waves are found on the electromagnetic spectrum, while ultraviolet and visible light are not.

B Infrared waves have the longest wavelength, followed by visible light and then ultraviolet light.

C Infrared waves and visible light are visible to the human eye, while ultraviolet light is not.

D Infrared waves consist of changing electric and magnetic fields, while ultraviolet light and visible light do not.

6 Your eyes detect a burning candle in a candleholder. Your eyes see the candle flame because it emits light. Why do your eyes see the opaque candleholder?

A It is luminous.

B It is illuminated.

C It absorbs light.

D It transmits light.

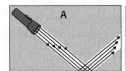

7 The diagrams above show how light interacts with two different surfaces. Which of the following statements is true?

A Diagram A illustrates the process of diffuse reflection.

B You will be able to see your reflection in surface B but not in surface A.

C Diagram B illustrates the process of regular reflection.

D You will be able to see your reflection in surface A but not in surface B.

☑ ASSESSMENT DOCTOR

Question 1: The correct answer is A. *Visible* means "that can be seen." *Audible* means "that can be heard." *Palpable* means "that can be tasted" or "that tastes good." *Sensible* means "that can be sensed" or "that is practical."

Question 2: The correct answer is C. *Light is detected by the eye.* This sentence needs a past participle to complete the verb phrase begun by the auxiliary *is.* Passive verbs are often used with the preposition *by.*

Question 3: The correct answer is D. *Light can be transmitted through matter.* This sentence needs a past participle to complete the verb phrase begun by the auxiliary *can. Through* is the correct preposition to use with the verb *transmit.*

Question 4: The correct answer is C. *React* and *respond* are similar in meaning. They both suggest an action to address a previous action.

Question 5: The correct answer is B. Infrared waves have the longest wavelength, followed by visible light, and then ultraviolet light. Infrared waves, ultraviolet light, and visible light are all part of the electromagnetic spectrum.

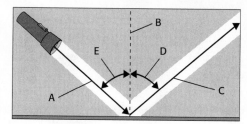

8 The diagram above illustrates the law of reflection. What is found at point E in the diagram?

A the angle of incidence

B the angle of reflection

C the incident beam

D the reflected beam

9 What happens to white light during refraction?

A It appears to be closer than it actually is.

B It absorbs the pigment of the medium it passes through.

C It separates into different wavelengths or colors.

D It is refracted at the same angle as the angle of incidence.

10 What part of a camera is most like the retina in the human eye?

A the lens   C the shutter

B the film   D the aperture

11 What happens when white light shines through a translucent, red, glass window?

A All colors of light except red are transmitted through the glass.

B Red light is transmitted through and reflected by the glass.

C Red light is absorbed by the glass.

D All colors of light except red are reflected by the glass.

REVIEWING PRIOR LEARNING

12 While you are conducting an experiment, your lab partner burns himself on a candle flame. After such an accident, you should

A take your partner to the bathroom and wash the burn with soap.

B perform first aid by rinsing the burned area with warm water.

C tell your teacher, even if the burn seems like a minor injury.

D continue with your lab and tell no one about what has happened.

13 Corals and producers live in the neritic zones of an ocean. Whales and squid live in the oceanic zone. Bacteria and worms live in the benthic zone. Which of the following factors most determines the types of organisms that live at each level?

A the strength of underwater currents and daily tides

B the amount of fresh water that falls as precipitation

C the number of predators living in the oceanic zone

D the depth to which sunlight can penetrate the water

14 If sunlight could not reach Earth's surface, which of the following would happen first?

A Producers would die.

B Consumers would die.

C Scavengers would die.

D Decomposers would die.

Standards Assessment

Question 10: The correct answer is B. The film in a camera is similar to the retina in the human eye. In the camera, images are focused on the film, just as images are focused on the retina of the eye. The lens in a camera is like the lens in the eye. The shutter is like the iris, and the aperture is like the pupil.

Question 11: The correct answer is B. When your eye detects light shining through red translucent glass, red light waves are the only ones that have been transmitted through and reflected by the glass. The other wavelengths present in white light have been absorbed.

Question 12: The correct answer is C. When an accident occurs in the classroom, even a minor one, tell your teacher, who will decide if other steps are necessary.

Question 13: The correct answer is D. The amount of sunlight that can penetrate the water decreases as depth increases. As a result, the upper levels of the ocean are warmer than the lower levels are. And the upper levels support different types of organisms than the lower levels do. Producers live in the surface levels, where there is sunlight for photosynthesis.

Question 14: The correct answer is A. Producers would die first because they need sunlight to make their food through photosynthesis.

Question 6: The correct answer is B. The candleholder is illuminated, which means that it is a visible object that is not a light source. Light is reflected from the candleholder, and the reflected light makes the candleholder visible to the eye.

Question 7: The correct answer is D. The smooth surface in diagram A allows regular reflection, which occurs when all of the light beams are reflected at the same angle. The rough surface in diagram B reflects the light at many different angles, creating a diffuse reflection. So, one could see a reflection in surface A but not in surface B.

Question 8: The correct answer is A. The angle of incidence is found at point E in the diagram. The angle of incidence indicates the angle between the incident beam (A) and the normal (B).

Question 9: The correct answer is C. White light consists of a combination of many different wavelengths of light. When white light is refracted, the amount that the light bends varies with wavelength. Therefore, white light separates into different wavelengths or colors when it is refracted.

Weird Science

Background

Luciferase assays have a number of relevant uses in medicine as well. Bacterial infections can be deadly. Researchers have developed luciferase assays to measure bacteria in the urine and blood. Antibiotics, the medicines used to treat bacterial infections, are not always effective. Luciferase tests can be used to evaluate the effectiveness of antibiotic therapy on particular patients.

Science, Technology, and Society

Background

At this point, bionic eyes are still in the testing and research stage. Scientists have already tested silicon-based bionic eyes on several people. One patient was even able to drive a car on a test course. However, the early version of the silicon chip has only 16 electrodes, so it does not deliver as clear an image as a healthy eye, which has millions of cells. At the level of sensitivity offered by these bionic eyes, patients can expect to be able to distinguish between light and dark areas and to be able to see general shapes. In the future, scientists expect to be able to use chips that have 1,000 electrodes or more.

Science in Action

Weird Science

Fireflies Light the Way

Just as beams of light from lighthouses warn boats of approaching danger, the light of an unlikely source—fireflies—is being used by scientists to warn food inspectors of bacterial contamination.

Fireflies use an enzyme called *luciferase* to make light. Scientists have taken the gene from fireflies that tells cells how to make luciferase. They put this gene into a virus that preys on bacteria. The virus is not harmful to humans and can be mixed into meat. When the virus infects bacteria in the meat, the virus transfers the gene into the genes of the bacteria. The bacteria then produce luciferase and glow! So, if a food inspector sees glowing meat, the inspector knows that the meat is contaminated with bacteria.

Social Studies ACTIVITY

Many cultures have myths to explain certain natural phenomena. Read some of these myths. Then, write your own myth titled "How Fireflies Got Their Fire."

Science, Technology, and Society

Bionic Eyes

Imagine bionic eyes that allow a person who is blind to see. Researchers working on artificial vision think that the technology will be available soon. Many companies are working on different ways to restore sight to people who are blind. Some companies are developing artificial corneas, while other companies are building artificial retinas. One item that has already been tested on people is a pair of glasses that provides limited vision. The glasses have a camera that sends a signal to an electrode implanted in the person's brain. The images are black and white and are not detailed, but the person who is wearing the glasses can see obstacles in his or her path.

Language Arts ACTIVITY

Write a one-page story in your **Science Journal** about a teen who has his or her eyesight restored by a bionic eye. What would the teen want to see first? What would the teen do that he or she couldn't do before?

Answer to Social Studies Activity

Accept all reasonable answers. Encourage students to be creative when writing their myths. Invite volunteers to read their myths to the class.

Answer to Language Arts Activity

Accept all reasonable answers. Students' stories should describe what the teen wants to see first and what the teen wants to do once his or her sight is restored. For example, a teen may want to see his or her family first and then may want to try playing a sport, such as soccer.

Careers

Edie Widder

Oceanographer When Dr. Edie Widder studies the waters of the world's oceans, she's always searching for the light. She is not searching for light from a lighthouse or a nearby coastal town. She is searching for the light given off by marine animals.

Widder received a Ph.D. in neurobiology from the University of California, Santa Barbara in 1982. She is now one of the world's leading researchers on bioluminescence. *Bioluminescence* is the production and emission of light by a living organism. Many marine animals emit light when chemical energy is converted into light energy. Thousands of deep-sea creatures, including various species of shrimp, squid, and jellyfish, are bioluminescent. Widder also studies animals that give off light through a process called *fluorescence*. In fact, Widder was part of a team that discovered the only known fluorescent shark!

To help her research, Widder designed a special camera system called *Eye-in-the-Sea*. Eye-in-the-Sea sits on the sea floor and automatically films bioluminescent organisms. Widder recently used this device to explore the depths of California's Monterey Bay.

Math ACTiViTY

The fluorescent shark filmed by Widder's team is about 36 in. long. If 1 in. is equal to 2.54 cm, how long is the shark in centimeters? Show your work in your **Science Journal.**

Internet Resources

- To learn more about careers in science, visit www.scilinks.org and enter the SciLinks code HY70225.
- To learn more about these Science in Action topics, visit go.hrw.com and type in the keyword HY7LOWF.
- Check out articles related to this chapter by visiting go.hrw.com. Just type in the keyword HY7LOWC.

Answer to Math Activity
36 in. × 2.54 cm/1 in. = 91.4 cm

UNIT 2

TIMELINE

Cells

Cells are everywhere. Even though most cells can't be seen with the naked eye, they make up every living thing. Living things may be made up of one cell or many cells. Your body alone contains trillions of cells!

In this unit, you will learn about different kinds of cells. You will also learn about what happens in a cell. This timeline shows some of the discoveries that scientists have made about cells. Each discovery has helped people understand more about these tiny, amazing structures.

1492

Christopher Columbus reaches North America after sailing from Europe.

Around 1595

Zacharias and Hans Janssen build the first compound microscope.

1838

Johannes Muller proves that cancerous tumors are made up of cells.

1869

Friedrich Miescher discovers a special material in the nucleus of a white blood cell. Later research on this material leads to the discovery of DNA.

White blood cell

1999

Elizabeth Gould and Charles Gross discover that cells in the brain can be repaired and regrown. This discovery contradicts previous scientific understanding.

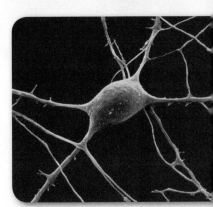

A neuron

1665

Robert Hooke looks at cork under a microscope and uses the name *cells* to describe the small structures that he sees.

1683

Anton van Leeuwenhoek uses a microscope to observe bacteria living on his teeth. He calls these bacteria *animalcules*.

Streptococcus sanguis found on teeth

1809

Abraham Lincoln, the 16th president of the United States, is born.

1873

Camillo Golgi develops a stain that allows scientists to view the structure of entire nerve cells.

1937

Sir Hans Adolf Krebs discovers how cells produce energy from nutrients through the citric acid cycle.

1967

Ragnar Granit, Haldan Hartline, and George Wald are awarded a Nobel Prize for describing how cells in the eye are sensitive to light.

Rods and cones in the eye

1999

The largest known bacterial species, *Thiomargarita namibiensis,* is discovered near Namibia. The cell of one bacterium is 0.3 mm long!

2001

Two separate groups publish the decoded human genome.

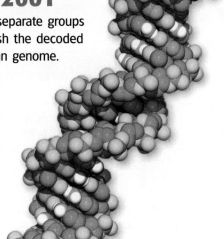

2003

Peter Agre receives a Nobel Prize for discovering water channels in human cells.

Standards Course of Study

The elements listed in the Standards Course of Study provide a base for presenting, supporting, and assessing the California Grade 7 Science Standards. Use this Standards Course of Study as a base for planning your lessons.

Why Teach

Cells: The Basic Units of Life

This chapter was designed to cover the California Grade 7 Science Standards about cell biology (7.1.a, 7.1.b, 7.1.c, 7.1.d, 7.1.f, and 7.5.a). It follows a chapter that introduced the basic characteristics of living things and a chapter that introduced how light and lenses are used in science. This chapter will explain the importance of the cell. This chapter will also explain how structure and function are related at the cellular level.

After they have completed this chapter, students will begin a chapter about cellular processes.

California Standards

Focus on Life Sciences

7.1.a Students know cells function similarly in all living organisms.

7.1.b Students know the characteristics that distinguish plant cells from animal cells, including chloroplasts and cell walls.

7.1.c Students know the nucleus is the repository for genetic information in plant and animal cells.

7.1.d Students know that mitochondria liberate energy for the work that cells do and that chloroplasts capture sunlight energy for photosynthesis.

7.1.f Students know that as multicellular organisms develop, their cells differentiate.

7.5.a Students know plants and animals have levels of organization for structure and function, including cells, tissues, organs, organ systems, and the whole organism.

Investigation and Experimentation

7.7.a Select and use appropriate tools and technology (including calculators, computers, balances, spring scales, microscopes, and binoculars) to perform tests, collect data, and display data.

7.7.d Construct scale models, maps, and appropriately labeled diagrams to communicate scientific knowledge (e.g., motion of Earth's plates and cell structure).

Chapter Pacing

Getting Started 45 min
pp. 112–113

The Big Idea All organisms are composed of one or more cells.
7.1.a, 7.7.a

Section 1 The Characteristics of Cells 90 min
pp. 114–119
Key Concept Cells function similarly in all living organisms.
7.1.a, 7.1.c 7.7.d

Section 2 Eukaryotic Cells 90 min
pp. 120–127
Key Concept Eukaryotic cells have organelles that perform important functions.
7.1.a, 7.1.b, 7.1.c, 7.1.d 7.7.d

Section 3 The Organization of Living Things 45 min
pp. 128–133
Key Concept As multicellular organisms develop, their cells differentiate and form levels of organization.
7.1.f, 7.5.a

Wrapping Up 180 min
pp. 134–143
7.1.b, 7.1.c, 7.7.a, 7.7.d

Basic Learners

TE Comparing Volume and Surface Area, p. 116
TE Cell Structures, p. 123
TE Cell Factory, p. 124
TE *Multi-* and *Uni-*, p. 132
TE Scale Diagrams, p. 136
Reinforcement Worksheet
Chapter Test A
Differentiated Datasheets A for Labs and Activities ■
Study Guide A ■

Advanced Learners/GATE

TE Dramatic Discoveries, p. 115
TE Cell Walls, p. 120
TE Golgi Mobiles, p. 125
TE Tissues, Organs, and Organ Systems, p. 131
Critical Thinking Worksheet
Chapter Test C
Differentiated Datasheets C for Labs and Activities ■

Teach

SE **Explore Activity** What Are Plants Made Of?, p. 113* ■

🖐 **Bellringer**
💿 **PowerPoint® Resources**
SE **Quick Lab** Observing Cells, p. 115* ■
🖐 L10 Math Focus: Surface Area–to–Volume Ratio
🖐 L11 Prokaryotic and Eukaryotic Cells

🖐 **Bellringer**
💿 **PowerPoint® Resources**
🖐 L12 Plant Cell
🖐 L13 Animal Cell
SE **Quick Lab** Cell Diagrams, p. 121* ■
🖐 L14 The Nucleus
🖐 L15 Organelles and Their Functions

🖐 **Bellringer**
💿 **PowerPoint® Resources**
SE **Quick Lab** A Division of Labor, p. 129* ■
🖐 L16 Levels of Organization in the Cardiovascular System

SE **Skills Practice Lab** Cells Alive!, pp. 134–135* ■

Practice

SE **Organize Activity** Layered Book, p. 112

SE **Section Review,** p. 119* ■

SE **Section Review,** p. 127* ■

SE **Section Review,** p. 133* ■

SE **Science Skills Activity** Constructing Scale Diagrams, p. 136* ■
🖐 **Concept Mapping***
SE **Chapter Review,** pp. 138–139* ■

Assess

📁 **Chapter Pretest**

SE **Standards Checks,** pp. 115, 117, 118
TE **Standards Focus,** p. 118
📁 **Section Quiz** ■

SE **Standards Checks,** pp. 120, 121, 122, 124, 126
TE **Standards Focus,** p. 126
📁 **Section Quiz** ■

SE **Standards Checks,** pp. 129, 131, 132
TE **Standards Focus,** p. 132
📁 **Section Quiz** ■

SE **Standards Assessment,** pp. 140–141*
📁 **Chapter Tests A, B** ■**, C**
📁 **Standards Review Workbook** ■

Resources for Universal Access • Differentiated Instruction

English Learners

TE Eukaryotic Cells, p. 119
TE Using the Figure, p. 122
TE Word Parts, p. 122
TE Activity, p. 123
TE Group Activity, p. 123
TE Personalizing Information, p. 130
TE Focus on Speaking, p. 137
📁 Vocabulary and Section Summary A ■, B

📁 Section Quizzes ■
📁 Chapter Tests A, B ■
📁 Differentiated Datasheets A, B, and C for Labs and Activities ■
📁 Study Guide A ■
📁 Multilingual Glossary

Struggling Readers

TE Reading Strategy, pp. 116, 124
TE Subheads, p. 124
TE Extended Definitions, p. 126
TE Terminology Explained, p. 132

Special Education Students

TE Discovery Timeline, p. 114
TE Standards Check Posters, p. 117
TE Describing Diagrams, p. 120
TE Cell Models, p. 122
TE Paragraph Discussions, p. 128
TE Scale Teams, p. 136

To help plan your lessons, refer to the On Course Mapping Instruction booklet.

Visual Resources

CHAPTER STARTER TRANSPARENCY

What If . . . ?

Imagine this scene from a horror film. A young man sits down to dinner to find that his mother has made asparagus again. The young man eats the dreaded asparagus stalks. Later, he finds out that instead of being digested, one of the stalks has taken up residence inside his body and is very much alive! Too horrifying to think about? What if the asparagus began to do wonderful things for the young man, such as giving him more energy than he ever dreamed possible? Lynn Margulis, a scientist, thinks that something similar may have happened to certain one-celled organisms that lived more than a billion years ago, giving rise to the kinds of cells that we are made of today.

According to Margulis's theory, about 1.2 billion years ago, some larger cells began eating smaller cells for dinner. Like the white blood cell on this page, these larger cells trapped the smaller cells with extensions of their cell body. But some of these smaller cells resisted being digested. In fact, they began to do very well in their new homes. The larger cells also benefited from their new guests. The smaller cells released large amounts of energy from food taken in by the larger cells. Other kinds of small cells used the energy in sunlight to make enough food to feed themselves and the larger cell. The energy-producing structures of most cells, including yours, are thought to have descended from these smaller cells.

BELLRINGER TRANSPARENCIES

Section: The Characteristics of Cells
Identify some of the functions that all cells have in common.

Write your ideas in your **science journal.**

Section: Eukaryotic Cells
What are three differences between prokaryotic and eukaryotic cells?

Write your answer in your **science journal.**

TEACHING TRANSPARENCIES

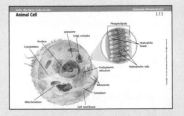
Math Focus: Surface Area-to-Volume Ratio — L10

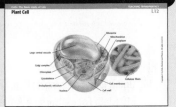
Plant Cell — L12

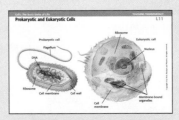
Prokaryotic and Eukaryotic Cells — L11

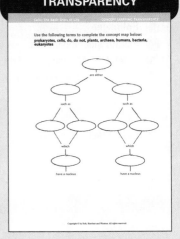
Animal Cell — L13

TEACHING TRANSPARENCIES

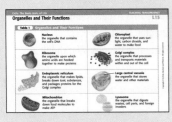
The Nucleus — L14

Levels of Organization in the Cardiovascular System — L16

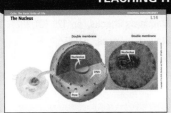
Organelles and Their Functions — L15

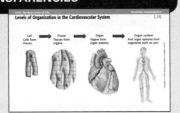
The Six Levels of Environmental Organization — E81

LINK TO EARTH SCIENCE

STANDARDS REVIEW TRANSPARENCIES

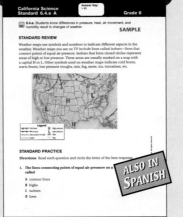
California Science Standard 6.4.e A — Grade 6

STANDARD REVIEW

Weather maps use symbols and numbers to indicate different aspects in the weather. Weather maps you see on TV include lines called *isobars*—lines that connect points of equal air pressure. Isobars that form closed circles represent areas of high or low pressure. These areas are usually marked on a map with a capital H or L. Other symbols used on weather maps indicate cold fronts, warm fronts, low pressure troughs, rain, fog, snow, ice, tornadoes, etc.

STANDARD PRACTICE

Directions Read each question and circle the letter of the best response.

1. The lines connecting points of equal air pressure on a map are called
   A contour lines
   B highs
   C isobars
   D lows

ALSO IN SPANISH

CONCEPT MAPPING TRANSPARENCY

Use the following terms to complete the concept map below: **prokaryotes, cells, do, do not, plants, archaea, humans, bacteria, eukaryotes**

Planning Resources

PARENT LETTER

SAMPLE

Dear Parent,

Your son's or daughter's science class will soon begin exploring the chapter entitled "The Nature of Physical Science." In this chapter, students will learn about how the scientific method applies to the world of physical science and the role of physical science in the world. By the end of the chapter, students should demonstrate a clear understanding of the chapter's main ideas and be able to discuss the following topics:

1. the role of questions in the process of investigation (Section 1)
2. how applying science saves lives and benefits the environment (Section 1)
3. careers that rely on science (Section 1)
4. the steps used in scientific methods (Section 2)
5. how scientific methods are used to answer questions and solve problems (Section 2)
6. the importance of safety precautions in the laboratory (Section 3)
7. examples of safety equipment and when to use them (Section 3)
8. how safety symbols are used to make laboratories safer (Section 3)

Questions to Ask Along the Way

You can help your child learn about these topics by asking interesting questions as he or she progresses through the chapter. For example, you may wish to ask your son or daughter the following questions:

What are some surprising careers that use science?

What is a characteristic of a good hypothesis?

What is the first step to take if an accident happens?

ALSO IN SPANISH

TEST ITEM LISTING

SAMPLE

Holt California Physical Science
Chapter 6 Introduction to Atoms
Test Item Listing
Multiple choice

1. The smallest particle into which an element can be divided and still have the properties of that element is called a(n)
   a. nucleus.   c. atom.
   b. electron.   d. neutron.
   ANS: C   DIF: 1   REF: 1   OBJ: 1   STO: 8.3.a   KEY: atom
   MSC: SQ.1.1

2. What particle did J. J. Thomson discover?
   a. neutron   c. atom
   b. electron   d. proton
   ANS: B   DIF: 1   REF: 1   OBJ: 2   STO: 8.3.a   KEY: electron
   MSC: SQ.1.2

3. How would you describe the nucleus?
   a. dense, positively charged
   b. mostly empty space, positively charged
   c. tiny, negatively charged
   d. dense, negatively charged
   ANS: A   DIF: 1   REF: 1   OBJ: 2   STO: 8.3.a   KEY: nucleus   MSC: SQ.1.3

4. Where are electrons likely to be found?
   a. in the nucleus
   b. in electron clouds
   c. mixed throughout an atom
   d. in definite paths
   ANS: B   DIF: 1   REF: 1   OBJ: 2   STO: 8.3.a   KEY: electron   MSC: SQ.1.4

5. Dalton believed that
   a. atoms of the same element are exactly alike.
   b. most, but not all, substances are made of atoms.
   c. atoms of different elements are the same.
   d. atoms can be divided.
   ANS: A   DIF: 1   REF: 1   OBJ: 1 2   STO: 8.3.a   KEY: atom
   MSC: SQ.1.5

6. Every atom of a given element has the same number of
   a. protons.
   b. neutrons.
   c. Electrons
   d. isotopes.
   ANS: A   DIF: 1   REF: 2   OBJ: 2   STO: 8.3.a   KEY: atom

ALSO IN SPANISH

 One-Stop Planner® CD-ROM

This CD-ROM package includes all of the resources shown here and the following time-saving tools:

- **Lab Materials QuickList Software**
- **Customizable Lesson Plans** Correlated to the California Science Standards
- **Holt Calendar Planner**
- **PowerPoint® Resources**
- **Printable Worksheets**
- **ExamView® Test Generator** Correlated to the California Science Standards
- **Holt PuzzlePro®**
- **Interactive Teacher's Edition**

For a correlation of each lab or activity to the **California Science Standards,** see pages T22–T27.

Meeting Individual Needs

DIRECTED READING A
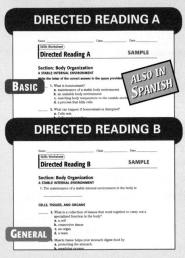

BASIC · ALSO IN SPANISH

DIRECTED READING B
GENERAL

VOCABULARY AND SECTION SUMMARY A
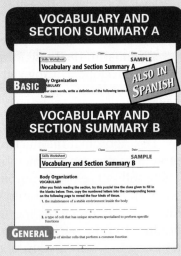

BASIC · ALSO IN SPANISH

VOCABULARY AND SECTION SUMMARY B
GENERAL

REINFORCEMENT
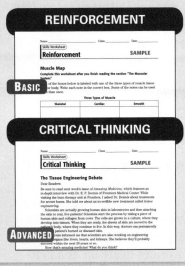

BASIC

CRITICAL THINKING
ADVANCED

INTERACTIVE READER AND STUDY GUIDE
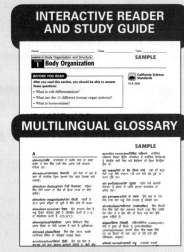

MULTILINGUAL GLOSSARY

Labs and Activities

DIFFERENTIATED DATASHEETS FOR EXPLORE ACTIVITY, QUICK LABS, AND CHAPTER LAB

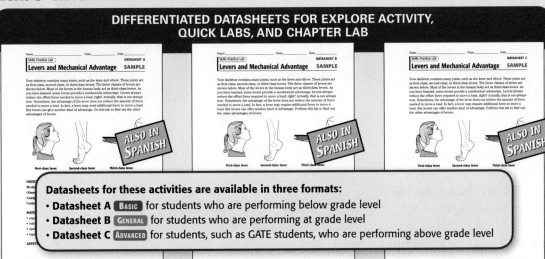

ALSO IN SPANISH · ALSO IN SPANISH · ALSO IN SPANISH

Datasheets for these activities are available in three formats:
- **Datasheet A** **BASIC** for students who are performing below grade level
- **Datasheet B** **GENERAL** for students who are performing at grade level
- **Datasheet C** **ADVANCED** for students, such as GATE students, who are performing above grade level

DATASHEET FOR SCIENCE SKILLS ACTIVITY
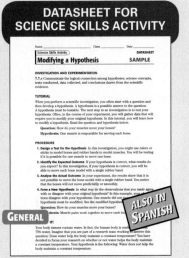

GENERAL · ALSO IN SPANISH

Reviews and Assessments

SECTION REVIEWS
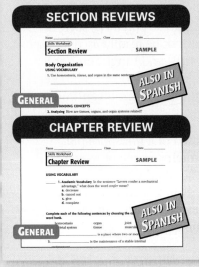

GENERAL · ALSO IN SPANISH

CHAPTER REVIEW
GENERAL · ALSO IN SPANISH

CHAPTER PRETEST
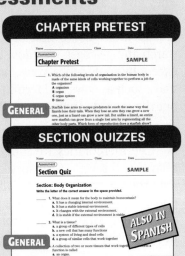

GENERAL

SECTION QUIZZES
GENERAL · ALSO IN SPANISH

CHAPTER TEST A
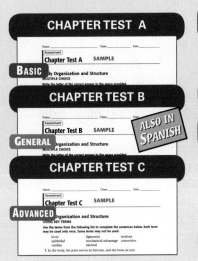

BASIC

CHAPTER TEST B
GENERAL · ALSO IN SPANISH

CHAPTER TEST C
ADVANCED

STANDARDS ASSESSMENT
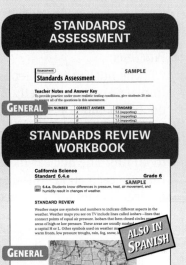

GENERAL

STANDARDS REVIEW WORKBOOK

GENERAL · ALSO IN SPANISH

This Teacher Background explains science concepts, principles, and theories that appear in the chapter. Use the information on these pages to refresh or enhance your understanding of the topics covered.

Section 1

The Characteristics of Cells

Similarities and Differences in Cells

All cells have similarities, regardless of the organism of which an individual cell is a part. All cells have a membrane, cytoplasm, and a deoxyribonucleic acid (DNA) genome. The DNA genome is expressed by a universal genetic code that includes nucleotides made up of a pentose sugar, phosphate groups, and the bases adenine, cytosine, guanine, and thymine. DNA determines the structure and function of each cell and the organism as a whole.

The biochemical pathways within cells, especially those for cell division and energy production (cellular respiration and fermentation), are also similar between cells, regardless of a cell's origin. Additionally, many of the proteins synthesized by cells have similar functions, such as catalyzing metabolic reactions (enzymes).

Significant functional and structural differences between cells arise as the cells within a multicellular organism become differentiated during development. For example, liver cells and brain cells have very different functions and structures. Cells also differ because of the environment in which they live. For example, the bacterium *Escherichia coli,* a member of Domain Bacteria, is adapted to live in the human digestive system, while the bacterium *Thermus aquaticus* is adapted to survive in extremely high temperatures. Despite differences that arise due to cell specialization or adaptation to an organism's environment, all cells still function to ensure the survival of the organism.

Nucleus

The nucleus is the repository for genetic information in plant and animal cells. The nucleus is surrounded by a double membrane, often referred to as the nuclear membrane or the nuclear envelope. The nuclear membrane and its associated proteins span a width of about 20 nm to 40 nm. The nuclear membrane is perforated by pores that are each about 100 nm in diameter. The layers of the nuclear membrane are fused at the pores, and the pores are lined by proteins that regulate the exit and entry of macromolecules. The nuclear lamina, a network of protein filaments, lines the inner side of the nuclear membrane and maintains the shape of the nucleus. The nucleus of a eukaryotic cell is illustrated in **Figure A.** This figure can be used to show that a eukaryotic cell has a nucleus surrounded by a porous nuclear membrane.

Chromatin, the loose form of DNA, lies within the nuclear envelope. During cell division, the chromatin condenses into chromosomes, the number of which is characteristic of a species. When cell division is not taking place, the nucleolus (or, in some cases, nucleoli) synthesizes ribosomal ribonucleic acid (rRNA) and other protein components, which become ribosomal subunits. These subunits exit the nucleus through the nuclear pores and are assembled into ribosomes in the cytoplasm. Ribosomes translate the messenger RNA (mRNA) that is produced in the nucleus during DNA transcription, resulting in the formation of proteins.

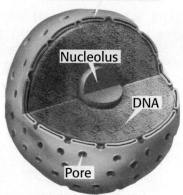

Figure A *Eukaryotic cells contain membrane-bound organelles and a nucleus surrounded by a nuclear membrane.*

Double membrane

Nucleolus

DNA

Pore

Section 2

Eukaryotic Cells

Cell Wall

Cell walls are a distinguishing feature of plant cells. They give plant cells a distinct shape and limited size. Plant cell walls are composed primarily of cellulose, a polymer of glucose molecules. Unlike other glucose polymers, such as starch and glycogen, cellulose cannot be readily used for fuel except by some prokaryotes, protists, and fungi. Some animals, such as cows and termites, can break down cellulose, but they can do so only with the aid of microorganisms.

Cell Membrane

Cell membranes are composed of a phospholipid bilayer and several accessory proteins, some of which facilitate the transport of materials across the membrane. Phospholipids are a class of lipids in which fatty acid molecules are bound to a glycerol molecule. In phospholipids, however, the third carbon of the glycerol is bound to a phosphate group instead of a fatty acid. The phosphate group is negatively charged, which makes the phosphate end of the molecule hydrophilic. The fatty acids are hydrophobic. These properties of phospholipids result in a bilayer when the phospholipids are surrounded by water. The hydrophilic phosphate group faces outward, while the hydrophobic fatty acids face inward. Use **Figure B** to explain to students that the hydrophilic phospholipids face the aqueous inside and outside of the cell, while the hydrophobic fatty acids face each other.

Figure B *The hydrophobic tails of the cell membrane face each other while the hydrophilic heads face the aqueous inside and outside of the cell.*

Cytoskeleton

In plant cells, the shape of the cell membrane is limited by the shape of the cell wall. In animal cells, however, the shape of the cell membrane is maintained by the cytoskeleton. The cytoskeleton is a network of microtubules and microfilaments that extend throughout the cytoplasm of the cell. In addition to giving the cell its shape, the cytoskeleton also plays a role in organizing the structures and activities of the cell.

Chloroplasts and Mitochondria

Chloroplasts are organelles that are found in plant cells. Chloroplasts capture light energy and through a series of chemical reactions, convert this light energy to chemical energy in the form of glucose. Plant cells use glucose to perform work. Chloroplasts are surrounded by two membranes and contain another membranous system that forms flattened sacs called thylakoids, which in turn form stacks called grana.

Mitochondria break down glucose and store the resulting energy in the phosphate bonds of adenosine triphosphate (ATP). When a cell needs energy, it breaks the bonds in ATP. Like chloroplasts, mitochondria are surrounded by a double membrane. The outer membrane is smooth, but the inner membrane has infoldings called cristae. The increased surface area that results from cristae improves the productivity of cellular respiration.

Section 3

The Organization of Living Things

Differentiation

The cell of a unicellular organism must perform all of the functions necessary to ensure the survival of the organism. In multicellular organisms, cells are specialized for specific functions, and each individual cell does not have to perform all of the activities necessary for the organism to survive.

Many multicellular organisms begin life as a fertilized egg, which undergoes repeated divisions. During the development of the embryo, some cells become differentiated, or structurally specialized for a certain function. For example, these differentiated cells may become brain cells, muscle cells, or skin cells. As development proceeds, these cells will continue to differentiate. For example, muscle cells could develop into one of three types of muscle tissue.

Unlike animal cells, some plant cells retain the ability to differentiate into different types of cells once the organism has developed. For example, the leaves of some plants will form roots for propagation, and the leaf cells may develop into root cells. This is not typically seen in animal cells. Once an animal cell has differentiated into a certain type of cell, it cannot change into a different type of cell.

Tissue

Tissues are composed of one or more types of cells that work together to perform specific functions. For example, epithelial tissue includes all tissues that cover the outside of the body and line organs and cavities within the body. Epithelial tissue forms sheets of tightly packed cells. Because of this trait, epithelial tissue plays a role in protecting the body from injury, preventing the entry of microorganisms and harmful substances, and preventing the loss of fluids. There are two types of epithelial tissue: simple epithelium, which has a single layer of cells, and stratified epithelium, which has multiple layers of cells.

Internet Resources

SciLinks is maintained by the National Science Teachers Association to provide you and your students with interesting, up-to-date links that will enrich your classroom presentation of the chapter.

Visit **www.scilinks.org** and enter the SciLinks code for more information about the topic listed.

Topic: Prokaryotic Cells
SciLinks code: HY71225

Topic: Eukaryotic Cells
SciLinks code: HY70541

Topic: Organization of Life
SciLinks code: HY71080

Chapter Preview

📁 **Chapter Pretest**

Use the Chapter Pretest in the Chapter Resource File to determine the prior knowledge of your students. The Test Doctors and diagnostic teaching tips in the Teacher Notes pages will help you tailor your instruction to your students' specific needs.

Improving Comprehension

Use the Graphic Organizer on this page of the Student Edition to introduce the topics that are covered in this chapter, to summarize the chapter material, or to show students how to make a comparison table.

Teaching Tips

• Explain to students that they may want to read the source information for a comparison table twice—once to determine the general characteristics that they want to compare and once to fill in the table.

• Explain to students that comparison tables allow for broader, more general comparisons than some other comparison organizers do. For example, unlike a Venn diagram, a comparison table does not need to contain both shared and unique characteristics.

• Encourage students to use the comparison table as a quick and efficient form of notes.

LS Logical

Improving Comprehension

Graphic Organizers are important visual tools that can help you organize information and improve your reading comprehension. The Graphic Organizer below is called a *comparison table*. Instructions for creating other types of Graphic Organizers are located in the **Study Skills** section of the Appendix.

How to Make a Comparison Table

❶ Draw a table like the one shown below. Draw as many columns and rows as you want to draw.

❷ In the top row, write the topics that you want to compare.

❸ In the left column, write the general characteristics that you want to compare. As you read the chapter, fill in the characteristics for each topic in the appropriate boxes.

When to Use a Comparison Table

A comparison table is useful when you want to compare the characteristics of two or more topics in science. Organizing information in a table helps you compare several topics at one time. In a table, all topics are described in terms of the same list of characteristics, which helps you make a thorough comparison. As you read, look for topics whose characteristics you may want to compare in a table.

	Prokaryotic cells	Eukaryotic cells
Nucleus	no	yes
DNA	yes	yes
Membrane-bound organelles	no	yes
Cell wall	yes	some
Cell membrane	yes	yes
Cytoplasm	yes	yes
Ribosomes	yes	yes

You Try It!

This Reading Strategy can also be used within the chapter that you are about to read. Practice making your own *comparison table* as directed in the Reading Strategies for Section ❷ and Section ❸. Record your work in your **Science Journal.**

Using Other Graphic Organizers

Students can practice using a variety of Graphic Organizers while reading this chapter. The following Graphic Organizers may also be useful in this chapter.

A **process chart** can be used to describe the development of the cell theory, which is discussed in Section 1.

A **Venn diagram** can be used to compare qualities of prokaryotes and qualities of eukaryotes, described in Section 1.

A **pyramid chart** can be used to illustrate the levels of organization in a living organism, discussed in Section 3.

Instructions for creating these Graphic Organizers are located on pp. 583–591 of the Appendix.

Unpacking the Standards

The information below "unpacks" the standards by breaking them down into basic parts. The higher-level, academic vocabulary is highlighted and defined to help you understand the language of the standards. "What It Means" restates the standards as simply as possible.

Unpacking the Standards

Use the following information with the *What It Means* in the Student Edition to help students understand why studying each standard is important.

California Standard	Academic Vocabulary	What It Means	Why It Matters
7.1.a Students know cells **function similarly** in all living organisms.	**function** (FUHNGK shuhn) to work **similarly** (SIM uh luhr lee) in almost the same way	Cells perform the same actions in all living things.	At the cellular level, all living organisms share common traits. Understanding this idea allows one to understand the nature of life on Earth.
7.1.b Students know the characteristics that distinguish plant cells from animal cells, including chloroplasts and cell walls.		Plant cells have some unique structures that make plant cells different from animal cells. These structures include chloroplasts and a cell wall.	Plants and animals are the organisms with which people interact the most.
7.1.c Students know the nucleus is the repository for genetic information in plant and animal cells.		The nucleus of a plant cell or an animal cell contains information that the cell uses as blueprints for building new cells.	Understanding the nature of heredity in organisms is beneficial. More and more, people's lives will be affected by the field of genetics.
7.1.d Students know that mitochondria **liberate** energy for the work that cells do and that chloroplasts capture sunlight **energy** for photosynthesis.	**liberate** (LIB uhr AYT) to release; to set free **energy** (EN uhr jee) the capacity to do work	Mitochondria release energy from sugar to power the cell's life processes. Chloroplasts turn energy from the sun into sugars and oxygen.	To understand digestion and the need to eat and breathe at the macro level, students must understand where their food originates at a cellular level and how your their cells make use of this food.
7.1.f Students know that as multicellular organisms develop, their cells **differentiate.**	**differentiate** (DIF uhr EN shee AYT) to become specialized in structure and function	As a living thing that is made of more than one cell grows, the structure of its cells change so that the cells perform specific jobs.	Differentiation allows multicellular organisms to accomplish the tasks of living efficiently. It also explains the presence of many types of cells.
7.5.a Students know plants and animals have levels of organization for **structure** and **function,** including cells, tissues, organs, organ systems, and the whole organism.	**structure** (STRUHK chuhr) the arrangement of the parts of a whole **function** (FUHNGK shuhn) use or purpose	Plants and animals are made of smaller parts which are organized by shape and purpose. These layers of organization include cells, tissues, organs, organ systems, and the whole organism.	Multicellular organisms, including humans, function because their cells are organized at many levels. Each subsequent level of organization has unique properties that the prior level of organization does not have.

Words with Multiple Meanings

Words that have both common and scientific meanings can be confusing to students. The following table identifies some of those words that are used in this chapter.

Term	Common meaning	Scientific meaning
cell	a small, confining room	the smallest structural and functional unit of all living organisms
organ	a musical instrument similar to a piano	a collection of tissues that carries out a specialized function of the body

Practice Have students complete the sentences below to help them understand how the scientific and common meanings of the word *organ* can differ.

a. The sound of the ___ filled the church. (organ)

b. The heart is an ___ that pumps blood through the body. (organ)

Have students write one definition for the common meaning of the word and one definition for the scientific meaning.

Chapter Overview

This chapter will help students understand both the diversity of and the similarities between cells. The chapter describes the discovery of cells and gives an overview of the cell theory. Students will learn about cell structures and how cells, tissues, organs, and organ systems form organisms.

Cells: The Basic Units of Life

The Big Idea

All organisms are composed of one or more cells.

California Standards

Focus on Life Sciences

7.1 All living organisms are composed of cells, from just one to many trillions, whose details usually are visible only through a microscope. (Sections 1, 2, and 3)

7.5 The anatomy and physiology of plants and animals illustrate the complementary nature of structure and function. (Section 3)

Investigation and Experimentation

7.7 Scientific progress is made by asking meaningful questions and conducting careful investigations. (Science Skills Activity)

Math

7.1.1 Algebra and Functions
7.2.3 Measurement and Geometry

English–Language Arts

7.1.3 Reading
7.2.1 Writing

About the Photo

Harmful bacteria may invade your body and make you sick. But wait—your white blood cells come to the rescue! In this image, a white blood cell (shown in yellow) reaches out to destroy bacteria (shown in purple). The red disks are red blood cells.

Organize

Layered Book

Before you read this chapter, create the FoldNote entitled "Layered Book." Label the tabs of the layered book with "Characteristics of all cells," "Prokaryotic cells," "Eukaryotic cells," and "Organization of living things." As you read the chapter, write information that you learn about each category under the appropriate tab.

Instructions for creating FoldNotes are located in the Study Skills section on p. 580 of the Appendix.

California Standards Alignment

Focus on Life Sciences

7.1.a Students know cells function similarly in all living organisms. **pp. 113–127, 138–140**

7.1.b Students know the characteristics that distinguish plant cells from animal cells, including chloroplasts and cell walls. **pp. 120–122, 124, 126–127, 134–135, 138–141**

7.1.c Students know the nucleus is the repository for genetic information in plant and animal cells. **pp. 117–119, 122, 126–127, 134–135, 138–140**

7.1.d Students know that mitochondria liberate energy for the work that cells do and that chloroplasts capture sunlight energy for photosynthesis. **pp. 124, 126–127, 138–141**

7.1.f Students know that as multicellular organisms develop, their cells differentiate. **pp. 128–133, 138–141**

7.5.a Students know plants and animals have levels of organization for structure and function, including cells, tissues, organs, organ systems, and the whole organism. **pp. 128, 130–133, 138–141**

Investigation and Experimentation

7.7.a Select and use appropriate tools and technology (including calculators, computers, balances, spring scales, microscopes, and binoculars) to perform tests, collect data, and display data. **pp. 113, 134–135**

7.7.d Construct scale models, maps, and appropriately labeled diagrams to communicate scientific knowledge (e.g., motion of Earth's plates and cell structure). **pp. 115, 121, 134–136**

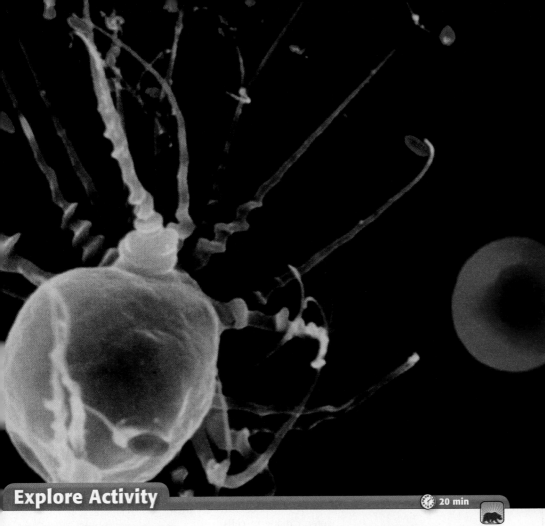

Explore Activity

 20 min

What Are Plants Made Of?

All living things, including plants, are made of cells. What do plant cells look like? Do this activity to find out.

Procedure

1. Follow your teacher's directions on how to set up and operate a **microscope.**

2. Tear off a **small leaf** from near the tip of an *Elodea* sprig. Using **forceps,** place the whole leaf in a **drop of water** on a **microscope slide.**

3. Place a **coverslip** on top of the water drop by putting one edge of the coverslip on the slide near the water drop. Next, lower the coverslip slowly so that the coverslip does not trap air bubbles.

4. Place the slide on your microscope.

5. Using the lowest-powered lens first, find the plant cells. When you can see the cells under the lowest-powered lens, switch to a higher-powered lens.

6. Draw a picture of what you see.

7.1.a
7.7.a

Analysis

7. Describe the shape of the *Elodea* cells. Are all of the cells the same?

8. Do you think that human cells look like *Elodea* cells? How do you think they are different? How might they be similar?

Math Standards

Algebra and Functions 7.1.1 Use variables and appropriate operations to write an expression, an equation, an inequality, or a system of equations or inequalities that represents a verbal description (e.g., three less than a number, half as large as area A). **p. 127**

Measurement and Geometry 7.2.3 Compute the length of the perimeter, the surface area of the faces, and the volume of a three-dimensional object built from rectangular solids. Understand that when the lengths of all dimensions are multiplied by a scale factor, the surface area is multiplied by the square of the scale factor and the volume is multiplied by the cube of the scale factor. **pp. 116, 119, 131, 133, 139**

English–Language Arts Standards

Reading 7.1.3 Clarify word meaning through the use of definition, example, restatement, or contrast. **p. 120**

Writing 7.4.2 Write fictional or autobiographical narratives: (a) Develop a standard plot line (having a beginning, conflict, rising action, climax, and denouement) and point of view; (b) Develop complex major and minor characters and a definite setting; (c) Use a range of appropriate strategies (e.g., dialogue; suspense; naming of specific narrative action, including movement, gestures, and expressions). **p. 139**

What If . . . ?

Imagine this scene from a horror film. A young man sits down to dinner to find that his mother has made asparagus again. The young man eats the dreaded asparagus stalks. Later, he finds out that instead of being digested, one of

According to Margulis's theory, about 1.2 billion years ago, some larger cells began eating smaller cells for dinner. Like the white blood cell on this page, these larger cells trapped the smaller cells with extensions of their cell body. But

Chapter Starter Transparency
Use this transparency to help students begin thinking about the characteristics of cells.

Preteach

Reviewing Prior Knowledge

Ask students to relate what they already know about cells. (Sample answer: All living organisms are made up of one or more cells and cells have DNA.) Then, ask volunteers to read the red and blue heads in the section aloud. Finally, ask students to describe what they think the section is about. (Sample answer: This section contains a general introduction to cells.)

🎧 Bellringer

Have students focus on standard 7.1.a by asking them to identify some of the functions that all cells have in common. (Students should note that the primary function of any cell is to survive or to help ensure the survival of the organism of which it is a part. Some students may note that all cells make proteins and have metabolic pathways in common.)

📦 Bellringer Transparency

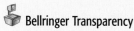

Motivate

Discussion

Cell Discovery Before students begin this section, have them examine a piece of cork. Ask them if they can see cells in the cork. (Some students may think that they can see cells because of the natural structures in cork. Remind students that nearly all cells are too small to be seen with the naked eye.) Ask students to identify what made Robert Hooke's discovery of cells possible. (the microscope) Ask students if they think that Hooke could have made his discovery without the microscope. (Students should conclude that Hooke likely would not have made his discovery.) **LS Visual/Logical**

The Characteristics of Cells

Key Concept Cells function similarly in all living organisms.

What You Will Learn

- The cell theory explains why cells are important for living things.
- All cells have a cell membrane, cytoplasm, and DNA.
- Prokaryotic cells and eukaryotic cells differ in how their genetic information is contained.

Why It Matters

Understanding how cells function makes it easier to learn how organisms function.

Vocabulary

- cell
- cell membrane
- organelle
- nucleus
- prokaryote
- eukaryote

READING STRATEGY

Asking Questions Read this section silently. In your **Science Journal,** write down questions that you have about this section. Discuss your questions in a small group.

cell (SEL) the smallest functional and structural unit of all living organisms; usually consists of a nucleus, cytoplasm, and a membrane

▶ Most cells are so small that they can't be seen with the naked eye. So, how did scientists find cells? They found cells by accident! The first person to see cells wasn't looking for them.

All living things are made of cells. A **cell** is the smallest structural and functional unit of living things. Because of their size, cells weren't discovered until microscopes were invented in the mid-1600s.

Cells and the Cell Theory

Robert Hooke was the first person to describe cells. In 1665, he built a microscope to look at tiny objects. One day, he looked at a thin slice of cork. Cork is found in the bark of cork trees. The cork looked as if it were made of little boxes. Hooke named these boxes *cells,* which means "little rooms" in Latin. Hooke's cells were really the outer layers of dead cork cells. His microscope and his drawing of the cork cells are shown in **Figure 1.**

Hooke also looked at thin slices of living plants. He saw that they too were made of cells. Some cells were even filled with "juice." The "juicy" cells were living cells.

Hooke also looked at feathers, fish scales, and the eyes of houseflies. But he spent most of his time looking at plants and fungi. The cells of plants and fungi have cell walls. Thus, they are easy to see. Animal cells do not have cell walls. The lack of cell walls makes seeing the outline of animal cells harder. Because Hooke couldn't see their cells, he thought that animals weren't made of cells.

Figure 1 *Hooke discovered cells by using this microscope. His drawing of cork cells is shown to the right of his microscope.*

7.1.a Students know cells function similarly in all living organisms.
7.1.c Students know the nucleus is the repository for genetic information in plant and animal cells.

Universal Access · Differentiated Instruction

Special Education Students

Discovery Timeline Presenting information visually can help make learning easier for struggling students, such as those with hearing impairments. Create a timeline on the board. Divide the timeline into five equal sections. Label the sections as follows: 1600s, 1700s, 1800s, 1900s, and 2000s. Explain to students that each section represents 100 years. Near the beginning of the 2000s, draw a line and

label it with the current year and the sentence, "You are studying cells." Ask volunteers to add the following items to the timeline: Hooke describes cells, 1665; Leeuwenhoek finds single-celled organisms, 1673; Schleiden finds that all plants are made of cells, 1838; Schwann concludes that animals are made of cells, 1839; and Virchow states that all cells form from other cells, 1858. **LS Visual/Kinesthetic**

Euglena

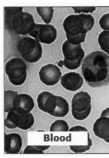
Blood

Yeast

Bacteria

Finding Cells in Other Organisms

In 1673, Anton van Leeuwenhoek (LAY vuhn HOOK), a Dutch merchant, made his own microscopes. He used one of his microscopes to look at pond scum. Leeuwenhoek saw small organisms in the water. He named these organisms *animalcules,* which means "little animals." Today, we call these single-celled organisms *protists* (PROH tists).

Leeuwenhoek also looked at animal blood. He saw differences in blood cells from different kinds of animals. For example, blood cells in fish, birds, and frogs are oval. Blood cells in humans and dogs are round and flat. Leeuwenhoek was also the first person to see bacteria. And he discovered that yeasts that make bread dough rise are single-celled organisms. Examples of the types of cells that Leeuwenhoek examined are shown in **Figure 2.**

The Cell Theory

Almost 200 years passed before scientists concluded that cells are present in all living things. Matthias Schleiden (muh THIE uhs SHLIE duhn) studied plants. In 1838, he concluded that all plant parts were made of cells. Theodor Schwann (THEE oh DAWR SHVAHN) studied animals. In 1839, Schwann concluded that all animal tissues were made of cells. Shortly thereafter, he wrote the first two parts of what is now known as the *cell theory:*

- All organisms are made up of one or more cells.
- The cell is the basic unit of all living things.

In his book published in 1858, doctor Rudolf Virchow (ROO DAWLF FIR koh), stated that all cells could form only from other cells. He then added the third part of the cell theory:

- All cells come from existing cells.

Standards Check What are the three parts of the cell theory?
7.1.a

Figure 2 *Leeuwenhoek examined many types of cells, including protists of the genus* Euglena *and the other types of cells shown above. The bacteria in the photo have been enlarged more than the other cells. Bacterial cells are much smaller than most other types of cells.*

Quick Lab

Observing Cells   7.1.a
7.7.d

1. Follow your teacher's directions on how to set up and operate a **microscope.**

2. Examine **prepared microscope slides** from a variety of living things.

3. Record your observations of the samples on the slides. Draw pictures of what you see, and label your drawings.

4. What similarities between the samples do you observe?

5. How do the samples differ?

🕐 **20 min**

Anticipation Guide Before students read this page, ask them which of the following reasons might explain why cells are so small:

1. There isn't enough microscopic food available for the cells.

2. There isn't enough room in a multicellular organism.

3. another reason (Ask students for suggestions.)

Have students evaluate their answer after they read the page.
LS Logical

Answers to Math Focus

1. Surface area of cube (*SA*) = (3 cm × 3 cm) × 6 = 54 cm² Volume of cube (*V*) = 3 cm × 3 cm × 3 cm = 27 cm³ *SA:V* ratio = 54:27 or 2:1

2. *SA* = (4 cm × 4 cm) × 6 = 96 cm² *V* = 4 cm × 4 cm × 4 cm = 64 cm³ *SA:V* = 96:64 or 1.5:1

3. The cube with sides that are 3 cm long has the greater surface area–to–volume ratio.

4. The larger the cell is, the smaller the surface area–to–volume ratio is.

Teaching Transparency:
L10 Math Focus: Surface Area–to–Volume Ratio

Cell Size

Most cells are too small to be seen without a microscope. It would take 50 human cells to cover the dot on this letter *i*.

A Few Large Cells

Most cells are small. A few, however, are big. The yolk of a chicken egg, shown in **Figure 3**, is one big cell. The size of most cells is controlled by the relationship between the surface area and the volume of the cell.

Many Small Cells

There is a reason why most cells are so small. Cells take in food and get rid of wastes through their outer surface. As a cell gets larger, it needs more food and produces more waste. Therefore, more materials pass through its outer surface.

As the cell's volume increases, its surface area grows, too. But the cell's volume grows faster than its surface area. If a cell gets too large, the cell's surface area will not be large enough to take in enough nutrients or pump out enough wastes. So, the surface area of a cell—relative to the volume of the cell—limits the cell's size. The ratio of the cell's surface area to the cell's volume is called the *surface area–to–volume ratio*. It can be calculated by using the following equation:

$$\text{surface area–to–volume ratio} = \frac{\text{surface area}}{\text{volume}}$$

Figure 3 *The white and yolk of this chicken egg provide nutrients for the development of a chick.*

Surface Area–to–Volume Ratio Calculate the surface area–to–volume ratio of a cube whose sides measure 2 cm.

Step 1: Calculate the surface area.

surface area of cube =
number of sides × area of side

surface area of cube = 6 × (2 cm × 2 cm)

surface area of cube = 24 cm²

Step 2: Calculate the volume.

volume of cube = side × side × side

volume of cube = 2 cm × 2 cm × 2 cm

volume of cube = 8 cm³

Step 3: Calculate the surface area–to–volume ratio.

$$\text{surface area–to–volume ratio} = \frac{\text{surface area}}{\text{volume}} = \frac{24}{8} = \frac{3}{1}$$

Now It's Your Turn

1. Calculate the surface area–to–volume ratio of a cube whose sides are 3 cm long.

2. Calculate the surface area–to–volume ratio of a cube whose sides are 4 cm long.

3. Of the cubes from questions 1 and 2, which has the greater surface area–to–volume ratio?

4. What is the relationship between the length of a side and the surface area–to–volume ratio of a cell?

Universal Access · Differentiated Instruction

Basic Learners

Comparing Volume and Surface Area

Have students work in pairs. Give each pair three cubes of varying sizes and a ruler. If possible, give students cubes that have lengths that are whole numbers in units of centimeters. This will make it easier for students to calculate surface area and volume. Have one student in each pair calculate the surface area of each cube. Have the other student in each pair calculate the volume of each cube. Then, have students switch roles. Finally, have students compare their results and calculate the surface area-to-volume ratios for each cube. **LS** Kinesthetic Co-op Learning

Parts of a Cell

Cells have many different functions and come in many shapes and sizes. But all cells have some parts in common.

The Cell Membrane and Cytoplasm

All cells are surrounded by a cell membrane. The **cell membrane** is a protective layer that covers the cell's surface and acts as a barrier. It separates the cell's contents from its environment. The cell membrane also controls materials going into and out of the cell. Inside the cell is a fluid. This fluid and almost all of its contents are called the *cytoplasm* (SIET oh PLAZ uhm).

Organelles

Cells have organelles that carry out many life processes. **Organelles** are structures that have specific jobs inside the cell. Different kinds of cells have different organelles. Most organelles are surrounded by membranes. For example, the algal cell in **Figure 4** has membrane-bound organelles. Some organelles float in the cytoplasm. Other organelles are attached to membranes or other organelles.

Genetic Material

All cells have DNA (**d**eoxyribo**n**ucleic **a**cid) at some point in their lives. DNA is genetic material. It carries information needed to make new cells and new organisms. DNA is passed on from parent cells to new cells and directs the activities of a cell. **Figure 5** shows the DNA of a bacterium.

In cells such as plant and animal cells, DNA does not float around the cell. The *repository*, or storage area, for DNA is an organelle called the **nucleus.** Other cells, such as bacterial cells, do not have a nucleus.

Some cells can live without DNA. When human red blood cells are first made, they have a nucleus with DNA. But as red blood cells mature, they lose their nucleus and DNA. Most cells, however, always need to have DNA. DNA gives these cells instructions on how to make proteins.

Standards Check Where is DNA located in plant and animal cells?
7.1.c

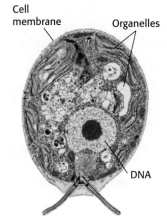

Figure 4 *The green alga in this photomicrograph has organelles. The organelles and the fluid surrounding them make up the cytoplasm.*

cell membrane (SEL MEM BRAYN) a phospholipid layer that covers a cell's surface and acts as a barrier between the inside of a cell and the cell's environment

organelle (AWR guh NEL) one of the small bodies in a cell's cytoplasm that are specialized to perform a specific function

nucleus (NOO klee uhs) in a eukaryotic cell, a membrane-bound organelle that contains the cell's DNA and that has a role in processes such as growth, metabolism, and reproduction

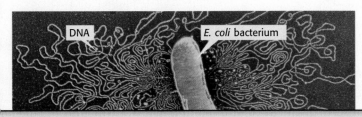

Figure 5 *This photomicrograph shows an Escherichia coli bacterium. The bacterium's cell membrane has been treated so that the cell's DNA is released.*

Homework

Smallest Living Thing Ask students to research the smallest living thing. Students should identify the organism that is considered the smallest living thing and compare the size of its cells to the size of human cells. (Accept all reasonable answers. Scientists are not certain what the smallest living organism is. *Mycoplasma genitalium* has been considered the smallest living thing by most scientists, but the recent discovery of nanobacteria may change this. However, nanobacteria do not always show the characteristics of living things. Continued research may settle this issue.) **LS Verbal/Logical**

MISCONCEPTION ALERT

Who's in Charge Here?

Some students may anthropomorphize the nucleus in a cell. In doing so, they may incorrectly think that the nucleus "bosses" the cell around. Help students overcome this misconception by having them create a model of a nucleus. Students should include representations of genetic material in their models. Help students understand that the nucleus is the repository for DNA, which is the molecule that controls the functions of the cell. The nucleus simply houses this control mechanism.

Answer to Standards Check

DNA is contained in an organelle called the nucleus in plant and animal cells.
7.1.c (mastering)

Universal Access · Differentiated Instruction

Special Education Students

Standards Check Posters Struggling learners may have a difficult time retaining details. To help students remember the detailed information in the standards checks, create posters of the standards checks to display in the classroom. Make one poster for each standards check in this section. Write the question from the textbook in one color. Write a succinct and simple answer for the question in another color. Place the posters around the room. Periodically, conduct standards reviews in which you ask the questions from the posters at random, and students recite the answers aloud, either from memory or by reading the posters. **LS Visual**

Standards Focus

This **Standards Focus** provides you with a quick way to **assess, reteach,** and **re-assess** one or more concepts in the section.

Assess

1. Name one structure that is common to all cells and describe its function. (Sample answer: The cell membrane is a protective layer that acts as a barrier.) **7.1.a**

2. Where is DNA located in a prokaryotic cell? (in the cytoplasm) in a eukaryotic cell? (in the nucleus) **7.1.c**

Reteach

Drawing Cells Ask students to draw diagrams with colored pencils. Have them draw a diagram of a typical prokaryotic cell on one page. Then, have them draw a diagram of a typical eukaryotic cell on the next page. Students should label the different parts of both types of cells and note which structures are common to both types of cells. **LS Visual 7.1.a, 7.1.c**

Re-Assess

Cell Theory Timeline Ask students to create a timeline that shows the creation and evolution of the cell theory. In their timeline, students should identify the individuals who contributed to the cell theory and the main points of the cell theory. **LS Verbal/Intrapersonal 7.1.a**

Answer to Standards Check

Prokaryotic cells do not have a nucleus. Eukaryotic cells have a nucleus.
7.1.a (supporting)

📦 Teaching Transparency:
L11 Prokaryotic and Eukaryotic Cells

---

prokaryote (proh KAR ee OHT) a single-celled organism that does not have a nucleus or membrane-bound organelles; examples are archaea and bacteria

Wordwise The prefix *pro-* means "before." The root *karyon* means "nut" or "kernel."

Two Kinds of Cells

All cells have cell membranes, organelles, cytoplasm, and DNA. But there are two basic types of cells. Cells without a nucleus are *prokaryotic* (proh KAR ee AHT ik) *cells.* Cells that have a nucleus are *eukaryotic* (yoo KAR ee AHT ik) *cells.* Prokaryotic cells are further classified into two groups: *bacteria* (bak TIR ee uh) and *archaea* (ahr KEE uh). **Figure 6** shows a prokaryotic cell and eukaryotic cell. Other prokaryotic and eukaryotic cells may look different from the cells in the diagrams below.

Standards Check How do prokaryotic cells differ from eukaryotic cells? **7.1.a**

Prokaryotes

Bacteria and archaea are prokaryotes. **Prokaryotes** are single-celled organisms that do not have a nucleus. Even though prokaryotes do not have a nucleus, they do have DNA. The DNA of a prokaryote is a long, circular molecule. It is shaped like a twisted rubber band. Prokaryotes also do not have membrane-bound organelles. But they do have ribosomes. *Ribosomes* are tiny, round organelles made of protein and other material. Prokaryotic cells also have strong, weblike cell walls.

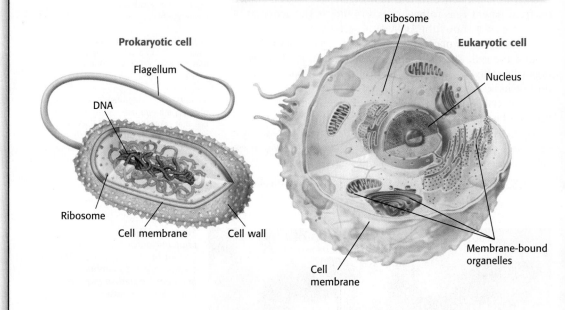

Figure 6 Two Kinds of Cells

Wordwise

Prefixes *eu-* and *pro-* The words *eukaryote* and *prokaryote* are related. Both words have the same root, *karyon,* which means "nut" or "kernel." The prefix *eu-* means "good" or "true;" the prefix *pro-* means "before." Other words that contain the prefixes *eu-* and *pro-* include *prologue, euphemism,* and *euphoria.* However, tell students to keep in mind that the prefix *pro-* has additional meanings: "in front of," "forward," and "for." These meanings apply in words such as *promote* and *produce.* Ask students to identify additional words that contain the prefixes *eu-* and *pro-*. Have students identify the meaning of each word and the other roots in the word. **LS Auditory/Verbal**

Eukaryotes

Eukaryotic cells are the largest cells. Most eukaryotic cells are still microscopic, but they are about 10 times as large as most prokaryotic cells.

Unlike bacteria and archaea, eukaryotic cells have a nucleus. The nucleus holds the cell's DNA. Eukaryotic cells have other membrane-bound organelles, too. Each kind of organelle has a specific job in the cell.

All living things that are not bacteria or archaea are made up of one or more eukaryotic cells. Organisms made up of eukaryotic cells are called **eukaryotes.** Yeasts and amoebas are single-celled eukaryotes. Plants and animals are eukaryotes that are made up of many cells.

eukaryote (yoo KAR ee OHT) an organism made up of cells that have a nucleus enclosed by a membrane; eukaryotes include protists, animals, plants, and fungi but not archaea or bacteria

---

SECTION Review

 7.1.a, 7.1.c

Summary

- The cell theory states that all organisms are made of cells, the cell is the basic unit of all living things, and all cells come from other cells.

- All cells have a cell membrane, cytoplasm, and DNA.

- Most cells are too small to be seen with the naked eye. The surface area–to–volume ratio of a cell limits the size of the cell.

- The two basic kinds of cells are prokaryotic cells and eukaryotic cells. Eukaryotic cells have a nucleus and membrane-bound organelles. Prokaryotic cells do not.

- Prokaryotes are single-celled.

- Eukaryotes can be single-celled or multicellular.

Understanding Concepts

1 Summarizing What does the cell theory tell us about cells?

2 Listing Name three structures that every cell has.

3 Describing Why are most cells small?

INTERPRETING GRAPHICS The picture below shows an organism that has one cell. Use the picture to answer the next two questions.

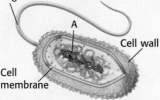
Flagellum
A
Cell wall
Cell membrane

4 Identifying Is this cell a prokaryotic cell or a eukaryotic cell? How can you tell?

5 Identifying What part of the organism is labeled "A"?

Critical Thinking

6 Making Comparisons Compare the ways in which eukaryotic cells and prokaryotic cells store their DNA.

7 Applying Concepts You have discovered a new single-celled organism. It has ribosomes and long, circular DNA. Is it a eukaryote or a prokaryote? Explain.

8 Identifying Relationships You are looking at a cell under a microscope. What characteristics would this cell have if the organism is a eukaryote? What characteristics would this cell have if the organism is a prokaryote? What would you look for first?

Math Skills

9 Analyzing Shapes Calculate the surface area–to–volume ratio of a cube whose sides are 3 cm long.

Internet Resources

For a variety of links related to this chapter, go to www.scilinks.org
Topic: Prokaryotic Cells
SciLinks code: HY71225

Universal Access · Differentiated Instruction

English Learners

Eukaryotic Cells Remind students that bacteria and archaea are prokaryotic cells and that plant and animal cells are eukaryotic cells. Tell students the following mnemonic to help them remember the difference between the two kinds of cells: *You* (and plants) have *eu*karyotic cells. **LS Auditory/Verbal**

Preteach

Reviewing Prior Knowledge

Review standard 7.1.b with students. Make sure that students understand what cell walls and chloroplasts are. Then, ask students to summarize the standard in their own words. (Sample answer: The cells of plants and animals contain different organelles.) Finally, ask students to predict how the standard may apply to this section. (Sample answer: This chapter will explain the ways that plant and animal cells are alike and different.)

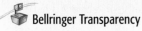 Bellringer

Have students focus on standard 7.1.c by answering the following question: What are three differences between prokaryotic and eukaryotic cells? (Prokaryotic cells have no nucleus, circular DNA, and no membrane-bound organelles. Eukaryotic cells have a nucleus, linear DNA, and membrane-bound organelles.)

Bellringer Transparency

Motivate

Discussion

Cellular Activity Ask students if they can feel the activity within their cells that keep them alive. (Students should indicate that they cannot feel cellular activity.) Then, ask students to explain how they know that their cells are working if they cannot feel cellular activity. (Sample answer: I know that my body's cells are working because I am alive and healthy. If cells are not working, an organism gets sick and may die.)
LS Logical/Interpersonal

Answer to Standards Check

One characteristic that distinguishes plant cells from animal cells is a cell wall, which is found in plant cells but not in animal cells. **7.1.b** (mastering)

Eukaryotic Cells

Key Concept Eukaryotic cells have organelles that perform important functions.

▶ Even though most cells are small, cells are complex. A eukaryotic cell has many parts that help the cell stay alive. Some eukaryotic cells can be classified as plant cells or animal cells. Compare the plant cell in **Figure 1** with the animal cell in **Figure 2** to see the differences between these two types of cells.

Cell Wall

Plant cells have an outermost structure called a **cell wall.** A cell wall is a rigid structure that gives support to a cell. The cell walls of plants, fungi, archaea, and bacteria can be made of different materials. For example, plants and algae have cell walls made of a complex sugar called *cellulose*. **Figure 1** shows the cellulose fibers in the cell wall of a plant cell. Animal cells do not have cell walls.

Standards Check What is one characteristic that distinguishes plant cells from animal cells? **7.1.b**

What You Will Learn

- Eukaryotic cells have many parts—such as cell membranes, a nucleus, and ribosomes—in common.
- Plant cells and animal cells have some cell parts that are different.

Why It Matters

Learning how organelles function helps you know how cells stay alive.

Vocabulary

- cell wall
- cytoskeleton
- ribosome
- endoplasmic reticulum
- mitochondrion
- chloroplast
- Golgi complex
- vesicle
- lysosome

READING STRATEGY

Graphic Organizer In your **Science Journal,** make a Comparison Table that compares the structure, function, location in the cell, and presence in animal and plant cells of all the organelles discussed in this section.

cell wall (SEL WAWL) a rigid structure that surrounds the cell membrane and provides support to the cell

Figure 1 A Plant Cell

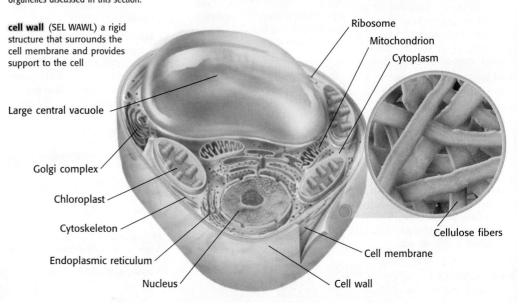

Ribosome
Mitochondrion
Cytoplasm
Large central vacuole
Golgi complex
Chloroplast
Cytoskeleton
Endoplasmic reticulum
Nucleus
Cellulose fibers
Cell membrane
Cell wall

Universal Access · Differentiated Instruction

Special Education Students

Describing Diagrams Students with visual impairments need alternative methods for learning information that is presented visually. Pair students who are not visually impaired with those who are. Have the students who are not visually impaired describe and explain each of the complex cell diagrams to their partners. Choose nonvisually impaired students who have a solid grasp of the information.
LS Auditory/Interpersonal

Advanced Learners/GATE

Cell Walls Have students investigate the molecular structure of cell walls. Then, have them make a molecular model of a cell wall based on their findings. Ask volunteers to present their models to the class. In their presentation, volunteers should explain why cell walls are rigid and why they are important to plants. You may wish to expand this activity by having students investigate and model cell membranes as well. **LS** Visual

Cell Membrane

All cells have a cell membrane made up of proteins and lipids. The *cell membrane* is a protective barrier that encloses a cell. It separates the cell's contents from the cell's environment. The cell membrane is the outermost structure in cells that lack a cell wall. In cells that have a cell wall, the cell membrane lies just inside the cell wall.

The cell membrane has two layers of phospholipids, shown in **Figure 2.** A *phospholipid* is a type of lipid. Each phospholipid has a *hydrophobic,* or "water fearing," end and a *hydrophilic,* or "water loving," end. The "water fearing" ends are on the inside of the cell membrane. The "water loving" ends form the outer part of the membrane. This structure makes it difficult for materials to pass through the membrane. Not allowing materials to pass through is one way the cell membrane protects the cell.

Some materials, such as nutrients and wastes, must pass through the cell membrane. These materials are able to pass through passageways made of proteins. Nutrients move into the cell—and wastes move out of the cell—through these protein passageways.

Standards Check How does the cell membrane protect the cell?
 7.1.a

Quick Lab

Cell Diagrams 7.1.b 7.7.d
1. Draw an outline of a plant cell and an animal cell on **separate pieces of paper.**
2. As you read about eukaryotic cells, use **colored pencils** to add the correct cell parts to each cell. Label the cell parts.
3. Which cell parts are found in both plant cells and animal cells?
4. Which cell parts are found either in plant cells or in animals cells but not in both types of cells?

⏱ **20 min**

Figure 2 An Animal Cell

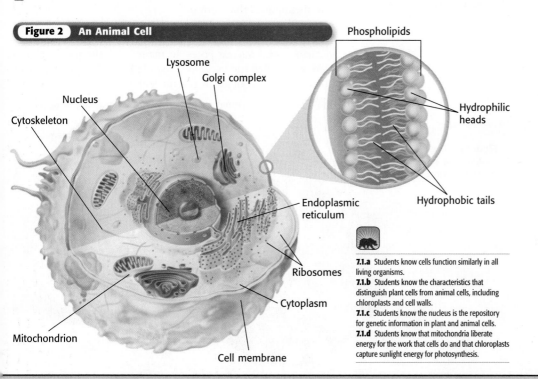

- Lysosome
- Golgi complex
- Nucleus
- Cytoskeleton
- Phospholipids
- Hydrophilic heads
- Hydrophobic tails
- Endoplasmic reticulum
- Ribosomes
- Cytoplasm
- Mitochondrion
- Cell membrane

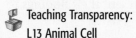
7.1.a Students know cells function similarly in all living organisms.
7.1.b Students know the characteristics that distinguish plant cells from animal cells, including chloroplasts and cell walls.
7.1.c Students know the nucleus is the repository for genetic information in plant and animal cells.
7.1.d Students know that mitochondria liberate energy for the work that cells do and that chloroplasts capture sunlight energy for photosynthesis.

Quick Lab

⏱ **20 min**

Teacher Notes

In this lab, students will draw a plant cell and an animal cell and label the different parts of each cell. This activity will help students learn about the similarities and differences between plant and animal cells (covers standards 7.1.b and 7.7.d).

Materials for Each Student
- colored pencils
- paper (2)

Answers

3. The cell membrane, cytoskeleton, nucleus, ribosomes, endoplasmic reticulum, mitochondria, Golgi complex, and cell compartments, including lysosomes, are found in both plant and animal cells.

4. Plant cells have a cell wall, chloroplasts, and a large central vacuole, but animal cells do not.

📁 Differentiated Datasheets
A **BASIC**, B **GENERAL**, C **ADVANCED**

Also editable on the Holt Lab Generator CD-ROM

Using the Figure

The Nucleus Have students examine the illustration of the nucleus in **Figure 4.** Ask students to describe the structure of the nucleus orally. (Sample answer: The nucleus is an organelle that has two membranes, nuclear pores, and a dark area called the nucleolus.) Answer to caption question: no; All eukaryotic cells have a nucleus at some point in their lives, but some cells, such as red blood cells, may lose the nucleus as they mature. Prokaryotic cells do not have a nucleus. **LS Visual/Auditory**

Connection To
Physical Science

The Physics of Cells Scientists in the field of biophysics use the tools and techniques of physics to study the life processes of cells. Techniques such as electron microscopy, X-ray diffraction, magnetic resonance spectroscopy, and electrophoresis allow biophysicists to study the structure of proteins, nucleic acids, and various parts of the cell. Ask students to research one of the techniques listed above. Students should identify and explain how the technique helps biophysicists better understand the cell. Have students present their findings to the class. **LS Verbal**

Answer to Standards Check

The function of the nucleus is to contain the cell's DNA. **7.1.c** (mastering)

Teaching Transparency:
L14 The Nucleus

Q: Why did the cell cross the microscope?

A: To get to the other slide!

Figure 3 *The cytoskeleton is a network of protein fibers that anchors the cell's organelles and other components of its cytoplasm.*

cytoskeleton (SIET oh SKEL uh tuhn) the cytoplasmic network of protein filaments that plays an essential role in cell movement, shape, and division

Cytoskeleton

The **cytoskeleton** is a web of proteins in the cytoplasm of some cells. Both plant cells and animal cells have a cytoskeleton. Many of the organelles in cells are attached to the cytoskeleton, as **Figure 3** shows. In an animal cell, the cytoskeleton defines the shape of the cell because the cell does not have a cell wall. Different cells in your body have different shapes because of how their cytoskeleton is arranged.

The cytoskeleton is also used for movement. The cytoskeleton can help objects move around within the cell. Some organisms use their cytoskeleton to form structures that help the organisms move.

Nucleus

All eukaryotic cells have a membrane-bound nucleus. The *nucleus* is a large organelle in a eukaryotic cell. It contains the cell's DNA. DNA is the genetic material that contains the information on how to make a cell's proteins. Proteins control the chemical reactions in a cell. They also provide structural support for cells and tissues. But proteins are not made in the nucleus. Messages for how to make proteins are given by the DNA. These messages are then sent out of the nucleus through the membranes that surround it.

The nucleus is covered by two membranes. Materials cross this double membrane by passing through pores. **Figure 4** shows a nucleus and nuclear pores. In many cells, the nucleus has a dark area called the *nucleolus* (noo KLEE uh luhs). A cell begins to make its ribosomes in the nucleolus.

Standards Check What is the function of the nucleus? **7.1.c**

Figure 4 *The nucleus contains the cell's DNA. **Does every cell have a nucleus?***

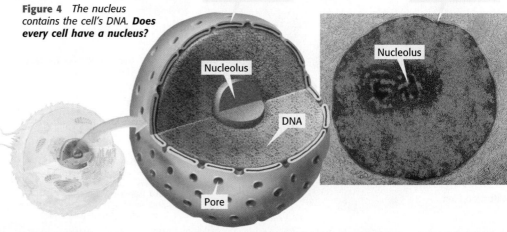

Double membrane

Double membrane

Nucleolus

DNA

Nucleolus

Pore

Universal Access · Differentiated Instruction

English Learners

Word Parts Group students together and ask them to list the vocabulary terms in this section. Help students break complicated words into word roots, prefixes, and suffixes. Students should look up the definitions for these word parts using the appendix of this book, dictionaries, and the Internet. Help students assemble a poster that shows vocabulary terms and their meanings based on their word parts. **LS Verbal Co-op Learning**

Special Education Students

Cell Models Make a salt, water, and flour solution (1/4 salt, 1/4 water, and 1/2 flour). Create a ball for the cell. Then have students color and shape cell organelles and glue them onto the salt/water/flour creation to make the cell come alive! When all the organelles are in place, wrap the "cell" in plastic wrap to represent the cell membrane. **LS Visual/Kinesthetic**

Ribosomes

Organelles that make proteins are called **ribosomes.** Ribosomes are the smallest organelles. And there are more ribosomes than there are any other organelles in a cell. Some ribosomes float freely in the cytoplasm. Others are attached to membranes or the cytoskeleton. Unlike most organelles, ribosomes are not covered by a membrane.

Ribosomes make proteins by assembling chains of amino acids. An *amino acid* is any of about 20 different organic molecules that are used to make proteins. All cells need proteins to live. Thus, all cells have ribosomes.

Endoplasmic Reticulum

Many chemical reactions take place in a cell. Many of these reactions happen on or in the endoplasmic reticulum. The **endoplasmic reticulum,** or ER, is a system of folded membranes in which proteins, lipids, and other materials are made. The ER is shown in **Figure 5.**

The ER is part of the internal delivery system of the cell. Its folded membrane contains many tubes and passageways. Substances move through the ER to different places in the cell.

The endoplasmic reticulum is either rough or smooth. The part of the ER covered in ribosomes is rough ER. Rough ER is usually found near the nucleus. Ribosomes on rough ER make many of the cell's proteins. The ER then delivers these proteins throughout the cell. The ER that lacks ribosomes is smooth ER. The functions of smooth ER include making lipids and breaking down toxic materials that could damage the cell.

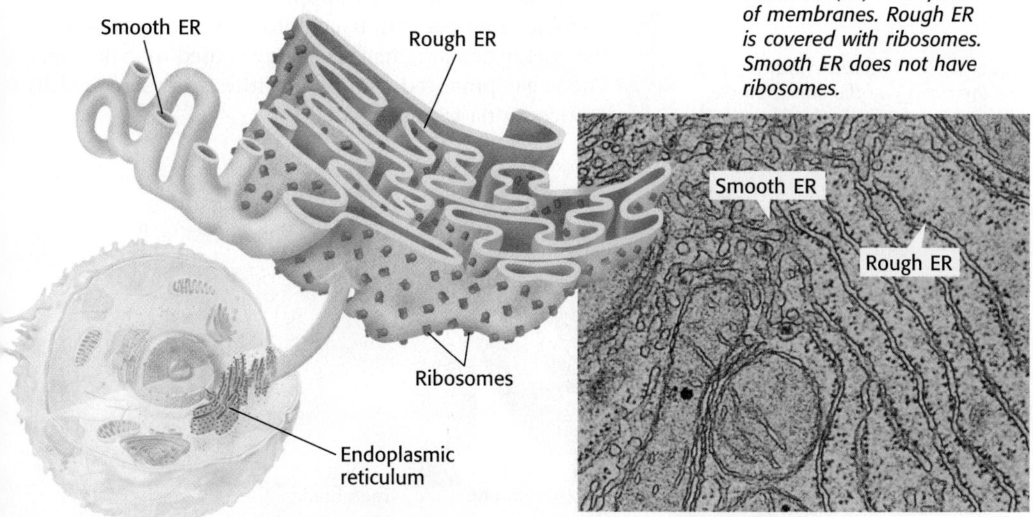

ribosome (RIE buh SOHM) a cell organelle composed of RNA and protein; the site of protein synthesis

endoplasmic reticulum (EN doh PLAZ mik ri TIK yuh luhm) a system of membranes that is found in a cell's cytoplasm and that assists in the production, processing, and transport of proteins and in the production of lipids

Figure 5 *The endoplasmic reticulum (ER) is a system of membranes. Rough ER is covered with ribosomes. Smooth ER does not have ribosomes.*

Smooth ER

Rough ER

Smooth ER

Rough ER

Ribosomes

Endoplasmic reticulum

📖 READING STRATEGY

Discussion Before students read this page, ask them if the following statement is true or false, and why: Animal cells are completely different from plant cells. (false; Animal cells and plant cells have many features in common, such as membrane-bound organelles and a cell membrane. The main difference between animal and plant cells is that animal cells do not have cell walls and chloroplasts.) **LS** Logical

Connection To
Language Arts

Writing **Far-Out Fiction** Have students write a short story about an animal whose cells are invaded by chloroplasts. In their story, students should describe how the animal's life processes would be affected at the cellular level by the invasion. Students may also describe how the animal might use the chloroplast invasion to its advantage. Encourage students to write about an animal other than a mammal. **LS** Intrapersonal

Answer to Standards Check

Mitochondria are the main power source of a cell. **7.1.d** (mastering)

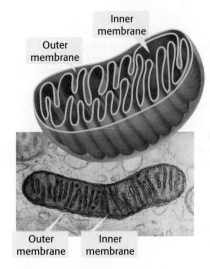

Figure 6 *Mitochondria break down sugar and make ATP. ATP is produced on the inner membrane.*

mitochondrion
(MIET oh KAHN dree uhn) in eukaryotic cells, the cell organelle that is surrounded by two membranes and that is the site of cellular respiration

chloroplast (KLAWR uh PLAST) an organelle found in plant and algae cells where photosynthesis occurs

Figure 7 *Chloroplasts harness and use the energy of the sun to make sugar. A green pigment—chlorophyll—captures the sun's energy.*

Mitochondria

A **mitochondrion** is the main power source of a cell. A mitochondrion is the organelle in which sugar is broken down to release energy. Mitochondria are covered by two membranes, as shown in **Figure 6.** Energy released by mitochondria is stored in a substance called *ATP* (**a**denosine **tri**phosphate). The cell then uses ATP to do work. ATP can be made at several places in a cell. But most of a cell's ATP is made on the inner membrane of the cell's mitochondria.

Most eukaryotic cells have mitochondria. Mitochondria are the size of some bacteria. Like bacteria, mitochondria have their own DNA, and mitochondria can divide within a cell.

Standards Check Why are mitochondria important for cells?
🔲 **7.1.d**

Chloroplasts

Animal cells cannot make their own food. Plant cells are different. Some of them have chloroplasts. **Chloroplasts** are organelles in which photosynthesis takes place. They are found in plant, algae, and some prokaryotic cells. Like mitochondria, chloroplasts have two membranes and their own DNA. A chloroplast is shown in **Figure 7.** *Photosynthesis* is the process by which cells, such as plant cells, use sunlight, carbon dioxide, and water to make sugar and oxygen.

Chloroplasts are green because they contain *chlorophyll,* a green pigment. Chlorophyll is found in an internal membrane system within a chloroplast. Chlorophyll traps the energy of sunlight. This energy is used to make sugar. The sugar produced by photosynthesis is then used by mitochondria to make ATP.

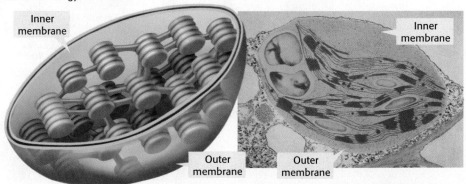

Universal Access · Differentiated Instruction

Basic Learners

Writing **Cell Factory** Cellular structures can be described as being part of a factory. Ask students to write a short story in which each organelle represents part of a factory. Students should describe the role that each cellular structure plays in the factory. Encourage students to be creative. **LS** Verbal

Struggling Readers

Subheads Show students that subheads are helpful guides for understanding the text. Show them that, in this section, the subheads are all words that students might not already know and so most of them are defined in the margins. Teach them to make flashcards. Have students write the word and pronunciation on one side and the definition and a labeled diagram on the other for each of the subheads on these two pages. **LS** Verbal/Kinesthetic

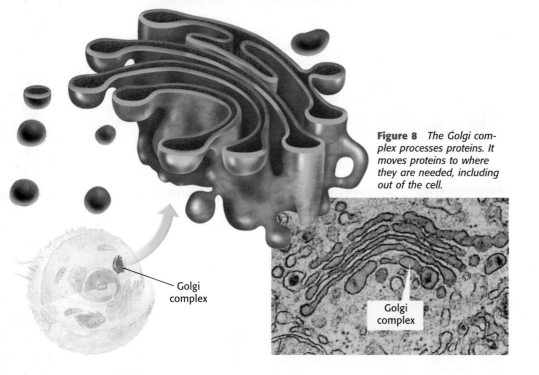

Figure 8 *The Golgi complex processes proteins. It moves proteins to where they are needed, including out of the cell.*

Golgi complex

Golgi complex

Golgi Complex

The organelle that packages and distributes proteins is called the **Golgi complex.** It is named after Camillo Golgi, the Italian scientist who first identified the organelle.

The Golgi complex, shown in **Figure 8,** looks like smooth ER. Lipids and proteins from the ER are delivered to the Golgi complex. There, the lipids and proteins may be modified to do different jobs. The final products are enclosed in a piece of the Golgi complex's membrane. This membrane pinches off to form a small bubble. The bubble transports its contents to other parts of the cell or out of the cell.

Golgi complex (GOHL jee KAHM PLEKS) a cell organelle that helps make and package materials to be transported out of the cell

vesicle (VES i kuhl) a small cavity or sac that contains materials in a eukaryotic cell

Cell Compartments

The bubble that forms from the Golgi complex's membrane is one example of a vesicle. A **vesicle** is a small sac that surrounds material to be moved into or out of a cell. All eukaryotic cells have vesicles. Vesicles also move material within a cell. For example, vesicles carry new proteins from the ER to the Golgi complex. Other vesicles carry material from the Golgi complex to other parts of the cell. Some vesicles form when part of the cell membrane surrounds an object that is outside the cell.

Cell World

What would a cell look like from the inside? Create a brochure inviting tourists to visit various parts of the cell. Go to **go.hrw.com,** and type in the keyword HY7CELW.

Standards Focus

This **Standards Focus** provides you with a quick way to **assess, reteach,** and **re-assess** one or more concepts in the section.

Assess

1. How are plant and animal cells similar? (Sample answer: They both have membrane-bound organelles, cell membranes, and DNA organized into chromosomes that are stored in the nucleus.) **7.1.a, 7.1.b, 7.1.c**

2. Which organelle captures light energy? (chloroplast) Which organelle releases energy? (mitochondrion) **7.1.d**

3. What three structures are found in plant cells, but not in animal cells? (chloroplasts, cell walls, and large central vacuoles) **7.1.b**

Reteach

Organelles and Their Functions
Create a table like the one shown on this page, but do not include the descriptions of the organelles. Distribute copies of the table to the class, and have students work in pairs to fill in the descriptions. **LS** Visual **7.1.a, 7.1.b, 7.1.c, 7.1.d**

Re-Assess

Plant Cell Model Have students use a shoebox to create a model of a plant cell. Provide students with materials that can be used to represent other cell parts. Ask students to label the structures that are found only in plant cells. **LS** Visual **7.1.a**

Answer to Standards Check

Lysosomes destroy worn-out organelles, attack foreign invaders, and get rid of waste material from inside the cell. **7.1.a** (supporting)

 Teaching Transparency:
L15 Organelles and Their Functions

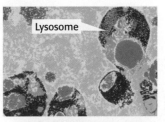

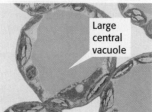

Figure 9 *Lysosomes digest materials inside a cell. In plant cells, the large central vacuole stores water.*

lysosome (LIE suh SOHM) a cell organelle that contains digestive enzymes

Lysosomes

Lysosomes are vesicles found mainly in animal cells. Lysosomes contain digestive enzymes. They are responsible for digestion inside a cell. Lysosomes destroy worn-out or damaged organelles, get rid of waste materials, and engulf foreign invaders. The foreign invaders are digested, and most of them are no longer harmful to the cell.

When eukaryotic cells engulf particles, they enclose the particles in vesicles. Lysosomes, shown in blue in **Figure 9,** bump into the vesicles, shown in purple, and pour enzymes into them. These enzymes digest the particles in the vesicles.

Standards Check Why are lysosomes important? **7.1.a**

Vacuoles

A *vacuole* (VAK yoo OHL) is another type of vesicle found in cells. In plant and fungal cells, some vacuoles act like lysosomes. They store digestive enzymes and aid in digestion within the cell. The large central vacuole in a plant cell stores water and other liquids. Large central vacuoles that are full of water, such as the one in **Figure 9,** help support the cell. Some plants wilt when their large central vacuoles lose water. Some organelles and their functions are shown in **Table 1.**

Table 1	Organelles and Their Functions
Nucleus the organelle that contains the cell's DNA	**Chloroplast** the organelle that uses sunlight, carbon dioxide, and water to make food
Ribosome the organelle upon which amino acids are hooked together to make proteins	**Golgi complex** the organelle that processes and transports materials within and out of the cell
Endoplasmic reticulum the organelle that makes lipids, breaks down toxic substances, and packages proteins for the Golgi complex	**Large central vacuole** the organelle that stores water and other materials
Mitochondrion the organelle that breaks down food molecules to make ATP	**Lysosome** the organelle that digests wastes, cell parts, and foreign invaders

Universal Access · Differentiated Instruction

Struggling Readers

Extended Definitions Direct students' attention to the first two sentences under the "Lysosomes" subhead. Discuss with students the fact that the two sentences are actually working together to explain the term *lysosome.* The first sentence classifies the word and the second sentence gives its function. Ask students to write the word *lysosomes* in their **Science Journal** and list important points about lysosomes underneath the word. Tell students to include the page number and details from the first two paragraphs in their list for future reference. **LS** Visual/Verbal

Summary

- Eukaryotic cells have organelles that perform functions that help cells remain alive.
- All cells have a cell membrane. Some cells have a cell wall. Some cells have a cytoskeleton.
- The nucleus of a eukaryotic cell contains the cell's genetic material, DNA.
- Ribosomes are the organelles that make proteins. Ribosomes are not covered by a membrane.
- The endoplasmic reticulum (ER) and the Golgi complex make and process proteins before the proteins are transported to other parts of the cell or out of the cell.
- Mitochondria and chloroplasts are organelles that provide chemical energy for the cell.
- Lysosomes are organelles responsible for digestion within a cell. In plant cells, the large central vacuole stores cell materials and sometimes acts like a large lysosome.
- Plant cells have cell parts that are not found in animal cells. Plant cells have cell walls, chloroplasts, and a large central vacuole.

Using Vocabulary

1 Write an original definition for *mitochondria*, *nucleus*, and *cell wall*.

Understanding Concepts

2 **Listing** What are two functions of the cytoskeleton in animal cells?

3 **Describing** What is the function of the Golgi complex? What is the function of the endoplasmic reticulum?

4 **Comparing** Describe three ways in which plant cells differ from animal cells.

5 **Applying** Every cell needs ribosomes. Explain why.

INTERPRETING GRAPHICS Use the diagram below to answer the next two questions.

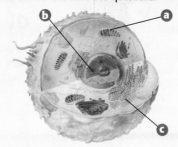

6 **Identifying** Is this a diagram of a plant cell or an animal cell? Explain how you know.

7 **Describing** What is the function of the organelle labeled "b"?

Critical Thinking

8 **Predicting Consequences** A certain virus attacks the mitochondria in cells. What would happen to a cell if all of its mitochondria were destroyed?

9 **Expressing Opinions** Do you think that having chloroplasts gives plant cells an advantage over animal cells? Support your opinion.

Math Skills

10 **Making Calculations** There are 11 foreign invaders and 4 lysosomes in Cell A. If it takes each lysosome 1 h to digest 1 foreign invader, how long will it take to digest all of the foreign invaders?

Challenge

11 **Making Inferences** Amoebas are single-celled eukaryotes. An amoeba moves by creating an extension of the cell. The cytoplasm from the rest of the cell flows into the extension. Given what you know about cell parts, determine which cell part inside of an amoeba is most likely used to make the extension.

Internet Resources

For a variety of links related to this chapter, go to www.scilinks.org
Topic: Eukaryotic Cells
SciLinks code: HY70541

6. This diagram is of an animal cell; the cell has no cell wall, chloroplasts, or central vacuoles, all of which are found in plant cells. **7.1.b** (mastering)

7. The nucleus stores the cell's DNA. **7.1.c** (mastering)

8. Sample answer: Mitochondria are organelles that produce most of the cell's energy. If mitochondria were destroyed, a cell would eventually die because it would not be able to produce enough energy to survive. **7.1.d** (exceeding)

9. Sample answer: I think plant cells have an advantage over animal cells because plant cells can make their own food using light, carbon dioxide, and water. Animals must eat other organisms to get food. **7.1.b** (mastering), **7.1.d** (exceeding)

10. about 3 hours

11. Sample answer: Most likely, the cell part that is used to make an amoeba's extension is the cytoskeleton. **7.1.a** (exceeding)

Section Review Standards Guide

	Supporting	Mastering	Exceeding
7.1.a	1, 3		5, 11
7.1.b	2	1, 4, 6, 9	
7.1.c		1, 7	
7.1.d		1	8, 9

Answers to Section Review

1. Sample answer: Mitochondria are organelles in which sugar is broken down to release energy. The nucleus contains the cell's DNA. The cell wall is the outermost structure in the cells of plants, fungi, and algae. **7.1.a** (supporting), **7.1.b** (mastering), **7.1.c** (mastering), **7.1.d** (mastering)

2. Sample answer: The cytoskeleton keeps the cell's membrane from collapsing and helps some cells move. **7.1.b** (supporting)

3. Sample answer: The Golgi complex packages and distributes proteins within the cell. The endoplasmic reticulum is a series of folded membranes on which lipids, proteins, and other materials are made. Materials are delivered to other places within the cell through the ER. **7.1.a** (supporting)

4. Sample answer: Plant cells have cell walls, but animal cells do not. Plant cells have chloroplasts, which animal cells do not have. Plant cells have large central vacuoles, but animal cells do not have these structures. **7.1.b** (mastering)

5. Sample answer: Ribosomes are the organelles on which proteins are made. All cells need proteins in order to live. **7.1.a** (exceeding)

Section Resources

- Directed Reading A **BASIC** (Also in Spanish), B **GENERAL**
- Interactive Reader and Study Guide
- Section Quiz **GENERAL** (Also in Spanish)
- Section Review **GENERAL** (Also in Spanish)
- Vocabulary and Section Summary A **BASIC** (Also in Spanish), B **GENERAL**

Preteach

Reviewing Prior Knowledge

Instruct students to study the figure of the development of multicellular organisms on this page. Then, ask students to explain what the figure is trying to illustrate. (Sample answer: The figure is showing how one cell grows and divides to become many specialized cells, eventually forming a new organism.)

Bellringer

Have students focus on standard 7.5.a by asking them the following questions: "Why can't you use your tongue to breathe?" (Sample answer: Your tongue is an organ that is specialized for aiding digestion and creating noise, not for breathing. Only respiratory cells, tissues, and organs can aid in respiration, or breathing.) "Why can't you use your arm muscles to digest food?" (Sample answer: Arm muscles are organs that are specialized to help move the arm. They are not specialized for digestion. Only digestive cells, tissues, and organs can digest food.)

Bellringer Transparency

Motivate

ACTIVITY

Concept Mapping Divide the class into small groups. Provide groups with pictures of cells, tissues, organs, organ systems, and organisms. Have students arrange the pictures into concept maps that demonstrate the levels of organization in multicellular organisms. Encourage students to note the similarities between different cells, tissues, and organs. **LS Visual/Interpersonal**

The Organization of Living Things

Key Concept As multicellular organisms develop, their cells differentiate and form levels of organization.

What You Will Learn

- Unicellular organisms are made up of one cell, and multicellular organisms are made up of many cells.
- The cells of multicellular organisms can differentiate to become specialized types of cells.
- The levels of organization in multicellular organisms are cells, tissues, organs, and organ systems.

Why It Matters

Because cells can differentiate, multicellular organisms, such as humans, can have different kinds of cells, tissues, organs, and organ systems.

Vocabulary

- organism
- tissue
- function
- organ
- structure
- organ system

READING STRATEGY

Graphic Organizer In your **Science Journal**, make a Comparison Table that compares various characteristics of unicellular and multicellular organisms.

In some ways, organisms are like machines. Some machines have just one part. But most machines have many parts. Some organisms exist as a single cell. Other organisms have many cells—trillions in some cases.

Anything that can perform life processes by itself is an **organism.** There are two types of organisms: unicellular organisms and multicellular organisms.

Unicellular Organisms

Organisms that are made up of one cell are called *unicellular.* Prokaryotes, such as bacteria and archaea, are unicellular organisms. Eukaryotes such as yeasts, some algae, and some protists are also unicellular. A unicellular organism performs all of the necessary functions to stay alive. Unicellular organisms need fewer resources and can live in harsher conditions than organisms that have many cells.

Multicellular Organisms

Organisms that are made up of many cells are called *multicellular.* Plants, animals, some protists, and many fungi are multicellular organisms. A multicellular organism starts as a single cell, such as the fertilized egg shown in **Figure 1.** As the single cell develops into many cells, the cells become *differentiated,* or fixed, into different types of cells.

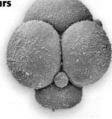

Figure 1 *Multicellular organisms that have differentiated cells, such as humans, can be traced back to a single fertilized egg.*

24 hours

40 hours

6 days

4 months

Universal Access · Differentiated Instruction

Special Education Students

Paragraph Discussions One way to minimize difficulty learning high-level vocabulary is to invite students to summarize each paragraph in their own words before moving on to the next paragraph. Have students perform this exercise in a large group. Allow students to read and then summarize each paragraph in an entire section. **LS Verbal/Auditory**

The Characteristics of Being Multicellular

Multicellular organisms differ from unicellular organisms in many ways. Characteristics of multicellular organisms include the following:

- **Larger Size** Many multicellular organisms are small. But usually they are larger than unicellular organisms. Multicellular organisms grow by making more small cells, not by making their cells larger. Being large can be an advantage. Large organisms are prey for fewer predators. Large predators can eat a wider variety of prey.

- **Longer Life** A unicellular organism dies if its cell dies. But if a single cell in a multicellular organism dies, the organism continues to live.

- **Specialization** Each type of cell has a particular job. Specialization makes the organism more efficient than a unicellular organism. In some ways, having specialized cells is similar to having an assembly line at a factory. The assembly line allows the factory to produce more products in less time than a single individual could.

Standards Check How are multicellular organisms more efficient than unicellular organisms? **7.1.f**

7.1.f Students know that as multicellular organisms develop, their cells differentiate.
7.5.a Students know plants and animals have levels of organization for structure and function, including cells, tissues, organs, organ systems, and the whole organism.

organism (AWR guh NIZ uhm) a living thing; anything that can carry out life processes independently

---

Quick Lab

A Division of Labor

In this activity, your teacher will ask you to model a unicellular organism or a multicellular organism. You will make paper chains according to the steps at right. The steps represent how organisms do work, such as making cell parts.

1. If you are a unicellular organism, you must complete all of the steps before you start over.

2. If you are a cell in a multicellular organism, you will be a member of a team. Each team will work together in an assembly line. Each team member represents a cell that completes only one step. Each team member will receive the product from the previous team member, complete the step, and pass the product to the next team member.

3. Listen for your teacher's directions about when to start and stop.

4. Who made longer chains: the multicellular organisms or the unicellular organisms?

5. How does this activity relate to cell specialization?

7.1.f

How to Make a Paper Chain

1. Use **scissors** to cut one 8 in. strip of paper.

2. Use a **marker** to draw a line down the middle of the length of one strip of paper.

3. Use a **marker of a different color** to draw three circles on the line.

4. Walk to a desk in the front of the classroom. For the first strip, tape the two ends together to form a loop. For the rest of the strips, thread one end of the strip through the previous loop, and tape the ends of the strip to form another loop.

🕐 15 min

Answer to Standards Check

The cells of multicellular organisms are specialized and therefore more efficient than the single cell of unicellular organisms. **7.1.f** (supporting)

Teaching Transparency: *LINK TO EARTH SCIENCE*
E81 The Six Levels of Environmental Organization

Connection to Ecology

Flowchart Poster Use the Earth Science transparency entitled "The Six Levels of Environmental Organization" to expand students' understanding of organization. Students should create a poster with three columns. In the middle column, ask students to make a flowchart starting with cells and ending with the biosphere. In the other columns, students should paste or draw images representing each level of organization and write a short description of each level. **LS** Logical/Visual

ACTiViTy

Writing **Friendly Explanations**
One effective way to learn a scientific concept, such as the organization of multicellular organisms, is to teach the concept to someone else. Have students write a letter to a friend explaining the relationship between cells, tissues, organs, organ systems, and organisms.
LS Interpersonal

MISCONCEPTION ALERT

Cellular Dependence Some students may not realize that the cells in multicellular organisms depend on other cells for their survival. A multicellular organism most likely will survive if a few individual cells are lost, but an individual cell from a multicellular organism typically cannot survive on its own. Show students a live plant. Tear off a very small section of a leaf and explain to students that both the leaf and the small torn piece are made of cells. Ask students to predict what will happen to the plant now that those cells are removed. (Students should recognize that the plant will continue to survive and may replace the lost cells.) Ask students to predict what will happen to the cells that were separated from the plant. (Students should recognize that the cells will die without the support of other cells from the organism.) Help students recognize that each cell in a multicellular organism depends on other cells for its survival.
LS Visual/Logical

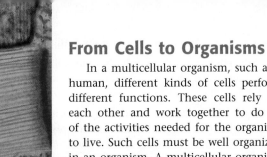

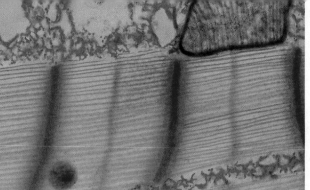

Figure 2 *This photomicrograph shows a small part of one heart muscle cell. The green line surrounds one of many mitochondria, the powerhouses of the cell. The pink areas are muscle filaments.*

function (FUHNGK shuhn) the special, normal, or proper activity of an organ or part

structure (STRUHK shuhr) the arrangement of parts in an organism

Figure 3 *Some plant cells have structures that allow the cells to perform specialized functions.*

From Cells to Organisms

In a multicellular organism, such as a human, different kinds of cells perform different functions. These cells rely on each other and work together to do all of the activities needed for the organism to live. Such cells must be well organized in an organism. A multicellular organism can have four levels of organization: cells, tissues, organs, and organ systems.

Cells: The First Level of Organization

Cells in a multicellular organism can be specialized. A *specialized* cell performs a specific function. The **function** of a cell is the activity that the cell performs. The function of a specialized cell relates to the cell's structure. **Structure** is the arrangement of parts in an organism. It includes the shape of a part and the material of which the part is made. For example, the cardiac muscle cell in **Figure 2** is a specialized muscle cell. Heart muscle cells have internal structures that contract and that make the heart pump blood.

Plants also have cells that perform specific functions. For example, a special type of cell is found in the layer between the inside of a plant and the outside of the plant. These cells are shaped like sausages, as **Figure 3** shows. Pairs of these sausage-shaped cells, which are called *guard cells,* control the size of openings called *stoma.* The stoma allow gases, such as carbon dioxide and oxygen, to move into and out of a leaf.

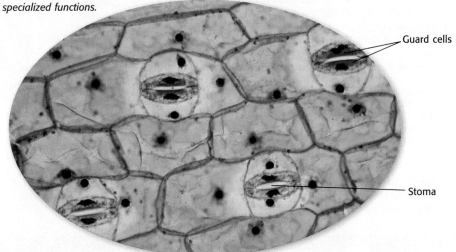

Guard cells

Stoma

Universal Access · Differentiated Instruction

English Learners
Materials
- marker, large
- shelf paper (1 roll)

Personalizing Information Have students use the text and their personal experiences to come up with examples of specialized cells that make up organs and tissues in their bodies or in the organisms around them. Have students add their examples to a class list on a roll of shelf paper, and see how long a list they can make. Tell students to keep their letters between one and two inches high, and make sure that they do not duplicate any examples. Hang the list on a wall. (Sample answers: cardiac muscle cells, plant barrier cells, cells that allow the human body to release water through sweat, and cells that make fingernails.)
LS Logical/Interpersonal

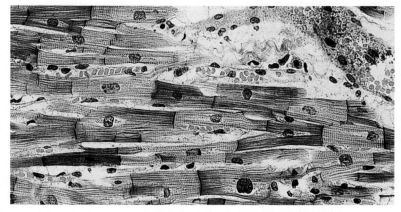

Figure 4 *This photomicrograph shows cardiac muscle tissue. Cardiac muscle tissue is made up of many cardiac cells.*

Tissues: The Second Level of Organization

A **tissue** is a group of cells that work together to perform a specific job. The material around and between the cells is also part of the tissue. The cardiac muscle tissue, shown in **Figure 4,** is made of many cardiac muscle cells. Cardiac muscle tissue is just one type of tissue in a heart.

Animals have four basic types of tissues: nerve tissue, muscle tissue, connective tissue, and protective tissue. In contrast, plants have three types of tissues: transport tissue, protective tissue, and ground tissue. Transport tissue moves water and nutrients through a plant. Protective tissue covers the plant. It helps the plant retain water and protects the plant from damage. Photosynthesis takes place in ground tissue.

Organs: The Third Level of Organization

A structure that is made up of two or more tissues working together to perform a specific function is called an **organ.** For example, your heart is an organ. It is made mostly of cardiac muscle tissue. But your heart also has nerve tissue and tissues of the blood vessels that work together to make your heart the powerful pump that it is.

Another organ is your stomach. It also has several kinds of tissues. Muscle tissue in the stomach makes food move in and through the stomach. Special tissues make chemicals that help digest your food. Connective tissue holds the stomach together, and nervous tissue carries messages back and forth between the stomach and the brain. Other organs include the intestines, brain, and lungs.

Plants also have different kinds of tissues that work together as organs. The leaf of a plant is an organ that contains tissue that traps sunlight energy to make food. Other examples of organs in plants are stems and roots.

Standards Check What is an organ? 📷 **7.5.a**

tissue (TISH oo) a group of similar cells that perform a common function

organ (AWR guhn) a collection of tissues that carry out a specialized function of the body

A Pet Protist
Imagine that you have a tiny, box-shaped protist for a pet. To care for your pet protist properly, you have to figure out how much to feed it. The dimensions of your protist are roughly 25 μm × 20 μm × 2 μm. If seven food particles can enter through each square micrometer of surface area per second, how many particles can your protist eat in 1 min? Record you work in your **Science Journal.**

Answers to Math Practice
The surface area of the protist is [(25 μm × 20 μm) + (20 μm × 2 μm) + (25 μm × 2 μm)] × 2 = 1,180 μm². Thus, it can eat 1,180 μm² × 7 particles per second = 8,260 particles per second, or 60 s/min × 8,260 particles per second = 495,600 particles per minute.

Answer to Standards Check

An organ is a structure that is made up of two or more tissues that work together to perform a specific function in the body. **7.5.a** (mastering)

Universal Access · Differentiated Instruction

Advanced Learners/GATE

Tissues, Organs, and Organ Systems
Have students use the Internet to research the major tissues, organs, and organ systems of the human body. Then, have students create a pamphlet in which they illustrate the major tissues, organs, and organ systems of the human body and provide an in-depth description of each.

Because there are so many tissues, organs, and organ systems in the human body, this can be assigned as an ongoing activity in which students focus on structures that perform specific functions (for example, cardiac functions: cardiac muscle tissue, the heart, and the cardiovascular system). **LS Verbal/Visual**

Close

Standards Focus

This **Standards Focus** provides you with a quick way to **assess, reteach,** and **re-assess** one or more concepts in the section.

**Assess**

1. What happens to the fertilized egg of a multicellular organism? (It divides into two cells, which each divide into two cells, and so on until there are many differentiated cells.) **7.1.f**

2. Put the following into order from simplest to most complex: organ system, organism, tissue, cell, and organ. (cell, tissue, organ, organ system, and organism) **7.5.a**

Reteach

Unicellular Versus Multicellular
Draw a three-column table on the board. In the first column, label three rows with the following headings: *Characteristics, Organization,* and *Examples.* Label the second column with the heading *Unicellular Organisms* and the third column with the heading *Multicellular Organisms.* Have students come up to the board to fill in information on the table.
LS Visual **7.1.f, 7.5.a**

Re-Assess

Organization   Give students an example of a multicellular organism. Then, ask students to identify a specific example for each level of organization of the organism. **LS** Verbal/Logical **7.5.a**

Answer to Standards Check

cells, tissues, organs, and organ systems
7.5.a (mastering)

 Teaching Transparency:
L16 Levels of Organization in the Cardiovascular System

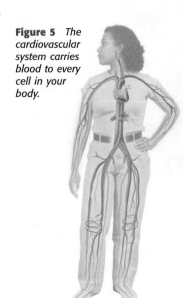

Figure 5 *The cardiovascular system carries blood to every cell in your body.*

organ system (AWR guhn SIS tuhm) a group of organs that work together to perform body functions

---

Organ Systems: The Fourth Level of Organization

A group of organs working together to perform a particular function is called an **organ system.** Each organ system has a specific job to do in the body. The cardiovascular system, shown in **Figure 5,** includes organs and tissues, such as the heart and blood vessels. The job of the cardiovascular system is to transport blood throughout the body.

The digestive system is an organ system made up of several organs, including the stomach and intestines. The digestive system's job is to break down food into small particles. Other parts of the body then use these small particles as fuel. In turn, the digestive system depends on the respiratory and cardiovascular systems for oxygen.

Plants also have organ systems. They include leaf systems, root systems, and stem systems.

Organisms

Multicellular organisms, such as plants and animals, have levels of organization. Cells form the tissues, the tissues form the organs, and the organs form the organ systems of a multicellular organism. The levels of organization in a multicellular organism are shown in **Figure 6.**

Standards Check   List the four levels of organization in multicellular organisms. **7.5.a**

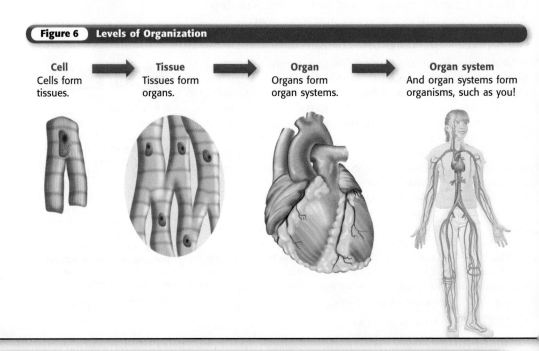

Figure 6   **Levels of Organization**

Cell
Cells form tissues.

Tissue
Tissues form organs.

Organ
Organs form organ systems.

Organ system
And organ systems form organisms, such as you!

Universal Access • Differentiated Instruction

Basic Learners

Multi-* and *Uni-   Write the following words on the board in two separate lists:

List 1: *multigrain, multitasking,* and *multicellular*

List 2: *unicycle, unicorn,* and *unicellular*

Ask volunteers to give the meanings of the prefixes *multi-* and *uni-*. (Sample answer: *multi-* means "more than one"; *uni-* means "one") Invite students to add more words to the lists. **LS** Verbal

Struggling Readers

Terminology Explained   Rewrite the first paragraph of this page on the board. Have students identify the scientific terminology and difficult words. Underline these terms. Ask students to come up with synonyms or short definitions to replace the underlined terms. Help students to rewrite the paragraph using synonyms and simple definitions. **LS** Verbal/Interpersonal

---

Unicellular Organization

Prokaryotes, most protists, and some kinds of fungi are unicellular. Although some of these organisms live in colonies, they are still unicellular. These unicellular organisms live together, and each cell in the colony is the same. However, each cell must carry out all life processes in order for that cell to survive. In contrast, even the simplest multicellular organism has specialized cells that depend on each other in order to survive.

A slime mold is shown in **Figure 7**. A slime mold is a unicellular organism in which individual cells can come together to form a large group.

Figure 7 *Slime molds eat small organisms and break down organic matter.*

SECTION Review

7.1.f, 7.5.a

Summary

Unicellular organisms have only one cell.

As a multicellular organism develops, its cells differentiate into specialized cells.

Multicellular organisms are made up of one or many cells and can have a larger size and a longer life than unicellular organisms.

The four levels of organization in multicellular organisms are cells, tissues, organs, and organ systems.

A tissue is a group of cells working together. An organ is made up of two or more tissues working together. An organ system is made up of two or more organs working together.

Using Vocabulary

1 Use *tissue, organ,* and *multicellular* in separate sentences.

Understanding Concepts

2 Describing Describe the four levels of organization in multicellular organisms.

3 Applying Explain how different types of tissues work together in the heart, an organ.

4 Demonstrating The layer between the outside of a plant leaf and the inside of the leaf contains specialized cells called *guard cells.* How does the structure of guard cells relate to the function of guard cells?

Critical Thinking

5 Predicting Consequences What would happen if the cells of a developing plant did not differentiate into guard cells?

6 Making Inferences Why can multicellular organisms be more complex than unicellular organisms?

7 Making Comparisons Organisms need to perform life functions. How do the ways in which a multicellular organism and a unicellular organism perform life functions differ?

Math Skills

8 Analyzing Shapes Multicellular organism A is a cube. Each of its sides is 3 cm long. The volume of each of its cells is 1 cm³. How many cells does the organism have?

Challenge

9 Applying Concepts Think of an environment on Earth in which you would expect to find unicellular organisms but no multicellular organisms. Why are unicellular organisms able to survive in this environment?

Internet Resources

For a variety of links related to this chapter, go to www.scilinks.org
Topic: Organization of Life
SciLinks code: HY71080

---

5. Sample answer: If guard cells were not differentiated during development, the plant likely would be unable to control the movement of carbon dioxide and oxygen into and out of the leaves. **7.1.f** (exceeding), **7.5.a** (supporting)

6. Multicellular organisms can be more complex than unicellular organisms because the cells of multicellular organisms differentiate and specialize. Specialization results in different kinds of cells. Also, a multicellular organism can grow larger and live longer than a unicellular organism can. **7.1.f** (mastering), **7.5.a** (supporting)

7. Sample answer: Unicellular organisms must perform all necessary life functions with a single cell. A multicellular organism has specialized cells that perform specific functions. The cells work together in a way that is similar to an assembly line, which allows the cells to make more products in less time. **7.1.f** (supporting), **7.5.a** (mastering)

8. 3 cm × 3 cm × 3 cm = 27 cm³, or 27 cells

9. Sample answer: An environment on Earth where I would expect to find unicellular organisms, but not multicellular organisms, is under the ice in Antarctica. Unicellular organisms would be able to survive here more easily than multicellular organisms could survive because unicellular organisms need fewer resources than multicellular organisms do. **7.5.a** (exceeding)

	Section Review Standards Guide		
	Supporting	**Mastering**	**Exceeding**
7.1.f	1, 4, 7	6	5
7.5.a	5, 6	1, 2, 3, 4, 7	9

Answers to Section Review

1. Sample answer: An organism has several kinds of tissue. I think that the most important organ in the body is the brain. A multicellular organism is organized into cells, tissues, organs, and organ systems. **7.1.f** (supporting), **7.5.a** (mastering)

2. A cell is the smallest structural and functional unit of living things. A tissue is made up of cells working together to perform a specific function. An organ is composed of multiple tissues that work together to perform a specific job. An organ system is a group of organs that work together. **7.5.a** (mastering)

3. Sample answer: The heart is made up of several types of tissue, including muscle and nerve tissue. The tissues work together to form the powerful pump that is the heart. **7.5.a** (mastering)

4. Sample answer: A guard cell is shaped like a sausage. Two guard cells put together have a small opening between them, called a stoma. The guard cells control the size of the stoma. When the guard cells increase in size, the stoma is closed. When the guard cells decrease in size, the stoma is open, which allows gases to enter and exit the plant. **7.1.f** (supporting), **7.5.a** (mastering)

Section Resources

- Directed Reading
  A **BASIC** (Also in Spanish), B **GENERAL**
- Interactive Reader and Study Guide
- Section Quiz **GENERAL** (Also in Spanish)
- Section Review **GENERAL** (Also in Spanish)
- Vocabulary and Section Summary
  A **BASIC** (Also in Spanish), B **GENERAL**

Teacher Notes

This lab has students observe the characteristics of cells including chloroplasts and nuclei (covers standards 7.1.b and 7.1.c). Students will operate microscopes and draw diagrams of the objects that they see (covers standards 7.7.a and 7.7.d). Before students begin this lab, you may want to instruct them on the proper procedure for transporting and using a microscope.

Time Required

One 45-min class period

Lab Ratings

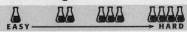

EASY ———————————→ HARD

Teacher Prep 🧪🧪
Student Set-Up 🧪
Concept Level 🧪
Clean Up 🧪

Materials

The materials listed on the student page are enough for a group of 1 to 3 students. Be sure to keep the algae in a warm, damp place that is out of direct sunlight.

Safety Caution

Remind students to review all safety cautions and icons before beginning this lab activity.

OBJECTIVES

Observe the structure of a eukaryotic organism.

Compare the structure of several organisms.

MATERIALS

- algae of the genus *Protococcus* (or other algae)
- eyedropper
- microscope
- saucer
- slide, microscope, and coverslip
- water

SAFETY

7.1.b Students know the characteristics that distinguish plant cells from animal cells, including chloroplasts and cell walls.
7.1.c Students know the nucleus is the repository for genetic information in plant and animal cells.

Investigation and Experimentation
7.7.a Select and use appropriate tools and technology (including calculators, computers, balances, spring scales, microscopes, and binoculars) to perform tests, collect data, and display data.
7.7.d Construct scale models, maps, and appropriately labeled diagrams to communicate scientific knowledge (e.g., motion of Earth's plates and cell structure).

Skills Practice Lab

Cells Alive!

You have probably used a microscope to look at single-celled organisms such as those shown below. These organisms can be found in pond water. In the following exercise, you will look at algae of the genus *Protococcus*, which form a greenish stain on tree trunks, wooden fences, flowerpots, and buildings.

Euglena

Amoeba

Paramecium

Procedure

1 Locate some algae of the genus *Protococcus*. Scrape a small sample into a container. Bring the sample to the classroom. If you can't find these algae outdoors, look for algae on the glass in an aquarium. Such algae may not be members of the genus *Protococcus* but will be very good substitutes.

2 Mix the scraping in a few drops of water in a saucer. Draw up the mixture with an eyedropper, and carefully squeeze one or two drops onto a slide.

3 Place one edge of the coverslip on one end of the slide face. Hold the coverslip at about a 45° angle to the slide.

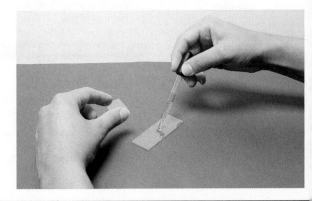

Lab Resources

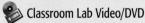

📋 Differentiated Datasheets
A **BASIC**, B **GENERAL**, C **ADVANCED**

💿 Classroom Lab Video/DVD

🔴 **Holt Lab Generator CD-ROM**

Search for any lab by topic, standard, difficulty level, or time. Edit any lab to fit your needs, or create your own labs. Use the Lab Materials QuickList software to customize your lab materials list.

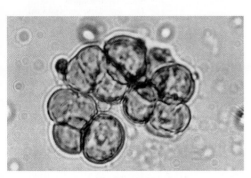

Protococcal cells

4 Draw the edge of the coverslip along the slide until the edge comes into contact with the liquid. Gently lower the coverslip onto the slide. Avoid trapping any air bubbles under the coverslip.

5 Set the microscope on low power to examine the algae. Draw the cells that you see.

6 Switch to high power to examine a single cell. Draw the cell on a separate sheet of paper.

7 You will probably see several chloroplasts in each cell. Label a chloroplast on your drawing. What is the function of the chloroplast?

8 Another structure that should be clearly visible in all the algae cells is the nucleus. Find a cell's nucleus, and label it on your drawing. What is the function of the nucleus?

9 What does the cytoplasm look like? Describe any movement that you see inside the cells.

Analyze the Results

10 **Examining Data** Is a protococcus unicellular or multicellular?

11 **Examining Data** How does a protococcus differ from an amoeba?

12 **Identifying Patterns** How can you tell if a protococcus is eukaryotic or prokaryotic?

Draw Conclusions

13 **Interpreting Results** Discuss how the shape of the cells and the structures within the cells differ between a protococcus and an amoeba.

14 **Interpreting Results** How does a protococcus get its nutrition? Is this method different from the method used by an amoeba?

15 **Making Predictions** If there were no light for some time, predict whether the protococcus or the amoeba would survive more easily, and explain why.

Big Idea Question

16 **Drawing Conclusions** What cell parts were you able to observe in the algae? Are these cell parts found in all living organisms? Explain your answer.

Procedure

7. The chloroplast is responsible for photosynthesis.

8. The nucleus contains DNA, the genetic information of the cell.

9. The cytoplasm is a clear, gel-like substance. Accept all reasonable answers regarding movement of organelles and other structures within the cell.

Analyze the Results

10. Protococci are unicellular algae.

11. Answers may vary. Sample answer: A protococcus cannot move about as an amoeba can. A protococcus contains green chloroplasts, but an amoeba does not. This means protococci can perform photosynthesis, but amoebas cannot.

12. A protococcus is eukaryotic because it has a nucleus. All eukaryotic cells have a nucleus at some stage in their life.

Draw Conclusions

13. Sample answer: An amoeba seems to have a softer body than a protococcus does. Amoebas do not have chloroplasts. Both amoebas and protococci have nuclei.

14. A protococcus makes its own food during photosynthesis. An amoeba must consume food particles and break them down for nutrition.

15. Sample answer: An amoeba would survive more easily because it does not rely on light to make its own food as a protococcus does.

Big Idea Question

16. Sample answer: I was able to observe the chloroplasts and nuclei in the algae. Only organisms that perform photosynthesis have chloroplasts. All eukaryotes have nuclei, but prokaryotes do not have nuclei.

Kelly Sullivan
Harry M. Marsh Junior
High School
Chico, California

Science Skills Activity

Teacher Notes

In this activity, students will learn how to construct a scale diagram and then create two scale diagrams on their own (covers standard 7.7.d). Each student will need a piece of graph paper. Students may not understand that scale diagrams are not only used to represent small things on a larger scale, but are also used to represent large things on a smaller scale. Show students the legend on a map, and explain that maps are also scale diagrams.

Answers to You Try It!

Diagrams may vary, but the number of scale units for each kind of cell should be as follows: Euglena has 20 scale units (100 μm ÷ 5 μm = 20) and red blood cells have 1.4 scale units (7 μm ÷ 5 μm = 1.4).

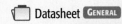 Datasheet **GENERAL**

> **Also editable on the Holt Lab Generator CD-ROM**

Science Skills Activity

Scientific Methods	Research	Data Analysis	Models, Maps & Diagrams

Investigation and Experimentation
7.7.d Construct scale models, maps, and appropriately labeled diagrams to communicate scientific knowledge (e.g., motion of Earth's plates and cell structure).

Constructing Scale Diagrams

▶ Tutorial

Procedure

When a scientist needs to study objects that are too big or too small to fit on a piece of paper, he or she uses a scale diagram. A scale diagram shows the relationship between the size of the object shown on the diagram and the actual size of the object. The following procedure explains how to construct a scale diagram.

1 Find the actual size of the object. You can measure the object if it is big enough, or do research to find its size. For example, if you wanted to draw a scale diagram of a yeast cell, you might research yeast cells and find that the longest yeast cell is 10 μm long.

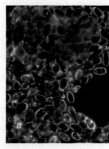

Yeast The longest individual cell is 10 μm long.

2 Once you determine the scale, the actual measurement divided by the scale gives you the measurement of the object in scale units. For example, to draw a scale diagram of a yeast cell, you might decide that one square unit, or scale unit on a piece of graph paper, is equal to 2 μm. Therefore, a yeast cell that is 10 μm in length would equal 5 scale units on a piece of graph paper.

> Scale: 1 scale unit:2 μm
> 10 μm ÷ 2 μm = 5 scale units

3 Mark the dimensions of your object in scale units on a piece of graph paper. Draw the object so that it begins and ends on the spots that you marked.

▶ You Try It!

Procedure

Scale diagrams can be used to compare objects. Construct a scale diagram of each cell shown below. The photos were taken using a microscope. Each photo has a different magnification. Use the actual dimensions of the cells to determine the measurement of the cells in scale units. Construct your diagram on graph paper using the following scale: 1 scale unit = 5 μm.

Euglena The average individual cell is 100 μm long.

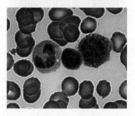

Red blood cell The average diameter is 7 μm.

Universal Access · Differentiated Instruction

Basic Learners

Scale Diagrams Some students will better understand the concept of scale diagrams if they begin with a concrete item that they can easily measure. Have students create a scale diagram that fits on an 8½" × 11" piece of graph paper and shows a single graphic from the cover photo of a textbook. **LS Visual**

Special Education Students

Scale Teams Some students may have a difficult time physically constructing scale diagrams, but they may be able to direct the process or present the results. Divide the class into groups of three students. Assign one student in each group to direct the process and another to construct the scale diagram. Have the third student be the group spokesperson. Teams should share their finished products with the class. **LS Interpersonal**

Chapter Summary

The Big Idea
All organisms are composed of one or more cells.

Section	Vocabulary

1 The Characteristics of Cells

Key Concept Cells function similarly in all living organisms.

- The cell theory explains why cells are important for living things.
- All cells have a cell membrane, cytoplasm, and DNA.
- Prokaryotic cells and eukaryotic cells differ in how their genetic information is contained.

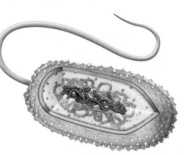

A bacterium is a prokaryotic cell.

cell p. 114
cell membrane p. 117
organelle p. 117
nucleus p. 117
prokaryote p. 118
eukaryote p. 119

2 Eukaryotic Cells

Key Concept Eukaryotic cells have organelles that perform important functions.

- Eukaryotic cells have many cell parts—such as cell membranes, a nucleus, and ribosomes—in common.
- Plant cells and animal cells have some cell parts that are different.

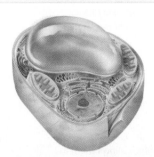

A plant cell is made of many cell parts, such as cell walls and chloroplasts.

cell wall p. 120
cytoskeleton p. 122
ribosome p. 123
endoplasmic reticulum p. 123
mitochondrion p. 124
chloroplast p. 124
Golgi complex p. 125
vesicle p. 125
lysosome p. 126

3 The Organization of Living Things

Key Concept As multicellular organisms develop, their cells differentiate and form levels of organization.

- Unicellular organisms are made up of one cell, and multicellular organisms are made up of many cells.
- The cells of multicellular organisms can differentiate to become specialized types of cells.
- The levels of organization in multicellular organisms are cells, tissues, organs, and organ systems.

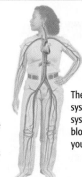

The cardiovascular system is an organ system that delivers blood throughout your body.

organism p. 128
function p. 130
structure p. 130
tissue p. 131
organ p. 131
organ system p. 132

Review Resources

- Reinforcement Worksheet **BASIC**
- Critical Thinking Worksheet **ADVANCED**
- Chapter Review **GENERAL** (Also in Spanish)
- Standards Review Workbook (Also in Spanish)
- Study Guide A **BASIC** (Also in Spanish), B **GENERAL**

Assessment Resources

- Chapter Tests A **BASIC**, B **GENERAL** (Also in Spanish), C **ADVANCED**
- Standards Assessment **GENERAL**

Chapter Summary

SUPER SUMMARY

Have students connect the major concepts in this chapter through an interactive Super Summary. Visit go.hrw.com and type in the keyword HY7CELS to access the Super Summary for this chapter.

Identifying Word Parts

Making Flashcards Have students create flashcards for the boldfaced and italicized key terms used in the chapter. Have students use a dictionary to identify any root words, prefixes, and suffixes in the words and include this information on their flashcards. Students should use the flashcards to study the terms until they understand the meaning of each one. **LS Verbal/Logical**

Focus on Speaking

Reviewing the Standards Ask students to work in pairs. Assign each pair a specific California Science Standard. Ask one member of the pair to read the standard aloud to the class. Then, ask the other member of the pair to explain to the class in his or her own words what the standard means. **LS Auditory Co-op Learning**

Chapter Review

Assignment Guide

Section	Questions
1	2, 7–10, 22
2	3, 12–14, 19, 21, 26
3	4–6, 11, 15–18, 20, 23–24

Answers

Using Vocabulary

1. b

2. cell **7.1.a** (supporting), **7.5.a** (supporting)

3. organelles **7.1.d** (supporting)

4. differentiate **7.1.f** (mastering)

5. tissue **7.5.a** (mastering)

Understanding Concepts

6. c **7.5.a** (mastering)

7. a **7.1.c** (mastering)

8. b **7.1.a** (mastering)

9. b **7.1.a** (supporting)

10. c **7.1.a** (supporting)

11. Sample answer: Cells are the smallest unit of all living things. Cells work together in tissues. Two or more tissues work together in organs, which have specific jobs in the body. Organs work together in organ systems, which are specialized for specific functions.
    7.5.a (mastering)

12. plant cell **7.1.b** (mastering)

13. b **7.1.d** (mastering)

14. c **7.1.a** (supporting)

Writing Skills

15. Accept all reasonable answers. Students should demonstrate an understanding of the structures within cells, particularly structures that are found only in plant cells.
    7.1.b (exceeding), **7.5.a** (exceeding)

Chapter Review

7.1.a, 7.1.b, 7.1.c, 7.1.d, 7.1.f, 7.5.a

Organize

Layered Book Review the FoldNote that you created at the beginning of the chapter. Add to or correct the FoldNote based on what you have learned.

Using Vocabulary

1. **Academic Vocabulary** Which of the following words is the closest in meaning to the word *structure*?
   a. evidence   c. duty
   b. shape   d. location

Complete each of the following sentences by choosing the correct term from the word bank.

cell	organ
cell membrane	prokaryote
organelles	differentiate
cell wall	tissue

2. A(n) ___ is the smallest structural and functional unit of living things.

3. Two types of ___ are ribosomes and mitochondria.

4. During development, the cells of a multicellular organism ___, which allows them to be specialized.

5. A(n) ___ is a group of cells working together to perform a specific function.

Understanding Concepts

Multiple Choice

6. Which of the following best describes an organ?
   a. a group of cells that work together to perform a specific job
   b. a group of tissues that belong to different systems
   c. a group of tissues that work together to perform a specific job
   d. a body structure, such as muscles or lungs

7. In eukaryotic cells, which organelle contains the DNA?
   a. nucleus   c. smooth ER
   b. Golgi complex   d. vacuole

8. Which of the following statements is part of the cell theory?
   a. All cells suddenly appear by themselves.
   b. All cells come from other cells.
   c. All organisms are multicellular.
   d. All cells have identical parts.

9. The surface area–to–volume ratio of a cell limits
   a. the number of organelles that the cell has.
   b. the size of the cell.
   c. where the cell lives.
   d. the types of nutrients that a cell needs.

10. Two types of organisms whose cells do NOT have a nucleus are
    a. prokaryotes and eukaryotes.
    b. plants and animals.
    c. bacteria and archaea.
    d. single-celled and multicellular organisms.

Short Answer

11. **Listing** Describe the four levels of organization in multicellular organisms.

INTERPRETING GRAPHICS Use the diagram below to answer the next three questions.

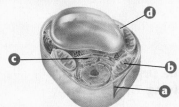

12. **Analyzing** Is this a plant or an animal cell?

13. **Identifying** Which letter identifies the structure that captures sunlight energy for photosynthesis?

14. **Applying** Which letter identifies the structure that makes proteins and lipids and that contains passageways through which substances move from place to place in the cell?

Writing Skills

15 **Creative Writing** Write a paragraph from the perspective of an organelle in a plant cell. Describe which organelle you are and what you do for the cell. Include information about how your structure relates to your function.

Critical Thinking

16 **Concept Mapping** Use the following terms to create a concept map: *cells, organisms, Golgi complex, organ systems, organs, nucleus, organelle,* and *tissues.*

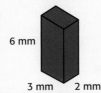

17 **Making Comparisons** Compare the functions of the endoplasmic reticulum with the functions of the Golgi complex.

18 **Evaluating Hypotheses** One of your classmates states a hypothesis that all organisms must have organ systems. Is your classmate's hypothesis valid? Explain your answer.

19 **Predicting Consequences** What would happen if all of the ribosomes in your cells disappeared?

INTERPRETING GRAPHICS Use the diagram below to answer the next question.

20 **Making Inferences** Describe what could happen to an organism if the organ system shown above failed to function properly.

21 **Making Comparisons** Compare how a plant cell retains its shape to how an animal cell retains its shape. Be sure to include in your explanation which cell parts are used by each type of cell to maintain its shape.

22 **Making Comparisons** Compare how a eukaryote stores DNA to how a prokaryote stores DNA.

23 **Applying Concepts** If you used a microscope to observe a heart cell and a skin cell, would you find that the two cells are exactly the same? Explain your answer.

24 **Expressing Opinions** How do you think cell differentiation affects an organism? Support your answer with examples.

Math Skills

INTERPRETING GRAPHICS Use the diagram below to answer the next question.

6 mm

3 mm   2 mm

25 **Analyzing Shapes** What is the surface area–to–volume ratio for a cell that has the shape depicted in the diagram?

Challenge

26 **Making Inferences** A plant cell has chloroplasts that capture sunlight for photosynthesis. Plant cells have mitochondria that release energy that the cell can use to do work. Animal cells have mitochondria but do not have chloroplasts. How do animal cells get the sugars that mitochondria use to release energy?

---

21. Sample answer: The cell wall defines the shape of plant cells. The shape of animal cells is determined by the cytoskeleton. **7.1.b** (exceeding)

22. Sample answer: A eukaryote stores DNA in the nucleus. A prokaryote does not have a structure in which to store it's circular DNA molecule. **7.1.c** (exceeding)

23. Sample answer: Heart cells and skin cells will not be exactly the same because the cells of eukaryotes differentiate. This means that they are specialized to perform specific functions. The functions of heart cells and skin cells are different, so they will probably have a different structure. **7.1.f** (exceeding)

24. Sample answer: I think cell differentiation helps an organism perform a wider variety of functions. Without cell differentiation, there would be no tissues, organs, or organ systems. **7.1.f** (mastering)

Math Skills

25. surface area $= [(6 \text{ mm} \times 3 \text{ mm}) + (6 \text{ mm} \times 2 \text{ mm}) + (3 \text{ mm} \times 2 \text{ mm})] \times 2 = 72 \text{ cm}^2$
volume $= 6 \text{ mm} \times 3 \text{ mm} \times 2 \text{ mm} = 36 \text{ cm}^3$
Ratio $= 2{:}1$

Challenge

26. Sample answer: Animals must consume other organisms to obtain the sugars that mitochondria use. Animals may consume plants or other animals. **7.1.d** (exceeding)

	Supporting	Mastering	Exceeding
7.1.a	2, 9, 10, 14, 17	8	18
7.1.b		12	15, 21
7.1.c		7	22
7.1.d	3	13	19, 26
7.1.f		4, 24	23
7.5.a	2, 17	5, 6, 11	15, 16, 20

Critical Thinking

16. An answer to this exercise can be found at the end of this book. **7.5.a** (exceeding)

17. Sample answer: The endoplasmic reticulum (ER) is a series of folded membranes within a cell in which many proteins, lipids, and other materials are made. Smooth ER also helps break down toxic materials. ER is part of the internal delivery system of the cell. The Golgi complex modifies, packages, and distributes proteins. It takes materials from the ER and encloses them in a vesicle. Then, the Golgi complex delivers the materials where they are needed in other parts of the cell or outside of the cell. **7.1.a** (supporting), **7.5.a** (supporting)

18. Sample answer: The hypothesis is not valid because some organisms are unicellular, so they do not have tissues, organs, or organ systems. **7.1.a** (exceeding)

19. Sample answer: Ribosomes make proteins, which all cells need to survive. If ribosomes disappeared, an organism could not get the proteins it needs to survive. **7.1.d** (exceeding)

20. Sample answer: The organ system shown is the cardiovascular system. If the cardiovascular system did not function properly, blood would not be pumped, nutrients would not be brought to cells, and wastes would not be carried away from cells. An organism might die if the cardiovascular system failed to function properly. **7.5.a** (exceeding)

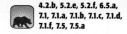
Teacher Notes

To provide practice under more realistic testing conditions, give students 20 min to answer all of the questions in this assessment.

Answer Key

Question Number	Correct Answer
1	D
2	B
3	C
4	A
5	B
6	C
7	C
8	C
9	D
10	B
11	C
12	A
13	B
14	D
15	B
16	A
17	A

Standards Guide

	Supporting	Mastering	Exceeding
4.2.b		14	
5.2.e		16	
5.2.f		15	
6.5.a		17	
7.1	5		
7.1.a	6		
7.1.b	13	9	
7.1.c	7, 8		
7.1.d	1		10
7.1.f	2	12	
7.5	3		
7.5.a	4	11	

📋 Standards Assessment GENERAL

📋 Teacher Notes for Standards Assessment contain a longer Assessment Doctor and Diagnostic Teaching Tips.

REVIEWING ACADEMIC VOCABULARY

1 Which of the following words is the closest in meaning to the word *liberate*?

A constrain

B tolerate

C protect

D free

2 Choose the appropriate form of the word *differentiate* for the following sentence: When cells ___ , they become specialized.

A different

B differentiate

C differ

D differentiation

3 Which of the following is the noun form of the word *illustrate?*

A illustrated

B illustrate

C illustration

D illustrating

4 Which of the following words means "the arrangement of the parts of a whole"?

A structure

B function

C inclusion

D container

5 Which of the following words means "something that can be seen"?

A dominant

B visible

C identical

D process

REVIEWING CONCEPTS

6 The cell theory has three parts. The first states that all organisms are made up of one or more cells. The second states that the cell is the basic unit of all living things. What does the third part state?

A Cells were discovered by accident.

B Single-celled organisms are protists.

C All cells come from existing cells.

D DNA is contained in a cell's nucleus.

7 Some cells have nuclei, and some do not. Cells that have nuclei are called

A prokaryotic.　　C eukaryotic.

B archaea.　　D ribosomes.

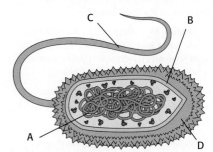

8 Which part of the cell is pictured at point A in the diagram above?

A cell wall　　C DNA

B flagellum　　D cell membrane

9 Eukaryotic plant and animal cells have many of the same organelles, but how do these cells differ?

A Animal cells have cytoskeletons, and plant cells do not.

B Animals cells have phospholipids, and plant cells do not.

C Plant cells have ribosomes, and animal cells do not.

D Plant cells have cell walls, and animal cells do not.

➕ ASSESSMENT DOCTOR

Question 1: The correct answer is D. *Liberate* means *free*. When cells liberate energy, they free it so that they can use it to perform necessary functions.

Question 2: The correct answer is B. Cells *differentiate*, or specialize, and become efficient at performing specific functions.

Question 3: The correct answer is C. To *illustrate* something is to show or make it clear. *Illustration* is the noun form of the verb *illustrate*.

Question 4: The correct answer is A. The *structure* of a cell determines whether it is a plant or animal, and prokaryote or eukaryote. Similarly, the structure of an organelle determines its function.

Question 5: The correct answer is B. Most cells are not *visible* to the naked eye. Viewing cells often requires the use of a microscope.

Question 6: The correct answer is C. The third part of the cell theory says that all cells come from existing cells. This part of the theory was added by Rudolf Virchow in 1858.

10 Mitochondria are important organelles within a cell. What would most likely happen if a cell's mitochondria were not functioning properly?

A The cell would use lysosomes to release energy.

B The cell's level of ATP would decrease.

C The cell would create new mitochondria by cell division.

D The cell's level of sugar would decrease.

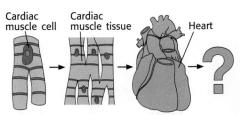

Cardiac muscle cell → Cardiac muscle tissue → Heart → ?

11 Which of the following choices correctly completes the diagram above?

A Cardiac organ

B Connective tissue

C Cardiovascular organ system

D Human organism

12 What types of cells differentiate to become specialized?

A the cells of multicellular organisms

B prokaryotic cells

C bacterial cells

D the cells of unicellular organisms

13 Why are a plant cell's chloroplasts green?

A because they trap sunlight

B because they contain chlorophyll

C because they make sugar

D because they have DNA

REVIEWING PRIOR LEARNING

14 Some unicellular organisms are decomposers. Others, including some bacteria, are

A protists.   C eukaryotes.

B organelles.   D producers.

15 Plants make their food through photosynthesis. What substances must plants have in order to begin photosynthesis?

A sunlight, oxygen, and water

B sunlight, carbon dioxide, and water

C water and carbon dioxide

D sunlight and oxygen

16 Multicellular plants have many specialized structures. What function does the xylem perform in multicellular vascular plants?

A The xylem transports water and minerals from the roots to the leaves.

B The xylem is the place where photosynthesis takes place in a plant.

C The xylem breaks down sugar into a form that plant cells can use.

D The xylem is a woody tissue that fills the stem of a plant.

17 How does energy enter an ecosystem?

A as sunlight

B as ATP

C as food

D as prokaryotes

Standards Assessment

Question 11: The correct answer is C. The specialized cells, tissues, and organs in the diagram are part of the cardiovascular organ system. The heart is made up of tissues including cardiac tissue, which is formed by cardiac cells.

Question 12: The correct answer is A. Only the cells of multicellular organisms are able to differentiate. Unicellular eukaryotes and all prokaryotes, including bacteria, are incapable of cell differentiation.

Question 13: The correct answer is B. Chloroplasts are green because they contain chlorophyll, a green pigment. Chlorophyll traps the energy of sunlight, which is used by the plant to make sugar molecules.

Question 14: The correct answer is D. Some bacteria and protists perform photosynthesis and therefore can be classified as producers. These unicellular organisms are primary producers of biomass in the oceans, and the food chain there is dependent upon them.

Question 15: The correct answer is B. Plants use the energy from sunlight to begin a chemical reaction between carbon dioxide and water. This reaction produces sugar molecules and releases oxygen molecules as waste.

Question 16: The correct answer is A. Xylem and phloem are the two types of vascular tissue in plants. Xylem transports water and minerals; phloem transports food.

Question 17: The correct answer is A. Energy enters an ecosystem as sunlight. Primary producers, found at the base of food chains, use sunlight to make food. When primary producers are consumed by other organisms, the energy is transferred to the consumer.

Question 7: The correct answer is C. Eukaryotic cells have nuclei. The nucleus of eukaryotic cells contains the genetic material, DNA.

Question 8: The correct answer is C. The DNA is pictured at point A in the diagram. In a prokaryotic cell, the DNA is not contained by a nucleus.

Question 9: The correct answer is D. Plant cells have cell walls, while animal cells do not. Eukaryotic plant and animal cells both have cytoskeletons, phospholipids, and ribosomes.

Question 10: The correct answer is B. Mitochondria release energy to the rest of the cell by breaking down sugar and making ATP, which is used by the cell to do work. Without properly functioning mitochondria, there would be less ATP in the cell.

Scientific Discoveries

Background

Stem cells are very different from other cells. All stem cells—embryonic or adult—have three unique characteristics. First, stem cells are unspecialized. Thus, a stem cell in its original form cannot perform the function of a muscle cell or a blood cell. However, stem cells can give rise to specialized cells that can perform functions such as a muscle cell or a blood cell. Second, stem cells can divide and renew for long periods of time. Scientists have shown that as long as a stem cell remains unspecialized, it can continue to divide for an extended period of time. Third, stem cells can evolve into specialized cells through the processes of differentiation.

Weird Science

Background

Within the last 20 years, biologists have begun to realize that more environments on Earth are suitable for life than they once thought. Discoveries of organisms that live under extreme conditions of temperature and pressure have led scientists to coin the term *extremophile* for these life forms.

Science in Action

Scientific Discoveries

Discovery of the Stem Cell

What do Parkinson's disease, diabetes, aplastic anemia, and Alzheimer's disease have in common? All of these diseases are diseases for which stem cells may provide treatment or a cure. Stem cells are unspecialized cells from which all other kinds of cells can grow. And research on stem cells has been going on almost since microscopes were invented. But scientists have been able to culture, or grow, stem cells in laboratories for only about the last 20 years. Research during these 20 years has shown scientists that stem cells can be useful in treating—and possibly curing—a variety of diseases.

Language Arts ACTIVITY

Imagine that you are a doctor who treats diseases such as Parkinson's disease. Design and create a pamphlet or brochure that you could use to explain some of the methods used to treat Parkinson's disease. Include a description of how stem cells might be used to treat one of your patients who has Parkinson's disease. Be sure to include information about Parkinson's disease.

Weird Science

Extremophiles

Are there organisms on Earth that can give scientists clues about possible life elsewhere? Yes, there are! Such organisms are called *extremophiles*. They live where the environment is extreme in some way, such as in temperature. Some extremophiles live in the hot volcanic thermal vents of the deep ocean. Other extremophiles live in the extreme cold of Antarctica. Most extremophiles are archaea, but some are bacteria, fungi, or animals.

Social Studies ACTIVITY

Do some research about an extremophile, and make a poster showing what you learned about it, including where it can be found, under what conditions it lives, how it survives, and how it is used.

Answer to Language Arts Activity

Students' pamphlets or brochures should contain a basic explanation of at least two methods of treatment for Parkinson's disease, including possible treatments involving stem cells. Students may need help in understanding the difference between a treatment and a cure.

Answer to Social Studies Activity

Students' posters should reflect their research. For example, a student who studies methanogens may relate that these extremophiles live in a wide variety of environments and in a number of geographical locations. Posters should include an explanation of how extremophiles obtain nutrients and how their metabolism differs from human metabolism. In their posters, students should also indicate any commercial, industrial, or medical uses of extremophiles.

People in Science

Caroline Schooley

Microscopist Imagine that your assignment is the following: Go outside. Look at 1 ft² of the ground for 30 min. Make notes about what you observe. Be prepared to describe what you see. If you look at the ground with just your naked eyes, you may quickly run out of things to see. But what would happen if you used a microscope to look? How much more would you be able to see? And how much more would you have to talk about? Caroline Schooley could tell you.

Caroline Schooley joined a science club in middle school. That's when her interest in looking at things through a microscope began. Since then, Schooley has spent many years at the University of California at Berkeley teaching about the study of life through a microscope. Schooley is a microscopist. A *microscopist* is someone who uses a microscope to explore the world of small things that cannot be seen by the naked eye. And with today's powerful electron microscopes, microscopists can study things that we could never see before, such as atoms.

Math ACTIVITY

An average bacterium is about 0.000002 m long. A pencil point is about 0.001 m wide. Approximately how many bacteria lined up end to end would fit across a pencil point? Record your work in your **Science Journal.**

Internet Resources

- To learn more about careers in science, visit www.scilinks.org and enter the SciLinks code HY70225.

- To learn more about these Science in Action topics, visit go.hrw.com and type in the keyword HY7CELF.

- Check out articles related to this chapter by visiting go.hrw.com. Just type in the keyword HY7CELC.

Answer to Math Activity
0.001 m ÷ 0.000002 m/bacteria = 500 bacteria

People in Science

Background

Caroline Schooley wants students to think about microscopes and microscopy. The field of microscopy is changing. One of the newest uses of microscopy is in nanotechnology. *Nanotechnology* is the science of manipulating materials at the atomic or molecular level to build microscopic devices. Scientists in the field of nanotechnology strive to develop tiny machines called *assemblers* that can manipulate atoms and molecules as directed. Tiny nanomachines called *replicators* will be programmed to build more assemblers. Nanotechnology can be thought of as molecular manufacturing.

Standards Course of Study

The elements listed in the Standards Course of Study provide a base for presenting, supporting, and assessing the California Grade 7 Science Standards. Use this Standards Course of Study as a base for planning your lessons.

Why Teach

The Cell in Action

This chapter was designed to cover the California Grade 7 Science Standards about cell processes (7.1.b, 7.1.d, 7.1.e, and 7.2.e). It follows a chapter about cell structure and function. Because all living things are made of cells, understanding basic processes that occur in cells is important to a student's understanding of himself or herself and of the world in general.

After they have completed this chapter, students will begin a chapter about heredity.

 California Standards

Focus on Life Sciences

7.1.b Students know the characteristics that distinguish plant cells from animal cells, including chloroplasts and cell walls.

7.1.d Students know that mitochondria liberate energy for the work that cells do and that chloroplasts capture sunlight energy for photosynthesis.

7.1.e Students know cells divide to increase their numbers through a process of mitosis, which results in two daughter cells with identical sets of chromosomes.

7.2.e Students know DNA (deoxyribonucleic acid) is the genetic material of living organisms and is located in the chromosomes of each cell.

Investigation and Experimentation

7.7.c Communicate the logical connection among hypotheses, science concepts, tests conducted, data collected, and conclusions drawn from the scientific evidence.

7.7.d Construct scale models, maps, and appropriately labeled diagrams to communicate scientific knowledge (e.g., motion of Earth's plates and cell structure).

Basic Learners
TE Flowers, p. 151
TE Cell Types, p. 153
☐ Reinforcement Worksheet
☐ Chapter Test A
☐ Differentiated Datasheets A for Labs and Activities ■
☐ Study Guide A ■

Advanced Learners/GATE
TE Cellular Respiration, p. 148
TE Cell Structures, p. 153
TE Awareness Colors, p. 156
☐ Critical Thinking Worksheet
☐ Chapter Test C
☐ Differentiated Datasheets C for Labs and Activities ■

Teach

SE Explore Activity The Purpose of Pigment, p. 147* ■

🗐 **Bellringer**
💿 **PowerPoint® Resources**
SE Quick Lab Currency of the Cell, p. 149* ■
🗐 **L17** The Connection Between Photosynthesis and Cellular Respiration

---

🗐 **Bellringer**
💿 **PowerPoint® Resources**
🗐 **L18** The Cell Cycle
SE Quick Lab The Mitosis Flipbook, p. 155* ■

SE Skills Practice Lab Phases of Mitosis, pp. 158-159* ■

Practice

SE Organize Activity Layered Book, p. 146

SE Section Review, p. 151* ■

SE Section Review, p. 157* ■

SE Science Skills Activity Drawing Conclusions from Data, p. 160* ■
🗐 **Concept Mapping***
SE Chapter Review, pp. 162-163* ■

Assess

🗐 **Chapter Pretest**

SE Standards Checks, pp. 148, 149, 151
TE Standards Focus, p. 150
🗐 **Section Quiz** ■

SE Standards Checks, pp. 153, 154, 156
TE Standards Focus, p. 156
🗐 **Section Quiz** ■

SE Standards Assessment, pp. 164-165* ■
🗐 **Chapter Tests A, B** ■**, C**
🗐 **Standards Review Workbook** ■

Resources for Universal Access • Differentiated Instruction

English Learners
TE Demonstration, p. 148
TE Mapping Photosynthesis, p. 148
TE Using the Figure, pp. 150, 153
TE Activity, pp. 152, 154
TE Pronunciation with Cells, p. 152
🗐 Vocabulary and Section Summary A ■, B

🗐 Section Quizzes ■
🗐 Chapter Tests A, B ■
🗐 Differentiated Datasheets A, B, and C for Labs and Activities ■
🗐 Study Guide A ■
🗐 Multilingual Glossary

Struggling Readers
TE Strengthening Key Vocabulary, p. 150
TE Reading Strategy, p. 153
TE Using Text Figures, p. 154

Special Education Students
TE Fermentation, p. 151
TE Alternate Mitosis "Movie," p. 155
TE Explaining Temperatures, p. 160

To help plan your lessons, refer to the On Course Mapping Instruction booklet.

Visual Resources

CHAPTER STARTER TRANSPARENCY

The Cell in Action — CHAPTER STARTER

What If . . . ?

How long would you like to live? What if you could live to be 120 years old? or 150 and beyond? Since ancient times, people have searched in vain for a magical fountain or potion that could give them eternal youth. No one has yet found the secret of immortality, but scientists have recently made a startling discovery that may help extend people's lives.

In January of 1998, researchers at the University of Texas reported that they had found an enzyme in the body that acts like a "cellular fountain of youth." In the laboratory, the enzyme enables human cells to stay young and multiply long

past the time when cells would normally stop dividing and die. Researchers hope that the enzyme can someday be used to understand and treat certain cancers and other incurable diseases. Although the so-called immortalizing enzyme won't help people live forever, it may help them live longer, healthier lives.

BELLRINGER TRANSPARENCIES

The Cell in Action — BELLRINGER TRANSPARENCY

Section: Cell Energy
Why might cells need energy?

List ways that cells might get energy.

Write your answers in your **science journal**.

Section: The Cell Cycle
Explain why the following statement is true:

Biology is a science in which multiplication means the same thing as division.

Write your response in your **science journal**.

TEACHING TRANSPARENCIES

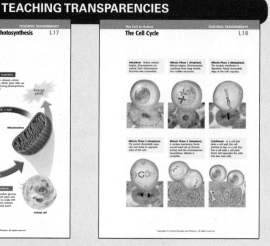

The Cell in Action — TEACHING TRANSPARENCY — L17
The Connection Between Photosynthesis and Cellular Respiration

The Cell in Action — TEACHING TRANSPARENCY — L18
The Cell Cycle

TEACHING TRANSPARENCIES

Rivers and Groundwater — TEACHING TRANSPARENCY — E51
The Water Cycle

LINK TO EARTH SCIENCE

STANDARDS REVIEW TRANSPARENCIES

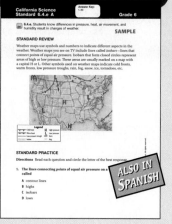

California Science Standard 6.4.e A — Grade 6 — Answer Key
SAMPLE

6.4.e. Students know differences in pressure, heat, air movement, and humidity result in changes of weather.

STANDARD REVIEW

Weather maps use symbols and numbers to indicate different aspects in the weather. Weather maps you see on TV line lines called isobars—lines that connect points of equal air pressure. Isobars that form closed circles represent areas of high or low pressure. These areas are usually marked on a map with a capital H or L. Other symbols used on weather maps indicate cold fronts, warm fronts, low pressure troughs, rain, fog, snow, ice, tornadoes, etc.

STANDARD PRACTICE

Directions Read each question and circle the letter of the best response.

1. The lines connecting points of equal air pressure on a called
   A contour lines
   B highs
   C isobars
   D lows

ALSO IN SPANISH

CONCEPT MAPPING TRANSPARENCY

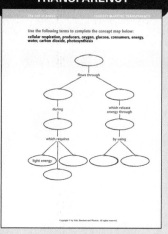

The Cell in Action — CONCEPT MAPPING TRANSPARENCY

Use the following terms to complete the concept map below:
cellular respiration, producers, oxygen, glucose, consumers, energy, water, carbon dioxide, photosynthesis

Planning Resources

PARENT LETTER

SAMPLE

Dear Parent,

Your son's or daughter's science class will soon begin exploring the chapter entitled "The Nature of Physical Science." In this chapter, students will learn about how the scientific method applies to the world of physical science and the role of physical science in the world. By the end of the chapter, students should demonstrate a clear understanding of the chapter's main ideas and be able to discuss the following topics:

1. the role of questions in the process of investigation (Section 1)
2. how applying science saves lives and benefits the environment (Section 1)
3. careers that rely on science (Section 1)
4. the steps used in scientific methods (Section 2)
5. how scientific methods are used to answer questions and solve problems (Section 2)
6. the importance of safety precautions in the laboratory (Section 3)
7. examples of safety equipment and when to use them (Section 3)
8. how safety symbols are used to make laboratories safer (Section 3)

Questions to Ask Along the Way

You can help your child learn about these topics by asking interesting questions as he or she progresses through the chapter. For example, you may wish to ask your son or daughter the following questions:

What are some surprising careers that use science?

What is a characteristic of a good hypothesis?

What is the first step to take if an accident happens?

ALSO IN SPANISH

TEST ITEM LISTING

SAMPLE

Holt California Physical Science
Chapter 6 Introduction to Atoms
Test Item Listing
Multiple choice

1. The smallest particle into which an element can be divided and still have the properties of that element is called a(n)
   a. nucleus.   c. atom.
   b. electron.   d. neutron.
   ANS: C   DIF: 1   REF: 1   OBJ: 2   STO: 8.3.a   KEY: atom
   MSC: SQ.1.1

2. What particle did J. J. Thomson discover?
   a. neutron
   b. electron
   c. atom
   d. proton
   ANS: B   DIF: 1   REF: 1   OBJ: 2   STO: 8.3.a   KEY: electron   MSC: SQ.1.2

3. How would you describe the nucleus?
   a. dense, positively charged
   b. mostly empty space, positively charged
   c. tiny, negatively charged
   d. dense, negatively charged
   ANS: A   DIF: 1   REF: 1   OBJ: 2   STO: 8.3.a   KEY: nucleus   MSC: SQ.1.3

4. Where are electrons likely to be found?
   a. in the nucleus
   b. in electron clouds
   c. mixed throughout an atom
   d. in definite paths
   ANS: B   DIF: 1   REF: 1   OBJ: 2   STO: 8.3.a   KEY: electron   MSC: SQ.1.4

5. Dalton believed that
   a. atoms of the same element are exactly alike.
   b. most, but not all, substances are made of atoms.
   c. atoms of different elements are the same.
   d. atoms can be divided.
   ANS: A   DIF: 1   REF: 1   OBJ: 2   STO: 8.3.a   KEY: atom   MSC: SQ.1.5

6. Every atom of a given element has the same number of
   a. protons.
   b. neutrons.
   c. Electrons
   d. isotopes.
   ANS: A   DIF: 1   REF: 2   OBJ: 2   STO: 8.3.a   KEY: atom

ALSO IN SPANISH

One-Stop Planner® CD-ROM

This CD-ROM package includes all of the resources shown here and the following time-saving tools:

- **Lab Materials QuickList Software**
- **Customizable Lesson Plans** Correlated to the California Science Standards
- **Holt Calendar Planner**
- **PowerPoint® Resources**
- **Printable Worksheets**
- **ExamView® Test Generator** Correlated to the California Science Standards
- **Holt PuzzlePro®**
- **Interactive Teacher's Edition**

Meeting Individual Needs

DIRECTED READING A

Skills Worksheet
Directed Reading A   SAMPLE

Section: Body Organization
A STABLE INTERNAL ENVIRONMENT
Write the letter of the correct answer in the space provided.

BASIC

ALSO IN SPANISH

DIRECTED READING B

Skills Worksheet
Directed Reading B   SAMPLE

Section: Body Organization
A STABLE INTERNAL ENVIRONMENT

CELLS, TISSUES, AND ORGANS

GENERAL

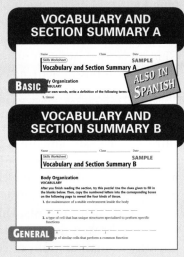

VOCABULARY AND SECTION SUMMARY A

Skills Worksheet
Vocabulary and Section Summary A   SAMPLE

BASIC

ALSO IN SPANISH

VOCABULARY AND SECTION SUMMARY B

Skills Worksheet
Vocabulary and Section Summary B   SAMPLE

Body Organization
VOCABULARY

GENERAL

REINFORCEMENT

Skills Worksheet
Reinforcement   SAMPLE

Muscle Map

BASIC

CRITICAL THINKING

Skills Worksheet
Critical Thinking   SAMPLE

The Tissue Engineering Debate

ADVANCED

INTERACTIVE READER AND STUDY GUIDE

Body Organization   SAMPLE

BEFORE YOU READ

MULTILINGUAL GLOSSARY

SAMPLE

Labs and Activities

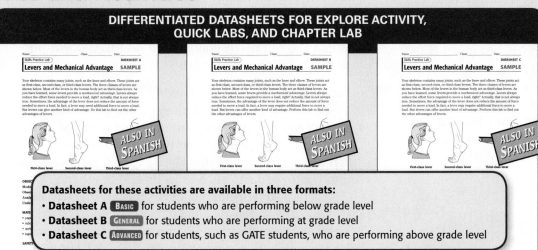

DIFFERENTIATED DATASHEETS FOR EXPLORE ACTIVITY, QUICK LABS, AND CHAPTER LAB

Skills Practice Lab
Levers and Mechanical Advantage   DATASHEET A   SAMPLE

Skills Practice Lab
Levers and Mechanical Advantage   DATASHEET B   SAMPLE

Skills Practice Lab
Levers and Mechanical Advantage   DATASHEET C   SAMPLE

ALSO IN SPANISH

Datasheets for these activities are available in three formats:
- **Datasheet A** BASIC for students who are performing below grade level
- **Datasheet B** GENERAL for students who are performing at grade level
- **Datasheet C** ADVANCED for students, such as GATE students, who are performing above grade level

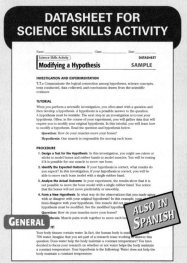

DATASHEET FOR SCIENCE SKILLS ACTIVITY

Science Skills Activity
Modifying a Hypothesis   DATASHEET   SAMPLE

INVESTIGATION AND EXPERIMENTATION

TUTORIAL

PROCEDURE

GENERAL

ALSO IN SPANISH

Reviews and Assessments

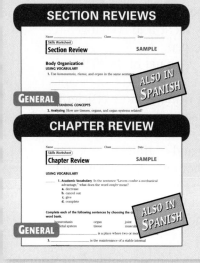

SECTION REVIEWS

Skills Worksheet
Section Review   SAMPLE

Body Organization
USING VOCABULARY

GENERAL

ALSO IN SPANISH

CHAPTER REVIEW

Skills Worksheet
Chapter Review   SAMPLE

USING VOCABULARY

GENERAL

ALSO IN SPANISH

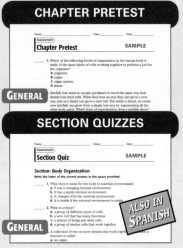

CHAPTER PRETEST

Assessment
Chapter Pretest   SAMPLE

GENERAL

SECTION QUIZZES

Assessment
Section Quiz   SAMPLE

Section: Body Organization

GENERAL

ALSO IN SPANISH

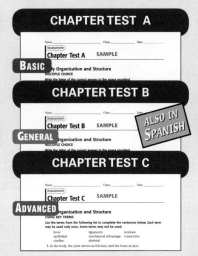

CHAPTER TEST A

Assessment
Chapter Test A   SAMPLE

BASIC

CHAPTER TEST B

Assessment
Chapter Test B   SAMPLE

GENERAL

ALSO IN SPANISH

CHAPTER TEST C

Assessment
Chapter Test C   SAMPLE

ADVANCED

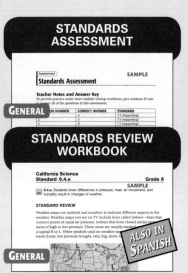

STANDARDS ASSESSMENT

Assessment
Standards Assessment   SAMPLE

Teacher Notes and Answer Key

GENERAL

STANDARDS REVIEW WORKBOOK

California Science Standard 6.4.e   Grade 6   SAMPLE

STANDARD REVIEW

GENERAL

ALSO IN SPANISH

This Teacher Background explains science concepts, principles, and theories that appear in the chapter. Use the information on these pages to refresh or enhance your understanding of the topics covered.

Section 1

Cell Energy

Photosynthesis and Cellular Respiration

Chloroplasts contain two chlorophyll pigments, a and b, which give plants their green color. Chlorophyll a and chlorophyll b absorb all wavelengths of light, except those in the blue-green and yellow-green ranges, respectively (around 500–575 nm). These pigments convert light energy to chemical energy, in the form of glucose. Additional pigments, called *accessory pigments,* also facilitate the conversion of light energy. For example, carotenoids tend to absorb all wavelengths of light except for yellow and orange (around 575–590 nm). Some of this energy is transferred to chlorophyll, but much is simply absorbed to protect chlorophyll from being damaged by too much light. Chloroplasts in a plant cell are shown in **Figure A.** This figure also shows a plant leaf. Point out to students that a leaf is part of the figure because leaves perform the majority of photosynthesis in plants, although other parts of the plant can also perform photosynthesis.

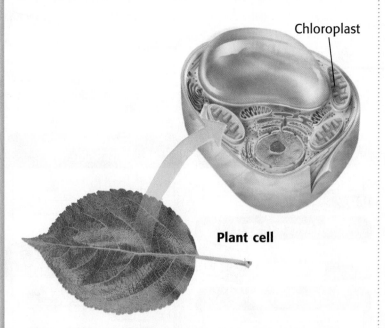

Chloroplast

Plant cell

Figure A *Photosynthesis occurs in plant cells that contain chloroplasts.*

Glucose is used by plant cells for energy or combined with other glucose molecules to form starch, which is stored by the plant. When organisms consume the plant, they use the stored glucose for energy. Glucose is used by both plant and animal cells during cellular respiration. During cellular respiration, which occurs in the mitochondria, glucose is broken down in the presence of oxygen into carbon dioxide and water.

The first step of cellular respiration is glycolysis. During glycolysis, glucose is broken down into pyruvic acid, and a small amount of energy is liberated. The next steps of cellular respiration, collectively called *aerobic respiration,* are the Krebs cycle, the electron transport chain, and chemiosmosis. During the Krebs cycle, pyruvic acid is broken down into CO_2. The Krebs cycle also liberates a small amount of energy. However, most of the energy obtained from cellular respiration is produced by the electron transport chain and chemiosmosis. The electron transport chain requires oxygen. The energy produced by cellular respiration is stored in the phosphate bonds of adenosine triphosphate (ATP). When the cell needs energy, ATP is broken down into adenosine diphosphate (ADP).

Fermentation

Fermentation liberates energy from glucose in the absence of oxygen. Fermentation begins with glycolysis, as in cellular respiration, but the pyruvic acid is not broken down into carbon dioxide. Instead, it is broken down into waste products, such as lactic acid or ethanol.

Lactic acid fermentation causes the burning sensation that humans and many animals may feel during strenuous exertion. When muscle cells do not receive enough oxygen for respiration, they produce energy through lactic acid fermentation. The low pH in muscles caused by lactic acid buildup is the direct cause of the burning sensation. When the exertion is ended, cells can obtain sufficient oxygen and can resume cellular respiration. The waste products of fermentation remain in the body until lactic acid is carried by blood to the liver, where the lactic acid is changed to other chemicals, primarily glycogen.

Cellular respiration produces a net of 36 ATP molecules, fermentation produces a net of 2 ATP molecules. Therefore, cellular respiration is much more efficient than fermentation is. Hence, aerobic organisms with high energy requirements, such as humans, can rely on fermentation for only a short period of time.

Humans use the products of fermentation made by other organisms. For example, the carbon dioxide released by yeasts causes bread to rise, and ethanol is used in beverages such as wine and beer.

Section 2

The Cell Cycle

Cell Cycle

Mitosis is the process by which eukaryotic cells duplicate. Mitosis has four phases: prophase, metaphase, anaphase, and telophase. Mitosis is preceded by interphase, during which the cell grows, and DNA and membrane-bound organelles are copied. Mitosis is followed by cytokinesis, during which the cytoplasm is divided between the daughter cells. After cytokinesis, cell division is complete. The original cell has divided into two identical daughter cells. Cytokinesis differs in plant and animal cells. In plant cells, a cell plate forms between the two daughter cells. The cell plate becomes cell membranes and cell walls for the new cells. In animal cells, the membrane pinches, forming two cells.

Interphase usually accounts for about 90% of the cell cycle and includes three subphases: G1 phase, S phase, and G2 phase. During each subphase, cell growth occurs. Chromosomal duplication occurs during S phase. The duration of the cell cycle varies between species and tends to be shorter in less complex organisms. In many complex organisms, the cell cycle lasts about 24 hours, of which mitosis comprises about 2 hours.

Prokaryotic cells reproduce by a process called binary fission, which results in two identical daughter cells. However, binary fission differs from mitosis. Prokaryotic binary fission does not involve the duplication of membrane-bound organelles, nor does it involve chromatids, which are the copied pairs of chromosomes found in eukaryotic cells.

DNA

Deoxyribonucleic acid (DNA) is a type of nucleic acid. DNA carries all of the information that determines the structure and function of an organism and its cells. Before eukaryotic cells begin mitosis, DNA is a long, uncoiled molecule, called *chromatin,* that is found in the nucleus of the cell. Shortly before cell division, DNA and proteins form dense, coiled structures called *chromosomes.* The proteins that aid in the coiling of chromosomes do not carry genetic information, but simply support the structure and function of the chromosome. Chromosomes carry the genetic information of the cell, and the number of chromosomes varies based on the type of organism. For example, humans have 23 pairs of chromosomes, which vary in size, as shown in the karyotype in **Figure B.** It should be noted to students that, during interphase, the chromosomes cannot be clearly seen, which is one way to identify a cell in interphase.

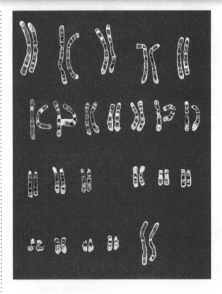

Figure B
This shows a karyotype of a human. Females have two X chromosomes that are equal in length. Males have an X and a Y chromosome. Y chromosomes are shorter and carry less genetic information than X chromosomes do.

Before mitosis, the chromosomes are copied, forming homologous pairs, which are held together by the centromere, forming chromatids. Mitosis begins when the chromatids separate. Mitosis is complete when the chromosomes have moved to opposite sides of the dividing cell and the nuclear membrane has reformed. However, cell division is complete only after cytokinesis.

DNA Replication

A DNA molecule consists of two chains of sugars and phosphate molecules and nitrogenous bases that are twisted into a double helix. A double helix looks like a twisted ladder. The nitrogenous bases—adenine, cytosine, guanine, and thymine—form the rungs of the ladder between the two sugar-phosphate chains. The nitrogenous bases exhibit complimentary pairing: adenine pairs with thymine and cytosine pairs with guanine.

The process of copying DNA is called replication. During replication, the double helix "unzips," separating the two strands of DNA. Then, the nitrogenous bases on each strand of DNA are used as a template to make a second strand of DNA.

Internet Resources

SciLinks is maintained by the National Science Teachers Association to provide you and your students with interesting, up-to-date links that will enrich your classroom presentation of the chapter.

Visit **www.scilinks.org** and enter the SciLinks code for more information about the topic listed.

Topic: Cell Energy
SciLinks code: HY70237

Topic: Cell Cycle
SciLinks code: HY70235

Topic: Photosynthesis
SciLinks code: HY71140

5 Chapter Preview

Chapter Preview

Improving Comprehension

Use the Graphic Organizer on this page of the Student Edition to introduce the topics that are covered in this chapter, to summarize the chapter material, or to show students how to make a cause-and-effect map.

Teaching Tips

• Remind students that a cause-and-effect map shows a process; it describes how, when, or why one event causes another event.

• Remind students that there can be multiple causes and effects in one cause-and-effect map. Explain that one cause may have several effects and one effect may have several causes.

LS Logical

Improving Comprehension

Graphic Organizers are important visual tools that can help you organize information and improve your reading comprehension. The Graphic Organizer below is called a *cause-and-effect map*. Instructions for creating other types of Graphic Organizers are located in the **Study Skills** section of the Appendix.

How to Make a Cause-and-Effect Map

1 Draw a box, and write a cause in the box. You can have as many cause boxes as you want. The diagram shown here is one example of a cause-and-effect map.

2 Draw another box to the right of the cause box to represent an effect. You can have as many effect boxes as you want. Draw arrows from each cause box to the appropriate effect boxes.

3 In the cause boxes, explain the process that makes up the cause. In the effect boxes, write a description of the effect or details about the effect.

When to Use a Cause-and-Effect Map

A cause-and-effect map is a useful tool for illustrating a specific type of scientific process. Use a cause-and-effect map when you want to describe how, when, or why one event causes another event. As you read, look for events that are either causes or results of other events, and draw a cause-and-effect map that shows the relationships between the events.

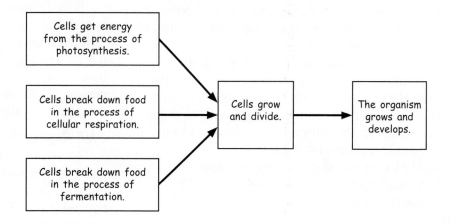

You Try It!

This Reading Strategy can also be used within the chapter that you are about to read. Practice making your own *cause-and-effect map* as directed in the Reading Strategy for Section **1**. Record your work in your **Science Journal**.

Using Other Graphic Organizers

Students can practice using a variety of Graphic Organizers while reading this chapter. The following Graphic Organizers may also be useful in this chapter.

A **concept map** can be used to describe photosynthesis, introduced in Section 1.

A **process chart** can be used to describe the stages of cell development, explained in Section 2.

Instructions for creating these Graphic Organizers are located on pp. 583–591 of the Appendix.

Unpacking the Standards

The information below "unpacks" the standards by breaking them down into basic parts. The higher-level, academic vocabulary is highlighted and defined to help you understand the language of the standards. "What It Means" restates the standards as simply as possible.

Unpacking the Standards

Use the following information with the *What It Means* in the Student Edition to help students understand why studying each standard is important.

California Standard	Academic Vocabulary	What It Means	Why It Matters
7.1.b Students know the characteristics that distinguish plant cells from animal cells, including chloroplasts and cell walls.		Plant cells have some unique structures that make plant cells different from animal cells. These structures include chloroplasts and a cell wall.	Plants and animals are the organisms with which people interact the most.
7.1.d Students know that mitochondria **liberate** energy for the work that cells do and that chloroplasts capture sunlight **energy** for photosynthesis.	**liberate** (LIB uhr AYT) to release; to set free **energy** (EN uhr jee) the capacity to do work	Mitochondria release energy from sugar to power the cell's life processes. Chloroplasts turn energy from the sun into sugars and oxygen.	To understand digestion and the need to eat and breathe at the macro level, students must understand where their food originates at a cellular level and how their cells make use of this food.
7.1.e Students know cells divide to increase their numbers through a **process** of mitosis, which results in two daughter cells with **identical** sets of chromosomes.	**process** (PRAH SES) a set of steps, events, or changes **identical** (ie DEN ti kuhl) being exactly the same	Cells split to make more cells through a process called mitosis. Through this process, a single cell becomes two cells that have the same genetic material.	To understand how the body grows and heals, students must understand mitosis and the role of heredity in this process.
7.2.e Students know DNA (deoxyribonucleic acid) is the genetic material of living organisms and is **located** in the chromosomes of each cell.	**located** (LOH KAYT id) to be in a certain place	DNA is the material that determines what traits are passed from one generation of living things to the next. DNA is found in the chromosomes of each cell.	DNA is the blueprint for running the cell's chemical manufacturing system and for making another copy of itself. Any change in the DNA can affect the products or offspring of the cell.

Words with Multiple Meanings

Words that have both common and scientific meanings can be confusing to students. The following table identifies some of those words that are used in this chapter.

Term	Common meaning	Scientific meaning
daughter	one's female child	the offspring of cell division; not dependent on gender
respiration	breathing	the process by which cells use oxygen to produce energy from food

Practice Have students define the following words: *daughter* and *respiration*. Then, give students the definitions for the scientific meanings of these terms. (These definitions can be found in the glossary of this book.) Have students write sentences that use the common meanings of these words. Then, have students write sentences that use the scientific meanings of the words.

Chapter Overview

This chapter will introduce students to photosynthesis and cellular respiration and describe the relationship between the two processes. The chapter also describes mitosis.

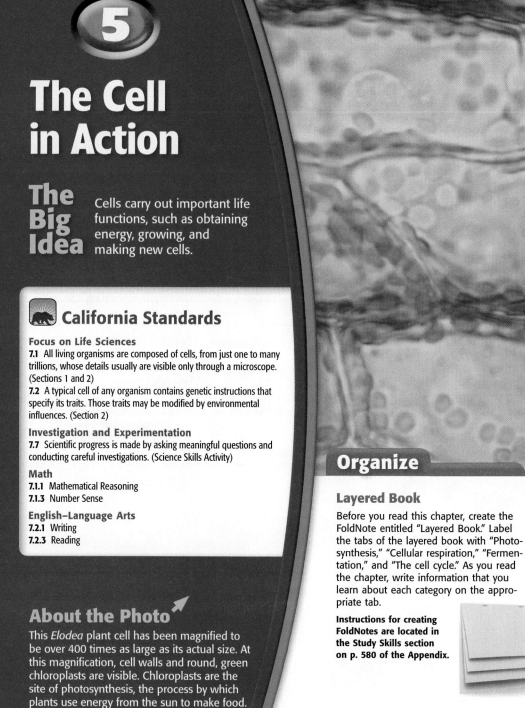

The Cell in Action

The Big Idea Cells carry out important life functions, such as obtaining energy, growing, and making new cells.

California Standards

Focus on Life Sciences

7.1 All living organisms are composed of cells, from just one to many trillions, whose details usually are visible only through a microscope. (Sections 1 and 2)

7.2 A typical cell of any organism contains genetic instructions that specify its traits. Those traits may be modified by environmental influences. (Section 2)

Investigation and Experimentation

7.7 Scientific progress is made by asking meaningful questions and conducting careful investigations. (Science Skills Activity)

Math

7.1.1 Mathematical Reasoning
7.1.3 Number Sense

English–Language Arts

7.2.1 Writing
7.2.3 Reading

About the Photo

This *Elodea* plant cell has been magnified to be over 400 times as large as its actual size. At this magnification, cell walls and round, green chloroplasts are visible. Chloroplasts are the site of photosynthesis, the process by which plants use energy from the sun to make food.

Organize

Layered Book

Before you read this chapter, create the FoldNote entitled "Layered Book." Label the tabs of the layered book with "Photosynthesis," "Cellular respiration," "Fermentation," and "The cell cycle." As you read the chapter, write information that you learn about each category on the appropriate tab.

Instructions for creating FoldNotes are located in the Study Skills section on p. 580 of the Appendix.

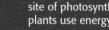

California Standards Alignment

Focus on Life Sciences

7.1.b Students know the characteristics that distinguish plant cells from animal cells, including chloroplasts and cell walls. **pp. 148–151, 154–155, 157, 162–165**

7.1.d Students know that mitochondria liberate energy for the work that cells do and that chloroplasts capture sunlight energy for photosynthesis. **pp. 147–151, 162–165**

7.1.e Students know cells divide to increase their numbers through a process of mitosis, which results in two daughter cells with identical sets of chromosomes. **pp. 152–159, 162–164**

7.2.e Students know DNA (deoxyribonucleic acid) is the genetic material of living organisms and is located in the chromosomes of each cell. **pp. 152–155, 157–159, 162–165**

Investigation and Experimentation

7.7.c Communicate the logical connection among hypotheses, science concepts, tests conducted, data collected, and conclusions drawn from the scientific evidence. **p. 160**

7.7.d Construct scale models, maps, and appropriately labeled diagrams to communicate scientific knowledge (e.g., motion of Earth's plates and cell structure). **pp. 155, 158–159**

Math Standards

Number Sense 6.2.1 Convert one unit of measurement to another (e.g., from feet to miles, from centimeters to inches). **p. 151**

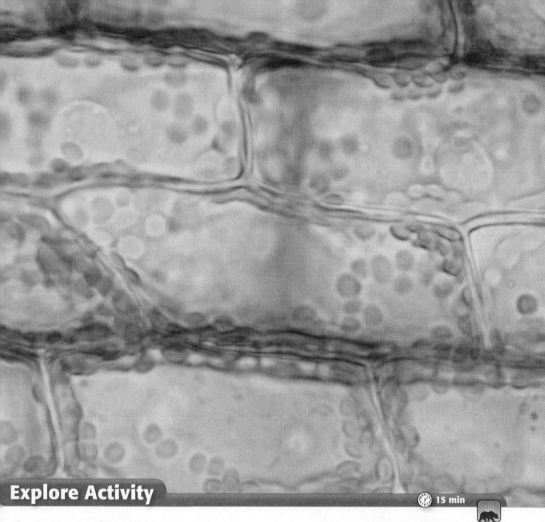

Explore Activity

7.1.d

The Purpose of Pigment

Chlorophyll is a green pigment found in the chloroplasts of plant cells. Chlorophyll gives plants their green color. Sunlight stimulates the formation of chlorophyll. Chlorophyll is important for photosynthesis because chlorophyll absorbs energy from the sun. In this activity, you will observe how chlorophyll affects the appearance of a plant.

Procedure

1. Gather a **large, presoaked lima bean** and a **magnifying lens**. A lima bean is actually the seed of the lima bean plant.

2. Carefully remove the softened outer shell that covers the seed. Gently separate the two larger halves of the seed.

3. Use the magnifying lens to examine the small plant between the two halves. Draw what you see.

4. Examine the **seedling** supplied by your teacher. Draw what you see.

Analysis

5. Compare the size and appearance of the two plants.

6. Both of these samples are the same type of plant. Why are they different colors?

7. Which plant is capable of absorbing energy from the sun? Explain your answer.

Mathematical Reasoning 7.1.1 Analyze problems by identifying relationships, distinguishing relevant from irrelevant information, identifying missing information, sequencing and prioritizing information, and observing patterns. **pp. 156–157**

Number Sense 7.1.3 Convert fractions to decimals and percents and use these representations in estimations, computations, and applications. **p. 163**

English–Language Arts Standards

Writing 7.2.1 Write fictional or autobiographical narratives: (a) Develop a standard plot line (having a beginning, conflict, rising action, climax, and denouement) and point of view; (b) Develop complex major and minor characters and a definite setting; (c) Use a range of appropriate strategies (e.g. dialogue; suspense; naming of specific narrative action, including movement, gestures, and expressions). **p. 162**

Reading 7.2.3 Analyze text which uses cause and effect patterns. **p. 148**

What If . . . ?

How long would you like to live? What if you could live to be 120 years old? or 150 and beyond? Since ancient times, people have searched in vain for a past the time when cells would normally stop dividing and die. Researchers hope that the enzyme can someday be used to understand and treat certain cancers

📦 **Chapter Starter Transparency**
Use this transparency to help students begin thinking about the life of a cell.

Explore Activity

Teacher Notes

This activity will introduce students to the functions of chlorophyll (covers standard 7.1.d). You may wish to explore students' prior knowledge of chlorophyll, chloroplasts, and photosynthesis. Prepare large lima bean seedlings about a week before the activity. First, soak the beans in water for 12–24 hours to soften the seed coat. Then, line a baking pan with 3 to 4 layers of wet paper towels. Place the softened beans on top of the towels and add 3 to 4 more layers of wet paper towels on top of the seeds. Add water as necessary throughout the week to keep the layers moist but not dripping. Keep the pan in a warm place. When the seedlings are a few inches tall, expose them to indirect sunlight for a few hours each day.

Materials for Each Group

- lima bean, presoaked
- magnifying lens
- seedling

Answers

5. Sample answer: The seedling is large, green, and has open leaves. The plant in the seed is small, cream-colored, and tightly curled.

6. Sample answer: Sunlight stimulates chlorophyll formation. The bean has not been exposed to sunlight, so it has not formed chlorophyll. Without chlorophyll, a plant is not green.

7. Sample answer: Chlorophyll absorbs energy from the sun during photosynthesis. The seedling is green in color and contains chlorophyll. The seedling can absorb sunlight.

📋 **Differentiated Datasheets**
A **BASIC**, B **GENERAL**, C **ADVANCED**

Also editable on the Holt Lab Generator CD-ROM

Preteach

Reviewing Prior Knowledge

Ask student volunteers to read the red and blue heads in the section aloud. Then, ask students to describe what they think the section is about. Finally, ask students to relate what they already know about photosynthesis and cellular respiration.

Bellringer

Have students focus on standard 7.1.d by asking them to list why they think cells might need energy. (Accept all reasonable answers. Students should recognize that cells need energy to stay alive.) Ask students to list ways that cells might get energy. (Accept all reasonable answers. Students may note that cells get energy from the nutrients they take in.)

📠 Bellringer Transparency

Motivate

Demonstration

Leaves and Light A few days before teaching this section, cover a leaf of a plant with black construction paper. Use a paper clip or tape to hold the paper in place. Ask students to predict what has happened to the leaf. (Accept all reasonable answers.) Remove the black paper. The leaf will be more pale than other leaves on the plant. Ask students to describe why this happens. (In the absence of light, chlorophyll is depleted.) **LS Visual/Logical**

Answer to Standards Check

Plant cells contain chloroplasts.
7.1.b (mastering)

Cell Energy

Key Concept All cells need energy to carry out cell functions. However, cells may obtain and process energy in different ways.

What You Will Learn

- In plant cells, chloroplasts capture energy from the sun in order to make food during photosynthesis.
- Cells release energy from food through either cellular respiration or fermentation.

Why It Matters

Understanding the differences in how plants and animals obtain energy is an important part of cell biology.

Vocabulary

- photosynthesis
- cellular respiration
- fermentation

READING STRATEGY

Graphic Organizer In your **Science Journal**, create a Cause-and-Effect Map about fermentation.

photosynthesis
(FOHT oh SIN thuh sis) the process by which plants, algae, and some bacteria use sunlight, carbon dioxide, and water to make food
Wordwise The root *phot-* means "light."

Wordwise   chloroplast
The root *chlor-* means "green." The root *plast-* means "to form."

▶ Why do you get hungry? Feeling hungry is your body's way of telling you that your cells need energy. All cells need energy to live, grow, and reproduce. Plant cells get their energy from the sun. Many animal cells get their energy from food.

From Sun to Cell

Nearly all of the energy that fuels life comes from the sun. Plants absorb energy from the sun and change the energy into food through a process called **photosynthesis.** The food that plants make gives them energy. This food also becomes a source of energy for the organisms that eat the plants.

Photosynthesis

Plant cells have molecules that absorb light energy. These molecules are called *pigments*. Chlorophyll (KLAWR uh FIL), the main pigment used in photosynthesis, gives plants their green color. Chlorophyll is found in *chloroplasts*.

Plants cannot use energy directly from the sun to perform life processes. Instead, they use the sun's energy to change carbon dioxide and water into food. The food is in the form of the simple sugar glucose. Glucose can be stored and used by the plant's cells. Photosynthesis also produces oxygen. The chemical equation for photosynthesis is shown in **Figure 1.**

Standards Check What kind of cell has chloroplasts? 🐻 **7.1.b**

Figure 1 *Photosynthesis takes place in chloroplasts. Chloroplasts are found inside plant cells.*

7.1.b Students know the characteristics that distinguish plant cells from animal cells, including chloroplasts and cell walls.
7.1.d Students know that mitochondria liberate energy for the work that cells do and that chloroplasts capture sunlight energy for photosynthesis.

Photosynthesis

$$6CO_2 + 6H_2O + \text{light energy} \longrightarrow C_6H_{12}O_6 + 6O_2$$

Carbon dioxide   Water   Glucose   Oxygen

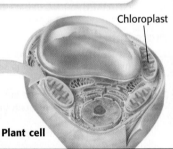

Chloroplast

Plant cell

Universal Access • Differentiated Instruction

English Learners

Mapping Photosynthesis To help students understand both the terms and the process of photosynthesis, ask them to create a flow chart showing the steps of photosynthesis. Have them work in pairs and use as many of the following words as they can: *photosynthesis, pigments, light energy, chlorophyll, carbon dioxide, water, food, glucose, stored energy,* and *oxygen*.
LS Visual Co-op Learning

Advanced Learners/GATE

Cellular Respiration Ask students who can benefit from more in-depth studies to work together to prepare an overhead presentation using words and pictures to show the difference between a person breathing and the cellular respiration that takes place within a person's cells. Allow time for the students to share the project with the whole class. **LS Visual/Interpersonal**

Getting Energy from Food

Animal cells cannot make their own food. Animals must eat to get food. No matter how an organism gets food, the food must be broken down in the organism's cells in order to free the energy stored in the food. Even plant cells must break down the food that they make during photosynthesis.

Cells can break down food in two ways. The first way is **cellular respiration,** a process that uses oxygen. The second way does not use oxygen. This process is called **fermentation.** Cellular respiration releases more energy from food than fermentation does. Most complex organisms, such as plants and animals, get most of their energy through cellular respiration.

Cellular Respiration

The word *respiration* means "breathing," but cellular respiration is different from breathing. Cellular respiration is a chemical process that happens in cells. In prokaryotic cells, cellular respiration happens in the cell membrane. In eukaryotic cells, cellular respiration takes place mostly in the mitochondria.

During cellular respiration, food (such as glucose) is broken down into CO_2 and H_2O, and energy is liberated, or freed. In animals, most of the freed energy is used to keep a constant body temperature. Some of the energy is used to form a**deno**sine **tri**phosphate (ATP). Molecules of ATP supply readily available energy that fuels cell activities, such as growth.

The process of cellular respiration is shown in **Figure 2.** Does the equation in the figure remind you of the equation for photosynthesis? On the next page, **Figure 3** shows how photosynthesis and respiration are related.

Standards Check Where does the process of cellular respiration take place in eukaryotes, such as plants and animals? 🐻 **7.1.d**

Cellular respiration
$$C_6H_{12}O_6 + 6O_2 \rightarrow 6CO_2 + 6H_2O + \text{energy (ATP)}$$
Glucose   Oxygen   Carbon dioxide   Water

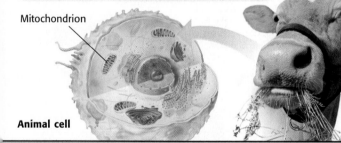

Mitochondrion

Animal cell

Figure 2 The mitochondria in the cells of this cow will use cellular respiration to release the energy stored in the grass.

Quick Lab

Currency of the Cell 7.1.d

1. Some of the energy in food is converted into ATP, which can be used to perform cell functions. Examine the table that your teacher has drawn.

2. Use the chart's data to explain why ATP is referred to as the *energy currency of the cell.*

3. Why do you think that the number of ATP molecules varies so much?

4. If each glucose molecule can produce 36 ATP, how many molecules of glucose are needed to produce enough ATP to assemble the protein molecule in the chart?

⏱ **10 min**

cellular respiration
(SEL yoo luhr RES puh RAY shuhn) the process by which cells use oxygen to produce energy from food

fermentation (fuhr muhn TAY shuhn) the breakdown of food without the use of oxygen

Quick Lab   ⏱ **10 min**

Teacher Notes

This activity reinforces the universal role of mitochondria and ATP for the activities of organisms (covers standard 7.1.d). Draw a table on the board and provide the following information in the table:

- Column 1: organism; bacterium; worm; human

- Column 2: process; assembling a DNA strand; assembling a protein molecule; holding a baseball

- Column 3: molecules of ATP required; 70 million; 1,500; 2 trillion

Answers

2. Different processes found in different organisms all depend on ATP to supply the required energy.

3. Different activities require different amounts of energy.

4. 42 glucose molecules

📁 Differentiated Datasheets
A **BASIC**, B **GENERAL**, C **ADVANCED**

Also editable on the Holt Lab Generator CD-ROM

Teach

CONNECTION ACTIVITY
Physical Science

PORTFOLIO **Solar Heating** Explain to students that conventional solar heating is much simpler than photosynthesis. Add that, in solar heating, the sun either heats the house or heats water, which then circulates through the house. Ask students to research methods of solar heating and to create a pamphlet that describes solar heating. Ask students to also relate solar heating and photosynthesis. **LS Verbal**

MISCONCEPTION ALERT

Cellular Respiration in Plants Some students may not recognize that plants use much of the glucose that they make during photosynthesis to support their own life functions. Ask students to diagram the relationship between cellular respiration and photosynthesis. In their diagrams, have students list examples of organisms that participate in each process.

Answer to Standards Check

Cellular respiration takes place in the mitochondria of eukaryotic cells.
7.1.d (mastering)

Wordwise

Photosynthesis and Chloroplast The roots of *photosynthesis, photo-* and *-synthesis,* mean "light" and "putting together," respectively. The roots of *chloroplast, chloro-* and *-plastid,* mean "green" and "mold," respectively. Ask students to think of other words that use any of these roots. Then, ask students to use various colored pencils to diagram what each part of the word means. **LS Verbal**

Close

Standards Focus

This **Standards Focus** provides you with a quick way to **assess**, **reteach**, and **re-assess** one or more concepts in the section.

Assess

1. What organelle is found in plant cells, but not in animal cells? (chloroplast) **7.1.b**

2. Where do chloroplasts get the energy used to perform photosynthesis? (sunlight) **7.1.d**

Reteach

Concept Mapping Have students make a concept map using the following terms and phrases: *plants, lactic acid, fermentation, cellular respiration, release energy, mitochondria, photosynthesis, pigment, chlorophyll, capture light energy, chloroplast, mitochondria,* and *ATP.* (Accept all reasonable answers.) **LS** Logical **7.1.d**

Re-Assess

Lungs of Earth Tell students that plants are considered the lungs of Earth. Ask students to apply the information from the section by making a poster that explains why this might be true. **LS** Verbal/Visual **7.1.b, 7.1.d**

Using the Figure

Relating Photosynthesis and Cellular Respiration Have students work in pairs to examine **Figure 3.** Then, have students take turns summarizing the figure to each other. **LS** Auditory

📦 Teaching Transparency: L17 The Connection Between Photosynthesis and Cellular Respiration

📦 Teaching Transparency: *LINK TO EARTH SCIENCE* E51 The Water Cycle

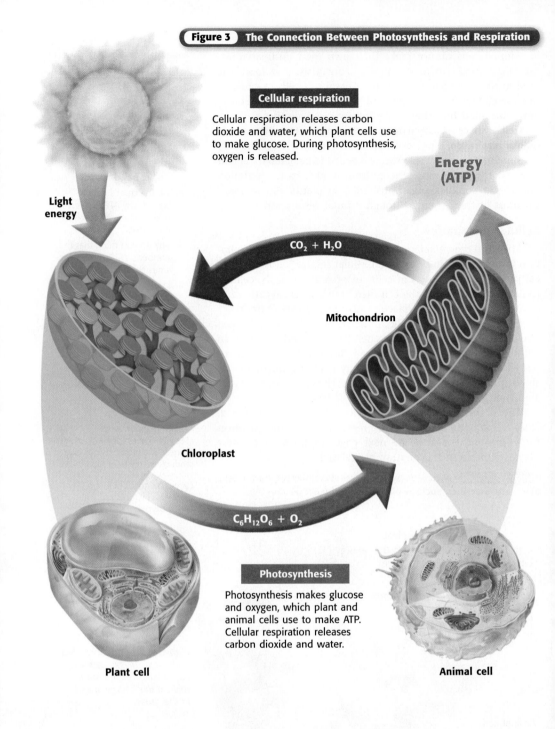

Figure 3 **The Connection Between Photosynthesis and Respiration**

Cellular respiration

Cellular respiration releases carbon dioxide and water, which plant cells use to make glucose. During photosynthesis, oxygen is released.

Energy (ATP)

Light energy

$CO_2 + H_2O$

Mitochondrion

Chloroplast

$C_6H_{12}O_6 + O_2$

Photosynthesis

Photosynthesis makes glucose and oxygen, which plant and animal cells use to make ATP. Cellular respiration releases carbon dioxide and water.

Plant cell

Animal cell

Universal Access · Differentiated Instruction

Struggling Readers

Strengthening Key Vocabulary As they work through a chapter, some students may benefit from answering short oral summary checks. Ask volunteers to finish the following sentences orally:

1. The chlorophyll in plants uses the sun's energy to change ____ and ____ into food. (carbon dioxide, water)

2. One way that animals are different from plants is animals cannot make their own ____. (food)

3. Animal and plant cells usually use ____ rather than fermentation to break down food. (cellular respiration)

4. One difference between prokaryotic cells and eukaryotic cells is that in prokaryotic cells, cellular respiration takes place in the ____ instead of the ____. (cell membrane, mitochondria) **LS** Verbal/Auditory

Connection Between Photosynthesis and Respiration

As shown in **Figure 3,** photosynthesis changes CO_2 and H_2O into glucose. During photosynthesis, cells use energy from the sun to make glucose. The process also releases O_2. During cellular respiration, cells use O_2 to break down glucose and to free energy and CO_2. Each process makes the materials that are needed for the other process to occur.

Standards Check List the products of cellular respiration. **7.1.d**

Fermentation

Have you ever had a burning feeling in your leg muscles while you were running? You may have these feelings during short, fast races. When muscle cells cannot get the oxygen that they need for cellular respiration, they use the process of fermentation to get energy. One kind of fermentation takes place in your muscles and makes lactic acid. The buildup of this acid leads to muscle fatigue and causes a burning feeling. This kind of fermentation also happens in the muscle cells of other animals and in some fungi and bacteria.

SECTION Review

 7.1.b, 7.1.d

Summary

- Most of the energy that fuels life comes from the sun.
- The sun's energy is changed into food by the process of photosynthesis, which occurs in the chloroplasts of plant cells.
- Cellular respiration breaks down glucose into water, carbon dioxide, and energy.
- Cellular respiration takes place in the mitochondria of plant and animal cells.
- Fermentation is a way that cells get energy from their food without using oxygen.

Using Vocabulary

1 Write an original definition for *cellular respiration.*

Understanding Concepts

2 **Applying** How are photosynthesis and cellular respiration related?

3 **Concluding** What type of cell has chloroplasts? How do chloroplasts affect the functions of the cell?

Critical Thinking

4 **Analyzing Relationships** Why are plants important for the survival of other organisms?

5 **Predicting Consequences** What would happen to an animal if all of its mitochondria disappeared?

Math Skills

6 **Making Conversions** Cells of plant A make 120 molecules of glucose per hour. Cells of plant B make half as many molecules of glucose as cells of plant A do. How many molecules of glucose does plant B make per minute?

Challenge

7 **Applying Concepts** Your classmate suggests that chlorophyll is not the only pigment contained in plant cells. Is your classmate correct? Explain your answer.

Internet Resources

For a variety of links related to this chapter, go to www.scilinks.org
Topic: Cell Energy; Photosynthesis
SciLinks code: HY70237; HY71140

Answers to Section Review

1. Cellular respiration is a process that breaks down food, releases energy, and takes place in the mitochondria. **7.1.d** (mastering)

2. Photosynthesis uses the waste materials of cellular respiration, CO_2, and H_2O, to generate glucose. Cellular respiration uses the products of photosynthesis, O_2, and glucose, to release energy. **7.1.d** (supporting)

3. The cells of plants have chloroplasts. This allows them to make food during photosynthesis. **7.1.b** (mastering), **7.1.d** (mastering)

4. Sample answer: Plants turn energy from the sun into chemical energy. Animals that eat the plants or eat other animals that ate the plants use the stored energy. Plants also produce O_2. **7.1.b** (exceeding), **7.1.d** (exceeding)

5. Sample answer: If all of an animal's mitochondria disappeared, it would not be able to use cellular respiration to break down food for energy. Without energy, the organism will die. **7.1.d** (mastering)

6. 120 molecules/hr $\times$ 1/2 = 60 molecules/hr $\div$ 60 min/hr = 1 molecule/min

7. Your classmate is correct. The pigment chlorophyll is green, but not all parts of plants are green. For example, flower petals are often purple, red, and yellow. These colors cannot be from chlorophyll, so there must be other pigments in some plant cells.

Section Review Standards Guide			
	Supporting	Mastering	Exceeding
7.1.b		3	4
7.1.d	2	1, 3, 5	4

Section Resources

- Directed Reading A **Basic** (Also in Spanish), B **General**
- Interactive Reader and Study Guide
- Section Quiz **General** (Also in Spanish)
- Section Review **General** (Also in Spanish)
- Vocabulary and Section Summary A **Basic** (Also in Spanish), B **General**

Universal Access • Differentiated Instruction

Special Education Students

Fermentation Many students learn best when information relates directly to them. Ask a student to read the paragraph on fermentation aloud. As a group, brainstorm situations, other than burning in the legs from running, where students' muscles were likely hurting due to a shortage of oxygen and the buildup of lactic acid. (Sample answers: arm hurts from lifting weights, hand is sore from writing a lot) **LS** Verbal/Intrapersonal

Basic Learners

Flowers Some students need a hands-on approach to really understand a concept. Ask a florist for a bunch of flowers that are still alive, but too old to sell and will have to be disposed of. Give each student (or pair of students) a flower. Ask students to explain the part of the flowers where most photosynthesis takes place. (the leaves; chlorophyll makes the leaves green and is used in photosynthesis) **LS** Visual/Kinesthetic

Reviewing Prior Knowledge

Ask students to relate what they already know about different types of cells. Have them identify how prokaryotic and eukaryotic organisms store genetic information differently. (Prokaryotes have a single, long strand of circular DNA; eukaryotes store their DNA in a nucleus.)

 **Bellringer**

Have students focus on standard 7.1.e by asking them to explain why the following statement is true:

Biology is a science in which multiplication means the same thing as division.

(Students should note that cells multiply by undergoing cell division.)

 Bellringer Transparency

Motivate

ACTIVITY

Making Exact Models Have students work in pairs. Have each pair use interlocking, colored blocks to build an object. Have each pair of students trade objects with another pair of students. Have students replicate the object created by the first pair of students, including the objects' colors. Have the pairs of students examine each other's replicas to be sure the objects are exact copies. Explain to students that the replicas represent the kind of exact copies that are created when cells divide. Tell students that they will learn about mitosis and cell division in this section. **LS Kinesthetic/Logical**
Co-op Learning

SECTION
2

What You Will Learn

- Before a cell divides, it must make a copy of its DNA.
- To increase their numbers, eukaryotic cells divide through the processes of mitosis and cytokinesis.
- Mitosis has four phases.
- Cytokinesis differs in animals and plants.
- Cancer occurs when cells replicate abnormally.

Why It Matters

Problems within the cell cycle can lead to cancer.

Vocabulary

- cell cycle
- cytokinesis
- chromosome
- cancer
- mitosis

READING STRATEGY

Prediction Guide Before reading this section, write each heading from this section in your **Science Journal.** Below each heading, write what you think you will learn.

cell cycle (SEL SIE kuhl) the life cycle of a cell

chromosome (KROH muh SOHM) in a eukaryotic cell, one of the structures in the nucleus that are made up of DNA and protein; in a prokaryotic cell, the main ring of DNA

mitosis (mie TOH sis) in eukaryotic cells, a process of cell division that forms two new nuclei, each of which has the same number of chromosomes

cytokinesis (SIET oh ki NEE sis) the division of the cytoplasm of a cell

Figure 1 *Bacteria reproduce by binary fission.* **How will the new cells compare to the parent cell?**

The Cell Cycle

Key Concept The cell cycle results in daughter cells, two new cells that are exact copies of the original cell.

▶ In the time that it takes you to read this sentence, your body will have made millions of new cells! Making new cells allows you to grow and to replace cells that have died. Your stomach is so acidic that the cells lining the inside must be replaced every few days. Other cells are replaced less often, but your body is always making new cells.

The Life of a Cell

As you grow, you pass through different stages in life. Your cells also pass through different stages in their life cycle. The life cycle of a cell is called the **cell cycle.**

The cell cycle begins when the cell is formed and ends when the cell divides and forms new cells. Before a cell divides, it must make a copy of its **d**eoxyribo**n**ucleic **a**cid (DNA). DNA is the hereditary material that directs all cell activities, including the making of new cells. The DNA of a cell is organized into structures called **chromosomes.** Chromosomes are made up of DNA and proteins. Copying chromosomes ensures that each new cell receives all of the DNA of the parent cell. Each new cell will be an exact copy of its parent cell. How a cell makes more cells depends on whether the cell is prokaryotic (has no nucleus) or eukaryotic (has a nucleus).

Making More Prokaryotic Cells

Prokaryotic cells are less complex than eukaryotic cells. Bacteria, which are prokaryotes, have a single, circular chromosome. Also, they do not have membrane-enclosed organelles. Cell division in bacteria is called *binary fission,* which means "splitting into two parts." Binary fission results in two cells, each of which has one copy of the circle of DNA. A few of the bacteria in **Figure 1** are undergoing binary fission.

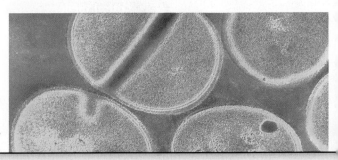

Eukaryotic Cells and Their DNA

Prokaryotic cells have a single chromosome, but eukaryotic cells have many chromosomes. Eukaryotes have more DNA than prokaryotes do. Different kinds of eukaryotes have different numbers of chromosomes. More-complex eukaryotes do not always have more chromosomes than simpler eukaryotes do. For example, fruit flies have 8 chromosomes, potatoes have 48, and humans have 46. **Figure 2** shows the 46 chromosomes of a human body cell lined up in pairs. These pairs are made up of similar chromosomes known as *homologous chromosomes* (hoh MAHL uh guhs KROH muh SOHMZ). Although chromosomes vary in size, the homologous chromosomes in each pair will be very similar.

Standards Check How many chromosomes are in the cells of the human body? **7.2.e**

Making More Eukaryotic Cells

The eukaryotic cell cycle has three stages. In the first stage, called *interphase,* the cell grows and copies its organelles and chromosomes. After each chromosome is duplicated, the two copies are called *chromatids.* Chromatids are held together at a region called the *centromere.* The joined chromatids condense into an X shape, as shown in **Figure 3.** After this step, the cell enters the second stage of the cell cycle.

In the second stage, the chromatids separate. The process by which chromosomes separate is called **mitosis.** During mitosis, each new cell receives a copy of each chromosome. Mitosis is divided into four phases: prophase, metaphase, anaphase, and telophase.

In the third stage, cytokinesis, the cell splits into two cells called *daughter cells.* **Cytokinesis** is the division of cytoplasm and all of the materials in the cytoplasm. The new daughter cells are exactly the same as each other and as the original cell. For example, each daughter cell receives exactly the same number of chromosomes.

Figure 2 *Human body cells have 46 chromosomes, or 23 pairs of chromosomes.*

INTERNET ACTIVITY

Mitosis Adventure

How does a cell change during a cell cycle? Describe cell division from inside the cell. Go to **go.hrw.com,** and type in the keyword HY7ACTW.

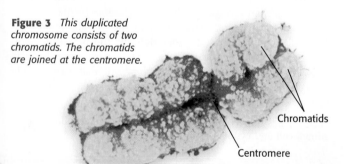

Figure 3 *This duplicated chromosome consists of two chromatids. The chromatids are joined at the centromere.*

Chromatids

Centromere

7.1.b Students know the characteristics that distinguish plant cells from animal cells, including chloroplasts and cell walls.

7.1.e Students know cells divide to increase their numbers through a process of mitosis, which results in two daughter cells with identical sets of chromosomes.

7.2.e Students know DNA (deoxyribonucleic acid) is the genetic material of living organisms and is located in the chromosomes of each cell.

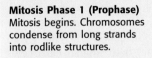
Figure 4 The Cell Cycle

Interphase Before mitosis begins, chromosomes are copied. Each chromosome becomes two chromatids.

Mitosis Phase 1 (Prophase) Mitosis begins. Chromosomes condense from long strands into rodlike structures.

Mitosis Phase 2 (Metaphase) The nuclear membrane is dissolved. Paired chromatids align at the cell's equator.

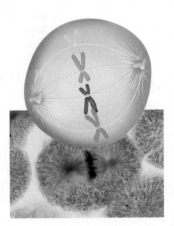

Teach, continued

Cytokinesis Many students may think that the end of mitosis coincides with the end of the cell cycle. Ask students to describe the end of the cell cycle. Then, ask students to take turns coming up to the board to draw the steps of the cell cycle in order. Ask students to draw a star next to steps that are part of mitosis. Students should recognize that mitosis is not the end of the cell cycle.

 Teaching Transparency: L18 The Cell Cycle

ACTIVITY

Vocabulary Dictionary Divide the class into small groups. Ask each group to divide up the vocabulary words from this chapter evenly among its members. Have each member of the group look up his or her word (or words) and identify and define its root (or roots). (Accept all reasonable answers. For example, *Chromosome* contains the roots *chromo-* and *-some*, which mean "color" and "body".) Then, have students work together to make a dictionary that describes their findings. **LS** Verbal Co-op Learning

Answer to Standards Check

During cytokinesis in plant cells, a cell plate forms between the cells. During cytokinesis in animal cells, a cell plate does not form. **7.1.b** (mastering)

SCIENCE HUMOR

Q: How do cells communicate with teach other?

A: By cell phone, of course!

Mitosis and the Cell Cycle

Figure 4 shows the cell cycle and the phases of mitosis in an animal cell. Mitosis has four phases, as shown and described above. This diagram shows only four chromosomes to make it easy to see what's happening inside the cell.

Cytokinesis

In animal cells and other eukaryotes that do not have cell walls, division of the cytoplasm begins at the cell membrane. The cell membrane begins to pinch inward to form a groove. Eventually, the cell is pinched in half, and two daughter cells form. Cytokinesis is shown at the last step of **Figure 4.**

Eukaryotic cells that have a cell wall—such as the cells of plants, algae, and fungi—go through cytokinesis differently. In this kind of cell, a *cell plate* forms in the middle of the cell. The cell plate contains the materials for the new cell membranes and for the new cell walls that will separate the new cells. After the cell splits in two, a new cell wall forms where the cell plate was. The cell plate and a late stage of cytokinesis in a plant cell are shown in **Figure 5.**

Standards Check What is the difference between cytokinesis in an animal cell and cytokinesis in a plant cell? **7.1.b**

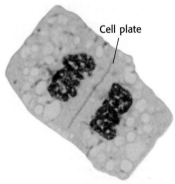

Cell plate

Figure 5 *When a plant cell divides, a cell plate forms and the cell splits into two cells.*

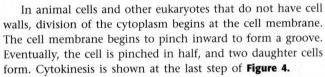

Universal Access · Differentiated Instruction

Struggling Readers

Using Text Features Struggling readers often think that one way to more easily handle a page of text is to ignore all the picture captions and focus only on the main text. Point out to students that pictures and their captions usually provide helpful information that make the text easier to understand. Ask volunteers to read the captions above each of the six steps in the cell cycle pictures on these two pages. After each caption is read, discuss how the caption relates to the pictures. After all the captions have been read and studied, ask students to look at the main text on p. 154 and note that the art and captions supply some information that the text does not. **LS** Visual/Logical

Mitosis Phase 3 (Anaphase)
The paired chromatids separate and move to opposite sides of the cell.

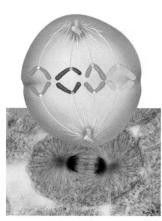

Mitosis Phase 4 (Telophase)
A nuclear membrane forms around each set of chromosomes, and the chromosomes decondense. Mitosis is complete.

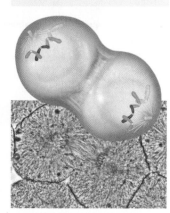

Cytokinesis In a cell that lacks a cell wall, the cell pinches in two. In a cell that has a cell wall, a cell plate forms and separates the cells into two new cells.

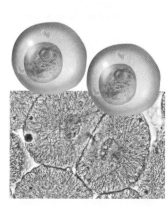

Quick Lab

The Mitosis Flipbook

The process of mitosis involves four phases, but the transition from one phase to the next involves many intermediate stages. In this activity, you will illustrate and assemble a flipbook. The flipbook will show the phases and intermediate stages of mitosis.

1. Punch two holes near the upper edge of **20 index cards.**

2. Take four cards from your stack. List a different phase of mitosis on each card.

3. Review the images above. Draw a diagram of each phase of mitosis on the correct card.

4. Use **colored pencils** to make each chromosome a different color. On each card where the cell part is present, label one example of the chromosome, centromere, and nuclear membrane.

5. On the blank cards, draw the intermediate stages between each phase. Show the gradual transitions of mitosis by making small changes on each card.

6. Put your cards in order. Place a **brad** in each hole to assemble your flipbook.

7. In what phase of mitosis does the nuclear membrane dissolve?

8. This flipbook shows the actions of chromosomes, centromeres, and the nuclear membrane during mitosis. Is it acceptable to leave out what is happening to the rest of the cell's organelles? Explain your answer.

9. Why is it important for eukaryotic cells to undergo mitosis?

7.1.e
7.7.d

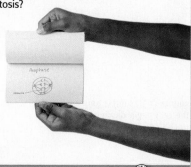

⏱ 30 min

Universal Access · Differentiated Instruction

Special Education Students

Alternate Mitosis "Movie" Some students may benefit from this adaptation to complete the Quick Lab. Create a mitosis "movie" by using digital presentation software. Following the procedure described in the Quick Lab, copy and paste pictures showing the stages of mitosis either from the Internet or from another source. Have students either quickly click individual page turns or scroll through the pages to create the movie effect. **LS** Visual

Quick Lab ⏱ 30 min

Teacher Notes

Students will model the gradual transitions throughout mitosis by making a flipbook (covers standards 7.1.e and 7.7.d). Students may work independently or in groups of two or four. If students have difficulty with Step 5, instruct them to place five blank cards between two of the consecutive cards from Step 3. Then, ask students to draw any features that all of the cards will have in common (e.g. shape of cell membrane, position of the dark yellow centrioles) on each of the blank cards. Finally, tell students to select one element that changes, such as a single color of chromosome, and to draw it as it changes over each card. Students should repeat this step until all changing elements have been added to the cards.

Materials for Each Group
• brad (2)
• hole punch
• index cards (20)
• pencils, colored

Answers

7. prophase

8. It is acceptable to leave the other organelles off the flipbook because mitosis only refers to replication of the nucleus. The other organelles replicate during interphase.

9. Eukaryotic cells must undergo mitosis because they need copies of their genetic material to pass on to the daughter cells. These new cells are needed to replace old, worn-out, or injured cells and to allow for the growth of the organism.

📋 Differentiated Datasheets
A **BASIC**, B **GENERAL**, C **ADVANCED**

Also editable on the **Holt Lab Generator CD-ROM**

This **Standards Focus** provides you with a quick way to **assess, reteach,** and **re-assess** one or more concepts in the section.

 Assess

1. What structure forms during cell division in plant cells but not in animal cells? (cell plate) **7.1.b**

2. What is the relationship between a parent cell and its daughter cells? (They are exactly the same.) **7.1.e**

3. What is the hereditary material of the cell called? (DNA) **7.2.e**

 **Reteach**

Writing **Biography of an Organism** Have students write a short biography of a multicellular eukaryotic organism in which they describe how an organism grows and divides. Encourage students to be creative, but their biographies must be accurate. **LS Verbal 7.1.e**

 **Re-Assess**

PORTFOLIO **Mitosis Diagram** Have students diagram mitosis and cytokinesis. Students should illustrate the steps of mitosis and the results of mitosis and cytokinesis (two identical daughter cells). Students should also relate the location of DNA throughout the cell cycle and its role in the cell. **LS Visual/Verbal 7.1.e, 7.2.e**

Answer to Math Practice

2 days/division × 24 h/day = 48 hours/division;
6 times faster = 48 h/6 divisions = 8 hours/division

Answer to Standards Check

The feedback from the cell needs to report that the cell is large and healthy in order to begin cell division. **7.1.e** (supporting)

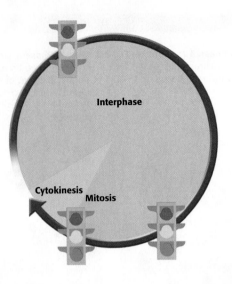

Figure 6 *The feedback switches of cells work like traffic signals. A "go" signal, like a green light, tells a cell to start or continue a process. A "stop" signal, like a red light, tells a cell to end a process.*

Interphase

Cytokinesis   Mitosis

MATH PRACTICE

Uncontrolled Division

Cell A normally divides once every two days. If control mechanisms are not functioning properly, cell A divides 6 times as fast. How many hours does it take cell A to divide when control mechanisms are not functioning properly? Record your work in your **Science Journal**.

cancer (KAN suhr) a tumor in which the cells begin dividing at an uncontrolled rate and can become invasive

Control of the Cell Cycle

Most of a cell's life is spent in interphase. During interphase, parent cells replicate their chromosomes and organelles. But what causes a cell to start or stop making copies of organelles and chromosomes? These activities are controlled by feedback switches.

Feedback Switches

Babies cry when they are hungry. Once they are fed, they stop crying. Crying is a baby's way of reporting conditions. Cells report conditions in messages called *feedback*. A cell may report that it needs more, has enough, or has too much of a certain molecule. This feedback turns on a set of switches that work like traffic lights. For example, if feedback indicates that there is too much of a molecule, proteins assembling that molecule get a "stop" signal. Thus, the production of the molecule stops. At the same time, proteins that break down the molecule may get a "go" signal. Thus, the breakdown of the molecule begins. This process continues until feedback indicates that levels of the molecule are ideal.

The cell cycle is controlled by the feedback switches shown in **Figure 6.** When feedback indicates that the cell is healthy and large enough for division, proteins get the first "go" signal. Organelles and chromosomes are copied. Then, the cell prepares for division.

Standards Check What feedback does the cell need to prepare for cell division? **7.1.e**

Universal Access · Differentiated Instruction

Advanced Learners/GATE

Awareness Colors Ask students if any of them wear colored bracelets or pins that denote awareness of certain diseases, such as cancer. Then, ask students to research the different colors used in these bracelets and pins and which diseases they denote. Have students create an informative pamphlet that describes what color is used for each disease.

(Students will find several colors denote various diseases. They will note that one color may denote several diseases, or may denote a specific form of that disease, such as pink for breast cancer and white for bone cancer.) **LS Verbal/Visual**

Cancer

The feedback switches that control the "stop" and "go" signals are proteins. A cell's DNA carries the information needed to make proteins. If the DNA is changed, the proteins also may be changed. Thus, the proteins may not be able to control cell growth and division. Cells may reproduce rapidly and form clumps called *tumors*. **Cancer** occurs when tumors affect the normal functions of the body.

There are more than a hundred kinds of cancer. All cancers are caused by the uncontrolled growth of cells. **Figure 7** shows *melanoma*, the most deadly kind of skin cancer. Wearing sunscreen and checking skin for abnormal moles may help prevent skin cancer.

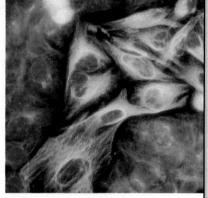

Figure 7 *Cancer cells, such as these melanoma cells, are growing uncontrollably.*

5. Sample answer: If cytokinesis occurred without mitosis, the DNA would not be divided equally between the two daughter cells. **7.1.e** (exceeding)

6. Sample answer: Mitosis ensures that each new cell receives a copy of each chromosome, and hence, an exact copy of the parent cell's genetic material. **7.1.e** (mastering)

7. Sample answer: The processes of animal and plant cells are different because plant cells have cell walls. Cytokinesis is different in plant cells, but all other stages of cell division are essentially the same as they are in animal cells. **7.1.b** (mastering)

8. Sample answer: no; The number of chromosomes is not always related to the complexity of an organism. A person is more complex than a potato because a person can think, move, speak, and so on. However, a potato has 48 chromosomes, while a person only has 46. **7.2.e** (mastering)

9. The image shows phase 3, anaphase. In this phase, chromatids separate and move to opposite sides of the cell. **7.1.e** (mastering)

10. Cell A: There are four 6-hour periods in 24 h, so $2 \times 2 \times 2 \times 2 = 16$ cells

Cell B: There are three 8-hour periods in 24 h, so $2 \times 2 \times 2 = 8$ cells

Cell A produces 8 more cells than Cell B does in a 24-hour period.

SECTION Review

7.1.b, 7.1.e,
7.2.e

Summary

- The life cycle of a cell is the cell cycle.
- A cell copies its chromosomes during interphase.
- Mitosis produces two nuclei that have the same number of chromosomes.
- Mitosis has four phases: prophase, metaphase, anaphase, and telophase.
- After mitosis, the cytoplasm is divided by cytokinesis into two daughter cells.
- In plant cells, a cell plate forms between the two new cells during cytokinesis.
- Cancer is a disorder of cell division.

Understanding Concepts

① **Comparing** Compare the organization of DNA in prokaryotic and eukaryotic cells.

② **Analyzing** Why must chromosomes be copied before cells divide?

③ **Describing** Describe mitosis.

④ **Summarizing** Summarize the control methods of the cell cycle.

Critical Thinking

⑤ **Predicting Consequences** What would happen if cytokinesis occurred without mitosis?

⑥ **Applying Concepts** How does mitosis ensure that a new cell is identical to its parent cell?

⑦ **Making Comparisons** Compare the processes that animal cells and plant cells use to make new cells. How are the processes different?

⑧ **Identifying Relationships** Do more-complex organisms always have more chromosomes than simpler organisms do? How do you know?

INTERPRETING GRAPHICS Use the diagram below to answer the next question.

⑨ **Evaluating Data** What step of mitosis does this image show? Describe what is happening.

Math Skills

⑩ **Solving Problems** Cell A takes 6 h to complete division. Cell B takes 8 h to complete division. After 24 h, how many more copies of cell A than copies of cell B are there?

Internet Resources

For a variety of links related to this chapter, go to www.scilinks.org
Topic: Cell Cycle
SciLinks code: HY70235

Answers to Section Review

1. Prokaryotic DNA is a single, circular ring. Eukaryotic DNA is condensed into several chromosomes that are stored in the nucleus. **7.2.e** (mastering)

2. Chromosomes need to be copied so that the two daughter cells have the same genetic material as the parent cell. **7.1.e** (mastering), **7.2.e** (supporting)

3. Sample answer: Before mitosis begins, the chromosomes are copied. In prophase, the chromosomes condense. In metaphase, the paired chromosomes line up along the equator of the cell. In anaphase, the chromatids move to opposite sides of the cell. In telophase, a nuclear membrane forms around the chromosomes and the chromosomes decondense. **7.1.e** (mastering)

4. Sample answer: The control methods of the cell cycle are similar to "stop" and "go" traffic signals. The signal is determined by feedback from the cell. **7.1.e** (supporting)

Section Review Standards Guide			
	Supporting	Mastering	Exceeding
7.1.b		7	
7.1.e	4	2, 3, 6, 9	5
7.2.e	2	1, 8	

Section Resources

- Directed Reading
  A **BASIC** (Also in Spanish), B **GENERAL**
- Interactive Reader and Study Guide
- Section Quiz **GENERAL** (Also in Spanish)
- Section Review **GENERAL** (Also in Spanish)
- Vocabulary and Section Summary
  A **BASIC** (Also in Spanish), B **GENERAL**

Skills Practice Lab

Teacher Notes

In this lab, students will observe and draw cells undergoing mitosis (covers standard 7.1.e). Students will identify and label chromosomes, centromeres, and the nuclear membrane on their drawings (covers standards 7.2.e and 7.7.d).

Time Required

One 45-minute class period

Lab Ratings

EASY ———————→ HARD

Teacher Prep 🧪🧪
Student Set-Up 🧪
Concept Level 🧪🧪🧪
Clean Up 🧪

Materials

The materials listed on the student page are enough for a group of 2 students. However, if at all possible, supply each student with his or her own microscope and a prepared onion root tip slide.

Safety Caution

Remind students to tell you immediately if slides or coverslips are broken.

Preparation Notes

Demonstrate the proper way to transport microscopes. Show students how to change lens power so that the cover slip is protected from shattering.

Phases of Mitosis

OBJECTIVES

Observe cells in the phases of mitosis.

Draw the phases of mitosis.

MATERIALS

- microscope
- paper (4 sheets)
- prepared slide, onion-root tip

Onion root tip

7.1.e Students know cells divide to increase their numbers through a process of mitosis, which results in two daughter cells with identical sets of chromosomes.

7.2.e Students know DNA (deoxyribonucleic acid) is the genetic material of living organisms and is located in the chromosomes of each cell.

Investigation and Experimentation
7.7.d Construct scale models, maps, and appropriately labeled diagrams to communicate scientific knowledge (e.g., motion of Earth's plates and cell structure).

Cell division is a step-by-step process that results in the formation of two identical daughter cells. All of the material inside the parent cell must be replicated before the new daughter cells can form. A cell's nucleus is replicated by the process of mitosis. Mitosis has four phases: prophase, metaphase, anaphase, and telophase. During each phase of mitosis, cell parts follow a routine that results in the formation of two identical nuclei. You can observe mitosis in the cells of onion-root tips. These cells reproduce often, so you can observe a large number of them in the stages of cell reproduction.

Procedure

1. Use the microscope's low-power setting to examine a prepared slide of an onion root tip.

2. Locate the growing region of the root tip.

3. Switch to the high-power setting.

4. Select the cells that are the best representatives of each of the four phases of mitosis. Draw each cell on a separate sheet of paper. Label the chromosomes, centromeres, and the nuclear membrane on your drawings.

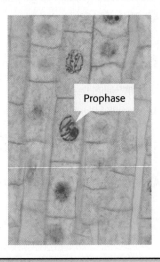

Prophase

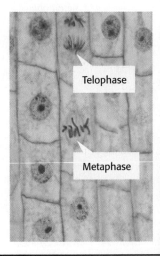

Telophase

Metaphase

Lab Resources

📋 Differentiated Datasheets
A **BASIC**, B **GENERAL**, C **ADVANCED**

💿 Classroom Lab Video/DVD

Holt Lab Generator CD-ROM

Search for any lab by topic, standard, difficulty level, or time. Edit any lab to fit your needs, or create your own labs. Use the Lab Materials QuickList software to customize your lab materials list.

Analyze the Results

5 **Analyzing Data** Which phase(s) have visible chromosomes? In which phase(s) are the chromosomes invisible?

6 **Recognizing Patterns** What feature of metaphase is most visible?

7 **Examining Data** During which phase do the two separate nuclei appear?

8 **Examining Data** In which phase(s) does the cell have a visible nuclear membrane?

Draw Conclusions

9 **Evaluating Results** Explain why the nuclear membrane is visible in some phases of mitosis but not in others.

10 **Interpreting Information** Although chromosomes are not visible during interphase, the cell still contains DNA. Where is the DNA and why can't it be seen?

11 **Making Predictions** The cell's DNA doubles during interphase. Suppose this increase in DNA never occurred. How would this affect the daughter cells produced during mitosis?

Big Idea Question

12 **Interpreting Information** Explain what the term *cycle* means and how the meaning applies to the cell cycle. Besides mitosis, what are the stages of the cell cycle?

Analyze the Results

5. Chromosomes are visible in all of the phases of mitosis: prophase, metaphase, anaphase, and telophase. Chromosomes are not visible in interphase or cytokinesis.

6. The chromosomes line up along the central axis of the cell.

7. Two separate nuclei appear in telophase.

8. The only phase of mitosis in which the nuclear membrane is visible is prophase.

Draw Conclusions

9. The nuclear membrane dissolves, so it cannot be seen during metaphase, anaphase, and telophase.

10. The genetic material is still within the nucleus. However it is found in loosely packed fibers, not the thicker, more visible chromosomes.

11. If the DNA did not double, then the daughter cells would receive only some of the DNA that was found in the parent cell. Each subsequent division would produce cells with only part of the genetic code of its parent. This lineage of cells would not survive.

Big Idea Questions

12. Sample answer: A cycle is a process that repeats itself and often ends at the same place it began. The cell cycle begins with one cell that has a certain number of chromosomes and organelles. The cell goes through the process of cell division and ends up as two cells that are identical to the first. Each of these cells can now start the process over again. Besides mitosis, the stages of the cell cycle are interphase and cytokinesis.

Karen Benitez
George V. Leyva
Intermediate School
San Jose, California

Teacher Notes

In this activity, students will learn to draw conclusions based on experimental data (covers standard 7.7.c).

Answers to You Try It!

1. Sample answer: The results show that bacterial populations increased in each sample. The bacterial populations increased the most in samples at the highest temperature, and they increased the least in the coolest temperatures. Cooler temperatures, like those found in refrigerators, reduce the amount of growth in bacterial populations on food. Of the temperatures tested, the smallest amount of increase was found in samples kept at 15°C. The refrigerator with the starting temperature of 10°C broke during the experiment. It was not able to maintain the required temperature. My conclusion does not use the data collected from this refrigerator.

2. The refrigerator with an initial temperature of 10°C broke during the experiment. This data should not be used because the temperature was not 10°C the entire time.

3. Sample answers: (a) The experimental factor was refrigeration temperature, not the type of food. A conclusion cannot be drawn that bacteria grows faster on Food X than on Food Y because I did not test Food Y. (b) The effect of bacteria on humans was not tested so this conclusion cannot be made. (c) No results can be based on the 10°C sample, because the equipment failed during the experiment.

4. Sample answer: yes; Cell growth and division leads to increased populations, but populations did not increase as much with refrigeration at lower temperatures than they did with refrigeration at higher temperatures. Therefore, the cooler the temperature, the smaller the increase in bacterial population.

☐ Datasheet GENERAL

Also editable on the Holt Lab Generator CD-ROM

Science Skills Activity

| Scientific Methods | Research | Data Analysis | Models, Maps & Diagrams |

Investigation and Experimentation
7.7.c Communicate the logical connection among hypotheses, science concepts, tests conducted, data collected, and conclusions drawn from the scientific evidence.

Drawing Conclusions from Data

▶ Tutorial

After scientists analyze the data from an experiment, they can draw conclusions. Conclusions reveal what was discovered through the experiment.

❶ First, determine which question you want to answer. Use your question to form a hypothesis. Then, plan and carry out your experiment.

❷ Collect data and other observations during your experiment. Your observations should also include any problems that you encountered during your experiment.

❸ Analyze your data. Complete mathematical calculations if necessary. Be sure to use the correct units.

❹ Begin your conclusions with a brief summary of your data. Describe what your data show.

❺ Explain how your data relate to the question you were trying to answer. Be sure to use the data that you collected, not the data that you expected to collect.

❻ Explain any errors or problems that occurred during experimentation. Major problems can result in incorrect data. Incorrect data can lead to incorrect conclusions.

▶ You Try It!

Why do we put food in the refrigerator? Perishable foods—foods that can go bad, such as meat—can support the growth of thousands of bacteria. Some bacteria, such as *Escherichia coli*, can cause sickness and even death when people eat foods contaminated by these bacteria. At cool temperatures, the chemical processes that lead to cell growth and division are slowed down or stopped. This environment helps control bacterial populations. Use the data in the table below to draw conclusions and to answer the following questions.

Bacterial Growth on Food X at Various Temperatures		
Starting temperature (°C)	Growth after 24 h (% increase)	Observations of refrigerator performance
30	42	normal
20	20	normal
15	5	normal
10	9	broke down

❶ **Drawing Conclusions** Analyze the table. Write a conclusion paragraph about the data. Begin with a summary of the data. What do the data show?

❷ **Examining Data** Explain any problems that occurred in the data. Are the data valid? Why or why not?

❸ **Defending Conclusions** Explain why each of the following conclusions CANNOT be drawn from the data: (a) bacteria grow faster on food X than on food Y, (b) you will get sick if you eat food X left at 30°C for one day, and (c) storing food X at a temperature of 15°C leads to fewer bacteria than storing it at 10°C.

❹ **Applying Conclusions** Does this experiment indicate that refrigeration slows the processes of cell growth and division? Explain your answer.

Universal Access • Differentiated Instruction

Special Education Students

Explaining Temperature For some students, neither the concept of 30°C nor the concept of the difference between 30°C and 10°C are meaningful. Use a marker to write the temperatures 30°C, 20°C, 15°C, and 10°C on glass cups or beakers. Using hot and cold tap water, fill the four glasses with water that is approximately 30°C (86°F), 20°C (68°F), 15°C (59°F) and 10°C (50°F). If necessary, add ice to obtain the lower temperatures. Have students use their fingers to feel the differences between the temperatures. ⬛ Kinesthetic

Chapter Summary

The Big Idea
Cells carry out important life functions, such as obtaining energy, growing, and making new cells.

Section

Vocabulary

① **Cell Energy**

Key Concept All cells need energy to carry out cell functions. However, cells may obtain and process energy in different ways.

- In plant cells, chloroplasts capture energy from the sun in order to make food during photosynthesis.
- Cells release energy from food through either cellular respiration or fermentation.

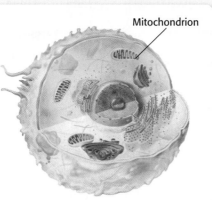

Mitochondrion

Eukaryotic cells, such as this animal cell, carry out cellular respiration in mitochondria.

photosynthesis p. 148
cellular respiration p. 149
fermentation p. 149

② **The Cell Cycle**

Key Concept The cell cycle results in daughter cells, two new cells that are exact copies of the original cell.

- Before a cell divides, it must make a copy of its DNA.
- To increase their numbers, eukaryotic cells divide through the processes of mitosis and cytokinesis.
- Mitosis has four phases.
- Cytokinesis differs in animals and plants.
- Cancer occurs when cells replicate abnormally.

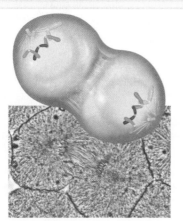

Telophase is the last phase of mitosis.

cell cycle p. 152
chromosome p. 152
mitosis p. 153
cytokinesis p. 153
cancer p. 157

Chapter Summary

SUPER SUMMARY

Have students connect the major concepts in this chapter through an interactive Super Summary. Visit go.hrw.com and type in the keyword HY7ACTS to access the Super Summary for this chapter.

Identifying Word Parts

Vocabulary Quiz Game Have students work in small groups. Ask each group to identify and define the root words for each of the vocabulary terms and secondary terms in the chapter. Then, have students write quiz questions about each term based on this information. Use the questions for a quiz game in which the student groups compete against each other. **LS** Verbal

Focus on Reading

Comparing Texts Have students read *Cells: Amazing Forms and Functions* by John K. Young. Then, have students make a table that compares the information presented in the chapter with the information presented in the book. **LS** Verbal/Logical

Review Resources

- Reinforcement Worksheet **BASIC**
- Critical Thinking Worksheet **ADVANCED**
- Chapter Review **GENERAL** (Also in Spanish)
- Standards Review Workbook (Also in Spanish)
- Study Guide A **BASIC** (Also in Spanish), B **GENERAL**

Assessment Resources

- Chapter Tests A **BASIC**, B **GENERAL** (Also in Spanish), C **ADVANCED**
- Standards Assessment **GENERAL**

Assignment Guide

Section	Questions
1	2–3, 5, 7, 9, 13, 18–20, 29
2	4, 6, 8, 10–12, 14–17, 21–27

Answers

Using Vocabulary

1. Sample answer: The word *process* means "a series of actions or changes."

2. photosynthesis **7.1.d** (mastering)

3. cellular respiration **7.1.d** (supporting)

4. Cytokinesis is the division of cytoplasm after mitosis. Mitosis is the process during which the nuclear material splits to form two new nuclei. **7.1.e** (mastering)

5. Cellular respiration releases stored energy by using oxygen. Fermentation releases stored energy without using oxygen. **7.1.d** (mastering)

Understanding Concepts

6. a **7.1.e** (mastering)

7. d **7.1.d** (supporting)

8. c **7.1.b** (mastering)

9. Chloroplasts are needed for photosynthesis. Cellular respiration requires mitochondria in eukaryotic cells. Prokaryotic cells that carry out cellular respiration do so on the cell membrane. **7.1.b** (supporting), **7.1.d** (mastering)

10. Sample answer: The first stage is interphase, which includes cell growth and copying of DNA (duplication). The second stage is mitosis, which involves separating the duplicated chromosomes. The third stage is cytokinesis, which results in two identical cells. **7.1.e** (mastering)

11. The four phases of mitosis are prophase, metaphase, anaphase, and telophase. **7.1.e** (mastering)

Chapter Review

Organize

Layered Book   Review the FoldNote that you created at the beginning of the chapter. Add to or correct the FoldNote based on what you have learned.

Using Vocabulary

1 **Academic Vocabulary**   In the sentence "The process of photosynthesis converts energy from the sun into food," what does the word *process* mean?

Complete each of the following sentences by choosing the correct term from the word bank.

  cellular respiration
  photosynthesis
  fermentation

2 Plants use ___ to make glucose.

3 During ___, oxygen is used to break down food molecules, releasing large amounts of energy.

For each pair of terms, explain how the meanings of the terms differ.

4 *cytokinesis* and *mitosis*

5 *cellular respiration* and *fermentation*

Understanding Concepts

Multiple Choice

6 What is the result of mitosis and cytokinesis?
  a. two identical cells
  b. two nuclei
  c. two chloroplasts
  d. two different cells

7 Before a cell can use the energy in food, the energy must be transferred to molecules of
  a. proteins.
  b. carbohydrates.
  c. DNA.
  d. ATP.

8 Which of the following cells would form a cell plate during the cell cycle?
  a. a human cell
  b. a prokaryotic cell
  c. a plant cell
  d. All of the above

Short Answer

9 **Identifying**   Name the cell structures that are needed for photosynthesis and the cell structures that are needed for cellular respiration.

10 **Describing**   Describe the three stages of the cell cycle of a eukaryotic cell.

11 **Listing**   List in order the four phases of mitosis.

12 **Evaluating**   How many pairs of chromosomes do humans have?

INTERPRETING GRAPHICS   The picture below shows a cell. Use the picture to answer the next question.

13 **Classifying**   Does the picture show a plant cell or an animal cell? How do you know?

Writing Skills

14 **Writing a Biography**   Write and illustrate the biography of a cell. The biography can be humorous or serious, but it should include accurate descriptions of how cells grow and reproduce.

---

12. Humans have 23 pairs of chromosomes. **7.2.e** (mastering)

13. The illustration shows a plant cell. The cell in the illustration has chloroplasts, and animal cells do not have chloroplasts. **7.1.b** (mastering)

Writing Skills

14. Answers may vary. **7.1.e** (mastering)

Critical Thinking

15. An answer to this exercise can be found at the end of this book. **7.1.e** (mastering)

16. Each new cell will receive a copy of each chromosome, so each new cell with have 10 chromosomes. **7.2.e** (mastering)

15 **Concept Mapping** Use the following terms to create a concept map: *chromosome duplication, cytokinesis, prokaryote, mitosis, cell cycle, binary fission,* and *eukaryote.*

16 **Applying Concepts** A parent cell has 10 chromosomes. How many chromosomes will each new cell have after the parent cell divides?

17 **Identifying Relationships** How is DNA related to cancer? How are chromosomes related to cancer?

18 **Analyzing Processes** How is ATP involved in cellular respiration? What would happen to cells if ATP did not exist?

19 **Making Comparisons** How are chlorophyll and chloroplasts related, and where are they found?

20 **Applying Concepts** How are mitochondria related to ATP?

INTERPRETING GRAPHICS Use the table below to answer the next two questions.

Cell Characteristics		
Cell	Number of chromosomes	Presence of chloroplasts
A	12	no
B	12	yes
C	10	yes
D	12	yes

21 **Evaluating Data** Two of these cells came from the division of one parent cell. Which two cells came from the same parent cell? Explain your answer.

22 **Applying Concepts** Which of the cells does NOT form a cell plate during cytokinesis? How do you know?

23 **Predicting Consequences** What would happen to a cell if it were unable to use feedback?

INTERPRETING GRAPHICS The image below shows a cell. Use the image to answer the next four questions.

24 **Applying Concepts** Is the cell prokaryotic or eukaryotic?

25 **Evaluating Data** Which stage of the cell cycle is this cell in?

26 **Identifying Relationships** What will happen to the cell after this stage is complete?

27 **Applying Concepts** Assume that 12 chromatids are present in the image above. How many chromosomes will be present in each of the new cells after the cell divides?

Math Skills

28 **Making Calculations** Cell A converts 80% of its food into usable fuel. Cell B is not as efficient as cell A. Cell B converts only half the amount of food into fuel as cell A does. What percentage of food does cell B convert into fuel? How many grams of fuel will cell B make if cell B starts with 150 g of food?

Challenge

29 **Identifying Relationships** Describe the path of energy conversions, beginning with light energy from the sun and ending with the energy in your muscles.

---

21. Cell B and cell D came from the division of one parent cell. The cell cycle ensures that the new cells have equal numbers of chromosomes and organelles. Cells B and D each have 12 chromosomes and chloroplasts. **7.1.e** (exceeding)

22. Cell A does not have chloroplasts, which means it is not a plant cell. Plant cells have cell walls, which form from cell plates. **7.1.b** (exceeding)

23. A cell that is unable to get feedback will not be able to regulate its cell cycle. **7.1.e** (supporting)

24. The cell is eukaryotic. **7.2.e** (supporting)

25. The cell is in interphase. **7.1.e** (mastering)

26. After interphase is complete, the cell will enter mitosis. **7.1.e** (mastering)

27. There will be 6 chromosomes present in each of the new cells after the cell divides. **7.1.e** (mastering)

Math Skills

28. Cell B converts 40% of food into fuel. 150 g × 0.40 = 60 g

Challenge

29. Sample answer: Light energy from the sun is changed into chemical energy, or glucose, in a grass plant. During cellular respiration, this chemical energy is changed to another type of chemical energy, ATP, which is used for growth and other cell processes. A cow eats the grass, taking in glucose. Cellular respiration releases energy from the glucose and stores it as ATP. The cow uses this energy to move around. A person eats a hamburger, which is made of meat from a cow. His or her body cells release energy from the meat by cellular respiration and store it as ATP. Later, the person uses ATP to walk home from school.
7.1.b (supporting), **7.1.d** (exceeding)

---

17. Cancer is abnormal cell growth and division. DNA and cancer are related because mutated DNA can produce proteins that do not regulate cell growth and division normally. Chromosomes are related to cancer because DNA, including mutated DNA, makes up chromosomes. **7.2.e** (exceeding)

18. Cellular respiration releases energy from food. Some of this energy is stored in ATP, which supplies energy to fuel cell functions. Without ATP, cells would not be able to function. **7.1.d** (supporting)

19. Chlorophyll is a green pigment found in chloroplasts. Chloroplasts are the site for photosynthesis. Both chlorophyll and chloroplasts are found in cells that are capable of photosynthesis, such as plants cells. **7.1.b** (mastering)

20. Cellular respiration occurs in the mitochondria. The energy released by cellular respiration is stored in ATP. **7.1.d** (mastering)

Chapter Review Standards Guide			
	Supporting	Mastering	Exceeding
7.1.b	9, 29	8, 13, 19	22
7.1.d	3, 7, 18	2, 5, 9, 20	29
7.1.e	23	4, 6, 10, 11, 14, 15, 25, 26, 27	21
7.2.e	24	12, 16	17

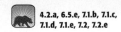
Standards Assessment

Teacher Notes

To provide practice under more realistic testing conditions, give students 20 min to answer all of the questions in this assessment.

Answer Key	
Question Number	Correct Answer
1	C
2	C
3	B
4	A
5	D
6	C
7	C
8	A
9	A
10	B
11	D
12	A
13	B
14	D
15	B
16	A
17	C

Standards Guide			
	Supporting	Mastering	Exceeding
4.2.a		17	
6.5.e		16	
7.1.b	12	6	
7.1.c		14	
7.1.d	4	5, 10	11
7.1.e	1, 7, 9	8	
7.2	3		
7.2.a		15	
7.2.e	2	13	

Standards Assessment **GENERAL**

Teacher Notes for Standards Assessment contain a longer Assessment Doctor and Diagnostic Teaching Tips.

REVIEWING ACADEMIC VOCABULARY

1 Which of the following words is the closest in meaning to the word *identical*?

A related

B common

C duplicate

D woven

2 Choose the appropriate form of the word *locate* for the following sentence: Genetic information is ___ in the nucleus of a cell.

A locates

B locative

C located

D location

3 Which of the following sets of words best completes the following sentence: A cell's traits may be ___ the environment.

A modify with

B modified by

C modifying

D modifies in

4 Which of the following words means "to release or to set free"?

A liberate

B characterize

C function

D specify

REVIEWING CONCEPTS

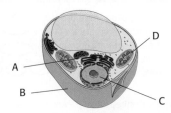

5 The diagram above shows a plant cell. Where in the diagram does the process of photosynthesis take place?

A part A   C part C

B part B   D part D

6 Which of the following best describes a major difference between plant cells and animal cells?

A Only plant cells use cellular respiration.

B Only plant cells have a nucleus containing DNA.

C Unlike plant cells, animal cells cannot make their own food.

D Only animal cells have a cell wall.

7 What is the life cycle of a cell called?

A mitosis   C cell cycle

B centromere   D chromatid

8 What is the purpose of the process of mitosis?

A to produce two identical nuclei

B to split a cell into two identical cells

C to copy each chromosome in a cell

D to create deoxyribonucleic acid in a cell

9 A parent cell has 24 chromosomes at the beginning of interphase. How many chromatids will it have during prophase?

A 48   C 12

B 24   D 6

ASSESSMENT DOCTOR

Question 1: The correct answer is C. *Duplicate* and *identical* have similar meanings. When DNA is copied in a cell, the copied DNA is a duplicate of the original DNA, meaning they are exactly the same, or identical.

Question 2: The correct answer is C. *Located* is the past participle of the verb *locate*. Genetic information is located or positioned in the nucleus of a cell.

Question 3: The correct answer is B. *Modified*, like many passive verbs, is often used with the preposition *by*.

Question 4: The correct answer is A. Mitochondria *liberate*, or free, energy that is stored in food through the process of cellular respiration.

Question 5: The correct answer is D. Point D indicates a chloroplast, whose function is to convert carbon dioxide, water, and light energy into food for the cell through photosynthesis.

$$C_6H_{12}O_6 + 6O_2 \longrightarrow 6CO_2 + 6H_2O + energy\ (ATP)$$

Glucose   Oxygen   Carbon dioxide   Water

10 Above is the chemical equation for a process that occurs in cells. What process is described by the chemical equation?

A cytokinesis

B cellular respiration

C fermentation

D photosynthesis

11 How are the processes of photosynthesis and cellular respiration connected?

A Both processes begin with oxygen.

B Both processes require sunlight.

C Each process takes place only in plant cells.

D Each process makes the material needed in the other process.

12 Which of the following is true of cytokinesis in the cells of a plant?

A A cell plate forms and separates the cytoplasm into two new cells.

B The cell divides its cytoplasm by a process called *binary fission.*

C The cell membrane pinches the cytoplasm of the cell in two.

D At this stage, the nuclear membrane of the cell dissolves.

13 Which of the following best describes the chromosomes of eukaryotic cells?

A More-complex eukaryotes have more chromosomes than simpler ones do.

B Different kinds of eukaryotes have different numbers of chromosomes.

C The chromosomes in a pair contain very different genetic information.

D Each of the chromosomes contains one copy of circular DNA.

REVIEWING PRIOR LEARNING

14 Where is DNA found within a eukaryotic cell?

A the Golgi apparatus

B the mitochondria

C the smooth endoplasmic reticulum

D the nucleus

15 Offspring are created by either sexual or asexual reproduction. How are the two kinds of offspring similar?

A Both share traits of two parents.

B Both have DNA.

C Both have multiple cells.

D Both are identical to one parent.

16 Which of the following is an abiotic factor that may affect the types and numbers of animals that can live in an area?

A the range of temperatures experienced in the area

B the types of plants available for food sources

C the number and types of predators in the area

D the number of plants available for food sources

17 What are the primary sources of energy and matter in most food chains?

A primary consumers

B decomposers

C plants

D carnivores

Standards Assessment

Question 11: The correct answer is D. The products of photosynthesis, glucose and oxygen, are the materials needed for cellular respiration. The products of cellular respiration are carbon dioxide and water, which a cell needs to begin the process of photosynthesis.

Question 12: The correct answer is A. In cytokinesis in plants, the cells are split apart by the formation of a cell plate. The cell plate will become new cell membranes and cell walls.

Question 13: The correct answer is B. Different eukaryotes have different numbers of chromosomes. More complex organisms do not necessarily have more chromosomes than simpler organisms do. The chromosomes in a pair are called *homologous chromosomes,* because they are similar.

Question 14: The correct answer is D. The nucleus is the repository for genetic information, DNA, in eukaryotic cells. Prokaryotic cells, which do not have a nucleus, store their DNA in a long, circular chromosome within the cytoplasm.

Question 15: The correct answer is B. Offspring produced from both sexual and asexual reproduction have DNA. All living organisms have DNA.

Question 16: The correct answer is A. Abiotic factors are the non-living components of an ecosystem. The range of temperature in an area is an abiotic component of an ecosystem.

Question 17: The correct answer is C. Energy enters an ecosystem as sunlight which is used by producers, such as plants, to make food. Organisms then eat plants and use the energy in the food made by plants. The energy continues to be moved from one organism to the next as organisms consume other organisms.

Question 6: The correct answer is C. Animal cells cannot make their own food, while plant cells can through photosynthesis. Both plant and animal cells use cellular respiration and have a nucleus containing DNA. Plant cells have cell walls, but animal cells do not.

Question 7: The correct answer is C. The cell cycle is the life cycle of a cell. This cycle lasts until a cell divides and forms two daughter cells identical to the parent cell.

Question 8: The correct answer is A. At the end of mitosis, two separate but identical nuclei exist. Mitosis is preceded by interphase in which chromosomes are duplicated. Mitosis is followed by cytokinesis, in which the parent cell splits to form two daughter cells.

Question 9: The correct answer is A. During interphase, a cell duplicates each of its chromosomes. A parent cell that has 24 chromosomes at the beginning of interphase will have double that number of chromatids, or 48, during prophase, the first phase of mitosis.

Question 10: The correct answer is B. The equation describes the process of cellular respiration. During this process, glucose and oxygen are broken down into carbon dioxide, water, and energy.

Science Fiction

Teaching Strategy

This is a relatively long story, containing quite a few medical terms. Students may find it easier to read if the class discusses some of the unfamiliar terms before they start reading the story.

LS Verbal Co-op Learning

Scientific Discoveries

Discussion

Explain some of the traditional methods of cancer treatment, such as chemotherapy and radiation. Present students with the pros and cons of each method.

LS Verbal/Logical

Science in Action

New branches of blood vessels supply nutrients to this tumor.

Science Fiction

"Contagion" by Katherine MacLean

A quarter mile from their spaceship, the *Explorer*, a team of doctors walk carefully along a narrow forest trail. Around them, the forest looks like a forest on Earth in the fall—the leaves are green, copper, purple, and fiery red. But it is not fall. And the team is not on Earth.

Minos is enough like Earth to be the home of another colony of humans. But Minos might also be home to unknown organisms that could cause severe illness or death among the crew of *Explorer*. These diseases might be enough like diseases on Earth to be contagious, but they might be different enough to be very difficult to treat.

Something large moves among the shadows—it looks like a man. What happens next? Read Katherine MacLean's "Contagion" in the *Holt Anthology of Science Fiction* to find out.

Language Arts ACTIVITY

In your **Science Journal**, write two to three paragraphs that describe what you think might happen next in the story.

HOLT ANTHOLOGY OF **Science Fiction**

Scientific Discoveries

"Smart Bombs" Can Fight Cancer?

There are more than 100 types of cancer. Cancer cells multiply rapidly in clumps called *tumors*. Current cancer treatment involves harsh side effects. However, Dr. David Cheresh of the University of California, San Diego, may have a better way to fight cancer.

In order to survive, cancer cells need nutrients supplied by the blood. As the number of cells in tumors grow, new branches of blood vessels form nearby. Without these blood vessels, tumors would have no access to blood. The new cancer treatment, called "smart bombs," destroys the new branches of blood vessels that supply blood to tumors. Although the "smart bombs" are still being tested, this new method of fighting cancer seems to be promising!

Math ACTIVITY

Cell A requires 18 h to complete division. When cell A experiences abnormal cell growth, cell division takes one-third of that time. How many hours will it take for 32 cells to be present? Solve the problem in your **Science Journal**.

Answer to Language Arts Activity

Students' predictions may vary. Whatever a student predicts, the prediction should be reasonably related to the information that the student has from reading this introductory paragraph.

Answer to Math Activity

Abnormal cell division = 6 hours;

5 cell divisions = 32 cells;

6 h × 5 cell divisions = 30 hours

Careers

Jerry Yakel

Neuroscientist Jerry Yakel credits a sea slug for making him a neuroscientist. In a college class studying neurons, or nerve cells, Yakel got to see firsthand how ions move across the cell membrane of *Aplysia californica,* also known as a *sea hare.* He says, "I was totally hooked. I knew that I wanted to be a neurophysiologist then and there. I haven't wavered since."

Today, Yakel is a senior investigator for the National Institute of Environmental Health Sciences, which is part of the U.S. government's National Institutes of Health. "We try to understand how the normal brain works," says Yakel of his team. "Then, we look at a diseased brain; we train to understand where the deficits are. Eventually, someone will have an idea about a drug that will tweak the system in this or that way."

Yakel studies the ways in which nicotine affects the human brain. "It is one of the most prevalent and potent neurotoxins in the environment," says Yakel. "I'm amazed that it isn't higher on the list of worries for the general public."

Social Studies Activity

Research a famous or historical figure in science. In your **Science Journal,** write a short report that outlines how he or she became interested in science.

Internet Resources

- To learn more about careers in science, visit www.scilinks.org and enter the SciLinks code HY70225.
- To learn more about these Science in Action topics, visit go.hrw.com and type in the keyword HY7ACTF.
- Check out articles related to this chapter by visiting go.hrw.com. Just type in the keyword HY7ACTC.

Background

Jerry Yakel grew up in Ventura County, California. After graduating from high school, he attended a nearby community college "ostensibly to continue running track, figuring out life." Eventually, he relocated to Oregon State University, where he obtained a B.S. in 1982. He was accepted into UCLA in 1983 and received a Ph.D. in 1988.

Working for the NIH was not something Yakel originally expected to do. "Most of us trained in universities think we will work there," he says. He does enjoy some aspects of being outside the typical university setting. "In the NIH, we are supposed to take more risks in our research." He also enjoys the focus he is able to bring to his work. "I miss having students to teach, but then again I get to spend more time doing research," Yakel says. His choice of environment hasn't affected his passion. "Honestly, the type of research I [would] do actually is the same."

Answer to Social Studies Activity

Students may write about any historical figure in science. Some students may go back as far as Archimedes; others may choose Hyupatia (the first woman to be a true astronomer), Benjamin Franklin, Marie Curie, Albert Einstein, Rosalind Franklin, or one of hundreds of other people. The important issues for the student are why the person is important to science and how the person became interested in science.

Heredity and Genes

How do organisms acquire their traits? The inheritance of traits is the subject of this unit. You will learn how characteristics are passed from one generation to another, how DNA contains genetic information, and how genes influence traits.

Many important discoveries have been made in the field of genetics. This timeline will give you an idea of some of the discoveries that have been made so far.

Around 250

Mayan farmers build terraces to control the flow of water to crops.

1860

Abraham Lincoln is elected the 16th president of the United States.

1865

Gregor Mendel publishes the results of his studies of genetic inheritance in pea plants.

1953

James Watson and Francis Crick figure out the structure of DNA.

1990

Ashanti DeSilva's white blood cells are genetically engineered to treat her immune deficiency disease.

1620

The Pilgrims settle Plymouth Colony.

1859

Charles Darwin suggests that natural selection is a mechanism of evolution.

1905

Nettie Stevens describes how human gender is determined by the X and Y chromosomes.

1941

George Beadle and Edward Tatum discover that genes control the chemical reactions in cells by directing protein production.

1951

Rosalind Franklin photographs DNA.

1997

A sheep named Dolly becomes the first animal to be cloned from a single body cell.

2002

An international team decodes the DNA sequences for both the protist that causes malaria and the mosquito that carries this protist. As a result, the door to more-effective antimalaria drugs is opened.

2003

The Human Genome Project is completed. Scientists spent 13 years mapping out the 3 billion DNA subunits of chromosomes.

Standards Course of Study

The elements listed in the Standards Course of Study provide a base for presenting, supporting, and assessing the California Grade 7 Science Standards. Use this Standards Course of Study as a base for planning your lessons.

Why Teach
Heredity

This chapter was designed to cover the California Grade 7 Science Standards about genetics (7.2.b, 7.2.c, 7.2.d, and 7.2.e). It follows a chapter about cell processes, which also introduced mitosis. In this chapter, meiosis, a cellular process involved in the passing of information from one generation to the next, is described in the context of heredity.

After they have completed this chapter, students will begin a chapter about genes and DNA.

California Standards

Focus on Life Sciences

7.2.b Students know sexual reproduction produces offspring that inherit half their genes from each parent.

7.2.c Students know an inherited trait can be determined by one or more genes.

7.2.d Students know plant and animal cells contain many thousands of different genes and typically have two copies of every gene. The two copies (or alleles) of the gene may or may not be identical, and one may be dominant in determining the phenotype while the other is recessive.

7.2.e Students know DNA (deoxyribonucleic acid) is the genetic material of living organisms and is located in the chromosomes of each cell.

Investigation and Experimentation

7.7.c Communicate the logical connection among hypotheses, science concepts, tests conducted, data collected, and conclusions drawn from the scientific evidence.

7.7.d Construct scale models, maps, and appropriately labeled diagrams to communicate scientific knowledge (e.g., motion of Earth's plates and cell structure).

7.7.e Communicate the steps and results from an investigation in written reports and oral presentations.

Chapter Pacing

Getting Started — 45 min, pp. 172–173
The Big Idea Heredity is the passing of the instructions for traits from one generation to the next.
 7.2.d

Section 1 Mendel and His Peas — 45 min, pp. 174–179
Key Concept The work of Gregor Mendel explains the rules of heredity and is the foundation of modern genetics.
 7.2.d

Section 2 Traits and Inheritance — 90 min, pp. 180–187
Key Concept Genes are the instructions for inherited traits.
7.2.c, 7.2.d, 7.7.c, 7.7.d

Section 3 Meiosis — 90 min, pp. 188–193
Key Concept Meiosis and sexual reproduction allow for the combination of genetic material from two different cells.
7.2.b, 7.2.e

Wrapping Up — 180 min, pp. 194–203
7.2.b, 7.2.d, 7.7.c, 7.7.d, 7.7.e

Basic Learners
TE Organisms in Research, p. 175
TE Describing Meiosis, p. 191
☐ Reinforcement Worksheet
☐ Chapter Test A
☐ Differentiated Datasheets A for Labs and Activities ■
☐ Study Guide A ■

Advanced Learners/GATE
TE Scientists' Discoveries, p. 175
TE Creating a Rubric, p. 196
☐ Critical Thinking Worksheet
☐ Chapter Test C
☐ Differentiated Datasheets C for Labs and Activities ■

Teach

SE Explore Activity Modeling Traits, p. 173＊ ■

▢ **Bellringer**
◉ **PowerPoint® Resources**
SE Quick Lab Flower Cross, p. 177＊ ■

▢ **Bellringer**
◉ **PowerPoint® Resources**
▢ L19 Punnett Squares
SE Quick Lab Completing a Punnett Square, p. 181＊ ■
SE Quick Lab Exploring Probability, p. 182＊ ■

▢ **Bellringer**
◉ **PowerPoint® Resources**
▢ L20 Homologous Chromosomes
▢ L21 Steps of Meiosis: A
▢ L22 Steps of Meiosis: B
SE Quick Lab Meiosis Skit, p. 191＊ ■
▢ L23 Meiosis and Dominance

SE Model-Making Lab Modeling Space Bug Genetics, pp. 194–195＊ ■

Practice

SE Organize Activity Key-Term Fold, p. 172

SE Section Review, p. 179＊ ■

SE Section Review, p. 187＊ ■

SE Section Review, p. 193＊ ■

SE Science Skills Activity Giving Oral Presentations, p. 196＊ ■
▢ **Concept Mapping**＊
SE Chapter Review, pp. 198–199＊ ■

Assess

▢ **Chapter Pretest**

SE Standards Checks, pp. 174, 177, 178
TE Standards Focus, p. 178
▢ **Section Quiz** ■

SE Standards Checks, pp. 180, 182, 185, 186
TE Standards Focus, p. 186
▢ **Section Quiz** ■

SE Standards Checks, pp. 188, 190, 193
TE Standards Focus, p. 192
▢ **Section Quiz** ■

SE Standards Assessment, pp. 200–201＊
▢ **Chapter Tests A, B** ■**, C**
▢ **Standards Review Workbook** ■

Resources for Universal Access • Differentiated Instruction

English Learners

TE Demonstration, pp. 176, 180
TE Using the Figure, p. 176
TE Activity, p. 177
TE Hyphenated Adjectives, p. 177
TE Words with Latin Roots, p. 180
TE Learning Science Vocabulary, p. 184
TE Practicing Words Out Loud, p. 188
TE Focus on Reading, p. 197

▢ Vocabulary and Section Summary A ■, B
▢ Section Quizzes ■
▢ Chapter Tests A, B ■
▢ Differentiated Datasheets A, B, and C for Labs and Activities ■
▢ Study Guide A ■
▢ Multilingual Glossary

Struggling Readers

TE Reading Strategy, pp. 175, 184, 190
TE Making Analogies, p. 189
TE Connecting Text with a Figure, p. 192

Special Education Students

TE Poster of Mendel's Experiments, p. 178
TE Genetic Variation, p. 186
TE Flow Charts, p. 190
TE Demonstrating Meiosis, p. 191
TE Computer Presentations, p. 196

To help plan your lessons, refer to the On Course Mapping Instruction booklet.

Visual Resources

CHAPTER STARTER TRANSPARENCY

BELLRINGER TRANSPARENCIES

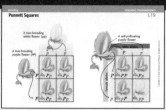

TEACHING TRANSPARENCIES

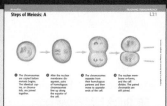
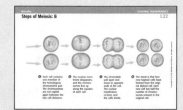
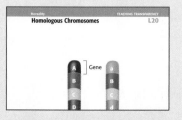

TEACHING TRANSPARENCIES

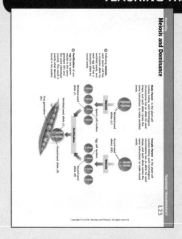
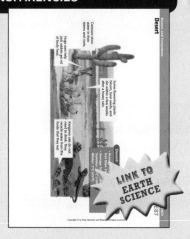

STANDARDS REVIEW TRANSPARENCIES

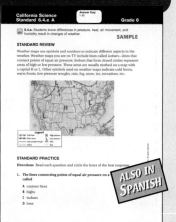

CONCEPT MAPPING TRANSPARENCY

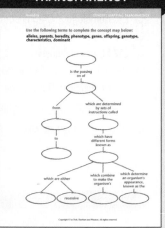

Planning Resources

PARENT LETTER

TEST ITEM LISTING

One-Stop Planner® CD-ROM

This CD-ROM package includes all of the resources shown here and the following time-saving tools:

- **Lab Materials QuickList Software**
- **Customizable Lesson Plans** Correlated to the California Science Standards
- **Holt Calendar Planner**
- **PowerPoint® Resources**

- **Printable Worksheets**
- **ExamView® Test Generator** Correlated to the California Science Standards
- **Holt PuzzlePro®**
- **Interactive Teacher's Edition**

Meeting Individual Needs

DIRECTED READING A

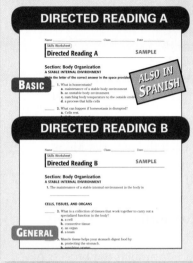

Skills Worksheet
Directed Reading A SAMPLE

Section: Body Organization
A STABLE INTERNAL ENVIRONMENT
Write the letter of the correct answer in the space provided.

BASIC

_____ 1. What is homeostasis?
a. maintenance of a stable body environment
b. an unstable body environment
c. matching body temperature to the outside environment
d. a process that kills cells

_____ 2. What can happen if homeostasis is disrupted?
a. Cells rest.

ALSO IN SPANISH

DIRECTED READING B

Skills Worksheet
Directed Reading B SAMPLE

Section: Body Organization
A STABLE INTERNAL ENVIRONMENT

1. The maintenance of a stable internal environment in the body is

CELLS, TISSUES, AND ORGANS

_____ 2. What is a collection of tissues that work together to carry out a specialized function in the body?
a. a cell
b. connective tissue
c. an organ
d. a team

_____ 3. Muscle tissue helps your stomach digest food by
a. protecting the stomach.

GENERAL

VOCABULARY AND SECTION SUMMARY A

Skills Worksheet
Vocabulary and Section Summary A SAMPLE

Body Organization
VOCABULARY
In your own words, write a definition of the following terms

1. tissue

BASIC

ALSO IN SPANISH

VOCABULARY AND SECTION SUMMARY B

Skills Worksheet
Vocabulary and Section Summary B SAMPLE

Body Organization
VOCABULARY
After you finish reading the section, try this puzzle! Use the clues given to fill in the blanks below. Then, copy the numbered letters into the corresponding boxes on the following page to reveal the four kinds of tissue.

1. the maintenance of a stable environment inside the body

2. a type of cell that has unique structures specialized to perform specific functions

GENERAL

REINFORCEMENT

Skills Worksheet
Reinforcement SAMPLE

Muscle Map
Complete this worksheet after you finish reading the section "The Muscular System."

of the boxes below is labeled with one of the three types of muscle tissue
ur body. Write each note in the correct box. Some of the notes can be used
than once.

Three Types of Muscle

Skeletal	Cardiac	Smooth

BASIC

CRITICAL THINKING

Skills Worksheet
Critical Thinking SAMPLE

The Tissue Engineering Debate

Dear Readers:
Be sure to read next week's issue of *Amazing Medicine*, which features an in-depth interview with Dr. E. P. Dermis of Frontiers Medical Center. While visiting the burn therapy unit at Frontiers, I asked Dr. Dermis about treatments for severe burns. She told me about an incredible new treatment called tissue engineering.

Scientists are actually growing human skin in laboratories and then attaching the skin to real, live patients! Scientists start the process by taking a piece of human skin and collagen from cows. The cells are grown in a culture, where they develop into tissues. When they are ready, the sheets of skin are moved to the patient's body, where they continue to live. In this way, doctors can permanently   patient's burned or diseased skin.
rmis informed me that scientists are also working on engineering
organs like livers, hearts, and kidneys. She believes they'll probably
succeed within the next 20 years or so.
Now that's amazing medicine! What do you think?

ADVANCED

INTERACTIVE READER AND STUDY GUIDE

CHAPTER 6 Body Organization and Structure
SECTION **Body Organization** SAMPLE

BEFORE YOU READ
After you read this section, you should be able to answer these questions:
• What is cell differentiation?
• What are the 11 different human organ systems?
• What is homeostasis?

California Science Standards
7.1.f, 7.6.b

MULTILINGUAL GLOSSARY

SAMPLE

A

Labs and Activities

DIFFERENTIATED DATASHEETS FOR EXPLORE ACTIVITY, QUICK LABS, AND CHAPTER LAB

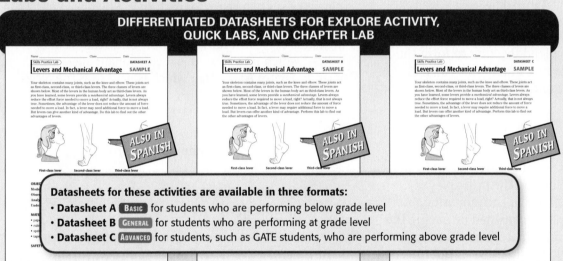

Skills Practice Lab
Levers and Mechanical Advantage DATASHEET A SAMPLE

Your skeleton contains many joints, such as the knee and elbow. These joints act as first-class, second-class, or third-class levers. The three classes of levers are shown below. Most of the levers in the human body act as third-class levers. As you have learned, some levers provide a mechanical advantage. Levers always reduce the effort force needed to move a load, right? Actually, that is not always true. Sometimes, the advantage of the lever does not reduce the amount of force needed to move a load. In fact, a lever may require additional force to move a load. But levers can give another kind of advantage. Do this lab to find out the other advantages of levers.

First-class lever   Second-class lever   Third-class lever

ALSO IN SPANISH

Skills Practice Lab
Levers and Mechanical Advantage DATASHEET B SAMPLE

Your skeleton contains many joints, such as the knee and elbow. These joints act as first-class, second-class, or third-class levers. The three classes of levers are shown below. Most of the levers in the human body act as third-class levers. As you have learned, some levers provide a mechanical advantage. Levers always reduce the effort force required to move a load, right? Actually, that is not always true. Sometimes, the advantage of the lever does not reduce the amount of force needed to move a load. In fact, a lever may require additional force to move a load. But levers can offer another kind of advantage. Perform this lab to find out the other advantages of levers.

First-class lever   Second-class lever   Third-class lever

ALSO IN SPANISH

Skills Practice Lab
Levers and Mechanical Advantage DATASHEET C SAMPLE

Your skeleton contains many joints, such as the knee and elbow. These joints act as first-class, second-class, or third-class levers. The three classes of levers are shown below. Most of the levers in the human body act as third-class levers. As you have learned, some levers provide a mechanical advantage. Levers always reduce the effort force required to move a load, right? Actually, that is not always true. Sometimes, the advantage of the lever does not reduce the amount of force needed to move a load. In fact, a lever may require additional force to move a load. But levers can offer another kind of advantage. Perform this lab to find out the other advantages of levers.

First-class lever   Second-class lever   Third-class lever

ALSO IN SPANISH

OBJE
Mod
Obse
Anal
Unde

MATE
• pip
• rule
• tap

SAFET

Datasheets for these activities are available in three formats:
• **Datasheet A** BASIC for students who are performing below grade level
• **Datasheet B** GENERAL for students who are performing at grade level
• **Datasheet C** ADVANCED for students, such as GATE students, who are performing above grade level

DATASHEET FOR SCIENCE SKILLS ACTIVITY

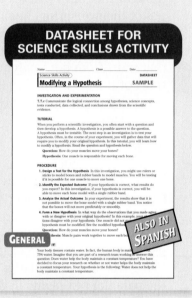

Science Skills Activity
Modifying a Hypothesis DATASHEET SAMPLE

INVESTIGATION AND EXPERIMENTATION
7.7.c Communicate the logical connection among hypotheses, science concepts, tests conducted, data collected, and conclusions drawn from the scientific evidence.

TUTORIAL
When you perform a scientific investigation, you often start with a question and then develop a hypothesis. A hypothesis is a possible answer to the question. A hypothesis must be testable. The next step in an investigation is to test your hypothesis. Often, in the course of your experiment, you will gather data that will require you to modify your original hypothesis. In this tutorial, you will learn how to modify a hypothesis. Read the question and hypothesis below.
Question: How do your muscles move your bones?
Hypothesis: One muscle is responsible for moving each bone.

PROCEDURE
1. **Design a Test for the Hypothesis** In this investigation, you might use rulers or sticks to model boxes and rubber bands to model muscles. You will be testing if it is possible for one muscle to move your bones.
2. **Identify the Expected Outcome** If your hypothesis is correct, what results do you expect? In this investigation, if your hypothesis is correct, you will be able to move each bone model with a single rubber band.
3. **Analyze the Actual Outcome** In your experiment, the results show that it is not possible to move the bone model with a single rubber band. You notice that the bones will not move properly or smoothly.
4. **Form a New Hypothesis** In what way do the observations that you made agree with or disagree with your original hypothesis? In this example, your observations disagree with your original hypothesis. One muscle did not   hypothesis must be modified. See the modified hypotheses
Question: Muscle pairs work together to move each b

IT!

GENERAL

Your body tissues contain water. In fact, the human body is
75% water. Imagine that you are part of a research team working
question: Does water help the body maintain a constant temperature
decided to focus your research on whether or not water helps the body maintain
a constant temperature. Your hypothesis is the following: Water does not help the
body maintain a constant temperature.

ALSO IN SPANISH

Reviews and Assessments

SECTION REVIEWS

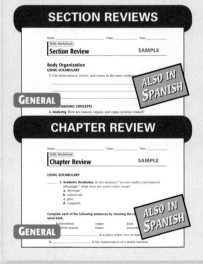

Skills Worksheet
Section Review SAMPLE

Body Organization
USING VOCABULARY
1. Use *homeostasis, tissue,* and *organ* in the same senten

ALSO IN SPANISH

ERSTANDING CONCEPTS
2. **Analyzing** How are tissues, organs, and organ systems related?

GENERAL

CHAPTER REVIEW

Skills Worksheet
Chapter Review SAMPLE

USING VOCABULARY
_____ 1. **Academic Vocabulary** In the sentence "Levers confer a mechanical advantage," what does the word *confer* mean?
a. decrease
b. cancel out
c. give
d. complete

Complete each of the following sentences by choosing the c   word bank.

homeostasis   tissue   muscles
letal system   joint

2. _____ is a place where two or mo

3. _____ is the maintenance of a stable internal

GENERAL

ALSO IN SPANISH

CHAPTER PRETEST

Assessment
Chapter Pretest SAMPLE

1. Which of the following levels of organization in the human body is made of the same kinds of cells working together to perform a job for the organism?
A organism
B organ
C organ system
D tissue

2. Starfish lose arms to escape predators in much the same way that lizards lose their tails. When they lose an arm they can grow a new one, just as a lizard can grow a new tail. But unlike a lizard, an entire new starfish can grow from a single lost arm by regenerating all the other body parts. Which form of reproduction does a starfish show?

GENERAL

SECTION QUIZZES

Assessment
Section Quiz SAMPLE

Section: Body Organization
Write the letter of the correct answer in the space provided.

_____ 1. What does it mean for the body to maintain homeostasis?
a. It has a changing internal environment.
b. It has a stable internal environment.
c. It changes with the external environment.
d. It is stable if the external environment is stable

_____ 2. What is a tissue?
a. a group of different types of cells
b. a new cell that has many functions
c. a system of living and dead cells
d. a group of similar cells that work together

_____ 3. A collection of two or more tissues that work togeth   a function is called a
a. an organ.

GENERAL

ALSO IN SPANISH

CHAPTER TEST A

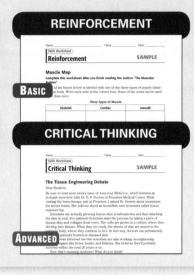

Assessment
Chapter Test A SAMPLE

BASIC

Body Organization and Structure
MULTIPLE CHOICE
Write the letter of the correct answer in the space provided

CHAPTER TEST B

Assessment
Chapter Test B SAMPLE

GENERAL

Body Organization and Structure
MULTIPLE CHOICE
Write the letter of the correct answer in the space provided

ALSO IN SPANISH

CHAPTER TEST C

Assessment
Chapter Test C SAMPLE

ADVANCED

Body Organization and Structure
USING KEY TERMS
Use the terms from the following list to complete the sentences below. Each term may be used only once. Some terms may not be used.

lever   ligaments   tendons
epithelial   mechanical advantage   connective
cardiac   skeletal

1. In the body, the joint serves as fulcrum, and the bone is a(n)

STANDARDS ASSESSMENT

Assessment
Standards Assessment SAMPLE

Teacher Notes and Answer Key
To provide practice under more realistic testing conditions, give students 20 min   of the questions in this section.

GENERAL

ON NUMBER	CORRECT ANSWER	STANDARD
		7.5 (supporting)
		7.6 (supporting)
	B	7.5 (supporting)

STANDARDS REVIEW WORKBOOK

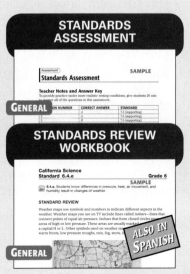

California Science Standard 6.4.e Grade 6

6.4.e. Students know differences in pressure, heat, air movement, and humidity result in changes of weather.

STANDARD REVIEW

Weather maps use symbols and numbers to indicate different aspects in the weather. Weather maps you see on TV include lines called *isobars*—lines that connect points of equal air pressure. Isobars that form closed circles   areas of high or low pressure. These areas are usually marked   a capital H or L. Other symbols used on weather maps indica   warm fronts, low pressure troughs, rain, fog, snow, l

GENERAL

ALSO IN SPANISH

This Teacher Background explains science concepts, principles, and theories that appear in the chapter. Use the information on these pages to refresh or enhance your understanding of the topics covered.

Section 1

Mendel and His Peas

Before Mendel

Many ideas have existed to try to explain *heredity*, the passing of genetic material from parents to offspring. These notions differed in how much genetic information each parent passed on to the offspring and in how the information was transmitted.

By the early nineteenth century, most scientists thought that both parents contributed to the characteristics of their offspring. The most widely-accepted idea of inheritance at the time of Mendel's experiments was that of *blending inheritance*. Blending inheritance is the idea that traits from both parents blend together to form the traits of the offspring. In blending inheritance, a cross between a brown rabbit a white rabbit would produce offspring with tan fur.

Mendel's Experiments

Gregor Mendel entered a monastery in 1843 in the city of Brünn, Austria (now known as Brno, a city in the Czech Republic). Mendel discovered the principles of heredity while studying pea plants at the monastery.

Mendel's studies of pea plants consisted of tracing the patterns of inheritance of seven different characteristics. Using true-breeding plants, he manually cross-pollinated the parental pea plants (P generation) to study the pattern of inheritance of each characteristic separately. In this first generation (F_1 generation), he found that one parental trait would disappear. For example, when Mendel cross-pollinated a pea plant that produced purple flowers with a pea plant that produced white flowers, he found that all of the offspring produced purple flowers.

Mendel then allowed the F_1 plants to self-pollinate. In the second generation plants (F_2 generation), he found that the trait for white flowers reappeared. He also discovered that the ratio of dominant traits (present in the F_1 generation) to recessive traits (absent in the F_2 generation) was 3:1. Mendel's work showed that blending inheritance was not a good explanation for the inheritance of traits because traits did not combine or mix together.

Section 2

Traits and Inheritance

Mendel's Model of Inheritance

From the results of his experiments, Mendel developed a hypothesis of inheritance. This hypothesis can be described as follows:

- The material which carries heritable characteristics can have multiple forms. Today, we call the material Mendel was describing a *gene*. The different forms of a gene are called alleles. The gene for seed color in pea plants has two alleles: yellow seeds and green seeds.

- Organisms inherit one allele from each parent for every inherited characteristic, or trait.

- Sex cells, or gametes, are produced through the process of meiosis. Gametes carry only one allele for each trait. When a sperm and egg unite during fertilization, the offspring receives two genes for each trait.

- When offspring receive two different alleles for a trait, one trait is expressed fully, while the other trait is masked. The trait which is expressed is the dominant allele, as shown in **Figure A;** the trait which is masked is the recessive allele.

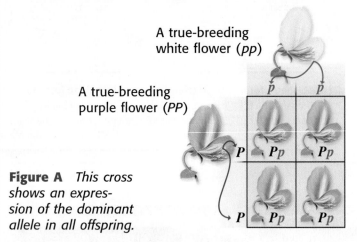

A true-breeding white flower (*pp*)

A true-breeding purple flower (*PP*)

Figure A *This cross shows an expression of the dominant allele in all offspring.*

Mendel's work on simple inheritance has led to exploration of more complex situations. Biologists have learned that there is not always a one-to-one correspondence between genes and traits. For example, genetic diseases often result in one gene affecting many traits. Human eye color is an example of one trait that is influenced by many genes.

Mendelian Genetics and Probability

During fertilization, an offspring will receive, at random, two alleles of a gene—one from each of its parents. The probability of an offspring receiving a certain allele can be calculated using the rule of multiplication in the probability of independent events.

Probability is the mathematical chance that an event will occur. Probability is written as a fraction or a percentage, because the probability that an event will happen is based on a probability scale of 0 to 1. An event that is certain to occur has a probability of 1. An event that is certain *not* to occur has a probability of 0. For example, in a coin toss, the probability of tossing either heads or tails is 1, and the probability of tossing neither heads nor tails is 0. The chance of tossing heads is 1/2, or 50%.

If two coins are tossed at the same time, then the probability of each coin tossed is determined separately, because the outcome for each coin is unaffected by the other coin. In other words, each coin being tossed is an independent event. According to the rule of multiplication, the probability of a compound event (two coins being tossed heads, for example) is equal to the product of the separate probabilities of the independent single events. So, if two coins are tossed, the probability of each coin being tossed heads can be described as 1/2 × 1/2, or 1/4, or 25%.

This same process can be applied to Mendel's experiments. In Mendel's second set of experiments, the F_1 generation was allowed to self-pollinate. If the parent plant was heterozygous for flower color (*Pp*), the chance that the egg has a *p* allele is 1/2 and the chance that the sperm has the *p* allele is 1/2, so the overall probability of the offspring having white flowers (*pp*) is 1/4.

Section 3

Meiosis

The Steps of Meiosis

Meiosis is the process by which sex cells are made. Meiosis produces cells which contain half of the usual number of chromosomes. Meiosis begins after the replication of chromosomes, followed by two cell divisions called meiosis I and meiosis II. The end results are shown in **Figure B.** The result is four cells which have half the original number of chromosomes. The process of meiosis occurs in the following series of cell phases:

Interphase

Before meiosis begins, the chromosomes in a cell replicate, forming sister chromatids for each chromosome.

Meiosis I

Prophase I: Homologous chromosomes come together as pairs. During this phase, homologous chromosomes may exchange information by crossing-over. The cell then prepares for division.

Metaphase I: The homologous chromosomes line up in the center of the cell.
Anaphase I: Homologous chromosomes are pulled away from each other to opposite sides of the cell.
Telophase I: The cell begins to divide, with each new cell containing a set of chromosomes which still have sister chromatids.

Meiosis II

During the second stage of meiosis, both resulting cells undergo a second division. This cell division includes the separation of each sister chromatid, which are now individual chromosomes. The result is four cells, each with their own set of chromosomes.

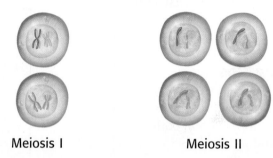

Meiosis I   Meiosis II

Figure B   *This figure shows the results of meiosis I and meiosis II for an organism with four chromosomes.*

Mitochondrial DNA

Mitochondria, which are the organelles responsible for ATP production, have their own DNA. The genetic material found in mitochondria is called mitochondrial DNA, or mtDNA, and is separate from the DNA found in the nucleus of a cell. Scientists have discovered that in most organisms, all of an offspring's mitochondria are received from its mother. Therefore, the mtDNA of an offspring is the same as its mother's. The genetic material in an organism's mitochondria can be traced along its maternal lines over several generations.

Internet Resources

SciLinks is maintained by the National Science Teachers Association to provide you and your students with interesting, up-to-date links that will enrich your classroom presentation of the chapter.

Visit **www.scilinks.org** and enter the SciLinks code for more information about the topic listed.

Topic: Heredity; Dominant and
    Recessive Traits
SciLinks code: HY70738; HY70423

Topic: Meiosis; Genetic Diseases,
    Screening, Counseling
SciLinks code: HY70935; HY70651

Topic: Genotypes; Phenotypes
SciLinks code: HY70664; HY71135

6 Chapter Preview

🗂 **Chapter Pretest**
Use the Chapter Pretest in the Chapter Resource File to determine the prior knowledge of your students. The Test Doctors and diagnostic teaching tips in the Teacher Notes pages will help you tailor your instruction to your students' specific needs.

Improving Comprehension

Use the Graphic Organizer on this page of the Student Edition to introduce the topics that are covered in this chapter, to summarize the chapter material, or to show students how to make combination notes.

Teaching Tips

• Remind students that combination notes provide a way to express information in both words and pictures.

• Remind students that the pictures on the right side of the chart are graphic representations of the information on the left.

LS Logical

Improving Comprehension

Graphic Organizers are important visual tools that can help you organize information and improve your reading comprehension. The Graphic Organizer below is called *combination notes*. Instructions for creating other types of Graphic Organizers are located in the **Study Skills** section of the Appendix.

How to Make Combination Notes

① Draw a table like the one shown below. Draw the columns to be as long as you want them to be.

② Write the topic of your notes in the section at the top of the table.

③ In the left column, write important phrases or sentences about the topic. In the right column, draw diagrams or pictures that illustrate the information in the left column.

When to Use Combination Notes

Combination notes let you express scientific information in words and pictures at the same time. Use combination notes to express information that a picture could help explain. The picture could be a diagram, a sketch, or another useful visual representation of the written information in your notes.

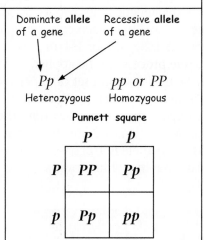

Heredity

- Gregor Mendel helped establish the basics of modern genetics.

- Mendel discovered that an offspring inherits two **alleles** for each gene, one allele from each parent.

- Through **meiosis** and sexual reproduction, genetic material combines.

- **Punnett squares** are used to predict the possible **genotypes** for a particular combination of genes.

You Try It!

This Reading Strategy can also be used within the chapter that you are about to read. Practice making your own *combination notes* as directed in the Reading Strategies for Section ② and Section ③. Record your work in your **Science Journal**.

Using Other Graphic Organizers

Students can practice using a variety of Graphic Organizers while reading this chapter. The following Graphic Organizers may also be useful in this chapter.

A **process chart** can be used to describe Mendel's first experiments and their results, described in Section 1. A **process chart** also can be used to illustrate the steps of meiosis, introduced in Section 3.

A **concept map** can be used to describe the structure of body cells and sex cells, explained in Section 3.

Instructions for creating these Graphic Organizers are located on pp. 583–591 of the Appendix.

Unpacking the Standards

The information below "unpacks" the standards by breaking them down into basic parts. The higher-level, academic vocabulary is highlighted and defined to help you understand the language of the standards. "What It Means" restates the standards as simply as possible.

California Standard	Academic Vocabulary	What It Means
7.2.b Students know **sexual** reproduction produces offspring that inherit half their genes from each parent.	**sexual** (SEK shoo uhl) having to do with sex	Offspring that are produced through sexual reproduction get half of their genetic material from one parent and half of their genetic material from the other parent.
7.2.c Students know an inherited trait can be determined by one or more genes.		A feature that is passed from parent to offspring can be caused by one gene or by the interaction of two or more genes.
7.2.d Students know plant and animal cells contain many thousands of different genes and typically have two copies of every gene. The two copies (or alleles) of the gene may or may not be **identical,** and one may be dominant in determining the phenotype while the other is recessive.	**identical** (ie DEN ti kuhl) being exactly the same	Plant and animal cells have many different genes and usually have two copies of each gene. The two copies of the gene, called alleles, may be the same or may be different. One of the two copies may be more important than the other in causing the features of the plant or animal.
7.2.e Students know DNA (deoxyribonucleic acid) is the genetic material of living organisms and is **located** in the chromosomes of each cell.	**located** (LOH KAYT id) to be in a certain place	DNA is the material that determines what traits are passed from one generation of living things to the next. DNA is found in the chromosomes of each cell.

Unpacking the Standards

Use the following information with the *What It Means* in the Student Edition to help students understand why studying each standard is important.

Why It Matters
Sexual reproduction is responsible for the variety that exists between individuals in a single species.
Understanding that traits are not always the product of one gene is important in understanding the field of genetics.
To understand the complex principles of heredity, one must be familiar with the vocabulary of science. Also, one should know that most organisms have more than one copy of each gene and that the interaction of these copies determines the trait expressed.
DNA is the blueprint for running the cell's chemical manufacturing system and for making another copy of itself. Any change in the DNA can affect the products or offspring of the cell.

Words with Multiple Meanings

Words that have both common and scientific meanings can be confusing to students. The following table identifies one of those words that are used in this chapter.

Term	Common meaning	Scientific meaning
egg	a thin-shelled product from a bird that is used in cooking	a sex cell produced by a female

Practice Have students complete the sentences below to help them understand how the scientific and common meanings of the word *egg* can differ.

a. The recipe calls for only one ____ yolk. (egg)

b. A sperm is the male sex cell that fertilizes a female's ____. (egg)

Have students write one definition for the common meaning of the word and one definition for the scientific meaning.

Chapter Overview

Tell students that this chapter will introduce heredity—the passing of traits from parents to offspring. The chapter describes how scientists study heredity and the role of sexual reproduction in inheritance.

MISCONCEPTION
**/// ALERT **

Meiosis

Identify It! Students may have misconceptions about the process of meiosis, such as confusing meiosis with mitosis. Ask students to compare meiosis with mitosis. (Students may mistakenly answer that both are the same process, except that meiosis occurs in sexually-reproducing organisms, while mitosis does not.)

Correct It! Illustrate the differences between mitosis and meiosis by drawing the steps of each process on the board. As you draw the steps of each process, have students point out the differences between the two, including in which types of cells each process occurs.

Assess It! Organize students into groups of 4 or 5. Give each group a set of index cards. Each index card should have a sketch of one step of meiosis. You may wish to have students make their own sets of meiosis index cards. Ask students to place the cards in order, and then take turns explaining the process of meiosis in their own words.

6

Heredity

The Big Idea

Heredity is the passing of the instructions for traits from one generation to the next.

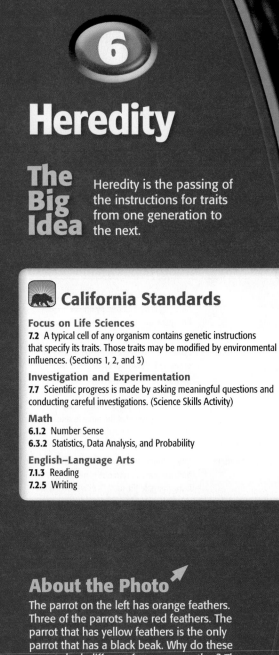

California Standards

Focus on Life Sciences

7.2 A typical cell of any organism contains genetic instructions that specify its traits. Those traits may be modified by environmental influences. (Sections 1, 2, and 3)

Investigation and Experimentation

7.7 Scientific progress is made by asking meaningful questions and conducting careful investigations. (Science Skills Activity)

Math

6.1.2 Number Sense
6.3.2 Statistics, Data Analysis, and Probability

English–Language Arts

7.1.3 Reading
7.2.5 Writing

About the Photo

The parrot on the left has orange feathers. Three of the parrots have red feathers. The parrot that has yellow feathers is the only parrot that has a black beak. Why do these parrots look different from one another? The colors of their feathers and of their beaks were determined before they were born. These are just two of the many traits determined by genetic information. Genetic information is passed on from parents to their offspring.

Organize

Key-Term Fold

Before you read this chapter, create the FoldNote entitled "Key-Term Fold." Write a key term from the chapter on each tab of the key-term fold. As you read the chapter, write the definition of each key term under the appropriate tab.

Instructions for creating FoldNotes are located in the Study Skills section on p. 581 of the Appendix.

California Standards Alignment

Focus on Life Sciences

7.2.b Students know sexual reproduction produces offspring that inherit half their genes from each parent. **pp. 189–191, 193–195, 198–200**

7.2.c Students know an inherited trait can be determined by one or more genes. **pp. 184–185, 187, 198–201**

7.2.d Students know plant and animal cells contain many thousands of different genes and typically have two copies of every gene. The two copies (or alleles) of the gene may or may not be identical, and one may be dominant in determining the phenotype while the other is recessive. **pp. 173–174, 176–183, 186–187, 194, 195, 198, 199, 200, 201**

7.2.e Students know DNA (deoxyribonucleic acid) is the genetic material of living organisms and is located in the chromosomes of each cell. **pp. 188, 198, 193, 199, 201**

Investigation and Experimentation

7.7.c Communicate the logical connection among hypotheses, science concepts, tests conducted, data collected, and conclusions drawn from the scientific evidence. **pp. 182, 194, 195**

7.7.d Construct scale models, maps, and appropriately labeled diagrams to communicate scientific knowledge (e.g., motion of Earth's plates and cell structure). **pp. 181, 194, 195**

7.7.e Communicate the steps and results from an investigation in written reports and oral presentations. **p. 196**

Math Standards

Number Sense 6.1.2 Interpret and use ratios in different contexts (e.g., batting averages, miles per hour) to show the relative sizes of two quantities, using appropriate notations (a/b, a to b, a:b). **pp. 178–179, 199**

Explore Activity

 15 min

Modeling Traits

In this activity, you will model how the combination of different traits creates variation.

Procedure

1. Your teacher will gather three boxes. Then, your teacher will place five hats in the first box, five gloves in the seond box, and five scarves in the third box.

2. Your teacher will allow students to select items from each box without looking in the boxes. Record the three items, or "outfit," each student chooses. Replace the clothes in the appropriate boxes. Repeat this process until each student in the class has picked an outfit.

Analysis

7.2.d

3. Were any two outfits exactly alike? Did you see all possible combinations? Explain your answer.

4. Choose a partner. Using your outfits, how many different combinations could you make by giving a third person one of your hats, gloves, and scarves? How is this process like parents passing traits to their children?

5. Based on what you have learned in this activity, why do you think parents often have children who look very different from each other?

Statistics, Data Analysis, and Probability 6.3.2 Use data to estimate the probability of future events (e.g., batting averages or number of accidents per mile driven). **pp. 182–183, 199**

English–Language Arts Standards

Reading 7.1.3 Use a variety of effective and coherent organizational patterns, including comparison and contrast; organization by categories; and arrangement by spatial order, order of importance, or climactic order. **pp. 182–183, 199**

Writing 7.2.5 2.5 Write summaries of reading materials: (a) Include the main ideas and most significant details; (b) Use the student's own words, except for quotations; (c) Reflect underlying meaning, not just the superficial details. **p. 199**

Would You Believe ... ?

It all started in ancient China. A fisherman caught an unusual carp. Usually these small freshwater fish are drab colored, but this one had a pale golden hue. It was too pretty to eat, so the fisherman took the fish home as a pet.

Months later, the fisherman caught another gold-tinged carp. He kept the two fish in the same bowl. When the fish reproduced, the offspring were even more brightly colored than their parents. The first goldfish had been born!

In the years that followed, throughout China began breeding the new, colorful fish. Many became goldfish, choosing only the most...

for their favorite fish. With each generation of hatchlings, the fish looked more and more distinctive. By 1500 CE, when the first shipments of goldfish arrived in Japan, goldfish no longer resembled carp. In fact, they were so regal looking that the commoners in Japan were forbidden to keep them as pets.

Without knowing it, these early goldfish breeders were using the principles of genetics to create many new kinds of goldfish.

Chapter Starter Transparency
Use this transparency to help students begin thinking about heredity.

Explore Activity 15 min

Teacher Notes

This activity demonstrates that combining traits can result in variability (covers standard 7.2.d).

Materials for Each Group
- boxes, 3
- hats, 5
- gloves, 5
- scarves, 5

Safety Caution

Infestations of head lice are a common problem in schools. Teachers may want to instruct students to pick hats, but to not wear the hats. Jackets and sweatshirts could be substituted for hats in this exercise. Clean clothing should be provided for each student to use for this activity.

Answers

3. Answers may vary. There should be many different combinations. It is not likely that students will see all of the possible combinations.

4. Sample answer: Eight new combinations (taken from the outfits of the two "parents") would be possible for the third person ("offspring"). This process is similar to inheritance because you are choosing combinations of hats, scarves, and gloves randomly. By combining the traits (outfits) of two "parents" (partners), there are many possible combinations of traits in the "offspring" (third person).

5. Sample answer: The number of possible genetic combinations is huge because we have so many genes. Each child has a different combination of the parents' genes.

Differentiated Datasheets
A **BASIC**, B **GENERAL**, C **ADVANCED**

Also editable on the
Holt Lab Generator CD-ROM

Preteach

Reviewing Prior Knowledge

Have students study **Figure 2** and to describe what they think the figure is trying to illustrate. Then, ask students to describe how self-pollination differs from cross-pollination. (Self-pollination occurs when pollen from one plant fertilizes the flower of the same plant to make a new plant. Cross-pollination occurs when pollen from one plant fertilizes the flower on a different plant.)

 Bellringer

Have students focus on standard 7.2.d by asking them to write a few sentences describing how they think traits are passed from parents to their offspring and why they think siblings look alike but are not always identical. (Sample answer: Parents carry two copies of each gene, and each parent passes one copy of each gene to their offspring. Offspring express different traits depending on the combination of the genes they receive from their parents.)

 Bellringer Transparency

Motivate

ACTIVITY

Trait Trends   Create a large table to record the number of students with the following traits: widow's peak, ability to roll tongue, and attached earlobes. Have pairs of students enter data for each other by adding tick marks on the table. Ask students if they can see any trends in the class data.

LS Kinesthetic/Interpersonal

Mendel and His Peas

Key Concept   The work of Gregor Mendel explains the rules of heredity and is the foundation of modern genetics.

What You Will Learn
- Heredity is the passing of genetic traits from parent to offspring.
- Gregor Mendel's experiments with pea plants led to the discovery of dominant and recessive traits.

Why It Matters
Heredity explains why you have many of your traits.

Vocabulary
- heredity
- dominant trait
- recessive trait

READING STRATEGY

Summarizing   Read this section silently. In pairs, take turns summarizing the material. Stop to discuss ideas and words that seem confusing.

▶ Imagine a puppy. The puppy has long, floppy ears like his mother has, and the puppy has dark brown fur like his father has. How did the puppy get these traits? The passing of traits from parents to offspring is called **heredity.** About 100 years ago, Gregor Mendel performed experiments about heredity that helped establish the field of *genetics*. Genetics is the study of how traits are inherited.

Before Mendel

Offspring often look a little like their mother and a little like their father. This observation led people to think that each trait of the offspring was the result of the traits of both parents mixed together. The idea that each trait of the offspring is a mixture of traits of both parents is called *blending inheritance*. According to the idea of blending inheritance, if a brown rabbit mates with a white rabbit, the offspring would be tan. And if a tan rabbit mates with a brown rabbit, the offspring would be dark tan.

However, when a brown rabbit and a white rabbit mate, the offspring often have brown fur. And when two brown rabbits mate, a white rabbit might be born. So, blending inheritance is not a good explanation of heredity. The experiments of Gregor Mendel provide evidence that blending inheritance is incorrect for many traits. Mendel's results have changed the way people think about inheritance.

Standards Check   What is blending inheritance?   **7.2.d**

Gregor Mendel's Work

Gregor Mendel, shown in **Figure 1,** was born in 1822 in Heinzendorf, Austria. Mendel grew up on a farm and learned a lot about flowers and fruit trees. When he was 21 years old, Mendel entered a monastery. A monastery is a place where monks study religion. The monks also taught science and performed scientific experiments.

As a monk, Mendel put most of his energy into research. Mendel decided to study only one kind of organism. Garden peas were a good choice because they grow quickly and because there are many varieties.

Figure 1   *Gregor Mendel discovered the principles of heredity while studying pea plants.*

Answer to Standards Check

Blending inheritance is the theory that each of the parent's trait are mixed together in the offspring.
7.2.d (supporting)

Self-Pollinating Peas

Pea plants, like many flowering plants, have both male and female reproductive structures. Many flowering plants reproduce through cross-pollination. In *cross-pollination*, sperm (in pollen) from one plant fertilizes the eggs (in an ovule) of a different plant. Pollen from one plant may be carried by insects, bats, birds, or other organisms to a flower on a different plant. Pollen can also be carried by the wind from one flower to another.

Most flowering plants cross-pollinate and therefore need another plant to reproduce. But a pea plant can reproduce through cross-pollination or self-pollination. In *self-pollination*, sperm from one plant fertilizes the eggs of the same plant.

What happens when pea plants self-pollinate? When a *true-breeding plant* self-pollinates, its offspring will have the same trait as the parent. For example, a true-breeding plant that has purple flowers will always have offspring that have purple flowers. Self-pollination is important because Mendel was able to grow true-breeding plants for his experiments. **Figure 2** shows flowers reproducing by cross-pollination and by self-pollination.

heredity (hee RED i tee) the passing of genetic traits from parent to offspring

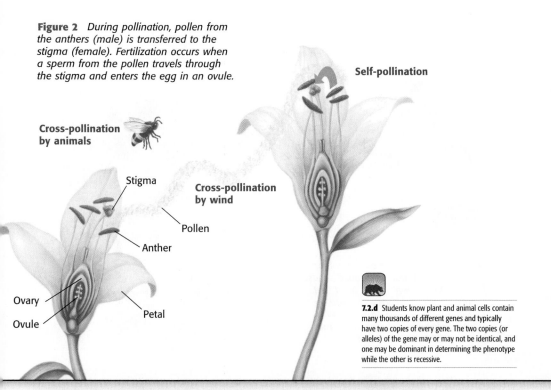

Figure 2 *During pollination, pollen from the anthers (male) is transferred to the stigma (female). Fertilization occurs when a sperm from the pollen travels through the stigma and enters the egg in an ovule.*

Self-pollination

Cross-pollination by animals

Stigma

Cross-pollination by wind

Pollen

Anther

Ovary

Petal

Ovule

7.2.d Students know plant and animal cells contain many thousands of different genes and typically have two copies of every gene. The two copies (or alleles) of the gene may or may not be identical, and one may be dominant in determining the phenotype while the other is recessive.

Discussion

Scientific Methods Have students identify the use of scientific methods in Mendel's work.

- **Ask a question:** How are traits inherited?

- **Form a hypothesis:** Inheritance has a pattern.

- **Test the hypothesis:** Cross true-breeding plants and offspring.

- **Analyze the results:** Identify patterns in inherited traits.

- **Draw conclusions:** Traits are inherited in predictable patterns.

- **Communicate the results:** Publish the results for peer review.

Ask students, "Why weren't Mendel's ideas accepted for so many years?" (because of problems with the last step—other scientists could not easily access or understand his findings) **LS** Logical/Verbal

Demonstration

Flower Dissection Obtain a flower that has anthers and a stigma, such as a pea flower, a tulip, or a lily. Use caution because pollen can stain clothing and cause allergic reactions. Dissect the flower, and show students the anthers and the stigma. Ask students if this flower could self-pollinate. (yes; Because it has both anthers and a stigma) Demonstrate how Mendel removed the anthers of his flowers and then used a small brush to transfer pollen from plant to plant. **LS** Visual/Verbal

Using the Figure

Flower Pollination Tell students to look at **Figure 3.** Explain to students that flowers must have anthers to complete self-pollination. Answer to caption question: Mendel removed anthers from the plant that produced round seeds so that he could fertilize the plant with pollen from a plant that produced wrinkled seeds.

dominant trait (DAHM uh nuhnt TRAYT) the trait observed in the first generation when parents that have different traits are bred

recessive trait (ri SES iv TRAYT) a trait that reappears in the second generation after disappearing in the first generation when parents with different traits are bred

Characteristics

Mendel studied one characteristic at a time. A *characteristic* is a feature that has different forms in a population. For example, hair color is a characteristic in humans. The different forms, or colors, such as brown or red hair, are called *traits*. Mendel used plants that had different traits for each of the characteristics he studied. For instance, for the characteristic of flower color, he chose plants that had purple flowers and plants that had white flowers. Mendel also studied other characteristics such as seed shape, pod color, and plant height.

Mix and Match

Mendel was careful to use plants that were true breeding for each of the traits he was studying. By choosing these plants, he would know what to expect if his plants were to self-pollinate. He decided to find out what would happen if he bred, or crossed, two plants that had different traits of a single characteristic. To be sure the plants cross-pollinated, he removed the anthers of one plant so that the plant could not self-pollinate. Then, he used pollen from another plant to fertilize the plant, as **Figure 3** shows. This step allowed Mendel to select which plants would be crossed to produce offspring.

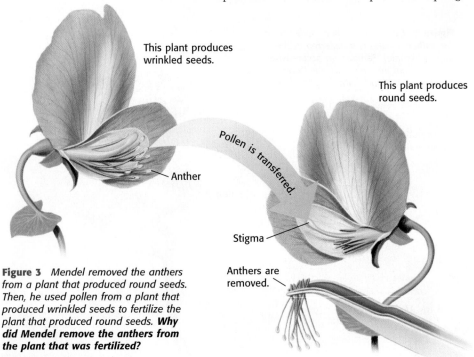

This plant produces wrinkled seeds.

This plant produces round seeds.

Pollen is transferred.

Anther

Stigma

Anthers are removed.

Figure 3 *Mendel removed the anthers from a plant that produced round seeds. Then, he used pollen from a plant that produced wrinkled seeds to fertilize the plant that produced round seeds.* **Why did Mendel remove the anthers from the plant that was fertilized?**

MISCONCEPTION ALERT

Recessive Traits Students may think that recessive traits are rare. Discuss with students that either dominant or recessive traits may be more common in a population. For example, blond hair (a recessive trait) is very common in parts of Scandinavia. Conversely, dominant traits are not always the most common.

For example, the trait for having six fingers on one hand is dominant. Have students research other dominant traits that are not common. Some examples are Marfan syndrome and Huntington's disease (both dominant traits), and the high frequency of sickle-cell anemia (a recessive trait) in some African populations.

Mendel's First Experiments

In his first experiments, Mendel crossed pea plants to study seven different characteristics. In each cross, Mendel used plants that were true breeding for different traits for each characteristic. For example, he crossed plants that had purple flowers with plants that had white flowers. The offspring from such a cross are called *first-generation plants*. All of the first-generation plants in this cross had purple flowers. Are you surprised by the results? What happened to the trait for white flowers?

Mendel got similar results for each cross. One trait was always present in the first generation, and the other trait seemed to disappear. Mendel chose to call the trait that appeared the **dominant trait.** Because the other trait seemed to fade into the background, Mendel called it the **recessive trait.** To *recede* means "to go away or back off." To find out what might have happened to the recessive trait, Mendel decided to do another set of experiments.

Mendel's Second Experiments

Mendel allowed the first-generation plants to self-pollinate. **Figure 4** shows what happened when a first-generation plant that had purple flowers was allowed to self-pollinate. As you can see, the recessive trait for white flowers reappeared in the second generation.

Mendel did this same experiment on seven different characteristics. In each case, some of the second-generation plants had the recessive trait.

Standards Check Describe the second set of experiments performed by Mendel. 🐻 **7.2.d**

Parent Generation

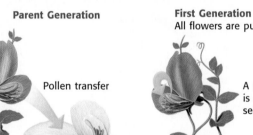

Pollen transfer

First Generation
All flowers are purple.

A mature plant is allowed to self-pollinate.

Second Generation
For every three plants that have purple flowers, there is one plant that has white flowers.

Figure 4 *Mendel used the pollen from a plant that had purple flowers to fertilize a plant that had white flowers. Then, he allowed the offspring to self-pollinate.*

Close

Standards Focus

This **Standards Focus** provides you with a quick way to **assess, reteach,** and **re-assess** one or more concepts in the section.

Assess

1. What did Mendel call the trait that appeared in all of his first-generation plants? (the dominant trait) **7.2.d**

2. In Mendel's experiments, all first-generation plants had purple flowers, but second-generation plants also had white flowers. What did this lead Mendel to hypothesize? (Each plant had two alleles for each characteristic.) **7.2.d**

 Reteach

Mendel's Experiments Have students re-enact Mendel's experiments using cups (to represent a plant), colored buttons or chips (to represent various alleles), and colored strips of paper (to represent visible traits). Have students perform crosses by putting alleles from "parent" cups into "offspring" cups, deciding which traits would then become visible. **LS** Kinesthetic/Logical **7.2.d**

 Re-Assess

The Missing Trait Have students create a skit or comic strip showing how Mendel solved the "mystery" of the disappearing trait in his experiments. Encourage students to be creative. **LS** Interpersonal/Visual **7.2.d**

Answer to Math Practice

The ratio of nougat to caramel-filled chocolates is 18:6, or 18/6, which can be reduced to 3/1. This fraction can be rewritten as 3:1 or 3 to 1.

Answer to Standards Check

A ratio is a relationship between two different numbers that is often expressed as a fraction.

Understanding Ratios

A ratio is a way to compare two numbers. Look at **Table 1.** The ratio of plants that have purple flowers to plants that have white flowers can be written as 705 to 224 or 705:224. This ratio can be reduced, or simplified, by dividing the first number by the second as follows:

$$\frac{705}{224} = \frac{3.15}{1}$$

which can be written as a ratio of 3.15:1. This means that for every 3 plants that have purple flowers, about 1 plant will most likely have white flowers. Try this problem:

A box of chocolates has 18 nougat-filled chocolates and 6 caramel-filled chocolates. What is the ratio of nougat-filled chocolates to caramel-filled chocolates?

Ratios in Mendel's Experiments

Mendel then decided to count the number of plants that had each trait and that turned up in the second generation. He hoped that this might help him explain his results. Take a look at Mendel's results shown in **Table 1.**

As you can see, the recessive trait did not show up as often as the dominant trait. Mendel decided to figure out the ratio of dominant traits to recessive traits. A *ratio* is a relationship between two different numbers that is often expressed as a fraction. Calculate the dominant-to-recessive ratio for each characteristic. (If you need help, look at the Math Practice at left.) Do you notice anything interesting about the ratios? Round to the nearest whole number. Are the ratios all the same, or are they different?

Standards Check What is a ratio? **7.2.d**

Table 1	Mendel's Results			
Characteristic	**Dominant traits**		**Recessive traits**	**Ratio**
Flower color	705 purple		224 white	3.15:1
Seed color	6,002 yellow		2,001 green	?
Seed shape	5,474 round		1,850 wrinkled	?
Pod color	428 green		152 yellow	?
Pod shape	882 smooth		299 bumpy	?
Flower position	651 along stem		207 at tip	?
Plant height	787 tall		277 short	?

Special Education Students
Materials For Each Group

- poster board, 1
- representations (such as construction paper shapes or squares) of one dominant trait from Table 1 (17)
- representations of the matching recessive trait (5)
- glue or clear tape

Poster of Mendel's Experiments Give small groups of students construction paper shapes to represent dominant traits from Table 1 and separate shapes for the matching recessive traits. Have small groups create a poster by gluing or taping one dominant trait and one recessive trait at the top. Across the middle, glue or tape four dominant traits to show the first generation. Under each of the items in the middle, glue or tape a set of three dominant traits and one recessive trait to show the second-generation plants. **LS** Visual/Kinesthetic

Gregor Mendel—Gone but Not Forgotten

Mendel realized that his results could only be explained if each plant had two sets of instructions for each characteristic. Therefore, he concluded that each parent gives one set of instructions to the offspring. The offspring's traits are then determined by the dominant set of instructions.

In 1865, Mendel published his findings. But good ideas are sometimes overlooked or misunderstood at first. It was not until after his death, more than 30 years later, that Mendel's work was widely recognized. Once Mendel's ideas were rediscovered and understood, the door was opened to modern genetics. Genetic research, as shown in **Figure 5,** is one of the fastest changing fields in science today.

Figure 5 *This researcher is continuing the work started by Gregor Mendel more than 100 years ago.*

SECTION Review

 7.2.d

Summary

- Heredity is the passing of traits from parents to offspring.
- Before Mendel's ideas were accepted, people explained inheritance as the blending of traits from each parent.
- Gregor Mendel's experiments using pea plants eventually changed the way people thought about heredity.
- When parents with different traits are bred, dominant traits are always present in the first generation. Recessive traits are not visible in the first generation but reappear in the second generation.
- Mendel found a 3:1 ratio of dominant-to-recessive traits in the second generation.
- Mendel's ideas are the foundation of modern genetics.

Using Vocabulary

1. Use *heredity, dominant trait,* and *recessive trait* in separate sentences.

Understanding Concepts

2. **Summarizing** Explain the difference between self-pollination and cross-pollination.

3. **Comparing** What is the difference between a trait and a characteristic? Give one example of each.

4. **Describing** Describe Mendel's first set of experiments.

5. **Describing** Describe Mendel's second set of experiments.

Critical Thinking

6. **Predicting Consequences** If Mendel had used plants that were not true breeding, do you think he would have discovered dominant and recessive traits? Explain your answer.

7. **Applying Concepts** Cats may have normal or curly ears. A curly-eared cat mated with a normal-eared cat, and all of the kittens had curly ears. Are curly ears a dominant or recessive trait? Explain your answer.

Math Skills

8. **Number Sense** Of the 52 students eating lunch, 17 students are eating a sandwich. The rest of the students are eating pizza. What is the ratio of students who are eating sandwiches to students eating pizza?

Challenge

9. **Predicting Consequences** If blending inheritance explained how flowers inherit traits, would you expect to see more flower colors? Explain your answer.

Internet Resources

For a variety of links related to this chapter, go to www.scilinks.org
Topic: Heredity; Dominant and Recessive Traits
SciLinks code: HY70738; HY70423

5. During Mendel's second experiments, he allowed the plants that were the offspring from his first experiments to self-pollinate. Most of the second-generation plants had the dominant trait, but some of the offspring had the recessive trait.

7.2.d (mastering)

6. Sample answer: If Mendel had used plants that were not true breeding, the dominant trait would not have been as clear for each characteristic, and he would not have gotten a clear ratio of 3:1. The concept of dominant and recessive may have remained hidden for a longer period of time.

7.2.d (exceeding)

7. Curly ears are the dominant trait because it is the trait that is represented in the first generation.

7.2.d (mastering)

8. The ratio of students eating sandwiches to students eating pizza is 17:35. **7.2.d** (exceeding)

9. If blending inheritance described how flowers inherited traits, each time two flowers with different traits had offspring, those two traits would be blended into one trait. Over time, there would be fewer and fewer traits. **7.2.d** (exceeding)

	Section Review Standards Guide		
	Supporting	Mastering	Exceeding
7.2.d	2, 3	1, 4, 5, 7	6, 8

Answer to questions on student p. 178

All the ratios are about the same. They can be rounded to 3:1.

Answers to Section Review

1. Sample answer: Heredity is the passing of traits from parents to their offspring. A dominant trait is a trait that is present in the first generation when parents with different traits produce offspring. A recessive trait is a trait that is not present in the first generation, but can reappear in the second generation. **7.2.d** (mastering)

2. Self-pollination occurs when pollen from a particular plant is deposited on a stigma from the same plant. Cross-pollination occurs when the pollen and stigma are from two different plants. **7.2.d** (supporting)

3. A characteristic is something that has different forms in a population, and a trait is each one of the possible forms. For example, eye color is a characteristic in humans, and brown eyes, green eyes, and blue eyes are all possible traits. **7.2.d** (supporting)

4. During Mendel's first experiments, he crossed two plants that were true breeding for different traits. The offspring always had the dominant trait. **7.2.d** (mastering)

Section Resources

- Directed Reading
  A **BASIC** (Also in Spanish), B **GENERAL**
- Interactive Reader and Study Guide
- Section Quiz **GENERAL** (Also in Spanish)
- Section Review **GENERAL** (Also in Spanish)
- Vocabulary and Section Summary
  A **BASIC** (Also in Spanish), B **GENERAL**

SECTION 2

Preteach

Reviewing Prior Knowledge

Ask student volunteers to read the red and blue headings in the section aloud. Then, ask students what they think the section is about. Finally, ask students what they already know about traits and the inheritance of traits.

 Bellringer

Have students focus on standard 7.2.d by asking them why Mendel proposed that the pea plants he used in his experiments contained two sets of instructions, one for each characteristic. (He realized the only way to explain why some characteristics were found only in the second generation was if each parent had two sets of instructions and passed only one set to its offspring.)

 Bellringer Transparency

Motivate

Demonstration

Ratios To review fractions and ratios, display three pennies and one nickel, and then ask students the following questions: "How many coins are there in all?" (4) "What fraction of the coins are pennies?" (3/4) "What fraction of the coins are nickels?" (1/4) "What is the ratio of pennies to nickels?" (3:1) **LS Visual/Verbal**

Answer to Standards Check

A gene contains instructions for an inherited trait. Different versions of a gene are called *alleles.* **7.2.d** (mastering)

Teaching Transparency: L19 Punnett Squares

SECTION 2

What You Will Learn

- Genes exist in multiple forms called alleles.
- An organism's phenotype is affected by the organism's genotype.
- Punnett squares are used to predict the possible genotypes of the offspring from particular parents.
- Patterns of inheritance can be more complicated than one gene influencing one trait.

Why It Matters

Understanding genes enables you to understand why you have many of your traits.

Vocabulary

- gene
- genotype
- allele
- probability
- phenotype

READING STRATEGY

Graphic Organizer In your **Science Journal,** create Combination Notes that explain genes, alleles, phenotype, and genotype both in words and in pictures or diagrams.

gene (JEEN) one set of instructions for an inherited trait

allele (uh LEEL) one of the alternative forms of a gene that governs a characteristic, such as hair color

phenotype (FEE noh TIEP) an organism's appearance or other detectable characteristic

7.2.c Students know an inherited trait can be determined by one or more genes.
7.2.d Students know plant and animal cells contain many thousands of different genes and typically have two copies of every gene. The two copies (or alleles) of the gene may or may not be identical, and one may be dominant in determining the phenotype while the other is recessive.

Traits and Inheritance

Key Concept Genes are the instructions for inherited traits.

▶ What did Mendel's experiments tell him about how traits are passed from parents to offspring?

A Great Idea

Mendel knew from his experiments with pea plants that there must be two sets of instructions for each characteristic. The first-generation plants carried the instructions for both the dominant trait and the recessive trait. Scientists now call these instructions for an inherited trait **genes.** Each parent gives one set of genes to the offspring. The offspring then has two versions, or forms, of the same gene for every characteristic—one from each parent. The different versions (often dominant and recessive) of a gene are known as **alleles.** Dominant alleles are shown as capital letters. A single dominant allele masks the expression of the instructions held on a recessive allele. When an organism has a dominant allele, the organism has the dominant trait. Recessive alleles are shown as lowercase letters. An organism has a recessive trait when two copies of the recessive allele are present in the organism.

Standards Check Compare the terms gene and allele. **7.2.d**

Phenotype

Genes affect the traits of offspring. An organism's appearance is known as the organism's **phenotype. Figure 1** shows the possible phenotypes for the characteristic of flower color in pea plants. The pea plants Mendel studied had either purple flowers or white flowers. The phenotypes for seed color are yellow and green. Phenotypes for humans also describe characteristics. For example, you most likely have a phenotype of either curly hair or straight hair.

Figure 1 Purple flowers and white flowers are the two possible phenotypes for the characteristic of flower color in pea plants.

Universal Access · Differentiated Instruction

English Learners

Words with Latin Roots English learners may need help in developing their vocabulary. Tell students that English contains many words from Latin. Write the word *genes* on the board. Explain the origin (Latin) and that the meaning of the Latin word *gene* is "people." Ask students for examples of words they know that may come from the Latin word *gene.* Write their examples on the board. (Students may say *generation, general, genetics*) Discuss the meanings of the words. Then, tell students to search the section for other words that start with *gen* (*genes, genotype, genetic*) Help students see the connections between the words by telling them to use each word in a sentence and to underline the Latin root in each. **LS Verbal**

180 Chapter 6 • Heredity

Genotype

Both inherited alleles together form an organism's **genotype.** Because the allele for purple flowers (*P*) is dominant, only one *P* allele is needed for the plant to have purple flowers. A plant with two dominant or two recessive alleles is said to be *homozygous* (HOH moh ZIE guhs). A plant that has the genotype *Pp* is said to be *heterozygous* (HET uhr OH ZIE guhs).

Punnett Squares

A Punnett square is used to predict the possible genotypes of offspring in a particular cross. **Figure 2** shows a Punnett square for a cross of a true-breeding, purple-flowered plant and a true-breeding, white-flowered plant. The alleles for a true-breeding, purple-flowered plant are written as *PP*. The alleles for a true-breeding, white-flowered plant are written as *pp*. Offspring get one allele from each parent. All of the offspring from this cross will have the same genotype: *Pp*. Because of the dominant allele, *P,* in the genotype, all of the offspring will have purple flowers.

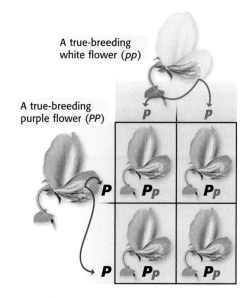

Figure 2 *All of the offspring for this cross have the same genotype—Pp.*

genotype (JEE nuh TIEP) the entire genetic makeup of an organism; *also* the combination of genes for one or more specific traits

Quick Lab

Completing a Punnett Square

1. Draw a square. Divide it into four sections.
2. Write the letters that represent alleles from one parent along the top of the square.
3. Write the letters that represent alleles from the other parent along the side of the square.
4. Fill in each column in the square with the letter on the top of that column.
5. Fill in each row in the square with the letter on the side of that row.
6. The cross shown at right is between two plants that produce round seeds. The genotype for each plant is *Rr*. Round seeds (*R*) are dominant, and wrinkled seeds (*r*) are recessive. Follow the arrows to see how the inside of the square was filled. The resulting alleles inside the square show the possible genotypes for the offspring from this cross.

7.2.d
7.7.d

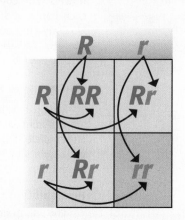

7. What are the possible phenotypes of the offspring from the cross above?

🕐 15 min

Quick Lab

🕐 15 min

Teacher Notes

This activity has students complete and interpret a Punnett square diagram (covers standard 7.2.d and 7.7.d).

Answers

7. The offspring with genotypes *RR* and *Rr* will have round-seed phenotypes. The offspring with the genotype *rr* will have wrinkled-seed phenotypes.

MISCONCEPTION ALERT

Genotype and Phenotype
Students may have trouble grasping that genotype determines phenotype. Ask students to name the possible genotypes for a purple flower of a pea plant. (Students may answer "only *PP*") Explain to students that a pea plant with purple flowers can have *PP* or *Pp* genotypes. Give the students another example. Tell students that the trait for a widow's peak is dominant. On the board, construct a Punnett square diagram between two people who have the genotype *Ww*. Ask students to write each genotype and phenotype resulting from this cross. (*WW, Ww,* and *Ww,* which indicates offspring that have a widow's peak, and *ww,* which indicates offspring that do not have a widow's peak) Then ask students how many possible genotypes there are for each phenotype. (There are two genotypes for the presence of a widow's peak; there is one genotype for absence of a widow's peak.)

CONNECTION ACTIVITY
Math

Probability of Independent Events The probability of two or more independent events is the product of the individual probabilities. For example, the probability of getting heads in a coin toss is 1/2, but the probability of getting heads twice in a row is 1/2 × 1/2, or 1/4. Have students consider the following parent genotypes for pea plants: *PpRr* and *Pprr*. Work out and discuss the probability of each possible combined phenotype. (For example, the probability of a plant with white flowers and round seeds is 1/4 × 1/2 = 1/8.)

Answer to Standards Check

Probability is the mathematical chance that something will happen. **7.2.d** (supporting)

MISCONCEPTION ALERT

The Role of Chance Students' lack of understanding of mathematical probability may block their understanding of the random and independent sorting of genes that occurs during meiosis. Be careful that students do not overextend mathematical probabilities to predict the outcome of single events. It is correct to predict that an average of many outcomes will be similar to, but not exactly match, a probability ratio. Explain to students that the probability of getting heads in a coin toss is 1/2. Ask students which situation can they more accurately predict the results: a single coin toss or the outcome of many coin tosses. (The more tosses, the more accurate the predictions.)

Quick Lab

Exploring Probability **7.2.d** **7.7.c**

In this activity, you will predict the color of fur for the offspring of two guinea pigs. Both parents have brown fur and the genotype *Bb*. The allele for brown fur, *B*, is dominant. The allele for white fur, *b*, is recessive.

1. Stick a **piece of masking tape** on each side of **two quarters.**
2. Label one side with a capital B and the other side with a lowercase b.
3. Toss both coins 10 times. Make note of your results each time.
4. How many times did you get the *bb* combination?
5. What is the probability that the next toss will result in *bb*?
6. What are the chances that the guinea pigs' offspring will have white fur?

🕐 15 min

probability (PRAHB uh BIL uh tee) the likelihood that a possible future event will occur in any given instance of the event

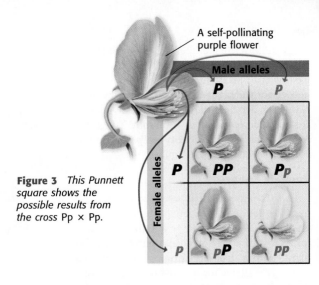

A self-pollinating purple flower

Figure 3 *This Punnett square shows the possible results from the cross Pp × Pp.*

More Evidence for Inheritance

In his second experiments, Mendel allowed the first-generation plants to self-pollinate. **Figure 3** shows a self-pollination cross of a plant that has the genotype *Pp*. What are the possible genotypes of the offspring?

Notice that one square shows the genotype *Pp*, while another shows *pP*. These are exactly the same genotype. The other possible genotypes of the offspring are *PP* and *pp*. The combinations *PP*, *Pp*, and *pP* have the same phenotype—purple flowers. The combinations have the same phenotype because each contains at least one dominant allele (*P*).

Only one combination, *pp*, produces plants that have white flowers. The ratio of dominant alleles to recessive alleles is 3:1, just as Mendel calculated from his data.

What Are the Chances?

Each parent has two alleles for each gene. When these alleles are different, as in *Pp*, offspring are equally likely to receive either allele. Think of a coin toss. There is a 50% chance you'll get heads and a 50% chance you'll get tails. The chance of receiving one allele or another is as random as a coin toss.

Probability

The mathematical chance that something will happen is known as **probability.** Probability is most often written as a fraction or percentage. If you toss a coin, the probability of tossing tails is 1/2—you will get tails half the time.

Standards Check What is probability? 🐻 **7.2.d**

Quick Lab

🕐 15 min

Teacher Notes

This activity helps students predict the probability of particular phenotypes. (covers standard 7.2.d and 7.7.c).

Materials for Each Group
- masking tape, 1 piece
- quarters, 2

Answers

4. Students should get bb about 1/4 or 25% of the time.
5. 1/4 or 25%
6. 1/4 (If brown fur results from genotype *Bb*, then brown fur is dominant, and white fur will result from the genotype *bb*.)

📋 Differentiated Datasheets
A **BASIC**, B **GENERAL**, C **ADVANCED**

Also editable on the Holt Lab Generator CD-ROM

Probability

If you roll a pair of dice, what is the probability that you will roll 2 threes?

Step 1: Count the number of faces on one die. Put this number in the denominator: 6.

Step 2: Count how many ways you can roll a three with one die. Put this number in the numerator: 1/6.

Step 3: To find the probability that you will throw 2 threes, multiply the probability of throwing the first three by the probability of throwing the second three:
$$1/6 \times 1/6 = 1/36.$$

Now It's Your Turn
If you roll a single die, what is the probability that you will roll an even number?

Calculating Probabilities

To find the probability that you will toss two heads in a row, multiply the probability of tossing the first head (1/2) by the probability of tossing the second head (1/2). The probability of tossing two heads in a row is 1/4.

Genotype Probability

To have white flowers, a pea plant must receive a *p* allele from each parent. Each offspring of a *Pp* × *Pp* cross has a 50% chance of receiving either allele from either parent. So, the probability of inheriting two *p* alleles is $1/2 \times 1/2$, which equals 1/4, or 25%. The traits Mendel chose to examine in pea plants are easy to predict because there were only two choices for each trait. Mendel studied sets of traits such as purple or white flowers and round or wrinkled seeds. Look at **Figure 4.** Do you see only two distinct choices for fur color?

Figure 4 *These kittens inherited one allele from their mother for each trait.*

Selective Breeding

Is breeding organisms for a particular characteristic an acceptable practice? Argue for or against selective breeding. Go to **go.hrw.com,** and type in the keyword HY7HERW.

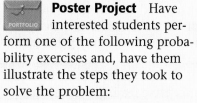

Poster Project Have interested students perform one of the following probability exercises and, have them illustrate the steps they took to solve the problem:

- What is the probability that you will draw two aces from a 52-card deck (without replacing the first card)? ($4/52 \times 3/51 = 12/2652$ or 1/221)

- What is the probability that you will roll two even numbers using a pair of dice? (1/4)

- If you toss a coin, what is the probability that you will toss heads three times in a row? (1/8)

Students should create a poster illustrating the concepts and fractions they used to solve the problem. Encourage students to be creative in their displays.

LS Visual/Logical

Homework

Punnett Squares Have students create Punnett squares for each of the different crosses in Mendel's experiments. Students should include the genotype and phenotype of each parent and each set of possible offspring. **LS** Visual/Logical

SCIENCE HUMOR

Q: What do you get when you cross a crocodile with an abalone?

A: a crocabaloney

Q: What do you get when you cross a bridge with a bicycle?

A: to the other side

CONNECTION ACTIVITY
Chemistry

Round and Wrinkled Explain to students that round seeds may look better, but wrinkled seeds taste sweeter. The dominant allele for seed shape, *R*, causes sugar to be changed into starch (which is a storage molecule for sugar). This change makes the seed round. Seeds with the genotype *rr* do not make or store this starch. Because the sugar has not been changed into starch, the seed tastes sweeter. Then, ask students what they would cross with a pea plant with round seeds (*Rr*) to get some offspring with wrinkled seeds. Have students draw a Punnett square showing their cross. (The *Rr* plant should be crossed with an *rr* plant to get offspring with wrinkled seeds. Students' Punnett squares should reflect this cross.)

LS Logical

 Teaching Transparency:
LINK TO EARTH SCIENCE E87 Desert

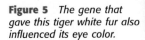
Figure 5 *The gene that gave this tiger white fur also influenced its eye color.*

More About Traits

Things are often more complicated than they first appear to be. Gregor Mendel uncovered the basic principles of how genes are passed from one generation to the next. But as scientists learned more about heredity, they began to find exceptions to Mendel's principles.

One Gene, Many Traits

In the traits that Mendel studied, one gene determined one trait. But sometimes one gene influences more than one trait. An example of this is shown by the white tiger in **Figure 5.** The white fur is caused by a single gene, but this gene influences more than just fur color. If you look closely, you will see that the tiger has blue eyes. Here, the gene that controls fur color also influences eye color.

Genetic disorders can be the result of an error on one allele of one gene. In some cases, the gene may affect many traits. For example, the genetic disorder sickle cell anemia is caused by an error on an allele of a single gene. This gene carries instructions for the structure of a protein in red blood cells. When a person has an allele with the error, she produces a protein with the wrong shape. This protein causes red blood cells to collapse into sickle-shapes, as **Figure 6** shows.

Sickle-shaped blood cells do not carry oxygen through the body as well as normal red blood cells do. Also, sickle-shaped blood cells can become stuck in small blood vessels. Both the ability of the cell to carry oxygen and the ability of the cell to move through the body are affected by the error in the alleles for this one gene.

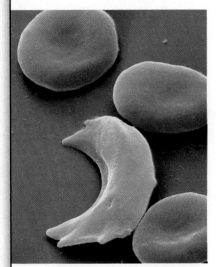
Figure 6 *One out of 500 African Americans has sickle cell anemia, which is caused by a mutation in the alleles for a gene that carries instructions for the protein hemoglobin.*

Figure 7 *At least two genes determine human eye color. That's why many shades of a single color are possible.*

Many Genes, One Trait

Some traits, such as the color of your skin, hair, and eyes, are the result of several genes acting together. Different combinations of alleles result in different eye-color shades, as shown in **Figure 7.** Multiple genes also affect many internal traits. For example, multiple genes influence how people break down food for energy. Because there is not always a one-to-one correspondence between trait and gene, many traits do not have simple patterns of inheritance.

Standards Check Give an example of many genes affecting one trait. 🐘 **7.2.c**

The Importance of Environment

Genes are not the only influences on traits. Traits are also determined by an organism's internal and external environment. For example, height is influenced by nutrition, which is an internal environmental condition. Also, skin color can be influenced by exposure to the sun, which is an external environmental condition.

Sometimes, the environment can have a great effect on an organism's phenotype. Look at the two grasshoppers in **Figure 8.** Would you believe that the grasshoppers are the same species? These grasshoppers develop a different coloration depending on the kind of food available when they are young. Some grasshoppers eat certain plants that make them poisonous to predators. Grasshoppers that eat these plants have a yellow and black coloration. Other grasshoppers that eat different kinds of plants will not be poisonous. They have a green coloration.

Figure 8 *These grasshoppers develop different colorations based on what they eat.*

Discussion

Codominance Caution students not to assume that all inherited traits follow the examples studied by Mendel. For instance, a cross between a red-haired horse and a white-haired horse can produce a horse with both red and white hair. Such a horse is said to have a roan coat. This is an example of codominance—the expression of two phenotypes at the same time within the same organism. Ask students to research other examples of codominance. One example of codominance is the inheritance of blood type in human. **LS** Logical

Cultural Awareness

Lactose Intolerance The protein lactase is an enzyme that allows humans to break down lactose, the sugar in milk. Infants produce a lot of lactase, but most adults produce much less. As a result, many adults cannot digest lactose and therefore have trouble digesting milk. While only about 10% of adult Americans of northern European ancestry are lactose intolerant, about 80% of African American adults and 60% of Hispanic adults are lactose intolerant. Scientists think that human populations that depended on cow's milk as a major food source evolved the ability to continue producing lactase as adults.

Standards Focus

This **Standards Focus** provides you with a quick way to **assess, reteach,** and **re-assess** one or more concepts in the section.

Assess

1. Give an example of how one gene can influence many traits. (Sample answer: Tiger fur and eye color are influenced by the same gene.) **7.2.c**

2. Explain why it may be difficult to tell if a trait, such as human eye color, is dominant or recessive. (Some traits are the result of several genes acting together.) **7.2.c**

Reteach

Rabbit Crosses Tell students that in rabbits, the allele for black fur, *B,* is dominant over the allele for white fur, *b.* Ask the class the following questions: Suppose two black rabbits produce one white rabbit and three black rabbits. What are the genotypes of the parents? (The parents must both have the recessive allele, so they both have the genotype *Bb.*) What are the possible genotypes of all four siblings? (White has genotype *bb,* and black may have *BB* or *Bb.*) **LS** **Verbal/Logical 7.2.d**

Re-Assess

Tracing Traits Ask students to imagine two true-breeding animal parents that have different genetic traits. Have them assign three characteristics, such as tall or short and red nosed or blue nosed, to each parent. Have students label each allele as either dominant or recessive. Then, have students use Punnett squares to determine the possible genotypes and phenotypes in the first and second generations of offspring. **LS** **Visual/Logical 7.2.d**

Figure 9 *Genetic variation explains why these corn snakes are different colors.*

Genetic Variation

How many genes do you have? Would you guess that you have a hundred genes or a thousand genes? Scientists estimate that humans have approximately 30,000 genes. For most genes, a person has two alleles, or copies. Because there are different alleles for most genes, every person has a unique set of alleles. One reason people look different from each other is that they do not have the same set of alleles. The differences in the sets of alleles between individuals in a population is called *genetic variation.*

Genetic variation is found in many populations. An example of genetic variation in a population of corn snakes is shown in **Figure 9.** The phenotypes of the corn snakes differ for the trait of skin color. Because skin color in corn snakes is determined by the alleles for skin color, you can see that there must be a large amount of genetic variation in the population of corn snakes shown in **Figure 9.**

Genes affect many things that are not easy to see. Some genes affect traits inside of your body. All of the enzymes, hormones, and other chemicals that your body makes are affected by genes. Different alleles direct the cells in your body to make different versions of these chemicals. So, even when two people look similar, the alleles for each of their genes may be very different.

Standards Check Approximately how many genes do people have? **7.2.d**

Universal Access · Differentiated Instruction

Special Education Students

Genetic Variation To help students understand genetic variation, divide students into pairs. Have each pair make a list of different traits that they can see between the two of them. For example, if one has black hair and one has red hair, they have different hair-color traits. On the other hand, if they both have brown eyes, they have the same eye-color traits. Allow time for students to share their lists. **LS** **Visual/Interpersonal**

Answer to Standards Check

People have about 30,000 genes. **7.2.d** (mastering)

Summary

- Instructions for an inherited trait are called *genes*. For each gene, there are two alleles, one inherited from each parent. Both alleles make up an organism's genotype.
- An organism's phenotype is the organism's observable characteristics.
- Punnett squares show all possible offspring genotypes.
- Probability can be used to describe possible outcomes in offspring and the likelihood of each outcome.
- Some genes influence more than one trait.
- Some traits are influenced by many genes.
- The environment can influence how genes are expressed.
- Scientists estimate that humans have approximately 30,000 genes.

Using Vocabulary

1 Use *gene* and *allele* in the same sentence.

2 Write an original definition for *genotype* and *phenotype*.

Understanding Concepts

3 **Describing** How are genes and alleles related to genotype and phenotype?

4 **Summarizing** What are three exceptions to Mendel's observations?

5 **Applying** What is the probability of rolling a five on one die three times in a row?

Critical Thinking

6 **Applying Concepts** The allele for a cleft chin, *C*, is dominant in humans. What are the possible results of a cross between parents that have genotypes *Cc* and *cc*?

---

7 **Evaluating Hypotheses** A student in your class believes that the number of genes an organism has is equal to the number of traits that organism has. Evaluate this hypothesis.

INTERPRETING GRAPHICS The Punnett square shows the alleles for fur color in rabbits. Black fur, *B*, is dominant over white fur, *b*. Use the Punnett square below to answer the next two questions.

	B	*B*
b	?	?
b	?	?

8 **Applying Concepts** What are the possible genotypes of the offspring from the cross above?

9 **Applying Concepts** What are the possible phenotypes of the offspring from the cross above?

Math Skills

10 **Making Calculations** In pea plants, the allele for purple flowers (*P*) is dominant. The allele for white flowers (*p*) is recessive. If you cross two flowers that have a genotype of *Pp*, what is the probability that the offspring will inherit a *PP* genotype?

Challenge

11 **Making Inferences** Some wild roses produce bigger flowers than other wild roses do. How could people use the genetic variation in wild roses to create roses that produce large flowers?

Internet Resources

For a variety of links related to this chapter, go to www.scilinks.org

Topic: Genotypes; Phenotypes

SciLinks code: HY70664; HY71135

---

5. $1/6 \times 1/6 \times 1/6 = 1/216$
   7.2.d (supporting)

6. Approximately half of the offspring will have the phenotype of cleft chins (genotypes *Cc*), and half of the offspring will not (genotypes *cc*). **7.2.d** (mastering)

7. Sample answer: The number of genes an organism has does not always equal the number of traits an organism has. Some genes influence more than one trait, and other traits are influenced by more than one gene. **7.2.d** (mastering)

8. *Bb* only **7.2.d** (mastering)

9. All of the offspring will have black fur. **7.2.d** (mastering)

10. $1/2 \times 1/2 = 1/4$ **7.2.d** (exceeding)

11. Sample answer: First, you would select plants with large flowers and cross them with other plants that have large flowers. Then, you would select the offspring from the cross that have large flowers and continue to propagate these plants. You could cultivate the offspring. **7.2.d** (exceeding)

	Section Review Standards Guide		
	Supporting	**Mastering**	**Exceeding**
7.2.c		3, 4	7
7.2.d	5	1, 2, 3, 6, 8, 9	10, 11

Answers to Section Review

1. Sample answer: Alleles are different versions of the same gene. **7.2.d** (mastering)

2. Sample answer: A genotype is the set of alleles an organism has inherited from its parents. A phenotype is the way the genes are expressed physically. **7.2.d** (mastering)

3. The genotype of an organism contains the two alleles for each characteristic. One allele of each pair was inherited from each of the organism's parents. The phenotype of the organism is the way the genotype affects the organism physically. For example, if an organism inherits one dominant allele for brown fur and one recessive allele for white fur, its phenotype will be brown fur. **7.2.c** (mastering)

4. Sample answer: Some exceptions to Mendel's observations include, the fact that one gene can influence many traits, and the fact that many genes can influence one trait. Also, the environment that an organism lives in may affect its traits. **7.2.c** (mastering)

Section Resources

- Directed Reading A **BASIC** (Also in Spanish), B **GENERAL**
- Interactive Reader and Study Guide
- Section Quiz **GENERAL** (Also in Spanish)
- Section Review **GENERAL** (Also in Spanish)
- Vocabulary and Section Summary A **BASIC** (Also in Spanish), B **GENERAL**

Reviewing Prior Knowledge

Instruct students to study **Figure 2.** Then, ask students what they think the figure is trying to illustrate. Ask students: What are these structures? How are these structures different? How are they similar?

Bellringer

To have students focus on standard 7.2.e, ask them to write the answers to the following questions in their **Science Journal:**

- Chromosomes contain DNA (deoxyribonucleic acid). What is DNA? (DNA, or deoxyribonucleic acid, is the genetic material of living organisms.)

- What do you think is an important function of DNA? (Answers may vary. Sample: DNA determines the characteristics of living organisms.)

Bellringer Transparency

Motivate

ACTIVITY

Crosses Have students model a cross between an organism with one pair of chromosomes and a member of the opposite sex of its species. Show the chromosomes in the cross as "$F_1F_2 \times M_1M_2$." Explain that F_1 and F_2 represent the father's chromosomes, and M_1 and M_2 represent the mother's chromosomes. Ask students, "If each parent contributes only one chromosome from his or her own pair to the offspring, what are the possible combinations in the offspring?" (F_1M_1, F_1M_2, F_2M_1, and F_2M_2) **LS Logical**

What You Will Learn

- In sexual reproduction, offspring receive half of their genetic material from each parent.
- Homologous chromosomes contain the same genes but may have different alleles for each gene.
- Meiosis results in the production of haploid cells that have half the number of chromosomes that diploid cells do.

Why It Matters

The combination of genetic material during sexual reproduction allows for genetic variation.

Vocabulary

- homologous chromosomes
- diploid
- haploid
- meiosis

READING STRATEGY

Graphic Organizer In your **Science Journal,** create Combination Notes about meiosis.

---

homologous chromosomes (hoh MAHL uh guhs KROH muh SOHMZ) chromosomes that have the same sequence of genes and the same structure

diploid (DIP LOYD) a cell that contains two haploid sets of chromosomes
Wordwise The root *dipl-* means "twice" or "double."

haploid (HAP LOYD) describes a cell, nucleus, or organism that has only one set of unpaired chromosomes

7.2.b Students know sexual reproduction produces offspring that inherit half their genes from each parent.
7.2.e Students know DNA (deoxyribonucleic acid) is the genetic material of living organisms and is located in the chromosomes of each cell.

Meiosis

Key Concept Meiosis and sexual reproduction allow for the combination of genetic material from two different cells.

▶ Offspring receive genetic information, or DNA, from their parents. In asexual reproduction, one parent contributes genetic information to its offspring. The offspring has the same genotype as the parent.

In sexual reproduction, two parents contribute genetic information to their offspring. Before sexual reproduction can occur, each parent must reduce his or her genetic material by half in a process called meiosis. Therefore, when the genetic information from two parents combine, the offspring will have the same amount of genetic information as each of its parents. Genetic information is located on structures called *chromosomes*.

Chromosome Numbers

Most species have a specific number of chromosomes in their body cells. For example, human cells usually have 46 chromosomes, corn cells usually have 20 chromosomes, and dog cells usually have 78 chromosomes. Most of the time, the chromosomes are spread out in long strands. Before a cell divides, the chromosomes in the cell condense and become shorter and thicker. **Figure 1** shows the 46 chromosomes of a human body cell that are visible during cell division.

Standards Check How many chromosomes does a human body cell have? 7.2.e

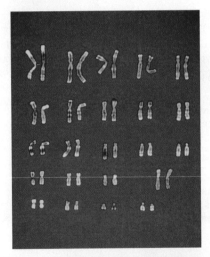

Figure 1 *This karyotype shows the 46 chromosomes from a human body cell.*

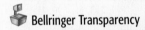

Wordwise

Word Connections Review the meaning of the term *diploid* by explaining to students that diploid comes from the Greek root *di-*, meaning "double" or "twice." Then, ask students to think of other words that contain the root *di-*. Some examples to tell the class are *dioxide* or *dilemma*. Have students look up the terms they have thought of and ask students how knowing the meaning of the Greek root can help them determine the definition of a word they may not already know.

Homologous Chromosomes

Organisms who reproduce sexually have two kinds of cells, body cells and sex cells. In body cells, the chromosomes are found in pairs that carry similar genetic information and have a similar structure. These chromosomes, that carry the same sets of genes, are called **homologous chromosomes.** Homologous chromosomes carry the same genes, but the chromosomes may have different alleles for those genes. **Figure 2** shows a diagram of a homologous pair of chromosomes.

Chromosomes in Reproduction

Cells that have homologous pairs of chromosomes are called **diploid.** Body cells are diploid cells. Before an organism can reproduce sexually, it must make *sex cells*. Sex cells have one copy of each chromosome. Sex cells do not have homologous chromosomes because the homologous chromosomes separate during the production of sex cells. So, each sex cell only has one copy of each gene. A cell that does not have homologous chromosomes is called **haploid.** Sex cells are haploid cells.

Figure 3 shows the role haploid sex cells play in the reproduction of diploid organisms. The male makes sex cells called *sperm*. The female makes sex cells called *eggs*. The sperm and eggs are haploid cells. Fertilization occurs when a sperm cell and an egg cell combine. A diploid cell is formed when the chromosomes from the sperm cell and the egg cell combine. The diploid cell divides and creates more diploid cells through the process of mitosis. These cells can develop into a new organism.

Figure 2 *Homologous chromosomes have the same genes. Genes can be the same version, or allele, such as the "B" allele found on both chromosomes. The genes can also be different alleles, such as the "A" and "a" alleles.*

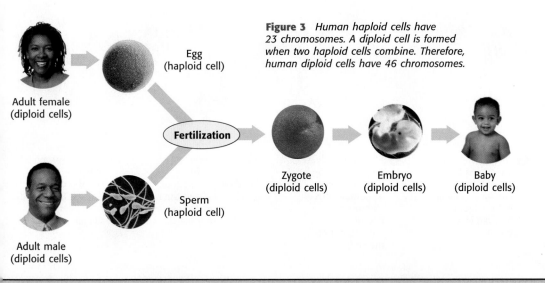

Figure 3 *Human haploid cells have 23 chromosomes. A diploid cell is formed when two haploid cells combine. Therefore, human diploid cells have 46 chromosomes.*

Adult female (diploid cells)

Egg (haploid cell)

Fertilization

Sperm (haploid cell)

Adult male (diploid cells)

Zygote (diploid cells)

Embryo (diploid cells)

Baby (diploid cells)

Universal Access · Differentiated Instruction

Struggling Readers

Making Analogies Ask students to think about how a gene is like a recipe. (A gene is the instructions for a trait.) Next, ask students to consider how a chromosome is like a cookbook. (Chromosomes contain many "recipes" for making traits). Finally, ask students to think about how homologous chromosomes could be like two cookbooks. (Two cookbooks could contain the same type of recipes in the same order, such as a cake and a side dish. The recipes in the cookbooks could be the same or different; one cookbook could have recipes for chocolate cake and mashed potatoes and the other book could have recipes for vanilla cake and mashed potatoes. **LS** **Verbal/Logical**

READING STRATEGY

Anticipation Guide Before students read the section on meiosis, ask them to predict the difference between meiosis and mitosis. Then, ask students if the following statements are true or false. Students will discover the answers as they explore the rest of the section.

- Only cells that produce sex cells undergo meiosis. (true)
- Sex cells contain half the number of chromosomes that other body cells do. (true)

LS Verbal/Auditory

ACTIVITY

Meiosis in Action
Have students make a flip book that animates the phases of meiosis. First, have students draw the events of meiosis in at least 15 sketches on sturdy cards. Explain that each drawing should vary only slightly from the one before it. When the book is flipped through quickly, the images should appear to be in motion, and students will be able to watch meiosis in action. This activity could be repeated to demonstrate mitosis. **LS** Visual/Kinesthetic

Discussion

Process of Meiosis Launch a discussion of meiosis to address any misconceptions students may have. Ask students if they think that meiosis and mitosis are related to each other. (Meiosis and mitosis are not linked processes. Cells do not go through one process and then the other. Meiosis occurs at certain stages and in certain cells, such as in the production of sex cells. Mitosis occurs in cells such as skin cells or muscle cells.) Then, ask students if Interphase is considered a stage of meiosis. (Students should answer that Interphase is not a stage of meiosis, rather it is a process which occurs before meiosis begins.) **LS** Verbal

meiosis (mie OH sis) a process in cell division during which the number of chromosomes decreases to half the original number by two divisions of the nucleus, which results in the production of sex cells (gametes or spores)

Meiosis

Sex cells are made during meiosis. **Meiosis** is a copying process that produces cells that have half the usual number of chromosomes. Each sex cell receives one-half of each homologous pair. For example, a human egg cell has 23 chromosomes, and a sperm cell has 23 chromosomes. The new cell that forms when an egg cell and a sperm cell join has 46 chromosomes.

Standards Check How many chromosomes does a human egg cell have? 🐻 **7.2.b**

The Steps of Meiosis

The steps of meiosis for a cell that has four chromosomes are shown in **Figure 4.** Before meiosis begins, each chromosome is copied. The original chromosome and the new copy form *chromatids*, which are joined together. The chromosomes shorten and thicken, which makes them visible under a microscope. During meiosis, the nucleus divides twice. The first time the nucleus divides, the homologous chromosomes separate. The second time the nucleus divides, the identical chromatids separate. Finally, meiosis results in four sex cells, which have half the number of chromosomes as the original cell.

Figure 4 **Steps of Meiosis**

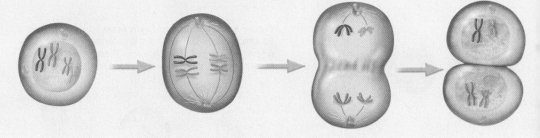

❶ The chromosomes are copied before meiosis begins. The identical copies, or chromatids, are joined together.

❷ After the nuclear membrane disappears, pairs of homologous chromosomes line up along the equator of the cell.

❸ The chromosomes separate from their homologous partners and then move to opposite ends of the cell.

❹ The nuclear membrane re-forms, and the cell divides. The paired chromatids are still joined.

Answer to Standards Check

A human egg cell has 23 chromosomes.

7.2.b (supporting)

Teaching Transparency:
L21 Steps of Meiosis: A
L22 Steps of Meiosis: B

Special Education Students

Flow Charts The flip book activity asks students to create a flip book to animate meiosis. To help students who do not have the physical dexterity to create the book, have them create a flow chart instead. Create an blank flow chart for these students to enter the steps into, or guide these students in using a computer to create the flow chart. **LS** Visual

Quick Lab

Meiosis Skit

After studying the steps of meiosis, perform a skit with your class about how a diploid cell that has four chromosomes undergoes meiosis.

1. To play the part of the genetic material, use four colors of **paper streamers** that are each 1 m long. Fold the streamers in half to represent chromosomes.

2. Students who are not holding genetic material can be the cell membrane by standing in a circle around the chromosomes. After the chromosomes separate, the membrane pinches to form separate cells.

3. As a group, you will act out each step of meiosis. For example, start with four students each holding one chromosome. When the chromosomes replicate before meiosis begins, four more students with chromosomes should enter the cell.

7.2.b

4. Continue the steps of meiosis until haploid cells are produced.

5. How many chromosomes are in each haploid cell?

20 min

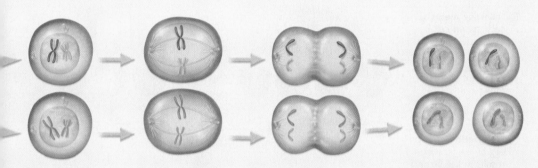

5. Each cell contains one member of the homologous chromosome pair. The chromosomes are not copied again between the two cell divisions.

6. The nuclear membrane disappears, and the chromosomes line up along the equator of each cell.

7. The chromatids pull apart and move to opposite ends of the cell. The nuclear membranes re-form, and the cells divide.

8. The result is that four new haploid cells have formed from the original diploid cell. Each new cell has half the number of chromosomes present in the original cell.

Universal Access · Differentiated Instruction

Special Education Students

Materials for Each Group
- jar lids, 4
- small snapbeads, 32, snapped to make 16 2-bead sets

Demonstrating Meiosis The descriptions of meiosis in **Figure 4** should be accessible to all students. Use small snapbeads as chromosomes and container lids as cells. Manipulate the props to explain **Figure 4** to students with visual impairments.

LS Verbal/Kinesthetic

Basic Learners

Describing Meiosis Have students write their own captions for the steps of meiosis illustrated on these pages. They should use language and descriptions that will help them understand and remember the material. **LS** Verbal/Visual

Quick Lab 20 min

Teacher Notes

This activity helps students understand meiosis, which is an important part of sexual reproduction and inheritance (covers standard 7.2.b).

Materials for Each Group
- paper streamers

Answers

5. There are 2 chromosomes in each haploid cell.

 Differentiated Datasheets
A **BASIC**, B **GENERAL**, C **ADVANCED**

Also editable on the Holt Lab Generator CD-ROM

CONNECTION ACTIVITY
Math

Chromosome Number Meiosis and sexual reproduction are beneficial to organisms because these processes maintain a variety of traits within a population. Meiosis and sexual recombination reshuffle the genetic material in each generation. Furthermore, the division of chromosomes during meiosis ensures that when the egg and sperm combine, the new organism has the same number of chromosomes as its parents. To explore these concepts, ask students the following questions:

- If the normal number of chromosomes for an organism is 30, how many chromosomes would be found in an egg or a sperm cell? (15)

- What would happen if eggs and sperm were produced by mitosis instead of by meiosis? (Sex cells would have a full set of 30 chromosomes. When the two sex cells combine, the offspring would have 60 chromosomes, which is twice the amount of chromosomes the parents have.) **LS** Logical

Standards Focus

This **Standards Focus** provides you with a quick way to **assess**, **reteach**, and **re-assess** one or more concepts in the section.

Assess

1. _____ in each cell are made up of DNA. **7.2.e** (Chromosomes)

2. Traits are determined by _____. **7.2.c** (genetic material)

3. Chromosomes contain _____, which is the genetic material of living organisms. **7.2.e** (DNA)

Reteach

Meiosis Flashcards Have students make a set of flashcards to help them review the steps of meiosis. Each flashcard should have a drawing of one step of meiosis on one side. On the back of the flashcard, students should identify the step and write an explanation of what is happening inside the cell during that step. **LS** Logical/Visual **7.2.b**

Re-Assess

Chromosome Chronicle

Have students write a short paragraph about the "history" of how a trait gets passed from parents to offspring. **LS** Verbal **7.2.b**

📦 Teaching Transparency:
L23 Meiosis and Dominance

Meiosis and Mendel

The steps in meiosis explain Mendel's results. **Figure 5** shows what happens to chromosomes during meiosis and fertilization. The cross shown is between a plant that is true breeding for round seeds and a plant that is true breeding for wrinkled seeds. All of the sperm formed by the male parent during meiosis have the wrinkled-seed allele, *r*, and all of the female parent's eggs have the round-seed allele, *R*. Each fertilized egg has one dominant allele and one recessive allele for seed shape. So, only one genotype, *Rr*, is possible for the offspring. Because the round-seed allele is dominant and the wrinkled-seed allele is recessive, the offspring have the round-seed phenotype.

Figure 5 **Meiosis and Dominance**

Male Parent In the plant-cell nucleus below, each homologous chromosome has an allele for seed shape, and each allele carries the same instructions: to make wrinkled seeds.

Female Parent In the plant-cell nucleus below, each homologous chromosome has an allele for seed shape, and each allele carries the same instructions: to make round seeds.

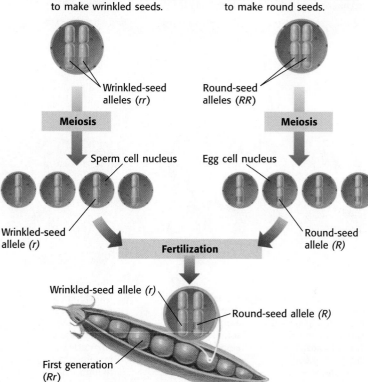

ⓐ Following **meiosis,** each sperm cell has a recessive allele for wrinkled seeds, and each egg cell has a dominant allele for round seeds.

ⓑ **Fertilization** of any egg by any sperm results in the same genotype (*Rr*) and the same phenotype (round). This result is exactly what Mendel found in his studies.

Wrinkled-seed alleles (*rr*)

Round-seed alleles (*RR*)

Meiosis

Meiosis

Sperm cell nucleus

Egg cell nucleus

Wrinkled-seed allele (*r*)

Round-seed allele (*R*)

Fertilization

Wrinkled-seed allele (*r*)

Round-seed allele (*R*)

First generation (*Rr*)

Universal Access · Differentiated Instruction

Struggling Readers

Connecting Text with a Figure Point out that the paragraph on this pages works with **Figure 5** to explain meiosis and dominance. Tell students to read the paragraph. Ask them to carefully study **Figure 5.** Have them read the paragraph again to make sure they understand the details. Ask a volunteer whether the peas in the pod at the bottom of the page have round or wrinkled seeds and how he or she knows.

(Sample answer: I can tell the pod has round seeds because that generation of peas has one wrinkled-seed allele and one round-seed allele and the round-seed allele is dominant. I know this information because the two paragraphs explain that Figure 5 shows a cross between a plant that is true breeding for round seeds and a plant that is true breeding for wrinkled seeds and the figure captions explain that the round seed trait is dominant.)
LS Visual/Verbal

Meiosis and Inheritance

In sexual reproduction, sex cells combine to produce offspring. Therefore, approximately half of the offspring's genetic material comes from its biological mother, and approximately half comes from its biological father. In eukaryotes, most of the genetic information is located in the nucleus. However, mitochondria, shown in **Figure 6,** also contain genetic material. Mitochondria are organelles that release energy. In most cases, all of an organism's mitochondria come from its mother. Therefore, mitochondrial DNA in the cells of offspring is the same as the mitochondrial DNA in the cells of the offspring's mother.

Standards Check From which parent does an offspring receive its mitochondrial DNA? 🐻 **7.2.b**

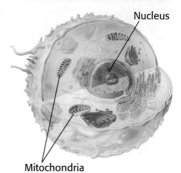

Figure 6   Animal Cell

Nucleus

Mitochondria

SECTION Review

7.2.b, 7.2.e

Summary

- Homologous pairs of chromosomes contain the same genes. The alleles for each gene may be the same or they may be different.

- Diploid cells have homologous pairs of chromosomes. Haploid cells do not.

- The process of meiosis produces haploid sex cells.

- During sexual reproduction, haploid sex cells combine to form a new diploid organism.

- Meiosis explains how organisms inherit one-half of their genetic information from each parent.

Using Vocabulary

① Use *meiosis* and *sex cells* in the same sentence.

② Write an original definition for the term *homologous chromosomes*.

Understanding Concepts

③ **Classifying** Are your body cells diploid or haploid?

④ **Describing** How many times does the nucleus divide during meiosis?

⑤ **Applying** If there are 14 chromosomes in pea plant cells, how many chromosomes are present in a sex cell of a pea plant?

⑥ **Describing** Approximately how much of an organism's genetic material is contributed by its mother?

⑦ **Describing** How many pairs of homologous chromosomes are found in human body cells?

Critical Thinking

⑧ **Identifying Relationships** Put the following in order of smallest to largest: chromosome, gene, and cell.

⑨ **Applying Concepts** A pea plant has purple flowers. What alleles for flower color could the sex cells carry?

Challenge

⑩ **Making Comparisons** Is the mitochondrial DNA in a baby more like the mitochondrial DNA from his mother's mother or the mitochondrial DNA from his father's mother? Explain your answer.

Internet Resources

For a variety of links related to this chapter, go to www.scilinks.org

Topic: Meiosis; Genetic Diseases, Screening, Counseling
SciLinks code: HY70935; HY70651

MISCONCEPTION ALERT

Mitosis and Meiosis Some students may think that mitosis always occurs before meiosis. Help students create a table that shows that mitosis and meiosis are separate processes. The column titles are "Types of cells," "Starting cell," "Ending cells," and "Purpose." As a class, complete rows describing mitosis and meiosis. (mitosis: occurs in most cells, starts with 1 diploid cell, ends with 2 diploid cells, and produces identical copies of cells; meiosis: occurs in sex cells, starts with one diploid cell, ends with 4 haploid cells, and produces cells that combine during sexual reproduction)

Modeling Space Bug Genetics

Teacher Notes

This activity has students model Mendelian genetics and the inheritance of traits (covers standards 7.2.b, 7.2.d, 7.7.c, and 7.7.d).

Time Required

Two 45-minute class periods

Lab Ratings

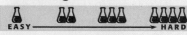

| EASY | | | HARD |

Teacher Prep 🧪🧪🧪
Student Set-Up 🧪🧪
Concept Level 🧪🧪🧪
Clean Up 🧪

Materials

The materials listed on the student page are enough for groups of three to four students.

Safety Caution

Remind students to review all safety cautions and icons before beginning this lab activity. Students should use caution with toothpicks and should not eat any of the materials used.

Model-Making Lab

Model-Making Lab

OBJECTIVES

Build models to further your understanding of inheritance.

Examine the traits of a population of offspring.

MATERIALS

- cup, paper
- gumdrops, green and black (feet)
- map pins (eyes)
- marshmallows, large (head and body segments)
- pipe cleaners (tails)
- pushpins, green and blue (noses)
- scissors
- toothpicks, red and green (antennae)

SAFETY

7.2.b Students know sexual reproduction produces offspring that inherit half their genes from each parent.
7.2.c Students know an inherited trait can be determined by one or more genes.
Investigation and Experimentation
7.7.c Communicate the logical connection among hypotheses, science concepts, tests conducted, data collected, and conclusions drawn from the scientific evidence.
7.7.d Construct scale models, maps, and appropriately labeled diagrams to communicate scientific knowledge (e.g., motion of Earth's plates and cell structure).

Modeling Space Bug Genetics

Imagine that you are working with a team of scientists that has discovered a new organism. The organism shares many characteristics with insects, but the species also has some very strange traits. Because the new organisms look like bugs from outer space, your team has decided to call the new organisms "space bugs." Space bugs inherit traits according to the principles of genetics discovered by Gregor Mendel. In this activity, you will use your knowledge of genetics to construct models of space bugs. You will then construct models of the offspring that could be created by crossing space bugs that have different traits.

Procedure

1. Seven characteristics of space bugs are shown in the table below. For each characteristic, there are two traits. The allele for the dominant trait is written with a capital letter. The allele for the recessive trait is written with a lowercase letter.

2. Create a table like the one entitled "Space Bug Family Traits." Notice that the genotypes of the parents are already entered into the table.

3. Determine the phenotype of each parent by using the table below and the genotypes listed for each parent. Enter the phenotypes in the table that you created.

Space Bug Traits and Alleles		
Characteristic	**Traits and Alleles**	
Antennae color	red antennae (*R*)	green antennae (*r*)
Number of body segments	three body segments (*S*)	two body segments (*s*)
Tail Shape	curly tail (*C*)	straight tail (*c*)
Number of leg pairs	three pairs of legs (*L*)	two pairs of legs (*l*)
Nose color	blue nose (*B*)	green nose (*b*)
Foot color	green feet (*G*)	black feet (*g*)
Number of eyes	two eyes (*E*)	three eyes (*e*)

Lab Resources

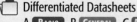

📁 **Differentiated Datasheets**
A **BASIC**, B **GENERAL**, C **ADVANCED**

💾 Classroom Lab Video/DVD

Holt Lab Generator CD-ROM

Search for any lab by topic, standard, difficulty level, or time. Edit any lab to fit your needs, or create your own labs. Use the Lab Materials QuickList software to customize your lab materials list.

Space Bug Family Traits

Characteristic	Female genotype	Female phenotype	Male genotype	Male phenotype	Offspring genotype	Offspring phenotype
Antennae color	Rr		rr			
Number of body segments	ss		Ss			
Tail shape	cc		CC			
Number of leg pairs	Ll		Ll			
Nose color	BB		Bb			
Foot color	Gg		Gg			
Number of eyes	Ee		ee			

DO NOT WRITE IN BOOK

4 In a group of four students, two students will construct a model of the female space bug and two students will construct a model of the male space bug. (Toothpicks can be used to hold body segments together and can be used as legs to attach the feet to the body.)

5 Based on the model that you created, determine which traits the offspring will inherit from the parent. First, write the parent's alleles for one characteristic on separate, small pieces of paper. For example, if your space bug has the genotype *Rr* for antennae, you will write "*R*" on one piece of paper and "*r*" on a second piece of paper.

6 Fold the pieces of paper, and place them in the paper cup. Without looking, draw one piece of paper. This is the allele that the offspring has inherited from the parent that you created. The other members of your group will tell you which allele the offspring has inherited from the other parent.

7 In your table, record the genotype of the offspring. Continue drawing alleles for the other characteristics.

8 Use the table entitled "Space Bug Traits and Alleles" and the genotype to determine the phenotype of the offspring.

9 As a group, construct a model of the offspring.

Analyze the Results

10 **Organizing Data** Take a poll of the traits of the offspring in your class. What are the ratios for each trait?

11 **Examining Data** Do any of the offspring models look the same? How many different models of offspring are there in your class?

Draw Conclusions

12 **Interpreting Information** Is it possible for an offspring to have a trait that neither of its parents have? If so, how could this occur?

Big Idea Question

13 **Drawing Conclusions** How does the inheritance of traits in the bug models you built represent how traits are inherited in humans?

Analyze the Results

10. Answers will depend on the traits of the offspring each group creates.

11. Answers will depend on the traits of the offspring each group creates.

Draw Conclusions

12. An offspring can have a trait that neither of its parents have. Both parents could have both the dominant allele and the recessive allele for a trait. If both parents pass the recessive allele to the offspring, the offspring will have two recessive alleles for that gene. The phenotype of the parents will be the dominant trait, and the phenotype of the offspring will be the recessive trait.

Big Idea Question

13. In both the bug models and in humans, traits are influenced by genes. Two copies of genes, or alleles, are inherited for most genes. How these genes interact determines what the offspring look like. Humans are more complicated, however, because many genes influence some traits. Also, one gene can influence many traits.

Procedure, Steps 2.–3.

Space Bug Family Traits

Trait	Female genotype	Female phenotype	Male genotype	Male phenotype	Offspring genotype	Offspring phenotype
Antennae color	Rr	red	rr	green		
Number of body segments	ss	two	Ss	three		
Tail shape	cc	straight	CC	curly		
Number of leg pairs	Ll	three	Ll	three		
Nose color	BB	blue	Bb	blue		
Foot color	Gg	green	Gg	green		
Number of eyes	Ee	two	ee	three		

Peggy Lubchenco
La Colina Junior
High School
Santa Barbara, California

Science Skills Activity

Teacher Notes

In the tutorial, students are asked to prepare an oral report (covers standard 7.7.e). Encourage them to carefully think about their topics to make sure that the topics are not too specific and not too broad. Assist them in making any necessary adjustments to their topic as they conduct their research.

Answers to You Try It!

Answers for questions 1, 2, 3, and 4 may vary depending on the genetic disorder students choose to research.

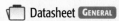 Datasheet GENERAL

Also editable on the Holt Lab Generator CD-ROM

Giving Oral Presentations

▶ Tutorial

Investigation and Experimentation
7.7.e Communicate the steps and results from an investigation in written reports and oral presentations.

Communicating your results is an important part of any scientific investigation. Results from an investigation can be communicated through written reports or oral presentations. In this tutorial, you will learn the steps for preparing and giving an oral presentation.

Procedure

1 The first step is to research the topic you will be discussing. Ask your teacher which sources you should use for the assignment. Sources might include newspapers, magazines, interviews, or information from the Internet.

2 To guide your research, make a list of topics you want to discuss in your presentation. You can update this list as you continue to gather information. Remember to take good notes!

3 When you have completed your research, think about the order in which you will discuss the information. Create an outline that lists the order of topics.

4 Consider what your introduction and conclusion will be. Your introduction should get your audience interested in your presentation. Your conclusion should review the information you have discussed.

5 Practice giving your presentation to family members. You can also practice your presentation in front of a mirror.

6 Use your outline as a guide when you give your presentation, but do not forget to make eye contact with your audience. Remember to stand up straight, to stay still, and to speak loudly and clearly.

▶ You Try It!

Procedure

Germs or other things in the environment can cause many health problems. But some health problems are inherited. A genetic disorder is a health condition that results from inheriting alleles that do not function properly. Research a genetic disorder, and give a presentation about it to your class. Your presentation should include information that answers the following questions:

1 What are the symptoms of this genetic disorder?

2 What treatment is available?

3 How is the genetic disorder inherited? Is it a dominant allele or a recessive allele?

4 How common is the genetic disorder in the human population?

Universal Access · Differentiated Instruction

Special Education Students

Computer Presentations Oral reports are difficult for students with hearing impairments. Allow these students to create slide presentations using a computer program. Encourage them to complete all of the steps in the Tutorial section. Have them create at least one separate slide for each of the four parts of the presentation. Have them use a combination of text and meaningful pictures. **LS** Visual

Advanced Learners/GATE

Creating a Rubric Some students can benefit from exploring additional aspects of a topic. Ask such students to work together to create a rubric to use when grading an oral report based on a scientific investigation. Make copies of the final version of the rubric and let all students use it to self-evaluate their presentations. **LS** Logical/Interpersonal

Chapter Summary

The Big Idea
Heredity is the passing of the instructions for traits from one generation to the next.

Section

Vocabulary

① Mendel and His Peas

Key Concept The work of Gregor Mendel explains the rules of heredity and is the of foundation of modern genetics.

- Heredity is the passing of genetic traits from parent to offspring.
- Gregor Mendel's experiments with pea plants led to the discovery of dominant and recessive traits.

Gregor Mendel discovered many properties of heredity.

heredity p. 174
dominant trait p. 177
recessive trait p. 177

② Traits and Inheritance

Key Concept Genes are the instructions for inherited traits.

- Genes exist in multiple versions called alleles.
- An organism's phenotype is affected by the organism's genotype.
- Punnett squares are used to predict the possible genotypes of the offspring from particular parents.
- Patterns of inheritance can be more complicated than one gene influencing one trait.

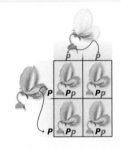

Punnett squares predict the possible genotypes for the offspring of a cross.

gene p. 180
allele p. 180
phenotype p. 180
genotype p. 181
probability p. 182

③ Meiosis

Key Concept Meiosis and sexual reproduction allow for the combination of genetic material from two different cells.

- In sexual reproduction, offspring receive half of their genetic information from each parent.
- Homologous chromosomes contain the same genes but may have different alleles for each gene.
- Meiosis results in the production of haploid cells that have half the number of chromosomes that diploid cells do.

The alleles for genes are found on chromosomes.

homologous chromosomes p. 189
diploid p. 189
haploid p. 189
meiosis p. 190

Review Resources

- Reinforcement Worksheet **BASIC**
- Critical Thinking Worksheet **ADVANCED**
- Chapter Review **GENERAL** (Also in Spanish)
- Standards Review Workbook (Also in Spanish)
- Study Guide A **BASIC** (Also in Spanish), B **GENERAL**

Assessment Resources

- Chapter Tests A **BASIC**, B **GENERAL** (Also in Spanish), C **ADVANCED**
- Standards Assessment **GENERAL**

Chapter Summary

SUPER SUMMARY

Have students connect the major concepts in this chapter through an interactive Super Summary. Visit go.hrw.com and type in the keyword HY7HERS to access the Super Summary for this chapter.

Identifying Roots
Counting Chromosomes

Have students research the root *-ploid* to find out how it relates to heredity. *Haploid* and *diploid* are common terms when talking about chromosomes. Ask students to note other words with the root *-ploid* that they encounter during their research. Then, ask students to illustrate *haploid* and *diploid* either through drawings or written explanations. **LS** Verbal

Focus on Reading
Genetic Research Have students work in pairs. Each pair should find a current newspaper article that relates to genetics. Have students research the genetic topic discussed in their article, and write a summary of what they have learned. **LS** Verbal
Co-op Learning

Chapter Review

7.2.b, 7.2.c,
7.2.d, 7.2.e

Assignment Guide

Section	Questions
1	6, 8, 10, 14, 16, 19, 24
2	3, 5, 11, 12, 13, 17, 21, 22, 23, 25
3	2, 4, 7, 9, 15, 18, 20

Answers

Using Vocabulary

1. The word *dominant* means the trait that will be observed.

2. haploid **7.2.b** (mastering)

3. phenotype, genotype **7.2.d** (mastering)

4. meiosis **7.2.d** (exceeding)

5. alleles **7.2.d** (mastering)

Understanding Concepts

6. d **7.2.c** (mastering)

7. c **7.2.b** (exceeding)

8. c **7.2.d** (mastering)

9. c **7.2.b** (exceeding)

10. self-pollination and cross-pollination

11. TT **7.2.d** (mastering)

12. Both of the parents and all of the offspring are tall pea plants. **7.2.d** (mastering)

13. Students should make two new Punnett squares. Self-fertilization of *TT (TT × TT)* will yield offspring that are all *TT*. Self-fertilization of *Tt (Tt × Tt)* will yield offspring that are *TT*, *Tt*, and *tt*. **7.2.d** (exceeding)

Organize

Key-Term Fold Review the FoldNote that you created at the beginning of the chapter. Add to or correct the FoldNote based on what you have learned.

Using Vocabulary

1 **Academic Vocabulary** In the sentence "The allele for round seeds is dominant to the allele for wrinkled seeds," what does the word *dominant* mean?

Complete each of the following sentences by choosing the correct term from the word bank.

diploid	genotype
haploid	alleles
phenotype	meiosis

2 Meiosis produces ___ cells.

3 The ___ is the expression of a trait and is determined by the combination of alleles called the ___.

4 ___ produces cells that have half the normal number of chromosomes found in body cells.

5 Different versions of the same genes are called ___.

Understanding Concepts

Multiple Choice

6 Genes carry information that determines
a. alleles.
b. ribosomes.
c. chromosomes.
d. traits.

7 The process that produces sex cells is
a. mitosis.
b. photosynthesis.
c. meiosis.
d. probability.

8 A male guinea pig that has long, orange fur mated with a female guinea pig that has short, black fur. The litter consisted of guinea pigs that have only long, black fur. Which of the following is probably dominant for both traits?
a. short, orange fur
b. long, orange fur
c. long, black fur
d. short, black fur

9 Which of the following statements about meiosis is true?
a. Chromosomes are copied twice.
b. The nucleus divides once.
c. Four cells are produced from a single cell.
d. Two cells are produced from a single cell.

Short Answer

10 **Identifying** What are the two methods of sexual reproduction used by pea plants?

INTERPRETING GRAPHICS Use the Punnett square below to answer the next three questions.

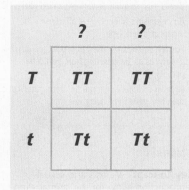

	?	?
T	TT	TT
t	Tt	Tt

11 **Applying** What is the unknown genotype?

12 **Analyzing** If *T* represents the allele for tall pea plants and *t* represents the allele for short pea plants, what is the phenotype of each parent and of the offspring?

13 **Concluding** If each of the offspring were allowed to self-fertilize, what are the possible genotypes in the next generation?

Writing Skills

14. Communicating Concepts Write a paragraph that describes Mendel's experiments with pea plants. Include information about how Mendel performed the experiments, what his results were, and what conclusions he made from the results.

Critical Thinking

15. Concept Mapping Use the following terms to create a concept map: *genes, dominant, heredity, homologous chromosomes, recessive,* and *alleles.*

16. Applying Concepts If a child does not have freckles and both of her parents have freckles, what does that tell you about the allele for freckles? Explain.

17. Applying Concepts In Mendel's experiments with pea plants, each trait was influenced by one gene. Describe an example in which there is not a one-to-one correspondence between trait and gene.

18. Identifying Relationships Explain the relationship between the alleles for a gene and homologous chromosomes.

19. Evaluating Hypotheses When two organisms that have different traits are crossed, some traits disappear in the offspring. But these traits can reappear in later generations. If the theory of blending inheritance explained how traits are inherited, could traits disappear and reappear? Explain your answer.

20. Analyzing Ideas How do the steps of meiosis explain Mendel's results?

21. Identifying Relationship How does the inheritance of mitochondrial DNA differ from the inheritance of DNA found in the nucleus of cells?

22. Applying Concepts Punnett squares can be used to predict many traits of offspring based on the traits of the offspring's parent. Why is it difficult to use a Punnett square to determine certain traits, such as eye color?

Math Skills

23. Making Calculations In pea plants, the allele for yellow seeds, *Y,* is dominant to the allele for green seeds, *y.* If a plant that has the genotype *Yy* is crossed with a plant that has the genotype *yy,* what is the probability that the offspring will have green seeds?

INTERPRETING GRAPHICS Use the table below to answer the next question.

Survey of Traits		
Trait	**Number of students with trait**	**Number of students without trait**
Dimples	9	21
Ability to roll tongue	23	7

24. Analyzing Data What is the ratio of students with dimples to students without dimples?

Challenge

25. Evaluating Hypotheses Hydrangeas are flowers that can produce either pink flowers or blue flowers. Your neighbor thinks that the color of the flowers is determined by the type of soil in which the hydrangeas are grown. Your friend thinks the color is determined by the plant's alleles. How could you perform an experiment to prove which hypothesis best explains how the flower color of hydrangeas is determined?

20. Mendel's results showed that living things have two copies of each gene. During meiosis, the two copies of each gene are separated when the homologous pairs separate. The product of meiosis is sex cells with one copy of each gene. When two sex cells combine, they contain all of the genetic material to make an organism with two copies of each gene. **7.2.d** (mastering)

21. Mitochondrial DNA is inherited from the mother; nuclear DNA comes equally from the mother and father. **7.2.b** (mastering)

22. Eye color is determined by multiple genes. **7.2.c** (mastering)

Math Skills

23. $1/2 \times 1 = 1/2$, or 50%
7.2.d (exceeding)

24. 9:21

Challenge

25. Sample answer: To test if the color is determined by soil, I would first obtain seeds from plants with blue flowers and plants with pink flowers. I would plant the seeds in different types of soil, and see what color flowers the plants produced. To test to see if the flower color was caused by alleles, I would make different crosses. I would cross plants with the same color of flowers together. I would also cross plants that have different colors of flowers. I would plant the seeds in the same type of soil. Then, I would make observations and analyze results to see which variable (the soil type or the crosses) determined the plant's flower color.

Chapter Review Standards Guide			
	Supporting	**Mastering**	**Exceeding**
7.2.b		2, 21	4, 7, 9, 20
7.2.c		6, 17	22
7.2.d		3, 5, 8, 11, 12, 14, 15, 15, 20	13, 19, 23
7.2.e			18

Writing Skills

14. Answers may vary, but should include a description of how Mendel performed the experiments, as well as what his results and conclusions were. **7.2.d** (mastering)

Critical Thinking

15. An answer to this exercise can be found at the back of the book. **7.2.b** (mastering)

16. The allele for freckles is dominant. **7.2.d** (mastering)

17. Sample answer: Many genetic disorders are caused by one gene affecting many traits. (Also accept examples of many genes affecting one trait, such as eye color or hair color.) **7.2.c** (mastering)

18. People inherit two forms, or alleles, of most genes. One form is found on each homologous chromosome. **7.2.e** (exceeding)

19. If traits were inherited through blending inheritance, traits would not reappear in later generations. In blending inheritance, traits from two parents mix together to form new traits. After being mixed, the original traits could not reappear. **7.2.d** (exceeding)

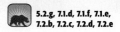
Standards Assessment

Teacher Notes

To provide practice under more realistic testing conditions, give students 20 min to answer all of the questions in this assessment.

Answer Key

Question Number	Correct Answer
1	C
2	A
3	A
4	B
5	D
6	D
7	C
8	C
9	C
10	A
11	A
12	B
13	B
14	B
15	A
16	D

Standards Guide

	Supporting	Mastering	Exceeding
7.1.e			13
7.1.f			14
7.2.b	3		6, 8
7.2.c		11	
7.2.d	1–2	7–10	
7.2.e		4, 12	5

📋 Standards Assessment **GENERAL**

📋 Teacher Notes for Standards Assessment contain a longer Assessment Doctor and Diagnostic Teaching Tips.

REVIEWING ACADEMIC VOCABULARY

1 Which of the following words is the closest in meaning to the word *instructions*?

A information

B advice

C directions

D threats

2 In the sentence "Traits may be modified by environmental influences," what does the word *modified* mean?

A changed

B exaggerated

C erased

D preserved

3 Which of the following words means "a way of doing something"?

A method

B product

C evaluation

D market

4 Choose the appropriate form of the word *locate* for the following sentence: DNA _____ in the chromosomes of each cell.

A was location

B is located

C have located

D locate

REVIEWING CONCEPTS

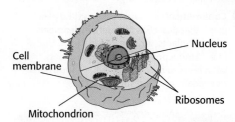

Cell membrane — Nucleus — Ribosomes — Mitochondrion

5 In which of the cell parts is DNA located?

A the mitochondrion

B the cell membrane

C the ribosomes

D the nucleus

6 Which cells are created during meiosis in humans?

A diploid cells with 46 chromosomes

B diploid cells with 23 chromosomes

C haploid cells with 46 chromosomes

D haploid cells with 23 chromosomes

7 How many genes do humans have?

A 1,000 to 2,000

B 3,000 to 6,000

C 20,000 to 30,000

D 100,000 to 200,00

8 Which statement best describes inheritance in humans?

A Offspring inherit two alleles for each gene from both parents.

B Offspring inherit two alleles for each gene from one parent.

C Offspring inherit one allele for each gene from both parents.

D Offspring inherit one gene for each allele from both parents.

➕ ASSESSMENT DOCTOR

Question 1: The correct answer is C. *Instructions* direct or tell how to do something.

Question 2: The correct answer is A. *Modified* is similar in meaning to *changed*.

Question 3: The correct answer is A. A *method* is a way of doing something.

Question 4: The correct answer is B. The tense and form of the helping verb is correct, as is the use of the past participle.

Question 5: The correct answer is D. DNA is found in the nucleus of eukaryotic cells.

Question 6: The correct answer is D. Haploid cells, or sex cells, are produced in humans and other animals during the process of meiosis. Sex cells have 23 chromosomes and when they combine with another sex cell during sexual reproduction, offspring will have 46 chromosomes in each cell.

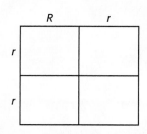

	R	r
r		
r		

9 The Punnett square above shows a cross between a pea plant that has round seeds (*Rr*) and a pea plant that has wrinkled seeds (*rr*). What are the possible genotypes of the offspring of this cross?

A *RR, Rr, rr*

B *RR, rr*

C *Rr, rr*

D *RR, Rr*

10 Why do identical twins have the same genotype?

A They have all the same sets of alleles.

B They come from two identical eggs.

C They look exactly like one another.

D They have heterozygous genotypes.

11 What is the best explanation for the many shades in human eye color?

A Eye color is determined by more than one gene.

B Blended inheritance creates offspring with mixed eye colors.

C One gene sometimes influences more than one characteristic.

D Many recessive alleles exist for different shades of eye color.

12 Which structure(s) contains DNA and protein?

A a genotype   C a nucleus

B chromosomes   D organelles

REVIEWING PRIOR LEARNING

13 What is the purpose of mitosis?

A to transform haploid sex cells into diploid cells

B to produce copies of cells

C to change cells in response to the environment

D to create sex cells for sexual reproduction

14 Why is cell differentiation necessary as a multicellular animal develops?

A to keep cells multiplying so that the animal will grow more quickly

B to create tissues, organs, and organ systems that keep the animal alive

C to prevent genetic disorders and other health problems from occurring

D to help the animal adapt to its environment as it grows to adulthood

15 Which structures in plant cells capture sunlight for photosynthesis?

A chloroplasts

B chromosomes

C genotypes

D nuclei

16 What is the process by which cells break down sugar molecules and release energy?

A sexual reproduction

B meiosis

C photosynthesis

D cellular respiration

Standards Assessment

ASSESSMENT DOCTOR

Question 7: The correct answer is C. Research indicates that humans have between 20,000 and 30,000 genes.

Question 8: The correct answer is C. Offspring inherit one allele for each gene from both parents.

Question 9: The correct answer is C. The completed Punnett square contains "Rr" in both boxes of the first column and "rr" in both boxes of the second column.

Question 10: The correct answer is A. Identical twins develop when one fertilized egg divides to form two fertilized eggs. Because identical twins come from the same original egg, their chromosomes are identical. Therefore, identical twins have the same sets of alleles and have the same phenotype.

Question 11: The correct answer is A. Many traits do not have a one-to-one correspondence between trait and gene. Different combinations of alleles for different genes results in different shades of eye color.

Question 12: The correct answer is B. Chromosomes are complexes of DNA and protein.

Question 13: The correct answer is B. Mitosis is the process by which identical copies of cells are made.

Question 14: The correct answer is B. Cells differentiate, or become different types of cells, so that tissues, organs, and organ systems can develop.

Question 15: The correct answer is A. Chloroplasts gather sunlight, carbon dioxide, and water, then initiate a chemical process that yields sugar molecules and oxygen. The sugar molecules are then used for energy while the oxygen is expelled.

Question 16: The correct answer is D. Cellular respiration is the chemical process by which cells break down sugar molecules, releasing energy for the cell to use for its functions. In plants and animals, cellular respiration produces carbon dioxide and water.

Science, Technology, and Society

Background

Genetic research has spawned a flurry of debate over ethical, social, and legal issues surrounding the use of genetic information. These issues include the privacy and ownership of personal genetic information and the possibility that people will selectively breed or control the birth of their children based on genetic knowledge.

Weird Science

Teaching Strategy

Offer the following analogies to help students grasp the concepts discussed in this article.

- Blueprints: Show students sample construction blueprints. Explain that genes are similar to these plans for a building and that mutations are similar to mistakes in copying, reading, or building from the blueprints.

- Recipes: Show students a book of cake recipes. Genes are similar to recipes, and an organism is similar to a cake made according to a recipe. A mutation is similar to using a different ingredient or a different amount of an ingredient. A mutation may or may not affect an organism.

This is a normal fruit fly under a scanning electron microscope.

This fruit fly has legs growing where its antennae should be.

Science in Action

Science, Technology, and Society

Mapping the Human Genome

In 2003, scientists finished one of the most ambitious research projects in history. Researchers with the Human Genome Project (HGP) mapped the human body's complete set of genetic instructions, which is called the *genome*. You might be wondering whose genome the scientists are decoding. Actually, it doesn't matter—only 0.1% of each person's genetic material is unique. The researchers' goals are to identify how tiny differences in that 0.1% make each of us who we are and to begin to understand how some differences can cause disease. Scientists are already using the map to think of new ways to treat genetic diseases, such as asthma, diabetes, and kidney disease.

Social Studies ACTIVITY

Research DNA fingerprinting. Write a short report that describes how DNA fingerprinting has affected the way criminals are caught.

Weird Science

Lab Rats with Wings

Drosophila melanogaster (droh SAHF i luh muh LAN uh GAS tuhr) is the scientific name for the fruit fly. This tiny insect has played a big role in helping scientists understand many illnesses. Because fruit flies reproduce every 2 weeks, scientists can alter a fruit fly gene and see the results of the experiment very quickly. Another important reason for using these "lab rats with wings" is that their genetic code is simple and well understood. Fruit flies have approximately 13,000 genes, but humans may have approximately 30,000. Scientists use fruit flies to find out about diseases such as cancer, Alzheimer's disease, and muscular dystrophy.

Language Arts ACTIVITY

The mythical creature called the *Chimera* (kie MIR uh) was said to be part lion, part goat, and part serpent. According to legend, the Chimera terrorized people for years until it was killed by a brave hero. The word *chimera* now refers to any organism that has parts from many organisms. Write a short story about the Chimera that describes what it looks like and how it came to be.

Answer to Social Studies Activity

Sample answer: DNA fingerprinting has made it much easier to match genetic material (evidence) at a crime scene to the genetic information of one particular individual. DNA can be found in hair, saliva, blood, and small skin cells. The DNA is analyzed and then compared to the DNA fingerprint of particular individuals. When the DNA fingerprints match, police can be sure that the person was at the scene of the crime.

Answer to Language Arts Activity

The Chimera (or Chimaera) was said to be a savage beast that spat fire from its mouth. In classical Greco-Roman stories, it wreaked havoc on the ancient lands until it was killed by the hero Bellerophon, who rode his winged horse Pegasus. This basic story is among the most ancient myths and appears in many texts from Homer's *Iliad* to traditional fairy tales.

Careers

Stacey Wong

Genetic Counselor If your family had a history of a particular disease, what would you do? Would you eat healthier foods, get more exercise, or visit your doctor regularly? All of those are good ideas, but Stacey Wong went a step farther. Her family's history of cancer helped her decide to become a genetic counselor. As a genetic counselor in Los Angeles, California, Wong is part of a team of health professionals that includes physicians, nurses, dieticians, social workers, laboratory personnel, and others. "If a diagnosis is made by the geneticist," says Wong, "then I provide genetic counseling." When a patient visits a genetic counselor, the counselor asks many questions and builds a family medical history. Although counseling involves discussing what it means to have a genetic condition, Wong says "the most important part is to get to know the patient or family we are working with, listen to their concerns, gain an understanding of their values, help them to make decisions, and be their advocate."

Math

The probability of inheriting genetic disease *A* is 1/10,000. The probability of inheriting genetic disease *B* is also 1/10,000. What is the probability that one person would inherit both genetic diseases *A* and *B*?

Internet Resources

- To learn more about careers in science, visit www.scilinks.org and enter the SciLinks code HY70225.

- To learn more about these Science in Action topics, visit go.hrw.com and type in the keyword HY7HERF.

- Check out articles related to this chapter by visiting go.hrw.com. Just type in the keyword HY7HERC.

Answer to Math Activity
$1/10{,}000 \times 1/10{,}000 = 1/100{,}000{,}000$

Careers

Background
Stacey Wong was born in Oakland, California, and grew up in the nearby suburb of Alameda. She received a B.S. in Cell and Molecular Biology from UCLA and an M.S. in Genetic Counseling from California State University Northridge. More information about genetic-counseling careers can be obtained from the National Society of Genetic Counselors.

Standards Course of Study

The elements listed in the Standards Course of Study provide a base for presenting, supporting, and assessing the California Grade 7 Science Standards. Use this Standards Course of Study as a base for planning your lessons.

Why Teach
Genes and DNA

This chapter was designed to cover the California Grade 7 Science Standards about genetics (7.1.a and 7.2.e). It follows a chapter about heredity. The genetic information that an organism inherits is contained in its genes and DNA.

After they have completed this chapter, students will begin a chapter about studying Earth's past.

California Standards

Focus on Life Sciences
7.1.a Students know cells function similarly in all living organisms.
7.2.e Students know DNA (deoxyribonucleic acid) is the genetic material of living organisms and is located in the chromosomes of each cell.

Investigation and Experimentation
7.7.c Communicate the logical connection among hypotheses, science concepts, tests conducted, data collected, and conclusions drawn from the scientific evidence.
7.7.d Construct scale models, maps, and appropriately labeled diagrams to communicate scientific knowledge (e.g., motion of Earth's plates and cell structure).

Chapter Pacing

Getting Started **45 min** pp. 206–207
The Big Idea DNA is the genetic material of living organisms and is located in the chromosomes of each cell.
7.2.e, 7.7.c

Section 1 What Does DNA Look Like? **90 min** pp. 208–211
Key Concept The structure of DNA is a double helix, which is shaped like a twisted ladder.
7.2.e, 7.7.d

Section 2 How DNA Works **90 min** pp. 212–217
Key Concept DNA stores a code that carries the instructions for making proteins. Proteins cause most of the differences among organisms.
 7.1.a, 7.2.e

Wrapping Up **180 min** pp. 218–227
 7.2.e, 7.7.c

Basic Learners
TE Scientific, Methods, p. 220
Reinforcement Worksheet
Chapter Test A
Differentiated Datasheets A for Labs and Activities ■
Study Guide A ■

Advanced Learners/GATE
TE Choose a Scientist, p. 209
TE Saluting Proteins, p. 215
Critical Thinking Worksheet
Chapter Test C
Differentiated Datasheets C for Labs and Activities ■

Teach

SE Explore Activity Fingerprint Identification, p. 207* ■

📙 **Bellringer**
💿 **PowerPoint® Resources**
📙 L24 DNA Structure
📙 L25 DNA Replication
SE Quick Lab Making a Model of DNA, p. 210* ■

📙 **Bellringer**
💿 **PowerPoint® Resources**
📙 L26 Unraveling DNA
📙 L27 The Making of a Protein: A
📙 L28 The Making of a Protein: B
SE Quick Lab Cracking the Code, p. 216* ■

SE Skills Practice Lab Extracting DNA, pp. 218–219* ■

Practice

SE Organize Activity Tri-Fold, p. 206

SE Section Review, p. 211* ■

SE Section Review, p. 217* ■

SE Science Skills Activity Connecting Scientific Methods, p. 220* ■
📙 **Concept Mapping***
SE Chapter Review, pp. 222–223* ■

Assess

📁 **Chapter Pretest**

SE Standards Checks, pp. 208, 211
TE Standards Focus, p. 210
📁 **Section Quiz** ■

SE Standards Checks, pp. 212, 215
TE Standards Focus, p. 216
📁 **Section Quiz** ■

SE Standards Assessment, pp. 224–225*
📁 **Chapter Tests A, B** ■**, C**
📙 **Standards Review Workbook** ■

Resources for Universal Access • Differentiated Instruction

English Learners

TE Abbreviations, p. 208
TE Group Activity, p. 209
TE Using the Figure, p. 211
TE Demonstration, p. 212
TE Using the Figure, p. 213
TE Homophones, p. 214
TE Group Activity, p. 214
📁 Vocabulary and Section Summary A ■, B

📁 Section Quizzes ■
📁 Chapter Tests A, B ■
📁 Differentiated Datasheets A, B, and C for Labs and Activities ■
📙 Study Guide A ■
📙 Multilingual Glossary

Struggling Readers

TE Reading Strategy, p. 209
TE Follow the Steps, p. 213
TE Meshing Text and Pictures, p. 214

Special Education Students

TE Variation in Eye Color, p. 209
TE Hands-on Chromatin, p. 212
TE Pictures of Proteins, p. 215

To help plan your lessons, refer to the On Course Mapping Instruction booklet.

Visual Resources

CHAPTER STARTER TRANSPARENCY

BELLRINGER TRANSPARENCIES

TEACHING TRANSPARENCIES

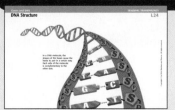

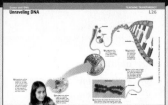

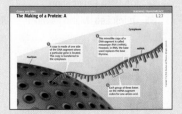

TEACHING TRANSPARENCIES

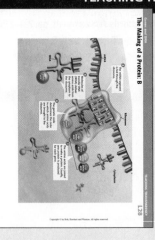

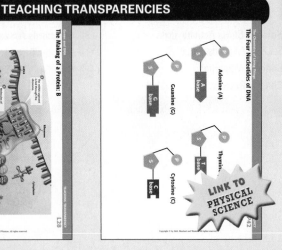

STANDARDS REVIEW TRANSPARENCIES

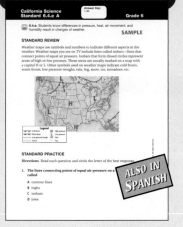

CONCEPT MAPPING TRANSPARENCY

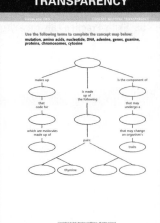

Planning Resources

PARENT LETTER

TEST ITEM LISTING

One-Stop Planner® CD-ROM

This CD-ROM package includes all of the resources shown here and the following time-saving tools:

- **Lab Materials QuickList Software**

- **Customizable Lesson Plans** Correlated to the California Science Standards

- **Holt Calendar Planner**

- **PowerPoint® Resources**

- **Printable Worksheets**

- **ExamView® Test Generator** Correlated to the California Science Standards

- **Holt PuzzlePro®**

- **Interactive Teacher's Edition**

Meeting Individual Needs

DIRECTED READING A

Skills Worksheet
Directed Reading A   SAMPLE

Section: Body Organization
A STABLE INTERNAL ENVIRONMENT
Write the letter of the correct answer in the space provided.

BASIC   *ALSO IN SPANISH*

DIRECTED READING B

Skills Worksheet
Directed Reading B   SAMPLE

Section: Body Organization
A STABLE INTERNAL ENVIRONMENT

GENERAL

VOCABULARY AND SECTION SUMMARY A

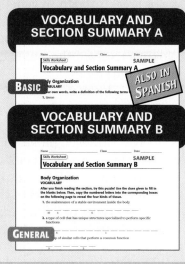

Skills Worksheet
Vocabulary and Section Summary A   SAMPLE

Body Organization
VOCABULARY

BASIC   *ALSO IN SPANISH*

VOCABULARY AND SECTION SUMMARY B

Skills Worksheet
Vocabulary and Section Summary B   SAMPLE

Body Organization
VOCABULARY

GENERAL

REINFORCEMENT

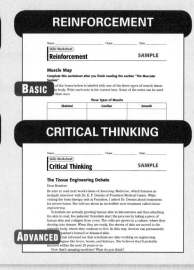

Skills Worksheet
Reinforcement   SAMPLE

Muscle Map
Complete this worksheet after you finish reading the section "The Muscular System."

Three Types of Muscle

Skeletal	Cardiac	Smooth

BASIC

CRITICAL THINKING

Skills Worksheet
Critical Thinking   SAMPLE

The Tissue Engineering Debate
Dear Readers:

ADVANCED

INTERACTIVE READER AND STUDY GUIDE

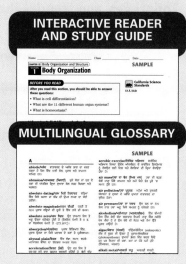

Body Organization   SAMPLE

BEFORE YOU READ
After you read this section, you should be able to answer these questions:
• What is cell differentiation?
• What are the 11 different human organ systems?
• What is homeostasis?

California Science Standards

MULTILINGUAL GLOSSARY

SAMPLE

Labs and Activities

DIFFERENTIATED DATASHEETS FOR EXPLORE ACTIVITY, QUICK LABS, AND CHAPTER LAB

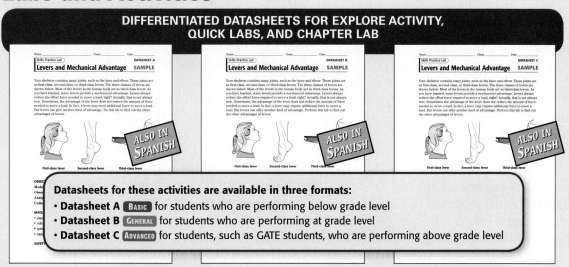

Skills Practice Lab
Levers and Mechanical Advantage   DATASHEET A   SAMPLE

Skills Practice Lab
Levers and Mechanical Advantage   DATASHEET B   SAMPLE

Skills Practice Lab
Levers and Mechanical Advantage   DATASHEET C   SAMPLE

ALSO IN SPANISH

First-class lever   Second-class lever   Third-class lever

Datasheets for these activities are available in three formats:
• **Datasheet A** BASIC for students who are performing below grade level
• **Datasheet B** GENERAL for students who are performing at grade level
• **Datasheet C** ADVANCED for students, such as GATE students, who are performing above grade level

DATASHEET FOR SCIENCE SKILLS ACTIVITY

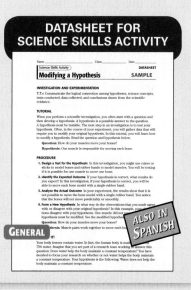

Science Skills Activity
Modifying a Hypothesis   DATASHEET   SAMPLE

INVESTIGATION AND EXPERIMENTATION
7.7.e Communicate the logical connection among hypotheses, science concepts, tests conducted, data collected, and conclusions drawn from the scientific evidence.

TUTORIAL

PROCEDURE

GENERAL   *ALSO IN SPANISH*

Reviews and Assessments

SECTION REVIEWS

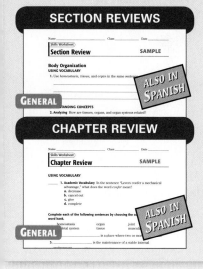

Skills Worksheet
Section Review   SAMPLE

Body Organization
USING VOCABULARY

GENERAL   *ALSO IN SPANISH*

CHAPTER REVIEW

Skills Worksheet
Chapter Review   SAMPLE

USING VOCABULARY

GENERAL   *ALSO IN SPANISH*

CHAPTER PRETEST

Assessment
Chapter Pretest   SAMPLE

GENERAL

SECTION QUIZZES

Assessment
Section Quiz   SAMPLE

Section: Body Organization
Write the letter of the correct answer in the space provided.

GENERAL   *ALSO IN SPANISH*

CHAPTER TEST A

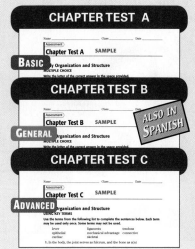

Assessment
Chapter Test A   SAMPLE

Body Organization and Structure
MULTIPLE CHOICE
Write the letter of the correct answer in the space provided.

BASIC

CHAPTER TEST B

Assessment
Chapter Test B   SAMPLE

Body Organization and Structure
MULTIPLE CHOICE

GENERAL   *ALSO IN SPANISH*

CHAPTER TEST C

Assessment
Chapter Test C   SAMPLE

Body Organization and Structure
USING KEY TERMS

ADVANCED   *ALSO IN SPANISH*

STANDARDS ASSESSMENT

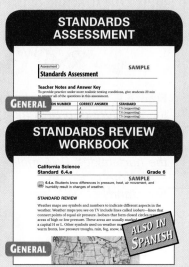

Assessment
Standards Assessment   SAMPLE

Teacher Notes and Answer Key

GENERAL

STANDARDS REVIEW WORKBOOK

California Science Standard 6.4.e   Grade 6
SAMPLE

6.4.e. Students know differences in pressure, heat, air movement, and humidity result in changes of weather.

STANDARD REVIEW

GENERAL   *ALSO IN SPANISH*

This Teacher Background explains science concepts, principles, and theories that appear in the chapter. Use the information on these pages to refresh or enhance your understanding of the topics covered.

Section 1

What Does DNA Look Like?

Purpose and Structure

In 1869, a 22-year-old Swiss scientist named Friedrich Miescher isolated DNA (deoxyribonucleic acid) from a cell nucleus. Miescher did not know the function of DNA and its role in heredity. In 1928, a British medical officer, Frederick Griffith, found that an unknown substance could be passed from dead bacteria to live ones. This substance was able to cause a heritable change in the phenotype of the live bacteria. In 1944, American bacteriologist Oswald Avery, along with colleagues Maclyn McCarty and Colin MacLeod, reported that DNA was the unknown heritable substance. Avery and colleagues tested various chemicals from the dead bacteria, including protein, RNA, lipids, and DNA. DNA was the only substance to work and therefore DNA was reported to be able to carry genetic information. At this time, not much was known about the structure of DNA. Discoveries about the structure of DNA led to a greater understanding of how DNA could carry hereditary information. Erwin Chargraff, a biochemist, discovered that within DNA molecules, the nucleotides adenine (A) and thymine (T) were present in relatively equal amounts. He found the same to be true for guanine (G) and cytosine (C). Chargaff's research provided the basis for the later understanding of nucleotide pairings.

In 1959, 35-year-old English scientist Francis Crick and 23-year-old American scientist James Watson determined the structure of DNA. Watson and Crick proposed the model of the double helix, the currently accepted model of the shape of DNA. Their work represented a major breakthrough in genetic research, providing an explanation for how DNA could store so much information. Watson and Crick, along with colleague Maurice Wilkins, received the Nobel Prize in physiology or medicine in 1962.

DNA is located in the chromosomes of each eukaryotic cell (cell with a membrane-bound nucleus). Prokaryotic cells (cells without a membrane-bound nucleus) also contain DNA. However, prokaryotic DNA is in the form of one circular chromosome. In eukaryotic cells, chromosomes organize strands of DNA into discrete units. Human DNA is organized into 23 pairs of chromosomes that vary in size. Other types of living organisms have different DNA arrangements. For example, carp have 52 pairs of chromosomes, and some beans have only 6 pairs of chromosomes.

The DNA double helix, as shown in **Figure A,** consists of two chains, or strands, that look like a twisted ladder. Each chain is made of sugars, phosphates, and bases. The bases make up the rungs of the ladder, while the sugars and phosphates make up the sides of the ladder. The bases are held together by hydrogen bonds, represented in **Figure A** as dots between the bases. Hydrogen bonds are weaker than covalent bonds, enabling the strands to separate during replication and transcription.

Nucleotides are often called the building blocks of DNA. The four bases are adenine (A), thymine (T), guanine (G), and cytosine (C). The molecular conformation of the nucleotides ensures that A always pairs with T and that G always pairs with C, as seen by the shapes of the nucleotide end-pieces in **Figure B.** Each strand of DNA contains millions of nucleotide bases, which are in a set order based on genetic ancestry. This order determines thousands of different characteristics, such as height, skin tone, eye color, and fingernail shape.

Figure A *This figure shows the structure of a DNA molecule, including the position of sugars, phosphates, and the nucleotides. DNA molecules are made up of two stands of DNA that, with the nucleotide pairings, form a ladder-like structure.*

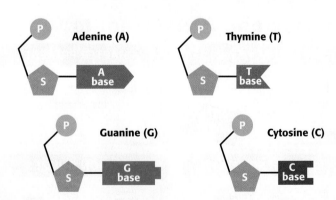

Figure B *Each DNA nucleotide consists of a phosphate, sugar, and a base. The base determines the type of nucleotide.*

Section 2

How DNA Works

The Genetic Code

DNA codons (sequences of three bases) are translated into amino acids, which is why DNA is often said to store information as a genetic code. Each DNA codon codes for a specific amino acid. Strings of codons form genes, and strings of genes form genomes. A genome is the total genetic content in a set of chromosomes.

When looking through a microscope at an appropriately stained section of an onion root tip, students may see cells that are engaged in mitosis and that have visible, condensed chromosome structures. The proteins in chromosomes help to support the chromosome's structure and function, but the genetic information of a cell is uniquely stored in the DNA component of the chromosome.

Ribonucleic acid (RNA), another type of nucleic acid, is a component of all living cells and many viruses. RNA consists of long chains of alternating phosphates and ribose, with the bases adenine, guanine, cytosine, and uracil bonded to the ribose. RNA functions as the "go-between" for DNA and proteins. Messenger RNA (mRNA) transmits information from DNA to ribosomes, while transfer RNA (tRNA) assembles strings of amino acids that form proteins.

The genetic code is nearly identical in all living organisms. If a codon encodes for a particular amino acid in humans, the same codon encodes for the same amino acid in bacteria. This similarity suggests that all life-forms have a common evolutionary ancestor.

Amino Acids

Most known organisms produce proteins using only 20 amino acids as building blocks (some use a rare 21st amino acid, selenocysteine). The human body can manufacture 10 of these amino acids. The other 10 must be obtained from proteins in the diet, and for this reason they are called the *essential* amino acids. Foods that contain all of the essential amino acids include eggs, milk, seafood, and meat. However, vegetarians can get all the amino acids that their body needs by eating a varied diet.

The 20 amino acids are listed in this table:

Alanine	Glutamine	Leucine	Serine
Arginine	Glutamic acid	Lysine	Threonine
Asparagine	Glycine	Methionine	Tryptophan
Aspartic acid	Histidine	Phenylalanine	Tyrosine
Cysteine	Isoleucine	Proline	Valine

Protein Synthesis

Protein synthesis begins with transcription. First, the two DNA strands in a gene for a given protein "unzip," or separate, from each other. Messenger RNA is synthesized from one strand of the gene, using the DNA as a template. Nucleotides pair with exposed DNA bases and are linked together by an enzyme called RNA polymerase. Since RNA does not contain the base thymine, uracil (U) pairs with adenine (A). Translation is the next part of the process of protein synthesis. The new mRNA leaves the cell nucleus and travels to a ribosome, where the mRNA code is translated by tRNA molecules and the ribosome. Amino acids are attached to the tRNA molecules. As tRNA molecules bring amino acids to the mRNA, a protein is formed when rRNA in the ribosome joins those amino acids together. These proteins carry out the biochemical processes that allow an organism to survive.

The DNA sequence may be changed by environmental conditions, such as exposure to radiation or by errors during DNA replication. A change to the nucleotide sequence of DNA is called a mutation. In protein synthesis, a mutation may cause no change, a harmful change, or a beneficial change. For example, since the codons GCT and GCA are both codes for the amino acid alanine, replacing the T with an A makes no difference. But, replacing an A with a T changes the codon GAG, encoding glutamic acid, to GTG, encoding valine. This single amino acid replacement results in sickle cell anemia. A mutation may result in a new amino acid sequence that leads to the development of traits that improve an organism's chances of survival in a particular environment. Mutations that improve an organism's chances of survival and reproduction are thought to be important for producing new traits in evolution.

If a mutation occurs in most body cells, such as the skin cells of a person, then any effects of that mutation will appear only in that individual and not in that individual's offspring. Mutations that occur in sex cells, however, can be passed on to future generations.

Chapter Preview

Chapter Pretest
Use the Chapter Pretest in the Chapter Resource File to determine the prior knowledge of your students. The Test Doctors and diagnostic teaching tips in the Teacher Notes pages will help you tailor your instruction to your students' specific needs.

Improving Comprehension

Use the Graphic Organizer on this page of the Student Edition to introduce the topics that are covered in this chapter, to summarize the chapter material, or to show students how to build a concept map.

Teaching Tips

• Remind students that the main topics and vocabulary terms in the chapter often make up the terms in a concept map.

• Explain to students that the words between the circled concepts indicate the relationship between the concepts that the words connect.

LS Logical

Improving Comprehension

Graphic Organizers are important visual tools that can help you organize information and improve your reading comprehension. The Graphic Organizer below is called a *concept map*. Instructions for creating other types of Graphic Organizers are located in the **Study Skills** section of the Appendix.

How to Make a Concept Map

1. Identify main ideas from the text, and write the ideas as short phrases or single words.
2. Select a main concept. Place this concept at the top or center of a piece of paper.
3. Place other ideas under or around the main concept based on their relationship to the main concept. Draw a circle around each idea.
4. Draw lines between the concepts, and add linking words to connect the ideas.

When to Use a Concept Map

Concept maps are useful when you are trying to identify how several ideas are connected to a main concept. Concept maps may be based on vocabulary terms or on main topics from the text. The concept map below shows how the important concepts of this chapter are related. As you read about science, look for terms that can be organized in a concept map.

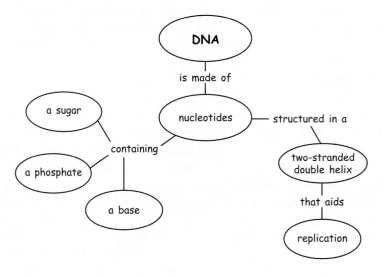

You Try It!

This Reading Strategy can also be used within the chapter that you are about to read. Practice making your own *concept map* as directed in the Reading Strategy for Section 2. Record your work in your **Science Journal**.

Using Other Graphic Organizers

Students can practice using a variety of Graphic Organizers while reading this chapter. The following Graphic Organizers may also be useful in this chapter:

An **idea wheel** can be used to show pioneering scientists' findings about the structure and function of DNA, discussed in Section 1.

A **process chart** can be used to illustrate how copies of DNA are made, explained in Section 1. A process chart can also be used to illustrate the steps involved in the making of a protein, introduced in Section 2.

Instructions for creating these Graphic Organizers are located on pp. 583–591 of the Appendix.

Unpacking the Standards

The information below "unpacks" the standards by breaking them down into basic parts. The higher-level, academic vocabulary is highlighted and defined to help you understand the language of the standards. "What It Means" restates the standards as simply as possible.

California Standard	Academic Vocabulary	What It Means
7.1.a Students know cells **function similarly** in all living organisms.	**function** (FUHNGK shuhn) to work **similarly** (SIM uh luhr lee) in almost the same way	Cells perform the same actions in all living things.
7.2.e Students know DNA (deoxyribonucleic acid) is the genetic material of living organisms and is **located** in the chromosomes of each cell.	**located** (LOH kayt id) to be in a certain place	DNA is the material that determines what traits are passed from one generation of living things to the next. DNA is found in the chromosomes of each cell.

Unpacking the Standards

Use the following information with the *What It Means* in the Student Edition to help students understand why studying each standard is important.

Why It Matters

At the cellular level, all living organisms share common traits. Understanding this idea allows one to understand the nature of life on Earth.

DNA is the blueprint for running the cell's chemical manufacturing system and for making another copy of itself. Any change in the DNA can affect the products or offspring of the cell.

Academic Vocabulary

Standards that are covered in this chapter may contain academic terms that are unfamiliar to students. The following table identifies some of the academic terms used in this chapter and their meanings.

Word	Definition
function	to work
located	to be in a certain place
similarly	in almost the same way

Practice Draw this table on the board. Fill in the words, but not the definitions. Have students write down what they think the words mean. Then, write the correct meanings of the words in the table on the board, and ask students to write sentences that demonstrate the meaning of each word. (The *function* of RNA is to help make proteins. Janet and Mark scored *similarly* on their exam; they both got a 92. Nobody knew where the puddle on the floor was coming from until a hole in the ceiling was *located*.

Chapter Overview

Tell students that this chapter is about deoxyribonucleic acid (DNA)—the substance that makes up genes—and about how DNA works within cells to direct the growth and function of every organism.

MISCONCEPTION ALERT

Dental Genes

Identify It! Students may not grasp the idea that inherited genes and learned behaviors together determine a person's traits. For example, students may think that they can completely prevent cavities by brushing and flossing their teeth after each meal.

Correct It! Explain that the tendency to develop cavities is an inherited trait, but that tooth care also plays a role in dental health. Point out that people who inherit cavity-prone teeth can reduce their chances of developing cavities by caring for their teeth. However, people who inherit teeth that are not prone to cavities can still develop cavities if they do not take care of their teeth. On the board, make a chart with the headings: Mother, Father, Me, My Tooth Care. Ask volunteers to use the letters H (High) and L (Low) to indicate the incidence of cavities in themselves and in their parents, and the student's level of dental care. Fill in students' responses on the chart.

Assess It! Ask volunteers what their cavity history tells them about their inherited tooth constitution. Ask students how this knowledge should affect their tooth care. (Answers may vary.)

Genes and DNA

The Big Idea

DNA is the genetic material of living organisms and is located in the chromosomes of each cell.

California Standards

Focus on Life Sciences
7.1 All living organisms are composed of cells, from just one to many trillions, whose details usually are visible only through a microscope. (Section 2)
7.2 A typical cell of any organism contains genetic instructions that specify its traits. Those traits may be modified by environmental influences. (Sections 1 and 2)

Investigation and Experimentation
7.7 Scientific progress is made by asking meaningful questions and conducting careful investigations. (Science Skills Activity)

Math
7.1.1, 7.1.2 Number Sense

English–Language Arts
7.1.3 Reading
7.2.5 Writing

About the Photo

In the cells of these adult mice, the genes that normally carry the signal to grow hair are not working. The genes were "turned off" by scientists who have learned to control the function of some genes. Scientists study defective genes in mice in order to learn more about a variety of medical problems, including cancer.

Organize

Tri-Fold

Before you read this chapter, create the FoldNote entitled "Tri-Fold." Write what you know about the structure of DNA in the column labeled "Know." Then, write what you want to know about the structure of DNA in the column labeled "Want." As you read the chapter, write what you learn about the structure of DNA in the column labeled "Learn."

Instructions for creating FoldNotes are located in the Study Skills section on p. 582 of the Appendix.

California Standards Alignment

Focus on Life Sciences

7.1.a Students know cells function similarly in all living organisms. **pp. 212–217, 222–225**

7.2.e Students know DNA (deoxyribonucleic acid) is the genetic material of living organisms and is located in the chromosomes of each cell. **pp. 207–208, 210–213, 217–218, 222–225**

Investigation and Experimentation

7.7.c Communicate the logical connection among hypotheses, science concepts, tests conducted, data collected, and conclusions drawn from the scientific evidence. **p. 207**

7.7.d Construct scale models, maps, and appropriately labeled diagrams to communicate scientific knowledge (e.g., motion of Earth's plates and cell structure). **p. 210**

Math Standards

Number Sense 7.1.1 Read, write, and compare rational numbers in scientific notation (positive and negative powers of 10) with approximate numbers using scientific notation. **p. 223**

Number Sense 7.1.2 Add, subtract, multiply, and divide rational numbers (integers, fractions, and terminating decimals) and take positive rational numbers to whole-number powers. **p. 223**

Explore Activity

Fingerprint Identification

One way to identify people is by taking their fingerprints. Does it really work? Are everyone's fingerprints unique? Try this activity to find out.

Procedure

1. Rub the tip of a **pencil** back and forth across a **piece of tracing paper.** Make a large, dark mark.

2. Rub the tip of one of your fingers on the pencil mark. Then place a small **piece of transparent tape** over the darkened area on your finger.

3. Remove the tape, and stick it on a **piece of white paper.** Repeat steps 1–3 for the rest of your fingers.

4. Look at the fingerprints with a **magnifying lens.** What patterns do you see?

Analysis

5. Compare your fingerprints with those of your classmates. Do any two people in your class have the same prints? Try to explain your findings.

7.2.e
7.7.c

English–Language Arts Standards

Reading 6.2.4 clarify understanding of texts by creating outlines, logical notes, summaries, or reports. p. 212

Reading 7.1.3 clarify word meaning through the use of definition, example, restatement, or contrast **p. 208**

Writing 7.2.5 Write summaries of reading materials: (a) Include the main ideas and most significant details; (b) Use the student's own words, except for quotations; (c) Reflect underlying meaning, not just the superficial details. **p. 223**

Chapter Starter Transparency
Use this transparency to help students begin thinking about the uses of DNA in a police investigation of a crime scene.

Explore Activity 🕐 20 min

Teacher Notes

This activity has students compare fingerprints and analyze why fingerprints are unique. This activity helps students begin thinking about the relationship between DNA, genes, and traits (covers standards 7.2.e and 7.7.e). The loop pattern is found in approximately 65% of the population, the whorl pattern is found in about 30%, and the arch pattern is found in approximately 5%.

Materials for Each Group

- magnifying lens
- paper, tracing (1 sheet)
- paper, white (1 sheet)
- pencil or piece of charcoal
- tape, transparent

Safety Caution

Remind students to review all safety cautions and icons before beginning this activity. Charcoal is nontoxic, but it can stain clothes.

Answer

5. The number of fingerprint types may vary for each class. No two students should have the same fingerprint (those of identical twins may be similar, but still unique). Accept any reasonable explanation that incorporates the concept of variation in inherited traits among populations.

📋 Differentiated Datasheets
A **BASIC**, B **GENERAL**, C **ADVANCED**

Also editable on the
**Holt Lab Generator
CD-ROM**

Preteach

Reviewing Prior Knowledge

Ask students to explain the purpose of DNA in our bodies. (DNA determines our genetic makeup.) Then, ask students if DNA is found only in humans. (No; DNA is found in all living things.)

🎧 Bellringer

To help students focus on standard 7.2.e, have them give examples of the difference between traits and characteristics. (Sample answer: Eye color is a characteristic. Blue eyes color is a trait.) Then ask, "Where are genes found in cells?" (in chromosomes; in cells that have nuclei, chromosomes are in the nucleus)

📀 Bellringer Transparency

Motivate

Modeling Code Have students create a code by pairing each letter of the alphabet with a numeral. For example, the numeral *1* could represent the letter *a*. Ask students to encode a brief message. Explain that a code is simply another way to represent information and that there are many types of codes. Make sure students realize that the genetic code is based on the sequences of the four nucleotide bases of DNA. **LS** Logical

What You Will Learn

- The discovery of the structure and function of DNA is a major achievement in life science.
- DNA is made up of nucleotides arranged in two strands. Together, the two strands form a double helix.
- The structure of DNA relates to how it functions, including how it is replicated.

Why It Matters

The structure of DNA allows for the storage of your genetic information.

Vocabulary

- DNA
- nucleotide

READING STRATEGY

Clarifying Concepts Take turns reading this section out loud with a partner. Stop to discuss ideas that seem confusing.

DNA (DEE EN AYE) **d**eoxyribo**n**ucleic **a**cid, a molecule that is present in all living cells and that contains the information that determines the traits that a living thing inherits and needs to live

nucleotide (NOO klee oh TIED) in a nucleic-acid chain, a subunit that consists of a sugar, a phosphate, and a nitrogenous base

7.2.e Students know DNA (deoxyribonucleic acid) is the genetic material of living organisms and is located in the chromosomes of each cell.

What Does DNA Look Like?

Key Concept The structure of DNA is a double helix, which is shaped like a twisted ladder.

▶ The study of heredity helped scientists understand how genetic information is transferred from parents to offspring. But what is genetic information made of, and how does it work?

Inherited characteristics are determined by genes, and genes are passed from one generation to the next. Genes are found on *chromosomes,* which are structures located in the nucleus of cells. Chromosomes are made of protein and DNA. **DNA** stands for *deoxyribonucleic acid* (dee AHKS ee RIE boh noo KLEE ik AS id). DNA is the genetic material of living things. It determines inherited characteristics. So, what does DNA look like?

The Pieces of the Puzzle

Scientists knew that the material that makes up genes must be able to do two things. First, it must be able to give instructions for building and maintaining cells. Second, it must be able to be copied each time a cell divides so that each cell contains identical genes. The structure of DNA allows for these two functions to occur.

Standards Check What are two functions of DNA? 📖**7.2.e**

Nucleotides: The Subunits of DNA

DNA is made of subunits called nucleotides. A **nucleotide** consists of a sugar, a phosphate, and a base. The nucleotides are identical except for the base. The four bases are *adenine, thymine, guanine,* and *cytosine.* Each base has a different shape. Scientists often refer to a base the first letter of the base—*A, T, G,* and *C.* **Figure 1** shows models of the four nucleotides.

Figure 1 The Four Nucleotides of DNA

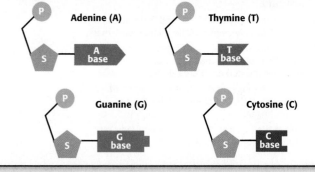

Adenine (A)   Thymine (T)

Guanine (G)   Cytosine (C)

Universal Access · Differentiated Instruction

English Learners

Abbreviations On the board, write the following abbreviations in the first column of a vertical list: C.O.D., P.M., M.D., and DNA. Ask students to give the general meaning of each abbreviation. (payment when package arrives, afternoon, physician or doctor, a type of genetic material) Write these meanings in the second column. Then, ask students what each letter in the abbreviation actually stands for. (cash on delivery, post meridian, medical doctor, deoxyribonucleic acid) Write this information in the third column. Challenge students to remember other abbreviations in previous chapters (UV, SI, mL). Discuss with the class that abbreviations are accepted shorthand for the words they represent. Point out that it is not always important to remember the exact words that the abbreviations stand for, but to know what the abbreviations mean. **LS** Verbal

Chargaff's Rules

In the 1950s, a biochemist named Erwin Chargaff found that the amount of adenine in DNA always equals the amount of thymine. He also found that the amount of guanine always equals the amount of cytosine. His findings are now known as *Chargaff's rules*. At the time of his discovery, no one knew the importance of these findings. But Chargaff's rules later helped scientists understand the structure of DNA.

Franklin's Discovery

More clues about the structure of DNA came from scientists in Britain. There, chemist Rosalind Franklin, shown in **Figure 2,** was able to make images of DNA molecules. She used a process known as *X-ray diffraction* to make these images. In this process, X rays are aimed at the DNA molecule. When an X ray hits a part of the molecule, the ray bounces off. The pattern made by the bouncing rays is captured on film. Franklin's images suggested that DNA has a spiral shape.

Figure 2 *Rosalind Franklin used X-ray diffraction to make images of DNA that helped reveal the structure of DNA.*

Watson and Crick's Model

At about the same time, two other scientists were also trying to solve the mystery of DNA's structure. They were James Watson and Francis Crick, shown in **Figure 3.** After seeing Franklin's X-ray images, Watson and Crick concluded that DNA must look like a long, twisted ladder. They were then able to build a model of DNA by using simple materials from their laboratory. Their model perfectly fit with both Chargaff's and Franklin's findings. The model eventually helped explain how DNA is copied and how it functions in the cell.

Figure 3 *This photo shows James Watson (left) and Francis Crick (right) with their model of DNA.*

Universal Access · Differentiated Instruction

Special Education Students

Variation in Eye Color Give students a chance to move around while they learn. Instruct students with green eyes to move to a certain part of the room, brown to a different part of the room, and blue to another part of the room. Then, have the students in each group line up from lightest shade to darkest shade of eye color. Assign a spokesperson for each group to explain how they decided the order of their lineup. Also, ask each group why they think there is so much variation in eye color. **LS Kinesthetic/Verbal**

Advanced Learners/GATE

Choose a Scientist Give students who can benefit from more in-depth information a chance to choose a scientist to research. Tell them they can choose any of the four scientists on this page. Ask students to present overviews of the scientists' careers, including the work described in this textbook. **LS Logical**

Teach

📖 READING STRATEGY

Mnemonics Have students create a mnemonic device that helps them remember the names of the bases and the way the bases form pairs. Examples such as "**A**toms are **T**iny" or "**A**dam is **T**errific" might help remind students that **a**denine pairs with **t**hymine. "**C**ats are **G**reat" might remind them that **c**ytosine pairs with **g**uanine. **LS Verbal**

Group ACTIVITY

A Place in History Have students imagine that they have just discovered the structure of DNA and must present their findings to a group of scientists. Have small groups of students use a model of DNA, a poster, or another visual aid to briefly describe the structure of DNA to their classmates. **LS Verbal/Logical**

MISCONCEPTION ALERT

Pre-Computer Research Since technological advancements have skyrocketed with the computer age, some students might think that DNA research is rather recent. Ask students to look at the picture of Watson and Crick and guess the year. (Sample answer: The picture looks like it was taken before color photos were common, perhaps in the 1950s.) Tell students that Watson and Crick determined the structure of DNA in 1953, before computer technology was available to them. Explain that scientists had been studying DNA since the 1860s.

 Teaching Transparency:

LINK TO PHYSICAL SCIENCE
P42 The Four Nucleotides of DNA

Close

Standards Focus

This **Standards Focus** provides you with a quick way to **assess, reteach,** and **re-assess** one or more concepts in the section.

 Assess

1. Name the four types of nucleotides. (adenine, thymine, guanine, and cytosine) **7.2.e**

2. Name two nucleotides that can form a pair and two that cannot. (Sample answer: Guanine and cytosine can form a pair; guanine and thymine cannot.) **7.2.e**

Reteach

DNA's Complementary Strands
To help students understand how the term *complementary* relates to the structure of DNA, point out that the term means "completing." Using **Figure 4** and **Figure 5,** explain that complementary base pairs join to complete each rung on the twisted-ladder structure of DNA because they complement each other, or fit together the way a lock and a key do. Help students review their knowledge by asking them what the letters on **Figure 4** stand for. (The letters *s* and *p* stand for sugar and phosphates. The letters *g, c, t,* and *a* stand for the four bases that make up nucleotide base pairs—guanine and cytosine, thymine and adenine.) **LS Visual/Verbal 7.2.e**

 Re-Assess

Standup DNA Divide the class into four equal groups. Assign each group one of the nucleotide letters: A, T, G, or C. Ask each student to write his or her assigned letter on paper in large print. Then, have students hold their papers up. Finally, tell them that when you call out, "mix it up," they should find and stand next to someone with whom they could form a base pair. (*As* and *Ts* must always choose each other, and *Gs* and *Cs* must always choose each other.)
LS Kinesthetic 7.2.e

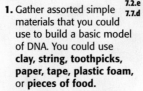

Quick Lab

Making a Model of DNA

7.2.e
7.7.d

1. Gather assorted simple materials that you could use to build a basic model of DNA. You could use **clay, string, toothpicks, paper, tape, plastic foam,** or **pieces of food.**

2. Work with a partner or a small team to build your model. Use your book and other resources to check the details of your model.

3. Show your model to your classmates. Give your classmates feedback about the scientific aspects of their models.

 25 min

DNA's Double Structure

The shape of DNA is shown in **Figure 4.** As you can see, a strand of DNA looks like a twisted ladder. This shape is known as a *double helix* (DUB uhl HEE LIKS). The two sides of the ladder are made of alternating sugar parts and phosphate parts. The rungs of the ladder are made of a pair of bases. Adenine on one side of a rung always pairs with thymine on the other side. Guanine always pairs with cytosine.

Notice how the double helix structure matches Chargaff's observations. When Chargaff separated the parts of a sample of DNA, he found that the matching bases were always present in equal amounts. To model how the bases pair, Watson and Crick tried to match Chargaff's observations. They also used information from chemists about the size and shape of each of the nucleotides. They found that the width of the DNA ladder matches the combined width of the matching bases. Only the correct pairs of bases fit within the ladder's width.

DNA Replication

The pairing of bases allows the cell to *replicate,* or make copies of, DNA. Each base always bonds with only one other base. Thus, pairs of bases are *complementary* to each other, and both sides of a DNA molecule are complementary. For example, the sequence CGAC will bond to the sequence GCTG.

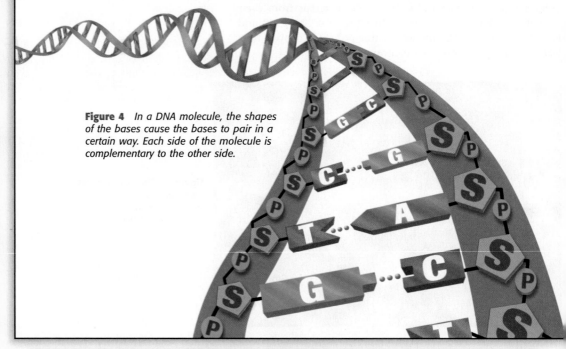

Figure 4 *In a DNA molecule, the shapes of the bases cause the bases to pair in a certain way. Each side of the molecule is complementary to the other side.*

Quick Lab

 **25 min**

Teacher Notes

In this activity, students construct an accurate model of DNA (covers standards 7.2.e and 7.7.d). If possible, display student models within the school. You may want to have students reevaluate or improve upon their models after learning more about DNA.

Materials for Each Group
• variety of craft materials, such as clay, string, toothpicks, paper, tape, plastic foam, beads or buttons, pipe cleaners or wire, and food items

Safety Caution

Remind students to review all safety cautions and icons. Ask students not to eat any of the food items.

Answers

3. Student models should resemble **Figure 4** in basic structure, but may vary in size, color, and construction. Students should suggest ways to make each other's models more accurate.

Differentiated Datasheets
A **BASIC**, B **GENERAL**, C **ADVANCED**

Also editable on the Holt Lab Generator CD-ROM

How Copies Are Made

During replication, a DNA molecule is split down the middle, as shown in **Figure 5**. The bases on each side of the molecule are used as a pattern for a new strand. As the bases on the original molecule are exposed, complementary nucleotides are added. Finally, two DNA molecules are formed. Half of each of the molecules is old DNA, and half is new DNA.

When Copies Are Made

DNA is copied every time that a cell divides. Each new cell gets a complete copy of all the DNA. The job of unwinding, copying, and rewinding the DNA is done by proteins within the cell. So, DNA is usually found with several kinds of proteins. Other proteins help with the process of carrying out the instructions written in the code of the DNA.

Standards Check What functions do proteins perform in DNA replication? **7.2.e**

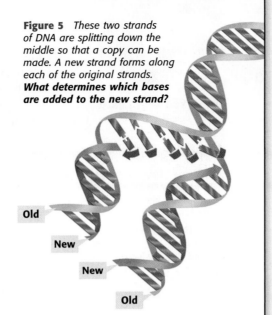

Figure 5 *These two strands of DNA are splitting down the middle so that a copy can be made. A new strand forms along each of the original strands.* **What determines which bases are added to the new strand?**

Old
New
New
Old

SECTION Review

 7.2.e

Summary

DNA is the material that makes up genes.

Investigations by Chargaff, Franklin, Watson, and Crick led to the discovery of DNA's structure and function.

The DNA molecule looks like a twisted ladder, or double helix. The two halves are long strings of nucleotides.

In DNA, adenine always pairs with thymine, and guanine always pairs with cytosine.

The structure of DNA allows it to be replicated accurately.

Understanding Concepts

1 **Describing** What is the relationship between DNA and chromosomes?

2 **Listing** What are three important events that led to understanding the structure of DNA?

3 **Listing** What substance is the genetic material of living things?

Critical Thinking

4 **Identifying Relationships** How are proteins involved in DNA replication?

5 **Analyzing Processes** How does the structure of DNA allow cells to replicate?

INTERPRETING GRAPHICS Use the diagram of DNA below to answer the next question.

6 **Applying Concepts** What would the complementary strand of DNA be for the sequence of bases shown?

Challenge

7 **Analyzing Processes** What scientific methods were used by the scientists who studied the structure of DNA?

Internet Resources

For a variety of links related to this chapter, go to www.scilinks.org
Topic: DNA
SciLinks code: HY70418

Using the Figure

Making New DNA Strands Ask students to look at **Figure 4.** Have them use the figure as a model to create a representation of a strand of DNA on a piece of paper. Tell them to create ten pairs of DNA in a straight line. Make sure that students realize that the bases T, A, G, and C can all fall on either side of the strand, but that T and A must always pair and that G and C must always pair. Then, have them cut their DNA strands in half lengthwise to represent the splitting of DNA strands. Finally, have them tape the two halves each on a separate piece of paper and create new halves for the two strands as shown in **Figure 5**. Again, remind them that T and A must always pair and that G and C must always pair. Answer to caption question: the bases on the old, original molecule are used to determine the complementary bases on the new strand.

 Teaching Transparency:
L25 DNA Replication
L24 DNA Structure

Section Resources

Directed Reading
A **Basic** (Also in Spanish), B **General**

Interactive Reader and Study Guide

Section Quiz **General** (Also in Spanish)

Section Review **General** (Also in Spanish)

Vocabulary and Section Summary
A **Basic** (Also in Spanish), B **General**

Preteach

Reviewing Prior Knowledge

Review standard 7.2.e with students. Ask students to answer these questions:

1. What is the cell doing when meiosis and mitosis take place? (dividing)

2. Why do chromosomes need to be compact during mitosis and meiosis? (Sample answer: Chromosomes are moving around. It is easier to move a compact object.)

3. Why do chromosomes need to be less compact during the rest of the life of the cell? (Sample answer: DNA must be accessible for replication and transcription, or for copying and making RNA.)

Bellringer

To help students focus on standard 7.1.a, have them unscramble the following words and use both of them in one sentence.

1. tpsoneir (proteins)

2. neesg (genes)

(Sample answer: Genes contain instructions for making proteins.)

Bellringer Transparency

Motivate

Demonstration

A Tight Fit   To illustrate the way that DNA is *supercoiled*, hold up a long rubber band or thick piece of string. Twist the ends in opposite directions until the band or string is compacted. Challenge students to fit 2 m of thread into a thimble, the cap of a pen, or an empty gelatin capsule. **LS Kinesthetic**

Answer to Standards Check

A gene tells a cell how to make a certain trait. **7.2.e** (mastering)

SECTION 2

How DNA Works

Key Concept   DNA stores a code that carries the instructions for making proteins. Proteins cause most of the differences among organisms.

▶ Almost every cell in your body contains about 2 m of DNA. How does all of the DNA fit in a cell? And how does the DNA contain a code that affects your traits?

What You Will Learn

- DNA is bundled with proteins to form chromosomes.
- DNA stores genetic information in the form of a code.
- Cells use the DNA code to make proteins. Proteins affect traits.
- A mutation is the result of a change in the genetic code.

Why It Matters

Your DNA code directs the growth and survival of your body.

Vocabulary

- RNA
- ribosome
- mutation

READING STRATEGY

Graphic Organizer   In your **Science Journal**, create a Concept Map by using the terms *DNA, proteins, RNA, traits, mutations,* and *chromosomes.*

Unraveling DNA

Large amounts of DNA can fit inside a cell because DNA is packaged tightly by proteins. The proteins found around DNA help support the structure and function of DNA. Together, the DNA molecule and the proteins it winds around make up a chromosome. In eukaryotic cells, chromosomes are usually spread out, and DNA and proteins exist as long strands called *chromatin.* Chromatin is bundled up to make chromosomes more compact before a cell divides. **Figure 1** shows how DNA is packaged with proteins so that it can fit inside a cell.

The structure of DNA allows DNA to contain information. The order of the bases on one side of DNA is a code that carries information. A *gene* consists of a string of nucleotides that give the cell information about how to make a specific trait.

Standards Check   What is the function of a gene? 🐻 **7.2.e**

Figure 1   **Unraveling DNA**

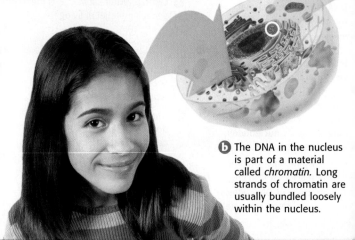

a A typical skin cell has a diameter of about 0.0025 cm. The DNA in the nucleus of each cell codes for proteins. Proteins are involved in many aspects of how your body looks and how it works.

7.1.a Students know cells function similarly in all living organisms.
7.2.e Students know DNA (deoxyribonucleic acid) is the genetic material of living organisms and is located in the chromosomes of each cell.

b The DNA in the nucleus is part of a material called *chromatin.* Long strands of chromatin are usually bundled loosely within the nucleus.

Universal Access • Differentiated Instruction

Special Education Students

Hands-on Chromatin   Students with special needs often learn better with hands-on activities. Help these students understand how chromatin is formed. Give each student an 8½″ × 2″ strip of paper. Have them fold their strips in 1″ accordion folds. Then, cut a rectangular notch a quarter of the way through the folded paper at both the center top and center bottom. (Folded paper will look like a wide H.) Have students unfold their papers to show ladder-like strips. Have several students tape their strips (DNA strands) together, wrap them around paper clips (proteins) to create a model of chromatin. **LS Visual/Kinesthetic**

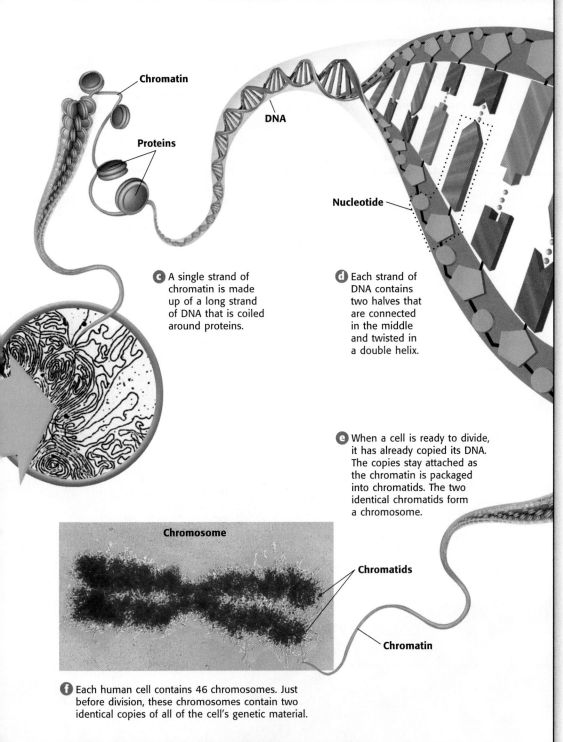

Chromatin

DNA

Proteins

Nucleotide

c A single strand of chromatin is made up of a long strand of DNA that is coiled around proteins.

d Each strand of DNA contains two halves that are connected in the middle and twisted in a double helix.

e When a cell is ready to divide, it has already copied its DNA. The copies stay attached as the chromatin is packaged into chromatids. The two identical chromatids form a chromosome.

Chromosome

Chromatids

Chromatin

f Each human cell contains 46 chromosomes. Just before division, these chromosomes contain two identical copies of all of the cell's genetic material.

 Teaching Transparency: L26 Unraveling DNA

📖 READING STRATEGY

Reading Hint Write the word *genetics* on the board. Ask a volunteer to define the term. Tell students that a word family is a group of words containing the same root. Ask students to identify the root of *genetics*. (gene) Remind students that a suffix is a group of letters added to the end of a root word that changes the meaning of the word a little. Ask students what suffix was added to the end of *genetics*. (tics or ics) Finally, ask volunteers to identify other terms that belong to this word family. (Sample answers: genealogy, gender, generation, genesis, genetically, geneticist, genic, genome, genotype) **LS** Verbal

Group ACTIVITY

Skit Have groups of students write and perform a short skit to demonstrate the formation of a protein. For example, students could play the roles of a ribosome, an amino acid, messenger RNA, transfer RNA, and a copy of DNA. **LS** Kinesthetic/Interpersonal

Homework

Research Have students collect information on the use of amino acids to build muscle. Suggest that they look at ads for amino acid supplements in health-food or fitness magazines or on labels of powdered amino acid drinks at the supermarket. Discuss with the class issues such as the expense of these types of products and how the amino acids in these products might be used by the body. Lead a class discussion on how amino acids might be acquired by eating a balanced diet. **LS** Verbal

🗄 Teaching Transparency:
L27 The Making of Protein: A
L28 The Making of Protein: B

INTERNET ACTIVITY

Anton Van Leeuwenhoek
How did Anton Van Leeuwenhoek help science advance? Write a biography about Anton Van Leeuwenhoek. Go to **go.hrw.com,** and type in the keyword HY7DNAW.

RNA (AHR EN AY) **r**ibo**n**ucleic **a**cid, a molecule that is present in all living cells and that plays a role in protein production

Figure 2 *Proteins are built in the cytoplasm by using RNA copies of genes, which are segments of DNA. The order of the bases on the RNA determines the order of amino acids that are assembled at the ribosome.*

Genes and Proteins

The DNA code is read like a book. Each gene has a starting point and an ending point, with DNA being read in one direction. The bases form the alphabet of the code. Groups of three bases are the codes for specific amino acids. A long string of amino acids forms a protein. Thus, each gene is usually a set of instructions for making a particular protein.

Proteins and Traits

How are proteins related to traits? Proteins are found throughout cells and cause most of the differences that you can see among organisms. Proteins act as chemical triggers and messengers for many of the processes within cells. Proteins help determine what colors you can see and whether your hair is curly or straight. A single organism typically has thousands of genes that code for thousands of proteins.

Help from RNA

Another type of molecule that helps make proteins is called **RNA,** or *ribonucleic acid* (RIE boh noo KLEE ik AS id). RNA is so similar to DNA that RNA can serve as a temporary copy of a DNA sequence. However, one difference between DNA and RNA is that RNA contains the base *uracil* (YOOR uh SIL) instead of thymine. Uracil is often referred to as *U*. **Figure 2** shows the forms of RNA that help in the process of changing the DNA code into proteins.

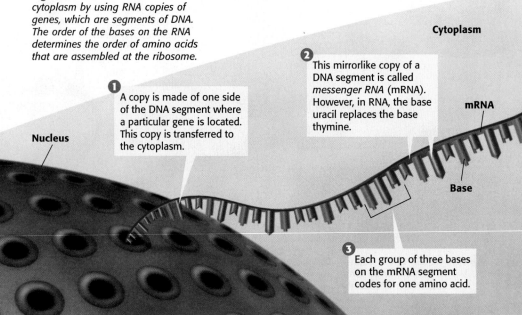

Cytoplasm

❶ A copy is made of one side of the DNA segment where a particular gene is located. This copy is transferred to the cytoplasm.

❷ This mirrorlike copy of a DNA segment is called *messenger RNA* (mRNA). However, in RNA, the base uracil replaces the base thymine.

mRNA

Nucleus

Base

❸ Each group of three bases on the mRNA segment codes for one amino acid.

Universal Access · Differentiated Instruction

English Learners

Homophones Explain to students that homophones are words that sound alike, but are spelled differently and have completely different meanings. Write these words on the board: *jeans, hare, strait,* and *won.* Ask students to look this page for homophones for these words. (genes, hair, straight, one) Ask volunteers to use each of the words in a sentence. **LS** Verbal

Struggling Readers

Meshing Text and Pictures Explain to students that some topics, such as the information under the head Genes and Proteins, are best explained using both text and pictures. Give each student seven tiny sticky notes. Have students write the numbers 1–7 on their sticky notes. Then, ask them to use the sticky notes to match the steps in the figure with the text. **LS** Visual

The Making of a Protein

The first step in making a protein is to copy one side of the segment of DNA containing a gene. A mirrorlike copy of the DNA segment is made out of RNA. This copy of the DNA segment is called *messenger RNA* (mRNA). It moves out of the nucleus and into the cytoplasm of the cell.

In the cytoplasm, the messenger RNA is fed through a protein assembly line. The "factory" that runs this assembly line is known as a ribosome. A **ribosome** is a cell organelle composed of RNA and protein. The messenger RNA is fed through the ribosome. Then, molecules of *transfer RNA* (tRNA) translate the RNA message. Each transfer RNA molecule picks up a specific amino acid from the cytoplasm. Inside the ribosome, bases on the transfer RNA match up with bases on the messenger RNA like pieces of a puzzle. The transfer RNA molecules then release their amino acids. The amino acids become linked in a growing chain. As the entire segment of messenger RNA passes through the ribosome, the growing chain of amino acids folds up into a new protein molecule.

Standards Check How are proteins made inside cells? 🐾 **7.1.a**

Code Combinations

A given sequence of three bases codes for one amino acid. For example, AGU and ACU are two possible sequence combinations. How many different sequences of the four RNA bases (adenine, guanine, uracil, and cytosine) are possible? (Hint: Make a list.)

ribosome (RIE buh SOHM) a cell organelle composed of RNA and protein; the site of protein synthesis

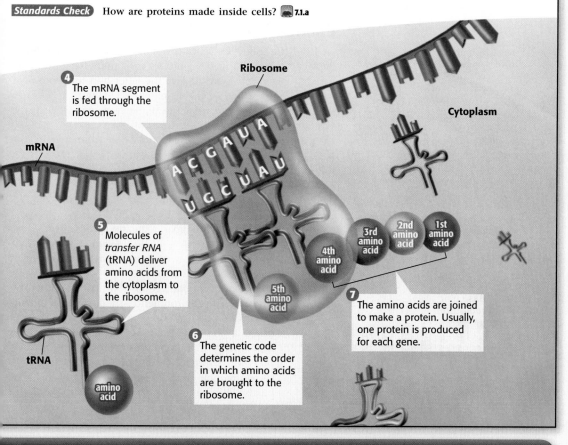

④ The mRNA segment is fed through the ribosome.

Ribosome

Cytoplasm

mRNA

⑤ Molecules of *transfer RNA* (tRNA) deliver amino acids from the cytoplasm to the ribosome.

tRNA

amino acid

⑥ The genetic code determines the order in which amino acids are brought to the ribosome.

⑦ The amino acids are joined to make a protein. Usually, one protein is produced for each gene.

1st amino acid
2nd amino acid
3rd amino acid
4th amino acid
5th amino acid

Answer to Standards Check

Proteins are built in the cytoplasm from RNA copies of a segment of DNA. Messenger RNA (mRNA) is read by a ribosome, and transfer RNA (tRNA) brings amino acids to the ribosome to be joined together to form proteins.
7.1.a (exceeding)

Connection To Math

Redundant Code Math has a lot to do with how DNA codes for amino acids. Each combination of three nucleotides that codes for one amino acid is called a *codon*. Yet cells use only 20 amino acids to build proteins. Thus, most amino acids have several, redundant corresponding codons. This redundancy is another reason that mutations in genes do not always result in changes in proteins. To physically model the possible base combinations that make up codons, organize the class into small groups. Give each group four pieces of paper, with one of the following four letters printed on it: *A, T, C,* or *G.* Ask students to come up with as many different three-letter "words" as possible by using the four different bases. [There are 4³, or 64, possible three-letter "words," or codons. For example, the four possible combinations that would start with the bases AA are AAA, AAT, AAG, and AAC.) Make sure that students realize that the order of letters in each combination also matters. For example, ATA is not the same "word" as TAA. **LS** Kinesthetic/Logical

Answer to Math Practice

With four possible nucleotides in three possible positions, there are 4×4×4, or 64, possible combinations. **7.1.a** (exceeding)

SCIENCE HUMOR

Q: What did one designer jean (gene) say to the other?

A: That's some fancy DNA you've got!

Standards Focus

This **Standards Focus** provides you with a quick way to **assess, reteach,** and **re-assess** one or more concepts in the section.

Assess

1. What is the function of a ribosome? (to translate mRNA code into proteins) **7.1.a**

2. List some causes of DNA mutations. (Answers may include random errors when DNA is copied, cigarette smoke, asbestos, high-energy radiation from X rays, or ultraviolet light.) **7.1.a**

Reteach

Find the Mutation Ask students to draw a set of 10 base pairs for a DNA strand. Then, have them draw the same set again with one mutation. Ask them to write a possible reason for the mutation at the top of the page. Then have them exchange papers with a partner and find each other's mutations. **LS Visual/Logical 7.2.e**

Re-Assess

DNA How-To Have students prepare an instruction manual for their DNA. The manual should include instructions for copying DNA and translating it into proteins. The manual should also include information about protecting their DNA from mutations by avoiding mutagens and correcting any mutations that occur. **LS Verbal 7.1.a**

Wordwise

The Use of *Mut-* Review the definition of *mutation,* and point out that the root *mut-* means "to change" and that is a derivative of the Latin word *mutare,* which also means "to change." Then, ask students what the term *mutant* means. (an organism that results from a mutation) **LS Logical**

Quick Lab

Cracking the Code

7.1.a

In messenger RNA, genetic information is stored in a code of four different bases: uracil (U), adenine (A), cytosine (C), and guanine (G). In this activity, you will crack a similar type of code.

▶ Try It!

1. Begin by tying a knot in one end of a **pipe cleaner.**

2. The code below shows the order in which **beads** should be placed on the pipe cleaner. Use the key to determine which color bead each group of three letters in the code represents.

Code:

C C U C U U C C U G U C C U A U C C C U U

Key	
Code	**Color**
CUU	blue
CCU	red
UUC	green
UCC	yellow
GUC	orange
CUA	blue

▶ Think About It!

3. Compare your string of beads with those of your classmates. Are the beads in the same order?

4. How is the code for the beads similar to the genetic code? What do the beads represent?

🕐 15 min

Changes in Genes

mutation (myoo TAY shuhn) a change in the nucleotide-base sequence of a gene or DNA molecule

Wordwise The root *mut-* means "to change." Another example is *mutant.*

Read the following sentence: "Put the book on the desk." Replace the letter *o* in the word *on* with the letter *i* and read the sentence again. Now replace the letter *b* in the word *book* with the letter *z* and read the sentence. Changing a letter in a sentence can change what the sentence means or keep the sentence from making any sense at all.

A change in the DNA sequence, like a change in the letters of a sentence, can affect the protein that DNA codes for. A change in the nucleotide-base sequence of DNA is called a **mutation.**

How Do Mutations Happen?

Mutations happen regularly because of random errors when DNA is copied. **Figure 3** shows what could happen if a nucleotide base were changed during DNA replication.

In addition, damage to DNA can be caused by things in the environment. Any physical or chemical agent that can cause a mutation in DNA is called a *mutagen.* Examples of mutagens include high-energy radiation from X rays and ultraviolet radiation. Ultraviolet radiation is one type of energy in sunlight. It is responsible for suntans and sunburns. Other mutagens include asbestos and the chemicals in cigarette smoke.

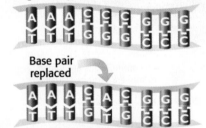

Original sequence

Base pair replaced

Figure 3 *The original base sequence on the top has been changed to show what happens when a nucleotide base is changed in DNA.*

Quick Lab

🕐 15 min

Teacher Notes

In this activity, students explore the role of RNA as a universal genetic code for the production of proteins (covers standard 7.1.a).

Materials for Each Group

• beads, (blue, green, orange, red, yellow)
• pipe cleaner

Safety Caution

Remind students to review all safety cautions and icons. Beads must be kept off the floor so that people do not slip and fall.

Answers

Code color order: red-blue-red-orange-blue-yellow-blue

3. The beads should all be in the same order.

4. The code is similar to DNA because there is a set of three bases that code for each bead. The beads represent amino acids. Chains of amino acids form proteins.

🗋 Differentiated Datasheets
A **BASIC**, B **GENERAL**, C **ADVANCED**

Also editable on the **Holt Lab Generator CD-ROM**

Do Mutations Matter?

Changes in DNA can cause an improved trait, no change, or a harmful trait. A mutation that makes an organism more likely to survive during a drought is an example of an improved trait. If a mutation does not change the protein that a gene codes for, then there will be no change to the trait.

Mutations can produce harmful traits. For example, a mutation that makes an animal a brighter color can make the animal easier for predators to find. Cells make proteins that detect and repair mutations. But not all errors are repaired correctly. If a mutation occurs in sex cells, the changed gene can be passed from one generation to the next.

SECTION Review

 7.1.a, 7.2.e

Summary

A gene is a set of instructions for making a protein. DNA stores these genetic instructions.

- Every organism has DNA in its cells. Humans have about 2 m of DNA in each cell.

- Traits of organisms are typically determined by proteins, which are coded for by segments of DNA called genes.

- Within a gene, each group of three bases codes for one amino acid. A sequence of amino acids is linked to make a protein.

- Proteins are built within the cytoplasm of cells.

- A mutation is a change in the DNA that can affect the traits of an organism.

Understanding Concepts

1 **Identifying** What structures in cells contain DNA and proteins?

2 **Describing** Explain how proteins help support the structure and function of DNA.

INTERPRETING GRAPHICS The illustration shows a sequence of bases on one strand of a DNA molecule. Use the illustration below to answer the next three questions.

3 **Applying** How many amino acids are coded for by the sequence on side A of this DNA strand?

4 **Demonstrating** What is the order of bases on side B, from left to right?

5 **Demonstrating** If *G* replaced *A* as the first base on side A, what would the order of bases be on side B of this DNA strand?

Critical Thinking

6 **Forming Hypotheses** What would happen if the proteins that support a DNA molecule failed to function?

7 **Applying Concepts** In which cell type could a mutation be passed from generation to generation? Explain.

8 **Analyzing Ideas** How does DNA store information in a code?

Challenge

9 **Forming Hypotheses** A beetle inherits a mutation that makes the beetle a darker green color than other beetles of its species. Explain how having the dark green trait could be a harmful trait or an improved trait for the beetle.

Internet Resources

For a variety of links related to this chapter, go to www.scilinks.org
Topic: Genes and Traits
SciLinks code: HY70647

---

6. Sample answer: The strands of DNA would not be able to condense and form chromosomes. This could keep the cell from passing on its DNA when the cell divides. **7.2.e** (mastering)

7. sex cells (germ cell, sperm cell, or egg cell); Because these cells contain the genes from which a new organism is formed. **7.1.a** (exceeding)

8. The order of base pairs in DNA represents a code for an amino acid. **7.1.a** (mastering)

9. The dark green trait could be harmful if it makes the beetle more visible and therefore more likely to be eaten by predators. It could be an improved trait if the color made the beetle blend in better with leaves, which would make it less likely to be eaten by predators. **7.1.a** (exceeding)

Section Review Standards Guide

	Supporting	Mastering	Exceeding
7.1.a		8	3, 5, 7, 9
7.2.e		1, 2, 6	4

Answers to Section Review

1. chromosomes (Chromatin is also acceptable.) **7.2.e** (mastering)

2. Sample answer: Proteins and DNA together form chromatin, which forms chromosomes. Proteins also assist DNA in making more proteins. **7.2.e** (mastering)

3. amino acids **7.1.a** (exceeding)

4. TGAGGACTT **7.2.e** (exceeding)

5. CGAGGACAA **7.1.a** (exceeding)

Section Resources

- Directed Reading A **BASIC** (Also in Spanish), B **GENERAL**

- Interactive Reader and Study Guide

- Section Quiz **GENERAL** (Also in Spanish)

- Section Review **GENERAL** (Also in Spanish)

- Vocabulary and Section Summary A **BASIC** (Also in Spanish), B **GENERAL**

Teacher Notes

This activity has students extract DNA from a living organism. The procedure reinforces the fact that DNA is found in chromosomes, where it is associated with proteins (covers standard 7.2.e). You may want to assist students by modeling many of the steps in the procedure.

Time Required

One 45-minute class period

Lab Ratings

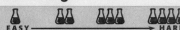

Teacher Prep 🧪🧪🧪
Student Set-Up 🧪🧪
Concept Level 🧪🧪🧪
Clean Up 🧪🧪

Materials

The materials listed on the student page are enough for 1 group of 2--4 students.

Safety Caution

Remind students to review all safety cautions and icons before beginning this activity. Remind students to review all safety precautions when working with hot liquids (hot tap water) and toxic chemicals (alcohol).

Preparation Notes

Raw wheat germ can be purchased at a health-food store and is critical to the success of this lab. Toasted wheat germ, which is more common, will not yield results. Water should be warm but not too hot; the temperature should not be above 50°C. You may want to test several liquid detergents to see which ones give the best results. Alcohol may be premeasured and placed in a freezer. Students may ask about viewing the DNA under a microscope. Explain to them that the structure of DNA is too small to be seen with a light microscope.

Skills Practice Lab

OBJECTIVES

Extract DNA from cells.

Observe and collect DNA.

MATERIALS

- balance
- beaker, 250 mL (2)
- dishwashing detergent
- isopropyl alcohol (chilled)
- paper clip
- paper towel
- pipet, 1 mL
- stirring rod
- test tubes (4)
- test-tube rack
- wheat germ, raw

SAFETY

7.2.e Students know DNA (deoxyribonucleic acid) is the genetic material of living organisms and is located in the chromosomes of each cell.

Extracting DNA

Every living thing has DNA. Within the nucleus of eukaryotic cells, DNA can be found in chromosomes. In chromosomes, strands of DNA are tightly packed and organized around several different proteins. DNA is packed so efficiently that if the DNA from one of your cells were unraveled, it would be about 2 m long! In this activity, you'll use common household items to release, unravel, and collect DNA. You will be extracting DNA from raw wheat germ, which is part of the seed of a wheat plant. Wheat germ is included in many products, such as whole wheat flour.

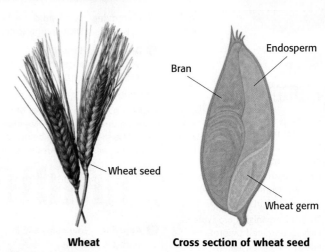

Endosperm

Bran

Wheat seed

Wheat germ

Wheat　　　　　**Cross section of wheat seed**

Procedure

① Measure 1 g of raw wheat germ. Place the raw wheat germ in a beaker.

② Use a separate beaker to measure about 50 mL of hot tap water. Add the water to the beaker containing the wheat germ. **Caution:** Be careful when handling hot water.

③ Using a pipet, add 2 mL of detergent to the wheat-germ mixture. Use a stirring rod to gently stir the mixture for 30 s. The detergent will help break down the cell membranes of the wheat germ.

Lab Resources

Differentiated Datasheets
A **BASIC**, B **GENERAL**, C **ADVANCED**

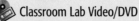
Classroom Lab Video/DVD

🔘 **Holt Lab Generator CD-ROM**

Search for any lab by topic, standard, difficulty level, or time. Edit any lab to fit your needs, or create your own labs. Use the Lab Materials QuickList software to customize your lab materials list.

4 Pour the contents of the beaker into several test tubes. Fill each test tube so it is about one-third full.

5 Holding a test tube at an angle, gently pour chilled isopropyl alcohol so that it runs down the inner surface of the test tube. Add enough alcohol so that the test tube is half full. The alcohol will form a layer on top of the wheat-germ mixture.

6 Place the test tubes in a test-tube rack. Observe the white strands that form in the alcohol layer. These strands are clumps of DNA. DNA is drawn to the alcohol layer. Most cell parts, including proteins that organize DNA, are drawn to the water level. Do not disturb the contents of the test tubes for several minutes.

7 Reshape a paper clip into a long, straight shaft with a hook on one end. Twirl the hook in the alcohol to collect the white stringy masses. The stringy masses are clumps of wheat DNA.

Analyze the Results

8 **Recognizing Patterns** What two materials make up chromosomes? What are their functions?

9 **Examining Data** Why was it important to tilt the test tube when introducing the alcohol?

Draw Conclusions

10 **Making Predictions** What other materials might be good sources of DNA? What materials would not be good to use for a DNA extraction?

11 **Evaluating Methods** Meat tenderizer contains chemicals that break down proteins. Explain why this substance may be used in some DNA extractions.

Big Idea Question

12 **Drawing Conclusions** How is it possible for a single cell to contain more than 2 m of DNA?

Analyze the Results

8. Chromosomes are made of DNA and proteins. DNA contains genes for making proteins. Proteins support the structure and function of DNA.

9. Tilting the test tube helps keep the alcohol and wheat germ mixtures separate.

Draw Conclusions

10. Sample answer: Plants or raw meat would also be good sources of DNA. Accept any answer that describes materials made of cells.

11. Because DNA is found coiled around proteins, the enzymes in meat tenderizers might break down the proteins and release the DNA.

Big Idea Question

12. Large amounts of DNA can fit inside of a cell because the DNA is wound around proteins in a compact shape.

Karen Benitez
George V. Leyva
Intermediate School
San Jose, CA

Teacher Notes

This activity has students communicate the logical connection between the parts of scientific methods (covers standard 7.7.c).

Answers to You Try It!

Sample answer: Michele formed a hypothesis when she stated: if strawberries are made of cells, then strawberries should have DNA. She tested the hypothesis when she smashed the strawberry, added warm water and soap, and added alcohol. Michele made observations when she observed white strands in the alcohol layer. Michele analyzed the results when she reasoned that the white strands were DNA.

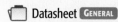 Datasheet GENERAL

Also editable on the Holt Lab Generator CD-ROM

Science Skills Activity

| Scientific Methods | Research | Data Analysis | Models, Maps & Diagrams |

 Investigation and Experimentation
7.7.c Communicate the logical connection among hypotheses, science concepts, tests conducted, data collected, and conclusions drawn from the scientific evidence.

Connecting Scientific Methods

▶ Tutorial

You can evaluate an investigation by examining whether scientific methods were properly used. For example, you can evaluate if the procedure of an investigation successfully tested the hypothesis.

The following questions can help you examine the scientific methods used in an investigation. But keep in mind that not all investigations will use the same scientific methods in the same order.

Procedure

1 **Ask a Question** What question did the investigation set out to answer?

2 **Make Observations** What was learned about the subject by observing it?

3 **Form a Hypothesis** What was the hypothesis? What predictions were made?

4 **Test the Hypothesis** How was the hypothesis tested? The answer to this question can include a description of the experiments performed, data collected, and observations made.

5 **Analyze the Results** How was the data organized and analyzed?

6 **Draw Conclusions** Did the results of the investigation support the hypothesis? Why or why not?

7 **Communicate Results** How were the results shared?

▶ You Try It!

Procedure

Read the following description of a scientific experiment. Then, use the procedure in the tutorial to examine the scientific methods used in the investigation. Finally, use your answers to write a short evaluation of the investigation.

Michele's Investigation

When Michele was studying DNA, she learned that all living things have DNA in their cells. She used the Internet to find a procedure for extracting DNA. She learned that DNA forms white, threadlike clumps when it is extracted from cells. Michele wondered if she could extract the DNA from a strawberry. She predicted yes, because if strawberries are made of cells, then strawberries should have DNA. Michele placed a strawberry into a plastic bag, sealed the bag, and smashed the strawberry. She opened the bag and added 15 mL of dish detergent and 100 mL of warm water to the bag. After sealing the bag, Michele mixed the contents by gently shaking the bag. Next, Michele poured the contents of the bag into a test tube. She then poured 20 mL of cold isopropyl alcohol into the test tube. Michele observed that the alcohol floated on top of the water. She could see a white, threadlike substance floating in the alcohol. Michele reasoned that the white substance was many strands of DNA clumped together.

Universal Access · Differentiated Instruction

Basic Learners

Scientific Methods To help students complete their evaluation of Michele's investigation, have them write down and answer each of these questions: 1. What question did Michele want to answer in her investigation? 2. What observations did Michele make? 3. What was Michele's hypothesis? What did she predict would happen in her investigation? 4. What steps did Michele take to test her hypothesis? 5. What information did Michele collect in her investigation? How did she interpret this information? 6. What conclusions did Michele draw from her investigation? **LS Verbal**

Chapter Summary

The Big Idea
DNA is the genetic material of living organisms and is located in the chromosomes of each cell.

Section

Vocabulary

1 What Does DNA Look Like?

Key Concept The structure of DNA is a double helix, which is shaped like a twisted ladder.

- The discovery of the structure and function of DNA is a major achievement in life science.
- DNA is made up of nucleotides arranged in two strands. Together, the two strands form a double helix.
- The structure of DNA relates to how it functions, including how it is replicated.

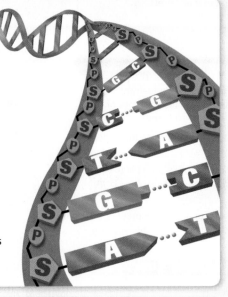

DNA is made of complementary nucleotides arranged in a double helix.

DNA p. 208
nucleotide p. 208

2 How DNA Works

Key Concept DNA stores a code that carries the instructions for making proteins. Proteins cause most of the differences among organisms.

- DNA is bundled with proteins to form chromosomes.
- DNA stores genetic information in the form of a code.
- Cells use the DNA code to make proteins. Proteins affect traits.
- A mutation is the result of a change in the genetic code.

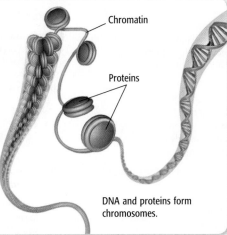

Chromatin

Proteins

DNA and proteins form chromosomes.

RNA p. 214
ribosome p. 215
mutation p. 216

Chapter Summary

SUPER SUMMARY

Have students connect the major concepts in this chapter through an interactive Super Summary. Visit go.hrw.com and type in the keyword HY7DNAS to access the Super Summary for this chapter.

Identifying Suffixes

Class Activity Write the word *ribosome* on the board. Ask students to identify the suffix (*-some*). Explain that *-some* means body. A *ribosome* is a body in cells. Then, ask students to name another word they know that ends in *-some*. (Sample answer: *chromosome*) **LS Verbal**

Focus on Writing

Super DNA Ask each student to write a short story about a person or animal whose DNA mutations result in some super skills or powers. Ask students to use all of the chapter vocabulary words in their stories. If time permits, have volunteers read their stories aloud. **LS Verbal/Intrapersonal**

Review Resources

- Reinforcement Worksheet **BASIC**
- Critical Thinking Worksheet **ADVANCED**
- Chapter Review **GENERAL** (Also in Spanish)
- Standards Review Workbook (Also in Spanish)
- Study Guide A **BASIC** (Also in Spanish), B **GENERAL**

Assessment Resources

- Chapter Tests A **BASIC**, B **GENERAL** (Also in Spanish), C **ADVANCED**
- Standards Assessment **GENERAL**

Assignment Guide

Section	Questions
1	5, 10, 13–14, 16–17, 20
2	1–4, 6–9, 11–12, 15, 18–19, 21–22

Answers

Using Vocabulary

1. Sample answer: *Located* means that the DNA is found in chromomes.

2. nucleotides **7.1.a** (mastering)

3. ribosome **7.1.a** (exceeding)

Understanding Concepts

4. b **7.2.e** (mastering)

5. d

6. a **7.1.a** (exceeding)

7. b **7.1.a** (exceeding), **7.2.e** (exceeding)

8. a **7.2.e** (mastering)

9. DNA has four nucleotides: adenine, thymine, cytosine, and guanine. RNA has uracil instead of thymine. Also, RNA is used to make temporary copies of DNA so that proteins can be made. **7.1.a** (exceeding)

10. C A G C T A G G A A T C
    7.2.e (exceeding)

11. 4 **7.1.a** (exceeding)

Organize

Tri-Fold Review the FoldNote that you created at the beginning of the chapter. Add to it or correct it based on what you have learned.

Using Vocabulary

1. **Academic Vocabulary** In the sentence "DNA is located in the chromosomes of cells," what does the word *locate* mean?

Correct each statement by replacing the underlined term.

2. The information in DNA is coded in the order of <u>amino acids</u> along one side of the DNA molecule.

3. The "factory" that puts together proteins based on the DNA code is called a <u>gene</u>.

Understanding Concepts

Multiple Choice

4. A gene can be all of the following EXCEPT
   a. a set of instructions for a trait.
   b. a complete chromosome.
   c. instructions for making a protein.
   d. a portion of a strand of DNA.

5. James Watson and Francis Crick
   a. took X-ray pictures of DNA.
   b. discovered that genes are in chromosomes.
   c. bred pea plants to study heredity.
   d. made models to figure out DNA's shape.

6. Within the cell, where are proteins made?
   a. the cytoplasm
   b. the nucleus
   c. the amino acids
   d. the chromosomes

7. Which of the following statements about DNA is NOT true?
   a. DNA is found in all organisms.
   b. DNA is made up of five subunits.
   c. DNA has a structure like a twisted ladder.
   d. Mistakes can be made when DNA is copied.

INTERPRETING GRAPHICS Use the illustration below to answer the next question.

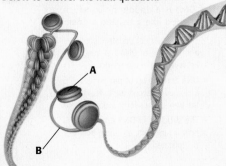

8. What molecule does A identify?
   a. protein
   b. RNA
   c. DNA
   d. ribosome

Short Answer

9. **Comparing** What is the difference between DNA and RNA?

INTERPRETING GRAPHICS Use the illustration below to answer the next two questions.

10. **Demonstrating** What is the order of bases on strand B, from left to right?

11. **Applying** How many amino acids are coded for by the sequence on strand A of this DNA strand?

Writing Skills

12. Communicating Concepts Write a paragraph explaining how the DNA in genes relates to the traits of an organism. Be sure to include information about where DNA is found and describe how it stores information in the form of a code.

Critical Thinking

13. Concept Mapping Use the following terms to create a concept map: *bases, adenine, thymine, nucleotides, guanine, DNA,* and *cytosine.*

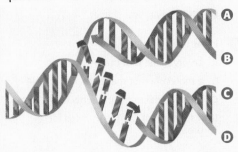

14. Analyzing Processes What role did scientific methods, such as communicating results, play in the discovery of the structure of DNA?

15. Evaluating Hypotheses Your classmate states that mutations to DNA are always harmful. Evaluate this statement.

INTERPRETING GRAPHICS The illustration shows the process of replication of a DNA strand. Use the illustration below to answer the next two questions.

A
B
C
D

16. Applying Concepts Which letters identify the two new strands that are being added to the original strands?

17. Applying Concepts How does the structure of DNA allow it to complete the process of replication?

18. Making Comparisons You are using a microscope to observe a cell that is ready to divide. What does the DNA look like? What does the DNA look like in a cell that is not ready to divide?

19. Making Inferences Why do governments make laws about the use of chemicals that are known to be mutagens?

Math Skills

20. Making Calculations The 46 chromosomes in a human cell contain 3.2 billion pairs of DNA bases in sequence. On average, about how many pairs of bases are in each chromosome?

21. Making Calculations Each cell in your body contains approximately 2.0 m of DNA. Your body has approximately 100 trillion cells. How long would the DNA in your body be if you laid it out end to end? Express your answer in scientific notation.

Challenge

22. Forming Hypotheses A house cat and a tiger have many similar traits, such as retractable claws and special teeth for tearing meat. A lion also shares these traits with a house cat. In addition, a lion and a tiger share other traits, such as the ability to roar and their large size. If you compared the sequence of nucleotide bases in a house cat, lion, and tiger, between which animals would you expect to find the most similarities? Explain your answer.

---

17. Because each nucleotide only forms a pair with one other nucleotide, an old strand can serve as a template for making a matching strand. **7.2.e** (exceeding)

18. In cells that are ready to divide, DNA is bundled into visible chromosomes. In cells that are not ready to divide, the chromosomes are spread out and are not visible. **7.2.e** (mastering)

19. Governments make laws about chemicals that are known to be mutagens because mutagens can change DNA. Mutations to DNA can result in harmful traits. **7.1.a** (exceeding)

Math Skills

20. About 70 million; $3,200,000,000 \div 46 = 69,565,217.39$

21. 200 trillion m; $2.0 \text{ m} \times 100,000,000,000,000 \text{ cells} = 200,000,000,000,000 \text{ m}$

Challenge

22. All three animals probably share a common ancestor because they all share many traits. Tigers and lions share more traits than either animal shares with house cats. Therefore, tigers and lions probably share a more recent common ancestor than either animal shares with a house cat. The DNA of lions, tigers, and cats should be similar in many ways. The DNA of lions and tigers should have the most similarities.

Chapter Review Standards Guide			
	Supporting	Mastering	Exceeding
7.1.a		2, 12	3, 6, 7, 9, 11, 15, 19
7.2.e		4, 8, 12, 18	7, 10, 13, 16, 17

Writing Skills

12. Answers may vary but should cover all requirements stated in the question. **7.1.a** (mastering), **7.2.e** (mastering)

Critical Thinking

13. An answer to this exercise can be found at the end of this book. **7.2.e** (exceeding)

14. Sample answer: Chargraff performed tests, analyzed results, and drew conclusions about the ratios of nucleotides in DNA. Franklin performed tests, analyzed results, and drew conclusions. Watson and Crick made observations, made a hypothesis, and tested the hypothesis by making a model. All of the scientists communicated results so that other scientists could learn about their work.

15. The statement that all mutations are harmful is not accurate. Many mutations do not change the protein that DNA encodes for, and so they do not have any effect on an individual's traits. Some mutations may even produce traits that help an individual survive. **7.1.a** (exceeding)

16. B and C are the new strands **7.2.e** (exceeding)

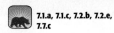
Teacher Notes

To provide practice under more realistic testing conditions, give students 20 min to answer all of the questions in this assessment.

Answer Key

Question Number	Correct Answer
1	B
2	D
3	C
4	A
5	B
6	D
7	A
8	D
9	B
10	A
11	B
12	D
13	C
14	D
15	B
16	A
17	B

Standards Guide

	Supporting	Mastering	Exceeding
7.1.a			6, 7, 9, 11, 12
7.1.c		15	
7.2.b		14	
7.2.e	8	10, 13	
7.7.b			16
7.7.d		17	

Standards Assessment **GENERAL**

Teacher Notes for Standards Assessment contain a longer Assessment Doctor and Diagnostic Teaching Tips.

REVIEWING ACADEMIC VOCABULARY

1 Which of the following terms means "to be in a certain place"?

A provide

B locate

C rest

D give

2 Which of the following words best completes the following sentence: Cells function _____ in all living organisms.

A periodically

B sporadically

C irregularly

D similarly

3 Which of the following words is the closest in meaning to the word *functioning*?

A thinking

B developing

C working

D dividing

4 Which of the following words means "able to be seen"?

A visible

B audible

C tangible

D sensible

5 Which of the following words is the closest in meaning to the word *instructions*?

A tests

B directions

C questions

D investigations

REVIEWING CONCEPTS

6 In the diagram above, what do the letters *S* and *P* stand for?

A sugars and proteins

B sucrose and proteins

C sugars and protons

D sugars and phosphates

7 What did Rosalind Franklin's experiment about DNA reveal?

A DNA has a spiral shape.

B DNA absorbs X rays.

C DNA is composed of X rays.

D DNA has an oval shape.

8 What is a gene?

A an organelle that makes proteins

B a molecule that makes copies of DNA

C the material outside the nucleus

D a segment of DNA that codes for proteins

9 What are the four nucleotide bases that form the genetic code?

A adenine, thymine, guanine, and cytoid

B adenine, thymine, guanine, and cytosine

C adenine, thyroid, guanine, and cytosine

D adenoid, thymine, guanine, and cytosine

ASSESSMENT DOCTOR

Question 1: The correct answer is B. *To be located* means "to reside." DNA is located in the chromosome of each cell.

Question 2: The correct answer is D. *Similarly* means "in the same way." Cells act similarly in all living organisms.

Question 3: The correct answer is C. *Functioning* means "working."

Question 4: The correct answer is A. *Visible* means "able to be seen."

Question 5: The correct answer is B. *Instructions* mean "directions." A typical cell contains genetic instructions, which give the cell its traits.

Question 6: The correct answer is D. Sugars and phosphates make up the sides of the DNA ladder. The rungs are made of the four bases: adenine, thymine, guanine, and cytosine.

Question 7: The correct answer is A. Rosalind Franklin discovered that when X rays are aimed at a DNA molecule, the X rays will bounce off. The pattern of deflected rays showed a spiral shape.

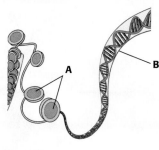

A   B

10   **What is the material identified by letter A in the diagram above?**

  A   proteins

  B   chromatin

  C   DNA

  D   chromosomes

11   **What did Watson and Crick discover?**

  A   DNA has two strands that form a branched chain called a *branched helix.*

  B   DNA is in the shape of a twisted ladder called a *double helix.*

  C   DNA is in the shape of a straight ladder called a *double helix.*

  D   DNA has three strands that form a *triple helix.*

12   **What is a change in the nucleotide-base sequence of DNA called?**

  A   variance

  B   ribosome

  C   chromatin

  D   mutation

13   **What are the structures that are in the nuclei of most cells and that are made of protein and DNA?**

  A   cytosine

  B   molecules

  C   chromosomes

  D   protons

REVIEWING PRIOR LEARNING

14   **Which type of reproduction leads to offspring that share characteristics of two parents?**

  A   binary fission

  B   asexual reproduction

  C   budding

  D   sexual reproduction

15   **Where is DNA stored in an animal cell?**

  A   mitochondria

  B   nucleus

  C   chloroplast

  D   Golgi complex

16   **If you are conducting research about how scientists study cells, what would be the best source to consult?**

  A   a Web site maintained by a cell research group

  B   a Web site written by a student who has written an essay on cell structure

  C   a Web site about the composition of molecules

  D   a Web site written by someone who is interested in cell research

17   **If you wanted to show cell structure, what would be the best way to show the information?**

  A   a flowchart showing what composes cells

  B   a model of what the cell looks like

  C   a chart listing the cell's function

  D   a list showing the amount of each molecule in the cell

Standards Assessment

Scientific Debate

Background

In the 1990s, The U.S. Food and Drug Administration began approving the use of genetically modified organisms (GMOs) in food products. Some consumer groups have protested the use of GMOs in food items and have boycotted these products. Several countries have banned the creation, sale, or importation of GMOs. In the United States, most foods containing GMOs are made with corn or soybeans that contain bacterial genes.

Most scientists recognize that the potential to create new and unknown types of organisms should be undertaken with careful scientific scrutiny, should involve ethical considerations, and should be regulated by governments.

Scientific Discoveries

Background

Polymerase Chain Reaction (PCR) amplifies DNA by allowing DNA fragments to replicate rapidly. Since PCR causes DNA to exponentially increase, it can quickly amplify a single molecule of DNA into billions of molecules. It is this capability that allows forensic scientists to expand very small samples of DNA material into a sufficient amount to conduct forensic tests. The scientists are able to increase the size of their sample by manipulating the temperature of the samples and adding nucleotides at the right times.

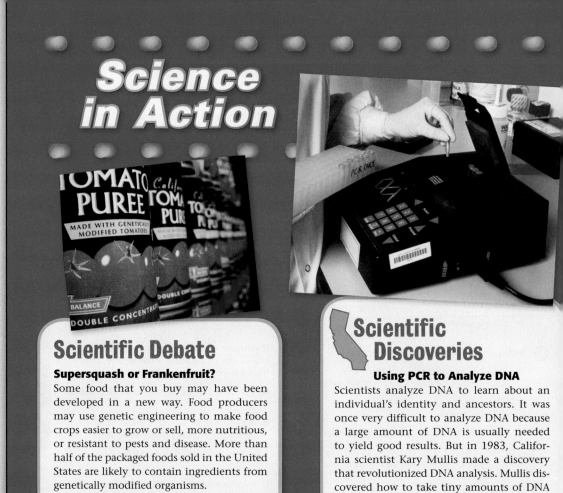

Science in Action

Scientific Debate

Supersquash or Frankenfruit?

Some food that you buy may have been developed in a new way. Food producers may use genetic engineering to make food crops easier to grow or sell, more nutritious, or resistant to pests and disease. More than half of the packaged foods sold in the United States are likely to contain ingredients from genetically modified organisms.

The U.S. government has stated that research shows that these foods are safe. But some people are concerned that genes introduced into crop plants could cause new environmental or health problems. For example, some people worry that crops engineered to be pest resistant might kill insects that are not pests, such as butterflies.

Scientific Discoveries

Using PCR to Analyze DNA

Scientists analyze DNA to learn about an individual's identity and ancestors. It was once very difficult to analyze DNA because a large amount of DNA is usually needed to yield good results. But in 1983, California scientist Kary Mullis made a discovery that revolutionized DNA analysis. Mullis discovered how to take tiny amounts of DNA and duplicate, or "amplify," them. The technique worked like a copy machine for DNA. Mullis called it *polymerase chain reaction* (PCR). PCR has many uses. For example, PCR is used in forensics to study clues left at a crime scene. Scientists can also use PCR to study the DNA of the remains of organisms that have been dead for thousands of years!

Math ACTIVITY

In a study measuring insect damage, 100 acres of land were planted with 32,000 corn plants per acre. Insects damaged an average of 19,200 corn plants per acre. What percentage of the corn plants survived? Record your work in your **Science Journal.**

Language Arts ACTIVITY

Research the use of PCR in forensics. In your **Science Journal**, write a newspaper article about an imaginary crime that was solved by using DNA analysis.

Answer to Math Activity
19,200 corn plants damaged/32,000 corn plant = 0.60 × 100 = 60%

Answer to Language Arts Activity
Answers may vary. Student's work should be in the form of a newspaper article.

Lydia Villa-Komaroff

Genetic Researcher When Lydia Villa-Komaroff was young, science represented "a kind of refuge" for her. She grew up in a very large family that lived in a very small house. "I always wanted to find things out. I was one of those kids who took things apart."

In college, Villa-Komaroff became interested in the process of embryonic development: how a simple egg grows into a complex animal. This interest led her to study genes and the way that genes code for proteins. For example, insulin is a protein that is normally produced by the human body. Often, people who suffer from diabetes lack the insulin gene, so their bodies can't make insulin. These people may need to inject insulin into their blood as a drug treatment.

Before the research by Villa-Komaroff's team was done, insulin was difficult to produce. Villa-Komaroff's team isolated the human gene that codes for insulin. Then, the scientists inserted the normal human insulin gene into the DNA of bacteria. This inserted gene caused the bacteria to produce insulin. This technique was a new and more efficient way to produce insulin. Now, most of the insulin used for diabetes treatment is made in this way. Many genetic researchers dream of making breakthroughs such as the one that Villa-Komaroff made in her work with insulin.

Social Studies ACTiViTY

Do some research about several women, such as Marie Curie, Barbara McClintock, or Maxine Frank Singer, who have done important scientific research. In your **Science Journal,** write a short biography about one of these women.

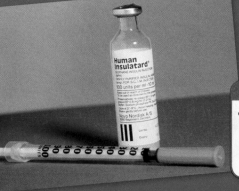

Internet Resources

- To learn more about careers in science, visit **www.scilinks.org** and enter the SciLinks code HY70225.

- To learn more about these Science in Action topics, visit **go.hrw.com** and type in the keyword HY7DNAF.

- Check out articles related to this chapter by visiting **go.hrw.com.** Just type in the keyword HY7DNAC.

Answer to Social Studies Activity

Suggest that students use library or Internet resources to find information on their chosen scientist.
Additional women scientists include the following:

- Jewel Plummer Cobb
- Ruth Fulton Benedict
- Emma Perry Carr
- Rosalyn Yalow

Check student biographies for accuracy, and comment on any interesting facts.

Careers

Background

Lydia Villa-Komaroff grew up in a family that loved to tell stories. One favorite was the story of Villa-Komaroff's grandfather, Encarnacion Villa, and his brush with the Mexican revolutionary Pancho Villa. Encarnacion was going to be killed by Pancho Villa's soldiers when he refused to join their fight. However, when Pancho Villa heard the captive's name, he ordered his release, but told the captive that he must have many sons. Pancho Villa probably could not imagine that a granddaughter of his former captive would someday become the third Mexican-American woman to earn a Ph.D. in the United States, and would go on to make many important contributions to science.

When Lydia Villa-Komaroff and her colleagues inserted the human gene that directs the production of insulin into the DNA of bacteria, they were using recombinant DNA technology. In recombinant DNA technology, researchers first identify which segment of the DNA is the gene that directs the production of the substance that they want to investigate. The researchers then cut this section out of the DNA with special enzymes and make copies, or clones, of the DNA. The researchers look for a location on the host DNA that will ensure that the host organism will read the DNA and produce the substance.

Earth and Life History

The rocks under your feet have a story to tell about what things have been like on Earth for the last three billion to four billion years! In this unit, you will learn how studying rocks helps us understand Earth and life history, how living things are classified based on their characteristics, and how these characteristics help living things survive. The timeline shows some events that have helped scientists understand Earth and life history.

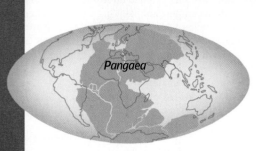

245 Million
Years Ago

The supercontinent Pangaea exists. Millions of years later, Pangaea breaks apart and the continents move to their current positions.

1864

Louis Pasteur uses heat to eliminate microbes. This process is later called *pasteurization*.

1913

Arthur Holmes develops a new technique for finding the absolute age of rocks and fossils.

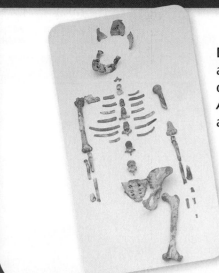

1974

Donald Johanson discovers a fossilized skeleton of one of the first hominids, *Australopithecus afarensis*, also called "Lucy."

1693

John Ray correctly identifies whales as mammals.

1753

Carolus Linnaeus publishes the first of two volumes containing the classification of all known species.

1960

Mary and Jonathan Leakey discover fossil bones of the human ancestor *Homo habilis* in Olduvai Gorge, Tanzania.

1969

Apollo 11 lands on the moon. Neil Armstrong becomes the first person to walk on the lunar surface.

1990

The most complete and largest known *Tyrannosaurus rex* skeleton is discovered. The skeleton is named Tyrannosaurus Sue.

2003

Researchers find that individual cloned pigs behave in very different ways. This finding shows that environmental conditions affect behavior.

The elements listed in the Standards Course of Study provide a base for presenting, supporting, and assessing the California Grade 7 Science Standards. Use this Standards Course of Study as a base for planning your lessons.

Why Teach
Studying Earth's Past

This chapter was designed to cover the California Grade 7 Science Standards about Earth and life history (7.3.c, 7.4.a, 7.4.b, 7.4.c, 7.4.d, and 7.4.e). It follows a chapter about genes and DNA and serves as an introduction to the history of life on Earth. This chapter describes the principles that help scientists determine the relative and absolute ages of rocks and introduces some of the evidence that influenced the development of the theory of evolution.

After they have completed this chapter, students will begin a chapter about the history of life on Earth.

 ## California Standards

Focus on Life Sciences
7.3.c Students know how independent lines of evidence from geology, fossils, and comparative anatomy provide the bases for the theory of evolution.

7.4.a Students know Earth processes today are similar to those that occurred in the past and slow geologic processes have large cumulative effects over long periods of time.

7.4.b Students know the history of life on Earth has been disrupted by major catastrophic events, such as major volcanic eruptions or the impacts of asteroids.

7.4.c Students know that the rock cycle includes the formation of new sediment and rocks and that rocks are often found in layers, with the oldest generally on the bottom.

7.4.d Students know that evidence from geologic layers and radioactive dating indicates Earth is approximately 4.6 billion years old and that life on this planet has existed for more than 3 billion years.

7.4.e Students know fossils provide evidence of how life and environmental conditions have changed.

Investigation and Experimentation
7.7.c Communicate the logical connection among hypotheses, science concepts, tests conducted, data collected, and conclusions drawn from the scientific evidence.

7.7.d Construct scale models, maps, and appropriately labeled diagrams to communicate scientific knowledge (e.g., motion of Earth's plates and cell structure).

 ## Chapter Pacing

Getting Started
The Big Idea The rock record can be used to determine the relative and absolute ages of rocks, which can be used to study Earth's history.
🕐 **45 min** pp. 232–233
 7.4.b

Section ① The Study of Earth's History
Key Concept Slow geologic processes and major catastrophic events have shaped Earth's surface in the past and continue to shape Earth today.
🕐 **75 min** pp. 234–237
7.4.a, 7.4.b, 7.4.e

Section ② Relative Dating
Key Concept Scientists can interpret the sequence of events in Earth's history by studying rock layers.
🕐 **75 min** pp. 238–245
7.3.c, 7.4.c

Section ③ Absolute Dating
Key Concept Because radioactive decay occurs at a constant rate, the age of a rock can be estimated by analyzing the amounts of different isotopes in a rock.
🕐 **75 min** pp. 246–249
7.3.c, 7.4.d

Wrapping Up
🕐 **180 min** pp. 250–259
7.4.d, 7.7.c, 7.7.d

Basic Learners
TE Creating Lakes, p. 234
TE Unconformities, p. 242
📄 Reinforcement Worksheet
📄 Chapter Test A
📄 Differentiated Datasheets A for Labs and Activities ■
📖 Study Guide A ■

Advanced Learners/GATE
TE Uniformitarianism Versus Catastrophism, p. 235
TE Road Cuts, p. 242
TE Half Dome, p. 246
TE 3-D Diagrams, p. 253
📄 Critical Thinking Worksheet
📄 Chapter Test C
📄 Differentiated Datasheets C for Labs and Activities ■

Teach

SE Explore Activity Model Craters, p. 233* ■

🎞 **Bellringer**
💿 **PowerPoint® Resources**
🎞 L29 Hutton and the Principle of Uniformitarianism
SE Quick Lab Geology Flip Book, p. 236* ■

🎞 **Bellringer**
💿 **PowerPoint® Resources**
🎞 L30 The Rock Cycle
🎞 L31 A Rock-Layer Sequence
SE Quick Lab Solve a Rock-Layer Puzzle!, p. 244* ■

🎞 **Bellringer**
💿 **PowerPoint® Resources**
🎞 L32 Radioactive Decay: Parent and Daughter Isotopes
SE Quick Lab Radioactive Decay, p. 248* ■

SE Skills Practice Lab The Half-Life of Pennies, pp. 250–251* ■

Practice

SE Organize Activity Three-Panel Flip Chart, p. 232

SE Section Review, p. 237* ■

SE Section Review, p. 245* ■

SE Section Review, p. 249* ■

SE Science Skills Activity Constructing Labeled Diagrams, p. 252* ■
🎞 **Concept Mapping***
SE Chapter Review, pp. 254–255* ■

Assess

📁 **Chapter Pretest**

SE **Standards Checks,** pp. 234, 235, 236, 237
TE **Standards Focus,** p. 236
📁 **Section Quiz** ■

SE **Standards Checks,** pp. 240, 243, 244
TE **Standards Focus,** p. 244
📁 **Section Quiz** ■

SE **Standards Checks,** pp. 246, 249
TE **Standards Focus,** p. 248
📁 **Section Quiz** ■

SE **Standards Assessment,** pp. 256–257*
📁 **Chapter Tests A, B** ■**, C**
📓 **Standards Review Workbook** ■

Resources for Universal Access • Differentiated Instruction

English Learners
TE Word Families, p. 238
TE Demonstration, p. 239
TE Using the Figure, pp. 239, 242, 243, 247
TE Cultural Awareness, p. 239
TE Rock Sculptures, p. 241
TE Group Activity, p. 242
TE Group Activity, p. 243
TE Activity, p. 246

📁 Vocabulary and Section Summary A ■, B
📁 Section Quizzes ■
📁 Chapter Tests A, B ■
📁 Differentiated Datasheets A, B, and C for Labs and Activities ■
📓 Study Guide A ■
📓 Multilingual Glossary

Struggling Readers
TE Words within Words, p. 234
TE Reading Strategy, p. 240
TE Visualizing Analogies, p. 240

Special Education Students
TE Rock Layers, p. 243
TE Raisin Dating, p. 247
TE Computer Diagrams, p. 252

To help plan your lessons, refer to the On Course Mapping Instruction booklet.

Visual Resources

CHAPTER STARTER TRANSPARENCY

Imagine . . .

BELLRINGER TRANSPARENCIES

Section: Earth's History
"The present is the key to the past" is the key to the uniformitarianism theory.

What can studying the present reveal about processes that occurred in the past?

Write your answers in your **science journal**.

Section: Relative Dating
Use arrows and words to indicate the relationships between the following phrases regarding the parts of the rock cycle:

- sedimentary rock
- heat and pressure
- igneous rock
- melting and cooling
- metamorphic rock
- pressure and cementation
- weathering and erosion

Write your answers in your **science journal**.

TEACHING TRANSPARENCIES

Hutton and the Principle of Uniformitarianism · L29

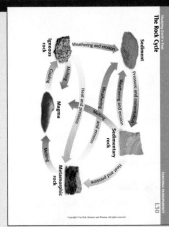

The Rock Cycle · L30

TEACHING TRANSPARENCIES

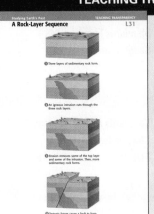

A Rock-Layer Sequence · L31

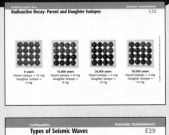

Radioactive Decay: Parent and Daughter Isotopes · L32

Types of Seismic Waves · E29

P waves are body waves that squeeze and stretch rock.

Direction of wave travel

S waves are body waves that move rock horizontally from side to side.

Direction of wave travel

LINK TO EARTH SCIENCE

STANDARDS REVIEW TRANSPARENCIES

California Science Standard 6.4.e A — Grade 6

6.4.e. Students know differences in pressure, heat, air movement, and humidity result in changes of weather.

STANDARD REVIEW
Weather maps use symbols and numbers to indicate different aspects of the weather. Weather maps you see on TV include lines called isobars—lines that connect circles of equal air pressure. Isobars that form closed circles represent areas of high or low pressure. These areas are usually marked on a map with a capital H or L. Other symbols used on weather maps indicate cold fronts, warm fronts, low pressure troughs, rain, fog, snow, ice, tornadoes, etc.

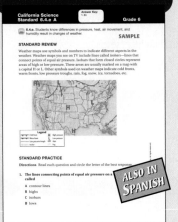

STANDARD PRACTICE
Directions Read each question and circle the letter of the best response.

1. The lines connecting points of equal air pressure on a map are called
   A contour lines
   B highs
   C isobars
   D lows

ALSO IN SPANISH

CONCEPT MAPPING TRANSPARENCY

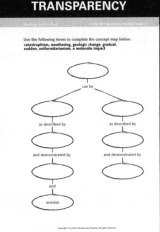

Use the following terms to complete the concept map below:
catastrophism, weathering, geologic change, gradual, sudden, uniformitarianism, a meteorite impact

Planning Resources

PARENT LETTER

SAMPLE

Dear Parent,

Your son's or daughter's science class will soon begin exploring the chapter entitled "The Nature of Physical Science." In this chapter, students will learn about how the scientific method applies to the world of physical science and the role of physical science in the world. By the end of the chapter, students should demonstrate a clear understanding of the chapter's main ideas and be able to discuss the following topics:

1. the role of questions in the process of investigation (Section 1)
2. how applying science saves lives and benefits the environment (Section 1)
3. careers that rely on science (Section 1)
4. the steps used in scientific methods (Section 2)
5. how scientific methods are used to answer questions and solve problems (Section 2)
6. the importance of safety precautions in the laboratory (Section 3)
7. examples of safety equipment and when to use them (Section 3)
8. how safety symbols are used to make laboratories safer (Section 3)

Questions to Ask Along the Way

You can help your child learn about these topics by asking interesting questions as he or she progresses through the chapter. For example, you may wish to ask your son or daughter the following questions:

What are some surprising careers that use science?
What is a characteristic of a good hypothesis?
What is the first step to take if an accident happens?

ALSO IN SPANISH

TEST ITEM LISTING

SAMPLE

Holt California Physical Science
Chapter 6 Introduction to Atoms
Test Item Listing
Multiple choice

1. The smallest particle into which an element can be divided and still have the properties of that element is called a(n)
   a. nucleus.   c. atom.
   b. electron.   d. neutron.
   ANS: C   DIF: 1   REF: 1   OBJ: 2   STO: 8.3.a   KEY: atom
   MSC: SQ.1.1

2. What particle did J. J. Thomson discover?
   a. neutron   c. electron
   b. electron
   c. proton
   ANS: B   DIF: 1   REF: 1   OBJ: 2   STO: 8.3.a   KEY: electron   MSC:
   SQ.1.2

3. How would you describe the nucleus?
   a. positively charged   c. mostly empty space, positively charged
   b. mostly empty space, positively charged
   c. tiny, negatively charged
   d. dense, negatively charged
   ANS: A   DIF: 1   REF: 1   OBJ: 2   STO: 8.3.a   KEY: nucleus   MSC:
   SQ.1.3

4. Where are electrons likely to be found?
   a. in the nucleus
   b. in electron clouds
   c. mixed throughout an atom
   d. in definite paths
   ANS: B   DIF: 1   REF: 1   OBJ: 2   STO: 8.3.a   KEY: electron   MSC:
   SQ.1.4

5. Dalton believed that
   a. atoms of the same element are exactly alike.
   b. most, but not all, substances are made of atoms.
   c. atoms of different elements are the same.
   d. atoms can be divided.
   ANS: A   DIF: 1   REF: 1   OBJ: 2   STO: 8.3.a   KEY: atom
   MSC: SQ.1.5

6. Every atom of a given element has the same number of
   a. protons.
   b. neutrons.
   c. Electrons
   d. isotopes.
   ANS: A   DIF: 1   REF: 1   OBJ: 2   STO: 8.3.a   KEY:

ALSO IN SPANISH

One-Stop Planner® CD-ROM

This CD-ROM package includes all of the resources shown here and the following time-saving tools:

- **Lab Materials QuickList Software**
- **Customizable Lesson Plans** Correlated to the California Science Standards
- **Holt Calendar Planner**
- **PowerPoint® Resources**
- **Printable Worksheets**
- **ExamView® Test Generator** Correlated to the California Science Standards
- **Holt PuzzlePro®**
- **Interactive Teacher's Edition**

For a correlation of each lab or activity to the **California Science Standards**, see pages T22–T27.

Meeting Individual Needs

DIRECTED READING A

BASIC

Skills Worksheet
Directed Reading A   SAMPLE

Section: Body Organization
A STABLE INTERNAL ENVIRONMENT
Write the letter of the correct answer in the space provided.

1. What is homeostasis?
   a. maintenance of a stable body environment
   b. an unstable body environment
   c. matching body temperature to the outside environment
   d. a process that kills cells

2. What can happen if homeostasis is disrupted?
   a. Cells rest.
   b. Cells become damaged.

ALSO IN SPANISH

DIRECTED READING B

GENERAL

Skills Worksheet
Directed Reading B   SAMPLE

Section: Body Organization
A STABLE INTERNAL ENVIRONMENT

1. The maintenance of a stable internal environment in the body is

CELLS, TISSUES, AND ORGANS

2. What is a collection of tissues that work together to carry out a specialized function in the body?
   a. a cell
   b. connective tissue
   c. an organ
   d. a team

3. Muscle tissue helps your stomach digest food by
   a. protecting the stomach.
   b. supplying oxygen.

VOCABULARY AND SECTION SUMMARY A

BASIC

Skills Worksheet
Vocabulary and Section Summary A   SAMPLE

Body Organization
VOCABULARY
In your own words, write a definition of the following terms.

1. tissue

ALSO IN SPANISH

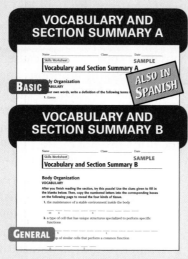

VOCABULARY AND SECTION SUMMARY B

GENERAL

Skills Worksheet
Vocabulary and Section Summary B   SAMPLE

Body Organization
VOCABULARY
After you finish reading the section, try this puzzle! Use the clues given to fill in the blanks below. Then, copy the numbered letters into the corresponding boxes on the following page to reveal the four kinds of tissue.

1. the maintenance of a stable environment inside the body

2. a type of cell that has unique structures specialized to perform specific functions

____ a group of similar cells that perform a common function

REINFORCEMENT

BASIC

Skills Worksheet
Reinforcement   SAMPLE

Muscle Map
Complete this worksheet after you finish reading the section "The Muscular System."

____ of the boxes below is labeled with one of the three types of muscle tissue in your body. Write each note in the correct box. Some of the notes can be used more than once.

Three Types of Muscle

Skeletal	Cardiac	Smooth

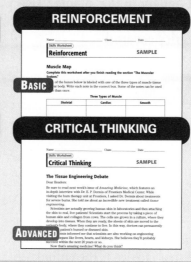

CRITICAL THINKING

ADVANCED

Skills Worksheet
Critical Thinking   SAMPLE

The Tissue Engineering Debate

Dear Readers:

Be sure to read next week's issue of *Amazing Medicine*, which features an in-depth interview with Dr. E. P. Dennis of Frontiers Medical Center. While visiting the burn therapy unit at Frontiers, I asked Dr. Dennis about treatments for severe burns. She told me about an incredible new treatment called *tissue engineering*.

Scientists are actually growing human skin in laboratories and then attaching the skin to real, live patients! Scientists start the process by taking a piece of human skin and collagen from cows. The cells are grown in a culture, where they develop into tissues. When they are ready, the sheets of skin are moved to the patient's burned or diseased skin.

____ is informed me that scientists are also working on engineering ____ like livers, hearts, and kidneys. She believes they'll probably succeed within the next 20 years or so.

Now that's amazing medicine! What do you think?

INTERACTIVE READER AND STUDY GUIDE

CHAPTER 11 Body Organization and Structure
Body Organization   SAMPLE

BEFORE YOU READ
After you read this section, you should be able to answer these questions:
• What is cell differentiation?
• What are the 11 different human organ systems?
• What is homeostasis?

California Science Standards 7.1.f, 7.6.b

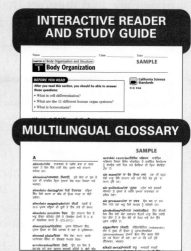

MULTILINGUAL GLOSSARY

SAMPLE

(glossary content in multiple languages)

Labs and Activities

DIFFERENTIATED DATASHEETS FOR EXPLORE ACTIVITY, QUICK LABS, AND CHAPTER LAB

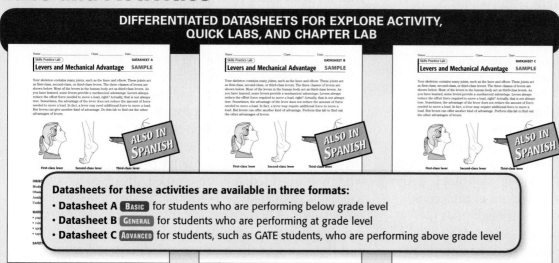

Skills Practice Lab   DATASHEET A
Levers and Mechanical Advantage   SAMPLE

Your skeleton contains many joints, such as the knee and elbow. These joints act as first-class, second-class, or third-class levers. The three classes of levers are shown below. Most of the levers in the human body act as third-class levers. As you have learned, some levers provide a mechanical advantage. Levers always reduce the effort force needed to move a load, right? Actually, that is not always true. Sometimes, the advantage of the lever does not reduce the amount of force needed to move a load. In fact, a lever may need additional force to move a load. But levers can give another kind of advantage. Do this lab to find out the other advantages of levers.

First-class lever   Second-class lever   Third-class lever

ALSO IN SPANISH

Skills Practice Lab   DATASHEET B
Levers and Mechanical Advantage   SAMPLE

Your skeleton contains many joints, such as the knee and elbow. These joints act as first-class, second-class, or third-class levers. The three classes of levers are shown below. Most of the levers in the human body act as third-class levers. As you have learned, some levers provide a mechanical advantage. Levers always reduce the effort force required to move a load, right? Actually, that is not always true. Sometimes, the advantage of the lever does not reduce the amount of force needed to move a load. In fact, a lever may require additional force to move a load. But levers can offer another kind of advantage. Perform this lab to find out the other advantages of levers.

First-class lever   Second-class lever   Third-class lever

ALSO IN SPANISH

Skills Practice Lab   DATASHEET C
Levers and Mechanical Advantage   SAMPLE

Your skeleton contains many joints, such as the knee and elbow. These joints act as first-class, second-class, or third-class levers. The three classes of levers are shown below. Most of the levers in the human body act as third-class levers. As you have learned, some levers provide a mechanical advantage. Levers always reduce the effort force required to move a load, right? Actually, that is not always true. Sometimes, the advantage of the lever does not reduce the amount of force needed to move a load. In fact, a lever may require additional force to move a load. But levers can offer another kind of advantage. Perform this lab to find out the other advantages of levers.

First-class lever   Second-class lever   Third-class lever

ALSO IN SPANISH

OBJECTIVE

MATERIALS

SAFETY

Datasheets for these activities are available in three formats:
• **Datasheet A** **BASIC** for students who are performing below grade level
• **Datasheet B** **GENERAL** for students who are performing at grade level
• **Datasheet C** **ADVANCED** for students, such as GATE students, who are performing above grade level

DATASHEET FOR SCIENCE SKILLS ACTIVITY

Science Skills Activity   DATASHEET
Modifying a Hypothesis   SAMPLE

INVESTIGATION AND EXPERIMENTATION
7.7.a Communicate the logical connection among hypotheses, science concepts, tests conducted, data collected, and conclusions drawn from the scientific evidence.

TUTORIAL
When you perform a scientific investigation, you often start with a question and then develop a hypothesis. A hypothesis is a possible answer to the question. A hypothesis must be testable. The next step in an investigation is to test your hypothesis. Often, in the course of your experiment, you will gather data that will require you to modify your original hypothesis. In this tutorial, you will learn how to modify a hypothesis. Read the question and hypothesis below.

Question: How do your muscles move your bones?
Hypothesis: One muscle is responsible for moving each bone.

PROCEDURE
1. **Design a Test for the Hypothesis** In this investigation, you might use rulers or sticks to model bones and rubber bands to model muscles. You will be testing if it is possible for one muscle to move one bone.
2. **Identify the Expected Outcome** If your hypothesis is correct, what results do you expect? In this investigation, if your hypothesis is correct, you will be able to move each bone model with a single rubber band.
3. **Analyze the Actual Results** In your experiment, the results show that it is not possible to move the bone model with a single rubber band. You notice that the bones will not move predictably or smoothly.
4. **Form a New Hypothesis** In what way do the observations that you made agree with or disagree with your original hypothesis? In this example, your results disagree with your hypothesis. One muscle did not move each bone. Now, your hypothesis must be modified. See the modified hypothesis below.

Question: How do your muscles move your bones?
____thesis: Muscle pairs work together to move each bone.

GENERAL

____ IT!
Your body tissues contain water. In fact, the human body is made ____ 75% water. Imagine that you are part of a research team working to answer this question: Does water help the body maintain a constant temperature? You have decided to focus your research on whether or not water helps the body maintain a constant temperature. Your hypothesis is the following: Water does not help the body maintain a constant temperature.

ALSO IN SPANISH

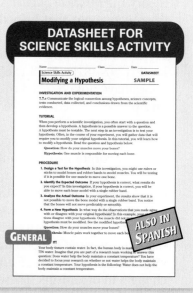

Reviews and Assessments

SECTION REVIEWS

GENERAL

Skills Worksheet
Section Review   SAMPLE

Body Organization
USING VOCABULARY
1. Use *homeostasis*, *tissue*, and *organ* in the same sentence.

UNDERSTANDING CONCEPTS
2. **Analyzing** How are tissues, organs, and organ systems related?

ALSO IN SPANISH

CHAPTER REVIEW

GENERAL

Skills Worksheet
Chapter Review   SAMPLE

Section: Body Organization
USING VOCABULARY
1. **Academic Vocabulary** In the sentence "Levers confer a mechanical advantage," what does the word *confer* mean?
   a. decrease
   b. cancel out
   c. give
   d. complete

Complete each of the following sentences by choosing the ____ word bank.

homeostasis   organ   joint
skeletal system   tissue

2. ____ is a place where two or more ____

3. ____ is the maintenance of a stable internal

ALSO IN SPANISH

CHAPTER PRETEST

GENERAL

Assessment
Chapter Pretest   SAMPLE

1. Which of the following levels of organization in the human body is made of the same kinds of cells working together to perform a job for the organism?
   A organism
   B organ
   C organ system
   D tissue

2. Starfish lose arms to escape predators in much the same way that lizards lose their tails. When they lose an arm they can grow a new one, just as a lizard can grow a new tail. But unlike a lizard, an entire new starfish can grow from a single lost arm by regenerating all the other body parts. Which form of reproduction does a starfish show?

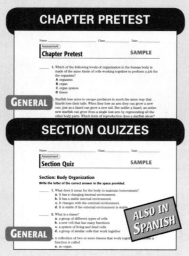

SECTION QUIZZES

GENERAL

Assessment
Section Quiz   SAMPLE

Section: Body Organization
Write the letter of the correct answer in the space provided.

1. What does it mean for the body to maintain homeostasis?
   a. It has a changing internal environment.
   b. It has a stable internal environment.
   c. It changes with the external environment.
   d. It is stable if the external environment is stable.

2. A different type of cell
   a. A group of different types of cells
   b. a new cell that has many functions
   c. a system of living and dead cells
   d. a group of similar cells that work together

3. A collection of two or more tissues that work together to ____ a function is called
   a. an organ.

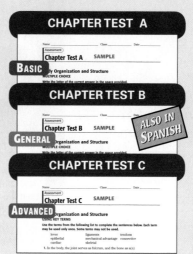

CHAPTER TEST A

BASIC

Assessment
Chapter Test A   SAMPLE

Body Organization and Structure
MULTIPLE CHOICE
Write the letter of the correct answer in the space provided.

CHAPTER TEST B

GENERAL

Assessment
Chapter Test B   SAMPLE

Body Organization and Structure
MULTIPLE CHOICE
Write the letter of the correct answer in the space provided.

ALSO IN SPANISH

CHAPTER TEST C

ADVANCED

Assessment
Chapter Test C   SAMPLE

Body Organization and Structure
USING KEY TERMS
Use the terms from the following list to complete the sentences below. Each term may be used only once. Some terms are not used.

lever   ligaments   tendons
epithelial   mechanical advantage connective
cardiac   skeletal

1. In the body, the joint serves as fulcrum, and the bone as ac(n)

STANDARDS ASSESSMENT

GENERAL

Assessment
Standards Assessment   SAMPLE

Teacher Notes and Answer Key
To provide practice under more realistic testing conditions, give students 20 min to answer all of the questions in this assessment.

QUESTION NUMBER	CORRECT ANSWER	STANDARD
1		7.5 (supporting)
2		7.6 (supporting)
3		7.6 (supporting)

STANDARDS REVIEW WORKBOOK

California Science Standard 6.4.e   Grade 6
SAMPLE

6.4.e. Students know differences in pressure, heat, air movement, and humidity result in changes of weather.

STANDARD REVIEW
Weather maps use symbols and numbers to indicate different aspects of the weather. Weather maps you see on TV include lines called *isobars*—lines that connect points of equal air pressure. Isobars that form closed circles represent areas of high or low pressure. These areas are usually marked with a capital H or L. Other symbols used on weather maps ____ warm fronts, low pressure troughs, rain, fog, snow, and ____

ALSO IN SPANISH

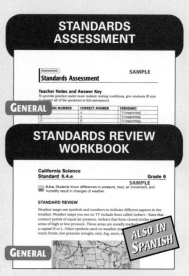

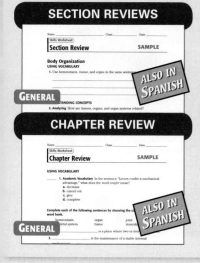

This Teacher Background explains science concepts, principles, and theories that appear in the chapter. Use the information on these pages to refresh or enhance your understanding of the topics covered.

Section 1

The Study of Earth's History

Uniformitarianism

The theory of uniformitarianism grew from the observations of James Hutton (1726–1797). Hutton, often considered the father of geology, proposed that it was possible to understand the mechanisms behind the formation of landforms by observing the processes that currently operate in the world. He theorized that change is the cumulative result of slow, continuous processes. Hutton called his theory the *theory of gradualism.* **Figure A** illustrates some of the observations that helped Hutton develop his theory.

Hutton's theory gained popularity and led to the theory of uniformitarianism through the studies of Charles Lyell (1797–1875). Lyell theorized that geological processes have not changed over time and that contemporary processes are the same as those that occurred throughout Earth's history. William Whewell (1794–1866) applied the term *uniformitarianism* to Lyell's theory, which incorporated Hutton's theory of gradualism.

The studies of Hutton and Lyell had a profound effect on Charles Darwin (1809–1882). Darwin saw that in geology, small changes over very long periods of time could result in large cumulative effects. He thought that the same thing could happen in biology—that small changes over very long periods of time could produce significant changes in organisms. These conclusions helped shape Darwin's theories of natural selection and evolution.

Catastrophism

Catastrophism is an idea based in part on the Biblical idea that Earth is very young—about 6,000 years old. If Earth is that young, the variety of geological forms observed could only be caused by catastrophic events, such as volcanic eruptions and floods. This idea was championed by Georges Cuvier (1769–1832). Because uniformitarianism contradicted religious interpretations of Earth's age, uniformitarianism had a profound effect on the discourse not only in geology but also in religion.

As scientists began to understand that Earth was much older than initially thought, they recognized that the idea of catastrophism inadequately described the geological processes they observed. Out of this understanding, uniformitarianism took hold. One of the tenets of uniformitarianism is that the present is the key to the past. For example, the ripples observed in ancient sedimentary rock are identical to the ripples that form as water runs through mud and sand today.

Paleontology

Paleontology is not just a geological science. It involves many areas of study, including biology, phylogeny, comparative anatomy, physiology, and evolution.

Paleontologists typically use two types of fossils: body fossils and trace fossils. Body fossils form from the actual remains of an organism—bones, shells, or leaves, for example. These fossils may be unaltered, which means they have undergone little change over time; or altered, which occurs if remains are crushed, dissolved, recrystallized, or carbonized. Body fossils include molds, which are impressions of body parts left in sediment, and casts, which result from the dissolution of the original parts and the filling of the resulting mold with sediment.

Figure A *These were some of the observations that Hutton used to develop his theory of gradualism.*

1 Hutton observed that rock is broken down into smaller particles.

2 He watched as these rock particles were carried downstream.

3 He saw that rock particles are deposited and that they form new layers of sediment. He predicted that these deposits would form new rock over time.

4 Hutton thought that in time, the new rock would be raised into new landforms, and then the cycle would begin again.

Trace fossils are evidence of an organism that does not involve bodily remains. Trace fossils include borings and burrows, which are evidence of worms and other tunneling organisms; coprolites, which are fossilized feces; footprints; and gastroliths, which are the smooth stones found with dinosaur skeletons that are thought to have functioned similarly to gizzard stones in birds.

Section 2

Relative Dating

The Rock Cycle

Rocks that are exposed to the atmosphere by geologic processes, such as uplifting, are subject to weathering processes that break down rocks. Weathering can include physical processes, such as freezing and thawing cycles and abrasion, and chemical processes such as acid rain. Abrasion and freezing and thawing cycles are mechanical processes that do not change the chemical nature of the rock. Exposure to acid rain and oxygen can result in chemical reactions and the formation of new materials.

Relative Dating

Relative dating does not establish the numerical age of a fossil or rock layer. It only establishes the relationships between geologic structures. For example, a scientist studying a core sample may not be able to tell how old the rock is, but the scientist can determine whether a given layer is older or younger than another layer. Relative dating establishes the order of events, but it does not establish the dates when those events occurred. The photographs in **Figure B** illustrate how superposition is used to identify the relative ages of rock layers. As long as the stack of photographs is undisturbed, the older photos, or older rock layers, will be at the bottom and more recent layers will be at the top.

Figure B *Rock layers can be compared to pictures stacked over time. In both sequences, the younger layers are at the top and the older layers are at the bottom.*

Geology and Evolution

As geologists determine the order of events based on superposition and crosscutting relationships, so too can this knowledge be used to help scientists understand the evolution of living things. Because of superposition, scientists can identify the relative relationships between fossils in the fossil record. When scientists cannot identify absolute ages, they can make reasonable conclusions about fossils based on relative ages. For example, a fossil found in an older rock layer lived at an earlier time than a fossil found in a younger rock layer did.

The relationship between fossils in the fossil record can also be studied by using comparative anatomy. Once the relative ages of fossils has been established, comparative anatomists and paleontologists can examine the fossils for an evolutionary relationship between the fossils. For example, there may be similarities between ancient and modern vertebrates. So, a scientist might conclude that all vertebrates evolved from a common ancestor.

Section 3

Absolute Dating

Radiometric Dating

The idea of radiometric dating was proposed in 1905 by Lord Ernest Rutherford (1831–1937), a British physicist. Actual radiometric dating was achieved in the 1950s.

Radiometric dating of rock varies with the type and origin of the rock. Some igneous rocks can be dated based on the presence of certain parent and daughter isotopes. If igneous rock is broken down and becomes part of a sedimentary layer, the igneous rock fragment can be dated. However, this date does not indicate the date the sedimentary layer formed, but rather when the igneous rock formed. Metamorphism can "reset" the radiometric clock of a rock. As a result, the absolute age indicates the date the rock was metamorphosed, not the date of formation of the original rock.

Internet Resources

SciLinks is maintained by the National Science Teachers Association to provide you and your students with interesting, up-to-date links that will enrich your classroom presentation of the chapter.

Visit **www.scilinks.org** and enter the SciLinks code for more information about the topic listed.

Topic: Earth's Story
SciLinks code: HY70450

Topic: The Rock Cycle
SciLinks code: HY71319

Topic: Relative Dating
SciLinks code: HY71288

Topic: Absolute Dating
SciLinks code: HY70003

Chapter Preview

📁 Chapter Pretest

Use the Chapter Pretest in the Chapter Resource File to determine the prior knowledge of your students. The Test Doctors and diagnostic teaching tips in the Teacher Notes pages will help you tailor your instruction to your students' specific needs.

Improving Comprehension

Use the Graphic Organizer on this page of the Student Edition to introduce the topics that are covered in this chapter, to summarize the chapter material, or to show students how to make a process chart.

Teaching Tips

• Remind students that a process chart can represent anything that is a process, such as a time-line, a list of steps, a chain of events, or a cycle.

• Explain to students that the arrangement of the boxes in a process chart should be appropriate for the content and should make sense. Explain that a process chart can have branches that represent points at which more than one event happens at the same time.

LS Logical

Improving Comprehension

Graphic Organizers are important visual tools that can help you organize information and improve your reading comprehension. The Graphic Organizer below is called a *process chart*. Instructions for creating other types of Graphic Organizers are located in the **Study Skills** section of the Appendix.

How to Make a Process Chart

❶ Draw a box. In the box, write the first step of a process, chain of events, or cycle.

❷ Under the box, draw another box, and draw an arrow to connect the two boxes. In the second box, write the next step of the process or the next event in the timeline.

❸ Continue adding boxes until each step of the process, chain of events, or cycle is written in a box. For cycles only, draw an arrow to connect the last box and the first box.

When to Use a Process Chart

Science is full of processes. A process chart shows the steps that a process takes to get from one point to another point. Timelines, chains of events, and cycles are examples of the kinds of information that can be organized well in a process chart. As you read, look for information that is described in steps or in a sequence, and draw a process chart that shows the progression of the steps or sequence.

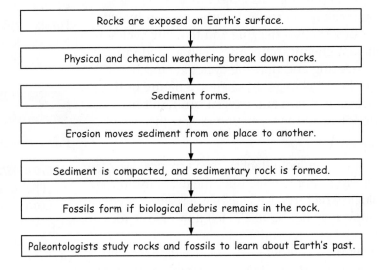

Rocks are exposed on Earth's surface.

Physical and chemical weathering break down rocks.

Sediment forms.

Erosion moves sediment from one place to another.

Sediment is compacted, and sedimentary rock is formed.

Fossils form if biological debris remains in the rock.

Paleontologists study rocks and fossils to learn about Earth's past.

You Try It!

This Reading Strategy can also be used within the chapter that you are about to read. Practice making your own *process chart* as directed in the Reading Strategy for Section ❶. Record your work in your **Science Journal**.

Using Other Graphic Organizers

Students can practice using a variety of Graphic Organizers while reading this chapter. The following Graphic Organizers may also be useful in this chapter.

A **cause-and-effect map** can be used to describe the causes and effects of erosion, discussed in Section 2.

Combination notes can be used to describe disturbed rock layers, introduced in Section 2.

Instructions for creating these Graphic Organizers are located on pp. 583–591 of the Appendix.

Unpacking the Standards

The information below "unpacks" the standards by breaking them down into basic parts. The higher-level, academic vocabulary is highlighted and defined to help you understand the language of the standards. "What It Means" restates the standards as simply as possible.

California Standard	Academic Vocabulary	What It Means
7.3.c Students know how independent lines of **evidence** from geology, fossils, and comparative anatomy provide the bases for the theory of evolution.	**evidence** (EV uh duhns) information showing whether an idea or belief is true or valid	The theory of evolution is based on several kinds of information that was gathered by studying rocks and fossils and by comparing the bodies of living and extinct organisms.
7.4.a Students know Earth **processes** today are **similar** to those that **occurred** in the past and slow geologic processes have large cumulative effects over long **periods** of time.	**process** (PRAH ses) a set of steps, events, or changes **similar** (SIM uh luhr) almost the same **occur** (uh KUHR) to happen **period** (PIR ee uhd) an interval or unit	Earth processes that happen today also happened in the past. These slow processes can cause large changes over long periods of time.
7.4.b Students know the history of life on Earth has been disrupted by **major** catastrophic events, such as major volcanic eruptions or the **impacts** of asteroids.	**major** (MAY juhr) of great importance or large scale **impact** (IM pakt) a striking together; collision	The history of life on Earth has been changed or upset by large-scale, disastrous events, such as the eruption of volcanoes or the impact of asteroids.
7.4.c Students know that the rock **cycle** includes the formation of new sediment and rocks and that rocks are often found in **layers,** with the oldest generally on the bottom.	**cycle** (SIE kuhl) a repeating series of changes **layer** (LAY uhr) a separate or distinct portion of matter that has thickness	The rock cycle includes the breakdown of rock into smaller fragments that may form new rock. Rocks are often found in layers, in which the oldest rock is usually on the bottom.
7.4.e Students know fossils provide evidence of how life and **environmental** conditions have changed.	**environment** (en VIE ruhn muhnt) the surrounding natural conditions that affect an organism	Fossils can be used to understand how living things and the environment have changed over time.

Unpacking the Standards

Use the following information with the *What It Means* in the Student Edition to help students understand why studying each standard is important.

Why It Matters

Evolution is a testable theory that is subject to change based on new discoveries and data.

Understanding geologic processes helps us explain the features of Earth.

Students should know that both slow, gradual changes and sudden changes alter the history of life on Earth.

Understanding the deposition of sediments helps scientists pinpoint the location of oil, natural gas, and other fossil deposits. It also helps geologists put events in geologic time in order.

Understanding patterns of change in the past can help us predict and plan for future conditions on Earth.

Words with Multiple Meanings

Words that have both common and scientific meanings can be confusing to students. The following table identifies some of those words that are used in this chapter.

Term	Common meaning	Scientific meaning
date	an engagement to go out socially	to measure the age of an event or object
daughter	one's female child	referring to the stable isotope produced by radioactive decay

Practice Have students define the following words: *date* and *daughter*. Then, give students the definitions for the scientific meanings of these terms. (These definitions can be found in the glossary of this book.) Have students write sentences that use the common meanings of these words. Then, have students write sentences that use the scientific meanings of the words.

Chapter Overview

This chapter describes how slow geologic processes and catastrophic events continue to shape Earth's surface. The chapter also describes relative and absolute dating techniques and explains how geologists use these dating techniques to understand Earth's history.

MISCONCEPTION ALERT

Rate of Change on Earth

Identify It! When students think of how Earth's surface has changed over time, they may think only of catastrophic events, such as volcanic eruptions and meteor strikes. They may not recognize that many geologic processes take place over very long periods of time. Ask students, "Does Earth's surface change quickly or slowly?"

Correct It! Show students examples of geologic features that formed over a long period of time, such as the Grand Canyon. Ask students to identify how long these features took to form. Help students recognize that many features on Earth formed over millions of years.

Assess It! Show students a series of photographs of geologic features. Ask them whether they think that the feature formed quickly or over a long period of time. Students who overcome the misconception will recognize that many geologic features form over a long period of time.

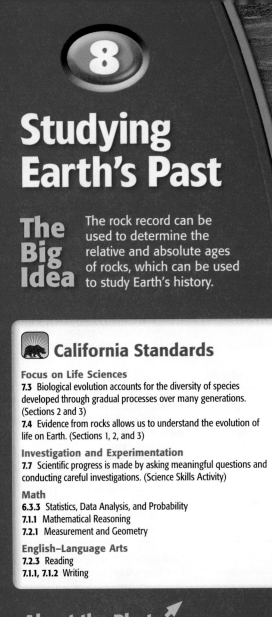

8
Studying Earth's Past

The Big Idea The rock record can be used to determine the relative and absolute ages of rocks, which can be used to study Earth's history.

California Standards

Focus on Life Sciences
7.3 Biological evolution accounts for the diversity of species developed through gradual processes over many generations. (Sections 2 and 3)
7.4 Evidence from rocks allows us to understand the evolution of life on Earth. (Sections 1, 2, and 3)

Investigation and Experimentation
7.7 Scientific progress is made by asking meaningful questions and conducting careful investigations. (Science Skills Activity)

Math
6.3.3 Statistics, Data Analysis, and Probability
7.1.1 Mathematical Reasoning
7.2.1 Measurement and Geometry

English–Language Arts
7.2.3 Reading
7.1.1, 7.1.2 Writing

About the Photo

The Barringer Meteorite Crater in the Arizona desert has a diameter of more than 1 km. The crater formed when an asteroid hit Earth about 40,000 years ago. Most geologic processes are slow and cause change on Earth over long periods of time. But rare catastrophic events can reshape Earth's surface suddenly and leave evidence, such as this crater.

Organize

Three-Panel Flip Chart

Before you read this chapter, create the FoldNote entitled "Three-Panel Flip Chart." Label each flap with the title of one of the sections in the chapter. As you read the chapter, write information from each section under the appropriate flap.

Instructions for creating FoldNotes are located in the Study Skills section on p. 581 of the Appendix.

California Standards Alignment

Focus on Life Sciences

7.3.c Students know how independent lines of evidence from geology, fossils, and comparative anatomy provide the bases for the theory of evolution. **pp. 239–241, 245–249, 254, 256**

7.4.a Students know Earth processes today are similar to those that occurred in the past and slow geologic processes have large cumulative effects over long periods of time. **pp. 234–237, 254–256**

7.4.b Students know the history of life on Earth has been disrupted by major catastrophic events, such as major volcanic eruptions or the impacts of asteroids. **pp. 233, 235–237, 254–256**

7.4.c Students know that the rock cycle includes the formation of new sediment and rocks and that rocks are often found in layers, with the oldest generally on the bottom. **pp. 238–245, 254–257**

7.4.d Students know that evidence from geologic layers and radioactive dating indicates Earth is approximately 4.6 billion years old and that life on this planet has existed for more than 3 billion years. **pp. 246–251, 254–257**

7.4.e Students know fossils provide evidence of how life and environmental conditions have changed. **pp. 237, 254–255**

Investigation and Experimentation

7.7.c Communicate the logical connection among hypotheses, science concepts, tests conducted, data collected, and conclusions drawn from the scientific evidence. **pp. 250–251, 256**

7.7.d Construct scale models, maps, and appropriately labeled diagrams to communicate scientific knowledge (e.g., motion of Earth's plates and cell structure). **p. 252**

This activity has students model the results of an object striking Earth's surface (covers standard 7.4.b).

Materials for Each Group

- bowl, basin, or tray
- marble
- flour
- meter stick
- gelatin powder, colored

Safety Caution

Remind students to review all safety cautions before beginning this activity. Ask students if they have allergies to any of the ingredients. Provide allergic students with safety equipment or ask other students to handle the materials.

Answers

5. Sample answer: The marble's impact created a crater.

6. Sample answer: yes; When dropped from greater heights, the marble made a deeper crater and scattered more debris.

7. Sample answer: It would have changed the landscape near the impact. Plants and animals might have been killed. The debris thrown into the air may have affected parts of Earth that were far from the impact, and might have changed the amount of sunlight that reached Earth's surface.

Differentiated Datasheets
A BASIC, B GENERAL, C ADVANCED

Also editable on the Holt Lab Generator CD-ROM

Explore Activity

20 min

7.4.b

Model Craters

Craters are part of the surface of many bodies in our solar system, including Earth! In this activity, you will make your own craters and observe what happens as the craters form.

Procedure

1. Fill a **bowl, basin,** or **tray** with **flour** to a depth of at least 7 cm.

2. Sprinkle **colored gelatin powder** over the flour's surface to produce a thin, uniform coating.

3. Using a **meterstick,** position a **marble** about 10 cm above the basin or tray. Release the marble, but do not throw it! The marble should not bounce out of the tray. Describe, measure, and sketch the appearance of the model crater.

4. Repeat step 3, positioning the marble at heights of 20 cm and 50 cm above areas of the undisturbed gelatin surface.

Analysis

5. How did the impact affect the flour and gelatin?

6. Did the height of the dropped marble have any effect on the crater's appearance? Explain.

7. How might such an event have affected Earth's surface?

Math Standards

6.3.3 Statistics, Data Analysis, and Probability Represent probabilities as ratios, proportions, decimals between 0 and 1, and percentages between 0 and 100 and verify that the probabilities computed are reasonable; know that if P is the probability of an event, 1 − P is the probability of an event not occurring. **pp. 250–251**

7.1.1 Mathematical Reasoning Analyze problems by identifying relationships, distinguishing relevant from irrelevant information, identifying missing information, sequencing and prioritizing information, and observing patterns. **pp. 237, 245, 255, 258**

7.2.1 Measurement and Geometry Use formulas routinely for finding the perimeter and area of basic two-dimensional figures and the surface area and volume of basic three-dimensional figures, including rectangles, parallelograms, trapezoids, squares, triangles, circles, prisms, and cylinders. **p. 237**

English–Language Arts Standards

7.2.3 Reading Analyze text that uses the cause-and-effect organizational pattern. **p. 234**

7.1.1 Writing Create an organizational structure that balances all aspects of the composition and uses effective transitions between sentences and ideas to unify key ideas. **pp. 254, 259**

7.1.2 Writing Support all statements and claims with anecdotes, descriptions, facts and statistics, and/or specific examples. **pp. 247, 258**

Chapter Starter Transparency
Use this transparency to help students begin thinking about Earth's history.

Preteach

Reviewing Prior Knowledge

Ask students to identify ways by which Earth's surface changes. (Answers may vary. Students may mention earthquakes, erosion, and volcanism.) Then, ask students to identify how much time is required to change Earth's surface. (Answers may vary. Students may say that Earth's surface changes suddenly or over long periods of time.)

Bellringer

Have students focus on standard 7.4.a by writing the following statement on the board: "The present is the key to the past." Tell students that this is the key to the uniformitarianism theory. Have students write a few sentences about what studying the present can reveal about processes that occurred in the past. (Accept all reasonable answers.)

📦 Bellringer Transparency

Motivate

ACTIVITY

Debate Posters Have students design a poster that announces a debate between a catastrophist and a uniformitarianist. Encourage students to use phrases and illustrations that would attract supporters from both sides. Have them summarize the main points of each side. **LS** Visual/Verbal

Answer to Standards Check

Uniformitarianism is the idea that the same geologic processes that shape Earth today have been at work throughout Earth's history. **7.4.a** (mastering)

What You Will Learn

- Uniformitarianism describes uniform change in Earth's geology, and catastrophism describes sudden change.
- Modern geology describes most change as gradual but acknowledges rare, sudden changes.

Why It Matters

Understanding the processes that shape Earth's surface today help us understand Earth's past.

Vocabulary

- uniformitarianism
- catastrophism
- paleontology

READING STRATEGY

Graphic Organizer In your **Science Journal,** create a Process Chart that shows how the theory of Earth's geologic history has changed over time.

The Study of Earth's History

Key Concept Slow geologic processes and major catastrophic events have shaped Earth's surface in the past and continue to shape Earth today.

▶ How do mountains form? How old is Earth? Have you ever asked these questions? Nearly 250 years ago, a Scottish farmer and scientist named James Hutton did. Searching for answers to his questions, Hutton spent more than 30 years studying rock formations in Scotland and England.

The Early Study of Geology

In 1788, James Hutton collected his notes and wrote *Theory of the Earth.* In *Theory of the Earth,* he stated that the key to understanding Earth's history is all around us. In other words, processes that we observe today—such as erosion and deposition—do not change over time. This idea is now called uniformitarianism. **Uniformitarianism** is the idea that the same geologic processes that shape Earth today have been at work during all of Earth's history. **Figure 1** shows some of the observations that Hutton used to develop the idea of uniformitarianism.

Standards Check What is uniformitarianism? 🐻 **7.4.a**

Figure 1 | **Hutton's Observations**

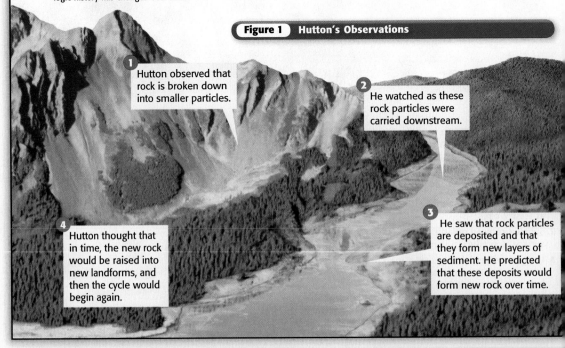

1. Hutton observed that rock is broken down into smaller particles.

2. He watched as these rock particles were carried downstream.

3. He saw that rock particles are deposited and that they form new layers of sediment. He predicted that these deposits would form new rock over time.

4. Hutton thought that in time, the new rock would be raised into new landforms, and then the cycle would begin again.

Universal Access • Differentiated Instruction

Struggling Readers

Words within Words Remind students that looking at small parts of long words can help them understand the meaning of the long words. Write these three words on the board: *uniformitarianism, observations,* and *unpredictable.* Ask students to find smaller words within each of the four words that can help explain the meaning of the word. (Sample answers: uniformitarianism: uniform; observations: observe; unpredictable: predict) **LS** Verbal

Basic Learners

Creating Lakes Ask students to demonstrate the difference between geologic changes resulting from uniform processes and those resulting from catastrophes. Divide the class into small groups. Ask half of the groups to describe a hypothetical way that a lake could form by slow, steady processes. Ask the other groups to describe the formation of a lake based on catastrophic events. **LS** Verbal/Interpersonal

Figure 2 This photograph shows Siccar Point on the coast of Scotland. Siccar Point is one of the places where Hutton observed the results of gradual geologic processes.

Uniformitarianism Versus Catastrophism

In Hutton's time, most people thought that Earth was only a few thousand years old. To explain Earth's history, most scientists supported catastrophism. **Catastrophism** is the idea that geologic change happens suddenly. Supporters of catastrophism thought that Earth's surface is shaped mainly by rare, sudden events. These unpredictable events caused rapid geologic change over large areas—sometimes over the whole planet.

Scientists debated Hutton's theory because it suggested that Earth is much older than most people thought it was. A few thousand years was not nearly enough time for the gradual geologic processes that Hutton described. Hutton thought that very slow processes needed a very long time to produce large effects. For example, the rocks that he saw at Siccar Point, shown in **Figure 2,** were deposited and folded. Hutton thought that the rock took a long time to form and to be deformed.

Standards Check What is catastrophism? **7.4.b**

A Victory for Uniformitarianism

Despite Hutton's work, most scientists continued to believe in catastrophism. Only after the work of British geologist Charles Lyell did people begin to think of uniformitarianism as geology's most important principle. From 1830 to 1833, Lyell published three books called *Principles of Geology.* In those books, he wrote about uniformitarianism. Using Hutton's notes and new evidence of his own, Lyell successfully challenged the principle of catastrophism. Lyell supported the idea that major geologic change happened gradually. For at least a century after Lyell's work, most geologists agreed with uniformitarianism and not catastrophism.

uniformitarianism
(YOON uh FAWRM uh TER ee uhn IZ uhm) a principle that geologic processes that occurred in the past can be explained by current geologic processes

catastrophism (kuh TAS truh FIZ uhm) a principle that states that geologic change occurs suddenly

Wordwise The prefix *cata-* means "against" or "very." The root *stroph-* means "to turn." The suffix *-ism* means "a belief in."

7.4.a Students know Earth processes today are similar to those that occurred in the past and slow geologic processes have large cumulative effects over long periods of time.
7.4.b Students know the history of life on Earth has been disrupted by major catastrophic events, such as major volcanic eruptions or the impacts of asteroids.
7.4.e Students know fossils provide evidence of how life and environmental conditions have changed.

Close

Standards Focus

This **Standards Focus** provides you with a quick way to **assess, reteach,** and **re-assess** one or more concepts in the section.

Assess

1. Which principle states that the processes that occur today have been at work throughout Earth's history? (uniformitarianism) **7.4.a**

2. What does a paleontologist study? (fossils) **7.4.e**

Reteach

Summarizing Geology Have students write a short essay that explains the roles of catastrophism and uniformitarianism in the history of modern geology. **LS** Verbal **7.4.a, 7.4.b**

Re-Assess

Paleontology Ask students to imagine they are paleontologists. Students should write a short article about their studies and discuss the theories of uniformitarianism and catastrophism in their articles. **LS** Verbal **7.4.a, 7.4.b, 7.4.e**

Teaching Transparency:
LINK TO EARTH SCIENCE
E29 Types of Seismic Waves

Answer to Standards Check

Sample answer: An asteroid impact formed a debris cloud that blocked the sun and caused the extinction of dinosaurs. **7.4.b** (mastering)

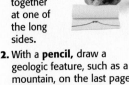

Quick Lab

Geology Flip Book   **7.4.a 7.4.b**

1. Arrange **25 pieces of blank paper** (about 8 cm × 12 cm) into a stack. Use a **stapler** to fasten the stack together at one of the long sides.

2. With a **pencil**, draw a geologic feature, such as a mountain, on the last page of your book. On each of the next pages in order, draw a slightly different scene to show gradual changes to the feature.

3. Watch the change happen by flipping through the book quickly.

4. Does your book better illustrate uniformitarianism or catastrophism? How could you change the drawings to illustrate both?

🕐 **25 min**

Modern Geology—A Happy Medium

During the late 1900s, scientists such as Stephen J. Gould challenged uniformitarianism. They thought that catastrophes can play an important role in shaping Earth's surface. Today, scientists realize that neither uniformitarianism nor catastrophism accounts for all geologic change during Earth's history. Most geologic change is slow and uniform, but catastrophes that cause sudden changes have also happened during Earth's history. For example, craters have been found where meteorites, asteroids, and comets are thought to have struck Earth.

Catastrophes can affect small areas or the whole Earth. They can have short-term or long-term effects on climate. Some scientists think that an asteroid strike about 65 million years ago may have contributed to the disappearance of the dinosaurs. **Figure 3** shows an imaginary re-creation of this asteroid strike. The asteroid impact could have thrown debris into the atmosphere. The debris spread around the whole planet and fell to Earth for decades. This global debris cloud may have blocked the sun's rays, causing a cooling of Earth's climate that doomed the dinosaurs. A volcanic eruption that injects debris into the atmosphere can cause similar changes in climate.

Standards Check What is one way that a catastrophe has disrupted the history of life on Earth? **7.4.b**

Figure 3 *Today, scientists think that sudden events are responsible for some changes during Earth's past. An asteroid hitting Earth, for example, may have contributed to the disappearance of the dinosaurs about 65 million years ago.*

Quick Lab   🕐 **25 min**

Teacher Notes
This activity has students demonstrate the way small changes can add up to large cumulative effects (covers standards 7.4.a and 7.4.b).

Materials for Each Group
- paper
- pencil
- stapler

Answers
4. Sample answer: uniformitarianism; If I added drawings of a sudden event, such as an asteroid impact, then both uniformitarianism and catastrophism would be illustrated.

 Differentiated Datasheets
A **BASIC**, B **GENERAL**, C **ADVANCED**

Also editable on the **Holt Lab Generator CD-ROM**

Paleontology—The Study of Past Life

Studying the rate of geologic change provides only part of the picture of Earth's past. To get a fuller picture, scientists also study the organisms that lived on Earth and the conditions in which they lived. The science that deals with the study of past life is called **paleontology.** Scientists who study this life are called *paleontologists,* and the data they use are fossils. *Fossils* are the remains of organisms preserved by geologic processes.

Paleontologists study fossils to see how the environment has changed. Fossils of sea life may be found almost anywhere on Earth. They may be found in a rock layer in the desert or on a mountain peak. These fossils are evidence that the rock layer formed when the area was part of the ocean. Fossils also provide evidence of how life has changed. As conditions on Earth's surface changed, organisms changed or died out. For example, the fossil record contains evidence of animals that no longer exist, such as saber-toothed cats and woolly mammoths.

Standards Check What are two things for which fossils can provide evidence? **7.4.e**

The Age of Earth
Today, geologists estimate that Earth is about 4.6 billion years old. How many times older is this age than early estimates of about 6,000 years? Record your work in your **Science Journal.**

paleontology
(PAY lee uhn TAHL uh jee) the scientific study of fossils
Wordwise The root *paleo-* means "old." The suffix *-logy* means "the science of."

SECTION Review

7.4.a, 7.4.b, 7.4.e

Summary

- Uniformitarianism assumes that geologic change is gradual. Catastrophism is based on the idea that geologic change is sudden.
- Modern geology is based on the idea that gradual geologic change is interrupted by catastrophes.
- Using fossils to study past life is called paleontology.

Using Vocabulary

1. Write an original definition for *uniformitarianism, catastrophism,* and *paleontology.*

Understanding Concepts

2. **Comparing** Compare catastrophism with uniformitarianism.

3. **Identifying** Give one example of catastrophic global change.

Critical Thinking

4. **Analyzing Methods** Describe how fossils can provide evidence of how environmental conditions and life have changed during Earth's history.

5. **Identifying Relationships** Why did many scientists disagree with the idea of uniformitarianism?

Math Skills

6. **Making Calculations** An impact crater left by an asteroid strike has a radius of 85 km. What is the area of the crater? (Hint: The area of a circle is πr^2.)

Challenge

7. **Analyzing Ideas** Imagine that you are explaining uniformitarianism and catastrophism to a friend. Describe an example of two related events that happen within the span of a human lifetime that demonstrate these two ideas.

Internet Resources

For a variety of links related to this chapter, go to www.scilinks.org
Topic: Earth's Story
SciLinks code: HY70450

Wordwise

Sciences Ask students to work in pairs to identify sciences other than *paleontology.* Then, have students identify the meaning of the prefix in each word. (Sample answer: The prefix *bio-* in *biology* means "life.") **LS** Verbal

Answer to Standards Check

Fossils can provide evidence for changes in the environment and changes in life on Earth. **7.4.e** (mastering)

Answer to Math Practice

$4,600,000,000 \div 6,000 = 766,667$ times

Preteach

Reviewing Prior Knowledge

Ask students to identify the process that breaks down rock. (*weathering*) Ask students to identify the two types of weathering. (*chemical weathering and physical weathering*) Finally, ask students to identify processes by which sediment is arranged in new layers. (*erosion transports sediment and deposition settles it in layers*)

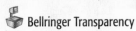 **Bellringer**

Have students focus on standard 7.4.c by using arrows and words to indicate the relationships between the following parts of the rock cycle:

- sedimentary rock
- heat and pressure
- igneous rock
- melting and cooling
- metamorphic rock
- pressure and cementation
- weathering and erosion

(*Accept all reasonable answers. Students should demonstrate an understanding of how rock forms, breaks down, and reforms.*)

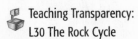 Bellringer Transparency

Teaching Transparency:
L30 The Rock Cycle

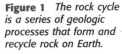

SECTION
2

What You Will Learn

- The rock cycle includes the formation and recycling of rock.
- Relative dating establishes the order in which rocks formed or events took place.
- The principle of superposition states that younger rocks lie above older rocks if the layers are undisturbed.

Why It Matters

Determining the sequence of events in Earth's history helps determine the story of life and environmental changes on Earth.

Vocabulary

- relative dating
- sedimentary rock
- superposition
- unconformity
- law of crosscutting relationships

READING STRATEGY

Asking Questions Read this section silently. In your **Science Journal**, write down questions that you have about this section. Discuss your questions in a small group.

Relative Dating

Key Concept Scientists can interpret the sequence of events in Earth's history by studying rock layers.

▶ If you were a detective investigating a crime scene, what would you do? You might dust the scene for fingerprints or search for witnesses. As a detective, you must figure out the sequence of events that took place before you reached the crime scene.

Geologists have a similar goal when investigating Earth. They try to determine the order in which events have happened during Earth's history. But instead of relying on fingerprints and witnesses, geologists rely on rocks and fossils to help them. Determining whether an object or event is older or younger than other objects or events is called **relative dating.**

The Rock Cycle

Geologic history, from Earth's formation to the present, includes a record of rocks and of changes in life on Earth. This geologic history is sometimes called the *geologic record*. The rock cycle is an important process in the development of the geologic record. **Figure 1** shows how each type of rock can become any other type of rock through the rock cycle. For example, all rock can melt to form magma. *Igneous rock* forms when magma cools. *Metamorphic rock* forms when any type of solid rock changes into another type of rock because of temperature or pressure changes. **Sedimentary rock** is the kind of rock that forms from fragments of other types of rocks. Sedimentary rocks are the most useful rocks for relative dating.

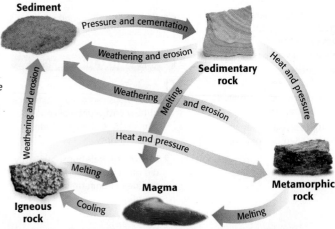

Figure 1 *The rock cycle is a series of geologic processes that form and recycle rock on Earth.*

Universal Access · Differentiated Instruction

English Learners

Word Families Write these words on the board: *geology, sediment, horizontal,* and *gravity*. Tell students that, if they know these four words, they can figure out the meanings of related words. Write a chart on the board and ask students to fill in the noun or adjective forms. Then, have partners find these words and identify the parts of speech. **LS** Verbal

Noun	Adjective
geology	geologic
sediment	sedimentary
horizon	horizontal
gravity	gravitational

Weathering, Erosion, and Deposition

When rocks are exposed on Earth's surface, they can be broken down into smaller pieces, or *weathered*. Rocks can be weathered when physical processes crack and break the rock. Chemical weathering can take place as rock material reacts with water or air. Through weathering, all three rock types can break down to form sediment. *Sediment* is composed of rock fragments, material dissolved in water, and sometimes, biological debris.

Erosion is the process that moves sediment from one place to another. Water, wind, ice, and gravity can cause erosion. Eventually, sediment is deposited in a new location. Deposition is the process in which material is laid down or dropped. Because the sediment is loose when it is deposited, it settles into relatively flat layers. A new, flat layer of sediment rests on top of whatever rock or other sediment is already in place. So, new layers of sedimentary rock are almost always flat. The results of erosion and deposition in Death Valley in California are shown in **Figure 2.**

Formation of Sedimentary Rock

After loose sediment is deposited, it may be *lithified,* or hardened, into sedimentary rock. In this process, the sediment is compacted and the grains of sediment are cemented together. Fossils form if biological debris or a trace of animal activity remains in a rock. The fossils are a record of the kind of life that existed where the sediment was deposited. And the type of rock that forms with a fossil can give clues about the environment in which the organism lived.

The type of rock that forms in any area depends on local conditions. So, no single rock layer is found in all areas of Earth. And during any one period of geologic time, many types of rock were forming in different areas of Earth. Therefore, no single area or history of an area can contain the geologic record for all of Earth.

Figure 2 *These mountains in Death Valley have been weathered, and the sediment has been eroded. The sediment has been deposited in a flat layer below the mountains.*

relative dating (REL uh tiv DAYT ing) any method of determining whether an event or object is older or younger than other events or objects

sedimentary rock (SED uh MEN tuhr ee RAHK) a rock that forms from compressed or cemented layers of sediment

7.3.c Students know how independent lines of evidence from geology, fossils, and comparative anatomy provide the bases for the theory of evolution.
7.4.c Students know that the rock cycle includes the formation of new sediment and rocks and that rocks are often found in layers, with the oldest generally on the bottom.

Discussion As students explore this section, ask them to answer the following questions:

- If a fault is observed in rock layers, which is older, the rock layers or the fault? (the rock layers)

- If rock layers are deposited horizontally but are sharply tilted, did the deposition happen first or did the tilting happen first? (the deposition) **LS** Verbal

ACTIVITY

Modeling Rock Disturbances

Have students model how faults, folding, and tilting disturb rock layers. Ask students to glue several sponges of different colors together to form a model rock sequence. Have students model folding and tilting with their sponge layers. Then, to show a fault, tell students to make a straight, diagonal cut through all of the sponge layers. Tell students to demonstrate fault movement. (Students should do so by moving the two sponge sections alongside each other.) **LS** Visual/Kinesthetic

Answer to Standards Check

The principle of superposition states that younger rocks lie above older rocks if the layers have not been disturbed. **7.3.c** (supporting), **7.4.c** (mastering)

The Principle of Superposition

Suppose that you have a brother who takes a lot of pictures of your family and piles them in a box. Over the years, he adds new pictures to the top of the stack. Think about the family history recorded in those pictures. Where are the oldest pictures—the ones taken when you were a baby? Where are the most recent pictures—those taken last week?

Superposition in Rock Layers

Layers of sedimentary rock, such as the ones shown in **Figure 3,** are like stacked photographs. As you move from top to bottom, the layers get older. The principle that states that younger rocks lie above older rocks in undisturbed sequences is called **superposition.** Superposition helps geologists determine the relative ages of rock layers.

Superposition also helps geologists determine the relative ages of fossils. Fossils represent organisms that lived when sediment collected to form sedimentary rock. So, fossils found in a younger rock layer are younger than fossils found in an older rock layer. And fossils found in lower, or older, rock layers are older than fossils found in higher, or younger, rock layers.

Standards Check What does the principle of superposition state about rocks that are found in layers? **7.3.c, 7.4.c**

superposition
(soo puhr puh ZISH uhn) a principle that states that younger rocks lie above older rocks if the layers have not been disturbed

Figure 3 These rock layers are in Red Rock Canyon in California. Rock layers are like pictures stacked over time—the younger ones are at the top of the stack over the older ones.

Universal Access · Differentiated Instruction

Struggling Readers

Visualizing Analogies Direct students' attention to the heading "The Principle of Superposition." Point out that, to explain superposition, an analogy is used to compare rock layers to a pile of photographs. Explain that one way to get the most benefit from an analogy is to stop reading and focus on a mental image of the description. Ask students to read the first paragraph under "The Principle of Superposition."

Then, ask them to stop, close their eyes, and picture the events described. Then, have students read the next paragraph. Tell them to stop again and think about how the rock layers are like the pile of pictures. Explain that, by briefly stopping to visualize the information, students will be more likely to understand and remember the information. **LS** Visual/Intrapersonal

Figure 4 **How Rock Layers Become Disturbed**

Folding *Folding* occurs when rock layers bend and buckle from forces inside Earth.

Tilting *Tilting* occurs when forces inside Earth slant rock layers.

Faults A *fault* is a break in Earth's crust along which blocks of rock slide relative to one another.

Intrusions An *intrusion* is molten rock from Earth's interior that squeezes into existing rock and cools.

Disturbed Rock Layers

Gravity causes sediment to be deposited in horizontal layers. So, if rock layers are not horizontal, something must have disturbed them after they formed. Sometimes, rock layers are even overturned by powerful forces in Earth's crust. In these sequences, older layers lie on top of younger layers.

Processes That Disturb Rock Layers

Folding and tilting are two events that disturb rock layers. *Folding* is the bending of rock layers that results from stress. *Tilting* happens when Earth's forces move rock layers so that they are slanted. Folding and tilting are shown in **Figure 4.**

Features That Cut Across Rock Layers

Geologists often find features that cut across existing layers of rock. These features include faults and intrusions. A *fault* is a break or crack in Earth's crust along which rocks shift position. An *intrusion* is a mass of igneous rock that forms when magma is injected into rock and then cools and solidifies. A fault and an intrusion are shown in **Figure 4.**

Group ACTiViTY

Rock-Layer Jigsaw Puzzle

Have students work in groups of three to construct a three-dimensional rock-layer jigsaw puzzle. Provide students with materials that can be shaped, such as foam. One student should create a model of sedimentary rock. The next student should add an intrusion to the model. The third student should add a fault to the model. Then, have groups exchange models and attempt to tell the relative ages of the parts of another group's model. **LS Kinesthetic**

Co-op Learning

Using the Figure

Geology Comic Strip Have students study the figure of unconformities on this page. Ask students to create a comic strip that continues the sequence of images in the figure. Students can illustrate geologic events such as intrusions, tilting, folding, faulting, or unconformities. **LS Visual**

unconformity
(uhn kuhn FAWRM uh tee) a break in the geologic record created when rock layers are eroded or when sediment is not deposited for a long period of time

law of crosscutting relationships
(LAW UHV KRAWS KUHT ing ri LAY shuhn SHIPS) the principle that a fault or body of rock is younger than any other body of rock that it cuts through

Gaps in the Record

Sometimes, layers of rock are missing, so there is a gap in the geologic record. To think of this another way, let's say that you stack your newspapers every day after reading them. Now, let's suppose that you want to look at a paper you read 10 days ago. You know that the paper should be 10 papers deep in the stack. But when you look, the paper is not there. What happened? Perhaps you didn't put the paper in the stack. Or maybe someone removed the paper. The same principles apply to a missing rock layer and the missing newspaper.

Unconformities

Missing rock layers create breaks in rock-layer sequences. An **unconformity** is a surface that represents a break in or a missing part of the geologic record. Unconformities also represent missing time—time that was not recorded in layers of rock. When geologists find an unconformity, they question whether the "missing layer" was never present or whether it was there once and was somehow removed. Unconformities can form when deposition stops after a supply of sediment is cut off. Unconformities also form when erosion removes layers. **Figure 5** shows these two processes.

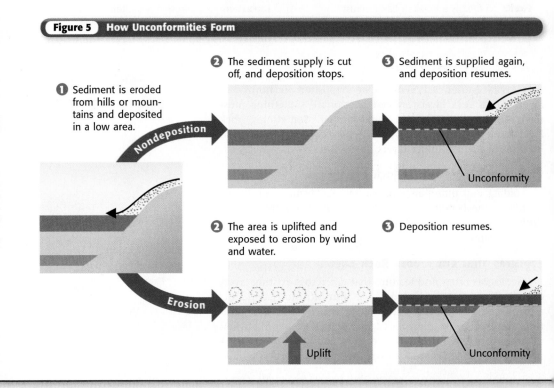

Figure 5 **How Unconformities Form**

❶ Sediment is eroded from hills or mountains and deposited in a low area.

Nondeposition

❷ The sediment supply is cut off, and deposition stops.

❸ Sediment is supplied again, and deposition resumes.

Unconformity

❷ The area is uplifted and exposed to erosion by wind and water.

Erosion

Uplift

❸ Deposition resumes.

Unconformity

Universal Access • Differentiated Instruction

Advanced Learners/GATE

Road Cuts When roads are built in hilly or mountainous terrain, they often cut through the hills and mountains. These road cuts often reveal several of the layers that make up the terrain. Have students find photographs of road cuts. Then, they should label geologic features, such as intrusions, tilting, folding, and faults. **LS Logical**

Basic Learners

Unconformities Have students demonstrate an unconformity. Give each student a sandwich cookie. Ask students to take apart the cookie and scrape out the filling. Then, have them put the cookie halves back together. Ask students:

• Where is the unconformity? (the missing frosting layer)

• How might an unconformity form? (Sample answer: erosion) **LS Visual**

Rock-Layer Puzzles

The principle of superposition states that younger layers of sedimentary rock are found on top of older layers if the layers have not been overturned. But what if the rock layers are more than just a stack of horizontal layers?

Geologists often find rock-layer sequences that have been affected by more than one process. Determining the order of events that led to the arrangement of these rock layers is like piecing together a puzzle. Geologists study rock-layer sequences to help piece together the history of Earth as told by the rock record.

The Law of Crosscutting Relationships

The **law of crosscutting relationships** states that a fault or a body of rock, such as an intrusion, is younger than any feature or layer of rock that the fault or rock body cuts through. For example, if a fault cuts through an unconformity, the fault is younger than the rock layers on either side of the unconformity. Remember that layers of rock have to be in place before anything can disturb them.

Standards Check How does the law of crosscutting relationships help with relative dating of rock layers and features? 🐻 **7.4.c**

Relative Ages of Rock Layers and Features

Figure 6 shows four stages in the formation of rock layers that contain an igneous intrusion, an unconformity, and a fault. A geologist studying rock layers has only the fourth view to look at when piecing together a rock-layer puzzle. Look at the bottom picture to see what the geologist is studying.

Now, start at the top to see the history of this area. You can see that the bottom three layers of sedimentary rock were formed first. Next, an intrusion cut through the three layers. The layers had to be there first before the intrusion could cut through them. An unconformity formed when the top of the sequence was eroded away. Then, two more layers of sediment were deposited. These layers were lithified and formed sedimentary rock. Finally, a fault cut through all of the sedimentary layers and the igneous intrusion.

Figure 6 **A Rock-Layer Sequence**

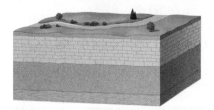

❶ Three layers of sedimentary rock form.

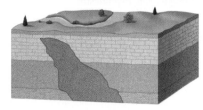

❷ An igneous intrusion cuts through the three rock layers.

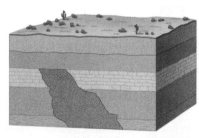

❸ Erosion removes some of the top layer and some of the intrusion. Then, more sedimentary rock forms.

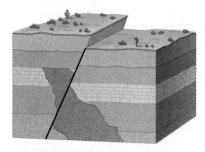

❹ Tectonic forces cause a fault to form.

Standards Focus

This **Standards Focus** provides you with a quick way to **assess, reteach,** and **re-assess** one or more concepts in the section.

 Assess

1. In the rock cycle, how does sediment form? (by weathering and erosion) **7.4.c**

2. What does the law of superposition state? (that younger rocks lie above older rocks if the layers have not been disturbed) **7.4.c**

Reteach

Flashcards Have students make flashcards for the following terms: *sedimentary rock, superposition, unconformity, folding, faulting, tilting,* and *intrusion.* On the opposite side of each card, students should draw an illustration that represents or defines each term. **LS Visual 7.4.c**

Re-Assess

Making Models Have students model folding, faulting, tilting, intrusions, and unconformities. Provide students with materials for their models, such as sponges, paper, or clay. **LS Kinesthetic 7.4.c**

Answer to Standards Check

Relative dating gives information about the order in which events took place but does not give information about when the events actually occurred. **7.4.c** (supporting)

Answer to School-to-Home Activity

Answers may vary depending on the area visited. Consider asking parents to take a photograph of the area to ensure that the student's drawing accurately represents the area.

Looking at Rock Layers

With a parent or guardian, look at road cuts, beaches, or other areas where rock layers are visible. Sketch the rock layers in your **Science Journal.** Discuss which rock layers are the oldest with your parent or guardian. Hypothesize what processes have affected the rocks since the rocks formed.

Order of Events

Geologists use superposition and crosscutting relationships to find the relative ages of rocks. Relative dating makes clear the order in which events happened. But relative dating does not tell scientists exactly when those events took place.

To form a more complete picture of Earth's history, geologists combine relative dating with information that can establish actual dates. For example, imagine that you are digging in layers of soil at the edge of a river. You know from superposition that the layers near the top were deposited more recently than the layers farther down. But without more information, you can't tell when any of the layers were deposited. Now, imagine that in one layer, you find a coin dated 1965. You can now tell that the layer in which you found the coin could not have been deposited before 1965. And you know that the layers above the coin were deposited in 1965 or in a later year.

Standards Check What information do geologists obtain from relative dating? **7.4.c**

Quick Lab

Solve a Rock-Layer Puzzle!

In this activity, you will put your scientific skills to work to determine the relative ages of the layers and features of this rock-layer puzzle.

▶ Try It!

1. On a **piece of paper,** use a **pencil** to draw 10 horizontal lines. Write "Youngest" above the top line and "Oldest" below the bottom line.

2. Study the rock layers shown in the drawing to the right. Use what you know about superposition and crosscutting relationships to determine the order in which layers and features A through J formed.

3. List the oldest layer or feature on the bottom line, and list the youngest feature or layer on the top line.

4. Fill in all 10 letters to show the relative ages of all of the layers and features. When you have finished, each line should contain one letter.

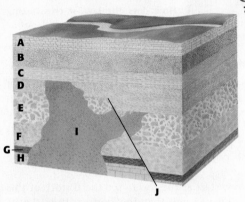

▶ Think About It!

5. Do the layers and features best represent geologic change as described by uniformitarianism or catastrophism? Explain your answer.

6. Can you tell how old any of the features or layers in this illustration are? If so, give the ages. If not, explain why not.

🕐 20 min

Quick Lab

🕐 20 min

Teacher Notes

This activity has students interpret a rock-layer sequence and determine the relative ages of the layers and features (covers standard 7.4.c).

Materials for Each Student

- paper
- pencil

Answers

4. from youngest to oldest: A, B, C, J, I, D, E, F, G, H

5. Sample answer: These layers and features best represent gradual geologic change, or uniformitarianism. The layers formed over a long period of time.

6. Sample answer: I cannot tell how old any of the features or layers are. Putting the events in order, or relative dating, does not give any information about the actual ages of the layers or features.

📋 Differentiated Datasheets
A **Basic**, B **General**, C **Advanced**

Also editable on the
**Holt Lab Generator
CD-ROM**

Summary

- Geologists use relative dating to determine the order in which events happen.
- The rock cycle describes processes that form and recycle rock on Earth.
- Sedimentary rock forms when layers of sediment are lithified. Fossils may be preserved in sedimentary rock.
- The principle of superposition states that in undisturbed rock sequences, younger sedimentary rock layers lie above older layers.
- Folding and tilting are two events that disturb rock layers. Faults and intrusions are two features that cut across rock layers.
- Unconformities occur when rock layers are eroded or when sediment is not deposited for a long time.
- The law of crosscutting relationships states that structures and features that cut across rock layers are younger than the rock layers.
- Superposition and crosscutting relationships allow geologists to determine the order in which rock layers and features form but not the age in years of rock layers and features.

Using Vocabulary

1 Write an original definition for *relative dating*, *superposition*, *sedimentary rock*, and *unconformity*.

Understanding Concepts

2 **Summarizing** What does the rock cycle demonstrate about the three types of rocks?

3 **Listing** What are two ways unconformities can form?

4 **Justifying** Explain how scientists use the law of crosscutting relationships to determine the relative ages of rock layers and a fault that cuts through the layers.

Critical Thinking

5 **Analyzing Processes** Put the following terms in the order in which they would likely occur as sedimentary rock forms: *weathering, lithification, deposition,* and *erosion.* Explain what happens during each of these steps.

6 **Analyzing Ideas** Does the law of crosscutting relationships involve sedimentary rock only? Explain why or why not.

INTERPRETING GRAPHICS Use the illustration below to answer the next three questions.

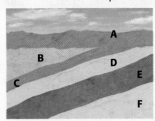

7 **Analyzing Processes** What process appears to have disturbed rock layers B, C, D, E, and F?

8 **Identifying Relationships** List the relative ages of these rock layers from youngest to oldest.

9 **Evaluating Data** There is an unconformity in this rock sequence. Describe its location, and describe how it may have formed.

Math Skills

10 **Making Calculations** Sediment in one area is deposited at a rate of 3 mm per year. At this rate, how many years must pass for 12 cm of sediment to be deposited?

Challenge

11 **Making Comparisons** Describe an example of something around your home or school that demonstrates superposition. Explain how you could use superposition to determine the order of events at home or at school.

Internet Resources

For a variety of links related to this chapter, go to www.scilinks.org
Topic: Relative Dating; The Rock Cycle
SciLinks code: HY71288; HY71319

6. Sample answer: The law of cross-cutting relationships does not involve only sedimentary rocks. For example, an intrusion can be made up of igneous rock. **7.4.c** (exceeding)

7. Rock layers B, C, D, E, and F appear to have been disturbed by tilting. **7.4.c** (supporting)

8. A, B, C, D, E, F **7.3.c** (supporting), **7.4.c** (exceeding)

9. Sample answer: The unconformity appears to be at the bottom of rock layer A. The probable sequence is: Layers B through F were tilted. The top of these layers then eroded. After the erosion, layer A was deposited. **7.4.c** (exceeding)

10. 12 cm $\times$ 10 mm/cm = 120 mm; 120 mm $\div$ 3 mm/y = 40 y

11. Sample answer: Layers of clothes in a laundry hamper at home are an example of superposition. Clothes that I wore more recently are deposited at the top of the hamper. Superposition could be used to determine the order in which I wore the clothes in the hamper. **7.3.c** (exceeding), **7.4.c** (exceeding)

Section Review Standards Guide

	Supporting	Mastering	Exceeding
7.3.c	1, 8		11
7.4.c	1, 2, 3, 4, 7	5	6, 8, 9, 11

Answers to Section Review

1. Sample answer: Relative dating is a method of determining whether an event or object is older or younger than other events or objects. Superposition is a principle that states that younger rocks lie above older rocks in undisturbed rock. A sedimentary rock is a rock that forms from layers of sediment. An unconformity is a break in the geologic record that forms when rock layers are eroded or when sediment is not deposited for a long period of time. **7.3.c** (supporting), **7.4.c** (supporting)

2. The rock cycle demonstrates how all three types of rock can become any other type of rock. **7.4.c** (supporting)

3. Unconformities can form when rock is eroded or when sediment is not deposited in an area for a long period of time. **7.4.c** (supporting)

4. Scientists would use the law of crosscutting relationships to determine that the fault was younger than the layers of rock through which it cuts. **7.4.c** (supporting)

5. weathering, erosion, deposition, and lithification; Weathering is the breakdown of rock into smaller particles. Erosion is the transport of the weathered fragments. Deposition is the process in which the sediment is deposited in a new location. Lithification is the hardening of sediment into sedimentary rock. **7.4.c** (mastering)

Section Resources

- Directed Reading A **BASIC** (Also in Spanish), B **GENERAL**
- Interactive Reader and Study Guide
- Section Quiz **GENERAL** (Also in Spanish)
- Section Review **GENERAL** (Also in Spanish)
- Vocabulary and Section Summary A **BASIC** (Also in Spanish), B **GENERAL**

SECTION
3

Absolute Dating

Key Concept Because radioactive decay occurs at a constant rate, the age of a rock can be estimated by analyzing the amounts of different isotopes in a rock.

Preteach

Reviewing Prior Knowledge

Ask students to describe the way minerals in igneous rock form from magma. (When magma cools enough, it solidifies to form igneous rock. Igneous rock can be made up of different minerals, depending on the composition of the magma and depending on how fast the magma cools.)

Bellringer

Have students focus on standard 7.4.d by asking them to identify how old Earth is. (4.6 billion years old) Then, ask students to identify how scientists determined how old Earth is. (Answers may vary. Students may recognize that radiometric dating was involved in this process.)

 Bellringer Transparency

Motivate

ACTIVITY

Isotope Skit Ask two or three students to play the role of geologists. The rest of the students play the part of isotopes in a newly formed rock sample. Have the geologists wait outside the classroom, and tell the students that their half-life is one minute. Have the isotopes stand, and have the geologists return to the classroom. Tell half of the isotopes to sit down after one minute. Continue until one student remains standing. Have the geologists guess the age of the sample.
LS Kinesthetic/Logical Co-op Learning

What You Will Learn

- Radioactive decay is the process by which a radioactive isotope changes into a stable isotope.
- Radiometric dating is the process in which parent and daughter isotopes are analyzed to determine the age of rocks and fossils.

Why It Matters

Estimating the age of rocks and fossils helps tell the story of Earth's past.

Vocabulary

- absolute dating
- radioactive decay
- radiometric dating
- half-life

READING STRATEGY

Clarifying Concepts Take turns reading this section out loud with a partner. Stop to discuss ideas that seem confusing.

absolute dating (AB suh LOOT DAYT ing) any method of measuring the age of an event or object in years

radioactive decay (RAY dee oh AK tiv dee KAY) the process in which a radioactive isotope tends to break down into a stable isotope of the same element or another element

7.3.c Students know how independent lines of evidence from geology, fossils, and comparative anatomy provide the bases for the theory of evolution.
7.4.d Students know that evidence from geologic layers and radioactive dating indicates Earth is approximately 4.6 billion years old and that life on this planet has existed for more than 3 billion years.

If you want to know exactly how old a person is, you can ask the person. But how can you find out the age of a rock? Finding the age of an object by determining the number of years the object has existed is called **absolute dating.** Read on to see how unstable atoms are used in one method of absolute dating.

Radioactive Decay

Atoms of the same element that have the same number of protons but have different numbers of neutrons are called *isotopes*. Most isotopes are stable, meaning that they stay in their original form. But some isotopes are unstable. Scientists call unstable isotopes *radioactive*. The breakdown of a radioactive isotope into a stable isotope of the same element or another element is called **radioactive decay. Figure 1** shows one example of how radioactive decay can happen.

Each kind of unstable isotope decays at a different rate. The rate of radioactive decay for a given isotope can be determined experimentally. For each kind of isotope, the rate of decay is constant. So, certain naturally occurring radioactive isotopes can be used as a kind of "clock" to find the ages of rocks that contain these isotopes.

Standards Check What is radioactive decay? 7.4.d

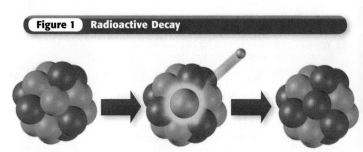

Figure 1 Radioactive Decay

Unstable Isotope
6 protons,
8 neutrons

Radioactive Decay
When some unstable isotopes decay, a neutron is converted into a proton. In the process, an electron is released.

Product of Decay: Stable Isotope
7 protons,
7 neutrons

Answer to Standards Check

Radioactive decay is the breakdown of an unstable isotope into a stable isotope of the same element or of another element. **7.4.d** (supporting)

Universal Access · Differentiated Instruction

Advanced Learners/GATE

Half Dome Ask students to work in small groups to research what geologists have discovered about the formation of Half Dome, which is located in Yosemite National Park in California. Have students present their findings in posters. Posters should include steps such as the cooling of magma, the uplift of Half Dome, and erosion by glaciers. **LS Visual/Verbal**

Dating Rocks—Parent and Daughter Isotopes

An unstable radioactive isotope is called a *parent isotope*. The stable isotope produced by radioactive decay is called the *daughter isotope*. Radioactive decay can occur as a single step or a series of steps. In either case, the rate of decay is constant.

To date rock, scientists compare the amount of parent isotope with the amount of daughter isotope. The more daughter isotope there is, the older the rock is. For this reason, radiometric dating works only on rocks that contained either no daughter isotope or a known amount of daughter isotope at the time the rock formed.

Radiometric Dating

If you know the rate of decay for a radioactive element in a rock, you can figure out the absolute age of the rock. Determining the absolute age of a sample based on the ratio of parent material to daughter material is called **radiometric dating.** For example, let's say that a rock sample contains an isotope with a half-life of 10,000 years. A **half-life** is the time needed for one-half of a radioactive sample to decay. In this rock sample, after 10,000 years, half of the parent material will have decayed and become daughter material. You analyze the sample and find equal amounts of parent material and daughter material. Half of the original radioactive isotope has decayed, so the sample must be about 10,000 years old. **Figure 2** shows how this steady decay happens.

The Most Useful Rock Samples

Igneous rocks are the best types of rock samples to use for radiometric dating. When igneous rock forms, elements are separated into different minerals in the rock. Thus, when they form, minerals in igneous rocks often contain only a parent isotope and none of the daughter isotope.

INTERNET ACTIVITY

Radioactive Benefits

Can radioactivity be a good thing? Write an essay that describes how radioactivity can be beneficial. Go to **go.hrw.com,** and type in the keyword HY7RADW.

radiometric dating (RAY dee oh MET rik DAYT ing) a method of determining the age of an object by estimating the relative percentages of a radioactive (parent) isotope and a stable (daughter) isotope

half-life (HAF lief) the time required for half of a sample of a radioactive isotope to break down by radioactive decay to form a daughter isotope

Figure 2 *After every half-life, the amount of parent material decreases by one-half.* **What fraction of parent material remains after two half-lives?**

0 years
Parent isotope = 16 mg
Daughter isotope = 0 mg

10,000 years
Parent isotope = 8 mg
Daughter isotope = 8 mg

20,000 years
Parent isotope = 4 mg
Daughter isotope = 12 mg

30,000 years
Parent isotope = 2 mg
Daughter isotope = 14 mg

Universal Access · Differentiated Instruction

Special Education Students

Raisin Dating Give students a general idea of how the absence of a substance can be used to determine time. Give each student 8 raisins (or other small food.) Explain that each student is to eat half their remaining raisins each time you say "Eat raisins." Explain that class will continue as planned between raisin "eatings."

Set a buzzer for 10 min, and when it rings, say "Eat raisins." Repeat this procedure two more times. Then, ask students to count the number of remaining raisins. (one) Then, ask students to determine how many half-lives elapsed. (three) Finally, ask students to determine how much time passed if the half-life of raisins is 10 min. (3 × 10 = 30 min) **LS** Visual/Kinesthetic

---

Teach

CONNECTION ACTIVITY
Math

Calculating Half-Life To help students understand the concept of half-life, ask them to calculate how old an object is when 1/4, 1/8, and 1/32 of its carbon-14 remains. The half-life of carbon-14 is 5,730 years. (1/4 = 2 half-lives = 11,460 y; 1/8 = 3 half-lives = 17,190 y; 1/32 = 5 half-lives = 28,650 y) **LS** Logical

MISCONCEPTION ALERT

Radioactive Decay Some students may think that radioactive decay is similar to organic decay. To help students overcome this misconception, ask them to research the mechanisms behind radioactive decay and organic decay. Have them work in pairs to create a table that compares the two types of decay. Students should recognize that radioactive decay happens at a constant rate because the isotopes are unstable, and they should recognize that organic decay does not happen at a constant rate and that it requires living organisms, or decomposers, to carry it out.

Using the Figure

Half-Life Have students examine **Figure 2.** Ask four volunteers to verbally describe what happened in each image. Then, ask students to predict what the isotope would look like after another half-life. (Sample answer: There would be 1 mg of the parent and 15 mg of the daughter.) Answer to caption question: After two half-lives, one-quarter of the parent material remains. **LS** Visual

 Teaching Transparency: L32 Radioactive Decay: Parent and Daughter Isotopes

Standards Focus

This **Standards Focus** provides you with a quick way to **assess, reteach,** and **re-assess** one or more concepts in the section.

Assess

1. How old is Earth? (4.6 billion years) **7.4.d**

2. How did scientists determine the age of Earth? (They dated meteorites and moon rocks to find that the age of the solar system, including Earth, is about 4.6 billion years.) **7.4.d**

Reteach

Modeling Radioactive Decay
Have students use two colors of marbles to demonstrate radioactive decay. Give each student 16 marbles of each color. Students should start with a sample that contains 16 marbles of one color. Have students use the other color of marbles to represent the daughter isotopes. The sample would have 8 marbles of each color after the first half-life. Students should demonstrate half-lives until only one marble of the original color, or the parent isotope, remains. **LS** Visual **7.4.d**

Re-Assess

Absolute Dating Ask students to create a Process Chart to describe the sequence of radioactive decay in a mineral containing 12 mg of potassium-40 when it forms. Ask students to show what happens as 3 half-lives go by in time. (Sample answer: 1. magma cools to form a mineral with 12 mg of potassium-40; 2. in 1.3 billion years there are 6 mg of potassium-40 and 6 mg of daughter isotopes; 3. in 2.6 billion years there are 3 mg of potassium-40 and 12 mg of daughter isotopes; 4. in 3.9 billion years there are 1.5 mg of potassium-40 and 10.5 mg of daughter isotopes. **LS** Logical **7.4.d**

Figure 3 *Half Dome in California's Yosemite National Park formed when a large mass of magma cooled very slowly below Earth's surface.*

Using Radiometric Dating

Scientists use different radiometric-dating techniques based on the estimated age of a sample. The half-life of an isotope determines how the isotope can be used for dating. The older the rock is, the more daughter material there will be in the rock. Isotopes with long half-lives can be used to date old rocks but not young rocks. For isotopes with long half-lives, younger rocks do not contain enough daughter material to allow accurate measurements.

Methods of Radiometric Dating

One isotope used for radiometric dating is potassium-40. Potassium-40 has a half-life of 1.3 billion years. It decays to argon and calcium. Geologists measure argon as the daughter material. This method can be used to date rocks older than 100,000 years.

Uranium-238 is a radioactive isotope that decays to lead-206. The half-life of uranium-238 is 4.5 billion years. Uranium-lead dating can be used to date rocks older than 10 million years.

Half Dome, in Yosemite National Park, is shown in **Figure 3.** This dome is composed of igneous rock. After the rock formed, it was uplifted and shaped by glaciers. Uranium-lead dating shows that the rock in Half Dome formed about 85 million years ago. So, geologists can use relative dating to determine that the uplift and glacial erosion happened sometime in the last 85 million years.

Quick Lab

Radioactive Decay

1. Use a **clock** or **watch with a second hand** to record the time. Wait 20 s, and then use **scissors** to carefully cut a **sheet of paper** in half. Select one piece, and set the other piece aside.

2. Repeat step 1 until nine 20 s intervals have elapsed.

3. What does the whole piece of paper used in this lab represent?

4. What do the pieces of paper you set aside in each step represent?

5. How much of your paper isotope was left after the first interval? after three intervals? after nine intervals? Express your answers as percentages.

6. What is the half-life of your paper isotope?

🕐 10 min

Quick Lab

🕐 10 min

Teacher Notes

This activity has students model radioactive decay (covers standard 7.4.d). For more advanced students, this lab could be done with several groups using different half-lives. The lab could go for 5 minutes and then groups could compare how much "radioactive" material they have remaining.

Materials for Each Group

• clock or watch with a second hand
• paper
• scissors

Safety Caution

Remind students to review all safety cautions and icons before beginning this activity.

Answers

3. parent isotope **5.** 50%; 12.5%; 0.195%

4. daughter isotopes **6.** 20 s

📄 **Differentiated Datasheets**
A **BASIC**, B **GENERAL**, C **ADVANCED**

Also editable on the
Holt Lab Generator
CD-ROM

The Age of Our Solar System

Can radiometric dating be used to find the age of Earth? Yes, but not by dating rocks from Earth. The first rocks that formed on Earth have been recycled by plate tectonics and erosion. Therefore, there are no Earth rocks left that are as old as our planet. But other bodies in space contain rock that is as old as our solar system.

For example, the moon and some meteorites contain rock that formed as our solar system, including Earth, was forming. *Meteorites* are small, rocky bodies that have traveled through space and fallen to Earth's surface. Geologists have found meteorites on Earth. Rocks from the moon have also been collected, as shown in **Figure 4**. Radiometric dating has been done on these rocks from other parts of our solar system. The absolute ages of these samples show that our solar system, including Earth, is about 4.6 billion years old.

Standards Check Approximately how old are Earth and the solar system? What is the evidence for this age? **7.4.d**

Figure 4 *Scientist-astronaut Harrison Schmitt collects samples of rock on the moon with the lunar rake during the* Apollo 17 *mission.*

---

3. Radioactive decay happens at a constant rate, so the amounts of parent and daughter isotopes can be measured during radiometric dating to determine the age of a sample.
7.3.c (supporting), **7.4.d** (supporting)

4. At the time the rock formed, the daughter material must either be absent from the rock or the amount present in the rock must be known.
7.4.d (supporting)

5. Geologists know that Earth and the solar system are about 4.6 billion years old because radiometric dating has shown that samples of moon rock and meteorites that formed as the solar system was forming are about 4.6 billion years old.
7.4.d (mastering)

6. Sample answer: If radioactive decay was not constant, scientists would not have a specific half-life number to compare with an object's ratio of parent material to daughter material. Therefore, a precise age could not be determined. **7.4.d** (supporting)

7. Sample answer: There are moon rocks that are older than any rocks on Earth because rocks on the moon are not recycled by the movement of tectonic plates and the rock cycle. So, the rocks that originally formed on the surface of the moon are still there. **7.4.d** (supporting)

8. Sample answer: The potassium-argon method would not be appropriate because the half-life of potassium-40 is 1.3 billion years. After 1,000 years, it is unlikely that there will be enough daughter isotope to accurately measure.
7.4.d (exceeding)

Section Review Standards Guide

	Supporting	Mastering	Exceeding
7.3.c	1, 3		
7.4.d	1, 2, 3, 4, 6, 7	5	8

Answer to Standards Check

The solar system, including Earth, is about 4.6 billion years old. The evidence for this age is radiometric dating of moon rocks and meteorites. **7.4.d** (mastering)

Answers to Section Review

1. Sample answer: Absolute dating is the process of determining the number of years that an object has existed. Radioactive decay happens when an unstable isotope breaks down and changes into another isotope. Radiometric dating is a method of absolute dating in which the age of a sample is determined by measuring the amounts of parent and daughter material in the sample. A half-life is the amount of time in which one-half of a radioactive sample decays. **7.3.c** (supporting), **7.4.d** (supporting)

2. Sample answer: One way radioactive decay can occur is when a neutron in an unstable atom is converted into a proton. **7.4.d** (supporting)

Section Resources

📄 Directed Reading
A **BASIC** (Also in Spanish), B **GENERAL**

📄 Interactive Reader and Study Guide

📄 Section Quiz **GENERAL** (Also in Spanish)

📄 Section Review **GENERAL** (Also in Spanish)

📄 Vocabulary and Section Summary A **BASIC** (Also in Spanish), B **GENERAL**

Teacher Notes

In this activity, students model radioactive decay and graph their results (covers standards 7.4.d and 7.7.c).

Time Required

One 45-minute class period

Lab Ratings

EASY ——————————→ HARD

Teacher Prep 🜊
Student Set-Up 🜊
Concept Level 🜊🜊🜊
Clean Up 🜊

Materials

The materials listed on the student page are enough for two to four students. Students can share containers and count pennies together, but each student should make his or her own data table and graph.

Preparation Notes

Recycled plastic containers, such as margarine tubs or sport drink bottles, are ideal for this activity. The mouth of the container should be wide enough to allow the coins to come out easily. Remind students to wash their hands after the activity.

Coin tosses are a good model for radioactive decay because about half of the coins will land heads up and half will land tails up any time the coins are shaken up. This probability is similar to the decay of a radioactive isotope because half of the atoms will decay during each half-life. Any two-sided coin can be used for this activity. However, make sure all students are using the same denomination of coin—all pennies, for example.

Skills Practice Lab

The Half-Life of Pennies

Uranium-238—or U-238—is a radioactive isotope of the element uranium. Uranium-238 decays to lead-206, which is a stable isotope of the element lead. The half-life of uranium-238 is 4.5 billion years. So, every 4.5 billion years, half of the uranium-238 in a sample will decay to lead-206. In other words, during any 4.5-billion-year period, the probability that a particular uranium-238 atom will decay is 1/2.

The absolute age of a rock can be found by analyzing the rock for uranium-238 and lead-206. Knowing the amounts of both of these isotopes enables scientists to calculate how long ago the rock formed. In the following experiment, you will use pennies to model radioactive decay.

OBJECTIVES

Model radioactive decay by using pennies to represent uranium atoms.

Demonstrate the concept of half-life and how it is used in radiometric dating.

MATERIALS

- container with a cover, plastic, large, wide mouthed
- paper, graph
- pennies (100)

Procedure

1. Place 100 pennies in a large, covered container. Shake the container several times, and remove the cover. Carefully empty the pennies onto a flat surface. Make sure that the pennies don't roll away.

7.4.d Students know that evidence from geologic layers and radioactive dating indicates Earth is approximately 4.6 billion years old and that life on this planet has existed for more than 3 billion years.

Investigation and Experimentation
7.7.c Communicate the logical connection among hypotheses, science concepts, tests conducted, data collected, and conclusions drawn from the scientific evidence.

Lab Resources

Differentiated Datasheets
A **BASIC**, B **GENERAL**, C **ADVANCED**

Classroom Lab Video/DVD

🔴 Holt Lab Generator CD-ROM

Search for any lab by topic, standard, difficulty level, or time. Edit any lab to fit your needs, or create your own labs. Use the Lab Materials QuickList software to customize your lab materials list.

2 Remove all of the pennies that have the "head" side of the coin turned upward. In a data table similar to the one below, record the number of pennies that you removed and the number of pennies that remain.

Shake number	Number of pennies remaining	Number of pennies removed
0	100	0
1		
2		

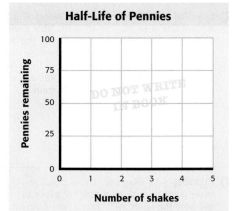

Half-Life of Pennies

Pennies remaining (y-axis: 0, 25, 50, 75, 100)
Number of shakes (x-axis: 0, 1, 2, 3, 4, 5)

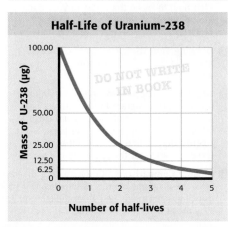

Half-Life of Uranium-238

Mass of U-238 (μg) (y-axis: 0, 6.25, 12.50, 25.00, 50.00, 100.00)
Number of half-lives (x-axis: 0, 1, 2, 3, 4, 5)

3 Repeat the process until no pennies are left in the container. Remember to remove only the pennies showing "heads."

4 Draw a graph similar to the one entitled "Half-Life of Pennies." Label the *x*-axis "Number of shakes," and label the *y*-axis "Pennies remaining." Plot the data from your table on the graph.

Analyze the Results

5 **Examining Data** Examine the graph entitled "Half-Life of Uranium-238." Compare the graph you have made for pennies with the one for U-238. Explain any similarities.

Draw Conclusions

6 **Evaluating Results** Recall that the probability of landing "heads" in a coin toss is 1/2. Use this information to explain why the remaining number of pennies is reduced by about half each time the pennies are shaken and tossed.

7 **Evaluating Models** Assume that pennies represent U-238 and lead-206 isotopes. In this model, which isotope does the "head" side of the pennies represent? Which isotope is represented by the "tail" side of the pennies?

8 **Applying Conclusions** If a "sample" of pennies contained 75 heads and 25 tails, how many half-lives would have passed since the "sample" formed? Explain your answer.

Big Idea Question

9 **Interpreting Information** Imagine that you are studying an area where two horizontal layers of sedimentary rock are cut by an igneous intrusion. Radiometric dating indicates that the igneous intrusion formed about 15 million years ago. What would you conclude about the history of the three rock formations? Explain your conclusions.

Analyze the Results

5. Sample answer: The lines in the two graphs are similar in shape. With each half-life and each time the container is shaken, the number of isotopes and pennies remaining is halved.

Draw Conclusions

6. Sample answer: The number of pennies is reduced by about half each time they are shaken because about half of the pennies come up heads.

7. heads: lead-206; tails: uranium-238

8. Two half-lives have passed because 75% of the sample has decayed, which would happen after two half-lives.

Big Idea Question

9. Sample answer: Relative dating techniques indicate that the igneous intrusion is younger than the rock through which it cuts. Because the intrusion is dated at 15 million years, the two layers must be older than 15 million years. If the layers are otherwise undisturbed, then the layer on top is younger than the layer on bottom, but we do not have enough data to determine the exact age of the layers. If students have trouble with this question, draw the two layers and the intrusion, as shown below, on the board to help them visualize the situation.

Marilyn K. Bachman
Montecito Union School
Santa Barbara, California

This activity walks students through the steps of constructing a labeled diagram to scale (covers standard 7.7.d).

Answers to You Try It!

1. Answers may vary. A student's drawing might use a scale of 1 millimeter = 1 meter, so that their drawing would be 150 mm or 15 cm high. Students should demonstrate an understanding of scale models. If students are having difficulty with scale, suggest they make their drawings on graph paper.

2. Answers may vary. Layers should be filled with different patterns to help distinguish the layers from each other.

3. Layer 1 should be just over half the height of layer 2, just under twice the height of layer 3, and a little over one-third the heights of both layers 4 and 5. See the sample drawing at the bottom of this page.

4. Labels and leaders should be precise and neat. The diagram should have a title such as "Rock Layers in a Canyon Wall."

5. Answers may vary. Students will note that other students used different patterns for each layer. Some students may note scale errors in either their own drawings or other students' drawings. Some students may have used different scales, such as 0.5 mm = 1 meter. This scale would give a drawing that is 7.5 cm high.

 Datasheet GENERAL

Also editable on the Holt Lab Generator CD-ROM

Science Skills Activity

Science Skills Activity

Scientific Methods	Research	Data Analysis	Models, Maps & Diagrams

Investigation and Experimentation
7.7.d Construct scale models, maps, and appropriately labeled diagrams to communicate scientific knowlege (e.g., motion of Earth's plates and cell structure).

Constructing Labeled Diagrams

▶ Tutorial

A diagram illustrates an item or place and shows how the parts of the item or place are related. Scientists use diagrams to show many things that may be hard to describe in words. When diagrams are drawn to scale, they can show the relative sizes of items. If a diagram is well labeled, it will be easy to see what makes up the item or place that is being illustrated. To construct a labeled diagram, follow these steps:

1 **Choosing Your Scale** Decide on the scale. The scale is the ratio of the size of the diagram to the size of the item or place being drawn. You will use the scale to determine the size of each part of your diagram. For example, imagine that you are making a diagram of a hill that is 20 m high. To fit it on a page, you choose a scale of 0.5 cm = 1 m. The hill will be 10 cm high in your diagram.

2 **Planning Your Diagram** Use a pencil to sketch a rough draft of your diagram on a scrap of paper. Plan how to make the parts of your diagram look different from one another.

3 **Drawing Your Diagram** If you know the overall size of your diagram, sketch the outlines. If not, start with the bottom or main part and build the rest of your diagram to scale around the first part.

4 **Labeling Your Diagram** After drawing all of the parts of your diagram to scale, label each part. Make neat labels for each part of the diagram close to where that part appears on the page. Use a ruler to draw a line from the label to the correct part of the diagram. Remember to put a title at the top of your diagram.

▶ You Try It!

A team of scientists has studied sedimentary rock layers exposed in a canyon. The team left notes about the layers but did not make any drawings. You have been asked to make a diagram of the layers so that others can see what the canyon wall looks like. Use these notes to make your diagram:

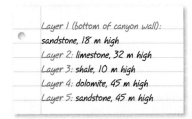

Layer 1 (bottom of canyon wall): sandstone, 18 m high
Layer 2: limestone, 32 m high
Layer 3: shale, 10 m high
Layer 4: dolomite, 45 m high
Layer 5: sandstone, 45 m high

1 **Choosing Your Scale** Decide what scale you will use so that your entire diagram will fit on a page. The total height of the layers in the canyon wall is 150 m.

2 **Planning Your Diagram** Use a pencil to make a rough draft on a scrap of paper to see how the layers will look in your diagram. Plan how to make the layers in your diagram look different to represent the different types of rock.

3 **Drawing Your Diagram** Start with Layer 1, and build the rest of your diagram to scale around that layer.

4 **Labeling Your Diagram** After drawing the layers of your diagram to scale, make neat labels for each part of the diagram close to where that part appears on the page. Use a ruler to draw a line from the label to each layer. Put a title at the top of your diagram.

5 **Making Comparisons** Compare your diagram with the diagrams of your classmates. Did your drawing differ in any way from theirs? Explain why these differences occurred.

Rock Layers in a Canyon Wall

— sandstone
— dolomite
— shale
— limestone
— sandstone

Universal Access · Differentiated Instruction

Special Education Students

Computer Diagrams Some students will have difficulty drawing the diagram by hand. Have these students use a computer program to create and shade boxes and stack them to represent the layers of rock on the canyon wall. Make sure students label their diagrams. **LS Visual/Kinesthetic**

Chapter Summary

The Big Idea The rock record can be used to determine the relative and absolute ages of rocks, which can be used to study Earth's history.

Section

Vocabulary

1 The Study of Earth's History

Key Concept Slow geologic processes and major catastrophic events have shaped Earth's surface in the past and continue to shape Earth today.

- Uniformitarianism describes uniform change in Earth's geology, and catastrophism describes sudden change.
- Modern geology describes most change as gradual but acknowledges rare, sudden changes.

Most geologic features are the result of gradual processes.

uniformitarianism
p. 234

catastrophism p. 235

paleontology p. 237

2 Relative Dating

Key Concept Scientists can interpret the sequence of events in Earth's history by studying rock layers.

- The rock cycle includes the formation and recycling of rock.
- Relative dating establishes the order in which rocks formed or events took place.
- The principle of superposition states that younger rocks lie above older rocks if the layers are undisturbed.

If things are found in undisturbed layers, the order of events can be determined.

relative dating p. 238
sedimentary rock
p. 238
superposition p. 240
unconformity p. 242
**law of crosscutting
relationships** p. 243

3 Absolute Dating

Key Concept Because radioactive decay occurs at a constant rate, the age of a rock can be estimated by analyzing the amounts of different isotopes in a rock.

- Radioactive decay is the process by which a radioactive isotope changes into a stable isotope.
- Radiometric dating is the process in which parent and daughter isotopes are analyzed to determine the age of rocks and fossils.

The half-life of an isotope is the time it takes for half of a sample to decay.

absolute dating p. 246
radioactive decay
p. 246
radiometric dating
p. 247
half-life p. 247

Chapter Summary

SUPER SUMMARY

Have students connect the major concepts in this chapter through an interactive Super Summary. Visit go.hrw.com and type in the keyword HY7STUS to access the Super Summary for this chapter.

Identifying Prefixes

Word Search Have students identify the meaning of the prefixes for *uniformitarianism, superposition,* and *radiometric.* (*uni-* means "one," *super-* means "above," and *radio-* comes from a root that means "ray") Then, challenge students to come up with as many words that use the same prefixes as they can in one minute.

Focus on Speaking

Persuasive Speech Ask students to deliver a persuasive speech that supports either uniformitarianism, catastrophism, or both. Challenge students to make presentations that persuade other people to embrace their point of view. Students' speeches should be accurate, engaging, and well-reasoned.

Universal Access · Differentiated Instruction

Advanced Learners/GATE
Materials List
- assorted materials such as boxes, sponges, Styrofoam, cardboard pieces, sandpaper, sand, gravel, salt, sugar, or birdseed
- glue

3-D Diagrams Have students create three-dimensional versions of their diagram. Make sure that the finished products are to scale and are labeled.
LS Visual/Kinesthetic

Review Resources

- Reinforcement Worksheet **BASIC**
- Critical Thinking Worksheet **ADVANCED**
- Chapter Review **GENERAL** (Also in Spanish)
- Standards Review Workbook (Also in Spanish)
- Study Guide A **BASIC** (Also in Spanish), B **GENERAL**

Assessment Resources

- Chapter Tests A **BASIC**, B **GENERAL** (Also in Spanish), C **ADVANCED**
- Standards Assessment **GENERAL**

Chapter Review

7.3.c, 7.4.a, 7.4.b,
7.4.c, 7.4.d, 7.4.e

Assignment Guide

Section	Questions
1	2, 6, 12–13, 21–22, 24
2	1, 5, 7–11, 15, 20, 25–31, 33
3	3–4, 14, 16–19, 23, 32

Answers

Using Vocabulary

1. Sample answer: Layers means sheets of rock or earth of one kind lying between sheets of other kinds. **7.4.c** (supporting)

2. Sample answer: Uniformitarianism is the theory that the gradual geologic processes that occur today also occurred in the past and that gradual changes shaped Earth. Catastrophism is the theory that episodes of sudden and drastic change shaped Earth. **7.4.a** (mastering), **7.4.b** (mastering)

3. Sample answer: Relative dating is a method of comparing rocks and fossils to each other to determine which are older. Absolute dating is a method of determining the actual age of something in years. **7.3.c** (supporting), **7.4.c** (supporting), **7.4.d** (supporting)

4. Sample answer: Radioactive decay is a process during which unstable isotopes decay to different isotopes. Radiometric dating uses rates of radioactive decay to determine the absolute age of a sample. **7.3.c** (supporting), **7.4.d** (supporting)

5. Sample answer: Superposition is the principle that states that the youngest layers are on top in undisturbed rock. The law of crosscutting relationships states that a fault or body of rock that cuts another rock is younger than the rock it cuts across. **7.4.c** (supporting)

Understanding Concepts

6. b

7. a **7.4.c** (supporting)

8. b **7.4.c** (supporting)

9. d **7.4.c** (supporting)

10. d **7.4.c** (mastering)

11. d **7.4.c** (supporting)

Organize

Three-Panel Flip Chart Review the FoldNote that you created at the beginning of the chapter. Add to or correct the FoldNote based on what you have learned.

Using Vocabulary

❶ **Academic Vocabulary** In the sentence "Younger rocks lie above older rocks if the layers have not been disturbed," what does the word *layers* mean?

For each pair of terms, explain how the meanings of the terms differ.

❷ *uniformitarianism* and *catastrophism*

❸ *relative dating* and *absolute dating*

❹ *radioactive decay* and *radiometric dating*

❺ *superposition* and *law of crosscutting relationships*

Understanding Concepts

Multiple Choice

❻ Paleontologists study
  a. craters on the moon and Earth.
  b. the history of life on Earth.
  c. the use of radioactivity for electric power.
  d. erosion and deposition.

❼ To determine relative ages, geologists use
  a. the principle of superposition.
  b. radiometric dating.
  c. half-lives.
  d. catastrophism.

❽ Rock layers that are cut by a fault formed
  a. after the fault.
  b. before the fault.
  c. at the same time as the fault.
  d. There is not enough information to determine the answer.

---

❾ An unconformity is
  a. evidence of past life.
  b. a tilted rock layer.
  c. an isotope that has no half-life.
  d. a gap in a rock-layer sequence.

❿ The rock cycle describes
  a. how round mineral crystals form.
  b. how to find the absolute age of a rock.
  c. how to find the relative age of a rock.
  d. how rock changes to form new rock.

⓫ Sedimentary rock
  a. forms from layers of sediment.
  b. forms when sediment is cemented.
  c. can be heated and squeezed to form metamorphic rock.
  d. All of the above

Short Answer

⓬ **Identifying** Identify the role of uniformitarianism in Earth science.

⓭ **Summarizing** Describe the role of paleontology in the study of Earth's history.

⓮ **Justifying** Approximately how old is our solar system? What evidence supports this estimate?

⓯ **Applying** How do geologists use the principle of superposition?

INTERPRETING GRAPHICS Use the table below to answer the next question.

Isotope Ratios		
	Parent isotope (mg)	**Daughter isotope (mg)**
Rock forms	8	0
Sample time A	4	4
Sample time B	2	6

⓰ **Applying** How many half-lives have elapsed at sample time A? at sample time B?

Writing Skills

⓱ **Outlining Topics** Describe how life on Earth has been affected by major catastrophic events.

---

12. Sample answer: Uniformitarianism states that the geologic processes that shape Earth today have been at work throughout Earth's history. **7.4.a** (mastering)

13. Sample answer: Paleontology is the study of the history of life on Earth and it is done by studying fossils. **7.4.e** (supporting)

14. 4.6 billion years old; This age is supported by radiometric dating of moon rocks and meteorites. **7.4.d** (mastering)

15. Sample answer: In undisturbed rock, the youngest layers are on top, and the oldest layers are on bottom. **7.4.c** (supporting)

16. A: 1 half-life; B: 2 half-lives **7.4.d** (supporting)

Writing Skills

17. Students' answers should describe at least one major catastrophic event in Earth's history, such as the asteroid impact that is thought to have led to a mass extinction 65 million years ago. **7.4.b** (mastering)

Critical Thinking

18 **Concept Mapping** Use the following terms to create a concept map: *age, half-life, absolute dating, radioactive decay, radiometric dating, relative dating, superposition,* and *isotopes.*

19 **Analyzing Methods** How could relative dating and absolute dating be used together?

20 **Identifying Relationships** How do geologists know that an intrusion is younger than the layers it cuts across?

21 **Making Inferences** What could you conclude about the formation of a sedimentary rock layer if you observed ripple marks preserved in the rock?

22 **Making Inferences** What might have happened in the atmosphere in the time just after the Barringer Meteorite Crater formed?

23 **Analyzing Methods** Would the uranium-lead method of radiometric dating be appropriate for determining the absolute age of a rock that is estimated to be between 1 million and 2 million years old? Explain your answer.

24 **Analyzing Ideas** Hutton's theory has been summarized in the statement "The present is the key to the past." Explain how this statement applies to studying Earth's history.

25 **Identifying Relationships** What are the source materials for sedimentary rocks?

26 **Identifying Relationships** Why are sedimentary rocks often found in layers? Why are the oldest layers generally on the bottom?

27 **Making Comparisons** Scientists are studying two sedimentary rock layers. One layer has no fossils in it, and the other layer has numerous fossils. Explain how fossils can provide evidence of how life and environmental conditions have changed. What might scientists be able to conclude about the layer with fossils that they cannot conclude about the layer with no fossils?

INTERPRETING GRAPHICS Use the diagram below to answer the next four questions.

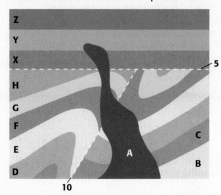

28 **Applying Concepts** Is intrusion A younger or older than layer X? Explain your answer.

29 **Applying Concepts** What is feature 5?

30 **Making Comparisons** Is intrusion A younger or older than feature 10? Explain your answer.

31 **Analyzing Relationships** Other than the intrusion and faulting, what event happened in layers B, C, D, E, F, G, and H? Number this event, the intrusion, and the fault in the order that they happened.

Math Skills

32 **Making Calculations** The half-life of uranium-238 is 4.5 billion years. How many years will three-fourths of a sample of uranium-238 take to decay?

Challenge

33 **Evaluating Data** Scientists discover a crater that has layers of sedimentary rock exposed on the inside walls of the crater. A layer of sandstone is visible near the bottom of the crater wall. A layer of limestone is visible above the sandstone. Both layers are below the edge of the crater. Describe the order of events that is most likely to have formed the limestone layer, the sandstone layer, and the crater.

Critical Thinking

18. An answer to this exercise can be found at the end of this book. **7.4.c** (supporting), **7.4.d** (supporting)

19. Sample answer: Absolute dating can be used to establish the age of one feature in a series of rock layers, such as an intrusion. Based on relative dating, the rock layers that are older than the intrusion are also older than the absolute age of the intrusion. **7.4.c** (exceeding), **7.4.d** (exceeding)

20. Sample answer: The layers had to be there before the intrusion could cut through them. **7.4.c** (supporting)

21. Sample answer: I could conclude that the sediment was deposited in an environment that had water. **7.4.a** (exceeding)

22. Sample answer: The atmosphere may have been filled with debris and dust. **7.4.b** (exceeding)

23. Sample answer: No, because the uranium-lead method is only appropriate in rocks that are older than 10 million years. In younger rocks there is not a measurable amount of the daughter isotope present. **7.4.d** (exceeding)

24. Sample answer: It applies to Earth's history because the processes we see today are the same as the processes that happened in the past. **7.4.a** (exceeding)

25. Sample answer: Source material for sedimentary rocks is sediment from weathering of rock. The sediment, which is moved by wind, water, or ice, forms horizontal layers. **7.4.c** (supporting)

26. Sedimentary rocks are often found in layers because sediment is usually deposited in horizontal layers. The oldest layers are found on the bottom because additional layers form on top of them as time passes. **7.4.c** (supporting)

27. Sample answer: Fossils provide evidence of how life and environmental conditions have changed because they show evidence of the types of life that existed in the past. The type of life represented by a fossil can provide evidence about the environment in which the fossil and rock layer formed. So, scientists have more evidence about life and environmental conditions in layers that include fossils than in layers that don't. **7.4.e** (mastering)

28. younger, because A cuts through X **7.4.c** (supporting)

29. unconformity **7.4.c** (supporting)

30. younger, because fault 10 is cut by intrusion A **7.4.c** (supporting)

31. folding; folding, fault, then intrusion **7.4.c** (supporting)

Math Skills

32. It will take two half-lives, so 9 billion years. **7.4.d** (exceeding)

Challenge

33. The sandstone formed first. Then, the limestone formed. The crater formed last. **7.4.c** (exceeding)

Chapter Review Standards Guide

	Supporting	Mastering	Exceeding
7.3.c	3, 4		
7.4.a		2, 12	21, 24
7.4.b		2, 17	22
7.4.c	1, 3, 5, 7, 8, 9, 11, 15, 18, 20, 25, 26, 28, 29, 30, 31	10	19, 33
7.4.d	3, 4, 16, 18	14	19, 23, 32
7.4.e	13	27	

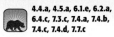
Standards Assessment

Teacher Notes

To provide practice under more realistic testing conditions, give students 20 min to answer all of the questions in this assessment.

Answer Key

Question Number	Correct Answer
1	C
2	C
3	D
4	A
5	B
6	C
7	D
8	B
9	B
10	A
11	A
12	C
13	D
14	A
15	C

Standards Guide

	Supporting	Mastering	Exceeding
4.4.a		11	
4.5.a			12
6.1.e		13	
6.2.a		14	
6.4.c		15	
7.3.c	1		
7.4.a		5	
7.4.b			6
7.4.c	10		7
7.4.d	2, 4	8, 9	
7.7.c	3		

📋 Standards Assessment **GENERAL**

📋 Teacher Notes for Standards Assessment contain a longer Assessment Doctor and Diagnostic Teaching Tips.

REVIEWING ACADEMIC VOCABULARY

1 Which of the following words means "a explanation of many related observations supported by a large body of evidence acquired through scientific investigation"?

A hypothesis

B question

C theory

D statement

2 Which of the following words is closest in meaning to the word *approximately*?

A exactly

B some

C about

D never

3 In the sentence "Students must know how to communicate the connection between a hypothesis and a theory," what does the word *communicate* mean?

A exchange ideas

B follow a series of steps

C be connected to

D make known or tell

4 In the sentence "The scientist found the fossil in the first layer of rock," what does the word *layer* mean?

A a single thickness lying above or below another

B a person who lays tile or bricks in horizontal sheets

C a single sheet of glass

D a depth or level of meaning

REVIEWING CONCEPTS

5 What is the main idea of the theory of uniformitarianism?

A Earth's surface is shaped by sudden events.

B Geologic change happens gradually.

C Fossils show how Earth has changed.

D Earth is approximately 4,000 years old.

6 Paleontologists believe that dinosaurs became extinct 65 million years ago. How do scientists explain this phenomenon?

A A volcanic eruption sent ash into the air, and Earth's climates cooled.

B A gradual global climate change caused extinctions of many of Earth's species.

C An asteroid hit Earth, and a debris cloud formed that blocked the light from the sun.

D Scientists have discovered fossils of the dinosaurs that lived on Earth 65 million years ago.

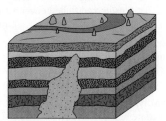

7 Determine what sequence of events occurred in the rock layers shown above.

A An intrusion formed, and then the rock layers formed around the intrusion.

B First, the bottom rock layer formed. Then, the intrusion formed. Finally, the other rock layers formed.

C The rock layers were folded, and then an intrusion cut through the layers.

D The rock layers formed, and then an intrusion cut through some of the layers.

➕ ASSESSMENT DOCTOR

Question 1: The correct answer is C. A theory is an explanation of related observations based on a large body of evidence. Scientific theories are based on research guided by questions and hypotheses.

Question 2: The correct answer is C. *Approximately* means "about or around." It is a word used to estimate time or quantity.

Question 3: The correct answer is D. *Communicate* means "make known or tell" in this case. Students may think "exchange ideas" also defines *communicate*, but it does not fit this sentence as well as "make known or tell."

Question 4: The correct answer is A. A layer of rock is a deposit or thickness of rock.

Question 5: The correct answer is B. The main idea of uniformitarianism is that major geologic change happens gradually, and that Earth has been shaped by millions of years of such change. Catastrophism supports the idea that Earth has been shaped by sudden, rare events.

Question 6: The correct answer is C. Scientists believe that an asteroid hit Earth 65 million years ago, creating a debris cloud that blocked the sun's rays and caused the global climate to cool, which in turn contributed to the dinosaurs' extinction.

Isotope Ratios

	Parent isotope (mg)	Daughter isotope (mg)
Rock forms	20	0
20,000 years	10	10
40,000 years		

8 According to the table above, what will the composition of the rock be in 40,000 years?

- A The rock will contain 3.75 mg of the parent isotope and 16.25 mg of the daughter isotope.
- B The rock will contain 5 mg of the parent isotope and 15 mg of the daughter isotope.
- C The rock will contain 3.75 mg of the parent isotope and 18.75 mg of the daughter isotope.
- D The rock will contain 5 mg of the parent isotope and 17.5 mg of the daughter isotope.

9 Which of the following methods has helped scientists determine the age of our solar system?

- A relative dating
- B radiometric dating
- C geologic columns
- D radioactive decay

10 What method is used to determine whether an object or event is older or younger than other objects or events?

- A relative dating
- B superposition
- C crosscutting
- D unconformity

REVIEWING PRIOR LEARNING

11 Rock that is formed by the process of lithification is called

- A sedimentary rock.
- B igneous rock.
- C metamorphic rock.
- D volcanic rock.

12 Which of the following processes best explains a mountain that has a smooth, rounded peak?

- A an earthquake
- B chemical erosion
- C wind erosion
- D volcanic eruption

13 Which of the following would most likely cause a volcano to form?

- A tectonic plates sliding past each other horizontally
- B tectonic plates becoming stuck against each other
- C tectonic plates colliding and crumpling
- D one tectonic plate sliding beneath another

14 Which of the following is the most important process in shaping Earth's landscape?

- A water running downhill
- B wind blowing across mountain ranges
- C glaciers sliding downhill
- D ocean waves striking the beach

15 Heat from Earth's interior reaches Earth's surface mostly through

- A conduction.
- B surface waves.
- C convection.
- D longitudinal waves.

Standards Assessment

Question 11: The correct answer is A. Sedimentary rock forms by lithification. Igneous rock forms when magma cools enough to become solid. Volcanic rock is a type of igneous rock. Metamorphic rock forms when increases in pressure and temperature cause changes in any type of rock.

Question 12: The correct answer is C. Wind erosion is the most likely explanation for a mountain that has a smooth, rounded peak. A volcanic eruption would usually leave a crater. Earthquakes generally do not smooth mountain peaks.

Question 13: The correct answer is D. Volcanoes may form when one tectonic plate slides beneath another. The subducted plate releases fluid as it sinks into the mantle, which causes the formation of magma that can rise toward Earth's surface because it is less dense than the surrounding mantle material.

Question 14: The correct answer is A. Water running downhill is the dominant process shaping Earth's landscape. Glaciers and ocean waves also shape the landscape but do not affect as much land as running water does. Wind can cause erosion, but water moves more material and causes more change than wind does.

Question 15: The correct answer is C. Heat from Earth's interior reaches the surface mostly through convection. Rock is a poor conductor of heat. Surface waves and longitudinal waves do not transfer much heat energy.

Question 7: The correct answer is D. The rock layers had to form first before the intrusion could cut through them. The rock layers shown are not folded.

Question 8: The correct answer is B. Because the amount of parent isotope is halved in 20,000 years, students should be able to tell that the half-life is 20,000 years. Therefore, in another 20,000 years, the amount of parent isotope will be halved again, leaving 5 mg of parent isotope. Therefore, the sample would have about 15 mg of daughter isotope at 40,000 years.

Question 9: The correct answer is B. Radiometric dating is a form of absolute dating that scientists have used to determine the age of Earth and our solar system. Because Earth's earliest rocks have been worn away through the rock cycle, scientists have dated meteorites and rocks from the moon to determine that Earth is about 4.6 billion years old.

Question 10: The correct answer is A. Relative dating is the process geologists use to determine whether an object or event is older or younger than other objects or events.

Weird Science

Group ACTIVITY

Adaptations for Different Environments Have students work in pairs to research the various conditions in which bacteria can exist. Then, have students choose one condition to focus on, and have them create a list of adaptations humans would need in order to live in those conditions.

Science, Technology, and Society

Background

Radon is one of the elements produced by the decay of uranium, a radioactive element that occurs naturally in Earth's crust. Radon gas can enter an indoor environment either through the soil or through the water. Radon that comes in through the soil is the most serious concern. Radon testing is very simple and very important, especially since the Environmental Protection Agency (EPA) estimates that about 1 in 15 homes has a high radon level and virtually any indoor environment can be affected. Two types of tests are available: a short-term test and a long-term test. A short-term test takes about 90 days to complete. Radon levels can vary from day to day and from season to season, so the short-term test is not always the best option. If high levels of radon are detected, the situation can be remediated with the installation of a venting system. More information about radon can be found on the EPA's Web site.

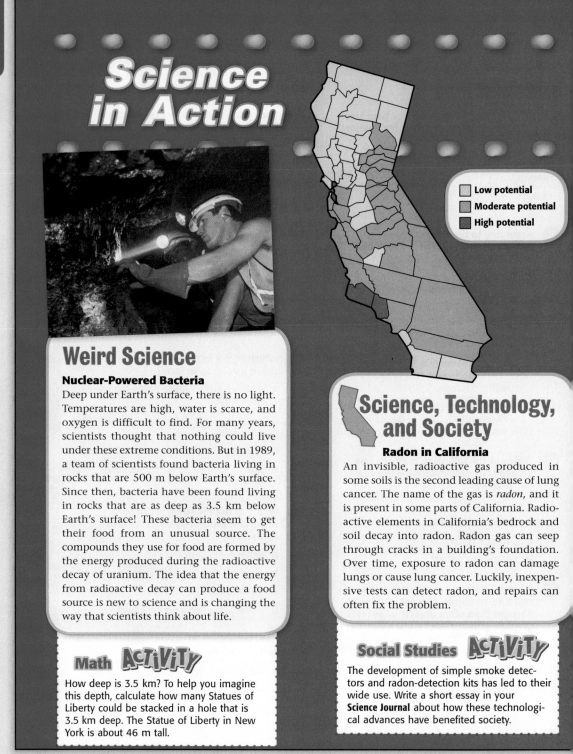

Science in Action

Weird Science

Nuclear-Powered Bacteria

Deep under Earth's surface, there is no light. Temperatures are high, water is scarce, and oxygen is difficult to find. For many years, scientists thought that nothing could live under these extreme conditions. But in 1989, a team of scientists found bacteria living in rocks that are 500 m below Earth's surface. Since then, bacteria have been found living in rocks that are as deep as 3.5 km below Earth's surface! These bacteria seem to get their food from an unusual source. The compounds they use for food are formed by the energy produced during the radioactive decay of uranium. The idea that the energy from radioactive decay can produce a food source is new to science and is changing the way that scientists think about life.

Low potential
Moderate potential
High potential

Science, Technology, and Society

Radon in California

An invisible, radioactive gas produced in some soils is the second leading cause of lung cancer. The name of the gas is *radon*, and it is present in some parts of California. Radioactive elements in California's bedrock and soil decay into radon. Radon gas can seep through cracks in a building's foundation. Over time, exposure to radon can damage lungs or cause lung cancer. Luckily, inexpensive tests can detect radon, and repairs can often fix the problem.

Math ACTIVITY

How deep is 3.5 km? To help you imagine this depth, calculate how many Statues of Liberty could be stacked in a hole that is 3.5 km deep. The Statue of Liberty in New York is about 46 m tall.

Social Studies ACTIVITY

The development of simple smoke detectors and radon-detection kits has led to their wide use. Write a short essay in your **Science Journal** about how these technological advances have benefited society.

Answer to Math Activity
3.5 km × 1,000 m/km = 3,500 m
3,500 m ÷ 46 m/Statue of Liberty = about 76 Statues of Liberty

Answer to Social Studies Activity
Answers may vary. Students may discuss the growth in consumer demand for affordable devices to warn of fires or radon contamination through the 1980s and 1990s. Since they have become more widely used, smoke detectors have reduced the incidence of death by fire and radon detectors have helped countless families reduce their chances of developing radon-related lung disease. Students may also discuss the impact of laws that were passed requiring certain kinds of buildings to include smoke detectors.

People in Science

Marie and Pierre Curie

A Great Team You may have heard the saying "Two heads are better than one." For scientific discoveries, this saying is often true. The husband and wife team Pierre and Marie Curie put their heads together and discovered the elements radium and polonium. Their work also helped them describe radioactivity.

Working side by side for long hours under poor conditions, Marie and Pierre Curie studied the mysterious rays given off by the element uranium. They processed huge amounts of an ore called *pitchblende* to collect the uranium from it. Strangely, the leftover material was more radioactive than uranium was. They spent several more months working with the material and discovered an element that was 300 times as radioactive as uranium was. Marie called it *polonium* in honor of Poland, the country in which she was born. For their research on radiation, the Curies were awarded the Nobel Prize in physics in 1903.

Language Arts ACTiViTy

Think of a time when you and a friend solved a problem together that neither of you could solve alone. Write a one-page story in your **Science Journal** about how you each helped solve the problem.

Internet Resources

- To learn more about careers in science, visit **www.scilinks.org** and enter the SciLinks code HY70225.

- To learn more about these Science in Action topics, visit **go.hrw.com** and type in the keyword HY7STUF.

- Check out articles related to this chapter by visiting **go.hrw.com**. Just type in the keyword HY7STUC.

Answer to Language Arts Activity
Answers may vary. Students' answers should focus on problem-solving techniques.

People in Science
Discussion

Teamwork Ask students to share what they think are the benefits of working as a part of a team. Then, ask them to share what they think might be some challenges of working as part of a team. Finally, have students discuss if there are certain tasks or situations that are better suited for teamwork than others.

To help students begin this discussion, have students talk about what it would be like to play a team sport in which only one person played all of the positions on the team. What would be some challenges? How does working as a team make this situation easier to handle?

The elements listed in the Standards Course of Study provide a base for presenting, supporting, and assessing the California Grade 7 Science Standards. Use this Standards Course of Study as a base for planning your lessons.

Why Teach

The History of Life on Earth

This chapter was designed to cover the California Grade 7 Science Standards about the history of life on Earth (7.3.c, 7.4.a, 7.4.c, 7.4.d, 7.4.e, 7.4.f, and 7.4.g). It follows a chapter about studying Earth's past, which introduced students to the evidence scientists use to understand the history of Earth. This chapter describes the geologic time scale and the fossil record. These topics are important to a student's understanding of the theory of evolution.

After they have completed this chapter, students will begin a chapter about the theory of evolution.

Chapter Pacing

Getting Started
The Big Idea Evidence from rocks allows us to understand the evolution of life on Earth.
 45 min
pp. 262–263
7.3.c, 7.4.c

Section ① Looking at Fossils
Key Concept Fossils provide evidence of how life and environmental conditions have changed.
 45 min
pp. 264–269
7.3.c, 7.4.c, 7.4.e

Section ② Earth's Changing Continents
Key Concept Movements of Earth's tectonic plates have affected climate, geographic connections, and the distribution of organisms.
 90 min
pp. 270–275
7.4.a, 7.4.e, 7.4.f

Section ③ Time Marches On
Key Concept Life has changed through Earth's history as life-forms have developed, or evolved, and become extinct.
 90 min
pp. 276–283
7.4.d, 7.4.e, 7.4.g

Wrapping Up
 180 min
pp. 284–293
7.4.e, 7.7.d

California Standards

Focus on Life Sciences

7.3.c Students know how independent lines of evidence from geology, fossils, and comparative anatomy provide the bases for the theory of evolution.

7.4.a Students know Earth processes today are similar to those that occurred in the past and slow geologic processes have large cumulative effects over long periods of time.

7.4.c Students know that the rock cycle includes the formation of new sediment and rocks and that rocks are often found in layers, with the oldest generally on the bottom.

7.4.d Students know that evidence from geologic layers and radioactive dating indicates Earth is approximately 4.6 billion years old and that life on this planet has existed for more than 3 billion years.

7.4.e Students know fossils provide evidence of how life and environmental conditions have changed.

7.4.f Students know how movements of Earth's continental and oceanic plates through time, with associated changes in climate and geographic connections, have affected the past and present distribution of organisms.

7.4.g Students know how to explain significant developments and extinctions of plant and animal life on the geologic time scale.

Investigation and Experimentation

7.7.d Construct scale models, maps, and appropriately labeled diagrams to communicate scientific knowledge (e.g., motion of Earth's plates and cell structure).

Basic Learners
TE Boundary Types, p. 270
TE Describing Eras, p. 278
TE Word Familiarity, p. 280
📄 Reinforcement Worksheet
📄 Chapter Test A
📄 Differentiated Datasheets A for Labs and Activities ■
📖 Study Guide A ■

Advanced Learners/GATE
TE Fossil Poster, p. 268
TE Research on Earth's Age, p. 277
TE End of the Cenozoic Era?, p. 282
TE Before Pangaea?, p. 286
📄 Critical Thinking Worksheet
📄 Chapter Test C
📄 Differentiated Datasheets C for Labs and Activities ■

Key
SE Student Edition
TE Teacher's Edition

📁 Chapter Resource File
📓 Workbook
🖥 Transparency

💿 CD or CD-ROM
* Datasheet or blackline master available

■ Also available in Spanish

All resources listed below are also available on the One-Stop Planner.

Teach

SE **Explore Activity** Making Fossils, p. 263* ■

🖥 **Bellringer**
💿 **PowerPoint® Resources**
SE **Quick Lab** Connecting Fossils to Climates, p. 267* ■

🖥 **Bellringer**
💿 **PowerPoint® Resources**
🖥 L33 Tectonic Plate Boundaries
🖥 L34 The Breakup of Pangaea
🖥 L35 Formation of the Panama Land Bridge
SE **Quick Lab** Climate Changes, p. 275* ■

🖥 **Bellringer**
💿 **PowerPoint® Resources**
🖥 L36 Geologic Time Scale
SE **Quick Lab** Timeline of Earth's History, p. 278* ■

SE **Skills Practice Lab** Interpreting Fossil Finds, pp. 284–285* ■

Practice

SE **Organize Activity** Four-Corner Fold, p. 262

SE **Section Review**, p. 269* ■

SE **Section Review**, p. 275* ■

SE **Section Review**, p. 283* ■

SE **Science Skills Activity** Constructing Models, p. 286* ■
🖥 **Concept Mapping***
SE **Chapter Review**, pp. 288–289* ■

Assess

📁 **Chapter Pretest**

SE **Standards Checks**, pp. 264, 265, 266, 268
TE **Standards Focus**, p. 268
📁 **Section Quiz** ■

SE **Standards Checks**, pp. 270, 273, 274
TE **Standards Focus**, p. 274
📁 **Section Quiz** ■

SE **Standards Checks**, pp. 276, 279, 281
TE **Standards Focus**, p. 282
📁 **Section Quiz** ■

SE **Standards Assessment**, pp. 290–291*
📁 **Chapter Tests A, B** ■**, C**
📓 **Standards Review Workbook** ■

Resources for Universal Access • Differentiated Instruction

English Learners
TE Describing Fossilization, p. 264
TE Group Activity, p. 264
TE Group Activity, p. 272
TE Fossil Questions, p. 272
TE Group Activity, p. 273
TE Using the Figure, p. 277
TE Activity, p. 279
📁 Vocabulary and Section Summary A ■, B

📁 Section Quizzes ■
📁 Chapter Tests A, B ■
📁 Differentiated Datasheets A, B, and C for Labs and Activities ■
📓 Study Guide A ■
📓 Multilingual Glossary

Struggling Readers
TE Fossil Outline, p. 266
TE Using Figures and Tables, p. 276

Special Education Students
TE Fossils, p. 265
TE Sliding Plates, p. 272
TE Extinction, p. 279
TE Partnering Pangaea, p. 286

To help plan your lessons, refer to the **On Course Mapping Instruction** booklet.

Visual Resources

CHAPTER STARTER TRANSPARENCY

What a Find!

Imagine that you are a scientist looking for fossils. You are climbing up a sandstone cliff in unexplored mountains in North Africa. The sun is scorching. The temperature is 120°F in the shade. You see a tooth in the 90-million-year-old rock. It looks like a shark's tooth, but it is more than 12 cm long! You dig around the tooth and discover that it is attached to a huge skull. Eventually, you uncover the entire skull, which contains a full set of these ferocious teeth. The skull measures about 1.6 m in length, which is about the height of a refrigerator. You realize that this skull with savage teeth belonged to a large dinosaur.

You take the skull back to your lab to study it more closely. Given the size of the skull, you decide the skeleton of the animal it came from must have been about 14 m long—about as big as a school bus. That's even larger than *Tyrannosaurus rex!* This 90-million-year-old giant you have found most likely chased other dinosaurs by running on large, powerful hind legs, and its blade-like teeth meant certain death for its prey. You have discovered a vicious predator from the past!

BELLRINGER TRANSPARENCIES

Section: Looking at Fossils
Imagine that 65 million years from now, scientists discover the fossilized remains of today's living organisms. In a few sentences, describe the types of fossils that the scientists might find.

Write your description in your **science journal**.

Section: Earth's Changing Continents
Imagine that two large sections of Earth's crust are slowly colliding or separating. Over time, what might happen at the site of the collision or separation?

Write your answer in your **science journal**.

TEACHING TRANSPARENCIES

Tectonic Plate Boundaries

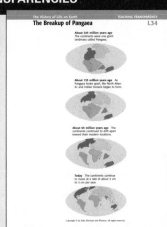

The Breakup of Pangaea   L34

TEACHING TRANSPARENCIES

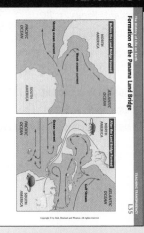

Formation of the Panama Land Bridge

Geologic Time Scale   L36

Formation of Coal   E12

LINK TO EARTH SCIENCE

STANDARDS REVIEW TRANSPARENCIES

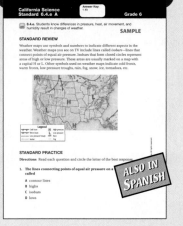

California Science Standard 6.4.e A   Grade 6

STANDARD REVIEW

STANDARD PRACTICE

ALSO IN SPANISH

CONCEPT MAPPING TRANSPARENCY

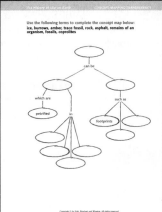

Use the following terms to complete the concept map below: ice, burrows, amber, trace fossil, rock, asphalt, remains of an organism, fossils, coprolites

Planning Resources

PARENT LETTER

SAMPLE

Dear Parent,

Your son's or daughter's science class will soon begin exploring the chapter entitled "The Nature of Physical Science." In this chapter, students will learn about how the scientific method applies to the world of physical science and the role of physical science in the world. By the end of this chapter, students should demonstrate a clear understanding of the chapter's main ideas and be able to discuss the following topics:

1. the role of questions in the process of investigation (Section 1)
2. how applying science saves lives and benefits the environment (Section 1)
3. careers that rely on science (Section 1)
4. the steps used in scientific methods (Section 2)
5. how scientific methods are used to answer questions and solve problems (Section 2)
6. the importance of safety precautions in the laboratory (Section 3)
7. examples of safety equipment and when to use them (Section 3)
8. how safety symbols are used to make laboratories safer (Section 3)

Questions to Ask Along the Way

You can help your child learn about these topics by asking interesting questions as he or she progresses through the chapter. For example, you may wish to ask your son or daughter the following questions:

What are some surprising careers that use science?

What is a characteristic of a good hypothesis?

What is the first step to take if an accident happens?

ALSO IN SPANISH

TEST ITEM LISTING

SAMPLE

Holt California Physical Science
Chapter 6 Introduction to Atoms
Test Item Listing
Multiple choice
1. The smallest particle into which an element can be divided and still have the properties of that element is called a(n)
   a. nucleus.   c. atom.
   b. electron.   d. neutron.
   ANS: C   DIF: 1   REF: 1   STO: atom.
   MSC: SQ.1.1
2. What particle did J. J. Thomson discover?
   a. neutron
   b. electron
   c. atom
   d. proton
   ANS: B   DIF: 1   REF: 1   STO: 8.3.a   KEY: electron   MSC: SQ.1.2
3. How would you describe the nucleus?
   a. in the nucleus
   b. mostly empty space, positively charged
   c. tiny, negatively charged
   d. dense, negatively charged
   ANS: A   DIF: 1   REF: 1   STO: 8.3.a   KEY: nucleus   MSC: SQ.1.3
4. Where are electrons likely to be found?
   a. in the nucleus
   b. in electron clouds
   c. mixed throughout an atom
   d. in definite paths
   ANS: B   DIF: 1   REF: OBJ: 2   STO: 8.3.a   KEY: electron   MSC: SQ.1.4
5. Dalton believed that
   a. atoms of the same element are exactly alike.
   b. most, but not all, substances are made of atoms.
   c. atoms of different elements are the same.
   d. atoms can be divided.
   ANS: A   DIF: 1   REF: OBJ: 1 12   STO: 8.3.a   KEY: atom
   MSC: SQ.1.5
6. Every atom of a given element has the same number of
   a. protons.
   b. electrons.
   c. isotopes.
   ANS: A   DIF: 1   REF: 2   OBJ: 8.3.a   KEY:

ALSO IN SPANISH

One-Stop Planner® CD-ROM

This CD-ROM package includes all of the resources shown here and the following time-saving tools:

- **Lab Materials QuickList Software**
- **Customizable Lesson Plans** Correlated to the California Science Standards
- **Holt Calendar Planner**
- **PowerPoint® Resources**
- **Printable Worksheets**
- **ExamView® Test Generator** Correlated to the California Science Standards
- **Holt PuzzlePro®**
- **Interactive Teacher's Edition**

Meeting Individual Needs

DIRECTED READING A

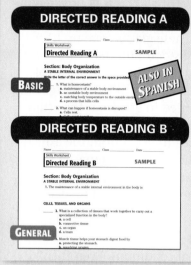

Skills Worksheet
Directed Reading A SAMPLE

Section: Body Organization
A STABLE INTERNAL ENVIRONMENT
Write the letter of the correct answer in the space provided.

BASIC

___ 1. What is homeostasis?
a. maintenance of a stable body environment
b. an unstable body environment
c. matching body temperature to the outside environment
d. a process that kills cells

___ 2. What can happen if homeostasis is disrupted?
a. Cells rest.

ALSO IN SPANISH

DIRECTED READING B

Skills Worksheet
Directed Reading B SAMPLE

Section: Body Organization
A STABLE INTERNAL ENVIRONMENT
1. The maintenance of a stable internal environment in the body is

CELLS, TISSUES, AND ORGANS

GENERAL

___ 2. What is a collection of tissues that work together to carry out a specialized function in the body?
a. a cell
b. connective tissue
c. an organ
d. a brain

___ 3. Muscle tissue helps your stomach digest food by
a. protecting the stomach.
b. squashing oxygen.

VOCABULARY AND SECTION SUMMARY A

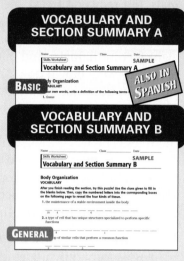

Skills Worksheet
Vocabulary and Section Summary A SAMPLE

Body Organization
VOCABULARY
In your own words, write a definition of the following terms.

BASIC

ALSO IN SPANISH

VOCABULARY AND SECTION SUMMARY B

Skills Worksheet
Vocabulary and Section Summary B SAMPLE

Body Organization
VOCABULARY
After you finish reading the section, try this puzzle! Use the clues given to fill in the blanks below. Then, copy the numbered letters into the corresponding boxes on the following page to reveal the four kinds of tissue.

GENERAL

1. the maintenance of a stable environment inside the body

2. a type of cell that has unique structures specialized to perform specific function

___ a group of similar cells that perform a common function

REINFORCEMENT

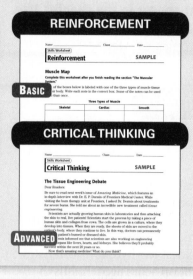

Skills Worksheet
Reinforcement SAMPLE

Muscle Map
Complete this worksheet after you finish reading the section "The Muscular System."

BASIC

Each of the bones below is labeled with one of the three types of muscle tissue for which it works. Write each note in the correct box. Some of the notes can be used more than once.

Three Types of Muscle

Skeletal	Cardiac	Smooth

CRITICAL THINKING

Skills Worksheet
Critical Thinking SAMPLE

The Tissue Engineering Debate
Dear Readers:
Be sure to read next week's issue of *Amazing Medicine*, which features an in-depth interview with Dr. E. P. Dermis of Frontiers Medical Center. While visiting the burn therapy unit at Frontiers, I asked Dr. Dermis about treatments for severe burns. She told me about an incredible new treatment called tissue engineering.

Scientists are actually growing human skin in laboratories and then attaching the skin to real, live patients! Scientists start the process by taking a piece of human skin and collagen from cows. The cells are grown in a culture, where they develop into tissues. When they are ready, the sheets of skin are moved to the patient's body, where they continue to live. In this way, doctors can permanently

ADVANCED

... patient's burned or diseased skin.
... informed me that scientists are also working on engineering ... organs like livers, hearts, and kidneys. She believes they'll probably succeed within the next 20 years or so.

Now that's amazing medicine! What do you think?

INTERACTIVE READER AND STUDY GUIDE

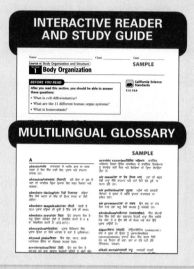

CHAPTER 15 Body Organization and Structure
SECTION 1 **Body Organization** SAMPLE

California Science Standards
7.1.c, 7.5.b

BEFORE YOU READ
After you read this section, you should be able to answer these questions:
• What is cell differentiation?
• What are the 11 different human organ systems?
• What is homeostasis?

MULTILINGUAL GLOSSARY

SAMPLE

A
abiotic/विविध ...
abrasion/घर्षण ...
absolute dating/पूर्ण तिथि ...
absolute magnitude/पूर्ण परिमाण ...
absolute zero/पूर्ण शून्य ...
absorption/अवशोषण ...
abyssal plain/अथाह मैदान ...
acceleration/त्वरण ...

aerobic exercise/वायवीय व्यायाम ...
air mass/वायु राशि ...
air pollution/वायु प्रदूषण ...
air pressure/वायु दाब ...
alcoholism/मदिरावाद ...
algae/शैवाल ...
alkali metal/क्षार धातु ...

Labs and Activities

DIFFERENTIATED DATASHEETS FOR EXPLORE ACTIVITY, QUICK LABS, AND CHAPTER LAB

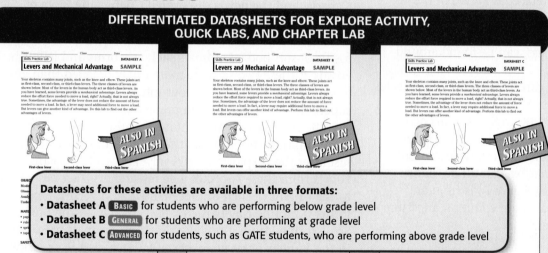

Name ___ Class ___ Date ___
Skills Practice Lab DATASHEET A
Levers and Mechanical Advantage SAMPLE

Your skeleton contains many joints, such as the knee and elbow. These joints act as first-class, second-class, or third-class levers. The three classes of levers are shown below. Most of the levers in the human body act as third-class levers. As you have learned, some levers provide a mechanical advantage. Levers always reduce the effort force needed to move a load, right? Actually, that is not always true. Sometimes, the advantage of the lever does not reduce the amount of force needed to move a load. In fact, a lever may require additional force to move a load. But levers can offer another kind of advantage. Do this lab to find out the other advantages of levers.

First-class lever   Second-class lever   Third-class lever

ALSO IN SPANISH

Name ___ Class ___ Date ___
Skills Practice Lab DATASHEET B
Levers and Mechanical Advantage SAMPLE

Your skeleton contains many joints, such as the knee and elbow. These joints act as first-class, second-class, or third-class levers. The three classes of levers are shown below. Most of the levers in the human body act as third-class levers. As you have learned, some levers provide a mechanical advantage. Levers always reduce the effort force needed to move a load, right? Actually, that is not always true. Sometimes, the advantage of the lever does not reduce the amount of force needed to move a load. In fact, a lever may require additional force to move a load. But levers can offer another kind of advantage. Perform this lab to find out the other advantages of levers.

First-class lever   Second-class lever   Third-class lever

ALSO IN SPANISH

Name ___ Class ___ Date ___
Skills Practice Lab DATASHEET C
Levers and Mechanical Advantage SAMPLE

Your skeleton contains many joints, such as the knee and elbow. These joints act as first-class, second-class, or third-class levers. The three classes of levers are shown below. Most of the levers in the human body act as third-class levers. As you have learned, some levers provide a mechanical advantage. Levers always reduce the effort force required to move a load, right? Actually, that is not always true. Sometimes, the advantage of the lever does not reduce the amount of force needed to move a load. In fact, a lever may require additional force to move a load. But levers can offer another kind of advantage. Perform this lab to find out the other advantages of levers.

First-class lever   Second-class lever   Third-class lever

ALSO IN SPANISH

OBJE...
Mod...
Obse...
Anal...
Unde...

MATE...
• pe...
• ru...
• sp...
• ta...

SAFET...

Datasheets for these activities are available in three formats:
• Datasheet A **BASIC** for students who are performing below grade level
• Datasheet B **GENERAL** for students who are performing at grade level
• Datasheet C **ADVANCED** for students, such as GATE students, who are performing above grade level

DATASHEET FOR SCIENCE SKILLS ACTIVITY

Science Skills Activity DATASHEET
Modifying a Hypothesis SAMPLE

INVESTIGATION AND EXPERIMENTATION
7.7.c Communicate the logical connection among hypotheses, science concepts, tests conducted, data collected, and conclusions drawn from the scientific evidence.

TUTORIAL
When you perform a scientific investigation, you often start with a question and then develop a hypothesis. A hypothesis is a possible answer to the question. A hypothesis must be testable. The next step in an investigation is to test your hypothesis. Often, in the course of your experiment, you will gather data that will require you to modify your original hypothesis. In this tutorial, you will learn how to modify a hypothesis. Read the question and hypothesis below.

Question: How do your muscles move your bones?
Hypothesis: One muscle is responsible for moving each bone.

PROCEDURE
1. **Design a Test for the Hypothesis** In this investigation, you might use rulers or sticks to model bones and rubber bands to model muscles. You will be testing if it is possible for one muscle to move one bone.
2. **Identify the Expected Outcome** If your hypothesis is correct, what results do you expect? In this investigation, if your hypothesis is correct, you will be able to move each bone model with a single rubber band.
3. **Analyze the Actual Outcome** In your experiment, the results show that it is not possible to move the bone model with a single rubber band. You notice that the bone will not move predictably or smoothly.
4. **Form a New Hypothesis** In what way do the observations that you made agree with or disagree with your original hypothesis? In this example, your observations disagree with your hypothesis. One muscle did not move the bone, so the hypothesis must be modified. See the modified hypothesis below.

Question: How do your muscles move your bones?
Hypothesis: Muscles pairs work together to move each bone.

IT
Your body tissues contain water. In fact, the human body is made up of about 70% water. Imagine that you are part of a research team working to answer this question: Does water help the body maintain a constant temperature? You have decided to focus your research on whether or not water helps the body maintain a constant temperature. Your hypothesis in the following: Water does not help the body maintain a constant temperature.

GENERAL

ALSO IN SPANISH

Reviews and Assessments

SECTION REVIEWS

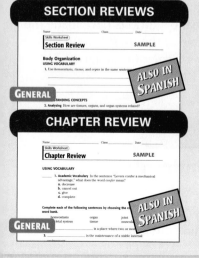

Skills Worksheet
Section Review SAMPLE

Body Organization
USING VOCABULARY
1. Use homeostasis, tissue, and organ in the same sentence.

UNDERSTANDING CONCEPTS
2. Analysing How are tissues, organs, and organ systems related?

GENERAL

ALSO IN SPANISH

CHAPTER REVIEW

Skills Worksheet
Chapter Review SAMPLE

USING VOCABULARY
1. **Academic Vocabulary** In the sentence "Levers confer a mechanical advantage," what does the word confer mean?
a. decrease
b. cancel out
c. give
d. complete

Complete each of the following sentences by choosing the correct term from the word bank.

___ 2. ___ skeletal systems

3. ___ is the maintenance of a stable internal ...

GENERAL

ALSO IN SPANISH

CHAPTER PRETEST

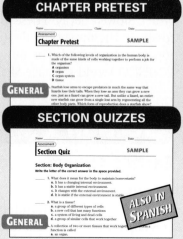

Assessment
Chapter Pretest SAMPLE

___ 1. Which of the following levels of organization in the human body is made of the same kinds of cells working together to perform a job for the organism?
A. organism
B. organ
C. organ system
D. tissue

GENERAL

___ Starfish lose arms to escape predators in much the same way that lizards lose their tails. When they lose an arm they can grow a new one, just as a lizard can grow a new tail. But unlike a lizard, an entire new starfish can grow from a single lost arm by regenerating all the other body parts. Which form of reproduction does a starfish show?

SECTION QUIZZES

Assessment
Section Quiz SAMPLE

Section: Body Organization
Write the letter of the correct answer in the space provided.

___ 1. What does it mean for the body to maintain homeostasis?
a. It has a changing internal environment.
b. It has a stable internal environment.
c. It changes with the external environment.
d. It is stable if the external environment is stable.

___ 2. What is a tissue?
a. all the different types of cells
b. a new cell that has many functions
c. a group of living and dead cells
d. a group of similar cells that work together

___ A collection of two or more tissues that work together in function is called
a. an organ.

GENERAL

ALSO IN SPANISH

CHAPTER TEST A

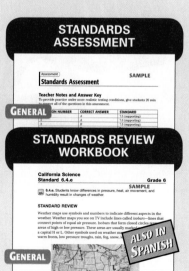

Assessment
Chapter Test A SAMPLE

BASIC

Body Organization and Structure
MULTIPLE CHOICE
Write the letter of the correct answer in the space provided.

CHAPTER TEST B

Assessment
Chapter Test B SAMPLE

GENERAL

Body Organization and Structure
MULTIPLE CHOICE
Write the letter of the correct answer in the space provided.

ALSO IN SPANISH

CHAPTER TEST C

Assessment
Chapter Test C SAMPLE

ADVANCED

Body Organization and Structure
USING KEY TERMS
Use the terms from the following list to complete the sentences below. Each term may be used only once. Some terms may not be used.

lever   ligaments   tendons
epithelial   mechanical advantage   connective
cardiac   skeletal

1. In the body, the joint serves as fulcrum, and the bone as a(n) ___

STANDARDS ASSESSMENT

Assessment
Standards Assessment SAMPLE

Teacher Notes and Answer Key
To provide practice under more realistic testing conditions, give students 20 min to answer all of the questions in this assessment.

GENERAL

QUESTION NUMBER	CORRECT ANSWER	STANDARD
1	A	7.5 (supporting)
2	B	7.5 (supporting)
3	B	7.5 (supporting)

STANDARDS REVIEW WORKBOOK

California Science
Standard 6.4.e Grade 6
SAMPLE

6.4.e. Students know differences in pressure, heat, air movement, and humidity result in changes of weather.

STANDARD REVIEW
Weather maps use symbols and numbers to indicate different aspects of the weather. Weather maps you see on TV include lines called isobars—lines that connect points of equal air pressure. Isobars that form closed circles indicate areas of high or low pressure. These areas are usually marked with a capital H or L. Other symbols used on weather maps, rain, fog, snow, and warm fronts, low pressure troughs, rain, fog, snow.

GENERAL

ALSO IN SPANISH

This Teacher Background explains science concepts, principles, and theories that appear in the chapter. Use the information on these pages to refresh or enhance your understanding of the topics covered.

Section 1

Looking at Fossils

California Fossils

Some of California's largest fossils are found in the sedimentary rock of the Mesozoic Era, an era when California was under shallow tropical seas. Fossils of ichthyosaurs, which were long marine reptiles, have been found in Kern County. The oldest ichthyosaur fossil dates to the Triassic Period (220 million years ago). Fossils of fish, gastropods, crinoids (sea lilies), and other ancient marine life dating from the Cretaceous Period of the Mesozoic Era (about 80 million years ago) can be found around Sacramento. Fossils of mammals from the Pliocene Epoch (about 2 million years ago) can be found around San Diego.

The best-preserved fossils can be found in Los Angeles at the Rancho La Brea Tar Pits. There, Ice Age herbivores and predators dating from 40,000 to 8,000 years ago were caught in the thick asphalt, which formed from evaporating crude oil. Dire wolves, ground sloths, and the saber-toothed tiger, or *Smilodon,* can all be found here. The *Smilodon,* pictured in **Figure A,** is from an extinct group of predators that share common ancestors with both cats and mongooses.

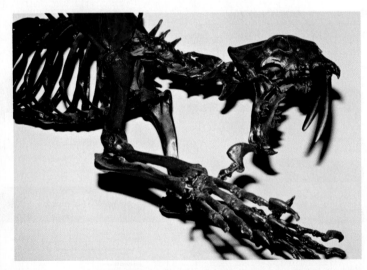

Figure A *The* Smilodon *is the most familiar of the fossils found at the La Brea Tar Pits in Los Angeles, California. It is the state fossil of California.*

The largest fossils found in California are not animals, but redwood trees. The Petrified Forest (a privately owned park and historic site) in Sonoma County contains petrified redwood trees. These giants were up to eight feet in diameter and once stood hundreds of feet tall. They were blown down by ash and glass from a volcanic eruption that occurred about 3 million years ago. The trees were then quickly buried in ash from the eruption. Over time, water seeped through the ash down to the trees. The water caused silica to leach from the ash. The silica gradually replaced the organic material of the trees, leaving nearly exact replicas of the original trees. The trees were discovered because erosion and modern uplift has begun to expose the trees.

Incredible Cambrian Fossils

Fossils form only under ideal conditions. Even then, typically only the hard body parts such as bones or shells are preserved. The Burgess Shale in British Columbia, Canada, and the newly discovered Chengjiang Biota of southwestern China are standouts even among the best fossil sites. The shale rocks at both of these sites contain fossils of soft-bodied animals such as worms and jellyfish. Fossils at these two sites are more finely detailed than elsewhere; even information about internal structures and superficial features has been preserved.

The two sites are also unique because they are from the Cambrian Period (more than 500 million years ago), just after the "explosion" of biodiversity in the oceans. Fossils from these two sites give researchers their best clues to the origins of such unprecedented biodiversity. Shale forms from fine clay particles, and shale from the Burgess Shale formed from especially fine clay. Animals preserved in the Burgess Shale are believed to have died in mudflows that periodically covered the reefs in a cloud of clay. The particles were fine enough to enter and encase even tiny appendages and internal structures. This encasement helped protect the organisms' bodies from being consumed by scavengers, and it cut off the oxygen supply, which slowed decay. These ideal conditions have made the fossils in the Burgess Shale some of the most important fossils in the world. The Burgess Shale was designated a UNESCO World Heritage Site in 1981.

Section 2

Earth's Changing Continents

San Andreas Fault

The transform boundary between the northwest-traveling Pacific plate and the North American plate is marked by several faults. By far the largest of these is the San Andreas fault. The San Andreas fault is a visible landscape feature; sag ponds and dips are visible along its length. The native vegetation is often noticeably different on opposing sides of the fault, as the underlying rocks are from different sources and have different characteristics. The land to the west side of the fault originated several hundred miles to the south. The Pacific plate and the North American plate are shown in **Figure B.**

The San Andreas fault is a classic "strike-slip" fault, in which two plates slide horizontally past each other. Some portions of the fault creep at a regular pace, while other portions experience more friction and bind. In the latter case, pressure can build until it is released in an earthquake. The San Francisco Bay area, which has at least six small faults in addition to the large San Andreas fault, is especially vulnerable to earthquakes. The Working Group on California Earthquake Probabilities estimates a 62% likelihood of a large earthquake (greater than 6.7 in magnitude) in the San Francisco Bay area by 2032.

Ring of Fire

In some areas, the Pacific plate is subducting beneath, or slipping under, the other tectonic plates that it is coming up against. This subduction has created the "Ring of Fire" around the Pacific Ocean, so named because three-fourths of all the world's volcanoes, both active and dormant, are found along this subduction zone. The Pacific plate and some of its neighboring plates are shown in **Figure B.** As the Pacific plate sinks downward, the crust forms viscous, gaseous magma that may erupt explosively. The interactions of the plates also lead to earthquakes and to the formation of some of the deepest ocean trenches in the world.

The Andes mountains of South America are part of the "Ring of Fire", but they did not form as a result of the subduction of the Pacific plate. Rather, the Andes formed from the subduction of the Nazca plate under the South American plate. The Cascade Range, including Mount St. Helens, owes its existence to subduction. The Aleutian Islands off the coast of Alaska are volcanic and mark the northern edge of the Pacific plate. The western edge of the Pacific plate is slipping under the Eurasian plate and has formed the Russian Kamchatka Peninsula and the volcanic Japanese islands. In the south, Micronesia and New Guinea formed where the Indo-Australian plate subducts under the Pacific plate. New Zealand marks the edge of the Indo-Australian plate.

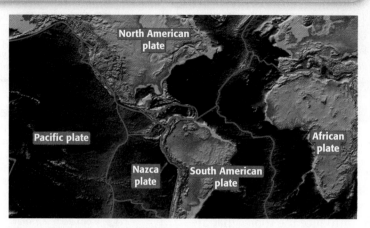

Figure B *The Pacific plate and the North American plate meet at a transform boundary in California.*

Section 3

Time Marches On

Permian Extinction

The Permian extinction was the largest of the five major extinctions recorded in the fossil record. The Permian extinction marked the end of the Paleozoic Era 251 million years ago. Point out to students that major extinctions mark the transition into most new eras. Scientists debate the causes of the Permian extinction and continue to find evidence that supports a number of theories, most of which involve global climate change. Pangaea was forming at the same time as the extinction, and one theory suggests that the loss of continental shelves and changing ocean currents and weather patterns led to extreme weather conditions and glaciations. These occurrences may have directly caused the extinction, or they may have been part of a series of events that led to the extinction. Also during this time, the largest volcanic eruptions in Earth's history took place in what is now known as Siberia.

Internet Resources

SciLinks is maintained by the National Science Teachers Association to provide you and your students with interesting, up-to-date links that will enrich your classroom presentation of the chapter.

Visit **www.scilinks.org** and enter the SciLinks code for more information about the topic listed.

Topic: Looking at Fossils
SciLinks code: HY70886

Topic: Earth's Story
SciLinks code: HY70450

Topic: Plate Tectonics
SciLinks code: HY71171

Topic: Geologic Time
SciLinks code: HY70668

Topic: Geologic Time Scale
SciLinks code: HY70669

⑨ Chapter Preview

Chapter Preview

Improving Comprehension

Use the Graphic Organizer on this page of the Student Edition to introduce the topics that are covered in this chapter, to summarize the chapter material, or to show students how to make a spider map.

Teaching Tips

• Point out to students that the structure of a spider map visually suggests levels of detail within a main topic. The circled idea is the main topic, the legs provide characteristics of the circled idea, and the horizontal lines provide details about the characteristics on the legs.

• Explain to students that a spider map works best when the characteristics of the main topic are analogous and the details about the characteristics can be written concisely.

LS Logical

Improving Comprehension

Graphic Organizers are important visual tools that can help you organize information and improve your reading comprehension. The Graphic Organizer below is called a *spider map*. Instructions for creating other types of Graphic Organizers are located in the **Study Skills** section of the Appendix.

How to Make a Spider Map

❶ Draw a diagram like the one shown below. In the circle, write the main topic.

❷ From the circle, draw legs to represent the main ideas or characteristics of the topic. Draw as many legs as you want to draw. Write an idea or characteristic along each leg.

❸ From each leg, draw horizontal lines. As you read the chapter, write details about each idea on the idea's horizontal lines. To add more details, make the legs longer and add more horizontal lines.

When to Use a Spider Map

A spider map is an effective tool for classifying the details of a specific topic in science. A spider map divides a topic into ideas and details. As you read about a topic, look for the main ideas or characteristics of the topic. Within each idea, look for details. Use a spider map to organize the ideas and details of each topic.

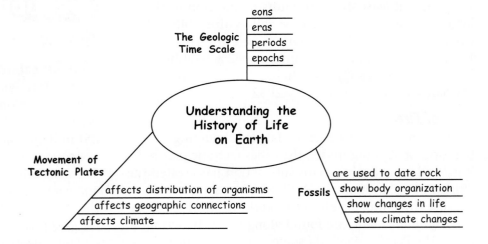

You Try It!

This Reading Strategy can also be used within the chapter that you are about to read. Practice making your own *spider map* as directed in the Reading Strategies for Section ❶ and Section ❷. Record your work in your **Science Journal**.

Using Other Graphic Organizers

Students can practice using a variety of Graphic Organizers while reading this chapter. The following Graphic Organizers may also be useful in this chapter.

An **idea wheel** can be used to describe the kinds of trace fossils, discussed in Section 1.

A **concept map** can be used to describe plate tectonics, introduced in Section 2.

A **cause-and-effect map** can be used to show the changes resulting from continental drift, discussed in Section 2.

A **process chart** can be used to describe the appearance of life on Earth, explained in Section 3.

Instructions for creating these Graphic Organizers are located on pp. 583–591 of the Appendix.

Unpacking the Standards

The information below "unpacks" the standards by breaking them down into basic parts. The higher-level, academic vocabulary is highlighted and defined to help you understand the language of the standards. "What It Means" restates the standards as simply as possible.

Unpacking the Standards

Use the following information with the *What It Means* in the Student Edition to help students understand why studying each standard is important.

California Standard	Academic Vocabulary	What It Means	Why It Matters
7.3.c Students know how independent lines of **evidence** from geology, fossils, and comparative anatomy provide the bases for the theory of evolution.	**evidence** (EV uh duhns) information showing whether an idea or belief is true or valid	The theory of evolution is based on several kinds of information that was gathered by studying rocks and fossils and by comparing the bodies of living and extinct organisms.	Evolution is a testable theory that is subject to change based on new discoveries and data.
7.4.c Students know that the rock **cycle** includes the formation of new sediment and rocks and that rocks are often found in **layers,** with the oldest generally on the bottom.	**cycle** (SIE kuhl) a repeating series of changes **layer** (LAY uhr) a separate or distinct portion of matter that has thickness	The rock cycle includes the breakdown of rock into smaller fragments that may form new rock. Rocks are often found in layers, in which the oldest rock is usually on the bottom.	Understanding the deposition of sediments helps scientists pinpoint the location of oil, natural gas, and other fossil deposits. It also helps geologists put events in geologic time in order.
7.4.d Students know that **evidence** from geologic **layers** and radioactive dating **indicates** Earth is **approximately** 4.6 billion years old and that life on this planet has existed for more than 3 billion years.	**indicate** (IN di KAYT) to be or give a sign of; to show **approximately** (uh PRAHK suh mit lee) almost; about	Rock layers and dating methods that use radioactive elements suggest that Earth is about 4.6 billion years old and that Earth has supported life for more than 3 billion years.	Understanding radioactive dating helps us to understand the significance of fossil finds and helps us piece together the history of life on Earth.
7.4.e Students know fossils provide evidence of how life and **environmental** conditions have changed.	**environment** (en VIE ruhn muhnt) the surrounding natural conditions that affect an organism	Fossils can be used to understand how living things and the environment have changed over time.	Understanding patterns of change in the past can help us predict and plan for future conditions on Earth.
7.4.f Students know how movements of Earth's continental and oceanic plates through time, with associated changes in climate and geographic connections, have **affected** the past and present **distribution** of organisms.	**affect** (uh FEKT) to change; to have an effect on; to influence **distribution** (DIS tri BYOO shuhn) the relative arrangement of objects or organisms in time or space	The movement of large chunks of Earth's lithosphere has caused changes in climate and changes in how landmasses are connected. These changes have affected where living things have existed on Earth in the past and where they live today.	This knowledge is critical for understanding the accepted theory of plate tectonics and critically reviewing other competing theories of the distribution and age of organisms on Earth.
7.4.g Students know how to explain **significant** developments and extinctions of plant and animal life on the geologic time scale.	**significant** (sig NIF uh kuhnt) important	You must know how to explain how, when, and why different plants and animals appeared and disappeared throughout Earth's history.	Understanding the history of life on Earth helps us understand how we interact with our environment and may help us prevent the extinction of more organisms.

The following identifies other standards that are covered in this chapter and where you can go to see them unpacked: **7.4.a** (Chapter 8)

Words with Multiple Meanings

Words that have both common and scientific meanings can be confusing to students. The following table identifies some of those words that are used in this chapter.

Term	Common meaning	Scientific meaning
period	a punctuation mark	an interval or unit
plate	a shallow dish	a large piece of the lithosphere (tectonic plate)
scale	a machine used to measure weight	the relationship between the measurements on a model, map, or diagram and the actual measurement or distance

Practice Have students define the following words: *period, plate,* and *scale.* Then, give students the definitions for the scientific meanings of these terms. (These definitions can be found in the glossary of this book.) Have students write sentences that use the common meanings of these words. Then, have students write sentences that use the scientific meanings of the words.

Chapter Overview

This chapter examines how scientists study the rock and fossil record to determine the sequence of events that led to life as we know it today. The chapter also describes the movements of the tectonic plates and outlines the events that mark the divisions of the geologic time scale.

MISCONCEPTION ALERT

Still Happening Today!

Identify It! Students may believe that tectonic plate movement and other geologic events, such as extinction or speciation, occurred only in the past. To help identify this misconception, ask students to provide evidence that Earth's crust is in motion. (Sample answers: earthquakes, volcanoes, and growing mountain ranges)

Correct It! Give students examples of active plate movements by showing them photos of the volcanoes along the "Ring of Fire" or the aftermath of an earthquake that occurred along the San Andreas fault. Ask students to make a map of the Pacific plate and neighboring plates and to use arrows to indicate the direction of the Pacific plate's current movements.

Assess It! Ask students to imagine the position of Earth's continents 200 million years from now. Have students draw a map of what Earth might look like. (Maps will vary, but should show some change in the relative position of the continents. Point out that ocean levels might be higher, so more land would be covered; ocean levels might also be lower, so more land would be exposed.)

The History of Life on Earth

The Big Idea Evidence from rocks allows us to understand the evolution of life on Earth.

California Standards

Focus on Life Sciences
7.3 Biological evolution accounts for the diversity of species developed through gradual processes over many generations. (Sections 1 and 2)
7.4 Evidence from rocks allows us to understand the evolution of life on Earth. (Sections 1, 2, and 3)

Investigation and Experimentation
7.7 Scientific progress is made by asking meaningful questions and conducting careful investigations. (Science Skills Activity)

Math
6.1.2, 6.2.1 Number Sense
7.1.2 Number Sense
6.2.1, 6.2.3 Algebra and Functions
7.1.1, 7.2.2 Mathematical Reasoning

English–Language Arts
7.1.3 Reading
7.2.5 Writing

About the Photo

Watch out! Saber-toothed cats, such as this *Smilodon*, were daunting predators in California long ago. This fossil skeleton was found in the sticky La Brea Tar Pits in Los Angeles, California. Predators were probably trapped as they ventured into the tar pits to eat animals already stuck there. *Smilodon* was about the size of a tiger and had sharp, dagger-like teeth, as you can see!

Organize

Four-Corner Fold

Before you read this chapter, create the FoldNote entitled "Four-Corner Fold." Label each flap of the four-corner fold with "Fossils," "Changes in Earth's environments," "Changes in life on Earth," and "The geologic time scale." As you read the chapter, add details about each topic under the appropriate flap.

Instructions for creating FoldNotes are located in the Study Skills section on p. 581 of the Appendix.

California Standards Alignment

Focus on Life Sciences

7.3.c Students know how independent lines of evidence from geology, fossils, and comparative anatomy provide the bases for the theory of evolution. **pp. 263–269, 288–289**

7.4.a Students know Earth processes today are similar to those that occurred in the past and slow geologic processes have large cumulative effects over long periods of time. **pp. 270–275, 288–291**

7.4.c Students know that the rock cycle includes the formation of new sediment and rocks and that rocks are often found in layers, with the oldest generally on the bottom. **pp. 263–269, 288–290**

7.4.d Students know that evidence from geologic layers and radioactive dating indicates Earth is approximately 4.6 billion years old and that life on this planet has existed for more than 3 billion years. **pp. 277–283, 288–291**

7.4.e Students know fossils provide evidence of how life and environmental conditions have changed. **pp. 264–269, 272–275, 277–285, 288–291**

7.4.f Students know how movements of Earth's continental and oceanic plates through time, with associated changes in climate and geographic connections, have affected the past and present distribution of organisms. **pp. 270–275, 288–291**

7.4.g Students know how to explain significant developments and extinctions of plant and animal life on the geologic time scale. **pp. 276–283, 288–291**

Explore Activity

 20 min

Teacher Notes

In this activity, students will make impressions of objects in clay and will use their observations to think about the kinds of information that can be learned from fossils (covers standards 7.3.c and 7.4.c). Include something soft such as gelatin or putty so students can see how difficult it is for fossils to form from soft organisms.

Materials for Each Group

- clay, modeling
- paper sack that contains small objects, such as shells, coins, paper clips, buttons, toys, or other objects that have recognizable textures or shapes

Answers

6. Sample answer: Textures and shapes were useful in identifying the model fossils. Small details, colors, and internal structures were not preserved. No, I can't tell what color the original objects were or what materials they were made from.

7. Sample answer: Fossils can provide only certain types of information about ancient organisms. Also, some organisms were not preserved as fossils.

☐ Differentiated Datasheets
A **BASIC**, B **GENERAL**, C **ADVANCED**

Also editable on the Holt Lab Generator CD-ROM

Explore Activity

 20 min

Making Fossils

How do scientists learn from fossils? In this activity, you will study "fossils" and identify the object that made each fossil.

Procedure

1. You and three or four of your classmates will be given **several pieces of modeling clay** and a **paper sack** containing a **few small objects.**

2. Press each object into a piece of clay, and then remove the object from the clay. Try to leave a "fossil" imprint showing as much detail as possible.

3. Trade your model fossils with another group.

4. On a **sheet of paper,** describe the fossils you have received. List as many details as possible. What patterns and textures do you observe?

5. Work as a group to identify each fossil, and check your results. Were you right?

7.3.c
7.4.c

Analysis

6. What kinds of evidence were important in identifying your fossils? What kinds of evidence were not preserved in the imprints? For example, can you tell what materials the objects were made of or what colors the objects were?

7. Why do you think fossils are sometimes called a "partial record" of past life?

Investigation and Experimentation

7.7.d Construct scale models, maps, and appropriately labeled diagrams to communicate scientific knowledge (e.g., motion of Earth's plates and cell structure). **pp. 284–286**

Math Standards

Number Sense 6.1.2 Interpret and use ratios in different contexts (e.g., batting averages, miles per hour) to show the relative sizes of two quantities, using appropriate notations (a/b, a to b, a:b). **p. 292**

Number Sense 6.2.1 Solve problems involving addition, subtraction, multiplication, and division of positive fractions and explain why a particular operation was used for a given situation. **p. 289**

Number Sense 7.1.2 Add, subtract, multiply, and divide rational numbers (integers, fractions, and terminating decimals) and take positive rational numbers to whole-number powers. **p. 283**

Algebra and Functions 6.2.1 Convert one unit of measurement to another (e.g., from feet to miles, from centimeters to inches). **p. 275**

Algebra and Functions 6.2.3 Solve problems involving rates, average speed, distance, and time. **p. 274**

Mathematical Reasoning 7.1.1 Analyze problems by identifying relationships, distinguishing relevant from irrelevant information, identifying missing information, sequencing and prioritizing information, and observing patterns. **p. 269**

Mathematical Reasoning 7.2.1 Use estimation to verify the reasonableness of calculated results. **p. 275**

English–Language Arts Standards

Reading 7.1.3 Clarify word meaning through the use of definition, example, restatement, or contrast. **pp. 264, 270**

Writing 7.2.5 Write summaries of reading materials: a. Include the main ideas and most significant details. b. Use the student's own words, except for quotations. c. Reflect underlying meaning, not just the superficial details. **pp. 288, 293**

Preteach

Reviewing Prior Knowledge

Ask students what they already know about superposition and radiometric dating. For example, ask students, "How can superposition be used to date fossils?" (Older rock layers and fossils are found below younger rock layers and fossils.) "What can radiometric dating tell you about fossils that superposition cannot?" (Radiometric dating is used to determine the actual age of a fossil, while superposition can identify only the age of a fossil relative to other fossils found at the same site in different layers.)

 **Bellringer**

Have students focus on standard 7.4.e by writing a few sentences to describe the fossil record that might be found 65 million years from now.

 Bellringer Transparency

Motivate

Group ACTiViTY

Carbon Impressions Carbon impressions of plants can form when the plants are buried in sediment. As plants decay, a thin film of carbon is left behind. Have students work in groups to make carbon "fossil" imprints. Have students place a flat leaf on the surface of plaster of Paris. After the plaster has dried, have students cover this layer with a second layer of plaster. When the second layer of plaster has dried, have students split the layers apart. Have students observe the leaf impression. They should note that a bit of the leaf material sticks to the impression made in the hard material. **LS Visual/Kinesthetic**

What You Will Learn

- Evidence of past life is preserved as fossils in sedimentary rock and in other materials.
- The study of fossils reveals information about how Earth's environments and organisms have changed.
- Index fossils can be used to date rock layers.

Why It Matters

Understanding fossils will help you understand how scientists piece together Earth's history.

Vocabulary

- fossil
- trace fossil
- index fossil

READING STRATEGY

Graphic Organizer In your **Science Journal**, make a Spider Map that shows the different ways that fossils can form.

7.3.c Students know how independent lines of evidence from geology, fossils, and comparative anatomy provide the bases for the theory of evolution.

7.4.c Students know that the rock cycle includes the formation of new sediment and rocks and that rocks are often found in layers, with the oldest generally on the bottom.

7.4.e Students know fossils provide evidence of how life and environmental conditions have changed.

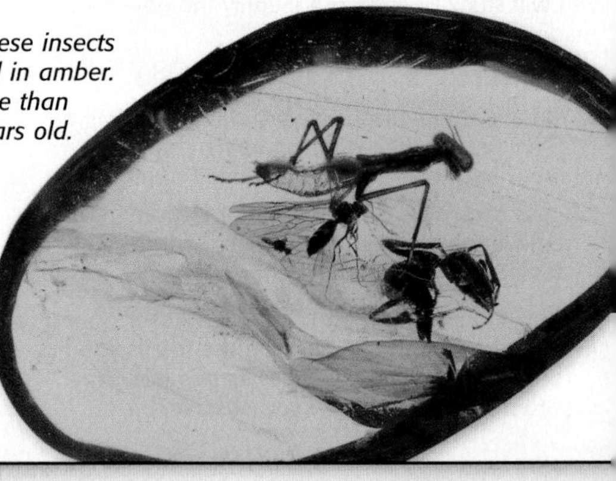

Answer to Standards Check

Evidence of past life is preserved as fossils in sedimentary rock. **7.4.c** (supporting), **7.4.e** (supporting)

Looking at Fossils

Key Concept Fossils provide evidence of how life and environmental conditions have changed.

▶ A paleontologist named Luis Chiappe found a dinosaur nesting ground in Argentina. How did he know the area had been a dinosaur nest? He studied fossil eggs found there.

Fossilized Organisms

The trace or remains of an organism that lived long ago is called a **fossil**. Fossils can form in several ways. The ways in which fossils form are outlined below.

Fossils in Rocks

When an organism dies, either it begins to decay or it is eaten by other organisms. Sometimes, however, organisms are quickly buried by sediment when they die. The sediment slows down decay and preserves the organisms. Hard parts, such as shells, teeth, and bones, are more resistant to decay than soft parts are. So, the hard parts of organisms are more often preserved than soft parts are. The fossils are preserved when sediment hardens to form sedimentary rock.

Standards Check How is evidence of past life preserved in sedimentary rock? **7.4.c, 7.4.e**

Fossils in Amber

Imagine that an insect is caught in soft, sticky tree sap. Suppose that the insect is covered by more sap. If the sap hardens quickly enough, it preserves the insect inside. Hardened tree sap is called *amber*. Some of the best insect fossils are found in amber, as shown in **Figure 1**. Frogs and lizards have also been found in amber.

Figure 1 These insects are preserved in amber. They are more than 38 million years old.

Universal Access · Differentiated Instruction

English Learners

Describing Fossilization The processes presented here that form fossils offer English learners a chance to practice reading comprehension and writing. Ask some students to write paragraphs that describe a method of fossilization and ask other students to draw an illustration. Have students take turns reading their description or showing their drawing to see if the class can guess which type of fossil formation is depicted. **LS Verbal/Visual Co-op Learning**

Frozen Fossils

In October 1999, scientists removed a 20,000-year-old woolly mammoth from the frozen ground of the Siberian tundra. Some of the remains of this mammoth are shown in **Figure 2.** Woolly mammoths, which are relatives of modern elephants, became extinct about 10,000 years ago. Cold temperatures slow down decay. So, many frozen fossils are preserved from the last ice age. By studying the fossils, scientists hope to learn more about the mammoth and its environment.

Fossils in Asphalt

There are places where asphalt wells up at Earth's surface in thick, sticky pools. The asphalt deposits known as the La Brea Tar Pits in Los Angeles, California, for example, are at least 38,000 years old. These pools of thick, sticky asphalt have trapped and preserved many kinds of organisms for the past 38,000 years. From these fossils, scientists have learned about the past environment of southern California.

Petrification

Organisms buried in sediment are sometimes preserved by petrification. *Petrification* is the filling or replacement of an organism's tissues with minerals that have different chemical compositions than the original tissues did. In one form of petrification, the space in an organism's hard tissue—for example, bone—is filled with a mineral. In another form of petrification, the organism's tissues are completely replaced by minerals. Petrified wood has undergone this type of replacement.

fossil (FAHS uhl) the trace or remains of an organism that lived long ago, most commonly preserved in sedimentary rock

Standards Check What is petrification? 7.3.c

Teach

ACTiViTY

Materials for Each Group

- cardboard, heavy, square
- leaves or shells, several
- milk carton
- petroleum jelly
- plaster of Paris
- stick for stirring
- water
- waxed paper

Making Fossils Divide the class into groups, and have each group fill the carton halfway with plaster of Paris. Have groups add water and stir the mixture to form a smooth, thick paste. Have students cover the cardboard square with waxed paper and pour the plaster mixture onto the cardboard square. Then, have them coat the leaves or the shells with petroleum jelly and place the items jelly side down into the plaster. Have students allow the plaster to dry for 24 h before removing the leaves or the shells. Have students exchange "fossil records" and interpret the records of other groups.
LS Kinesthetic/Visual

Answer to Standards Check

Petrification is the process in which minerals replace an organism's tissues.
7.3.c (supporting)

Universal Access · Differentiated Instruction

Special Education Students
Materials List

- clay, a fist-size glob for each student
- small flower boxes to represent ice encasements
- clear glue with yellow food coloring to represent amber
- clear glue with dark blue food coloring to represent asphalt
- model organisms such as small shells, model insects, and plant parts such as leaves or pine cones

Fossils Some students may have difficulty imagining the different processes of fossilization. Divide the class into groups. Ask each group to create one "fossil" for each of the fossilization processes presented on pages 264 through 266. Tell each group to select an organism for each type of fossilization. Make sure students choose organisms that are likely to go through each process. **LS** Kinesthetic

Debate

Amateur Fossil Collecting

Have students debate the pros and cons of amateur fossil collecting. Students should understand that amateur fossil collectors have made important discoveries and have helped advance the field of paleontology. On the other hand, amateur fossil collectors have lost important information by improperly removing fossils, by not recording data about the locations of fossils, and by failing to donate fossils to research institutions for study. Point out that it is illegal to collect fossils from state or national parks without a permit, or to remove vertebrate fossils from public lands without a permit. Have students conclude their debate by writing a handbook for amateur fossil collectors. **LS** Interpersonal/Verbal

---

MISCONCEPTION ALERT

Museum Displays Many people assume that when they see dinosaur fossils in a museum, they are looking at the actual fossils of the dinosaur. In older museums, this may be the case. However, point out to students that many newer museums do not display the actual fossilized dinosaur bones. They make casts of the bones and use these casts to make fiberglass reproductions of the bones. The fiberglass bones are much lighter than the original bones and can stand without support. Have students contact the closest museum that has dinosaur exhibits to find out whether the skeletons on display are actual fossils or fiberglass casts.

Answer to Standards Check

Sample answer: tracks, burrows, and coprolites, or fossilized dung

7.4.e (supporting)

Figure 3 *These dinosaur tracks are located in Arizona. They show that the dinosaur was running when it made these tracks.*

trace fossil (TRAYS FAHS uhl) a fossilized structure, such as a footprint or a coprolite, that formed in sedimentary rock by animal activity on or within soft sediment

---

Other Types of Fossils

Besides their hard parts—and in rare cases their soft parts—do organisms leave behind any other clues? What other evidence of past life do paleontologists look for? Many fossils are not body parts at all!

Trace Fossils

Any fossilized evidence of animal activity is called a **trace fossil.** Tracks, such as the ones shown in **Figure 3,** are an example of a trace fossil. These fossils form when animal footprints fill with sediment and are preserved in rock. Tracks reveal a lot about the animal that made them, including how big it was and how fast it was moving. Scientists have found parallel paths of tracks showing that a group of dinosaurs moved in the same direction. These discoveries have led paleontologists to hypothesize that some dinosaurs moved in herds.

Burrows are another kind of trace fossil. Burrows are shelters made by animals, such as clams, that bury themselves in sediment. Like tracks, burrows are preserved when they are filled with sediment and are buried quickly. A *coprolite* (KAHP roh LIET), a third kind of trace fossil, is preserved animal dung.

Standards Check Name three kinds of trace fossils. **7.4.e**

Molds and Casts

Molds and casts are two more kinds of fossils. The impression left in sediment or in rock where a plant or animal was buried is called a *mold.* **Figure 4** shows two types of molds from the same organism—an internal mold and an external mold. A *cast* is an object that forms when sediment fills a mold and becomes rock. Like a mold, a cast can show what the inside or the outside of an organism looked like.

Figure 4 *The fossil on the left is the internal mold of an ammonite. It formed when sediment filled the ammonite's shell. The shell later dissolved away. On the right is the external mold of the ammonite. It shows the external features of the shell.*

Universal Access • Differentiated Instruction

Struggling Readers

Fossil Outline Tell students that one way to remember and study information from a textbook is to take notes while reading. Write a skeleton outline on the board and have partners work together to read the pages and fill in the outline. A sample outline is shown to the right. Leave blanks for the magenta terms.

Other Types of Fossils
I. Trace Fossil
    A. Tracks - footprints filled with sediment
    B. Burrows - shelters made by animals
    C. Coprolite - preserved dung
II. Molds and Casts
    A. Mold - impression left in sediment where a plant or animal was buried
    B. Cast - an object that forms when sediment fills a mold and becomes a rock **LS** Visual/Logical

Using Fossils to Interpret the Past

All of the fossils that have been discovered on Earth are part of the fossil record. The *fossil record* is the history of life in the geologic past as indicated by the traces or remains of living things. Read on to find out more about the fossil record, including what scientists can learn from it.

The Information in the Fossil Record

The fossil record offers only a partial history of life on Earth. Some parts of this history are more complete than others. For example, scientists know more about organisms that had hard body parts than about organisms that had only soft body parts. Scientists also know more about organisms that lived in environments that favored fossilization. The fossil record is incomplete because most organisms never became fossils. And many fossils have not been discovered yet.

A History of Environmental Changes

Would you expect to find marine fossils on the mountain shown in **Figure 5**? The presence of marine fossils means that the rocks in these mountains formed in a very different environment. They formed at the bottom of an ocean.

Fossils can also contain evidence of climate change. For example, scientists have found fossil evidence of forests and freshwater organisms in Antarctica. The climate must have been warmer in the past for forests to grow and for fresh water to remain unfrozen. So, fossils are evidence of climate change in Antarctica. By studying life in the fossil record, scientists can tell what climates were like in the past.

Figure 5 *This scientist has found fossils of marine life at the top of mountains in the Yoho National Park in Canada. The marine fossils are evidence that these rocks were pushed up from below sea level.*

ACTiViTY

Materials for Each Group
- magazines, enough to find pictures of five different biomes

Imagining Environmental Change
Have small groups of students search in magazines for photographs that represent five different biomes. Then, have the groups place the five photographs in a sequence. Tell them to imagine that they are paleontologists and that this sequence represents roughly 300 million years in the geologic history of a single location. Have them study their photographs and brainstorm what the fossil record for each biome might contain. Ask students, "How would the fossil record indicate the environmental changes that occurred between each photograph in the sequence?" Have group members work together to write a press release announcing their description of 300 million years of environmental change. In their press release, students should describe what field techniques they used and how they reached their conclusions. They should also show illustrations of the fossils that they found and should explain why these fossils suggest the environmental changes shown in the sequence of photographs. **LS Visual/Logical**

Quick Lab

🕐 15 min

Teacher Notes

In this activity, students will interpret fossil evidence to determine a past environment and will explain how the environment could have changed over time (covers standard 7.4.e).

Answers

2. Sample answer: The fossil on the left is a fish. The fossil on the right appears to be an organism such as a shrimp or crayfish.

3. Sample answer: The fish had to live in water, so its environment must have been a place where water was always present and was deep enough for the fish to swim and find food. The shrimp or crayfish lived where there was water most of the time, and may have lived in water constantly, like the fish.

4. Sample answer: Yes, that environment is very different from a dry desert environment like the one in which the fossils were found. The environment changed between the time when the fossils formed and today. The area could

have been an ocean or lake when the organisms died and were buried by sediment, but later, the area became a desert.

📋 **Differentiated Datasheets**
A **BASIC**, B **GENERAL**, C **ADVANCED**

Also editable on the Holt Lab Generator CD-ROM

Standards Focus

This **Standards Focus** provides you with a quick way to **assess, reteach,** and **re-assess** one or more concepts in the section.

Assess

1. If two fossils are found in different sedimentary layers on the face of a cliff, how can you tell which fossil is older? (The older fossil would generally be found lower in the layers of the cliff, in older sedimentary rock.) **7.4.c**

2. How can plant fossils be used to determine changes in the environment over time? (Sample answer: Older rock layers may include fossils of plants from wetter, warmer conditions, while younger rock layers may include fossils of plants from cool, dry environments. This pattern would suggest a shift over time from warm, wet conditions to cool, dry conditions.) **7.4.e**

Reteach

Section Review Have students write two questions for each heading in the section. Then, have students exchange questions and attempt to answer each other's questions. **LS Verbal 7.3.c, 7.4.c, 7.4.e**

Re-Assess

Fossilization Have students prepare a guide for the fossilization processes described in this section. Students should imagine that the guide will explain to younger students how organisms are preserved in sedimentary rock, amber, asphalt, and ice, or by petrification. Emphasize to students that younger students may not know anything about fossilization, so details are important. **LS Verbal 7.4.c, 7.4.e**

Answer to Standards Check

Sample answer: younger rock layers, because fossils found in older rock layers are from older life forms

7.3.c (supporting)

SCHOOL to HOME

Fossil Hunt
Go on a fossil hunt with a parent or guardian. Find out what kinds of rocks in your local area may contain fossils. Take pictures or draw sketches of your trip and of any fossils that you find. Keep your notes and drawings in your **Science Journal**.

ACTIVITY

index fossil (IN DEKS FAHS uhl) a fossil that is used to establish the age of a rock layer because the fossil is distinct, abundant, and widespread and the species that formed that fossil existed for only a short span of geologic time

Figure 6 *Paleontologists know that any rock layer that contains a fossil of the trilobite* Phacops *is about 400 million years old.*

A History of Changing Organisms

To determine how life on Earth has changed, scientists look for similarities between different fossils. Scientists also look for similarities between fossils and living organisms. By studying these relationships, scientists can interpret how life has changed over time. However, only a small fraction of the organisms that have existed in Earth's history have been fossilized. As a result, the fossil record is incomplete. So, it does not provide paleontologists with a continuous record of changes in life on Earth.

Dating the Fossil Record

To understand the history of life on Earth, paleontologists put fossils in order based on age. In some cases, scientists can use absolute dating methods, such as radiometric dating, to determine the age of fossils. More commonly, they use relative dating methods, especially superposition, to establish the relative ages of fossils. Fossils found in older layers of rock are from more ancient life-forms. Fossils found in younger rock layers are from organisms that lived more recently.

Standards Check Would you expect to find fossils of an organism that lived recently in very old rock layers or in younger rock layers? Why? **7.3.c**

Using Fossils to Date Rocks

Scientists have found that some types of fossils appear all over the world, but only in certain rock layers. Scientists date the rock layers above and below these fossils. Then, scientists can determine the time span in which the organisms that formed the fossils lived. These types of fossils are called index fossils. **Index fossils** are fossils of organisms that lived during a relatively short, well-defined geologic time span. To be considered an index fossil, a fossil must be found in rock layers throughout the world. It must also be easy to identify, and many fossils of that organism must exist. Scientists use index fossils to date rock layers in which the fossils are found.

Trilobites as Index Fossils

Fossils in a group of trilobites (TRIE loh BIETS) called *Phacops* are an example of an index fossil. Trilobites are extinct. Their closest living relatives are horseshoe crabs, spiders, and scorpions. Through the dating of rock, paleontologists have determined that *Phacops* lived approximately 400 million years ago. So, when scientists find *Phacops* in rock layers anywhere on Earth, they know that the rock layers are approximately 400 million years old. A *Phacops* fossil is shown in **Figure 6.**

Universal Access · Differentiated Instruction

Advanced Learners/GATE

Materials List

- glue
- markers
- poster board
- research materials

Fossil Poster Ask a small group of students to create a poster that shows examples of index fossils that are used to date rock layers. In the poster, students should include the names of specific countries and locations within the countries where the index fossils were found, as well as discovery dates and the types of index fossils found. Encourage students to include pictures and/or drawings of the fossils and organisms. **LS Visual/Interpersonal**

Ammonites as Index Fossils

Ammonites (AM uh NIETS), another index fossil, were marine mollusks similar to a modern squid. Ammonites were common in ancient oceans and lived in coiled shells. A genus of ammonites called *Tropites*, shown in **Figure 7**, is a common index fossil. *Tropites* lived between 230 million and 208 million years ago. So, it is an index fossil for that period of time. If scientists find *Tropites* in a rock layer, they know the rock layer formed between 230 and 208 million years ago.

Figure 7 *Tropites* is a kind of coiled ammonite. *Tropites* existed for only about 20 million years, which makes it a good index fossil.

SECTION Review

7.3.c, 7.4.c, 7.4.e

Summary

- Fossils are the traces or remains of an organism that lived long ago.

- Fossils can be preserved in sedimentary rock, amber, asphalt, or ice and by petrification.

- Trace fossils are any naturally preserved evidence of animal activity. Tracks, burrows, and coprolites are examples of trace fossils.

- Scientists study fossils to determine how environments and organisms have changed over time.

- An index fossil is a fossil that can be used to establish the age of rock layers.

Using Vocabulary

❶ Use *fossil*, *trace fossil*, and *index fossil* in separate sentences.

Understanding Concepts

❷ **Listing** Describe five ways fossils can form.

❸ **Applying** Explain how an index fossil can be used to date rock.

❹ **Demonstrating** How can fossils be used to provide evidence of how life and environmental conditions on Earth have changed?

❺ **Concluding** Explain why the fossil record contains an incomplete record of the history of life on Earth.

Critical Thinking

❻ **Making Inferences** You find a fossil of clam A in rock layer A and a fossil of clam B in rock layer B. If rock layer B is older than rock layer A, what can you infer about the relative ages of clams A and B?

❼ **Applying Concepts** What could you conclude if you found a fossil of a tropical plant in a rock that is in a polar climate?

Math Skills

❽ **Solving Problems** If a scientist finds the remains of a plant between a rock layer that contains 400 million–year-old *Phacops* fossils and a rock layer that contains 230 million–year-old *Tropites* fossils, how old could the plant fossil be?

Challenge

❾ **Applying Concepts** Imagine that you have discovered a dinosaur fossil in Antarctica. What types of information would you look for in order to determine the environment in which the dinosaur lived?

Internet Resources

For a variety of links related to this chapter, go to www.scilinks.org
Topic: Looking at Fossils
SciLinks code: HY70886

6. Because clam B was found in the older rock layer, clam B is older than clam A. **7.3.c** (exceeding), **7.4.c** (exceeding)

7. Sample answer: A fossil of a tropical plant that was found in a polar environment would indicate that at some time in the past, the environment on that landmass had been tropical and not polar. **7.4.e** (exceeding)

8. The plant fossil is between 230 million and 400 million years old. **7.4.c** (exceeding)

9. Sample answer: Can the dinosaur be identified from the fossil? If so, what else do we know about that type of dinosaur? What type of rock is the fossil in? What does it tell us about the environment in which the dinosaur lived? What other fossils are found in the same rock layer as the dinosaur fossil? What types of organisms do these other fossils represent and what type of environment did they live in? **7.4.e** (exceeding)

Section Review Standards Guide

	Supporting	Mastering	Exceeding
7.3.c	1, 2, 3		6
7.4.c	1, 2, 3		6, 8
7.4.e	1, 2, 3	4	5, 7, 9

Answers to Section Review

1. Sample answer: A fossil is the remains or evidence of an organism preserved in rock. A trace fossil is evidence of an organism that is not the remains of an actual body part. An index fossil is the remains of an organism that lived for a relatively short time, and is found in a variety of places on Earth, so it can be used to help date the rocks in which it is found. **7.3.c** (supporting), **7.4.c** (supporting), **7.4.e** (supporting)

2. Fossils can form when an organism is trapped in sediment that becomes sedimentary rock, in amber, in ice, in asphalt, or when an organism's tissues are replaced by petrification. **7.3.c** (supporting), **7.4.c** (supporting), **7.4.e** (supporting)

3. An index fossil is the remains of an organism that lived during a relatively short time span. When scientists find an index fossil, they can tell that the rock containing the index fossil is a certain age. **7.3.c** (supporting), **7.4.c** (supporting), **7.4.e** (supporting)

4. Scientists can examine fossils in different rock layers to see how life-forms have changed during Earth's history. The types of life-forms found in an area can provide evidence about how the environment has changed. **7.4.e** (mastering)

5. The fossil record is incomplete because most organisms, especially those that had soft bodies, did not become fossils and because many fossils have yet to be discovered. **7.4.e** (exceeding)

Section Resources

- **Directed Reading**
  A **BASIC** (Also in Spanish), B **GENERAL**

- **Interactive Reader and Study Guide**

- **Section Quiz** **GENERAL** (Also in Spanish)

- **Section Review** **GENERAL** (Also in Spanish)

- **Vocabulary and Section Summary**
  A **BASIC** (Also in Spanish), B **GENERAL**

Preteach

Reviewing Prior Knowledge

Ask students to name the outer layer of Earth as defined by the physical properties of the layers. (the lithosphere, which contains the crust and the rigid upper part of the mantle) Then, ask students to explain how the lithosphere and mantle interact. (Movement within the mantle causes the tectonic plates of the lithosphere to move.)

Bellringer

Have students focus on standard 7.4.a by telling them to imagine that two large sections of Earth's crust are slowly colliding or separating. Then, ask students, "Over time, what might happen at the site of the collision or separation?" (Sample answers: Earthquakes may occur; mountain ranges and volcanoes may form.)

🗔 Bellringer Transparency

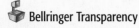

Motivate

ACTIVITY

Moving Towns Tell students that since the San Andreas fault formed about 25 million years ago, the part of California that is west of the fault has moved to the northwest at least 350 miles. Pair students and give each pair of students a map of California that shows towns and cities as well as the San Andreas fault. Have students find two towns on opposite sides of the fault. Assuming the same rate of movement in the future as in the last 25 million years, ask students to determine where the towns will be relative to each other in 25 million years. (The town on the west side will be 350 miles farther northwest.)
LS Logical

What You Will Learn

- Earth's continents have moved around Earth's surface throughout Earth's history and have only recently arrived at their current locations.
- Rocks and fossils provide evidence of continental drift. They also provide evidence of the changes in life and climate that have occurred during Earth's history.

Why It Matters

Understanding the history of climate change and life on Earth will help you better understand today's Earth.

Vocabulary

- plate tectonics
- continental drift

READING STRATEGY

Graphic Organizer In your **Science Journal,** make a Spider Map that organizes the types and details of plate boundaries.

Earth's Changing Continents

Key Concept Movements of Earth's tectonic plates have affected climate, geographic connections, and the distribution of organisms.

▶ The surface of Earth on which we live is constantly moving. Sometimes, we feel this movement as earthquakes. But did you know that Earth's surface has changed so much during Earth's long history that the continents have changed locations?

Plate Tectonics

The thin, cool "skin" of Earth is called the *lithosphere*. This layer is broken into several smaller blocks called *tectonic plates*. These plates rest on a thick layer of solid rock called the *mantle*. Earth's mantle is solid, but it moves very slowly. As the mantle moves, it drags on the bottom of the cold tectonic plates lying on top of it. As a result, the tectonic plates move. Earth's surface currently has about 12 large plates and many small ones. Some of the large plates are labeled in **Figure 1.** Most plates move as fast as your fingernails grow—between 2 cm and 5 cm per year. Over geologic time scales, this movement can cause large cumulative effects—plate movements may total thousands of miles. The theory that explains how Earth's tectonic plates move and change shape is called **plate tectonics.**

Standards Check What is plate tectonics? 🐾 **7.4.a, 7.4.f**

Figure 1 Earth's Tectonic Plates

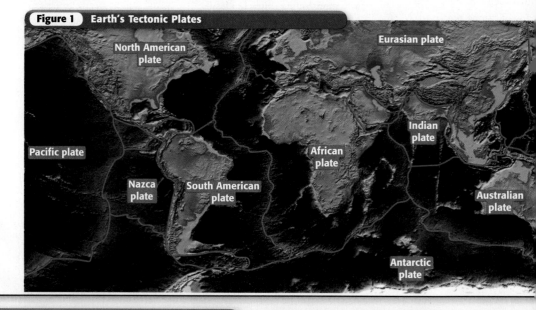

North American plate
Eurasian plate
Pacific plate
Nazca plate
South American plate
African plate
Indian plate
Australian plate
Antarctic plate

Universal Access • Differentiated Instruction

Basic Learners

Boundary Types Help students remember the different types of plate boundaries by giving them the following mnemonic clues:

DIVergent boundaries: plates DIVide.

COnvergent boundaries: plates COme together and COllide.

TRAnsform boundaries: plates TRAvel side by side.
LS Verbal/Auditory

Answer to Standards Check

Plate tectonics is the theory that explains how pieces of Earth's lithosphere move and change shape. **7.4.a** (supporting), **7.4.f** (supporting)

Figure 2 Tectonic Plate Boundaries

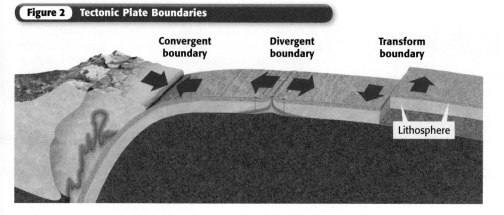

Convergent boundary   Divergent boundary   Transform boundary

Lithosphere

Where Tectonic Plates Meet

Tectonic plates may contain oceanic lithosphere, continental lithosphere, or both types of lithosphere. As tectonic plates move, they collide, separate, and grind past each other. Places where two or more tectonic plates meet are called *plate boundaries*. There are three main types of plate boundaries. The type of plate boundary that forms is a result of how the plates move relative to each other.

Convergent Boundaries

Plates move toward each other at a *convergent boundary*, as shown in **Figure 2.** If both plate edges are continental lithosphere, the rocks are forced together until they crumple to make great mountain belts. But if one plate is thin, dense oceanic lithosphere, it may sink downward into the mantle. As the plate sinks, surrounding rock may melt. Some of this molten rock rises to the surface and makes a line of volcanoes.

Divergent Boundaries

Plates move apart at a *divergent boundary*, as shown in **Figure 2.** This process forms a rift—a giant crack in the lithosphere. Volcanic eruptions fill the crack with lava that cools to form new oceanic lithosphere. If a rift tears apart a continent and then widens for millions of years, a new sea forms. The sea may gradually grow into a new ocean.

Transform Boundaries

Two plates slide horizontally past each other along a *transform boundary*, as shown in **Figure 2.** The movement of the plates can cause earthquakes in the area of a transform boundary. One of the world's most well known transform boundaries is the San Andreas fault, which cuts right across California.

plate tectonics (PLAYT tek TAHN iks) the theory that explains how large pieces of Earth's outermost layer, called *tectonic plates,* move and change shape

7.4.a Students know Earth processes today are similar to those that occurred in the past and slow geologic processes have large cumulative effects over long periods of time.
7.4.e Students know fossils provide evidence of how life and environmental conditions have changed.
7.4.f Students know how movements of Earth's continental and oceanic plates through time, with associated changes in climate and geographic connections, have affected the past and present distribution of organisms.

Maps in Motion Have students use the map of tectonic plates in **Figure 1** on page 270 to create their own map of plate boundaries. Point out to students that sometimes plate boundaries and continental boundaries are the same, but this is not always the case. Have students highlight their maps to show which plate boundaries are also continental boundaries. **LS Visual**

Group ACTIVITY

More Fossil Evidence Have students research other fossils that provide evidence of continental drift. For example, fossils of *Cynoganthus,* a 3 m long reptile, have been found across mid-South America and mid-Africa. Fossils of another Triassic Period reptile, *Lystrosaurus,* have been found across parts of India, Africa, and Antarctica. Have students create a world map that shows the distribution of such fossils on Pangaea and on present-day continents. **LS Visual/Logical**

Answer to Math Practice

40 km (4 cm = 0.00004 km; 0.00004 km/year × 1,000,000 years = 40 km)

SCIENCE HUMOR

Q: Why did the continents finally go their separate ways?

A: There was a great rift between them.

Tectonic Motion

Tectonic plates move slowly but may be in motion for millions of years. If a plate moves 4 cm per year, how many kilometers would it move in 1 million years? Record your work in your **Science Journal.**

---

continental drift (KAHN tuh NENT'l DRIFT) the hypothesis that a single large landmass broke up into smaller landmasses to form the continents, which then drifted to their present locations; the movement of continents

---

Continental Drift

As the tectonic plates move, they carry the continents along as passengers. **Continental drift** is the term that is used to describe how continents have moved around Earth's surface throughout Earth's history. As a continent moves across Earth's surface, it carries rocks and fossils with it. Sometimes, the rocks and fossils provide evidence of how the continent has moved.

Geologic Evidence of Continental Drift

Rocks in India show scratches and scars that formed when glaciers ground over their surfaces. So, at one time, India must have been covered by ice. Such a thick layer of ice could not form at sea level in the tropical zone where India is today. Southern Africa and Brazil also have ice-scratched rocks of the same age. This evidence suggests that at one time, the rocks were joined and were located in a colder climate. Scientists now know that India, South America, and Africa were part of a single landmass that was located near the South Pole about 280 million years ago.

Fossil Evidence of Continental Drift

A fossil of a little reptile called *Mesosaurus* is shown in **Figure 3.** Mesosaurs ate fishes in rivers and lakes about 270 million years ago. Today, *Mesosaurus* fossils are found in South America and southwestern Africa. These areas are separated by 3,000 miles of ocean. Mesosaurs could not have swum across this ocean. And there is no evidence of land bridges between these continents. Thus, mesosaurs must have lived at a time when the two continents were joined. This fossil evidence supports continental drift.

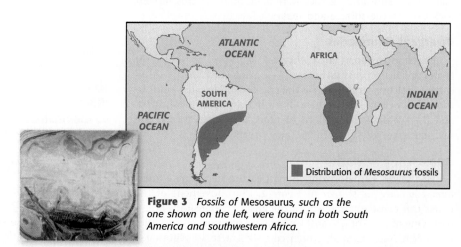

Figure 3 *Fossils of* Mesosaurus, *such as the one shown on the left, were found in both South America and southwestern Africa.*

Universal Access · Differentiated Instruction

Special Education Students

Sliding Plates The breakup of Pangaea and the movement of the continents to their present positions can be "visualized" by feel. Construct models of the early continents out of thick cardboard, foam, or plastic. Help students fit the continent models together into a model that represents Pangaea. Then, have students slide the "continents" apart into their current positions. **LS Kinesthetic**

English Learners

Fossil Questions Give English learners an opportunity to practice question formation by having them write questions about fossils. Remind them to use past tense and to start questions with *What, Where, When,* or *What kind,* and to put *was* or *were* in front of the subject or to add *did* when necessary. Sample: What did *Mesosaurus* eat? (fishes) What kind of an animal was *Mesosaurus?* (a reptile) **LS Verbal/Interpersonal**

History of Continental Drift

By putting together all of the evidence, scientists can draw maps that show how Earth's geography has changed over time. For example, all of Earth's continents made up a supercontinent called *Pangaea* (pan JEE uh) about 245 million years ago. At the same time, Earth also had a single super-ocean. Pangaea split into several new plates beginning about 200 million years ago. As the plates drifted apart, those new continents separated, and new oceans formed between them. The breakup of Pangaea is shown in **Figure 4.**

These huge changes moved rocks and fossils all over Earth. The rocks and fossils give scientists evidence of the plate movements. In addition, plate movements changed Earth's climate and affected *evolution*, or how populations of species have changed over time.

Changes in Climate

As continents moved, they changed the way land and sea were placed on Earth's surface. If continents moved toward the equator, they received more energy from the sun and developed warmer climates. Continental drift caused ocean currents and winds to flow differently. These changes affected heat flow. As a result, temperature and precipitation patterns around the planet changed.

For example, Antarctica was not frozen 40 million years ago. But as the other continents moved, Antarctica was left surrounded by the cold water near the South Pole. As cold water currents moved around Antarctica, the polar icecap formed. Antarctica slowly became the icy land we see today.

Changes in Life

When Pangaea split apart, the organisms living on each continent were separated. As their environments changed, the organisms that lived in those environments also changed. And as new oceans formed, changes also occurred in sea life. This explains why different organisms live on different continents. It also explains why fossils of the same organisms are found on different continents.

Standards Check How have tectonic plate motions affected the distribution of organisms? 7.4.f

---

Figure 4 The Breakup of Pangaea

About 245 million years ago The continents were one giant landmass called Pangaea.

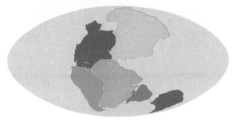

About 135 million years ago As Pangaea broke apart, the North Atlantic and Indian Oceans began to form.

About 65 million years ago The continents continued to drift apart toward their modern locations.

Today The continents continue to move at a rate of about 2 cm to 5 cm per year.

Answer to Standards Check

Tectonic plate motions have affected the distribution of organisms by changing geographic connections and by causing climate changes that affect where organisms can live. **7.4.f** (mastering)

Connection To Earth Science

Sudden Climate Change?
Climate change in the past has occurred both gradually and suddenly. The same may be true for present-day climate change. Many scientists are concerned that while people are adjusting to the idea of gradual global climate change, a sudden climate change may already be in motion. The Gulf Stream transports warm waters of the Atlantic up to Northern Europe. Melting ice caps are changing the density of the water in Northern Europe, and this may disrupt the normal flow of the Gulf Stream. New England and Europe could suddenly become colder even while global temperatures continue to rise.

Close

Standards Focus

This **Standards Focus** provides you with a quick way to **assess, reteach,** and **re-assess** one or more concepts in the section.

Assess

1. How do scientists know that the continents were once joined in the giant landmass Pangaea? (Fossil evidence, ancient rock formations, and the current rate of movement observed in continental plates all suggest that Pangaea once existed.) **7.4.a, 7.4.e, 7.4.f**

2. Which type of boundary between tectonic plates can lead to great mountain belts? (convergent) **7.4.a**

3. How did fossils of *Mesosaurus* provide evidence for continental drift? (*Mesosaurus* fossils were found in both Africa and South America, which suggests that South America and Africa were once connected.) **7.4.e, 7.4.f**

 Reteach

Replacing Headings Have students read through this section and replace each heading with a complete sentence. **LS** Verbal **7.4.a, 7.4.e, 7.4.f**

Re-Assess

Convincing Argument Have students create a presentation to convince an audience that the continental drift hypothesis is valid. Tell students to carefully consider what evidence to use in their presentations. **LS** Verbal **7.4.a, 7.4.e, 7.4.f**

Answer to Standards Check

It allowed organisms to migrate back and forth between North and South America and isolated marine organisms in the Atlantic and Pacific Oceans from each other. **7.4.f** (supporting)

📦 Teaching Transparency: L35 Formation of the Panama Land Bridge

---

Case Study: The Panama Land Bridge

North and South America drifted close together about 3 million years ago. At that time, a narrow strip of land joined North and South America for the first time, as shown in **Figure 5.** This strip of land was called the Panama Land Bridge.

Changes in Life

Animals could now walk across the Panama Land Bridge. As they migrated, they competed with one another. Many animals became extinct, but successful ones flourished. Opossums and armadillos invaded North America, whereas camels and cats invaded South America. At the same time, creatures in the sea were separated by the new land bridge. Some populations of clams, corals, whales, and sea urchins evolved into separate species on the Pacific and Caribbean coasts of Panama.

Standards Check How did the formation of the Panama Land Bridge affect the distribution of organisms in the Americas? **7.4.f**

Changes in Climate

The land bridge forced warm, tropical water that had once flowed between the continents to flow around the Gulf of Mexico and north past Florida. The new flow of water formed the Gulf Stream—a strong ocean current. The Gulf Stream changed the climate of western Europe by transporting warm water across the Atlantic Ocean. This water heats the air and makes climates milder.

Figure 5 *After North and South America were joined by the Panama Land Bridge, animals migrated across the bridge and ocean currents changed dramatically.*

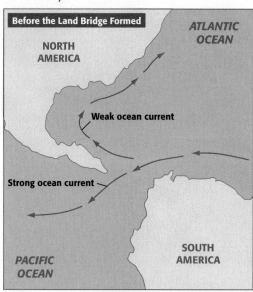

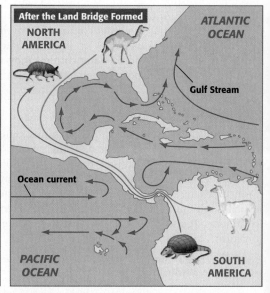

Quick Lab

🕐 **20 min**

Teacher Notes

In this lab, students will identify how environments can change and will discuss how the changes could occur (covers standard 7.4.f). To prepare for this lab, find photographs of diverse environments. Each student group will need two photos.

Answers

1. Students should describe the environment shown in each of their photos. Descriptions should include information on temperature, likely precipitation patterns, and likely latitude range.

2. Students might describe continental drift taking a landmass to a different latitude on Earth's surface, changes in geography causing different ocean currents to affect the area, or changes in geography causing the area to be closer to or farther from the ocean.

3. Students should list plant and animal life appropriate for each environment.

📋 Differentiated Datasheets
A **BASIC**, B **GENERAL**, C **ADVANCED**

Also editable on the Holt Lab Generator CD-ROM

Quick Lab

Climate Changes

1. Each lab group will receive **two pictures** of environments on Earth. Describe each environment. Describe each climate, making estimates about the temperature and precipitation patterns in each environment.

2. Now, imagine that your two pictures represent the same place during different times in Earth's history. Discuss with your lab group how the climate in your first picture could have changed into the one shown in your second picture.

3. With your lab group, discuss the kinds of animal and plant life that might be found in each of your environments.

 20 min

SECTION Review

 7.4.a, 7.4.e, 7.4.f

Summary

- Earth's tectonic plates drift over time, moving continents and changing oceans.

- Evidence from rocks and fossils shows how Earth's continents have drifted and how climate and life have changed as a result.

- The breakup of Pangaea about 245 million years ago divided Earth's land into separate continents.

- The movement of continents alters climates by changing the patterns of air currents and ocean currents.

- The formation of the Panama Land Bridge is an example of how the movement of tectonic plates affects the distribution of organisms on Earth.

Using Vocabulary

1. Use *continental drift* and *plate tectonics* in separate sentences.

Understanding Concepts

2. **Describing** Name the three types of plate boundaries, and describe how plates move at each type of boundary.

3. **Summarizing** Name two types of evidence for continental drift, and give examples of each type.

4. **Identifying** How do tectonic plate movements affect climate?

5. **Applying** Describe a change in geographic connections that has affected the distribution of organisms during Earth's history.

Critical Thinking

6. **Applying Concepts** How do fossils of extinct species provide evidence of how life on Earth has changed?

7. **Analyzing Processes** Explain how the slow process of continental drift has a large effect over long periods of time.

Evaluating Assumptions

8. What assumption do scientists make when they state that if continents separate, the land animals on the continents are separated from each other?

Math Skills

9. **Solving Problems** The San Andreas fault moves 5 cm per year in some areas. Which of the following is more likely—that in 1,000 years the fault will move 50 m or that it will move 50 km?

Challenge

10. **Predicting Consequences** Imagine that the Panama Land Bridge eroded and water began flowing between North and South America. Predict changes that might occur in the climate and the distribution of organisms.

Internet Resources

For a variety of links related to this chapter, go to www.scilinks.org
Topic: Earth's Story; Plate Tectonics
SciLinks code: HY70450; HY71171

6. Fossils of extinct species provide evidence of what life was like on Earth in the past, and by comparing past life to organisms on Earth today, scientists can see how life has changed over time. **7.4.e** (mastering)

7. Continental drift is slow, but over millions of years continents can move across much of Earth's surface. **7.4.a** (mastering), **7.4.f** (mastering)

8. Scientists are making the assumption that the animals cannot swim between the continents. **7.4.f** (supporting)

9. It is more reasonable that in 1000 years the fault will move 50 m. (5 cm = 0.05 m; 0.05 m/year × 1000 years = 50 m) **7.4.a** (supporting), **7.4.f** (supporting)

10. Sample answer: If water began flowing between North and South America, organisms on the two landmasses would be separated and might start evolving differently. The Gulf Stream might not flow so strongly into the North Atlantic, and the climate of northern Europe might become colder. **7.4.f** (exceeding)

Section Review Standards Guide			
	Supporting	Mastering	Exceeding
7.4.a	1, 3, 9	7	
7.4.e	3	6	
7.4.f	1, 2, 3, 8, 9	4, 5, 7	10

Answers to Section Review

1. Sample answer: Continental drift is the hypothesis that the continents drifted to their present locations. Plate tectonics is the theory that explains how Earth's tectonic plates move and change shape. **7.4.a** (supporting), **7.4.f** (supporting)

2. At convergent boundaries, plates push into each other. At divergent boundaries, plates move apart. At transform boundaries, plates slide past each other horizontally. **7.4.f** (supporting)

3. Sample answer: Two types of evidence for continental drift are geologic evidence and fossil evidence. An example of geologic evidence is the glacial scars on rocks of the same age in India,

South America, and Africa, which show that these landmasses were once joined. An example of fossil evidence is the location of *Mesosaurus* fossils, which shows that Africa and South America were once part of the same landmass. **7.4.a** (supporting), **7.4.e** (supporting), **7.4.f** (supporting)

4. Tectonic plate movements affect climate by changing where landmasses are located on Earth and by changing geographic connections between landmasses. **7.4.f** (mastering)

5. Sample answer: The formation of the Panama Land Bridge affected the distribution of organisms between North and South America and also in the Atlantic and Pacific Oceans. **7.4.f** (mastering)

Section Resources

- Directed Reading A **BASIC** (Also in Spanish), B **GENERAL**

- Interactive Reader and Study Guide

- Section Quiz **GENERAL** (Also in Spanish)

- Section Review **GENERAL** (Also in Spanish)

- Vocabulary and Section Summary A **BASIC** (Also in Spanish), B **GENERAL**

Preteach

Reviewing Prior Knowledge

Have students look at the geologic time scale on the next page. Point out that the earliest era and the earliest epoch both begin with the prefix *paleo-*, as does the term *paleontologist*. Ask students what they think the prefix *paleo-* means. (*Paleo-* is a Greek root that means "ancient or early".)

 **Bellringer**

Have students focus on standard 7.4.g by asking them, "If the history of Earth was condensed into one calendar year, on what date do you think that modern humans would arrive?" (December 31)

 Bellringer Transparency

Motivate

ACTIVITY

Personal Time Scale Have students create a time scale of their own lives up to the present time. Students should divide their lives broadly into eons, divide the eons into eras, and divide the eras into periods. Tell students to think of logical names for each time period, as well as logical reasons for the end and beginning of each new time period.
LS Logical

Answer to Standards Check

The geologic time scale is the standard method of dividing Earth's history into distinct units of time. **7.4.g** (supporting)

 Teaching Transparency:
LINK TO EARTH SCIENCE
E12 Formation of Coal

Time Marches On

Key Concept Life has changed through Earth's history as life-forms have developed, or evolved, and become extinct.

What You Will Learn

- The geologic time scale organizes Earth's history into intervals of time.
- Life first appeared on Earth more than 3.6 billion years ago.
- Life-forms changed as environmental changes happened during the Paleozoic, Mesozoic, and Cenozoic Eras.

Why It Matters

Understanding the history of life on Earth will help you understand how life-forms evolve.

Vocabulary

- geologic time scale
- extinction

READING STRATEGY

Outlining In your **Science Journal**, create an outline of the section. Use the headings from the section in your outline.

▶ Try to think of Earth's history in "fast forward." If you could watch Earth change in this way, you would see mountains rise up like wrinkles in fabric and quickly wear away. You would see life-forms appear, change, and disappear, or become extinct. In this section, you will learn that geologists must "fast forward" Earth's history when they write or talk about it. You will also learn about some incredible events in the history of life on Earth.

The Geologic Time Scale

Fossils of dinosaurs that lived 150 million years ago are shown in **Figure 1.** You may think that 150 million years is a very long time. But 150 million years is less than 3% of the time Earth has existed. All together, geologists study 4.6 billion years of Earth's history! To help keep track of this history, geologists have developed the geologic time scale, shown in **Figure 2.** The **geologic time scale** divides Earth's 4.6 billion–year history into distinct intervals of time. Each interval is distinct because life and environments have changed throughout Earth's history.

Standards Check Define the term *geologic time scale*. 🐻 **7.4.g**

Figure 1 *Bones of dinosaurs that lived about 150 million years ago are exposed in this quarry at Dinosaur National Monument in Utah.*

7.4.d Students know that evidence from geologic layers and radioactive dating indicates Earth is approximately 4.6 billion years old and that life on this planet has existed for more than 3 billion years.
7.4.e Students know fossils provide evidence of how life and environmental conditions have changed.
7.4.g Students know how to explain significant developments and extinctions of plant and animal life on the geologic time scale.

Universal Access · Differentiated Instruction

Struggling Readers

Using Figures and Tables Make sure that students realize that each of the figures and tables in the book are explained in the text at least once. Tell students that they can easily find the explanations for figures and tables in the text by looking for the word *figure* or *table* in boldface print. Make sure that students realize that the figure captions often provide additional information that is not given in the text.

Ask students how many times the text discusses **Figure 1** (once) and what information is given in the caption that is not given in the text. (The picture was taken in a quarry at Dinosaur National Park Monument in Utah.) Ask students how many times the text discusses **Figure 2** (twice) and what information is given in the caption that is not given in the text (The dates given on the geologic time scale are estimates.) **LS** Visual

Geologic Time Scale

Eon	Era	Period	Epoch	Millions of years ago
PHANEROZOIC	Cenozoic	Quaternary	Holocene	0.01
			Pleistocene	1.8
		Tertiary	Pliocene	5.3
			Miocene	23.0
			Oligocene	33.9
			Eocene	55.8
			Paleocene	65.5
	Mesozoic	Cretaceous		146
		Jurassic		200
		Triassic		251
	Paleozoic	Permian		299
		Carboniferous		359
		Devonian		416
		Silurian		444
		Ordovician		488
		Cambrian		542
PROTEROZOIC ARCHEAN HADEAN	These three eons together are known as *Precambrian time* because they came before the Cambrian Period.			4,600

Figure 2 *The geologic time scale is divided into four major parts called eons. Dates given for intervals on the geologic time scale are approximate.* ***What percentage of Earth's history does the Cenozoic Era represent?***

Divisions of Time

Geologists have divided Earth's history into chunks of time, as shown on the geologic time scale in **Figure 2.** The largest divisions of geologic time are *eons* (EE AHNZ). Together, the first three eons of Earth's history are known as Precambrian time. The Phanerozoic Eon is divided into three *eras,* which are the second-largest divisions of geologic time. The three eras are further divided into *periods*. Periods are divided into *epochs* (EP uhks).

The boundaries between geologic time intervals usually correspond to significant changes in Earth's history. Most boundaries are defined by the appearance or disappearance of a significant number of species. Some boundaries are defined by the appearance or disappearance of index fossils. Other boundaries are defined by major changes in Earth's surface or climate, such as the advance or retreat of glaciers.

geologic time scale (JEE uh LAHJ ik TIEM SKAYL) the standard method used to divide Earth's long natural history into manageable parts

Universal Access • Differentiated Instruction

Advanced Learners/GATE

Research on Earth's Age Before the development of the theory of plate tectonics and the use of radiometric dating, scientists developed many elaborate experiments to determine the age of Earth. In the mid-1700s, a French scientist estimated that Earth was 75,000 years old. He based his estimate on the cooling rate of iron cannonballs. By the 1930s, the estimated age of Earth reached 1 billion years, but it was not until the middle of the twentieth century that the current estimate of 4.6 billion years was determined. Have advanced students research the different methods that have been used to estimate the age of Earth. LS **Verbal**

Teach

CONNECTION ACTIVITY
Earth Science

Paleobotany The study of ancient life involves the crossover of life science and Earth science. Paleobotany, for example, is the study of the history of the plant kingdom through fossils. Have students find out how scientists have used plant and pollen fossils to learn about environmental changes over time. LS **Verbal**

Using the Figure

Cenozoic Era Remind students that the extinction of the dinosaurs marks the beginning of the Cenozoic Era. The start of the Cenozoic Era also marks the beginning of the "Age of Mammals." Ask students why they think scientists know more about the Cenozoic Era than any other period of time. (The fossils of the Cenozoic Era formed more recently than those of other time periods. They are more commonly exposed at Earth's surface and so are more often found than older fossils.) Answer to caption question: The Cenozoic Era is about 1.4% of Earth's history. LS **Logical**

Teaching Transparency: L36 Geologic Time Scale

ACTIVITY

What's in a Name? There are 25 different time periods listed in the geologic time scale on this page. Tell students that, in North America, the Carboniferous Period is divided into the Pennsylvanian and Mississippian Periods. Assign each student one of the divisions of geologic time, and have him or her research that particular division of time. Students should find out what the name of their assigned division of time means and why it might be a good descriptor for that eon, era, period, or epoch. LS **Verbal**

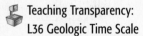

Quick Lab ⏱ 30 min

Teacher Notes

In this activity, students will make a timeline of Earth's history to help them visualize geologic time (covers standards 7.4.d and 7.4.g). This activity can be done in 30 minutes if students mark off only the three eras and Precambrian time. As students study this section, have them add details about each time interval to their timelines. This lab activity may be easier to conduct in the hallway.

Materials for Each Group
- meterstick
- paper strip, adding machine, 5 m
- pencils, colored, (5 different colors)

Answers
8. Precambrian time represents 88% of Earth's history.

9. Answers should include relevant details from various divisions of geologic time.

📋 Differentiated Datasheets
A **BASIC**, B **GENERAL**, C **ADVANCED**

Also editable on the Holt Lab Generator CD-ROM

Debate

The Next Mass Extinction?
Divide the class into groups. Ask groups to debate whether we are now entering another period of mass extinction, and whether human activities are the cause. Give groups time to find information to support or refute each stance. Then, allow groups to debate the issue. Students should state the sources of all of the data they present. **LS Verbal/Logical**

Figure 3 *Hallucigenia, named for its "bizarre and dreamlike quality," was one of numerous marine organisms to make its appearance during the early Cambrian Period.*

The Appearance and Disappearance of Organisms

At certain times in Earth's history, the number of different kinds of organisms has increased or decreased dramatically. These increases can happen because of increases in competition or environmental changes. *Hallucigenia,* shown in **Figure 3,** appeared in the Cambrian Period, when the number of different kinds of marine organisms greatly increased.

The diversity of organisms can decrease dramatically over a short period of time during a mass extinction. **Extinction** is the death of every member of a certain kind of organism. Gradual events, such as climate change and changes in ocean currents, can cause mass extinctions. Catastrophic events, such as the impact of an asteroid, can also cause mass extinctions.

extinction (ek STINGK shuhn) the death of every member of a species

Quick Lab

🐻
7.4.d
7.4.g

Timeline of Earth's History

1. Lay a **5 m strip of adding machine paper** flat on a hard surface. With a **pencil,** put a mark at the top of the paper. Near this mark write "Present time."

2. Using a **meterstick,** measure off 1 m sections from your first mark. At the first mark beyond "Present time," write "1 bya" (1 billion years ago), and at the second, write "2 bya." Continue marking 1 m sections until you have a mark labeled "4 bya."

3. Make a mark 4.6 m from "Present time," and label this mark "Earth forms, 4.6 bya."

4. Use a **colored pencil** to mark off and label the Cenozoic Era from the present time to 0.065 bya (6.5 cm from "Present time").

5. Use **another colored pencil** to mark off and label the Mesozoic Era from 0.065 bya to 0.25 bya (from the beginning of "Cenozoic Era" to 25 cm from the "Present time" mark).

6. Use **another colored pencil** to mark off and label the Paleozoic Era from 0.25 bya to 0.54 bya (from the beginning of "Mesozoic Era" to 54 cm from the "Present time" mark).

7. Use **another colored pencil** to mark off and label Precambrian time from 4.6 bya to 0.54 bya (from the beginning of "Paleozoic Era" to the "Earth forms, 4.6 bya" mark).

8. What percentage of the geologic time scale does Precambrian time represent?

9. Add to your timeline as you learn about events and life-forms in Precambrian time and in the Paleozoic, Mesozoic, and Cenozoic Eras.

⏱ 30 min

Universal Access • Differentiated Instruction

Basic Learners

Describing Eras Breaking down information in a chart can help struggling students make better sense of a complex topic. As you begin to discuss the geologic time scale, write the names *Cenozoic Era, Mesozoic Era, Paleozoic Era,* and *Precambrian time* on the board. Have students copy this information into their **Science Journal,** and instruct them to leave some space between each pair of labels. Have students fill in relevant information about each era and about Precambrian time as they learn about the major events that have occurred throughout geologic time. **LS Visual/Logical**

Precambrian Time—Life Develops

Precambrian time is the time from the formation of Earth 4.6 billion years ago to about 542 million years ago. Early Earth was very different from today's Earth. The early atmosphere did not contain oxygen as it does today. Intense radiation from the sun bombarded Earth's surface. Life on Earth began during this time. The first organisms appeared in Earth's oceans more than 3.6 billion years ago. These organisms were *prokaryotes*, or single-celled organisms that lack a nucleus.

Standards Check When did life first appear on Earth? 🐾 **7.4.d, 7.4.g**

Life and Oxygen

Cyanobacteria, a kind of prokaryotic organism, were some of the first organisms on Earth. Some cyanobacteria are shown in **Figure 4.** Cyanobacteria use sunlight to produce their own food through a process called *photosynthesis*. During this process, the cyanobacteria make oxygen. Cyanobacteria began to release oxygen gas into the oceans and the air.

Oxygen began to accumulate in the atmosphere. Some of the oxygen formed a new layer of gas in the upper atmosphere. This gas, called *ozone*, absorbs harmful radiation from the sun, as shown in **Figure 5.** Before ozone formed, life existed only in the oceans and underground. The new ozone layer reduced the amount of radiation that reached Earth's surface. The decrease in radiation allowed life to survive on land.

Organisms That Are More Complex

After about 1 billion years, organisms that were larger and more complex than prokaryotes appeared in the fossil record. These organisms, known as *eukaryotes*, contain a nucleus and other structures in their cells. Eukaryotes may have evolved into more complex multicellular organisms.

INTERNET ACTIVITY

A Fossil's Life

Can you discover how an organism lived by studying its fossil? Describe a day in the life of an extinct organism. Go to **go.hrw.com,** and type in the keyword HY7FOSW.

Figure 4 *Cyanobacteria are the simplest living organisms that use the sun's energy to produce their own food. They are still common on Earth and are very similar to the cyanobacteria that existed on Earth billions of years ago.*

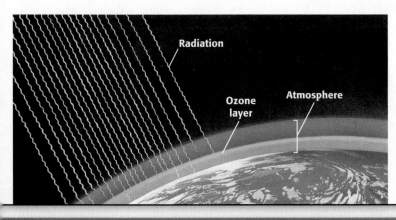

Radiation

Ozone layer

Atmosphere

Figure 5 *Oxygen in the atmosphere formed a layer of ozone, which absorbs harmful radiation from the sun.*

Discussion

Earth's Early Atmosphere Ask students, "How do scientists know when cyanobacteria began to produce oxygen? How do they know when ozone began to form?" (The presence of free oxygen changes characteristics of rocks and changed the kinds of living things that survived.) Then, ask students to describe what happens to iron in the presence of oxygen, especially if the iron is wet. (Iron rusts, or oxidizes, in the presence of oxygen.) Scientists can find signs of oxidized iron in the rock of ancient seabed sediments. Eventually, the oceans began to release oxygen into the atmosphere, and some of this oxygen in the air oxidized rocks on the surface. Over time, the ozone layer began to form from the oxygen, which allowed the survival of life on land, as seen in the fossil record. **LS Verbal**

ACTIVITY

Early Earth Illustrated
PORTFOLIO Have students use the information in this section and any other available information to create a poster that illustrates the events, organisms, and environments of ancient Earth. To ensure that a variety of time periods are represented, assign students different divisions of time. Display completed posters in chronological order around the room. You may wish to assist students who are working on particularly abstract early developments, such as the formation of the ozone layer. **LS Visual Co-op Learning**

Answer to Standards Check

Life first appeared on Earth more than 3.6 billion years ago. **7.4.d** (mastering), **7.4.g** (supporting)

Universal Access · Differentiated Instruction

Special Education Students

Extinction Because most of the animals that students are familiar with still exist on Earth, the idea of "extinction" may be difficult for some students to comprehend. Discuss with the class that the appearance and disappearance of species is not something that typically happens within a human life span. Explain that the process takes hundreds, thousands, or even millions of years, so it is not unusual that students would not notice the appearance or

disappearance of a species. Draw a long timeline on the board. In the middle of the timeline, write "20ᵗʰ and 21ˢᵗ centuries." At the far left of the timeline, write "1 billion years ago." At the far right of the timeline, write "1 billion years from now." Tell students that their lifetime and the lifetimes of their parents, grandparents, and great-grandparents fall in the middle of the timeline. Point out that over the span of 2 billion years, a couple of centuries is a very small amount of time. **LS Visual/Logical**

CONNECTION ACTIVITY
Language Arts

Writing **Prehistoric Newspapers**
As students read about the geologic time scale, encourage them to consider why scientists chose to divide geologic time in this way. Have students think about the important geologic, climatological, and biological differences between the eras. After students read about each era, have them write the front-page headlines for an imaginary newspaper that was printed at the close of each era. The headlines should detail the important events and characteristics of the era. (Sample answer: The front page of the *Mesozoic Times* might read, "Mammals Appear—Warm-Blooded" and "Furry Critters—Can We Trust Them?") Give students who wish to research more about geologic history the opportunity to write creative stories for each headline. **LS Verbal**

MISCONCEPTION ALERT

Creative Interpretations
Students may think that illustrations of dinosaurs and ancient environments are completely based on scientific information. Make students aware that such illustrations are based partly on artists' interpretations. For example, scientists are reasonably certain about the skeletal structure of many dinosaurs, but features such as skin coverings and color are unknown. *Tyrannosaurus rex* may have been green, spotted like a leopard, or striped like a tiger. Have students use existing birds and reptiles as models to suggest new colors and skin coverings for various dinosaurs, and have them share their models with the class.

The Paleozoic Era

The Paleozoic Era (PAY lee OH ZOH ik ER uh) began about 542 million years ago and ended about 251 million years ago. The word *Paleozoic* comes from Greek words that mean "ancient life." When scientists first named this era, they thought it held the earliest forms of life. Scientists now know that earlier forms of life existed, but less is known about those life-forms. Before the Paleozoic Era, most organisms lived in the oceans and left few fossils.

The Cambrian Explosion

The Cambrian Period was the first period in the Paleozoic Era. Many marine life-forms appeared during this period in what scientists call the "Cambrian explosion." This event was not an actual explosion. It was the appearance of many new and more-complex life-forms. For the first time, some had preservable hard parts such as shells and exoskeletons.

Life on Land

Rocks from the Paleozoic Era are rich in fossils of animals such as sponges, corals, snails, squids, and trilobites. Fishes, the earliest animals with backbones, also appeared during this era. During the middle of this era, plants, fungi, and animals colonized land.

By the end of the era, forests of giant ferns, horsetails, and conifers covered much of Earth. All major plant groups except for flowering plants appeared during this era. The plants provided food and shelter for animals. Fossils indicate that arthropods such as scorpions were the first land animals. Large salamander-like animals also evolved. Near the end of the era, reptiles and insects appeared. **Figure 6** is an artist's depiction of life in the Paleozoic Era.

The Permian Extinction

The largest known mass extinction was the Permian extinction. It took place about 251 million years ago, at the end of the Permian Period of the Paleozoic Era. Earth's continents had joined to form Pangaea, and shallow inland seas had disappeared. As many as 90% of marine species and 78% of land species had become extinct. The fossil record shows that groups such as reptiles and amphibians survived the Permian extinction.

Figure 6 *Organisms that first appeared in the Paleozoic Era include reptiles, amphibians, fishes, worms, and ferns.*

Universal Access • Differentiated Instruction

Basic Learners

Word Familiarity Students may have difficulty understanding text that contains a large number of unfamiliar words. Before students begin reading these two pages, help them become somewhat familiar with the pronunciations and meanings of unfamiliar words. On the board, write the following sentences:

1. The word *Paleozoic* comes from Greek words that mean "ancient life."

2. The Cambrian Period was the first part of the Paleozoic Era.

3. The Permian Period was at the end of the Paleozoic Era.

4. Pangaea was one giant landmass that included all of the land on Earth.

5. The word *Mesozoic* comes from Greek words that mean "middle life."

6. The Tertiary Period followed the Mesozoic Era.

As a group, practice reading the sentences aloud. **LS Verbal/Auditory**

The Mesozoic Era

The *Mesozoic Era* (MES oh ZOH ik ER uh) began about 251 million years ago. *Mesozoic* comes from Greek words meaning "middle life." Scientists think that the reptiles that survived the Permian extinction evolved into many reptile species in the Mesozoic Era. Therefore, the Mesozoic Era is commonly called the *Age of Reptiles.*

Life in the Mesozoic Era

Dinosaurs are the most well-known reptiles that lived during the Mesozoic Era. Dinosaurs dominated Earth for about 150 million years. Some had unique adaptations, such as ducklike bills for feeding or large spines on their bodies for defense. In addition to dinosaurs on land, giant marine reptiles swam in the oceans. The first birds also appeared during the Mesozoic Era. Scientists think that some dinosaurs were the ancestors of birds. The first mammals also appeared during the Mesozoic Era.

The most important plants during the early part of the Mesozoic Era were conifers, which formed large forests. Flowering plants appeared later in the Mesozoic Era. Some of the organisms of the Mesozoic Era are illustrated in **Figure 7.**

The Cretaceous-Tertiary Extinction

The Mesozoic Era ended about 65 million years ago. Around this time, all of the dinosaurs and about half of the animal and plant species became extinct. This event is called the *Cretaceous-Tertiary* (or *K-T*) *extinction* because it defines the boundary between the Cretaceous and Tertiary Periods. Scientists find evidence for this mass extinction in the disappearance of many types of fossils from the fossil record during this time.

What happened? According to one hypothesis, an object from our solar system hit Earth. The impact formed giant dust clouds and enough heat to cause worldwide fires. The dust and smoke blocked out some sunlight and caused many plants to die out. Without enough plants to eat, the plant-eating dinosaurs died out. As a result, the meat-eating dinosaurs that fed on the plant-eating dinosaurs died.

Standards Check What fossil evidence is there for the Cretaceous-Tertiary extinction? 🐾 **7.4.e, 7.4.g**

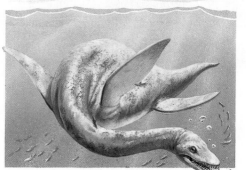

Figure 7 *The Mesozoic Era ended with the mass extinction of many of the large animals, such as the ankylosaur and the aquatic plesiosaur shown above.*

Answer to Standards Check

The fossil evidence for the K-T extinction includes the disappearance of all dinosaurs and about half of the plant and animal species from the fossil record. **7.4.e** (exceeding), **7.4.g** (supporting)

Close

Standards Focus

This **Standards Focus** provides you with a quick way to **assess, reteach,** and **re-assess** one or more concepts in the section.

Assess

1. How did the ozone layer allow organisms to live on land for the first time? (The ozone layer protects organisms from excessive solar radiation.) **7.4.e, 7.4.g**

Reteach

Geologic Time Scale Have students reproduce the geologic time scale from the beginning of this section in their **Science Journal.** Students should leave enough space so that they can add details about the history of life on Earth for each eon and era.

[LS] Verbal/Visual

Re-Assess

Making a Fossil History Book
Have students work independently to make construction-paper cutouts of plant and animal fossils that might be found in each era of Earth's history. Students should then annotate each cutout by describing the time period and environment in which the fossils formed.

[LS] Visual **7.4.d, 7.4.e, 7.4.g**

Wordwise

Using Roots Remind students of the words and meanings of *Paleozoic* (from the Greek root *paleo-,* meaning "ancient") and *Mesozoic* (from the Greek root *meso-,* meaning "middle"). Have students create a list of words that use *meso-* and *paleo-* as prefixes. Challenge students to identify and define the made-up words. (Examples of actual words: *paleontologist,* one who studies ancient bones; *mesosphere,* the layer of the atmosphere between the stratosphere and the thermosphere) [LS] Verbal/Logical

Figure 8 *Many types of mammals, including humans, appeared during the Cenozoic Era.*

Wordwise Cenozoic
The root *-cene* means "new" or "recent." The suffix *-zoic* means "pertaining to animals."

The Cenozoic Era

The *Cenozoic Era* (SEN uh ZOH ik ER uh) began about 65 million years ago and continues today. *Cenozoic* comes from Greek words meaning "recent life." Scientists have more information about the Cenozoic Era than about any of the previous eras. Because Cenozoic rocks formed on top of rocks from previous eras, many Cenozoic fossils are closer to Earth's surface. The closer the fossils are to the surface, the more likely they are to be found.

During the Cenozoic Era, many kinds of mammals, birds, insects, and flowering plants appeared. Some organisms that appeared in the Cenozoic Era are shown in **Figure 8.**

The Age of Mammals

The Cenozoic Era is sometimes called the *Age of Mammals.* Mammals have dominated the Cenozoic Era the way reptiles dominated the Mesozoic Era. Early Cenozoic mammals were small forest dwellers. Larger mammals appeared later in the era. Some of these larger mammals had long legs for running, teeth that were specialized for eating different kinds of food, and large brains. Cenozoic mammals have included mastodons, saber-toothed cats, camels, giant ground sloths, and horses. Humans appeared very late in the Cenozoic Era.

Standards Check What significant organisms appeared during the Cenozoic Era? **7.4.g**

The Cenozoic Era Today

The environment and landscapes that we see around us today developed during the Cenozoic Era. For example, the Alps and the Himalayas formed during this era. The climate has also changed many times during the Cenozoic Era. Earth's history includes some lengths of time called *ice ages,* during which the climate was very cold. During the ice ages, ice sheets and glaciers extended from Earth's poles. To survive, many organisms migrated toward the equator. Other organisms adapted to the cold or became extinct.

We are currently living in the Cenozoic Era. When will this era end? No one knows. In the future, geologists might draw the line at a time when life on Earth again undergoes major changes.

Universal Access · Differentiated Instruction

Advanced Learners/GATE

End of the Cenozoic Era? Ask interested students to write an essay that predicts the timing and cause of the end of the Cenozoic Era. Make sure that students understand that they should incorporate a logical major change on Earth in their predictions. [LS] Verbal/Logical

---

Answer to Standards Check

many kinds of insects, birds, flowering plants, and mammals, including humans **7.4.g** (mastering)

Summary

- The geologic time scale divides Earth's 4.6 billion–year history into time intervals. These intervals include eons, eras, periods, and epochs.
- At certain times in Earth's history, the number of different kinds of organisms has increased or decreased dramatically.
- Life on Earth developed more than 3.6 billion years ago, during Precambrian time. After cyanobacteria added oxygen to the atmosphere, more-complex forms of life evolved.
- A variety of marine organisms appeared at the beginning of the Paleozoic Era in what is called the Cambrian explosion. Near the end of the Paleozoic Era, the Permian extinction resulted in the disappearance of many organisms from the fossil record.
- Dinosaurs dominated Earth during the Mesozoic Era. They all became extinct during the Cretaceous-Tertiary extinction.
- Mammals have dominated the Cenozoic Era. Modern humans appeared during this era.

Using Vocabulary

1. Write an original definition for *extinction* and *geologic time scale*.

Understanding Concepts

2. **Listing** What are the major types of time intervals represented by the geologic time scale?

3. **Describing** Explain how cyanobacteria were important to the development of life on Earth.

4. **Listing** What kinds of environmental changes can cause mass extinctions?

5. **Describing** Describe the types of life that were common in the Paleozoic, Mesozoic, and Cenozoic Eras.

6. **Concluding** How do scientists study life-forms that are extinct?

7. **Applying** What environmental changes may have caused the Cretaceous-Tertiary extinction? What may have caused the changes?

8. **Identifying** About how much time elapsed between the formation of Earth and the appearance of the first life-forms?

Critical Thinking

9. **Making Inferences** Name three possible reasons why less is known about Precambrian life-forms than is known about more recent life.

10. **Analyzing Ideas** Why do scientists think the first organisms did not need oxygen to survive?

Math Skills

INTERPRETING GRAPHICS Use the figure below to answer the next question.

Phanerozoic Eon   Hadean Eon

Proterozoic Eon   Archean Eon

11. **Making Calculations** On the Earth-history clock shown, 1 h equals 383 million years, and 1 min equals 6.4 million years. In millions of years, how much more time is represented by the Proterozoic Eon than by the Phanerozoic Eon?

Challenge

12. **Making Comparisons** Describe a future event or sequence of events that might mark the end of the Cenozoic Era.

Internet Resources

For a variety of links related to this chapter, go to www.scilinks.org

Topic: Geologic Time; Geologic Time Scale

SciLinks code: HY70668; HY70669

7. The K-T extinction may have taken place when the impact of a large body, such as a meteorite or asteroid, formed large clouds of dust and smoke in the atmosphere. These clouds could have caused a decrease in the amount of sunlight that reached Earth's surface. As a result, some plants to died out, then some plant-eating animals died out, and then some meat-eating animals died out. **7.4.g** (mastering)

8. About 1 billion years elapsed between the formation of Earth (4.6 bya) and the appearance of the first life-forms (about 3.6 bya). **7.4.d** (mastering)

9. Sample answer: Less is known about Precambrian life because most Precambrian life-forms had soft body parts that were not usually preserved. Also, Precambrian life was mostly very small organisms, and Precambrian rocks are not as common as rocks from more recent geologic time. **7.4.g** (supporting)

10. Scientists think that the first organisms did not need oxygen to survive because Earth's early atmosphere did not contain oxygen. **7.4.e** (exceeding)

11. 25×6.4 million years $= 160$ million years; 7×6.4 million years $= 44.8$ million years; 160 million years $- 44.8$ million years $= 115.2$ million years **7.4.g** (exceeding)

12. Sample answer: A change in climate that causes a mass extinction might mark the end of the Cenozoic Era. Global warming might change the temperature of the oceans and cause extinction of many species of ocean life. **7.4.g** (exceeding)

Section Review Standards Guide

	Supporting	Mastering	Exceeding
7.4.d		8	
7.4.e		6	10
7.4.g	1, 2, 4, 9	3, 5, 7	11, 12

Section Resources

- Directed Reading A **BASIC** (Also in Spanish), B **GENERAL**
- Interactive Reader and Study Guide
- Section Quiz **GENERAL** (Also in Spanish)
- Section Review **GENERAL** (Also in Spanish)
- Vocabulary and Section Summary A **BASIC** (Also in Spanish), B **GENERAL**

Answers to Section Review

1. The geologic time scale is a method used to divide Earth's history into shorter intervals. Extinction occurs if every member of a species dies. **7.4.g** (supporting)

2. The major types of time intervals on the geologic time scale are eons, eras, periods, and epochs. **7.4.g** (supporting)

3. Cyanobacteria produced oxygen that entered the early atmosphere, which did not previously contain oxygen. **7.4.g** (mastering)

4. Mass extinctions can be caused by climate change, changes in ocean currents, and changes in the atmosphere that change the temperature. **7.4.g** (supporting)

5. Paleozoic Era: Common life-forms included marine life such as sponges, trilobites, and fishes; fern, horsetail, and conifer forests; and arthropods, reptiles, and insects. Mesozoic Era: Common life-forms included many reptile species, including dinosaurs and large conifer forests. Cenozoic Era: Common life-forms included mammals, birds, insects, and flowering plants. **7.4.g** (mastering)

6. Scientists study extinct life forms by studying fossils of these life forms and trace fossils of their activities. **7.4.e** (mastering)

Skills Practice Lab

Skills Practice Lab

Teacher Notes

In this lab, students will create maps of fossils in two rock layers. Students will then use the fossil evidence to infer what the past environments were like in the two time periods and how the environment changed over time (covers standards 7.4.e and 7.7.d).

Time Required

One 45-minute class period

Lab Ratings

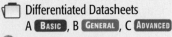

EASY ———————————— HARD

Teacher Prep 🜊
Student Set-Up 🜊
Concept Level 🜊🜊🜊
Clean Up 🜊

Materials

The materials listed on the student page are enough for one student or one group of students.

Preparation Notes

To save time, you may want to provide students with grids that already have A–J across the top and 1–10 down the side. To help students who struggle with the map-making procedure, model the procedure for the first one or two fossils by using an overhead transparency or the board. You may also wish to have several fossils on hand for students to examine. Ideally, each fossil should include information about its age and where it was collected. Allow students to make inferences about the original environment of each fossilized organism.

OBJECTIVES

Map locations of fossils found in two rock layers.

Determine what past environments may have been like based on the fossil record in the area of your maps.

MATERIALS

- paper, graph, 1 cm grid (2 sheets)
- pencil
- pencil, blue

7.4.e Students know fossils provide evidence of how life and environmental conditions have changed.

Investigation and Experimentation
7.7.d Construct scale models, maps, and appropriately labeled diagrams to communicate scientific knowledge (e.g., motion of Earth's plates and cell structure).

Interpreting Fossil Finds

At a remote desert site, a scientist searched for fossils in two layers of sedimentary rock. In addition to identifying each fossil, she recorded its location by using map coordinates consisting of a letter and a number. She also noted whether the fossil was found in the upper or lower rock layer. The data she collected are shown in Table 1.

Table 1	Locations of Fossils Uncovered at Site		
Rock layer	**Shark**	**Crab**	**Fern**
Upper layer	A4, B1, C2, C5, D3, E1	A5, B6, C6, D4, F1, F3	B9, E8, H5, H9, I2, J7
Lower layer	A1, B4, D2, D7, E5, E10, G3, G6, I2, J5	G7, G9, H10, I6, J7	I8, J9, J10

Procedure

1. Use your graph paper to create two maps of the fossil site, similar to Table 2. Each map will be formed by a grid pattern made up of 10 rows and 10 columns. The two maps should be the same size.

Table 2	Location of Fossils in Rock Layer									
	A	B	C	D	E	F	G	H	I	J
1										
2										
3										
4										
5										
6										
7										
8										
9										
10										

DO NOT WRITE IN BOOK

Lab Resources

📁 Differentiated Datasheets
A **BASIC**, B **GENERAL**, C **ADVANCED**

💿 Classroom Lab Video/DVD

💿 Holt Lab Generator CD-ROM

Search for any lab by topic, standard, difficulty level, or time. Edit any lab to fit your needs, or create your own labs. Use the Lab Materials QuickList software to customize your lab materials list.

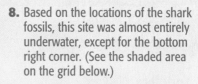

2 Use letters *A* through *J* to label the columns along the top of each grid. Use numbers 1 through 10 to label the rows along the side of each grid.

3 Label one grid "Location of Fossils in the Upper Rock Layer." Label the other grid "Location of Fossils in the Lower Rock Layer."

4 Begin with the map of the upper rock layer. For each fossil, mark a letter in pencil (*S* for a shark fossil, *C* for a crab fossil, and *F* for a fern fossil) in the square that corresponds to the coordinates listed in Table 1.

5 Repeat step 4 on your other map for the lower rock layer.

Analyze the Results

6 **Classifying** Describe the environment in which each organism was likely to have lived.

7 **Examining Data** Examine the map of the fossils found in the upper layer. According to the fossil distribution, which part of this site was probably underwater when these organisms died? How can you tell? Color this area of your map blue.

8 **Examining Data** Examine the map of the fossils found in the lower layer. Which part of this site was probably underwater when these organisms died? How can you tell? Color this area blue.

Draw Conclusions

9 **Drawing Conclusions** Which is older, the upper layer or the lower layer of sedimentary rock? Explain your answer.

10 **Drawing Conclusions** Which came first in Earth's history, the organisms and environment in the upper layer or those in the lower layer of sedimentary rock? Explain your answer.

11 **Interpreting Information** Before mapping the fossil finds, one scientist thought that sea level had risen between the time that the two rock layers formed. Did the fossil distribution support her hypothesis? Explain your answer.

Big Idea Question

12 **Applying Conclusions** How can fossils provide evidence of how environmental conditions change over time?

Horseshoe crab fossil

Fossilized shark teeth

Fern fossil

8. Based on the locations of the shark fossils, this site was almost entirely underwater, except for the bottom right corner. (See the shaded area on the grid below.)

	A	B	C	D	E	F	G	H	I	J
1	S									
2				S					S	
3							S			
4	S									
5					S					S
6							S		C	
7			S				C		C	
8									F	
9					C					F
10				S				C		F

Draw Conclusions

9. The lower layer of sedimentary rock is older, because the sediments of this layer were deposited first. The upper layer of sedimentary rock formed from sediments deposited on top of the older layer of sediments.

10. Organisms and environments in the lower layer came first in Earth's history, because the lower layer is the older layer.

11. no; The fossil evidence in this area does not support the hypothesis that sea level rose between the time that the two rock layers formed. The distribution of marine fossils suggests a drop in sea level.

Big Idea Question

12. Sample answer: Ancient species, like living species, were found only in certain environments. By comparing the distribution of fossils from one time period to another, scientists can draw conclusions about changes in the environment.

Analyze the Results

6. The sharks probably lived in deeper ocean water, while the crabs probably lived in shallow ocean water or a beach environment. The ferns probably lived on land in a moist environment.

7. The part where the sharks lived was probably underwater because sharks live only in water. The area where the crabs lived could have been shallow ocean water or the beach. (See the shaded area on the grid to the right.)

	A	B	C	D	E	F	G	H	I	J
1		S			S	C				
2			S					F		
3				S		C				
4	S			C						
5	C		S					F		
6		C	C							
7										F
8				F						
9		F					F			
10										

Marilyn K. Bachman
Montecito Union School
Santa Barbara, California

Science Skills Activity

Investigation and Experimentation

7.7.d Construct scale models, maps, and appropriately labeled diagrams to communicate scientific knowledge (e.g., motion of Earth's plates and cell structure).

Teacher Notes

This activity has students research the process of continental drift and make models to show the motion of Earth's plates (covers standard 7.7.d). Teachers may want to have some sets of continents already cut out to save time. Once students have positioned their models to show the breakup of Pangaea, they can modify their models to predict the future positions of the continents. As they continue to slide the continents, students should see that the continents continue to move farther away from each other. On a flat surface, the continents could continue on this trajectory forever, but on the spherical surface of Earth, the continents would eventually collide again, forming a new supercontinent. Ask students to modify their models to show this. (With help from others, students could move their continents along the surface of a ball.) If animation software is available, have students do the activity using the software.

Answers to You Try It!

1.–4. Answers may vary. Students should use their models to show how the continents may have fit together and then to show the movement of continents starting with Pangaea and progressing to present locations.

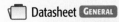

📄 Datasheet **GENERAL**

Also editable on the Holt Lab Generator CD-ROM

Constructing Models

▶ Tutorial

The following general instructions will show you one way to understand and model a process. You can also communicate scientific knowledge to others this way.

1 Research Read about the process in which you are interested. Start with your textbook and encyclopedias. Then, find written information in other places, including your library and the Internet. Be sure that your information comes from reliable sources. Take notes as you read to help you understand and remember what you have learned. Do more research with maps, videos, and other resources. If possible, talk with someone knowledgeable who can tell you about the process.

2 Make a Model Make a model of your process. A model could be
- a physical model such as a globe, a map, or a sculpture
- a mathematical model such as a graph or an equation

3 Use the Model for Understanding Use your model to better understand the process that you are studying by using the model to simulate movement or interactions.

4 Communicate Use your model to explain the process to another person.

▶ You Try It!

Learn about the breakup of the supercontinent Pangaea, which started about 245 million years ago. Then, make a model of the process and communicate your results to others.

1 Research Research continental drift and the breakup of Pangaea.

2 Make a Model Gather a copy of a world map that shows the Himalayas, a pencil, and a pair of scissors. Label Africa, Antarctica, Australia, Eurasia, India, North America, and South America. Cut out each continent. Cut India from Eurasia along the Himalayas.

3 Use the Model for Understanding
- Starting with the continents in their current positions, move them in ways that seem to make their coastlines fit together.
- Starting with the continents in the positions they occupied 245 million years ago in Pangaea, move them away from each other into their present locations.

4 Communicate Using your model of the continents, explain to a partner how Pangaea changed into the continents on Earth today. Then, listen to your partner's explanation of the same process. Include in your discussions evidence for continental drift and how this process affected life and climate.

Universal Access · Differentiated Instruction

Advanced Learners/GATE

Before Pangaea? The farther back in time we look, the more speculative things become. However, some evidence exists for supercontinents that predate Pangaea: Rodinia and Pannotia. Have advanced students research these ancient supercontinents and create a model that shows the progression from Rodinia to Pangaea. **LS** Logical

Special Education Students

Partnering Pangaea For some students, this activity will be easier if the world map already has the continents labeled. Also, some students do not have the physical dexterity needed to use scissors. Accommodate these students by having the class work in pairs to create the models. Pair students who have limited physical dexterity with those whose dexterity is not compromised. Make sure that both partners have tasks to perform. **LS** Interpersonal

Chapter Summary

The Big Idea Evidence from rocks allows us to understand the evolution of life on Earth.

Section

Vocabulary

1 Looking at Fossils

Key Concept Fossils provide evidence of how life and environmental conditions have changed.

- Evidence of past life is preserved as fossils in sedimentary rock and in other materials.
- The study of fossils reveals information about how Earth's environments and organisms have changed.
- Index fossils can be used to date rock layers.

Fossils provide evidence about organisms from Earth's past.

fossil p. 264
trace fossil p. 266
index fossil p. 268

2 Earth's Changing Continents

Key Concept Movements of Earth's tectonic plates have affected climate, geographic connections, and the distribution of organisms.

- Earth's continents have moved around Earth's surface throughout Earth's history and have only recently arrived at their current locations.
- Rocks and fossils provide evidence of continental drift. They also provide evidence of the changes in life and climate that have occurred during Earth's history.

Earth's continents move over Earth's surface.

plate tectonics p. 270
continental drift p. 272

3 Time Marches On

Key Concept Life has changed through Earth's history as life-forms have developed, or evolved, and become extinct.

- The geologic time scale organizes Earth's history into intervals of time.
- Life first appeared on Earth more than 3.6 billion years ago.
- Life-forms changed as environmental changes happened during the Paleozoic, Mesozoic, and Cenozoic Eras.

Many life-forms have developed and become extinct during Earth's history.

geologic time scale p. 276
extinction p. 278

Review Resources

- 📁 Reinforcement Worksheet **BASIC**
- 📁 Critical Thinking Worksheet **ADVANCED**
- 📁 Chapter Review **GENERAL** (Also in Spanish)
- 📖 Standards Review Workbook (Also in Spanish)
- 📖 Study Guide A **BASIC** (Also in Spanish), B **GENERAL**

Assessment Resources

- 📁 Chapter Tests A **BASIC**, B **GENERAL** (Also in Spanish), C **ADVANCED**
- 📁 Standards Assessment **GENERAL**

Chapter Summary

SUPER SUMMARY

Have students connect the major concepts in this chapter through an interactive Super Summary. Visit go.hrw.com and type in the keyword HY7FOSS to access the Super Summary for this chapter.

Identifying Roots

Recent Epochs Word Match
Each of the epochs within the Cenozoic Era end with the root word *-cene*, which means "recent." Have students research the meanings of the prefixes of each epoch in the Cenozoic Era. (See **Figure 2** on page 277.) (*holo-* means "whole or entire"; *pleisto-* means "most"; *plio-* means "more"; *mio-* means "less"; *oligo-* means "small"; *eo-* means "dawn"; and *paleo-* means "old") Then, have students use these newly defined terms to create a word-matching game. Students can then exchange and complete the word games. **LS** Verbal/Interpersonal

Focus on Reading

Expanding Summaries Have students read the bulleted summaries presented on this page. Ask students to add one more important point to each section of the summary after rereading the information in the section pages. Students can then share their additional points with the class. **LS** Verbal

Chapter Review
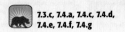
7.3.c, 7.4.a, 7.4.c, 7.4.d,
7.4.e, 7.4.f, 7.4.g

Assignment Guide

Section	Questions
1	1, 4, 10, 26
2	8–9, 11, 15–17, 19–20, 22–23
3	2–3, 5–7, 12–14, 18, 21, 24–25, 27–28

Answers

Using Vocabulary

1. b

2. The geologic time scale is the method used to divide Earth's history into manageable parts. **7.4.g** (supporting)

3. The death of every member of a species is called *extinction*. **7.4.g** (supporting)

Understanding Concepts

4. d **7.4.c** (supporting), **7.4.e** (supporting)

5. c **7.4.g** (supporting)

6. a **7.4.g** (mastering)

7. d **7.4.g** (mastering)

8. d **7.4.a** (supporting), **7.4.f** (mastering)

9. c **7.4.f** (supporting)

10. Sample answer: Fossils form when an organism is preserved in sediment that becomes sedimentary rock, when an organism is preserved in ice, and when organisms become trapped in tree sap which hardens into amber. **7.3.c** (supporting), **7.4.c** (supporting), **7.4.e** (supporting)

11. Scientists use fossils to reconstruct past climates and see how climates have changed, and to see whether an area was part of an ocean floor or dry land in the past. **7.4.e** (mastering)

12. Precambrian time: prokaryotes and eukaryotes; Paleozoic Era: marine life and land plants; Mesozoic Era: small mammals and birds; Cenozoic Era: large mammals and humans **7.4.g** (mastering)

13. Scientists think that a large asteroid struck Earth at the end of the Mesozoic and that the resulting climate change contributed to a mass extinction. **7.4.g** (mastering)

Organize

Four-Corner Fold Review the FoldNote that you created at the beginning of the chapter. Add to or correct the FoldNote based on what you have learned.

Using Vocabulary

1 **Academic Vocabulary** In the sentence "Fossils provide evidence of how life has changed," what does the word *evidence* mean?
   a. information presented in a legal proceeding
   b. information showing whether an idea is true or valid
   c. a separation or division
   d. a visual aid

Use a term from the chapter to correct each sentence below.

2 Continental drift is the method used to divide Earth's history into manageable parts.

3 The death of every member of a species is called an index fossil.

Understanding Concepts

Multiple Choice

4 Which of the following is a trace fossil?
   a. an insect preserved in amber
   b. a mammoth frozen in ice
   c. wood replaced by minerals
   d. a dinosaur footprint

5 The largest divisions of geologic time are called
   a. periods.
   b. eras.
   c. eons.
   d. epochs.

6 The first life on Earth appeared in
   a. Precambrian time.
   b. the Paleozoic Era.
   c. the Mesozoic Era.
   d. the Cenozoic Era.

7 In which time period are we currently living?
   a. Precambrian time
   b. the Paleozoic Era
   c. the Mesozoic Era
   d. the Cenozoic Era

8 Movements of continental and oceanic plates during Earth's history have
   a. affected the distribution of organisms.
   b. caused changes in climate.
   c. caused changes in geographic connections.
   d. All of the above

9 At a divergent plate boundary, tectonic plates
   a. move toward each other.
   b. slide horizontally against each other.
   c. move apart from each other.
   d. crumple up to form mountain ranges.

Short Answer

10 **Describing** Describe three processes by which fossils form.

11 **Summarizing** Explain two ways in which scientists use fossils to determine environmental change.

12 **Listing** List two important groups of organisms that appeared during each time interval: Precambrian time, the Paleozoic Era, the Mesozoic Era, and the Cenozoic Era.

13 **Describing** Describe the event that some scientists think caused the mass extinction at the end of the Mesozoic Era.

14 **Listing** How long has life existed on Earth?

15 **Classifying** Give one example of how continental drift has caused a change in geographic connections and one example of how continental drift has caused a change in climate.

16 **Describing** Give an example of how continental drift has affected the distribution of organisms during Earth's history.

Writing Skills

17 **Writing from Research** Find out more about *Mesosaurus,* and write a one-page report about this reptile.

14. Life has existed on Earth for more than 3.6 billion years. **7.4.d** (mastering)

15. Sample answer: Continental drift caused a change in geographic connections when the Panama Land Bridge formed and connected North and South America. Continental drift caused a change in climate when the land that is now Antarctica was left surrounded by cold water as other landmasses drifted away, and Antarctica became much colder than it had been. **7.4.f** (mastering)

16. Continental drift affected the distribution of organisms in North and South America when the Panama Land Bridge formed about 3 million years ago. Animals could move back and forth between the two continents for the first time, and organisms in the Atlantic and Pacific Oceans were isolated from each other. **7.4.f** (mastering)

Writing Skills

17. Students should include information about *Mesosaurus* and about how the location of *Mesosaurus* fossils provides evidence for continental drift.

Critical Thinking

18 **Concept Mapping** Use the following terms to create a concept map: *geologic time scale, fossils, rock record, eons, eras, periods, epochs, Earth's history, life on Earth,* and *environmental conditions.*

19 **Applying Concepts** Identify how fossil evidence supports plate tectonics and continental drift.

20 **Analyzing Processes** Explain how the breakup of Pangaea affected climate and organisms.

21 **Making Inferences** How does the fossil record provide evidence for the Cretaceous-Tertiary extinction?

INTERPRETING GRAPHICS The chart below shows data about fossilized teeth that were found within a series of rock layers. Use the chart below to answer the next two questions.

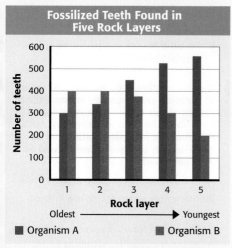

Fossilized Teeth Found in Five Rock Layers

Number of teeth (y-axis: 0 to 600)
Rock layer (x-axis: 1 to 5)
Oldest ——→ Youngest
■ Organism A   ■ Organism B

22 **Evaluating Data** Describe the changes in the populations of organisms A and B that are suggested by the evidence in the chart.

23 **Forming Hypotheses** Develop a hypothesis to explain these population changes.

24 **Identifying Relationships** Describe conditions that can cause the number of species to increase dramatically and conditions that can cause the number of species to decrease dramatically.

25 **Identifying Relationships** How does the Cretaceous-Tertiary extinction relate to the Age of Mammals?

26 **Identifying Relationships** Two undisturbed rock layers are being studied by paleontologists. One of the layers is directly on top of the other, and both layers contain fossils. Describe the relative ages of the layers, and tell which layer is likely to contain fossils of life-forms that are similar to living organisms.

Math Skills

INTERPRETING GRAPHICS Use the diagram of a portion of the geologic time scale below to answer the following question.

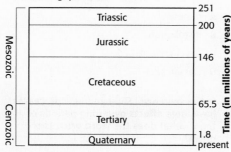

Mesozoic	Triassic	251
	Jurassic	200
		146
	Cretaceous	
		65.5
Cenozoic	Tertiary	
	Quaternary	1.8 present

Time (in millions of years)

27 **Making Calculations** Which period shown in the diagram was the longest? How many years did that period last?

Challenge

28 **Applying Concepts** Identify a type of organism that is found in the fossil record of a different geologic era but that is still living on Earth today. Also identify a type of organism that has become extinct. Compare the two organisms, and try to explain why one has survived and the other has become extinct.

My hypothesis is that both A and B were predators, but that A adapted better to a gradually cooler climate. As the climate became cooler, organism B migrated to warmer areas, and the population of organism A increased because of the decrease in competition for food. **7.4.e** (exceeding)

24. The number of species can increase dramatically when competition increases or if the environment changes in ways that are favorable to certain organisms. The number of species can decrease dramatically if climate changes are not favorable for existing species, such as when a catastrophic event causes a sudden change in climate. **7.4.g** (supporting)

25. During the K-T extinction, dinosaurs became extinct. The disappearance of animals that had flourished during the Mesozoic Era may have allowed a variety of mammals to evolve during the Cenozoic Era. **7.4.g** (mastering)

26. The rock layer on top is younger than the layer on the bottom. Because the top layer is younger, the fossils in the top layer are more likely to be similar to living organisms. **7.3.c** (exceeding), **7.4.c** (exceeding)

Math Skills

27. the Cretaceous Period; It lasted 80.5 million years. **7.4.g** (supporting)

Challenge

28. Students' answers should identify an organism from another era, such as the Mesozoic Era, that is still living on Earth. Most will be an insect, a plant, or something like a crocodile. Students should identify an organism, such as a type of dinosaur, that has become extinct. Students should explain why they think one organism survived and the other became extinct. **7.4.g** (exceeding)

| **Chapter Review Standards Guide** | | | |
	Supporting	**Mastering**	**Exceeding**
7.3.c	10		26
7.4.a	8, 19		
7.4.c	4, 10, 18		26
7.4.d		14	
7.4.e	4, 10, 18	11, 19, 21	22, 23
7.4.f	9	8, 15, 16, 20	
7.4.g	2, 3, 5, 18, 24, 27	6, 7, 12, 13, 25	20, 21, 28

Critical Thinking

18. An answer to this question can be found at the end of this book. **7.4.c** (supporting), **7.4.e** (supporting), **7.4.g** (supporting)

19. Fossil evidence shows that the continents were once joined in a supercontinent. **7.4.a** (supporting), **7.4.e** (mastering)

20. The breakup of Pangaea affected climate as landmasses drifted to different latitudes where they received more or less of the sun's energy. Other landmasses were affected because they were isolated. For example, Antarctica became colder after other landmasses drifted away and Antarctica was surrounded by cold water.

Organisms were affected by continental drift because climates may have changed and because changing geographic connections either separated the organisms in new ways or allowed them to travel to new areas. **7.4.f** (mastering), **7.4.g** (exceeding)

21. The fossil record provides evidence for the K-T extinction because many types of fossils disappeared from the fossil record at that time. **7.4.e** (mastering), **7.4.g** (exceeding)

22. The number of A organisms increased and the number of B organisms decreased. **7.4.e** (exceeding)

23. Sample answer: Because these changes happened in different rock layers, the changes probably happened over long periods of time.

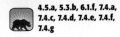
Teacher Notes

To provide practice under more realistic testing conditions, give students 20 min to answer all of the questions in this assessment.

Answer Key

Question Number	Correct Answer
1	D
2	A
3	B
4	B
5	C
6	D
7	D
8	A
9	B
10	C
11	C
12	A
13	C
14	D
15	B
16	A

Standards Guide

	Supporting	Mastering	Exceeding
4.5.a		15	
5.3.b		14	
6.1.f			16
7.4.a	4		12
7.4.c	5, 7		
7.4.d	2	10	
7.4.e	2		11
7.4.f	3, 6, 13		8, 12
7.4.g	1	9	

📋 Standards Assessment **GENERAL**

📋 Teacher Notes for Standards Assessment contain a longer Assessment Doctor and Diagnostic Teaching Tips.

Standards Assessment

4.5.a, 5.3.b, 6.1.f, 7.4.a, 7.4.c, 7.4.d, 7.4.e, 7.4.f, 7.4.g

REVIEWING ACADEMIC VOCABULARY

1 Which of the following words is the closest in meaning to the word *significant*?

- A minor
- B signify
- C identify
- D important

2 In the sentence "Fossils provide evidence of how life on Earth has changed," what does the word *evidence* mean?

- A data showing whether an idea is true
- B signal of changes to come
- C method of investigation
- D description of a situation

3 Which of the following words means "the geographic arrangement of organisms"?

- A remote
- B distribution
- C development
- D classification

4 In the sentence "Slow geologic processes have large effects over long periods of time," what does the word *processes* mean?

- A prepares, treats, or converts
- B series of occurrences that produce change
- C moves forward in an orderly way
- D parts that project from the main body

5 Which of the following words means "a repeating series of changes"?

- A experiment
- B effect
- C cycle
- D occurrence

REVIEWING CONCEPTS

6 What type of plate boundary is shown in the diagram above?

- A mantle boundary
- B divergent boundary
- C transform boundary
- D convergent boundary

7 Why are fossils from the Cenozoic Era, which began 65 million years ago, the easiest to find?

- A The number of species greatly increased during this era.
- B Life on Earth, in the form of cyanobacteria, began during this era.
- C Fossils of the largest creatures are from this era.
- D Fossils from this era are found in layers closest to Earth's surface.

8 A small reptile called *Mesosaurus* lived 260 million years ago and is now extinct. Fossils of this reptile have been found in both South America and southern Africa. Which of the following statements best explains why the fossils were found on both continents?

- A At one time, the continents were joined.
- B The reptile swam across the Atlantic Ocean.
- C The reptile traveled across a land bridge.
- D People brought the reptile to South America.

➕ ASSESSMENT DOCTOR

Question 1: The correct answer is D. Something that is significant is important. Significant developments in life or geology help divide Earth's history into chunks of time.

Question 2: The correct answer is A. Evidence is proof that something is true. While evidence might include a description of a situation, evidence is more than a description.

Question 3: The correct answer is B. Distribution is the geographic range of an organism. Classification can be used to describe an organism, but classification refers to characteristics of the organism itself and not its geographic range.

Question 4: The correct answer is B. The word *process* in this sentence refer to series of occurrences that produce change. *Processes* can be used as a verb to mean "prepares, treats, or converts," but that usage does not fit into the sentence.

9 Which of the following life-forms dominated the Mesozoic Era?

A mammals

B dinosaurs

C marine creatures

D one-celled organisms

10 When did the first organisms most likely appear on Earth?

A 251 million years ago

B 542 million years ago

C 3.6 billion years ago

D 4.6 billion years ago

11 Which of the following provides evidence that environmental conditions on Earth have changed?

A A fossilized footprint is found in lava rock.

B An insect fossil is found in amber.

C A marine fossil is found on a mountaintop.

D A dinosaur fossil is found in sedimentary rock.

12 If two tectonic plates form a divergent boundary on a continent and slowly move apart for millions of years, which of the following is most likely to happen?

A A new ocean will develop.

B A fault line will be created.

C A line of volcanoes will appear.

D A mountain chain will form.

13 Every year, Earth's lithospheric plates move between 2 cm and 5 cm. What causes these plates to move?

A currents in the ocean

B earthquakes in the ocean

C movement in Earth's mantle

D volcanoes under Earth's crust

REVIEWING PRIOR LEARNING

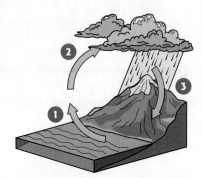

14 The diagram above shows the water cycle. What process in the water cycle is found at point 2 in the diagram?

A evaporation

B transpiration

C runoff

D condensation

15 Which of these processes slowly changes Earth's surface?

A landslide

B erosion

C earthquake

D volcanic eruption

16 The San Andreas fault is a major fault line in California. Why does this fault exist?

A It is the transform boundary of tectonic plates.

B A strong earthquake split the tectonic plate.

C It is the convergent boundary of tectonic plates.

D There are volcanoes under the tectonic plate.

Standards Assessment

Question 9: The correct answer is B. The Mesozoic Era is often called the *Age of Reptiles.* Mammals were just starting to appear in the Mesozoic Era.

Question 10: The correct answer is C. The first organisms appeared on Earth about 3.6 billion years ago. They were simple prokaryotes.

Question 11: The correct answer is C. Finding marine fossils on a mountaintop suggests that an ocean environment once existed where a mountain is now. This kind of fossil evidence supports the theory that environmental conditions on Earth have changed.

Question 12: The correct answer is A. When two continental plates diverge for millions of years, an ocean will form between the continents.

Question 13: The correct answer is C. Tectonic plates move because they are resting upon Earth's mantle, which is slowly moving by convection.

Question 14: The correct answer is D. Condensation takes place when water vapor cools and changes into droplets that form clouds. Condensation is shown at point 2 in the diagram.

Question 15: The correct answer is B. Erosion is a slow process that is not easily detected but that changes Earth's surface slowly over a long period of time. Landslides, earthquakes, and volcanic eruptions are all processes that happen quickly.

Question 16: The correct answer is A. The San Andreas fault is a transform boundary where two plates are sliding past each other horizontally. Transform boundaries can cause earthquakes, but earthquakes do not cause transform boundaries to form.

Question 5: The correct answer is C. A cycle is a repeating series of changes. An occurrence is something that happens or takes place, but an occurrence does not necessarily involve a series or repetition of the events.

Question 6: The correct answer is D. The boundary shown is a convergent boundary at which oceanic lithosphere is sinking below continental lithosphere.

Question 7: The correct answer is D. The Cenozoic Era is the most recent era. Fossils of organisms from this time period are found in layers of rock that are often more accessible to geologists than some older layers of rock are.

Question 8: The correct answer is A. Scientists think that the reptile lived during a time when all of the continents were joined. Later, the continents split apart and oceans formed between them.

Scientific Discoveries

Background

Since the 1990s, well-preserved fossils of dinosaurs that have featherlike structures have been found in northern China. For many vertebrate paleontologists, these fossils provide support for the theory that birds are descended from theropods, a group of dinosaurs that includes *Velociraptor*. Paleontologists think that the "feathered" dinosaurs were flightless and that the feathers were used for warmth or display.

Place to Visit

ACTIVITY

Cats Then and Now The saber-toothed cat, or *Smilodon*, was about the size of a lion, but weighed twice as much, and had 15 cm long canine teeth. Have students create a poster that compares different species of wild cats, both living and extinct. In their posters, students should include the size of each type of cat and where the animal is (or was) found. Also, for extinct cats, have students indicate the time period when the animal lived.

Science in Action

Scientific Discoveries

Feathered Dinosaurs

In 1996, a Chinese farmer broke open a rock that he found in an ancient dry lake. What he found inside the rock became one of the most exciting paleontological discoveries of the 20th century. Preserved inside were the remains of a dinosaur. The dinosaur had a large head; powerful jaws; sharp, jagged teeth; and, most importantly, a row of featherlike structures along its backbone.

Scientists named the dinosaur *Sinosauropteryx*, or "Chinese dragon wing." Since the discovery of *Sinosauropteryx*, other fossils have been found that provide evidence that some dinosaurs had feathers. These discoveries lend support to the hypothesis that birds and dinosaurs shared a common ancestor.

Language Arts ACTIVITY

Paleontologists often give dinosaurs names that describe something unusual about the animal's head, body, feet, or size. The names have Greek or Latin roots. Research the names of some dinosaurs, and find out what the names mean. In your **Science Journal**, create a list of dinosaur names and their meanings.

Place to Visit

La Brea Tar Pits

Fierce roars rumble through the air. A hungry saber-toothed cat has pounced on a young bison. Suddenly, the roars turn into panicked yowls. The big cat is stuck in asphalt! Along with the bison, she will die of exhaustion and thirst while trying to free herself.

Scenes like this happened 25,000 years ago in what is now Los Angeles, California. Natural tar deposits trapped millions of animals during the late Pleistocene Epoch. You can visit the La Brea Tar Pits and see fossils of these animals at the Page Museum. Visitors to the La Brea Tar Pits in Los Angeles can see fossils that have been discovered there, can watch scientists at work, and can watch a film that shows what scientists think downtown Los Angeles looked like when saber-toothed cats ruled!

Math ACTIVITY

Since 1906, fossils of 231 species of vertebrate animals, 159 species of plants, and 234 species of invertebrate animals have been identified at the La Brea Tar Pits. What is the ratio of vertebrate to invertebrate fossil species that have been found? What is the ratio of plant to animal species? Show your work in your **Science Journal**.

Answer to Language Arts Activity
Answers may vary.

Answer to Math Activity
The ratio of vertebrate to invertebrate species found is 231:234, or about 1:1 (0.99); the ratio of plants to animals (231 + 234 = 465) is 159:465, or about 1:3 (0.340).

People in Science

Lizzie May

Amateur Paleontologist For Lizzie May, summer vacations have meant trips into the Alaskan wilderness with her stepfather, geologist and paleontologist Kevin May. The purpose of these trips has not been merely for fun. Instead, Kevin and Lizzie have been exploring the Alaskan wilderness for the remains of ancient life—dinosaurs, in particular.

At age 22, Lizzie May has gained the reputation of being Alaska's most famous young paleontologist. It is a reputation that is well deserved. To date, Lizzie has collected hundreds of dinosaur bones and located important sites of dinosaur, bird, and mammal tracks. In her honor and as a result of her hard work in the field, scientists named the skeleton of a dinosaur discovered by the Mays "Lizzie." "Lizzie" is a duck-bill dinosaur, or hadrosaur, that lived approximately 90 million years ago. "Lizzie" is the oldest dinosaur ever found in Alaska and one of the earliest known duckbill dinosaurs in North America.

The Mays have made other, equally exciting discoveries. On one summer trip, Kevin and Lizzie located six dinosaur and bird track sites that dated back 97 million to 144 million years. On another trip, the Mays found a fossilized marine reptile more than 200 million years old—an ichthyosaur—that had to be removed with the help of a military helicopter. You have to wonder what other exciting adventures are in store for Lizzie and Kevin!

Social Studies

Lizzie May is not the only young person to have made a mark in dinosaur paleontology. Using the Internet or another source, research people such as Bucky Derflinger, Johnny Maurice, Brad Riney, and Wendy Sloboda, who as young people made contributions to the field of dinosaur study. Write a short essay in your **Science Journal** summarizing your findings.

Internet Resources

- To learn more about careers in science, visit **www.scilinks.org** and enter the SciLinks code HY70225.
- To learn more about these Science in Action topics, visit **go.hrw.com** and type in the keyword HY7FOSF.
- Check out articles related to this chapter by visiting **go.hrw.com**. Just type in the keyword HY7FOSC.

Answer to Social Studies Activity
Answers may vary.

People in Science
Teaching Strategy

Share with students the following fossil-hunting tips from Lizzie May:

- If you are interested in finding bones, figure out in advance what the bones look like. This advice sounds obvious, but it's really helpful to know exactly what you are looking for.

- Bones are usually a different color from the dirt around them. So, you can look for white objects in the middle of brown or black dirt. Sometimes, the bone will be the same color as the dirt, but as you sift through dirt, the inner portion of bones may stand out if the inner portion is still white.

- To find tracks, you need to be in the right place at the right time. Learn about the kind of lighting that is right for finding tracks. Then, go out at that time of day to look for depressions in the ground.

- Here's a clue for finding the right place to locate tracks: Tracks are often preserved in sedimentary rock that formed near rivers. Being able to tell where the river channel was can be helpful.

- Stay in good shape—you don't want anything to slow you down when you are out in the field. It's hard work, but it's really fun!

- Volunteer at a museum.

The elements listed in the Standards Course of Study provide a base for presenting, supporting, and assessing the California Grade 7 Science Standards. Use this Standards Course of Study as a base for planning your lessons.

Why Teach
The Evolution of Living Things

This chapter was designed to cover the California Grade 7 Science Standards about evolution (7.3.a, 7.3.b, 7.3.c, 7.3.d, 7.3.e, and 7.4.f). It follows two chapters that describe some of the evidence on which the theory of evolution is based. This chapter describes the theory of evolution, a theory central to every field of life science.

After they have completed this chapter, students will begin a chapter about classification.

Chapter Pacing

Getting Started **45 min** pp. 296–297
The Big Idea Biological evolution explains how populations change over time. 7.3.a, 7.7.c

Section ① Change over Time **90 min** pp. 298–305
Key Concept Independent lines of evidence from geology, fossils, and comparative anatomy provide the bases for the theory of evolution.
7.3.c, 7.3.d

Section ② How Does Evolution Happen? **45 min** pp. 306–311
Key Concept After making observations and analyzing evidence, Charles Darwin concluded that natural selection is the mechanism of evolution.
7.3.b

Section ③ Natural Selection in Action **90 min** pp. 312–317
Key Concept Natural selection explains how populations adapt to changes in their environment and why some species become extinct.
7.3.a, 7.3.e, 7.4.f, 7.7.c

Wrapping Up **180 min** pp. 318–327
7.3.a, 7.7.c, 7.7.e

California Standards

Focus on Life Sciences
7.3.a Students know both genetic variation and environmental factors are causes of evolution and diversity of organisms.
7.3.b Students know the reasoning used by Charles Darwin in reaching his conclusion that natural selection is the mechanism of evolution.
7.3.c Students know how independent lines of evidence from geology, fossils, and comparative anatomy provide the bases for the theory of evolution.
7.3.d Students know how to construct a simple branching diagram to classify living groups of organisms by shared derived characteristics and how to expand the diagram to include fossil organisms.
7.3.e Students know that extinction of a species occurs when the environment changes and the adaptive characteristics of a species are insufficient for its survival.
7.4.f Students know how movements of Earth's continental and oceanic plates through time, with associated changes in climate and geographic connections, have affected the past and present distribution of organisms.

Investigation and Experimentation
7.7.c Communicate the logical connection among hypotheses, science concepts, tests conducted, data collected, and conclusions drawn from the scientific evidence.
7.7.e Communicate the steps and results from an investigation in written reports and oral presentations.

Basic Learners
TE Understanding Relationships, p. 300
TE Traits and Characteristics Review, p. 308
TE Genetic Variation, p. 312
TE Group Work, p. 320
▢ Reinforcement Worksheet
▢ Chapter Test A
▢ Differentiated Datasheets A for Labs and Activities ■
▢ Study Guide A ■

Advanced Learners/GATE
TE Whale Evolution Research, p. 302
TE Endangered Animals, p. 316
▢ Critical Thinking Worksheet
▢ Chapter Test C
▢ Differentiated Datasheets C for Labs and Activities ■

Teach

SE **Explore Activity** Modeling Successful Traits, p. 297* ◼

🖨 **Bellringer**
💿 **PowerPoint® Resources**
🖨 L37 Branching Diagram
🖨 L38 Evidence of Whale Evolution: A
🖨 L39 Evidence of Whale Evolution: B
🖨 L40 Comparing Skeletal Structures
SE **Quick Lab** Similarities in Anatomy, p. 304* ◼

🖨 **Bellringer**
💿 **PowerPoint® Resources**
SE **Quick Lab** Population Growth Vs. Food Supply, p. 309* ◼
🖨 L41 Four Parts of Natural Selection

🖨 **Bellringer**
💿 **PowerPoint® Resources**
SE **Quick Lab** Adaptations of Bird Beaks, p. 313* ◼
🖨 L42 Evolution of the Galápagos Finches

SE **Inquiry Lab** Survival of the Chocolates, pp. 318–319* ◼

Practice

SE **Organize Activity** Tri-Fold, p. 296

SE **Section Review**, p. 305* ◼

SE **Section Review**, p. 311* ◼

SE **Section Review**, p. 317* ◼

SE **Science Skills Activity** Scientific Methods: Testing Hypotheses, p. 320* ◼
🖨 **Concept Mapping***
SE **Chapter Review**, pp. 322–323* ◼

Assess

📁 **Chapter Pretest**

SE **Standards Checks**, pp. 300, 301, 302, 304
TE **Standards Focus**, p. 304
📁 **Section Quiz** ◼

SE **Standards Checks**, pp. 307, 308, 309, 310
TE **Standards Focus**, p. 310
📁 **Section Quiz** ◼

SE **Standards Checks**, pp. 313, 315, 316
TE **Standards Focus**, p. 316
📁 **Section Quiz** ◼

SE **Standards Assessment**, pp. 324–325*
📁 **Chapter Tests A, B** ◼**, C**
📁 **Standards Review Workbook** ◼

Resources for Universal Access • Differentiated Instruction

English Learners

TE Definition of Population, p. 298
TE Using the Figure, pp. 299, 301, 302, 309, 314, 315
TE Demonstration, p. 307
TE Homophones, p. 310
📁 Vocabulary and Section Summary A ◼, B

📁 Section Quizzes ◼
📁 Chapter Tests A, B ◼
📁 Differentiated Datasheets A, B, and C for Labs and Activities ◼
📓 Study Guide A ◼
📓 Multilingual Glossary

Struggling Readers

TE Summarizing, p. 306
TE Reading Strategy, p. 308
TE Using Text and Figures, p. 314

Special Education Students

TE Comparing Anatomy, p. 305
TE Assisting Students with Hearing Impairments, p. 320

To help plan your lessons, refer to the On Course Mapping Instruction booklet.

Visual Resources

CHAPTER STARTER TRANSPARENCY

What If . . . ?

BELLRINGER TRANSPARENCIES

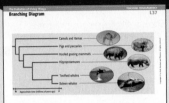

TEACHING TRANSPARENCIES

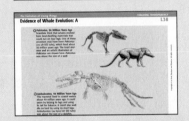
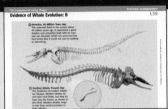

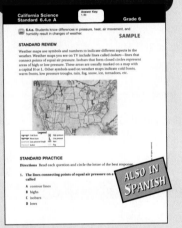

TEACHING TRANSPARENCIES

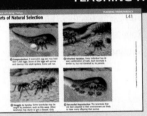

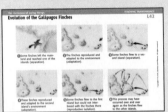

LINK TO EARTH SCIENCE

STANDARDS REVIEW TRANSPARENCIES

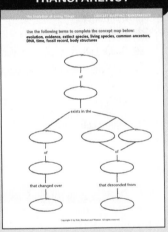

ALSO IN SPANISH

CONCEPT MAPPING TRANSPARENCY

Planning Resources

PARENT LETTER

SAMPLE

Dear Parent,

ALSO IN SPANISH

TEST ITEM LISTING

SAMPLE

ALSO IN SPANISH

One-Stop Planner® CD-ROM

This CD-ROM package includes all of the resources shown here and the following time-saving tools:

- **Lab Materials QuickList Software**

- **Customizable Lesson Plans** Correlated to the California Science Standards

- **Holt Calendar Planner**

- **PowerPoint® Resources**

- **Printable Worksheets**

- **ExamView® Test Generator** Correlated to the California Science Standards

- **Holt PuzzlePro®**

- **Interactive Teacher's Edition**

Meeting Individual Needs

DIRECTED READING A
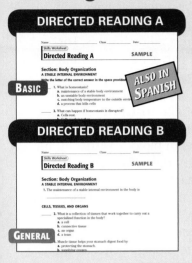
Skills Worksheet
Directed Reading A   SAMPLE

BASIC

Section: Body Organization
A STABLE INTERNAL ENVIRONMENT

ALSO IN SPANISH

VOCABULARY AND SECTION SUMMARY A
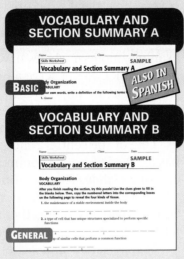
Skills Worksheet
Vocabulary and Section Summary A   SAMPLE

BASIC

ALSO IN SPANISH

REINFORCEMENT
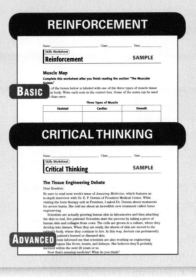
Skills Worksheet
Reinforcement   SAMPLE

BASIC

Muscle Map

INTERACTIVE READER AND STUDY GUIDE

Body Organization   SAMPLE

DIRECTED READING B
Skills Worksheet
Directed Reading B   SAMPLE

Section: Body Organization
A STABLE INTERNAL ENVIRONMENT

GENERAL

VOCABULARY AND SECTION SUMMARY B
Skills Worksheet
Vocabulary and Section Summary B   SAMPLE

Body Organization
VOCABULARY

GENERAL

CRITICAL THINKING
Skills Worksheet
Critical Thinking   SAMPLE

The Tissue Engineering Debate

ADVANCED

MULTILINGUAL GLOSSARY
SAMPLE

Labs and Activities

DIFFERENTIATED DATASHEETS FOR EXPLORE ACTIVITY, QUICK LABS, AND CHAPTER LAB

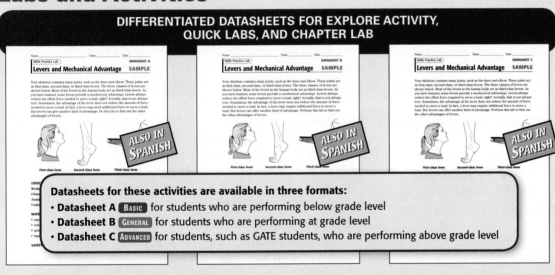

Skills Practice Lab   DATASHEET A
Levers and Mechanical Advantage   SAMPLE

Skills Practice Lab   DATASHEET B
Levers and Mechanical Advantage   SAMPLE

Skills Practice Lab   DATASHEET C
Levers and Mechanical Advantage   SAMPLE

ALSO IN SPANISH

Datasheets for these activities are available in three formats:
- **Datasheet A** BASIC for students who are performing below grade level
- **Datasheet B** GENERAL for students who are performing at grade level
- **Datasheet C** ADVANCED for students, such as GATE students, who are performing above grade level

DATASHEET FOR SCIENCE SKILLS ACTIVITY
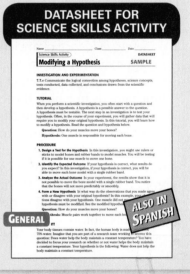
Science Skills Activity   DATASHEET
Modifying a Hypothesis   SAMPLE

GENERAL

ALSO IN SPANISH

Reviews and Assessments

SECTION REVIEWS
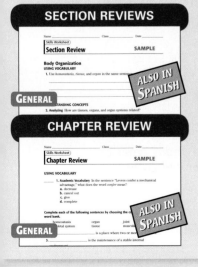
Skills Worksheet
Section Review   SAMPLE

Body Organization
USING VOCABULARY

GENERAL

ALSO IN SPANISH

CHAPTER PRETEST
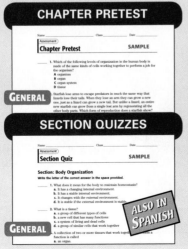
Assessment
Chapter Pretest   SAMPLE

GENERAL

CHAPTER TEST A
Assessment
Chapter Test A   SAMPLE

BASIC

STANDARDS ASSESSMENT
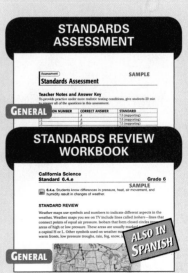
Assessment
Standards Assessment   SAMPLE

Teacher Notes and Answer Key

GENERAL

CHAPTER REVIEW
Skills Worksheet
Chapter Review   SAMPLE

USING VOCABULARY

GENERAL

ALSO IN SPANISH

SECTION QUIZZES
Assessment
Section Quiz   SAMPLE

Section: Body Organization

ALSO IN SPANISH

CHAPTER TEST B
Assessment
Chapter Test B   SAMPLE

GENERAL

ALSO IN SPANISH

CHAPTER TEST C
Assessment
Chapter Test C   SAMPLE

ADVANCED

ALSO IN SPANISH

STANDARDS REVIEW WORKBOOK
California Science Standard 6.4.e   Grade 6   SAMPLE

STANDARD REVIEW

GENERAL

ALSO IN SPANISH

For a correlation of each lab or activity to the **California Science Standards,** see pages T22–T27.

This Teacher Background explains science concepts, principles, and theories that appear in the chapter. Use the information on these pages to refresh or enhance your understanding of the topics covered.

Section 1

Change over Time

Centuries of Change

Independent lines of evidence from geology, the fossil record, molecular biology, and studies of comparative anatomy support the theory of evolution. Many decades before Darwin proposed his theory, geologists knew that sedimentary rocks held important information about the history of life on Earth. Some organisms that lived in or were buried by ancient sediments were preserved as fossils when the sediment hardened into rock. Many organisms, like the dinosaurs shown in **Figure A,** are only known to us because of fossil evidence. The process of fossilization preserves evidence of ancient life forms, and geological interpretation of the enclosing sedimentary rock yields valuable information about the environments and relative time periods in which those ancient organisms lived.

Comparative anatomists study similarities and differences among organisms. Anatomists have been able to discover significant similarities in the skeletal architecture and other anatomical structures of all vertebrates from fish to humans. The most plausible explanation for this finding is that all vertebrates descended from a common ancestor.

Studying anatomical structures has lead to the discovery of vestigial structures. *Vestigial structures* seem to serve no function for an organism, but resemble structures with functional roles in related organisms. For example, modern whales have pelvic bones. Although pelvic bones do not serve a function in modern whales, these bones are important in the closest related animals of whales, land mammals. Vestigial structures are evidence that organisms have changed over time.

One of the central concepts in biology is that all life has descended from a common origin through the process of *evolution*. The evolutionary history of a species, which tells the characteristics of the various species from which it descended, together with a species' genealogical relationship to every other species is called its *phylogeny*.

Widely varied approaches to biology generate information about phylogeny. These include the comparisons of DNA sequences conducted through molecular biology or genomics, and comparisons of fossils of organisms in paleontology. The growing field of *bioinformatics* combines the power of computing technology with information science to analyze DNA sequence and protein sequence data and then compile, organize, interpret, and predict biological structure and function.

Major catastrophic events are important because such events, although rare in the history of Earth, have had a significant effect on the shaping of Earth's surface and on the evolution of life. Most of the time, geologic processes proceed almost imperceptibly, only to be interrupted periodically by the impact of a large meteor or by a major volcanic eruption. Major events like these are capable of greatly increasing the amounts of particulate matter in the atmosphere. Large amounts of particulate matter can reduce the amount of solar radiation that reaches Earth's surface. Less solar radiation can lead to global cooling. Many organisms are unable to survive significant temperature changes. And when organisms become extinct, their disappearance impacts the ecosystem in which they lived.

Figure A *Over time, many types of organisms have inhabited Earth.*

Section 2

How Does Evolution Happen?

Effects of Isolation

Darwin observed that finches isolated on the Galápagos Islands had distinctive anatomy that helped each kind of bird eat the food found in its habitat. The shape and size of the birds' beaks seemed to match the seeds or insects found on the island where the bird lived, as shown in **Figure B.** Darwin's observations of finches suggested that isolation affects the distribution of organisms. Geographic separation of individuals in a species prevented the populations from interbreeding. This separation may have led to the accumulation of genetic changes in the two populations, changes that eventually defined them as different species.

One way that populations can become isolated is when members of a population colonize different islands and the population is divided into separate, isolated populations. Geological processes, such as plate tectonic movements and the uplift of mountain ranges, can also divide and isolate populations of organisms.

Mechanism of Evolution

In his book, *On the Origin of Species by Means of Natural Selection,* Charles Darwin observed that individual members of a population have different traits. Some of these differences are inherited and affect an individual's ability to survive and reproduce within a particular environment and ecological setting. With the passage of succeeding generations, the individuals that are best suited to particular environments would tend to have more progeny than those less well suited to that environment. Darwin called this process *natural selection* because environmental and ecological conditions essentially "select" certain characteristics of plants and animals for survival and reproduction.

In developing the theory that natural selection is the mechanism of evolution, Darwin's was influenced by the ideas presented in Thomas Malthus' *Essay on the Principles of Population.* Malthus' work described how human populations can increase more quickly than food supplies, but are limited by conditions such as disease or lack of food. Darwin saw that all populations, not just humans, could produce more offspring than the environment could support, and that some individuals must have traits that enabled them to survive and reproduce more than other individuals.

Section 3

Natural Selection in Action

Environmental Factors and Genetic Variation

Genetic variation and environmental factors are causes of evolution. Before natural section can occur the members of a population must have different traits. A population with different traits has high genetic variability. Environmental factors, such as temperature, availability of resources, and competition with other organisms, determine which traits, and thus which genes, are favorable or unfavorable. For example, traits that are favorable for an organism living in an arctic environment may be unfavorable for an organism living in a forest ecosystem.

Natural Selection and Extinction

Species can become extinct for many reasons, such as loss of habitat, decreased availability of resources, or the introduction of new predators. The amount of genetic variability in a species influences the species ability to survive. Large populations are able to sustain genetic variability much more readily than can small populations. Small populations often have low genetic variability, which results in a lack of evolutionary flexibility. If the environmental factors effecting a species change, such as increased competition for resources or a loss of habitat, species with low genetic variability are less likely to have members with traits that help them survive. Therefore, species with low genetic variability face a higher likelihood of extinction.

Figure B *Finches' beaks have adapted to their food sources.*

Internet Resources

SciLinks is maintained by the National Science Teachers Association to provide you and your students with interesting, up-to-date links that will enrich your classroom presentation of the chapter.

Visit **www.scilinks.org** and enter the SciLinks code for more information about the topic listed.

Topic: Species and Adaptation
SciLinks code: HY71433

Topic: Galápagos Islands
SciLinks code: HY70631

Topic: Fossil Record
SciLinks code: HY70615

Topic: Darwin and Natural Selection
SciLinks code: HY70378

Chapter Pretest
Use the Chapter Pretest in the Chapter Resource File to determine the prior knowledge of your students. The Test Doctors and diagnostic teaching tips in the Teacher Notes pages will help you tailor your instruction to your students' specific needs.

Improving Comprehension

Use the Graphic Organizer on this page of the Student Edition to introduce the topics that are covered in this chapter, to summarize the chapter material, or to show students how to make a concept map.

Teaching Tips

• Remind students that the main topics and vocabulary terms in the chapter often make up the terms in a concept map.

• Explain to students that the words between the circled concepts indicate the relationship between the concepts that the words connect.

LS Logical

Improving Comprehension

Graphic Organizers are important visual tools that can help you organize information and improve your reading comprehension. The Graphic Organizer below is called a *concept map*. Instructions for creating other types of Graphic Organizers are located in the **Study Skills** section of the Appendix.

How to Make a Concept Map

❶ Identify main ideas from the text, and write the ideas as short phrases or single words.

❷ Select a main concept. Place this concept at the top or center of a piece of paper.

❸ Place other ideas under or around the main concept based on their relationship to the main concept. Draw a circle around each idea.

❹ Draw lines between the concepts, and add linking words to connect the ideas.

When to Use a Concept Map

Concept maps are useful when you are trying to identify how several ideas are connected to a main concept. Concept maps may be based on vocabulary terms or on main topics from the text. The concept map below shows how the important concepts of this chapter are related. As you read about science, look for terms that can be organized in a concept map.

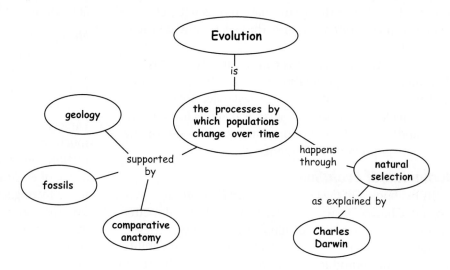

You Try It!

This Reading Strategy can also be used within the chapter that you are about to read. Practice making your own *concept map* as directed in the Reading Strategy for Section ❶. Record your work in your **Science Journal**.

Using Other Graphic Organizers

Students can practice using a variety of Graphic Organizers while reading this chapter. The following Graphic Organizers may also be useful in this chapter.

An **idea wheel** can be used to describe Darwin's thinking about different ideas of his time, discussed in Section 2.

A **process chart** can be used to describe the process of speciation, described in Section 3.

Instructions for creating these Graphic Organizers are located on pp. 583–591 of the Appendix.

Unpacking the Standards

The information below "unpacks" the standards by breaking them down into basic parts. The higher-level, academic vocabulary is highlighted and defined to help you understand the language of the standards. "What It Means" restates the standards as simply as possible.

Unpacking the Standards

Use the following information with the *What It Means* in the Student Edition to help students understand why studying each standard is important.

California Standard	Academic Vocabulary	What It Means	Why It Matters
7.3.a Students know both genetic **variation** and environmental **factors** are causes of evolution and **diversity** of organisms.	**variation** (VER ee AY shuhn) a difference in the usual form or function **factor** (FAK tuhr) a condition or event that brings about or contributes to a result **diversity** (duh VUHR suh tee) variety	Differences in the genes of individuals and the ways in which the natural surroundings affect organisms have caused living things to change and have caused many kinds of living things to develop on Earth.	Students should be familiar with the ways in which diversity and variety are introduced into a species of organisms.
7.3.b Students know the reasoning used by Charles Darwin in reaching his **conclusion** that natural **selection** is the mechanism of evolution.	**conclusion** (kuhn KLOO zhuhn) an idea developed from reasoning and investigating **selection** (suh LEK shuhn) the process of choosing	You must know what information and thought processes led Charles Darwin to form the idea that living things change over time because not all organisms survive and reproduce.	To understand the principles of biological evolution, students should be familiar with the proof and reasoning of Charles Darwin, who is thought of as the originator of the theory of evolution.
7.3.c Students know how independent lines of **evidence** from geology, fossils, and comparative anatomy provide the bases for the theory of evolution.	**evidence** (EV uh duhns) information showing whether an idea or belief is true or valid	The theory of evolution is based on several kinds of information that was gathered by studying rocks and fossils and by comparing the bodies of living and extinct organisms.	Evolution is a testable theory that is subject to change based on new discoveries and data.
7.3.d Students know how to **construct** a simple branching diagram to classify living groups of organisms by shared **derived** characteristics and how to **expand** the diagram to include fossil organisms.	**construct** (kuhn STRUHKT) to build; to make from parts **derived** (di RIEVD) gotten from something else **expand** (ek SPAND) to make more detailed; to enlarge	You must know how to draw a simple branching diagram to sort living things into groups based on features that the organisms share. You must also know how to add extinct organisms to the branching diagram.	Simple branching diagrams can summarize large quantities of information and can allow students to recognize patterns that they may otherwise miss.
7.3.e Students know that extinction of a species **occurs** when the environment changes and the **adaptive** characteristics of a species are **insufficient** for its **survival.**	**occur** (uh KUHR) to happen **adaptive** (uh DAP tiv) able to adjust to changes **insufficient** (IN suh FISH uhnt) not enough **survival** (suhr VIE vuhl) the continuing to live or exist	Extinction of a species happens when the surroundings of a species change and the species does not have the right traits to allow it to survive.	Extinction reduces the diversity of life in an area and affects the health and viability of the entire ecosystem.

The following identifies other standards that are covered in this chapter and where you can go to see them unpacked: **7.4.f** (Chapter 9)

Academic Vocabulary

Standards that are covered in this chapter may contain academic terms that are unfamiliar to students. The following table identifies some of the academic terms used in this chapter and their meanings.

Term	Definition
adaptive	able to adjust to changes
diversity	variety
variation	a difference in the usual form or function

Write the above table on the board.

Synonyms and Antonyms Have students choose a term from the table on the board. Have them list words whose meanings are similar to and words whose meanings are opposite that of their word. Below are terms, synonyms, and antonyms.

Term	Synonyms	Antonyms
adaptive	adjustable, flexible, changeable	inflexible, fixed
diversity	variety, mixture, range, assortment	uniform, homogeneous
variation	difference, change	similarity, likeness

Chapter Overview

Tell students that this chapter will introduce them to *evolution*—the process by which organisms change over time. Evolution explains the variation and adaptations that we see in organisms around us and in evidence of life in the past.

The Evolution of Living Things

The Big Idea

Biological evolution explains how populations change over time.

 California Standards

Focus on Life Sciences
7.3 Biological evolution accounts for the diversity of species developed through gradual processes over many generations. (Sections 1, 2, and 3)
7.4 Evidence from rocks allows us to understand the evolution of life on Earth. (Section 3)

Investigation and Experimentation
7.7 Scientific progress is made by asking meaningful questions and conducting careful investigations. (Science Skills Activity)

Math
7.1.2 Number Sense

English–Language Arts
7.1.3 Reading
7.2.5 Writing

About the Photo ↗

Can you find two eyes and a mouth in this photo? The eyes and mouth belong to an adult flounder. Adult flounders swim on their sides and have both eyes on one side of their body. These characteristics allow flounders to lie flat and still see all of their surroundings. Flounders also look like the sandy bottoms of coastal areas. These adaptations help flounders survive in their environment.

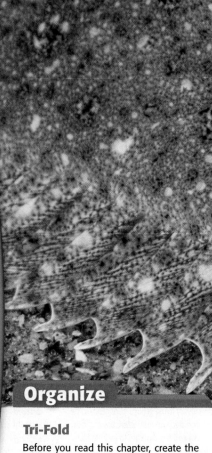

Organize

Tri-Fold

Before you read this chapter, create the FoldNote entitled "Tri-Fold." Write what you know about evolution in the column labeled "Know." Then, write what you want to know about evolution in the column labeled "Want." As you read the chapter, write what you learn about evolution in the column labeled "Learn."

Instructions for creating FoldNotes are located in the Study Skills section on p. 582 of the Appendix.

 California Standards Alignment

Focus on Life Sciences

7.3.a Students know both genetic variation and environmental factors are causes of evolution and diversity of organisms. **pp. 297, 312–313, 317–319, 322–323, 325**

7.3.b Students know the reasoning used by Charles Darwin in reaching his conclusion that natural selection is the mechanism of evolution. **pp. 306–311, 322–323, 325**

7.3.c Students know how independent lines of evidence from geology, fossils, and comparative anatomy provide the bases for the theory of evolution. **pp. 299–305, 322–323, 325**

7.3.d Students know how to construct a simple branching diagram to classify living groups of organisms by shared derived characteristics and how to expand the diagram to include fossil organisms. **pp. 301, 305, 323–324**

7.3.e Students know that extinction of a species occurs when the environment changes and the adaptive characteristics of a species are insufficient for its survival. **pp. 313, 316–317, 322–324**

7.4.f Students know how movements of Earth's continental and oceanic plates through time, with associated changes in climate and geographic connections, have affected the past and present distribution of organisms. **pp. 314–315, 317, 323–324**

Investigation and Experimentation

7.7.c Communicate the logical connection among hypotheses, science concepts, tests conducted, data collected, and conclusions drawn from the scientific evidence. **pp. 297, 318–320**

7.7.e Communicate the steps and results from an investigation in written reports and oral presentations. **pp. 318–319**

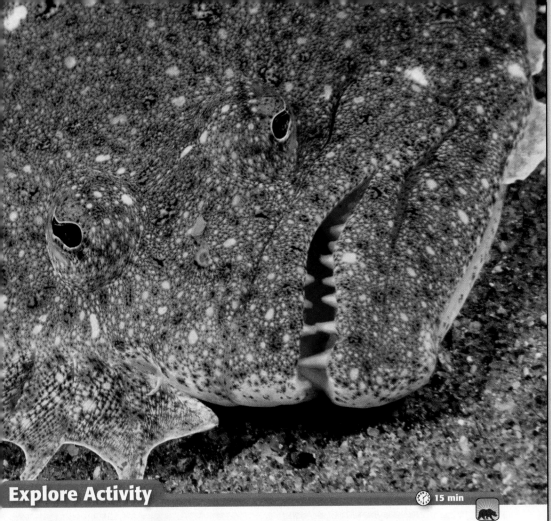

Explore Activity

Modeling Successful Traits

In this activity, you will see how traits can affect the success of an organism in a particular environment.

Procedure

1. Count out **25 colored marshmallows** and **25 white marshmallows.**

2. Ask your partner to look away while you spread out the marshmallows on a **white cloth.** Do not make a pattern with the marshmallows. Now, ask your partner to turn around and pick the first marshmallow that he or she sees.

3. Repeat step 2 ten times.

Analysis

⏱ 15 min

7.3.a
7.7.c

4. How many white marshmallows did your partner pick? How many colored marshmallows did he or she pick?

5. What did the marshmallows and the cloth represent in your investigation? What effect did the color of the cloth have?

6. When an organism blends into its environment, the organism is *camouflaged.* How does this activity model camouflaged organisms in the wild? What are some weaknesses of this model?

Math Standards

Number Sense 7.1.2 Add, subtract, multiply, and divide rational numbers (integers, fractions, and terminating decimals) and take positive rational numbers to whole-number powers. **p. 323**

English–Language Arts Standards

Reading 6.2.4 Clarify understanding of texts by creating outlines, logical notes, summaries, or reports. **p. 298**

Writing 7.2.5 2.5 Write summaries of reading materials: (a) Include the main ideas and most significant details; (b) Use the student's own words, except for quotations; (c) Reflect underlying meaning, not just the superficial details. **p. 323**

Chapter Starter Transparency
Use this transparency to help students begin thinking about changes in species over time.

Teacher Notes

This activity has students make observations and draw conclusions about how certain characteristics are more favorable than others in certain environments (covers standards 7.3.a and 7.7.c).

Materials for Each Group

- cloth, white, approximately 20 cm × 20 cm
- marshmallows, colored, miniature (25)
- marshmallows, white, miniature (25)

Safety Caution

Remind students to review all safety cautions and icons before beginning this activity.

Answers

4. Answers may vary, but students are likely to pick up more colored marshmallows than white ones.

5. The marshmallows represent organisms that could be eaten; the cloth represents the area where they live. The color of the cloth affected which organisms were easier to see.

6. Sample answer: Many organisms in the wild blend into their surroundings by having colors or patterns that make them hard to see. This might help them hide from predators. A weakness of this model is that it's very simple— a real "wild" environment would be more than two colors and would contain a variety of organisms. Another weakness is that this model does not include the behavior of the prey organisms, which would try to escape or defend themselves if a predator approached.

📋 **Differentiated Datasheets**
A **BASIC**, B **GENERAL**, C **ADVANCED**

Also editable on the Holt Lab Generator CD-ROM

Preteach

Reviewing Prior Knowledge

Instruct students to study **Figure 1.** Then, ask students what they think the figure is trying to illustrate. (Sample answer: Animal coloring sometimes helps animals to blend in with their habitats and sometimes makes them more noticeable.)

Bellringer

Have students focus on standard 7.3.c by asking them the following question: Imagine that you have found fossils of crocodiles in several different layers of rock. How would you compare the fossils to learn about the crocodiles? (Sample answer: I would compare the size of the skeletons.) **7.3.c**

Bellringer Transparency

Motivate

Discussion

Adaptations Ask students if a polar bear could live comfortably in Hawaii. Ask them to explain why or why not. Then, ask if a fish could survive in a forest, and why or why not. Discuss various characteristics of animals, such as physical adaptations that make animals well suited for a particular environment. **LS** Verbal

---

What You Will Learn

- The fossil record provides evidence that species have changed over time.
- Fossils support the hypothesis that modern whales evolved from land mammals.
- Comparing the anatomy and DNA of organisms provides evidence that organisms have common ancestors.

Why It Matters

The theory of evolution is a good example of how scientists develop and use scientific theories.

Vocabulary

- adaptation   • fossil
- species   • fossil record
- evolution

 **READING STRATEGY**

Graphic Organizer In your **Science Journal,** create a Concept Map by using the terms *fossils, sediment, sand, dust, soil, fossil record, estimated ages, physical similarities,* and *branching diagrams*.

Change over Time

Key Concept Independent lines of evidence from geology, fossils, and comparative anatomy provide the bases for the theory of evolution.

▶ What makes a frog a frog? Is it a frog's bulging eyes, its long hind legs, its croak, or the color of its skin?

Once you start to think about frogs, you realize that frogs differ in many ways. These differences set one kind of frog apart from another. The frogs in **Figure 1** look different from each other, yet they may live in the same area.

Differences Between Organisms

As you can see, each frog has different characteristics that may help the frog survive. A characteristic that helps an organism survive and reproduce in its environment is called an **adaptation.** Some adaptations, such as a long neck or striped fur, are physical. Other adaptations are behaviors that help an organism find food, protect itself, or reproduce.

Living things that have the same characteristics may be members of the same species. A **species** is a group of organisms that can mate with one another to produce fertile offspring. For example, all strawberry poison frogs are members of the same species. Therefore, strawberry poison frogs can mate with each other to produce fertile strawberry frogs. A group of individuals of the same species living in the same place is a *population*.

Figure 1 Adaptations in Species of Frogs

The **red-eyed tree frog** hides among a tree's leaves during the day and comes out at night.

The **smokey jungle frog** blends into the forest floor.

The bright coloring of the **strawberry poison frog** warns predators that the frog is poisonous.

Universal Access · Differentiated Instruction

English Learners

Definition of Population Some students might not understand the meaning of *population* as it is used in this chapter. Clarify the meaning by asking volunteers to define the following populations and identifying one living entity that is not part of the named population:

1. population of the class (Sample answer: The teacher and the students in the class make up the population. The principal is not in the class and is not part of the population.)

2. population of the school (Sample answer: The teachers, students, administrators, and other staff make up the population of the school. The students' parents are not part of the population.)

3. a population at the local zoo (The common squirrel monkeys make up a population at the local zoo. Although baboons live with the monkeys, they are not part of the population of squirrel monkeys since they are part of a different species.) **LS** Verbal/Logical

---

Do Species Change over Time?

In a single square mile of rain forest, there may be dozens of species of frogs. Across Earth, there are millions of different species of organisms. The species that live on Earth today range from single-celled bacteria and archaea to multicellular fungi, plants, and animals. Have these species always existed on Earth?

Scientists think that Earth has changed a great deal during its history and that living things have changed, too. They estimate that the planet is 4.6 billion years old. Since life first appeared on Earth, many species have died out, and many new species have appeared. **Figure 2** shows some of the species that have existed during Earth's history.

Scientists observe that species have changed over time. They also observe that the inherited characteristics in populations change over time. Scientists think that as populations change over time, new species may form. Thus, newer species descend from older species. The process in which populations change over time is called **evolution.**

7.3.c Students know how independent lines of evidence from geology, fossils, and comparative anatomy provide the bases for the theory of evolution.

7.3.d Students know how to construct a simple branching diagram to classify living groups of organisms by shared derived characteristics and how to expand the diagram to include fossil organisms.

adaptation (AD uhp TAY shuhn) a characteristic that improves an individual's ability to survive and reproduce in a particular environment

species (SPEE seez) a group of organisms that are closely related and can mate to produce fertile offspring

evolution (EV uh LOO shuhn) the process in which inherited characteristics within a population change over generations such that new species sometimes arise

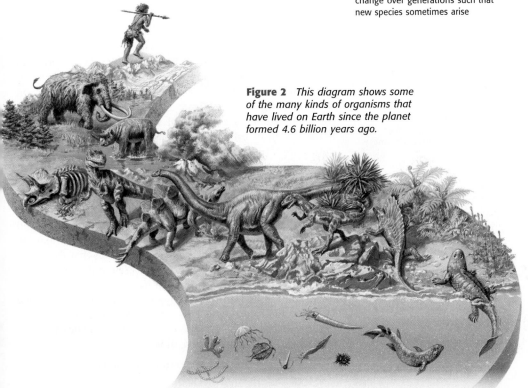

Figure 2 *This diagram shows some of the many kinds of organisms that have lived on Earth since the planet formed 4.6 billion years ago.*

Historic Paleontologist
Mary Anning (1799–1847) made some of the most important fossil discoveries of her time. She was born in Lyme Regis in southern Great Britain, an area with many fossils. Anning's fossil-finding skills provided the family with needed income after her father's death. Even before she reached her teens, Anning had discovered part of the first *Ichthyosaurus* to be recognized by scientists in London.

In the early 1820s, a professional fossil collector sold his private collection and gave the proceeds to the Anning family. He recognized that they had contributed many specimens for scientific investigation. Soon after, Mary Anning took charge of the family fossil business. However, many of Anning's finds ended up uncredited. Many scientists could not accept that a person of her financial and educational background could have acquired such expertise. Have students research to find out one of Anning's significant fossil finds. (For example, she discovered the first plesiosaur fossil.)

Answer to Standards Check

The fossil record is a history of life on Earth based on the traces or remains of living things. **7.3.c** (mastering)

Wordwise

Word Connections Review the definition of *sedimentary,* and point out that the prefix *sedi-* means "to sit" or "settle." Then, ask students what the terms *session* and *sedentary* mean. (*session:* a meeting (or sitting) of a legislative or judicial body; *sedentary:* characterized by or requiring much sitting) **LS Logical**

Figure 3 *The fossil on the left is of a trilobite, an ancient aquatic animal. The fossils on the right are of seed ferns.*

Wordwise **sedimentary**
The root *sed-* means "to sit" or "to settle." The suffix *-ment* means "result of."

fossil (FAHS uhl) the trace or remains of an organism that lived long ago, most commonly preserved in sedimentary rock

fossil record (FAHS uhl REK uhrd) the history of life in the geologic past as indicated by the traces or remains of living things

Evidence of Changes over Time

The layers of Earth's crust are made up of different kinds of rock and soil stacked on top of each other. Evidence that organisms have changed over time is buried in sedimentary rock. *Sedimentary* rock is formed when particles of sand, dust, or soil, are deposited in horizontal layers. After a rock layer forms, newer rock layers form on top of it. So, older layers are found below younger rock layers.

Fossils

The remains or imprints of once-living organisms found in layers of rock are called **fossils.** Examples of fossils are shown in **Figure 3.** Fossils usually form when a dead organism is covered by a layer of sediment. Over time, more sediment settles on top of the organism. Minerals in the sediment may seep into the organism and gradually replace the organism with stone. If the organism rots away completely after being covered, it may leave an imprint of itself in the rock.

The Fossil Record

All of the fossils that have been found make up the **fossil record.** By examining the fossil record, scientists can learn about the history of life on Earth. Fossils found in newer layers of Earth's crust tend to be similar to present-day organisms. This similarity indicates that the fossilized organisms were close relatives of present-day organisms. Fossils from older layers are less similar to present-day organisms than fossils from newer layers are. The older fossils are of earlier life-forms, which may not exist anymore. Comparing organisms in the fossil record provides evidence for how organisms have changed over time.

Standards Check What is the fossil record? **7.3.c**

Universal Access · Differentiated Instruction

Basic Learners

Understanding Relationships Some students may have difficulty understanding the relationships between the species presented in **Figure 4.** Help clarify the relationships by asking students to use the figure to answer these questions:

1. Which animal is more closely related to a camel, a hippopotamus or a buffalo? (buffalo)

2. Which animal is more closely related to a camel, a llama or a pig? (llama)

3. Which animal is more closely related to a pig, a camel or a hippopotamus? (camel)

LS Visual/Logical

Evidence of Ancestry

The fossil record provides evidence about the order in which species have existed. Scientists observe that all living organisms have characteristics in common and inherit characteristics in similar ways. So, they think that all living species descended from common ancestors. Evidence of common ancestors is found in fossils and in living organisms.

Drawing Connections

As scientists analyze fossils and living organisms, they develop hypotheses about how species are related. Scientists draw *branching diagrams* that illustrate their hypotheses. A branching diagram, such as the one shown in **Figure 4,** shows the relationships between species. The short horizontal line at the top left in the diagram represents a species that lived in the past. Each branch in the diagram represents a group of organisms that descended from that species.

Scientists think that whales and some types of hoofed mammals have a common ancestor, as **Figure 4** shows. This ancestor was probably a land mammal that lived between 50 million and 70 million years ago. The fossil record shows that many mammals appeared during this time period. The first ocean-dwelling mammals appeared about 50 million years ago. Scientists think whales evolved from these ocean-dwelling mammals.

Scientists use information about organisms to sketch a "tree of life" that includes all known living things. As scientists gather new information, they reexamine how all organisms are related.

Standards Check How do scientists use branching diagrams to show how all organisms are related? 7.3.d

Figure 4 *This diagram is a model of the proposed relationships between some modern mammals.* ***According to the diagram, which animals share the closest common ancestor with whales?***

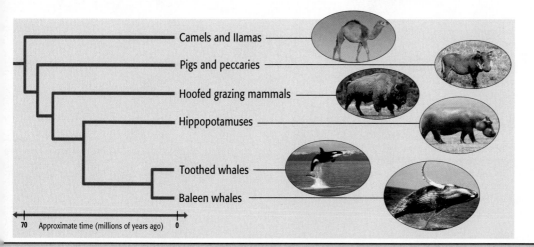

Camels and llamas

Pigs and peccaries

Hoofed grazing mammals

Hippopotamuses

Toothed whales

Baleen whales

70   Approximate time (millions of years ago)   0

Using the Figure

Evidence of Whale Evolution

Have students examine each of the skeletons in the diagram on these two pages. Ask them to describe one similarity and one difference between each successive species. (Sample answer: *Pakicetus* and *Ambulocetus* have similar limbs and feet, but those of *Ambulocetus* are shorter. *Dorudon* had hind limbs that it could not use for walking or swimming. Modern toothed whales have no hind limbs, but have tiny hip bones.) Point out that the hip bones of modern whales are examples of vestigial structures. *Vestigial structures,* such as hip bones in whales or the appendix in humans, have no function. Because structures similar to vestigial structures perform functions in other organisms, they are evidence that organisms have changed over time.

📦 Teaching Transparency:
L38 Evidence of Whale Evolution: A
L39 Evidence of Whale Evolution: B

CONNECTION ACTiViTY
Art

Scientific Illustrations The role of a scientific illustrator is to create accurate pictures of organisms and things that scientists study. In the case of long-extinct species, such as dinosaurs, artists must sometimes fill in where science leaves off. Have students look for and compare several examples of illustrations of a specific extinct organism. Have students try to identify ways in which artistic interpretation is used. For comparison, show students examples of similar illustrations from one hundred years ago, when much less was known about many fossil organisms.
LS Visual

Examining Organisms

Examining an organism carefully can give scientists clues about its ancestors. For example, whales seem similar to fish. But unlike fish, whales breathe air, give birth to live young, and produce milk. These traits show that whales are *mammals.* Thus, scientists think that whales evolved from ancient mammals.

Case Study: Evolution of the Whale

Scientists think that the ancient ancestor of whales was probably a mammal that lived on land and that could run on four legs. A more recent ancestor was probably a mammal that spent time both on land and in water. Comparisons between modern whales and a large number of fossils support this hypothesis. **Figure 5** shows some of this evidence.

Standards Check What evidence supports the hypothesis that the ancient ancestor of whales was a land mammal? 🦫 **7.3.c**

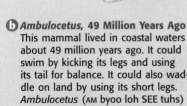 **Figure 5** **Evidence of Whale Evolution**

ⓐ *Pakicetus,* **50 Million Years Ago**
Scientists think that whales evolved from land-dwelling mammals that could run on four legs. One of these ancestors may have been *Pakicetus* (PAK uh SEE tuhs), which lived about 50 million years ago. The fossil skeleton and an artist's illustration of *Pakicetus* are shown here. *Pakicetus* was about the size of a wolf.

ⓑ *Ambulocetus,* **49 Million Years Ago**
This mammal lived in coastal waters about 49 million years ago. It could swim by kicking its legs and using its tail for balance. It could also waddle on land by using its short legs. *Ambulocetus* (AM byoo loh SEE tuhs) was about the size of a dolphin.

Universal Access • Differentiated Instruction

Advanced Learners/GATE

Whale Evolution Research Some students benefit from exploring a topic in greater depth. Ask these students to research current theories about the evolution of whales from ancient land mammals. Tell them to include the following at each stage: a picture (skeletons or artists' conception), how it walked or moved, what the animal probably ate, what type of an environment it probably lived in, and how it breathed. **LS** Visual/Verbal

---

Answer to Standards Check

Whales breathe air, give birth to live young, and produce milk. Also, comparisons between modern whales and a large number of fossils have supported the idea that whales are descendants of a land mammal.
7.3.c (exceeding)

Walking Whales

The organisms in **Figure 5** form a sequence between ancient four-legged mammals and modern whales. Several pieces of evidence indicate that these species are related by ancestry. Each species shared some traits with an earlier species. Some species had new traits that were shared with later species. Each species had traits that allowed it to survive in a particular time and place in Earth's history.

Further evidence can be found inside the bodies of living whales. For example, although modern whales do not have hind limbs, they have tiny hip bones, as **Figure 5** shows. Scientists think that these hip bones were inherited from the whales' four-legged ancestors. Scientists often look at this kind of evidence when trying to determine the relationships between organisms.

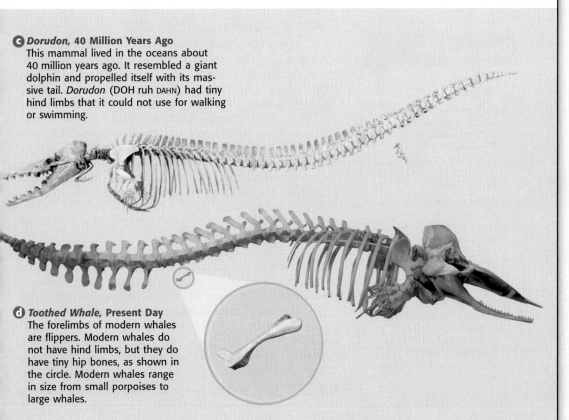

ⓒ Dorudon, 40 Million Years Ago
This mammal lived in the oceans about 40 million years ago. It resembled a giant dolphin and propelled itself with its massive tail. *Dorudon* (DOH ruh DAHN) had tiny hind limbs that it could not use for walking or swimming.

ⓓ Toothed Whale, Present Day
The forelimbs of modern whales are flippers. Modern whales do not have hind limbs, but they do have tiny hip bones, as shown in the circle. Modern whales range in size from small porpoises to large whales.

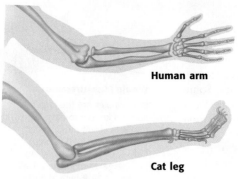

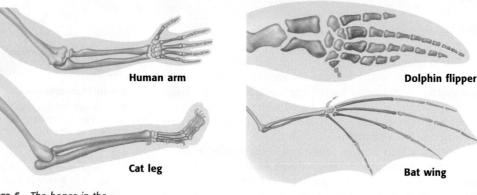

Human arm

Dolphin flipper

Cat leg

Bat wing

Figure 6 *The bones in the front limbs of humans, cats, dolphins, and bats are similar. Similar bones are shown in the same color. These limbs are not shown to scale.*

Close

Standards Focus

This **Standards Focus** provides you with a quick way to **assess, reteach,** and **re-assess** one or more concepts in the section.

Assess

1. Use the words *adaptations, population,* and *evolution* together in a sentence. (Sample answer: Evolution is the process by which a population acquires inherited adaptations over time.) **7.3.c**

2. Why do scientists make educated guesses about some parts of the "tree of life" on Earth? (Sample answer: There are many species to consider, and the information is incomplete. Also, some parts of Earth's history lack a fossil record because fossils are formed only rarely.) **7.3.d**

Reteach

Concept Map While prompting students for input, create a large concept map with the main ideas from this chapter. **LS** Visual **7.3.c, 7.3.d**

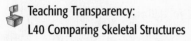

Re-Assess

Writing

Researching Relationships The giant panda and the red panda seem similar, but scientists now think that the red panda is more closely related to raccoons than to the giant panda. Have students investigate and write a report on recent studies on the classification of the two pandas. **LS** Logical **7.3.d**

Teaching Transparency: L40 Comparing Skeletal Structures

Answer to Standards Check

The two species are probably closely related through a common ancestor. **7.3.c** (exceeding)

Quick Lab

Similarities in Anatomy   7.3.c

1. Each member of a group should select one of the bone arrangements in **Figure 6.**

2. On a piece of **paper,** draw an outline of your selected animal's limb.

3. Shape **modeling clay** into the limb bones. Position the model bones within the outline. If possible, use colors that are consistent with the illustration. Otherwise, decide as a group which colors will be used for specific bones.

4. Compare the shape of each bone as it appears in different limbs. Discuss how the size and shape of each bone relates to its function.

⏱ 15 min

Comparing Organisms

The scientific fields of comparative anatomy and molecular biology provide evidence that organisms share common ancestors. Comparative anatomy is the study of the physical similarities and differences between organisms. Molecular biology is the study of the molecules found in living things.

Comparing Anatomy

When scientists study the anatomy, or structure, of different organisms, they find that related organisms share many traits. The arm of a human, the front leg of a cat, the front flipper of a dolphin, and the wing of a bat do not look alike and are not used in the same way. But under the surface, they are similar. Look at **Figure 6.** The bones of a human arm are similar in structure and order to the bones in the front limbs of a cat, a dolphin, and a bat. These similarities suggest that cats, dolphins, bats, and humans had a common ancestor. Over millions of years, changes occurred in the limb bones. Eventually, the bones performed different functions in each type of animal.

Comparing DNA Molecules

The genetic information stored in an organism's DNA determines the organism's traits. DNA, along with RNA and proteins, are important molecules found in all living things. Scientists compare many organisms' DNA, RNA, proteins, and other molecules. The greater the number of similarities between the DNA of any two species, the more recently the two species shared a common ancestor. Scientists use molecular data, comparative anatomy, and fossils to support the theory that populations change over time and sometimes give rise to new species.

Standards Check If two species have similar DNA, what would you infer about their ancestry? **7.3.c**

Quick Lab   ⏱ 15 min

Teacher Notes

This activity has students compare the anatomy of several vertebrates (covers standard 7.3.c).

Materials for Each Group

• paper, blank piece
• clay, modeling, in five colors

Answer

4. Sample answer: Bats have long, thin finger bones that support the skin that forms the wings.

📋 Differentiated Datasheets
A **BASIC**, B **GENERAL**, C **ADVANCED**

Also editable on the **Holt Lab Generator CD-ROM**

SECTION Review

7.3.c, 7.3.d

Summary

- Evolution is the process in which the inherited characteristics within a population change over generations, sometimes giving rise to new species.

- Fossils provide clues about the animals that have lived on Earth. Comparing fossils and living organisms supports the idea that organisms have changed over time.

- Scientists think that modern whales evolved from an ancient, land-dwelling mammal ancestor. Fossil organisms that support this hypothesis have been found.

- Comparing the anatomy and molecules of different organisms provides evidence of common ancestry among living organisms. The traits and DNA of species that have a common ancestor are more similar to each other than they are to the traits and DNA of distantly related species.

Understanding Concepts

1 **Describing** What are three lines of evidence that support the theory of evolution?

2 **Sumarizing** What evidence about the ancestors of whales do fossils provide?

3 **Describing** How does comparative anatomy support the idea that organisms share ancestors?

Critical Thinking

4 **Making Comparisons** Name some ways in which whales differ from fishes.

5 **Forming Hypotheses** Is a person's DNA likely to be more similar to the DNA of his or her biological parents or to the DNA of one of his or her first cousins? Explain your answer.

6 **Evaluating Data** A poodle and a wolf have similar physical characteristics. In addition, by using current DNA technology, scientists have learned that the DNA of a poodle is similar to the DNA of a wolf. Describe how DNA technology can be used to support the theory that poodles and wolves share a common ancestor.

7 **Making Comparisons** Modern whales share many similarities with the animals that are thought to be their ancestors. However, whales also differ from their ancestors. Name three or more adaptations that whales have for living in water.

INTERPRETING GRAPHICS Use the photograph of rock layers below to answer the next question.

8 **Making Inferences** The photograph shows the layers of sedimentary rock exposed during the construction of a road. Imagine that a species that lived 200 million years ago is found in layer **b**. Would the ancestor of the species, which lived 250 million years ago, most likely be found in layer **a** or in layer **c**? Explain your answer.

Challenge

9 **Forming Hypotheses** You are drawing a branching diagram that shows the relationships between cows, horses, and zebras. Which two organisms would you indicate as having the closest common ancestor? Explain your answer.

Internet Resources

For a variety of links related to this chapter, go to www.scilinks.org

Topic: Species and Adaptation; Fossil Record

SciLinks code: HY71433; HY70615

Answers to Section Review

1. Evidence from the fossil record, comparative anatomy, and DNA molecules support the theory of evolution. **7.3.c** (mastering)

2. There are fossils of four-legged mammals that share some characteristics with modern whales and other hoofed mammals. Also, there is a sequence of fossil organisms that have characteristics in between those of the ancient fossils and modern whales. **7.3.c** (mastering)

3. Comparing the anatomy of organisms shows that organisms share many characteristics. More closely related organisms tend to show more similarities. **7.3.c** (mastering)

4. Unlike fish, whales breathe air, produce milk, and have bones that are more similar to mammal bones than to fish bones. **7.3.c** (mastering)

5. A person's DNA is likely to be most similar to that of his or her biological parents, because the parents are more closely related to the person. **7.3.c** (mastering)

6. Organisms that share a recent common ancestor should have similar DNA. **7.3.c** (mastering)

7. Whales have fins for swimming, blow holes for breathing air, and the ability to hold their breath for long periods of time. **7.3.c** (mastering)

8. layer c; That layer is under layer b, so layer c was probably deposited earlier than layer b was and is older. **7.3.c** (mastering)

9. Horses and zebras share the most recent common ancestor. Horses and zebras share more anatomical structures than either animal shares with cows. **7.3.c** (mastering)

Section Review Standards Guide

	Supporting	Mastering	Exceeding
7.3.c	4	1, 3, 6	2, 5, 7, 8
7.3.d		9	

Section Resources

- Directed Reading A **BASIC** (Also in Spanish), B **GENERAL**

- Interactive Reader and Study Guide

- Section Quiz **GENERAL** (Also in Spanish)

- Section Review **GENERAL** (Also in Spanish)

- Vocabulary and Section Summary A **BASIC** (Also in Spanish), B **GENERAL**

Universal Access · Differentiated Instruction

Special Education Students

Comparing Anatomy Give students with visual impairments a chance to benefit from **Figure 6** by pairing these students (A) with students without visual impairments (B). Ask Student B to hold the arm of Student A and clarify the part of the human body shown in the diagram. Then, have Student B explain how each of the other diagrams compares to the human

arm. Make sure the explanation continues as a physical explanation based on the human arm. For example, for the cat leg, the explanation might include "the first bend in the cat leg looks a lot like the human elbow, except that it has a bone that appears to stick an inch or so past the joint right about here" (touch the upper back of Student A's elbow).

LS **Verbal/Kinesthetic**

Preteach

Reviewing Prior Knowledge

Direct students' attention to the vocabulary words in the left column.

1. Ask students to explain what *adaptations* do for animals. (they make them better suited to their environment)

2. Ask students to look at **Figure 3** on page 307 and explain why animals that are separated and end up in different parts of the world have different adaptations. (They have different environmental factors to survive such as climate and predators.)

 Bellringer

Have students focus on standard 7.3.b by asking them to respond to the following prompt: "Darwin traveled around the world in a ship. What findings resulted from this trip that could not have been understood if he had stayed at home and studied nature?"
(Sample answer: He discovered that animals from the same species evolved differently in different locations.) **7.3.b**

 Bellringer Transparency

Motivate

Discussion

Dinosaurs Have students explain why there are no dinosaurs alive today. (Dinosaurs are extinct.) Then, have students explain why they think dinosaurs became extinct. (Sample answer: A catastrophic event changed the environment faster than the dinosaurs could adapt). **LS Verbal**

What You Will Learn

● Darwin made many observations and was influenced by ideas from other fields.

● The four parts of natural selection are overproduction, inherited variation, struggle to survive, and successful reproduction.

Why It Matters

Natural selection causes populations to change to become better adapted to their environment.

Vocabulary

• trait
• selective breeding
• natural selection

READING STRATEGY

Graphic Organizer In your **Science Journal**, create a Process Chart that shows how Darwin arrived at his conclusions about evolution and natural selection.

How Does Evolution Happen?

Key Concept After making observations and analyzing evidence, Charles Darwin concluded that natural selection is the mechanism of evolution.

▶ Imagine that you are a scientist in the 1800s. Fossils of some very strange animals have been found. How would you explain the existence of these fossils?

In the 1800s, geologists began to realize that Earth was much older than anyone had previously thought. Evidence showed that gradual processes had changed Earth's surface over millions of years. Some scientists saw evidence of evolution in the fossil record. However, no one had been able to explain *how* evolution happens—until Charles Darwin.

Charles Darwin

In 1831, 21-year-old Charles Darwin, shown in **Figure 1,** graduated from college. Darwin didn't know what he wanted to do with his life. Although he eventually earned a degree in theology, Darwin was most interested in the study of plants and animals. So, he signed on for a five-year voyage around the world. He served as the *naturalist*—a scientist who studies nature—on the HMS *Beagle,* a British ship similar to the ship in **Figure 1.** During the trip, Darwin made observations that helped him form a theory about how evolution happens.

Figure 1 *Charles Darwin wanted to understand the natural world. He sailed around the world on a ship similar to the one shown here.*

7.3.b Students know the reasoning used by Charles Darwin in reaching his conclusion that natural selection is the mechanism of evolution.

Universal Access • Differentiated Instruction

Struggling Readers

Summarizing At the end of each paragraph in this section, have students write a one-sentence summary before reading on. Tell students that this process will help them understand what they are reading. Give students this example for the first paragraph: In the 1800s, geologists began to realize that Earth was much older than anyone realized, but these geologists did not yet understand evolution. Point out that they can make a flashcard labeled Darwin on one side and their sentences on the other to use as a study tool. **LS Logical**

Figure 2 *The course of the HMS* Beagle *is shown by the red line. The journey began and ended in England.*

Darwin's Journey

The *Beagle*'s journey is shown in **Figure 2.** Darwin observed plants and animals from places such as the Galápagos Islands. These islands are found 965 km (600 mi) west of Ecuador, a country in South America.

Darwin's Finches

Darwin noticed that the animals and plants on the Galápagos Islands were like those in Ecuador. But the plants and animals were not identical. For example, the finches on the Galápagos Islands differed slightly from the finches in Ecuador. And the finches on each island differed from the finches on the other islands. One difference between the finches was the shape of their beaks. As **Figure 3** shows, the beak of each finch is adapted to the way the bird usually gets food.

Standards Check What did Darwin notice about the finches of Ecuador and the Galápagos Islands? 🐘 **7.3.b**

Figure 3 **Some Finches of the Galápagos Islands**

The **large ground finch** has a wide, strong beak that it uses to crack open big, hard seeds. This beak works like a nutcracker.

The **cactus finch** has a tough beak that it uses for eating cactus parts and insects. This beak works like a pair of needle-nosed pliers.

The **warbler finch** has a small, narrow beak that it uses to catch small insects. This beak works like a pair of tweezers.

Answer to Standards Check

Darwin noticed that all of the finches shared many similarities. But he also noticed some differences, such as how the beak of each type of finch was adapted to what that finch ate. **7.3.b** (mastering)

Prediction Guide   Before students read this page, have them answer the following questions:

• Why did the finches Darwin saw on the Galápagos Islands look similar to those he saw in South America? (The finches were originally from South America.)

• Why did they look a little different? (Over time, the finches adapted to the conditions on the Galápagos Islands.)

Have students share and evaluate their answers with a partner after they read the page.

LS Verbal/Logical

MISCONCEPTION ALERT

Selective Breeding   Some students might think that breeds of dogs, such as collies, poodles, and bulldogs, have developed naturally. To correct this misconception, ask them to describe a mutt. (A mutt is the offspring of parents that are different breeds, or are mutts themselves.) Point out that the reason all dogs are not mutts is because people have been selectively breeding dogs for 12,000 years Breeds develop as people choose specific traits and allow dogs with these traits to reproduce. By selecting for traits in this manner, over 150 breeds have been produced. Explain that a breed is not a species because different breeds can still mate with each other and produce fertile offspring.

Answer to Standards Check

Beak shape changed relative to the available food. **7.3.b** (mastering)

Darwin's Thinking

Darwin puzzled over the animals that he had seen on his journey. He tried to explain why some of the animals, such as the Galápagos finches, were very similar yet had unique adaptations. Darwin hypothesized that the island finches descended from South American finches. He proposed that the first finches on the islands were blown there from South America by a storm. He suggested that the finches evolved adaptations for the various island environments over many generations. For example, Darwin noticed that the shape of the beak was directly related to the finch's food. Darwin's hypothesis about the Galápagos finches explained his observations.

Standards Check   What structural change helped the Galápagos finches adapt to their environment? 🐻 **7.3.b**

Ideas About Breeding

In Darwin's time, farmers and breeders had produced many kinds of farm animals and plants. These plants and animals had traits that were desired by the farmers and breeders. A **trait** is a form of an inherited characteristic. For example, redness is a trait, and fruit color is the corresponding characteristic. The practice by which humans select plants or animals for breeding based on desired traits is **selective breeding.** Most pets, such as the dogs in **Figure 4,** have been bred for various desired traits. Selective breeding shows that the traits of organisms can change and that certain traits can spread through populations.

trait (TRAYT) a genetically determined characteristic

selective breeding (suh LEK tiv BREED ing) the human practice of breeding animals or plants that have certain desired traits

Figure 4   *Over the past 12,000 years, dogs have been selectively bred to produce more than 150 breeds.*

Universal Access · Differentiated Instruction

Basic Learners

Traits and Characteristics   Make sure students understand the difference between traits and characteristics. Divide the class into two teams. Tell students that you are going to play a game called "Traits of Named Characteristics." Explain that you will name a characteristic of an animal or plant and the first team to come up with three corresponding traits will win a point. Begin with the following characteristics.

1. fruit color (Sample answers: red, yellow, green)

2. nature of dog hair (Sample answers: curly, straight, short)

3. human eye color (Sample answers: brown, blue, hazel)

4. leaf shape (Sample answers: oblong, pointed, lobed)

LS Verbal/Interpersonal

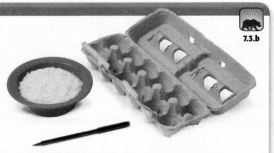
Ideas About Population

During Darwin's time, Thomas Malthus wrote *An Essay on the Principle of Population*. Malthus noted that the human population can grow more rapidly than food supplies can grow. **Figure 5** shows this relationship. Malthus also pointed out that the size of human populations is limited by problems such as starvation and disease.

After reading Malthus's work, Darwin realized that any species can produce many offspring. He also knew that the populations of all species are limited by starvation, disease, competition, and predation. Only a limited number of individuals live long enough to reproduce. Darwin reasoned that the survivors had traits that helped them survive in their environment. He also thought that some of these traits would be inherited by the offspring of the survivors.

Standards Check How did Thomas Malthus's ideas about population influence Darwin? 7.3.b

Ideas About Earth's History

During Darwin's time, most geologists thought that Earth was very young. But important books, such as *Principles of Geology* by Charles Lyell, were changing ideas about Earth. Lyell's book presented evidence that Earth had formed by natural processes over a long period of time. Darwin reasoned that if Earth were very old, then there would be enough time for organisms to slowly change.

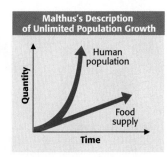

Malthus's Description of Unlimited Population Growth

Human population

Food supply

Quantity

Time

Figure 5 *Malthus thought that the human population could increase more quickly than the food supply. Such an increase would result in a worldwide food shortage.*

Standards Focus

This **Standards Focus** provides you with a quick way to **assess, reteach,** and **re-assess** one or more concepts in the section.

🐻 Assess

1. Who was Charles Lyell? (a British geologist) **7.3.b**

2. What did Darwin learn from Lyell's data about the age of Earth? (Darwin learned from Lyell that Earth was old enough for slow changes to happen in a population.) **7.3.b**

🐻 Reteach

Vocabulary Review Have students list the vocabulary words and any other unfamiliar terms from this chapter. For each word, have students write a definition and then write sample sentences using the word. **LS Logical 7.3.b**

🐻 Re-Assess

Darwin's Journal Point out that Charles Darwin's journals contain notes and records from his travels. Ask students to imagine that they are traveling with Darwin and are keeping their own journals. Their notes and drawings should reflect what they see, the questions that arise from their observations, and the hypotheses that they form. Encourage students to write journal entries about other animals on the Galápagos Islands besides the finches, such as the Galápagos tortoise or the marine iguanas. **LS Intrapersonal 7.3.b**

Answer to Standards Check

Natural selection is the mechanism or process by which organisms that are better adapted to their environment survive and reproduce more successfully than less well-adapted organisms do. **7.3.b** (mastering)

🗄 Teaching Transparency: L41 Four Parts of Natural Selection

Darwin's Theory of Natural Selection

After his voyage on the HMS *Beagle*, Darwin privately struggled with his ideas for about 20 years. Then, in 1858, Darwin received a letter from a naturalist named Alfred Russel Wallace. Wallace had arrived at the same ideas about evolution that Darwin had. In 1859, Darwin published a famous book called *On the Origin of Species by Means of Natural Selection*. In his book, Darwin proposed the theory that evolution happens by natural selection. **Natural selection** is the mechanism, or process by which organisms that are better adapted to their environment survive and reproduce more successfully than less well adapted organisms do. The process has four steps and is explained in **Figure 6.**

natural selection (NACH uhr uhl suh LEK shuhn) the process by which individuals that are better adapted to their environment survive and reproduce more successfully than less well adapted individuals do; a theory to explain the mechanism of evolution

Standards Check What is natural selection? 🐻 **7.3.b**

Figure 6 Four Parts of Natural Selection

❶ **Overproduction** A tarantula's egg sac may hold 500 to 1,000 eggs. Some of the eggs will survive and develop into adult spiders. Some will not.

❷ **Inherited Variation** Every individual has its own combination of traits. Each tarantula is similar but not identical to its parents.

❸ **Struggle to Survive** Some tarantulas may be caught by predators, such as this wasp. Other tarantulas may starve or get a disease. Only some of the tarantulas will survive to adulthood.

❹ **Successful Reproduction** The tarantulas that are best adapted to their environment are likely to have many offspring that survive.

Universal Access · Differentiated Instruction

English Learners

Homophones Explain to students who are English learners that homophones are two or more words that sound alike, but are spelled differently and have different meanings. Tell them that recognizing homophones can help them to understand the meaning of text and to spell words correctly. Write the following words (without the answers) in a vertical line on the board. Ask students to look on these two pages for matching homophones.

bye (by), dyed (died), knew (new), knot (not), inn (in), pray (prey), read (red), sew (so), they're (their, there), too, (two, to), witch (which) Test students by asking them to choose the correct homophone in sentences about the reading. (Sample: Dinosaurs are extinct because they have all _____ (died/dyed). When new predators _____ (pray/prey) on a population, it may become endangered.) **LS Visual/Auditory**

Genetics and Evolution

Darwin knew that organisms inherit traits, but not *how* they inherit traits. He also knew that there is great variation among organisms, but not *how* that variation occurs. Today, scientists know that variation happens as genetic information is passed from parent to offspring in sexual reproduction. Some genes make an organism more likely to survive to reproduce. Natural selection happens when organisms that carry these genes survive and reproduce more than organisms that do not carry these genes. New fossil discoveries and new information about genes add to scientists' understanding of natural selection and evolution.

SECTION Review

 7.3.b

Summary

- Finch species of the Galápagos Islands evolved adaptations in response to their environment.

- Natural selection is the process by which organisms that are better adapted to their environment are more likely to survive and reproduce than less well adapted organisms do.

- The four steps of Darwin's theory of evolution by natural selection include overproduction, inherited variation, struggle to survive, and successful reproduction.

- Variation in each species is due to the exchange of genetic information as it is passed from parent to offspring.

Using Vocabulary

1 Write an original definition for *trait*.

Understanding Concepts

2 **Describing** Describe Darwin's observations about the finches on the Galápagos Islands.

3 **Describing** Describe the four parts of Darwin's theory of evolution by natural selection.

4 **Identifying** What ideas from geology influenced Darwin?

Critical Thinking

5 **Identifying Relationships** Summarize Malthus's ideas about population. How did Darwin relate Malthus's ideas to evolution by natural selection?

6 **Evaluating Assumptions** Explain overproduction in natural selection. Can a species that reproduces at a slow rate, such as a whale that produces one offspring every six years, still overproduce?

7 **Analyzing Processes** How did Darwin use scientific methods, such as making observations, analyzing data, and drawing conclusions, before presenting his ideas on the theory of evolution by natural selection?

8 **Making Comparisons** How are selective breeding and natural selection similar? How are they different?

Challenge

9 **Identifying Relationships** Although both Charles Darwin and Gregor Mendel lived during the same time period, Darwin was unaware of Mendel's work. How do Mendel's ideas about the inheritance of traits relate to Darwin's theory of evolution by natural selection?

Internet Resources

For a variety of links related to this chapter, go to www.scilinks.org

Topic: Galápagos Islands; Darwin and Natural Selection
SciLinks code: HY70631; HY70378

---

6. Overproduction means that organisms can produce more offspring than can survive to maturity. Even if an animal reproduces at a slow rate, more offspring can be born than the environment could support. **7.3.b** (exceeding)

7. Sample answer: Darwin made many observations and kept detailed records during his voyage. Darwin analyzed his results and drew conclusions. Darwin communicated his results when he published a book describing his findings. **7.3.b** (mastering)

8. Selective breeding is similar to natural selection because both processes favor certain traits, and individuals with those traits reproduce and have more offspring than other individuals do. In selective breeding, humans determine which traits are favorable. In natural selection, the favorable traits are the ones that are best suited for the living thing's environment. **7.3.b** (exceeding)

9. Darwin thought that some organisms had traits that helped them compete for resources, and that these traits were passed on to their offspring. Mendel discovered how traits were passed from generation to generation. Mendel's ideas about heredity explain why an organism is likely to have offspring that have some of its traits. **7.3.b** (exceeding)

Section Review Standards Guide

	Supporting	Mastering	Exceeding
7.3.b	1	2, 3, 5, 7	4, 6, 8, 9

Answers to Section Review

1. Sample answer: A trait is a specific characteristic that is inherited from ancestors. **7.3.b** (supporting)

2. Darwin observed that many of the finch species of the Galápagos Islands were similar to those of South America, but they had unique adaptations. **7.3.b** (mastering)

3. Overproduction means that every organism can produce more offspring than will likely survive; inherited variation means that all offspring will have some differences; struggle to survive means the offspring have to compete with each other and with other organisms around them; and successful reproduction means those that are best adapted will probably have more offspring like themselves. **7.3.b** (mastering)

4. Darwin was influenced by Charles Lyell's idea that Earth was formed by natural processes over a long period of time. **7.3.b** (exceeding)

5. Malthus thought that human populations had a tendency to grow faster than their food supply. Darwin thought that populations in the wild could also grow faster than their food supply. Because the supply of resources is limited, there must be competition for resources. Therefore, individuals with certain traits would be able to obtain more resources. **7.3.b** (mastering)

Section Resources

- Directed Reading A **BASIC** (Also in Spanish), B **GENERAL**

- Interactive Reader and Study Guide

- Section Quiz **GENERAL** (Also in Spanish)

- Section Review **GENERAL** (Also in Spanish)

- Vocabulary and Section Summary A **BASIC** (Also in Spanish), B **GENERAL**

Reviewing Prior Knowledge

Ask students to describe examples of each of the four parts of natural selection: overproduction, inherited variation, struggle to survive, and successful reproduction. (Sample answer: overproduction: There is not enough food for all the deer that are born to survive to adulthood; inherited variation: In a population of deer, individuals have different traits such as being able to run at different rates; struggle to survive: Deer compete with each other for resources such as food and shelter. Deer must also avoid predators; successful reproduction: Deer that avoid predators and obtain the resources they need are more likely to survive and reproduce. The deer that survive will pass on some of their favorable traits to their offspring.)

 Bellringer

Have students focus on standard 7.3.a by responding to this prompt:

Choose an environment anywhere in the world. Make a list of traits that would help an organism survive in that environment. (Sample answer: Animals in Antarctica need to be able to stay warm and find food.)

 Bellringer Transparency

Debate

People and Nature During the past several hundred years, a rapidly expanding human population has caused some species to become extinct from habitat destruction or overhunting. Have students debate the following issue: If people are part of the environment, are people's actions just another natural process? **LS** Logical/Verbal

---

Natural Selection in Action

Key Concept Natural selection explains how populations adapt to changes in their environment and why some species become extinct.

What You Will Learn

- Genetic variation and environmental factors affect evolution by natural selection.
- Separation, adaptation, and reproductive isolation can produce new species.
- Extinction occurs when the adaptations of a species are insufficient for survival in a changing environment.

Why It Matters

Natural selection accounts for the great diversity of living things.

Vocabulary

- speciation
- extinct

READING STRATEGY

Prediction Guide Before reading this section, write each heading from this section in your **Science Journal.** Below each heading, write what you think you will learn.

Figure 1 *Cheetah populations have low genetic variation, which puts cheetahs at risk of extinction.*

▶ A unique insect species lives on a particular island. A storm carries a few members of a bird species to the island. Will the birds survive in their new environment? Will the insect species survive if the birds prey on the insects?

Many factors determine if a population will survive in its environment or become extinct. Over time, a population may evolve new adaptations to survive in its environment. The theory of evolution by natural selection explains how a population can change in response to its environment.

Changes in Populations

For natural selection to occur, a population must have genetic variation and thus a variety of traits. Environmental factors determine which traits in a population are favorable and which are unfavorable.

Genetic Variation

Genetic differences are responsible for the differences between species and between members of the same population. The *genetic variation* of a population is a measure of how much individuals in a population differ genetically. In a population that has high genetic variation, members have different *alleles,* or forms of their genes. As a result, the population will have a large variety of traits. The individuals in a population that has low genetic variation have many of the same alleles. Therefore, the population has a small variety of traits.

Genetic variation is important for the survival of a species. For example, populations of cheetahs, as shown in **Figure 1,** and other endangered species, have a low genetic variation. Populations with a low genetic variation are less likely than populations that have a high genetic variation to adapt to changes in their environment. For example, if a some members of a population cannot naturally resist a disease, the species is less likely to survive a major outbreak.

Universal Access · Differentiated Instruction

Basic Learners

Genetic Variation Large populations often have more genetic variation than small populations. Demonstrate this concept by filling a jar with different types of beans. Use different amounts of different types of bean. For example, you may use a large amount of pinto beans and only a few small lima beans. Explain to the students that the beans represent a large population of animals, and that the different types of beans represent individuals with different traits. Demonstrate that smaller populations often have less genetic variation by placing small handfuls of beans from the jar into piles to represent small populations. (If the lima beans are only present in small amount in the jar, then some of the piles will contain few, if any, lima beans.) Tell students that a

Environmental Factors

Individuals in a population often have different traits. But which traits are favorable, and which traits are unfavorable? The answer depends on environmental factors. *Environmental factors* are the conditions in an environment that affect the organisms that live there.

Different environments have different environmental factors. For example, organisms that live in a desert need to be able to survive in an area that receives little water. And organisms that live near coral reefs need to be able to survive in salt water. Also, organisms living near a coral reef have different food sources and different predators than organisms in deserts do.

Certain traits are better in certain environments. For example, a snake that lives in tall, green grass may benefit from being green. In this environment, a green snake will be able to hide from predators more easily than a brown snake will. Therefore, green snakes will survive and reproduce more than brown snakes will. But being brown may be more beneficial if the snake lives on a forest floor that has a large amount of dead leaves. On a forest floor, a brown snake will probably survive and reproduce more than a green snake will.

Standards Check What are environmental factors? **7.3.a**

7.3.a Students know both genetic variation and environmental factors are causes of evolution and diversity of organisms.

7.3.e Students know that extinction of a species occurs when the environment changes and the adaptive characteristics of a species are insufficient for its survival.

7.4.f Students know how movements of Earth's continental and oceanic plates through time, with associated changes in climate and geographic connections, have affected the past and present distribution of organisms.

Quick Lab

Adaptations of Bird Beaks

The shape of a bird's beak is adapted to the way that the bird usually obtains food. In this activity, you will observe how some beak shapes are more favorable than other beak shapes based on the type of food that a bird eats.

7.3.a
7.3.e
7.7.c

▶ Try It!

1. Your teacher will provide you with a **tray of small objects,** such as nuts and rice. These objects represent different types of seeds.

2. You will also select different **tools,** such as pliers and tweezers. The tools represent different types of bird beaks.

3. Use the tools to pick up the different objects. Record which tool works best to pick up each object.

▶ Think About It!

4. Imagine an island on which all of the plants that produce small seeds are killed by a drought. Which type of bird is most likely going to be able to survive and reproduce on this island: birds that have small beaks or birds that have large beaks?

5. For the situation described in question 4, what is the important environmental factor?

6. Imagine returning to the island after many years and observing that plants that produce small seeds no longer exist. Would you expect to find more small-beaked birds or more large-beaked birds?

⏱ **20 min**

Connection to Earth Science

Environmental Factors Begin a class by displaying the transparency "Ocean Zones: A." Ask students to describe the environmental factors that affect organisms that live in the ocean. (Sample answers: water temperature, amount of sunlight. types of predators)

 Teaching Transparency:
LINK TO EARTH SCIENCE E90 Ocean Zones: A

predator frequently catches the pinto beans and occasional catches the lima beans. Ask students which population among all the small populations and the large population in the jar is most likely to survive. Then, ask which population is least likely to survive. (The populations with the most lima beans are most likely to survive. The populations with the fewest lima beans are less likely to survive.) **LS** Visual/Kinesthetic

Teach

Quick Lab ⏱ 20 min

Teacher Notes
This activity has students model how different environmental factors can favor certain traits (covers standard 7.3.a, 7.3.e, and 7.7.c). Instead of using nuts and rice, you might choose to use birdseed that includes a variety of seed sizes.

Materials for Each Group
- several different tools for picking up small things, such as regular pliers, needle-nose pliers, tweezers, kitchen tongs
- tray with small objects, such as nuts and rice

Safety Caution
Remind students to review all safety cautions and icons before beginning this activity. Point out that the tools used in this experiment are not toys and should be handled carefully to prevent injuries.

Answers
4. With no small seeds to feed on and being unable to crack open large seeds, birds with small beaks would die off in large numbers, leaving mostly large-beaked birds.

5. The environmental factor is the availability of larger seeds.

6. You would probably find more birds with large beaks because those birds would be able to find more resources and reproduce more than birds with small beaks would be able to.

📋 Differentiated Datasheets
A **BASIC**, B **GENERAL**, C **ADVANCED**

Also editable on the Holt Lab Generator CD-ROM

Answer to Standards Check

Environmental factors are the conditions in an environment that affect the organisms that live there. **7.3.a** (mastering)

Using the Figure

Separating Populations Use the three pictures at the bottom of this page to lead a discussion about ways that populations can be separated. Ask students to suggest ways that animals can be separated other than those shown in the pictures. (Sample answers: volcano, hurricane or other storm, transportation by humans, ice freezing and melting, road or building construction by humans)
LS Visual/Verbal

Teaching Transparency:
L42 Evolution of the Galápagos Finches

Debate

Separating People Lead a debate about whether or not separating people by oceans and mountains creates separate populations in the same way that other animal groups develop separate populations. Encourage students to consider languages, daily activities, clothing, food choices, educational choices, habitats, and nature of communities, as well as transportation options that decrease the actual separation of people.
LS Verbal/Logical

Group ACTiViTy

Amazing Adaptations Have groups of students collaborate to create depictions of hypothetical organisms with interesting adaptations for bizarre imaginary environments or conditions, or perhaps other planets. Ask students to create captions to explain each organism's unique traits. As an alternative, have students research and make posters about interesting animals with adaptations that actually exist in extreme environments, such as the Arctic or deserts.
LS Interpersonal/Logical Co-op Learning

Figure 2 After squirrel populations by the Grand Canyon became separated, they formed two species: the Kaibab squirrel (left) and the Abert squirrel (right).

Forming a New Species

Sometimes, drastic changes that can form a new species take place. A new species may form after a group becomes separated from the original population. This group forms a new population. Over time, the new population adapts to its new environment. Over time, both populations evolve different adaptations. The two populations differ so greatly that they can no longer mate successfully. The new population may then be considered a new species.

The formation of a new species as a result of evolution is called **speciation. Figure 2** shows two species of squirrels that live on opposite sides of the Grand Canyon. At one time, these squirrels were probably part of one population. As the Grand Canyon became larger, the population became separated and evolved into two species.

speciation (SPEE shee AY shuhn) the formation of new species as a result of evolution

Separation

Speciation often begins when a part of a population becomes separated from the rest. The process of separation can happen in many ways. For example, a newly formed canyon, mountain range, or lake can divide a population as **Figure 3** shows. Movements of Earth's continental and oceanic plates can also affect the distribution of organisms.

Figure 3 Populations can become separated in a variety of ways.

Universal Access • Differentiated Instruction

Struggling Readers

Using Text and Figures Make sure students realize that the information in the figures adds important details to the information in the text. Direct students' attention to **Figure 4**. Ask them to read the caption below each part. Then, ask them to read the paragraph in the text where **Figure 4** is mentioned. Ask students to identify details that are given in the

Figure 4 captions that are not included in the text. (The captions show step-by-step how the finches evolved into separate species.) Ask students how the details in the captions relate to the information in the text. (The text says that a geographical barrier can cause a species to split into separate species. The captions give a detailed example of this situation.)
LS Visual/Logical

Adaptation

After two groups have separated, natural selection continues to act on the groups. Over many generations, the groups may evolve different sets of traits. If the environmental conditions for each group differ, the groups' adaptations will differ. For example, a population of birds may become separated into two groups living on two different islands. The birds living on the island that has bigger, tougher seeds will probably evolve different adaptations for eating than the birds living on the island that has small, soft seeds will.

Reproductive Isolation

Natural selection can cause two separated groups to become very different. If the groups are reunited and cannot interbreed anymore, the groups have undergone *reproductive isolation*. If they cannot interbreed, the two groups are no longer the same species. **Figure 4** shows how species of Galápagos finches may have evolved through separation, adaptation, and reproductive isolation.

Standards Check What are the three parts of speciation? 7.4.f

INTERNET ACTIVITY

Environment and Evolution

Can you balance the need for food with the needs of the environment? Argue for or against the use of insecticides. Go to **go.hrw.com**, and type in the keyword HY7EVOW.

Figure 4 The Evolution of Species of Galápagos Finches

① Some finches left the mainland and reached one of the islands (separation).

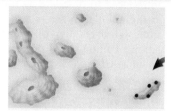

② The finches reproduced and adapted to the environment (adaptation).

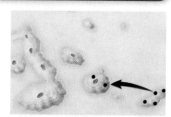

③ Some finches flew to a second island (separation).

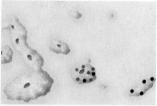

④ These finches reproduced and adapted to the second island's environment (adaptation).

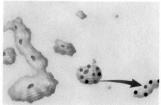

⑤ Some finches flew to the first island but could not interbreed with the finches there (reproductive isolation).

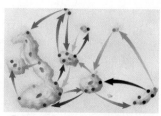

⑥ This process may have occurred over and over again as the finches flew to the other islands.

Teach, continued

Group ACTIVITY

Adaptation Selection Poster Tell students to imagine that a population of rabbits is divided into two populations when a levee breaks. Explain that one of the groups remains in the forest where the original population lived and the other group now lives in a residential suburb.

Divide students into small groups. Ask each group to create a poster showing some adaptations they expect to see in the suburban rabbits. (Sample answers: adjust to different foods (eat garden vegetables and yard grasses instead of wild plants—may develop sharper teeth to consume the garden vegetables); adjust to different predators (run from dogs, cars, and people instead of wild animals); adjust to a different habitat (live under a bush next to a house instead of under a pile of brush in the forest) **LS Visual/Interpersonal**

Using the Figure

Counting Generations Use **Figure 4** to lead a discussion about changes within generations. Point out that some animal adaptations take thousands of years, but finches have been known to acquire some adaptations within a few years. Ask students what must be true about the time between finch generations for adaptations to appear so quickly. (Sample answer: Finches must reproduce often for adaptations to appear within years.) **LS Verbal**

Answer to Standards Check

Three parts of speciation are separation, adaptation, and reproductive isolation. **7.4.f** (mastering)

Standards Focus

This **Standards Focus** provides you with a quick way to **assess, reteach,** and **re-assess** one or more concepts in the section.

Assess

What role can habitat play in extinction? (Sample answer: Animals that lose their habitat must adapt to new habitats or they could face extinction.) **7.3.e**

Reteach

Raccoon Adaptations Ask students if they have ever seen a raccoon getting into a garbage can or bag. Ask students what a dog might do if it is outside and a raccoon is in the garbage. (A dog will probably scare the raccoon off.) Ask students how raccoons in suburban areas are different from raccoons that live in forests. (Raccoons in suburban areas eat human garbage and interact with dogs.) **LS** Logical **7.3.a**

Re-Assess

Extinction Concept Map Ask students to create a concept map showing how animals could become extinct. Tell them to be sure to include these terms: *extinct, competition, predators, food supply, habitat,* and *failure to adapt.* (Accept any reasonable concept map.) **LS** Visual/Logical **7.3.a, 7.3.e**

MISCONCEPTION ALERT

Preventing Extinction
Some students may think that extinction can be prevented by keeping organisms in zoos. Ask students to research the birth rate of cheetahs in captivity. Discuss how zookeepers can take many steps to prevent extinction, but they cannot assure healthy births. Also discuss whether preserving species in zoos is as valuable as preserving them in the wild.

SCHOOL to HOME

Caring For A New Pet
If you could have one extinct animal to keep as a pet, which would you choose? With a family member, select an extinct animal to research. You will want the food and habitat that you provide for your pet to be similar to what the animal had before it went extinct. In your **Science Journal,** describe how you will care for your new pet.

ACTIVITY

extinct (ek STINGKT) describes a species that has died out completely

Figure 5 *Since European red foxes (left) were introduced to Australia, they prey on many animals, such as numbats (right).*

Extinction

Organisms have adaptive characteristics that help them survive in their environment. But what happens when the environmental factors change? Sometimes organisms can survive and reproduce after the environment has changed. However, if the adaptations of a species are not sufficient for organisms to survive, the species may become extinct. A species is **extinct** when all individuals of the species have died. Increased competition, new predators, and the loss of habitat are examples of environmental conditions that can lead to extinction.

Increased Competition

Resources such as food, water, shelter, space, or sunlight are in limited supply in the environment. Populations of different species often compete for resources. When the quantity of resources in an environment decreases, competition for the remaining resources increases. If the members of a species cannot gather the resources that they need, the species may become extinct.

New Predators

Sometimes, a new species enters an area. The new species may come from a nearby area or may be introduced by humans. For example, the European red fox, shown in **Figure 5,** was introduced to Australia by humans. Species in Australia, such as the numbat in **Figure 5,** do not have adaptations to escape foxes. So, foxes prey on numbats and have caused the population of numbats to decrease. Many species in Australia are endangered because of the introduction of new predators.

Standards Check How can a new predator cause a species to go extinct? **7.3.e**

Universal Access · Differentiated Instruction

Advanced Learners/GATE

Endangered Animals Point out to students that, just as there have been many animals that have become extinct in the past, there are many animals now that are in danger of becoming extinct. Write a list of endangered animals on the board. Ask students to choose one animal from the list and research to find out how or why these animals face extinction. Make sure all animals are chosen once before any are chosen a second time.

Examples of endangered or threatened animals in California:

San Bernardino kangaroo rat, California freshwater shrimp, Steller sea lion, California condor, California red-legged frog, El Segundo blue butterfly, Chinhook salmon, Steelhead, Loggerhead sea turtle, Santa Cruz Island fox **LS** Verbal/Logical

Loss of Habitat

Most species get the food, water, and shelter that they need from the habitat in which they live. What happens if a habitat is destroyed? **Figure 6** shows a forest that was harvested for timber. The trees that many living things once depended on for food and shelter are gone. Pollution can damage a habitat so that organisms can no longer live there. Habitats can also be destroyed by natural disasters, such as floods, storms, and forest fires.

When a population loses its habitat, it may move to a new area. Sometimes, the population may not have adaptations that allow it to live in nearby environments. As a result, species may go extinct.

Figure 6 *These trees can no longer supply food and shelter for other organisms.*

SECTION Review

7.3.a, 7.3.e, 7.4.f

Summary

- A population that has high genetic variation will have many individuals with different sets of traits.

- Environmental factors determine which traits are favorable and which traits are unfavorable.

- Natural selection explains how one species evolves into another.

- Separation, adaptation, and reproductive isolation can lead to speciation.

- If environmental conditions change, a species may not be able to survive and may go extinct.

- Environmental conditions that can lead to extinction of species include increased competition, new predators, and loss of habitat.

Using Vocabulary

① Write an original definition for *genetic variation*.

Understanding Concepts

② **Describing** Describe how the introduction of a new predator can cause a species to go extinct.

③ **Identifying** What environmental factors may affect an organism that lives on a rocky beach?

④ **Describing** Describe how new species of Galápagos finches may have formed.

⑤ **Describing** Explain how genetic variation and environmental factors affect evolution by natural selection.

Critical Thinking

⑥ **Forming Hypotheses** Suppose that the distance between some islands is small enough for birds to fly frequently between all of the islands. Is this situation likely to lead to speciation? Explain.

⑦ **Making Inferences** Mass extinctions are periods in Earth's history when many species have become extinct. Some evidence suggests that major environmental changes occurred during mass extinctions. Explain how changes in the environment could be related to mass extinctions.

Challenge

⑧ **Forming Hypotheses** When dinosaurs were alive, most of the mammals were small. After the dinosaurs became extinct, mammals evolved into many different forms, such as cats and elephants. Explain how the extinction of dinosaurs may be related to the increase in the number of species of mammals.

Internet Resources

For a variety of links related to this chapter, go to www.scilinks.org
Topic: Species and Adaptation
SciLinks code: HY71433

---

4. After living on separate islands, populations of finches evolved different adaptations. When some finches from one island flew to an islands that had a different population of finches living on it, the two populations were so different that they could not interbreed. **7.4.f** (mastering)

5. Environmental factors determine which traits are favorable or unfavorable. Genetic variation measures how many different genes are found in a population. If the genetic variation is high, there will be more traits that can be either favorable or unfavorable, depending on the environment. **7.3.a** (mastering)

6. no; This situation probably will not lead to speciation because separation is not likely to occur. **7.4.f** (exceeding)

7. If the environment changed over a short period of time, organisms may not have adaptive characteristics that enable them to survive in the new environment. So, mass extinctions could occur because the organisms fail to adapt to changes in the environment. **7.3.e** (exceeding)

8. Sample answer: When the dinosaurs were alive, they were able to get more resources than mammals. Mammals could only get resources if they were small. After the dinosaurs died, the mammals could obtain different types of resources. Mammals evolved different adaptations that helped them get specific resources. As mammals evolved different traits, they evolved into different species. **7.3.a** (exceeding)

Section Review Standards Guide

	Supporting	Mastering	Exceeding
7.3.a		1, 3, 5	8
7.3.e		2	7
7.4.f		4	6

Section Resources

- Directed Reading A **BASIC** (Also in Spanish), B **GENERAL**

- Interactive Reader and Study Guide

- Section Quiz **GENERAL** (Also in Spanish)

- Section Review **GENERAL** (Also in Spanish)

- Vocabulary and Section Summary A **BASIC** (Also in Spanish), B **GENERAL**

Answer to Standards Check

If a new predator is introduced, existing species may not have adaptive characteristics that enable individuals to escape the predator. **7.3.e** (mastering)

Answers to Section Review

1. Sample answer: Genetic variation describes how genetically similar individuals in a population are. **7.3.a** (mastering)

2. A species may not have adaptations that help them escape a new predator, so the predators are able to catch many individuals. The species can become extinct if too many of the members are killed. **7.3.e** (mastering)

3. An animal that lives on a rocky beach has to be able to withstand storms, salt water, and wind. The animal must be able to find shelter, find food, and avoid predators. **7.3.a** (mastering)

Inquiry Lab

Teacher Notes

This activity has students model how genetic variability and environmental factors interact to cause evolution by natural selection (covers standards 7.3.a, 7.7.c, and 7.7.e).

Time Required

One or two 45-minute class periods

Lab Ratings

Teacher Prep 🧪

Student Set-Up 🧪🧪

Concept Level 🧪🧪

Clean Up 🧪

Materials

The materials listed on the student page are enough for ten students working in pairs.

Safety Caution

Remind students to review all safety cautions before beginning this lab activity. Safety concerns will vary with each design.

Preparation Notes

Be prepared for a variety of experimental designs. For example, students may wish to test which color will crack easiest under physical stress or which color will dissolve more quickly in water. This lab is an opportunity to reinforce scientific methods and practice designing experiments. Encourage students to brainstorm a variety of possible hypotheses and ways of testing the hypotheses. Have students identify scientific methods in their experiments.

OBJECTIVES

Form a hypothesis about the fate of the candy-coated chocolates.

Predict what will happen to the candy-coated chocolates.

Design and conduct an experiment to test your hypothesis.

MATERIALS

- chocolates, candy-coated, small, in a variety of colors (about 100)
- items to be determined by the students and approved by the teacher

SAFETY

7.3.a Students know both genetic variation and environmental factors are causes of evolution and diversity of organisms.

Investigation and Experimentation
7.7.c Communicate the logical connection among hypotheses, science concepts, tests conducted, data collected, and conclusions drawn from the scientific evidence.
7.7.e Communicate the steps and results from an investigation in written reports and oral presentations.

Survival of the Chocolates

Imagine a world populated with candy, and hold that delicious thought in your head for just a moment. Try to apply the idea of natural selection to a population of candy-coated chocolates. According to the theory of natural selection, individuals who have favorable adaptations are more likely to survive. In the "species" of candy-coated chocolates that you will study in this experiment, the characteristics of individual chocolates may help the chocolates "survive." For example, shell strength (the strength of the candy coating) could be an adaptive advantage. Plan an experiment to find out which characteristics of the chocolates are favorable "adaptations."

Ask a Question

1. What might "survival" mean for a candy-coated chocolate? What are some ways to test which chocolates are the "strongest" or "most fit" for their environment? Also, write down any other questions that you could ask about the "survival" of the chocolates.

Form a Hypothesis

2. Form a hypothesis, and make a prediction. If you choose to study candy color, your prediction may be similar to the following: If the ___ colored shell is the strongest, then fewer of the chocolates with this color of shell will ___ when ___.

Lab Resources

📋 Differentiated Datasheets
  A **Basic**, B **General**, C **Advanced**

💿 Classroom Lab Video/DVD

🔴 **Holt Lab Generator CD-ROM**

Search for any lab by topic, standard, difficulty level, or time. Edit any lab to fit your needs, or create your own labs. Use the Lab Materials QuickList software to customize your lab materials list.

Test the Hypothesis

3 Design a procedure to determine which type of candy-coated chocolate is most likely to survive. In your plan, be sure to include materials and tools that you may need to complete this procedure.

4 Before you begin, ask your teacher to check your experimental design. Your teacher will supply the candy and will assist you in gathering materials and tools.

5 Record your results in a data table. Be sure to organize your data in a clear and understandable way.

Analyze the Results

6 **Describing Events** Write a report that describes your experiment. Be sure to include tables and graphs of your data.

Draw Conclusions

7 **Evaluating Data** In your report, explain how your data either support or do not support your hypothesis. Include possible errors and ways to improve your procedure.

Big Idea Question

8 **Making Predictions** If the candy-coated chocolates were living things, which chocolates would survive and reproduce more than the others?

Applying Your Data

Can you think of another characteristic that can be tested to determine which type of chocolate is best adapted to survive? Explain your idea, and describe how you might test it.

Ask a Question

1. Sample answer: For chocolates, survival might mean that the shell is not cracked or that the colored covering is not smeared.

Form a Hypothesis

2. Answers may vary. The example statement is only an example for format. Students may wish to investigate a characteristic other than candy shell hardness. Help them make a prediction about their own experiments. Check that all students have formed testable hypotheses.

Test the Hypothesis

4. Answer may vary. Check that students have planned a controlled experiment and that each factor is accounted for. Also, check that they have planned for all materials they will need.

5. Answers may vary. Students should conduct their own experiments and record all procedures, observations, and results. Students should use data tables to record results where appropriate.

Analyze the Results

6. Reports may vary but should describe all parts of the experiment and present the results with tables, diagrams, or graphs as appropriate.

Draw Conclusions

7. Reports may vary but should include a conclusion whether the hypothesis was supported or not. Check that student conclusions are directly related to the hypothesis and were logically drawn from the experimental results.

Big Idea Question

8. Answers may vary depending on the results of the tests performed by students.

Carol Lindstrom
Leonard Herman
Intermediate School
San Jose, California

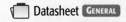
Science Skills Activity

| Scientific Methods | Research | Data Analysis | Models, Maps & Diagrams |

Investigation and Experimentation

7.7.c Communicate the logical connection among hypotheses, science concepts, tests conducted, data collected, and conclusions drawn from the scientific evidence.

Scientific Methods: Testing Hypotheses

▶ **Tutorial**

When you perform a scientific investigation, you will often start with a question and develop a hypothesis. A hypothesis is a possible answer to a question. In this tutorial, you will learn how to use a hypothesis to design an investigation.

Question: Does the size of a flowerpot affect how much fruit a tomato plant produces?

Hypothesis: If tomato plants are grown in large pots, then the plants will produce more fruit than plants grown in small pots will.

Procedure

1 Identify the Outcome The outcome describes what you will observe or measure during the investigation. The "then" part of the hypothesis includes the outcome.

Outcome: amount of tomatoes

2 Define the Outcome Sometimes you need to define how you will measure the outcome.

The number of tomatoes could be misleading because the plants could produce many small fruits or a few large fruits. I will measure the total mass of the tomatoes produced by each plant.

3 Identify Factors A factor is anything in the experiment that can influence the outcome.

Factors: amount of water, amount of sunlight, size of pot, type of soil, and temperature

4 Identify Variables A variable is a factor that can be changed. Often, you can change many of the factors. But the variable must test the hypothesis.

Variable: size of flower pot

5 Monitoring Controlled Factors In a controlled experiment, all of the factors that are not variables should be kept constant. If there are multiple variables, only one variable should be changed at a time. You may need to make a plan to keep the factors constant during the investigation.

I will use the same type of potting soil in each pot. Each plant will get 50 mL of water per day. Plants will be kept in a green house, where they will all receive the same amount of sunlight and be kept at the same temperature.

▶ **You Try It!**

Procedure

Insects can carry diseases that affect humans. For example, mosquitoes in tropical areas transmit malaria. One way to reduce the number of cases of diseases, such as malaria, is to use insecticides. Insecticides are chemicals that can be sprayed to kill insects.

Some populations of insects have become resistant to insecticides. Insecticide resistance is an example of natural selection in action. Some insects are naturally resistant to insecticides. In an environment where these chemicals are being used, the insects resistant to insecticides survive and reproduce more than other insects do. So,

more insects in the next generation will inherit the insecticide resistance genes.

In this activity, you will design an experiment that will test the following hypothesis: If a mosquito population is exposed to insecticides, then the number of mosquitoes that are resistant to the insecticide will increase in later generations.

1 Identify the outcome and define how you will measure it.

2 Identify controlled factors and the variables.

3 Make a plan for keeping controlled factors the same during the investigation.

Chapter Summary

The Big Idea Biological evolution explains how populations change over time.

Section

Vocabulary

① Change over Time

Key Concept Independent lines of evidence from geology, fossils, and comparative anatomy provide the bases for the theory of evolution.

- The fossil record provides evidence that species have changed over time.
- Fossils support the hypothesis that modern whales evolved from land mammals.
- Comparing the anatomy and DNA of organisms provides evidence that organisms have common ancestors.

Trilobite fossils are the remains of an extinct species.

adaptation p. 298
species p. 298
evolution p. 299
fossil p. 300
fossil record p. 300

② How Does Evolution Happen?

Key Concept After making observations and analyzing evidence, Charles Darwin concluded that natural selection is the mechanism of evolution.

- Darwin made many observations and was influenced by ideas from other fields.
- The four parts of natural selection are overproduction, inherited variation, struggle to survive, and successful reproduction.

Charles Darwin developed the theory of evolution by natural selection.

trait p. 308
selective breeding p. 308
natural selection p. 310

③ Natural Selection in Action

Key Concept Natural selection explains how populations adapt to changes in their environment and why some species become extinct.

- Genetic variation and environmental factors affect evolution by natural selection.
- Separation, adaptation, and reproductive isolation can produce new species.
- Extinction occurs when the adaptations of a species are insufficient for survival in a changing environment.

The numbat is an animal that faces extinction because of new predators.

speciation p. 314
extinct p. 316

Review Resources

- Reinforcement Worksheet BASIC
- Critical Thinking Worksheet ADVANCED
- Chapter Review GENERAL (Also in Spanish)
- Standards Review Workbook (Also in Spanish)
- Study Guide A BASIC (Also in Spanish), B GENERAL

Assessment Resources

- Chapter Tests A BASIC, B GENERAL (Also in Spanish), C ADVANCED
- Standards Assessment GENERAL

Chapter Summary

SUPER SUMMARY

Have students connect the major concepts in this chapter through an interactive Super Summary. Visit go.hrw.com and type in the keyword HY7EVOS to access the Super Summary for this chapter.

Identifying Suffixes

Independent Activity Have students fold a piece of paper in half lengthwise. On one half, have them write the vocabulary words and the definition of each word. On the second half of the paper, have them write the suffix for each of the vocabulary word that is a combination of a root and a suffix. Explain to the students that they can use a dictionary to determine the meaning of each suffix. Have them write the meaning of the suffix on the second column with the suffix. (Sample answer: adaptation; An adaptation is a characteristic that improves an individuals ability to survive and reproduce in a particular environment; -ation; The root "-ation" means "the act of.")
LS Logical

Focus on Writing

Short Story Have students write a short story about a young scientist who discovers some unusual fossils and works to find out about the species from which the fossil came. **LS** Intrapersonal

Chapter Review

7.3.a, 7.3.b, 7.3.c,
7.3.d, 7.3.e, 7.4.f

Assignment Guide

Section	Questions
1	2, 3, 5, 8, 9, 12, 15, 18
2	6, 7, 10, 13, 17, 19, 20, 21, 23
3	1, 4, 11, 16

Answers

Using Vocabulary

1. Sample answer: Mechanism is the means or process by which something gets done.

2. species **7.3.d** (supporting)

3. adaptation **7.3.b** (supporting)

Understanding Concepts

4. c **7.3.a** (mastering)

5. b **7.3.c** (mastering)

6. c **7.3.b** (mastering)

7. d **7.3.b** (mastering)

8. Sample answer: The body structure of living organisms can be compared with other living organisms and with organisms from the fossil record. Also, the DNA of living organisms can be compared. A large amount of similarities likely indicates that individuals shared a recent common ancestor. **7.3.c** (mastering)

9. Sample answer: Whales share many internal similarities with hoofed land mammals. Ancient fossils of four-legged land mammals share characteristics with modern whales and other hoofed mammals. A sequence of fossil organisms shows how the characteristics of modern whales could have evolved from those of ancient land mammals. **7.3.c** (exceeding)

10. Sample answer: Those animals that are better adapted to the conditions of their environment are more likely to survive to adulthood. **7.3.b** (exceeding)

Organize

Tri-Fold Review the FoldNote that you created at the beginning of the chapter. Add to or correct the FoldNote based on what you have learned.

Using Vocabulary

1. **Academic Vocabulary** In the sentence "Natural selection is the mechanism of evolution," what does the term *mechanism* mean?

Complete each of the following sentences by choosing the correct term from the word bank.

adaptation   species
natural selection

2. A group of organisms that can mate with each other to produce fertile offspring is known as a(n) ___.

3. A(n) ___ makes an organism better able to survive in its environment.

Understanding Concepts

Multiple Choice

4. Charles Darwin observed variations between individuals within a population, but he did not know how variations occur. Which of the following causes variation in a population?
   a. interbreeding
   b. differences in food
   c. genetic variation
   d. selective breeding

5. The fossil record is a history of life indicated by fossils found in Earth's crust. What information about organisms in an environment can the fossil record provide?
   a. how natural selection occurs
   b. how organisms in an environment changed over time
   c. how selective breeding occurs
   d. how genetic variation occurs

6. Darwin puzzled over the various species of Galápagos finches. He eventually concluded that over time, the finches adapted to various environments on the islands. On which of the following traits did Darwin base his conclusions?
   a. eye color
   b. flight patterns
   c. beak size and shape
   d. bone structure of the wings

7. Darwin developed the theory of evolution by making careful observations and by studying ideas from different fields. Which of the following did NOT influence Darwin?
   a. *Principles of Geology* by Charles Lyell
   b. *An Essay on the Principle of Population* by Thomas Malthus
   c. observations of selective breeding
   d. evidence from molecular biology

Short Answer

8. **Identifying** Identify two ways that organisms can be compared to provide evidence of evolution from a common ancestor.

9. **Describing** Describe evidence that supports the hypothesis that whales evolved from land-dwelling mammals.

10. **Comparing** Why are some animals more likely to survive to adulthood than other animals are?

11. **Describing** Describe how environmental changes can cause species to become extinct.

INTERPRETING GRAPHICS Use the photograph below to answer the next question.

12. **Identifying** Identify some of the adaptations that sea turtles have for living in the ocean.

11. If a species does not have adaptations that allow it to survive in a new environment, that species may become extinct when the environment changes. **7.3.e** (mastering)

12. Sample answer: Sea turtles have large, flat fins for swimming, a flat shell that helps them move through the water, and coloration that helps them blend in with the ocean floor. **7.3.b** (supporting)

Writing Skills

13. Communicating Concepts Write a paragraph explaining how natural selection occurs. Be sure to include the four parts of natural section.

Critical Thinking

14. Concept Mapping Use the following terms to create a concept map: *struggle to survive, theory, genetic variation, Darwin, overpopulation, natural selection,* and *successful reproduction.*

15. Analyzing Relationships A team of scientists is studying three species of frogs. How would the scientists use comparative anatomy and molecular biology to determine which two of the three species of frogs share the most recent common ancestor?

16. Analyzing Relationships Geologists have evidence that the continents were once a single giant landmass. This giant landmass eventually split apart, and the individual continents moved to their current positions. What role might this movement of continents have played in evolution?

17. Forming Hypotheses Tarantulas defend themselves by flicking hairs into the eyes of their predators. In a population of tarantulas, a few tarantulas do not have these hairs. Why are the tarantulas that have these hairs more likely to produce offspring than the hairless tarantulas are?

18. Identifying Relationships You are drawing a branching diagram to show the relationships between turtles, frogs, and alligators. Which two organisms does the diagram indicate as having the most recent common ancestor?

19. Analyzing Processes Similar species of lizards can be found on several Caribbean islands. But the species have some different traits that match the different environments in which they live. Explain how speciation could have produced the different species of lizards.

INTERPRETING GRAPHICS Use the graph below to answer the next two questions.

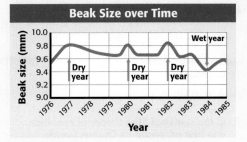

20. Evaluating Data During dry years, fewer seeds are produced. Birds have to be able to eat the large, tough seeds. How does the change of this environmental factor affect the average beak size of Galápagos finches?

21. Predicting Consequences Imagine that a storm blew some of the birds on the Galápagos Islands to a new island. The new island receives a large amount of rain. After several generations on the new island, what would you expect to happen to the average beak size of the finches?

Math Skills

22. Making Calculations A biologist studying Anaconda snakes captures five snakes of the following lengths: 8.9 m, 7.3 m, 6.6 m, 7.5 m, and 8.7 m. What is the average length of the snakes?

Challenge

23. Forming Hypotheses Whales share a more recent common ancestor with land mammals than they do with fishes. Whales breathe air, give birth to live young, and produce milk like mammals. The DNA of whales is more similar to the DNA of land mammals than it is to the DNA of fishes. Still, whales do share some characteristics with fishes. For example, both fishes and whales use flat fins to swim. How does natural selection explain how whales and fishes can have similar adaptations despite not having a recent common ancestor?

16. Sample answer: The splitting of one giant continent would cause populations of a species to be isolated from each other. This separation is a key part of the process of speciation as isolated populations would then adapt to their individual environments. **7.4.f** (mastering)

17. Tarantulas that have hairs will be better able to defend themselves. If they can defend themselves, the tarantulas are more likely to survive and reproduce than tarantulas that do not have hairs and cannot defend themselves. **7.3.b** (exceeding)

18. Turtles and alligators have the most recent common ancestor because they are both reptiles. **7.3.d** (exceeding)

19. Speciation can produce different species when populations are separated. While the lizards were separated on different islands, they may have evolved different traits. The different groups became so different over time that they can no longer interbreed, so they are different species. **7.4.f** (mastering)

20. During dry years, the average beak size increases. **7.3.a** (exceeding)

21. Based on the trend in the table, the beak size would probably decrease. **7.3.a** (exceeding)

Math Skills

22. 7.8 m; (8.9 m + 7.3 m + 6.6 m + 7.5 m + 8.7 m)/5 = 7.8 m

Challenge

23. Even though they do not share a recent common ancestor, whales and fishes are still influenced by the same environmental factors. So, both whales and fishes with strong fins would be more likely to survive and reproduce than members of their species that did not have those characteristics.

Writing Skills

13. Answers may vary but should include overproduction, inherited variation, struggle to survive, and successful reproduction. **7.3.b** (mastering)

Critical Thinking

14. An answer to this exercise can be found at the end of this book. **7.3.b** (mastering)

15. The scientists could compare the anatomical structures of the different frogs. They could also compare the DNA sequences of the frogs. The species that have the most similarities of anatomical structures and DNA sequences probably share the most recent common ancestor. **7.3.c** (mastering)

Chapter Review Standards Guide			
	Supporting	**Mastering**	**Exceeding**
7.3.a		4	20–21
7.3.b	3, 12	6–7, 10, 13–14	17
7.3.c		5, 8, 15	9
7.3.d	2		18
7.3.e		11	
7.3.f		16, 19	

Standards Assessment

6.5.c, 6.5.e, 7.2.b, 7.2.e, 7.3.a, 7.3.b, 7.3.c, 7.3.d, 7.3.e

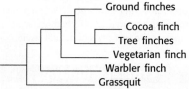

Teacher Notes

To provide practice under more realistic testing conditions, give students 20 min to answer all of the questions in this assessment.

Answer Key

Question Number	Correct Answer
1	B
2	D
3	C
4	D
5	C
6	D
7	A
8	A
9	A
10	C
11	A
12	B
13	A
14	C

Standards Guide

	Supporting	Mastering	Exceeding
6.5.a		11	
6.5.e		12	
7.2.b		14	
7.2.e		13	
7.3.a		1, 9	
7.3.b	2	4	8
7.3.c		10	
7.3.d		5	
7.3.e	6	3	
7.4.f			7

📁 Standards Assessment **GENERAL**

📁 Teacher Notes for Standards Assessment contain a longer Assessment Doctor and Diagnostic Teaching Tips.

REVIEWING ACADEMIC VOCABULARY

1 Which of the following words is the closest in meaning to the word *diversity*?

- A change
- B variety
- C availability
- D adaptation

2 In the sentence "The theory of evolution was first proposed by Charles Darwin," what does the word *theory* mean?

- A an idea that is not based on evidence
- B a belief that guides a person's actions
- C a thought or plan that exists in the mind
- D an explanation developed using scientific methods

3 Choose the appropriate form of the word *adapt* for the following sentence: Species that evolve _____ characteristics are more likely to survive environmental changes than species that do not develop these characteristics are.

- A adapt
- B adapting
- C adaptive
- D adaptation

4 Which of the following words means "any system or means by which something gets done"?

- A characteristic
- B sequence
- C attention
- D mechanism

REVIEWING CONCEPTS

- Ground finches
- Cocoa finch
- Tree finches
- Vegetarian finch
- Warbler finch
- Grassquit

5 According to the diagram above, which of the following statements about finch species is true?

- A Cocoa finches evolved from tree finches.
- B Grassquits and ground finches do not have a common ancestor.
- C Warbler finches are an older species than cocoa finches are.
- D Tree finches are better adapted to their environment than grassquits are.

6 Which term best describes a species in which all of the members have died?

- A evolved
- B decayed
- C endangered
- D extinct

7 Charles Darwin noticed that finches on different islands of the Galápagos Islands were similar but that their beaks differed. What explanation for these differences did he propose?

- A The beaks of the finches are adapted to the way the bird usually gets food.
- B The beaks of the finches are randomly selected by genetic mutation.
- C The different beaks would one day evolve into identical beaks.
- D Beak size is related to the size of the finch.

➕ ASSESSMENT DOCTOR

Question 1: The correct answer is B. Diversity and variety are both characterized by many different forms or kinds.

Question 2: The correct answer is D. A theory is an explanation developed using scientific methods. Darwin collected evidence of changes in and diversity among life forms and used it to formulate a theory about evolution.

Question 3: The correct answer is C. Species that develop *adaptive* characteristics are more likely to survive.

Question 4: The correct answer is D. A mechanism is a method, procedure, or process involved in how something works. Natural selection is the mechanism of evolution, meaning it is the method by which evolution works.

Question 5: The correct answer is C. Because warbler finches branch off earlier in the diagram than cocoa finches do, they are the older species.

Question 6: The correct answer is D. A species is *extinct* when all of its members have died.

Average Beak Measurements of Birds of the Colores Islands			
Island	Average beak length (mm)	Average beak width (mm)	Number of unique species
Verde	9.7	6.5	5
Azul	8.9	8.7	15
Rosa	5.2	8.0	10

8 The table above shows average beak measurements for birds living on three islands. Narrow beaks are best for eating insects. On which island would you expect to find the most birds that eat insects?

A Verde Island

B Azul Island

C Rosa Island

D Verde Island and Azul Island

9 Which of the following factors is necessary for natural selection to occur in a species?

A genetic variation within a population

B an abundance of food resources

C a hospitable environment

D a strong family structure

10 Scientists have noticed similarities between a bat's wings and a dolphin's flippers. What does this evidence tell us about the evolution of bats and dolphins?

A Bats probably evolved from dolphins.

B Bats and dolphins probably adapted to similar environments.

C Bats and dolphins probably have a common ancestor.

D Bats and dolphins use their wings and flippers for the same purposes.

REVIEWING PRIOR LEARNING

11 Which of the following environmental changes would directly affect primary consumers?

A the loss of plant life

B the degradation of soil

C the disappearance of insects

D the disappearance of scavengers

12 Which of the following is an abiotic factor most likely to affect the development of organisms living in a river?

A the plant life in the river

B the speed at which the river travels

C the width of the river

D the bacteria living in the river

13 What is the primary structure that contains genetic information?

A DNA

B proteins

C mitochondria

D RNA

14 Organisms that reproduce sexually contribute _____ of their genes to their offspring.

A none

B all

C about one-half

D about one-quarter

Standards Assessment

Question 7: The correct answer is A. Darwin proposed that the finches had evolved adaptations to their beaks that made them well suited to consuming the food available in their separate habitats.

Question 8: The correct answer is A. The birds on Verde Island had the smallest average width, so these birds would probably be the best at eating insects.

Question 9: The correct answer is A. Genetic mutations are necessary for adaptation, and thus natural selection, to occur. Such mutations guarantee a wide genetic variety within a species and allow those most suited to the environment to be selected for survival and reproduction.

Question 10: The correct answer is C. Bats and dolphins probably have similarities in their front limbs because they share a common ancestor.

Question 11: The correct answer is A. Primary consumers eat plants, so they would be directly affected by the loss of plant life.

Question 12: The correct answer is B. The speed at which water flows in a river is an important abiotic factor that affects the development of the creatures living there.

Question 13: The correct answer is A. Genetic information is passed down to future generations through the DNA in chromosomes.

Question 14: The correct answer is C. Organisms that reproduce sexually contribute about one-half of their genes to their offspring.

Scientific Discoveries

Discussion

Camouflage and Mimicry Discuss that some animals use camouflage or mimicry as a means of protection from predators or to surprise prey. Have students research insects that look like leaves, sea horses that look like coral, corpse flowers that smell like rotting meat, or other plants or animals that employ camouflage or mimicry.

Science Fiction

Background

About the Author Scott Sanders (1945–) writes many different kinds of stories. Early in life, Sanders chose to become a writer rather than a scientist, although he still has an interest in science. Sanders has written about folklore, physics, the naturalist John James Audubon, and settlers of Indiana. Much of his work is nonfiction. His writing has been published in books and periodicals, such as the *Chicago Sun Times*, *Harper's*, and *Omni*.

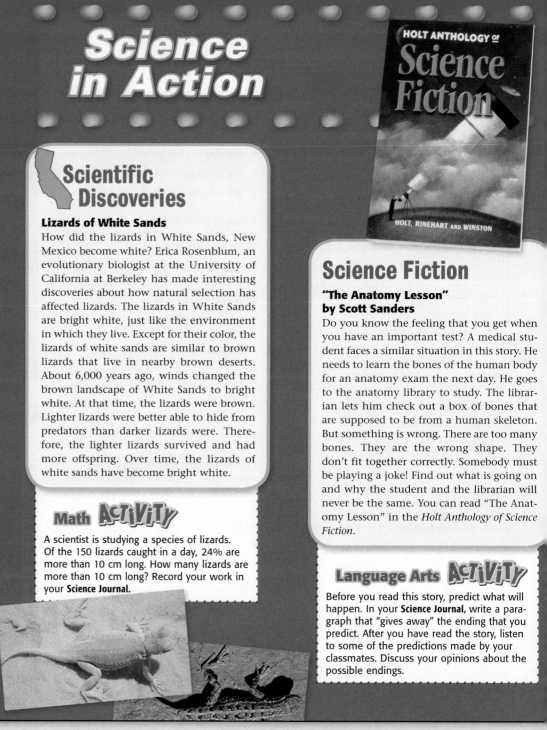

Science in Action

HOLT ANTHOLOGY OF
Science Fiction

HOLT, RINEHART AND WINSTON

Scientific Discoveries

Lizards of White Sands

How did the lizards in White Sands, New Mexico become white? Erica Rosenblum, an evolutionary biologist at the University of California at Berkeley has made interesting discoveries about how natural selection has affected lizards. The lizards in White Sands are bright white, just like the environment in which they live. Except for their color, the lizards of white sands are similar to brown lizards that live in nearby brown deserts. About 6,000 years ago, winds changed the brown landscape of White Sands to bright white. At that time, the lizards were brown. Lighter lizards were better able to hide from predators than darker lizards were. Therefore, the lighter lizards survived and had more offspring. Over time, the lizards of white sands have become bright white.

Math ACTIVITY

A scientist is studying a species of lizards. Of the 150 lizards caught in a day, 24% are more than 10 cm long. How many lizards are more than 10 cm long? Record your work in your **Science Journal.**

Science Fiction

"The Anatomy Lesson" by Scott Sanders

Do you know the feeling that you get when you have an important test? A medical student faces a similar situation in this story. He needs to learn the bones of the human body for an anatomy exam the next day. He goes to the anatomy library to study. The librarian lets him check out a box of bones that are supposed to be from a human skeleton. But something is wrong. There are too many bones. They are the wrong shape. They don't fit together correctly. Somebody must be playing a joke! Find out what is going on and why the student and the librarian will never be the same. You can read "The Anatomy Lesson" in the *Holt Anthology of Science Fiction*.

Language Arts ACTIVITY

Before you read this story, predict what will happen. In your **Science Journal**, write a paragraph that "gives away" the ending that you predict. After you have read the story, listen to some of the predictions made by your classmates. Discuss your opinions about the possible endings.

Answer to Math Activity

$150 \times 0.24 = 36$

Answer to Language Arts Activity

Student paragraphs may vary. Have students compare their predictions to the story's ending and to other students' predictions.

People in Science

Raymond Pierotti

Canine Evolution Raymond Pierotti thinks that it is natural that he became an evolutionary biologist. He grew up exploring the desert around his home in New Mexico. He was fascinated by the abundant wildlife surviving in the bleak landscape. "One of my earliest memories is getting coyotes to sing with me from my backyard," he says.

Pierotti now studies the evolutionary relationships between wolves, coyotes, and domestic dogs. Some of his ideas come from the traditions of the Comanches. According to a Comanche creation story, humans came from wolves. Although Pierotti doesn't believe that humans evolved from wolves, he sees the creation story as a suggestion that humans and wolves have evolved together. "Wolves are very similar to humans in many ways," says Pierotti. "They live in family groups and hunt together. It is possible that wolves actually taught humans how to hunt in packs, and there are ancient stories of wolves and humans hunting together and sharing the food. I think it was this relationship that inspired the Comanche creation stories."

Social Studies ACTIVITY

Research a story of creation that comes from a Greek, Roman, or Native American civilization. In your **Science Journal**, write a paragraph summarizing the myth, and share it with a classmate.

Internet Resources

- To learn more about careers in science, visit www.scilinks.org and enter the SciLinks code HY70225.

- To learn more about these Science in Action topics, visit go.hrw.com and type in the keyword HY7EVOF.

- Check out articles related to this chapter by visiting go.hrw.com. Just type in the keyword HY7EVOC.

Answer to Social Studies Activity
Student summaries may vary. Have students share their summaries with each other or with the entire class, and then have them discuss similarities.

People in Science
ACTIVITY

Dog Report Have every student write or present a report on a breed of dog. The report should focus on the origin and evolution of the breed, with particular attention paid to the culture that bred it and why those characteristics were chosen. The report could also explore whether these breeds make good household pets and why. Students can easily find information on dog breeds on the Internet by searching for either the name of a breed or for "dog breeds" and visiting any of several sites that collect information on different breeds.

The elements listed in the Standards Course of Study provide a base for presenting, supporting, and assessing the California Grade 7 Science Standards. Use this Standards Course of Study as a base for planning your lessons.

Why Teach
Classification

This chapter was designed to cover the California Grade 7 Science Standards about the characteristics of organisms and the classification of organisms (7.1.a and 7.3.d). This chapter follows a chapter about the theory of evolution. The study of evolution has influenced the ways in which organisms are classified by providing an understanding of how differences in DNA and RNA indicate relatedness among species. With this understanding, classification provides biologists with a framework within which new species may be classified. This understanding of DNA and RNA also helps scientists increase their knowledge of the evolution and development of over one million known and described species.

After they have completed this chapter, students will begin a chapter about plants.

 California Standards

Focus on Life Sciences

7.1.a Students know cells function similarly in all living organisms.

7.3.d Students know how to construct a simple branching diagram to classify living groups of organisms by shared derived characteristics and how to expand the diagram to include fossil organisms.

Investigation and Experimentation

7.7.d Construct scale models, maps, and appropriately labeled diagrams to communicate scientific knowledge (e.g., motion of Earth's plates and cell structure).

7.7.e Communicate the steps and results from an investigation in written reports and oral presentations.

Chapter Pacing

Getting Started
The Big Idea Organisms can be classified into groups based on their characteristics.
🕐 **45 min** pp. 330–331
 7.3.d, 7.7.d

Section ❶ Sorting It All Out
Key Concept An eight-level classification system and branching diagrams are two basic tools that scientists use to study living and extinct organisms.
🕐 **90 min** pp. 332–337
7.3.d, 7.7.d

Section ❷ Domains and Kingdoms
Key Concept All organisms can be classified into three domains based on their shared derived characteristics.
🕐 **90 min** pp. 338–343
7.1.a, 7.3.d, 7.7.d

Wrapping Up
🕐 **180 min** pp. 344–353
7.3.d, 7.7.d, 7.7.e

Basic Learners
TE Insects, p. 332
TE Plant Identification, p. 341
📁 Reinforcement Worksheet
📁 Chapter Test A
📁 Differentiated Datasheets A for Labs and Activities ■
📘 Study Guide A ■

Advanced Learners/GATE
TE Researching Protists, p. 340
📁 Critical Thinking Worksheet
📁 Chapter Test C
📁 Differentiated Datasheets C for Labs and Activities ■

Key

SE Student Edition
TE Teacher's Edition

📁 Chapter Resource File
📓 Workbook
🖥 Transparency

💿 CD or CD-ROM
*   Datasheet or blackline master available

■ Also available in Spanish

All resources listed below are also available on the One-Stop Planner.

Teach

SE Explore Activity Analyzing a Branching Diagram, p. 331* ■

🖥 **Bellringer**
💿 **PowerPoint® Resources**
🖥 L43 Evolutionary Relationships Between Organisms
SE Quick Lab Constructing a Branching Diagram, p. 333* ■
🖥 L44 Levels of Classification
🖥 L45 Fossils in a Branching Diagram

🖥 **Bellringer**
💿 **PowerPoint® Resources**
🖥 L46 The Three Domains
🖥 L47 Domain Eukarya
SE Quick Lab Fossils and Branching Diagrams, p. 342* ■

SE Skills Practice Lab Grouping Life-Forms by Their Characteristics, pp. 344–345* ■

Practice

SE Organize Activity Booklet, p. 330

SE Section Review, p. 337* ■

SE Section Review, p. 343* ■

SE Science Skills Activity Communicating Through Written Reports, p. 346* ■
🖥 **Concept Mapping***
SE Chapter Review, pp. 348–349* ■

Assess

📁 **Chapter Pretest**

SE Standards Checks, pp. 332, 335, 337
TE Standards Focus, p. 336
📁 **Section Quiz** ■

SE Standards Checks, pp. 338, 339, 340
TE Standards Focus, p. 342
📁 **Section Quiz** ■

SE Standards Assessment, pp. 350–351*
📁 **Chapter Tests A, B** ■, **C**
📓 **Standards Review Workbook** ■

Resources for Universal Access • Differentiated Instruction

English Learners
TE Demonstration, p. 332
TE Using the Figure, pp. 335, 336
TE Conversation Starters, p. 339
📁 Vocabulary and Section Summary A ■, B

📁 Section Quizzes ■
📁 Chapter Tests A, B ■
📁 Differentiated Datasheets A, B, and C for Labs and Activities ■
📓 Study Guide A ■
📓 Multilingual Glossary

Struggling Readers
TE Reading Strategy, pp. 334, 339
TE Classification Flow, p. 335
TE Understanding Hyphens, p. 338

Special Education Students
TE Classification, p. 334
TE Fungi and Plants, p. 341
TE Research Report Outline, p. 346

To help plan your lessons, refer to the On Course Mapping Instruction booklet.

Chapter Resources

Visual Resources

CHAPTER STARTER TRANSPARENCY

This Really Happened!

BELLRINGER TRANSPARENCIES

Section: Sorting It All Out
Write a few sentences describing how you think that scientists categorize organisms into groups.

Write your response in your **science journal.**

Section: Domains and Kingdoms
Write a short paragraph describing how shared derived characteristics play a role in classifying organisms.

Write your response in your **science journal.**

TEACHING TRANSPARENCIES

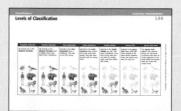
Evolutionary Relationships Between Organisms — L43

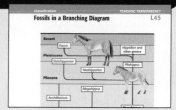
Fossils in a Branching Diagram — L45

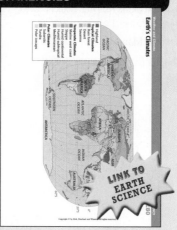
Levels of Classification — L44

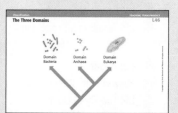
The Three Domains — L46

TEACHING TRANSPARENCIES

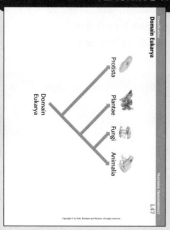
Domain Eukarya — L47

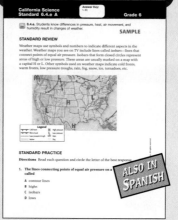
Earth's Climates

LINK TO EARTH SCIENCE

STANDARDS REVIEW TRANSPARENCIES

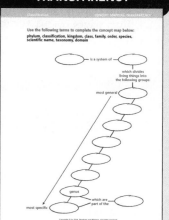

California Science Standard 6.4.e A — Grade 6

STANDARD REVIEW

STANDARD PRACTICE

ALSO IN SPANISH

CONCEPT MAPPING TRANSPARENCY

Use the following terms to complete the concept map below:
phylum, classification, kingdom, class, family, order, species, scientific name, taxonomy, domain

Planning Resources

PARENT LETTER

SAMPLE

Dear Parent,

Your son's or daughter's science class will soon begin exploring the chapter entitled "The Nature of Physical Science." In this chapter, students will learn about how the scientific method applies to the world of physical science and the role of physical science in the world. By the end of the chapter, students should demonstrate a clear understanding of the chapter's main ideas and be able to discuss the following topics:

1. the role of questions in the process of investigation (Section 1)
2. how applying science saves lives and benefits the environment (Section 1)
3. careers that rely on science (Section 1)
4. the steps used in scientific methods (Section 2)
5. how scientific methods are used to answer questions and solve problems (Section 2)
6. the importance of safety precautions in the laboratory (Section 3)
7. how safety equipment and when to use them (Section 3)
8. how safety symbols are used to make laboratories safer (Section 3)

Questions to Ask Along the Way

You can help your child learn about these topics by asking interesting questions as he or she progresses through the chapter. For example, you may wish to ask your son or daughter the following questions:

What are some surprising careers that use science?

What is a characteristic of a good hypothesis?

What is the first step to take if an accident happens?

ALSO IN SPANISH

TEST ITEM LISTING

SAMPLE

Holt California Physical Science
Chapter 6 Introduction to Atoms
Test Item Listing
Multiple choice

1. The smallest particle into which an element can be divided and still have the properties of that element is called a(n)
   a. nucleus.   c. atom.
   b. electrons.   d. neutron.
   ANS: C   DIF: 1   REF: 1   OBJ: 1   STO: 8.3.a   KEY: atom
   MSC: SQ.1.1

2. What particle did J. J. Thomson discover?
   a. neutron
   b. electron
   c. atom
   d. proton
   ANS: B   DIF: 1   REF: 1   OBJ: 2   STO: 8.3.a   KEY: electron   MSC:
   MSC: SQ.1.3

3. How would you describe the nucleus?
   a. dense, positively charged
   b. mostly empty space, positively charged
   c. tiny, negatively charged
   d. dense, negatively charged
   ANS: A   DIF: 1   REF: 1   OBJ: 2   STO: 8.3.a   KEY: nucleus   MSC:
   SQ.1.4

4. Where are electrons likely to be found?
   a. in the nucleus
   b. in electron clouds
   c. mixed throughout an atom
   d. in definite paths
   ANS: B   DIF: 1   REF: 1   OBJ: 2   STO: 8.3.a   KEY: electron   MSC:

5. Dalton believed that
   a. atoms of the same element are exactly alike.
   b. most, but not all, substances are made of atoms.
   c. atoms of different elements are the same.
   d. atoms can be divided.
   ANS: A   DIF: 1   REF: 1   OBJ: 112   STO: 8.3.a   KEY: atom
   MSC: SQ.1.5

6. Every atom of a given element has the same number of
   a. protons.
   b. neutrons.
   c. Electrons
   d. isotopes.
   ANS: A   DIF: 1   REF: 1   OBJ: 1   STO: 8.3.a   KEY: atom

ALSO IN SPANISH

One-Stop Planner® CD-ROM

This CD-ROM package includes all of the resources shown here and the following time-saving tools:

- **Lab Materials QuickList Software**
- **Customizable Lesson Plans** Correlated to the California Science Standards
- **Holt Calendar Planner**
- **PowerPoint® Resources**

- **Printable Worksheets**
- **ExamView® Test Generator** Correlated to the California Science Standards
- **Holt PuzzlePro®**
- **Interactive Teacher's Edition**

Meeting Individual Needs

DIRECTED READING A

Skills Worksheet
Directed Reading A   SAMPLE

Section: Body Organization
A STABLE INTERNAL ENVIRONMENT

BASIC   *ALSO IN SPANISH*

DIRECTED READING B

Skills Worksheet
Directed Reading B   SAMPLE

Section: Body Organization
A STABLE INTERNAL ENVIRONMENT

CELLS, TISSUES, AND ORGANS

GENERAL

VOCABULARY AND SECTION SUMMARY A

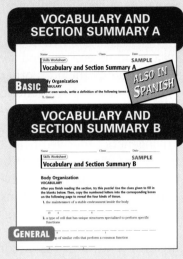

Skills Worksheet
Vocabulary and Section Summary A   SAMPLE

Body Organization
VOCABULARY

BASIC   *ALSO IN SPANISH*

VOCABULARY AND SECTION SUMMARY B

Skills Worksheet
Vocabulary and Section Summary B   SAMPLE

Body Organization
VOCABULARY

GENERAL

REINFORCEMENT

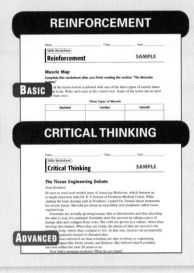

Skills Worksheet
Reinforcement   SAMPLE

Muscle Map

Three Types of Muscle

Skeletal	Cardiac	Smooth

BASIC

CRITICAL THINKING

Skills Worksheet
Critical Thinking   SAMPLE

The Tissue Engineering Debate
Dear Readers:

ADVANCED

INTERACTIVE READER AND STUDY GUIDE

CHAPTER 11 Body Organization and Structure
1 Body Organization   SAMPLE

BEFORE YOU READ

California Science Standards

MULTILINGUAL GLOSSARY

SAMPLE

Labs and Activities

DIFFERENTIATED DATASHEETS FOR EXPLORE ACTIVITY, QUICK LABS, AND CHAPTER LAB

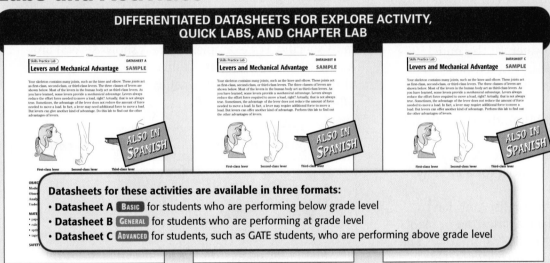

Skills Practice Lab
Levers and Mechanical Advantage   DATASHEET A / DATASHEET B / DATASHEET C   SAMPLE

ALSO IN SPANISH

Datasheets for these activities are available in three formats:
- **Datasheet A BASIC** for students who are performing below grade level
- **Datasheet B GENERAL** for students who are performing at grade level
- **Datasheet C ADVANCED** for students, such as GATE students, who are performing above grade level

DATASHEET FOR SCIENCE SKILLS ACTIVITY

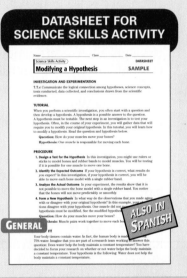

Science Skills Activity
Modifying a Hypothesis   DATASHEET   SAMPLE

INVESTIGATION AND EXPERIMENTATION

TUTORIAL

PROCEDURE

GENERAL   *ALSO IN SPANISH*

Reviews and Assessments

SECTION REVIEWS

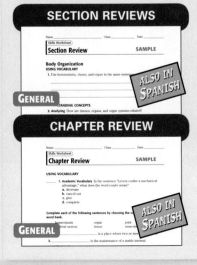

Skills Worksheet
Section Review   SAMPLE

Body Organization
USING VOCABULARY

GENERAL   *ALSO IN SPANISH*

CHAPTER REVIEW

Skills Worksheet
Chapter Review   SAMPLE

USING VOCABULARY

GENERAL   *ALSO IN SPANISH*

CHAPTER PRETEST

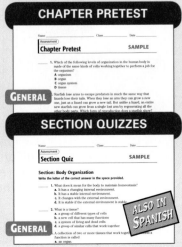

Assessment
Chapter Pretest   SAMPLE

GENERAL

SECTION QUIZZES

Assessment
Section Quiz   SAMPLE

Section: Body Organization

GENERAL   *ALSO IN SPANISH*

CHAPTER TEST A

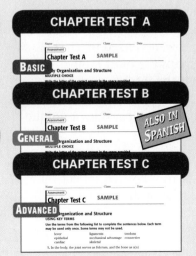

Assessment
Chapter Test A   SAMPLE

Body Organization and Structure
MULTIPLE CHOICE

BASIC

CHAPTER TEST B

Assessment
Chapter Test B   SAMPLE

Body Organization and Structure
MULTIPLE CHOICE

GENERAL   *ALSO IN SPANISH*

CHAPTER TEST C

Assessment
Chapter Test C   SAMPLE

Body Organization and Structure
USING KEY TERMS

ADVANCED

STANDARDS ASSESSMENT

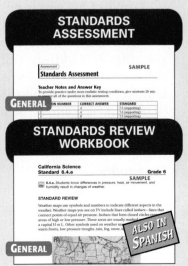

Assessment
Standards Assessment   SAMPLE

Teacher Notes and Answer Key

GENERAL

STANDARDS REVIEW WORKBOOK

California Science Standard 6.4.e   Grade 6   SAMPLE

STANDARD REVIEW

GENERAL   *ALSO IN SPANISH*

This Teacher Background explains science concepts, principles, and theories that appear in the chapter. Use the information on these pages to refresh or enhance your understanding of the topics covered.

Section 1

Sorting It All Out

History of Biological Classification

The history of biological classification is complex, as classification systems change with expanding knowledge of organisms, both living and extinct. The discovery and study of more and more organisms, as well as advancements in the study of evolution and evolutionary relationships between organisms, will continue to affect classification methodology.

Aristotle is credited with the earliest known method of biological classification. He classified organisms based on how the organism moved or the medium it moved through, such as air, land, or water. In the mid 1500s, Conrad von Gesner published a compilation of all organisms that were known at the time. As exploration of the New World took place, the discovery of new forms of life continued; in addition, the study of animals became more widespread in the late 1600s and early 1700s. This growing body of knowledge regarding organisms further increased the need for a broader basis for classification.

In the late 1600s, English naturalist John Ray proposed a new method for the classification of plants. Ray classified plants according to their similarities and differences based upon his own observations. This method of classification paved the way toward a more modern form of taxonomy.

Carolus Linnaeus is the scientist who is most often credited for advancements in classification. Linnaeus divided organisms into three realms (mineral, vegetable, and animal), and those realms were ranked by class, order, genus, and species. Perhaps the most famous of Linnaeus's accomplishments is the introduction of *binomial nomenclature*, the process by which organisms are given a two-word Latin name that provides a unique description of an organism.

Taxonomy

Biologists group organisms in ways that reflect the similarities and evolutionary relationships among organisms. The process of classifying organisms into groups is known as biological or scientific classification. Taxonomy is the study of the science of classification. The term is derived from the Greek words *taxis*, which means "arrangement," and *nomia*, which means "method."

Taxonomy includes other areas of study, such as systematics and phylogenetics. Systematics is the study of the diversity of characteristics shared by organisms and how these characteristics are evolutionarily related. Phylogenetics (derived from the Greek words *phylon*, meaning "tribe," and *genetikos*, meaning "relative to birth") is the study of the evolutionary relationships between groups of organisms. Phylogenetics focuses mainly on sets of related organisms. Phylogenetic systematics is the process by which groups of organisms are classified according to their evolutionary relationships.

Today, modern taxonomy classifies organisms into the following hierarchal system: domain, kingdom, phylum, class, order, family, genus, and species. Domain is the broadest, most inclusive category while species is the most specific. For example, Figure A shows several animals that are in Kingdom Animalia. However, only one of these animals, the house cat, is in the species *Felis catus*, as shown in **Figure A.**

Kingdom Animalia	Species *Felis catus*

Figure A *Although all animals in the first panel are in the domain Eukarya and kingdom Animalia, only the house cat is in the species* Felis catus.

For background information about teaching strategies and issues, refer to the
Professional Reference for Teachers.

Binomial Nomenclature

Binomial nomenclature refers to the widely accepted scientific method of naming organisms. As the name implies, binomial nomenclature proposes a two-part name for a species. This two-part name is composed of an organism's genus name and specific name.

Binomial nomenclature is widely used because it has many valuable aspects. First, all species can be identified with only two words. Second, the same name can be used internationally, making translation unnecessary. Third, if species are transferred between genera or reclassified in some other way, the specific name will remain the same. This allows for a smooth transition when revisions to the biological classification system become necessary.

Section 2

Domains and Kingdoms

Domains

In order to accommodate new evidence regarding the evolutionary relationships between organisms, taxonomists have significantly changed the modern biological classification system. Changes within the traditional five-kingdom system began with R.H. Whittaker's system, which classifies organisms according to whether they are prokaryotic or eukaryotic, whether they are unicellular or multicellular, and whether they obtain food by photosynthesis, ingestion, or absorption of nutrients from their environment.

Studies of prokaryotic DNA indicate that significant genetic differences exist between prokaryotic organisms. These differences are so fundamentally important that the prokaryotes formerly known as archaebacteria are no longer considered to be bacteria—they are now called archaea. Likewise, the prokaryotes once known as eubacteria are now called bacteria. As a result of this new evidence, the largest divisions in modern taxonomic systems are three domains: Archaea, Bacteria, and Eukarya. The traditional kingdoms and smaller divisions have been incorporated into this three-domain system.

Prokaryotes are divided between the domains Archaea and Bacteria. The domain Archaea, which contains the traditional kingdom Archaebacteria, is made up of archaea (singular, archaeon). The domain Bacteria, which contains the traditional kingdom Eubacteria, is made up of bacteria. All eukaryotes belong to the domain Eukarya. Domain Eukarya contains the traditional kingdoms: Protista, Plantae, Animalia, and Fungi.

Branching Diagrams

Modern taxonomy is moving from classifying organisms based on observable and anatomical similarities to classifying organisms based on evolutionary relationships. As DNA and RNA technologies advance, the study of phylogenetics and molecular-based systematics will also advance, and the methods of classification will have to adapt to new evidence. Scientists have already begun using fossil data, DNA and RNA sequencing, and comparison techniques to reclassify organisms based on their evolutionary relationships. To visually represent these relationships between organisms, scientists use evolutionary trees, or branching diagrams.

Phylogenetic trees, also known as phylogenies, are representations of the hypothesized evolutionary relationships between organisms. Phylogenetic trees include both living and extinct species. Cladograms are branching diagrams that are based on the presence of derived characteristics shared by all members of a group of organisms. Branching diagrams, such as the one in **Figure B,** are used throughout this text. Explain to students that this diagram indicates that Kingdoms Animalia and Fungi are more closely related to each other than either kingdom is to Kingdom Plantae.

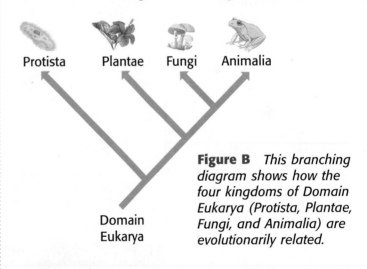

Figure B *This branching diagram shows how the four kingdoms of Domain Eukarya (Protista, Plantae, Fungi, and Animalia) are evolutionarily related.*

Internet Resources

SciLinks is maintained by the National Science Teachers Association to provide you and your students with interesting, up-to-date links that will enrich your classroom presentation of the chapter.

Visit **www.scilinks.org** and enter the SciLinks code for more information about the topic listed.

Topic: Basis for Classification
SciLinks code: HY70138

Topic: Kingdoms
SciLinks code: HY71397

Topic: Levels of Classification
SciLinks code: HY70870

Chapter Preview

📁 **Chapter Pretest**
Use the Chapter Pretest in the Chapter Resource File to determine the prior knowledge of your students. The Test Doctors and diagnostic teaching tips in the Teacher Notes pages will help you tailor your instruction to your students' specific needs.

Improving Comprehension

Use the Graphic Organizer on this page of the Student Edition to introduce the topics that are covered in this chapter, to summarize the chapter material, or to show students how to build a pyramid chart.

Teaching Tips

• Make sure that students understand the meaning of *hierarchy*.

• Explain how the shape of the pyramid suggests that the bottom of the pyramid is the broadest level and the top is the most specific level.

LS Logical

Improving Comprehension

Graphic Organizers are important visual tools that can help you organize information and improve your reading comprehension. The Graphic Organizer below is called a *pyramid chart*. Instructions for creating other types of Graphic Organizers are located in the **Study Skills** section of the Appendix.

How to Make a Pyramid Chart

❶ Draw a triangle that is divided into sections like the one shown below. Draw as many sections as you need to draw.

❷ Draw a box to the left of the triangle, as shown in the example. Write the topic of your pyramid chart in the box.

❸ In each section of your triangle, write information about the topic in the appropriate level of the pyramid.

When to Use a Pyramid Chart

A pyramid chart is used to organize information in a hierarchy of magnitude or detail. As the shape of the pyramid suggests, the pyramid's bottom level contains information that is largest in terms of magnitude and broadest, or least specific, in terms of detail. As you read about science, look for information that you can organize into a hierarchy.

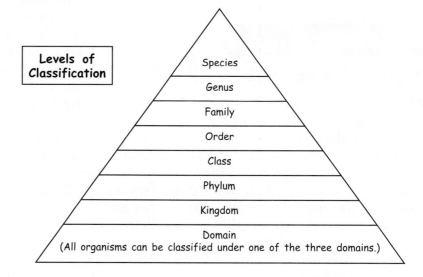

Levels of Classification

Species
Genus
Family
Order
Class
Phylum
Kingdom
Domain
(All organisms can be classified under one of the three domains.)

You Try It!

This Reading Strategy can also be used within the chapter that you are about to read. Practice making your own *pyramid chart* as directed in the Reading Strategy for Section ❶. Record your work in your **Science Journal**.

Using Other Graphic Organizers

Students can practice using a variety of Graphic Organizers while reading this chapter. The following Graphic Organizers may also be useful in this chapter:

A **spider map** can be used to describe characteristics of Linnaeus' naming system, discussed in Section 1.

An **idea wheel** can be used to organize details about the three domains, described in Section 2.

Instructions for creating these Graphic Organizers are located on pp. 583–591 of the Appendix.

Unpacking the Standards

The information below "unpacks" the standards by breaking them down into basic parts. The higher-level, academic vocabulary is highlighted and defined to help you understand the language of the standards. "What It Means" restates the standards as simply as possible.

California Standard	Academic Vocabulary	What It Means
7.1.a Students know cells **function similarly** in all living organisms.	**function** (FUHNGK shuhn) to work **similarly** (SIM uh luhr lee) in almost the same way	Cells perform the same actions in all living things.
7.3.d Students know how to **construct** a simple branching diagram to classify living groups of organisms by shared **derived** characteristics and how to **expand** the diagram to include fossil organisms.	**construct** (kuhn STRUHKT) to build; to make from parts **derived** (di RIEVD) gotten from something else **expand** (ek SPAND) to make more detailed; to enlarge	You must know how to draw a simple branching diagram to sort living things into groups based on features that the organisms share. You must also know how to add extinct organisms to the branching diagram.

Unpacking the Standards

Use the following information with the *What It Means* in the Student Edition to help students understand why studying each standard is important.

Why It Matters
At the cellular level, all living organisms share common traits. Understanding this idea allows one to understand the nature of life on Earth.
Simple branching diagrams can summarize large quantities of information and can allow students to recognize patterns that they may otherwise miss.

Words with Multiple Meanings

Words that have both common and scientific meanings can be confusing to students. The following table identifies some of those words that are used in this chapter.

Term	Common meaning	Scientific meaning
kingdom	a region ruled by a king or queen	the taxonomic category below the domain and above the phylum
order	a command	the taxonomic category below the class and above the family

Practice Have students complete the sentences below to help them understand how the scientific and common meanings of the word *order* can differ.

a. The general gave the soldiers an ___ to be silent for the rest of the evening. (order)

b. Animals in the ___ Carnivora have a backbone and nurse their young. (order)

Have students write one definition for the common usage of the word and one for the scientific meaning of the word.

Chapter Overview

This chapter introduces students to classification in life science. The chapter covers methods of classification and the three-domain system of biological classification of organisms.

Classifying Organisms

Identify It! Students may be confused about how scientists classify organisms. Students may mistakenly rely on misleading information found in the common names of organisms. Ask students, "What type of animal is a jellyfish?" Students may answer incorrectly that a jellyfish is a type of fish.

Correct It! Tell students that scientists classify organisms by sorting them into groups based on similar characteristics. Ask students to look up the biological classification of a jellyfish. What characteristics do jellyfish share with other members of their group? Do jellyfish share any characteristics with fishes?

Assess It! Show the class a box of donuts. The box should contain a variety of donuts. For example, some donuts should be frosted, some should be cream-filled, some should have sprinkles, and some should not have sprinkles. Then, ask students to create a classification system to organize the donuts into groups.

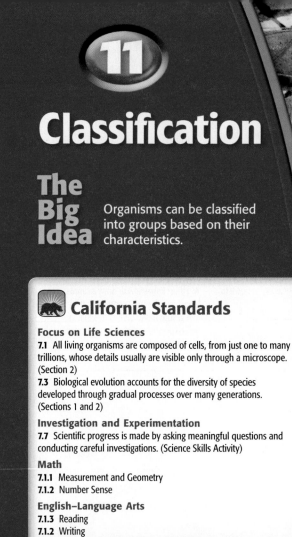

11
Classification

The Big Idea Organisms can be classified into groups based on their characteristics.

California Standards

Focus on Life Sciences

7.1 All living organisms are composed of cells, from just one to many trillions, whose details usually are visible only through a microscope. (Section 2)

7.3 Biological evolution accounts for the diversity of species developed through gradual processes over many generations. (Sections 1 and 2)

Investigation and Experimentation

7.7 Scientific progress is made by asking meaningful questions and conducting careful investigations. (Science Skills Activity)

Math

7.1.1 Measurement and Geometry
7.1.2 Number Sense

English–Language Arts

7.1.3 Reading
7.1.2 Writing

About the Photo

Look at the katydids, grasshoppers, and mantids in the photo. Every insect has a label that describes the insect. These descriptions will help a scientist find out if each insect has already been discovered and named. When scientists discover a new organism, they name the organism. The name chosen is unique and should help other scientists understand some basic facts about the organism.

Organize

Booklet

Before you read the chapter, create the FoldNote entitled "Booklet." On the front cover, title the booklet "Classification." Label each page of the booklet with "Classification," "Domain Archaea," "Domain Bacteria," and "Domain Eukarya." As you read the chapter, write what you learn about each topic on the appropriate page of the booklet.

Instructions for creating FoldNotes are located in the Study Skills section on p. 580 of the Appendix.

California Standards Alignment

Focus on Life Sciences

7.1.a Students know cells function similarly in all living organisms. **pp. 338–339, 351**

7.3.d Students know how to construct a simple branching diagram to classify living groups of organisms by shared derived characteristics and how to expand the diagram to include fossil organisms. **pp. 331–343, 350–351**

Investigation and Experimentation

7.7.d Construct scale models, maps, and appropriately labeled diagrams to communicate scientific knowledge (e.g., motion of Earth's plates and cell structure). **pp. 331, 333, 342, 344–345**

7.7.e Communicate the steps and results from an investigation in written reports and oral presentations. **p. 346**

Math Standards

Number Sense 7.1.2 Add, subtract, multiply, and divide rational numbers (integers, fractions, and terminating decimals) and take positive rational numbers to whole-number powers. **pp. 341, 343**

Measurement and Geometry 7.1.1 Compare weights, capacities, geometric measures, times, and temperatures within and between measurement systems (e.g., miles per hour and feet per second, cubic inches to cubic centimeters). **p. 349**

Explore Activity
🕐 15 min

Teacher Notes
In this activity, students will learn what a branching diagram represents (covers standards 7.3.d and 7.7.d). You may want to give students who are struggling with the activity hints on how the branching diagram incorporates variation of the subject along a timeline.

Answers
3. Sample answer: This diagram shows how clothing can be divided into groups based on the age of the person wearing the clothes.
4. teenager
5. infant, toddler, and preteen
6. Sample answer: Teenager clothing may be divided into radical and conservative kinds of clothing.

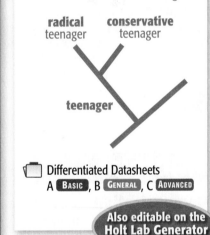

radical teenager   conservative teenager

teenager

📋 Differentiated Datasheets
A **BASIC**, B **GENERAL**, C **ADVANCED**

Also editable on the
**Holt Lab Generator
CD-ROM**

Explore Activity
🕐 15 min

Analyzing a Branching Diagram
Scientists use branching diagrams to show how different kinds of organisms are related to each other. The branching diagram below shows one way that clothes can be organized into groups.

Infant Toddler Preteen Teenager Adult Elder

Procedure
7.3.d
7.7.d

1. Redraw the diagram.
2. On the branch that slopes towards the right, draw a mark between each of the other branches in your diagram. Label each mark with what changed between the branches that are on either side of the mark.

Analysis
3. Write a statement that explains what you think the diagram shows.
4. Which branch of clothing category do you fit in?
5. Which categories of clothing have you already worn?
6. Can you think of how one of these groups of clothing can be split into two new groups? Show the two new groups on your diagram.

English–Language Arts Standards
Reading 7.1.3 Clarify word meaning through the use of definition, example, restatement, or contrast. **p. 332**

Writing 7.1.2 Support all statements and claims with anecdotes, descriptions, facts and statistics, and/or specific examples. **p. 349**

Classification   CHAPTER STARTER

This Really Happened!
Skunks have been thrown out of their family. It wasn't their awful smell that got them thrown out, though. It was their DNA.

Skunks were once thought to be most closely related to weasels, badgers, and otters. These short-legged, long-bodied animals are grouped together in a family called Mustelidae (*muh STEL uh dee*). Mustelidae is from a Latin word meaning "mouse." Skunks were classified as weasels and ferrets because of several physical characteristics, such as short, round ears.

However, a researcher at the University of New Mexico's Southwestern Biology Museum found that the DNA of skunks is very different from the DNA of the other members of Mustelidae. By comparing the DNA of different species, scientists can tell how closely related the species are. The DNA of two closely related animals—a house cat and...

Chapter Starter Transparency
Use this transparency to help students begin thinking about how scientists determine the relationships among organisms.

Preteach

Reviewing Prior Knowledge

Ask students to brainstorm ideas about ways to organize different things such as books, pencils, tables, and chairs into categories, such as study materials and furniture. Ask students, "What are some other strategies that could be used to organize things into categories? (Answers may vary, accept all reasonable answer.) Could these strategies be applied to grouping different kinds of organisms?

Bellringer

Have students focus on standard 7.3.d by asking them to describe how they think scientists categorize organisms into groups. Have students write their ideas in their **Science Journal.** (Sample answer: Scientists classify organisms by their characteristics, such as if the organism is a plant or an animal.)

Bellringer Transparency

Motivate

Demonstration

Classifying Objects Show the students a variety of small, solid objects. Ask students for their ideas on ways to organize the objects into groups. For each grouping method, record the defining characteristics of each group and the objects that belong in the group. Identify objects that can be classified into more than one group, and have students consider how the groups change according to the grouping method that is used. Discuss with the class how putting objects into groups can be helpful. **LS Visual**

SECTION
1

Sorting It All Out

Key Concept An eight-level classification system and branching diagrams are two basic tools that scientists use to study living and extinct organisms.

What You Will Learn

- Scientists use classification to study organisms and how organisms are related to each other.
- The eight levels of classification are domain, kingdom, phylum, class, order, family, genus, and species.
- Each organism that has been described is given a scientific name.
- Branching diagrams show the relatedness between living and extinct organisms over time.

Why It Matters

Classifying organisms will help you identify how living and extinct organisms are related.

Vocabulary

- classification
- taxonomy

READING STRATEGY

Graphic Organizer In your **Science Journal,** make a Pyramid Chart that follows a general note-taking structure. At the top, write the topic of this section. In the next level down, ask two questions about the topic. In the next level, answer the questions. In the bottom level, add more details to your answers.

Imagine that you live in a tropical rain forest and must get your own food, shelter, and clothing from the forest. What do you need to know to survive in the forest? You need to know which plants are safe to eat and which are not. You need to know which animals you can eat and which animals might eat you. In other words, you need to study the organisms around you and organize them into categories, or classify them. **Classification** is putting things into orderly groups based on similar characteristics.

Why Classify?

For thousands of years, humans have classified organisms based on usefulness. The Chácabo people of Bolivia know of 360 kinds of plants in the forest where they live. Of these 360 plant types, 305 types are useful to the Chácabo.

Some biologists, such as those shown in **Figure 1,** classify living and extinct organisms. Scientists classify organisms to help make sense and order of the many kinds of organisms in the world. Biologists use a system to classify organisms. This system is a tool to group organisms according to the characteristics that they share. The classification of organisms allows biologists to answer many important questions, such as the following:

- What are the defining characteristics of each species?
- When did the characteristics of an organism evolve?
- What are the relationships between various species?

Standards Check What are three questions that classifying organisms can help answer? **7.3.d**

Figure 1 *These biologists are sorting rain-forest plant material.*

7.3.d Students know how to construct a simple branching diagram to classify living groups of organisms by shared derived characteristics and how to expand the diagram to include fossil organisms.

Answer to Standards Check

The three questions that classifying organisms can help answer are as follows: What are the defining characteristics of each species? When did the characteristics of an organism develop? What are the relationships between different species?
7.3.d (supporting)

Universal Access • Differentiated Instruction

Basic Learners

Insects Give students the following information: "Suppose that there were about 1,260,000 known species of insects in the world and that the number of insect species accounted for about 70% of all known species." Have students calculate the approximate total number of known species in the world based on this data.
(1,260,000/0.7 = 1.8 million species) **LS Logical**

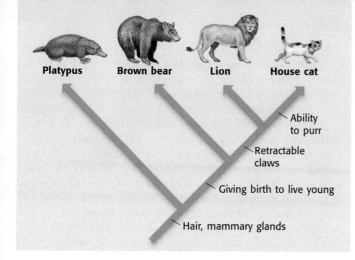

Platypus   Brown bear   Lion   House cat

Ability
to purr

Retractable
claws

Giving birth to live young

Hair, mammary glands

Figure 2 *This branching diagram shows the similarities and differences between four mammals. The bottom of the branching diagram begins in the past, and the tips of the branches end in the present day.*

How Do Scientists Classify Organisms?

In the 1700s, Carolus Linnaeus (KAR uh luhs li NAY uhs), a Swedish scientist, founded modern taxonomy. **Taxonomy** is the science of describing, classifying, and naming organisms. Linnaeus classified organisms based on their structure or characteristics. Classifying organisms by their characteristics is called *systematics*. The classification system used today is based on the one that Linnaeus developed.

Classification Today

Taxonomists use an eight-level system to classify organisms by their *shared derived characteristics*. A shared derived characteristic is a characteristic that two or more kinds of organisms share with their most recent common ancestor. Scientists use these characteristics to hypothesize how closely related organisms are. The more derived characteristics organisms share, the more closely related the organisms probably are. For example, the platypus, brown bear, lion, and house cat all have hair and mammary glands. Therefore, they are grouped together as mammals.

Branching Diagrams

Branching diagrams show which characteristics organisms share and when these organisms evolved. In **Figure 2**, each characteristic listed on the branching diagram is only shared by the animals above it. All of the animals shown have hair and mammary glands. But only the bear, lion, and house cat give birth to live young. Characteristics shown higher on the diagram are more recent than the characteristics below them. Therefore, more-recent organisms are at the ends of branches that begin higher on the diagram. For example, the house cat evolved more recently than the platypus.

classification (KLAS uh fi KAY shuhn) the division of organisms into groups, or classes, based on specific characteristics

taxonomy (taks AHN uh mee) the science of describing, naming, and classifying organisms

Wordwise The root *tax-* means "to arrange" or "to put in order." The suffix *-nomy* means "the science of."

Quick Lab

Constructing a Branching Diagram   7.3.d   7.7.d

1. Construct a diagram similar to the one in **Figure 2**. On the diagram, write "frog", "snake", "kangaroo", and "rabbit" in this order, from left to right.

2. Think of one major change that happened before the frog evolved.

3. For the last three organisms, write a change that happened between one of these organisms and the other two in your diagram.

4. How does this diagram show that the organisms are related?

⏲ 15 min

Teach, *continued*

READING STRATEGY

Paired Summarizing Pair students and have them read silently about the levels of classification and scientific names. Then, have one student in each pair summarize the information that they have read. The other student in each pair should listen to the summary and should point out any inaccuracies or ideas that were left out. Allow students to refer to the text as needed. **LS Verbal**

Discussion

Classification Drill To help students understand what constitutes a species, genus, family, order, class, phylum, kingdom, and domain, have students answer the following questions:

- What does a species contain? (organisms that have the same characteristics)
- What does a genus contain? (similar species)
- What does a family contain? (similar genera)
- What does an order contain? (similar families)
- What does a class contain? (similar orders)
- What does a phylum contain? (similar classes)
- What does a kingdom contain? (similar phyla)
- What does a domain contain? (similar kingdoms)

LS Logical/Auditory

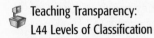

Teaching Transparency: L44 Levels of Classification

Answer to Standards Check

The first part of a two-part scientific name is the genus name. The second part of the scientific name is the specific name. **7.3.d** (supporting)

INTERNET ACTIVITY

Kingdom Competition!
Do you have a favorite kingdom? Choose one, and write which of its characteristics you most like. Create an advertisement for your favorite kingdom! Go to **go.hrw.com,** and type in the keyword HY7CLSW.

Levels of Classification

Every living thing is classified into one of three domains. Domains are the largest, most general groups. All organisms in a domain are sorted into kingdoms. The members of one kingdom are more like each other than they are like the members of another kingdom. All organisms in a kingdom are further sorted into phyla (singular, *phylum*). The members of a phylum are sorted into classes. Each class includes one or more orders. Orders are separated into families. Families are sorted into genera (singular, *genus*). And genera are sorted into species. A species is a group of organisms that are closely related and that can mate to produce fertile offspring. **Figure 3** shows the classification of a house cat in the domain Eukarya, from the level of kingdom Animalia to the species *Felis catus*.

Scientific Names

By classifying organisms, biologists can give organisms scientific names. A scientific name remains the same for a specific kind of organism even if the organism has many common names. Before Linnaeus's time, scholars used names that were as long as 12 words to identify species. This system was hard to work with because the names were so long. The system was also hard to use because different scientists named organisms differently, so an organism could have more than one name.

Kingdom Animalia	Phylum Chordata	Class Mammalia
All animals are in the **kingdom Animalia.**	All animals in the **phylum Chordata** have a hollow nerve cord. Most have a backbone.	Animals in the **class Mammalia** have a backbone. They also nurse their young.

Figure 3 *Levels of classification begin with domain, followed by kingdom, phylum, class, order, family, genus, and species. This diagram shows the levels of classification of the house cat, in domain Eukarya.*

BRAIN FOOD

Dragon Fossils The term *dinosaur* was not coined until the 19th century. Until then, the most widely accepted understanding of dinosaur fossils was that the fossils were the remains of dragons.

Universal Access • Differentiated Instruction

Special Education Students

Classification Some students might not understand the purpose of the faded pictures in **Figure 3.** Point out that the faded pictures are included to show which of the animals from the previous level of classification are not included in the next level of classification. To make sure that the point is clear, ask volunteers to name the animals in the diagram that are included in some of the different levels of classification. **LS Visual**

Two-Part Names

Linnaeus simplified the naming of living things by giving each species a two-part scientific name. For example, the scientific name for the Asian elephant is *Elephas maximus* (EL uh fuhs MAK suh muhs). The first part of the name, *Elephas,* is the genus name. The second part, *maximus,* is the specific name. No other species has the name *Elephas maximus.* Naming rules help scientists communicate clearly about living things.

All genus names begin with a capital letter. All specific names begin with a lowercase letter. Usually, both words are underlined or italicized. But if the surrounding text is italicized, the scientific name is not, as **Figure 4** shows. These printing styles show a reader which words are genus names and specific names.

Scientific names, which are usually Latin or Greek, contain information about an organism. The name of the animal shown in **Figure 4** is *Tyrannosaurus rex. Tyrannosaurus* is a combination of two Greek words and means "tyrant lizard." The word *rex* is Latin for "king." The name tells you that this animal was probably not a passive grass eater! *Tyrannosaurus rex* can also be referred to as *T. rex.* A correct scientific name consists of the genus name (or its abbreviation) and the specific name.

Standards Check What are the two parts of a scientific name?
■ **7.3.d**

Figure 4 *You would never call* Tyrannosaurus rex *just* rex!

Using the Figure

Classification Have students use **Figure 3** to answer the following questions:

- Which animals are shown at the kingdom level? (beetle, bird, lion, lynx, bear, human, house cat)
- Which of the animals shown at the kingdom level does not have a backbone? (the beetle)
- Which of the animals shown at the phylum level is not a mammal? (the bird)

LS Visual

BRAIN FOOD

Classifying Ideas Have students consider the importance of classification. Ask students to think of something that cannot be classified. Suggest that they test any item or concept that they come up with by placing it in the sentence: A(n) _____ is a type of _____. For example, if the word is *speech,* the sentence may be filled in as follows: Speech is a type of communication. Have students share their examples.
LS Logical/Verbal

Order Carnivora	Family Felidae	Genus *Felis*	Species *Felis catus*
Animals in the **order Carnivora** have a backbone and nurse their young. They also have special teeth for tearing meat.	Animals in the **family Felidae** are cats. They have a backbone, nurse their young, have special teeth for tearing meat, and have retractable claws.	Animals in the **genus *Felis*** share traits with other animals in the same family. However, these cats cannot roar; they can only purr.	The **species *Felis catus*** is the common house cat. The house cat shares traits with all of the organisms in the levels above the species level, but it also has unique traits.

MISCONCEPTION ALERT

Two-Part Names Some students may not realize that the two-part scientific name of an organism is only a part of the organism's classification. Give students the following example: The scientific name of the Asian elephant is a combination of the genus and specific name. The elephant is first classified in Domain Eukarya and then Kingdom Animalia. Have students research the classification of the Asian elephant and list the names of the phylum, class, order, and family to which the Asian elephant belongs.

Universal Access · Differentiated Instruction

Struggling Readers

Classification Flow Make sure students completely understand the classification system before going on. Divide students into small groups. Give each group a piece of poster board and a marker. Ask each group to create a flow chart that shows how the classification system builds and how different levels relate to the other levels. Tell them to begin with Domain Eukarya, which has four kingdoms, and at least three of the other classification levels. Make sure they realize that they do not have to fill in names of plants and animals, but rather they are to write only the classification levels, such as domain, kingdom, phyla, classes, etc. Tell them that they should write small since they will have many pieces to add. **LS** Visual/Logical

Standards Focus

This **Standards Focus** provides you with a quick way to **assess**, **reteach**, and **re-assess** one or more concepts in the section.

Assess

1. What is a shared derived characteristic? (*A characteristic that two or more kinds of organisms share with their most recent common ancestor.*) Why are branching diagrams useful? (*Because branching diagrams can be used to show the evolutionary relationships between organisms.*) **7.3.d**

Reteach

Branching Diagram Have students construct a branching diagram that shows the evolutionary relationships between the following organisms: a sponge, a mosquito, a horse, and a human. Provide students with details about these organisms that will help them construct the diagram. For example, the development of a skeleton occurred after sponges evolved leading them to place sponges on the oldest branch. Ask students how scientists might determine the evolutionary relationships between four different breeds of horses in order to construct a branching diagram. (*Sample answer: Scientists would compare the DNA of the horses to determine the evolutionary relationships between different breeds of horses.*) **LS** Visual **7.3.d**

Re-Assess

Branching Diagram Manual Have students create a manual for younger readers that describes how to construct branching diagrams. In their manual, students should help the reader make decisions based on the available information. The manual should also mention the importance of the timeline and how fossils are included. **LS** Visual **7.3.d**

Extinct Organisms and Living Organisms

Extinct organisms can also be placed in a branching diagram with living organisms. Scientists identify the characteristics of an extinct organism from fossils of that organism. The more shared derived characteristics that an extinct organism has in common with a living organism, the more closely related these organisms probably are. By studying fossils scientists can better understand the evolutionary relationships between organisms or how organisms have evolved. **Figure 5** shows a branching diagram that has extinct and living genera. Notice that extinct genera never appear at the tips of branches that reach the top of the diagram.

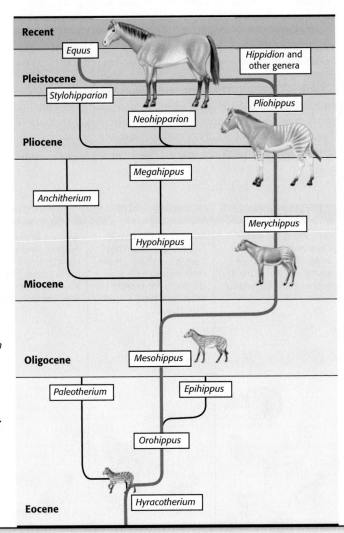

Figure 5 *This branching diagram shows the modern horse, and other related genera. The diagram also shows how these genera have probably evolved from currently extinct genera through the epochs of the Cenozoic era.* **List all the genera that evolved from the genus Mesohippus, according to this diagram.**

Using the Figure

Fossils and Branching Diagrams

Use **Figure 5** on this page to lead a discussion of how studying the fossils of extinct organisms can help classify living organisms. (*Studying the fossils of extinct organisms allows scientists to identify shared derived characteristics that extinct organisms have in common with living organisms.*) Ask students to use the figure to identify which genera exist today. (*Equus, Hippidion,* and other genera) Answer to caption question: The genera that developed from the *Mesohippus* are *Hypohippus, Megahippus, Anchitherium, Merychippus, Neohipparion, Stylohipparion, Pliohippus, Equus, Hippidion,* and other genera.

 Teaching Transparency:
L45 Fossils in a Branching Diagram

Fossils and Branching Diagrams

Branching diagrams that include fossils of extinct organisms show when the extinct organisms evolved and when those organisms became extinct. For example, as **Figure 5** shows that the members of the genus *Neohipparion* appeared near the beginning of the Pliocene Epoch and became extinct near the end of the Pliocene Epoch. In some cases, extinct organisms are on a branch that is on a direct line to other organisms. For example, the genus *Mesohippus* appeared in the Oligocene Epoch and is on a direct line to the genera *Hypohippus* and *Merychippus*.

Standards Check How are fossils of extinct organisms included in branching diagrams? 🐻 **7.3.d**

SECTION Review

 7.3.d

Summary

- Classification groups organisms based on their shared derived characteristics.
- Classification is a tool that helps us understand the relationships between organisms.
- The are eight levels of classification.
- The scientific name of an organism has two parts.
- Branching diagrams show evolutionary relationships between extinct and living organisms.

Using Vocabulary

1. Write an original definition for *classification* and *taxonomy*.

Understanding Concepts

2. **Analyzing** Why do scientists use scientific names for organisms?

3. **Listing** What are the eight levels of classification?

INTERPRETING GRAPHICS Use the branching diagram below to answer the next two questions.

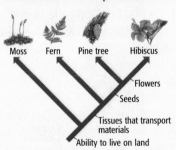

Moss Fern Pine tree Hibiscus

Flowers
Seeds
Tissues that transport materials
Ability to live on land

4. **Identifying** Which kind of organism evolved earliest? Which kind of organism evolved most recently?

5. **Inferring** Which organisms have tissues that transport materials?

Critical Thinking

6. **Analyzing Processes** You have found a fossil of an organism. The organism has characteristics that have never been described. What would you have to do to identify this fossil?

7. **Making Inferences** What is the difference between organisms that share many derived charateristics and organisms that do not?

8. **Applying Concepts** There is an organism halfway up a branch in a branching diagram, and a different organism at the tip of the branch. What can you infer about these organisms?

9. **Making Inferences** In branching diagrams, what can you infer about the organisms at the tips of the branches that do not reach the tops of the diagrams?

Internet Resources

For a variety of links related to this chapter, go to www.scilinks.org

Topic: Basis for Classification; Levels of Classification
SciLinks code: HY70138; HY70870

---

6. Sample answer: I would make a list of the new organism's characteristics. **7.3.d** (exceeding)

7. Sample answer: Organisms that have many shared derived characteristics are more closely related to each other than organisms that do not have many shared derived characteristics are. **7.3.d** (mastering)

8. Sample answer: I would infer that the species at the tip of the branch evolved from the species that occurs halfway up the branch. **7.3.d** (exceeding)

9. Sample answer: I would infer that species at the tips of branches that did not reach the top of the branching diagram were extinct. **7.3.d** (mastering)

🐻	**Section Review Standards Guide**		
	Supporting	Mastering	Exceeding
7.3.d	1–3	4–5, 7, 9	6, 8

Answer to Standards Check

Fossils of extinct organisms are shown at the tips of branches that do not reach the top of the branching diagrams. **7.3.d** (mastering)

Answers to Section Review

1. Sample answer: Classification is putting things into orderly groups based on similar characteristics. Taxonomy is the science of describing, classifying, and naming organisms. **7.3.d** (supporting)

2. Sample answer: Scientists use scientific names for organisms to make it easier for people all over the world to understand which organism is being referred to. **7.3.d** (supporting)

3. Domain, kingdom, phylum, class, order, family, genus, and species. **7.3.d** (supporting)

4. Moss is the oldest kind of organism. The hibiscus or the pine tree may be considered the youngest kinds of organisms. **7.3.d** (mastering)

5. The fern, pine tree, and hibiscus have tissues that transport materials. **7.3.d** (mastering)

Section Resources

- Directed Reading A **BASIC** (Also in Spanish), B **GENERAL**
- Interactive Reader and Study Guide
- Section Quiz **GENERAL** (Also in Spanish)
- Section Review **GENERAL** (Also in Spanish)
- Vocabulary and Section Summary A **BASIC** (Also in Spanish), B **GENERAL**

Reviewing Prior Knowledge

Review standard 7.3.d with students. Ask students to summarize the standard in their own words. Then, ask students to predict how that standard may apply to this section. Ask students how branching diagrams may have helped scientists develop the classification system that they use today.

 Bellringer

Have students focus on standard 7.3.d by asking them to describe how shared derived characteristics play a role in classifying organisms. Have students write a short paragraph describing their ideas in their **Science Journal.**

 Bellringer Transparency

ACTIVITY

Grouping Animals Have students write letters to zoos requesting a copy of their visitor's map. (Be sure that students include a self-addressed, stamped envelope with their letter.) Ask students to compare the layouts of the zoos by how the animals are grouped.

LS Logical

Answer to Standards Check

Scientists use shared derived characteristics to classify organisms. **7.3.d**

Teaching Transparency: L46 The Three Domains

Domains and Kingdoms

Key Concept All organisms can be classified into three domains based on their shared derived characteristics.

What You Will Learn
- Classification systems change as greater numbers of different organisms are described.
- All prokaryotes are divided into one of two domains, domain Archaea or domain Bacteria.
- All eukaryotes are classified into the domain Eukarya, which is divided into four kingdoms.

Why It Matters
Learning about the characteristics of organisms in each domain and kingdom can help you recognize similarities and differences between organisms.

Vocabulary
- Archaea
- Fungi
- Bacteria
- Plantae
- Eukarya
- Animalia
- Protista

READING STRATEGY

Summarizing Read this section silently. In pairs, take turns summarizing the material. Stop to discuss ideas and words that seem confusing.

Archaea (ahr KEE uh) in a modern taxonomic system, a domain made up of prokaryotes that differ from other prokaryotes in the makeup of their cell walls and in their genetics

7.1.a Students know cells function similarly in all living organisms.
7.3.d Students know how to construct a simple branching diagram to classify living groups of organisms by shared derived characteristics and how to expand the diagram to include fossil organisms.

▶ For hundreds of years, all organisms were classified as either plants or animals. But over time, scientists discovered species that did not fit easily into these two kingdoms. For example, an organism of the genus *Euglena,* has characteristics of both plants and animals. How would you classify this organism?

Three Domains

Organisms are classified by their shared derived characteristics. Euglena are single-celled organisms that live in pond water. Euglena perform photosynthesis, move around, and can feed on other organisms. Therefore, euglena are neither plants nor animals. Scientists solved this classification problem by adding another kingdom, the kingdom Protista, for organisms such as euglena. However, scientists soon realized that new kingdoms could not solve some larger problems in classification.

As greater differences among organisms were discovered, scientists had to create a new level of classification, the level of domain. **Figure 1** shows the three domains in the eight-level classification system that is used today. Domains represent the largest differences among organisms. At each level of classification, organisms within a group are more like other organisms in the same group than organisms that belong to different groups. Therefore, organisms in each domain are more like each other than organisms in another domain. Domains are subdivided into kingdoms. Scientists are still working to describe the kingdoms in each of the three domains.

Standards Check What do scientists use to classify organisms today? **7.3.d**

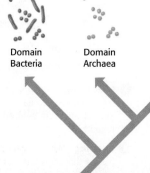

Domain Bacteria   Domain Archaea   Domain Eukarya

Figure 1 *This branching diagram shows the three domains into which all organisms are classified.*

Struggling Readers

Understanding Hyphens Point out the following hyphenated terms in the text:

single-celled (2nd paragraph, on this page);
eight-level (3rd paragraph, on this page);
single-celled (1st paragraph, p. 339);
disease-causing (last paragraph, p. 339)

Explain that these terms are all hyphenated because each set includes two side-by-side adjectives that describe the

same noun. Explain that these hyphenated words will not be found in a dictionary as hyphenated words because they are hyphenated as a punctuation point, not because they are actually single words. Ask volunteers to name the noun each pair of hyphenated words describes. (Answers: organisms, classification system, organisms, bacteria) **LS** Verbal/Interpersonal

Figure 2 The Grand Prismatic Spring in Yellowstone National Park contains water that is about 90°C (194°F). The spring is home to archaea that thrive in its hot water.

Domain Archaea

The domain **Archaea** is made up entirely of archaea. Archaea are one of two kinds of prokaryotes. *Prokaryotes* (proh KAR ee OHTS) are single-celled organisms that do not have a nucleus. Archaea were first discovered living in extreme environments, where other organisms could not survive. **Figure 2** shows a hot spring in Yellowstone National Park. The yellow and orange rings around the edge of the hot spring are made up of the billions of archaea that live there. Some archaea can also be found in more-moderate environments, such as the open ocean.

Bacteria (bak TIR ee uh) in a modern taxonomic system, a domain made up of prokaryotes that differ from other prokaryotes in the makeup of their cell walls and in their genetics

Domain Bacteria

All bacteria belong to the domain **Bacteria.** Bacteria are another kind of prokaryote. Bacteria can be found in the soil, in water, and even on and inside the human body! For example, *Escherichia coli* (ESH uh RIK ee uh KOH LIE), pictured in **Figure 3,** is present in large numbers in human intestines, where it produces vitamin K. One kind of bacterium converts milk into yogurt. Some bacteria cause diseases, such as pneumonia. Other bacteria make chemicals that help us fight disease-causing bacteria. Although bacteria and archaea are prokaryotes, differences in their characteristics allow them to live in very different kinds of environments.

Figure 3 Specimens of E. coli are shown on the point of a pin under a scanning electron microscope. These bacteria live in the intestines of animals and decompose undigested food.

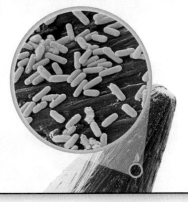

Standards Check Describe one major difference between archaea and bacteria. 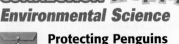 **7.1.a**

Cooking with Mushrooms
Tell students that mushrooms are found in a variety of recipes for different dishes. Mushrooms are sometimes used in vegetarian dishes as a substitute for meat. Ask students to research recipes that contain mushrooms. Have students plan a meal that includes only dishes containing mushrooms. Tell the students to include recipes that use different type of mushrooms (white, portabella, shitake, etc.), if possible. You may want to assign different students breakfast, lunch, or dinner. **LS** **Kinesthetic/Verbal**

Answer to Standards Check

The two kingdoms that evolved most recently in Eukarya are Fungi and Animalia. **7.3.d** (mastering)

ACTIVITY

The Distribution of Organisms
Use the teaching transparency "Earth's Climate" to discuss how climate and distances limit the distribution of related organisms. For example, plants from the tropics are unlikely to survive in the tundra. Also, most organisms do not travel long distances. Discuss how humans have changed these factors. (Humans use technology to move organisms worldwide and create the conditions in which the organisms thrive.) **LS** **Verbal**

 Teaching Transparency:
LINK TO *EARTH SCIENCE* E80 Earth's Climate

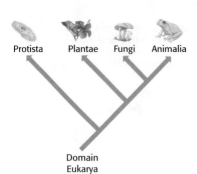

Protista   Plantae   Fungi   Animalia

Domain Eukarya

Figure 4 *This branching diagram shows the four kingdoms in the domain Eukarya.*

Eukarya (yoo KAR ee uh) in a modern taxonomic system, a domain made up of all eukaryotes

Figure 5 *The slime mold on the left is a protist. The brightly colored fungus on the right is of the genus* Amanita *and is poisonous.*

Domain Eukarya

All organisms whose cells have a nucleus and membrane-bound organelles are called *eukaryotes*. Eukaryotes belong to the domain **Eukarya.** The four kingdoms within the domain Eukarya are Protista, Fungi, Plantae, and Animalia, as **Figure 4** shows.

Standards Check Based on the branching diagram, what are the the two kingdoms in Eukarya that evolved most recently?  **7.3.d**

Kingdom Protista

Members of the kingdom **Protista** commonly called *protists* (PROH tists), are single-celled or simple multicellular organisms. Scientists think that the first protists evolved from ancient bacteria about 2 billion years ago. Much later, ancient protists gave rise to fungi, plants, and animals. The kingdom Protista contains many kinds of organisms. Animal-like protists are called *protozoa*. Plantlike protists are called *algae*. Slime molds, such as the one shown in **Figure 5,** belong to the kingdom Protista.

Kingdom Fungi

Molds and mushrooms are examples of the complex, multicellular members of the kingdom **Fungi.** Unlike plants, fungi do not perform photosynthesis. Unlike animals, fungi do not eat food. Instead, fungi absorb nutrients from substances in their surroundings. They use digestive juices to break down the substances. **Figure 5** shows a very poisonous fungus. Never eat wild fungi.

SCIENCE HUMOR

Q: What did the carrot say to the mushroom?
A: You are a fun guy (fungi).

Universal Access • Differentiated Instruction

Advanced Learners/GATE

Researching Protists Have students research three kinds of protists, such as *Paramecium*, slime mold, and giant kelp. Have students write descriptions of each kind of protist. Descriptions should include information about the size, form, method of obtaining nutrients, method of reproduction, and, if applicable, the commercial uses of each kind of organism. **LS** **Verbal**

Figure 6 *Giant sequoias can be found in California. Giant sequoias can measure 30 m around at the base and can grow to more than 91.5 m tall.*

MATH PRACTICE

Ring-Around-the-Sequoia
How many students would have to join hands to form a human chain around a giant sequoia that has a circumference of 30 m? Assume for this calculation that the average student can extend his or her arms about 1.3 m.

Protista (proh TIST uh) a kingdom of mostly one-celled eukaryotic organisms that are different from plants, animals, bacteria, archaea, and fungi

Fungi (FUHN JIE) a kingdom made up of nongreen, eukaryotic organisms that have no means of movement, reproduce by using spores, and get food by breaking down substances in their surroundings and absorbing the nutrients

Plantae (PLAN tee) a kingdom made up of complex, multicellular organisms that are usually green, have cell walls made of cellulose, cannot move around, and use the sun's energy to make sugar by photosynthesis

Kingdom Plantae

Although plants vary remarkably in size and form, most people easily recognize the members of the kingdom Plantae. **Plantae** consists of organisms that are eukaryotic, have cell walls, and make food through photosynthesis. For photosynthesis to occur, most plants need sunlight. Plants can therefore be found on land and in water that light can penetrate.

The food that plants make is important not only for the plants but also for all of the organisms that get nutrients from plants. Most life on Earth is dependent on plants. For example, some animals, fungi, protists, and bacteria consume plants. When these organisms digest the plant material, they get energy and nutrients made by the plants.

Plants also provide habitat for other organisms. The giant sequoias in **Figure 6** provide a home for birds, insects, and other animals.

Standards Focus

This **Standards Focus** provides you with a quick way to **assess**, **reteach**, and **re-assess** one or more concepts in the section.

Assess

1. A scientist discovered a previously undocumented organism in a cave. It can move around on its own and eats insects. But it has no eyes and is white. Into which kingdom of Eukarya would you classify this organism? (Animalia) **7.3.d**

2. What causes the number of kingdoms in the modern classification system to increase? (discovery of new organisms that do not fit into the established kingdoms) **7.3.d**

Reteach

New Kingdom Have students describe and illustrate in their **Science Journal** an organism that might require the formation of a new kingdom. Students should explain why they think that the organism should be classified in its own kingdom. Ask students to describe how using a branching diagram could help scientists decide to create a new kingdom for this novel organism. **LS** Visual/Logical **7.3.d**

Re-Assess

Making a Chart Have students construct a chart of the six kingdoms. On the chart, students should list the major characteristics of each kingdom and include a representative organism for each kingdom. **LS** Visual/Logical **7.3.d**

Animalia (AN i MAY lee uh) a kingdom made up of complex, multicellular organisms that lack cell walls, can usually move around, and quickly respond to their environment

Kingdom Animalia

The kingdom **Animalia** contains complex, multicellular organisms that lack cell walls, are usually able to move around, and have specialized sense organs. These sense organs help most animals quickly respond to their environment. Organisms in the kingdom Animalia are commonly called *animals*. The bald eagle in **Figure 7** belongs to the kingdom Animalia.

Animals depend on the organisms from other kingdoms. For example, animals depend on plants for food. Animals also depend on bacteria and fungi to recycle the nutrients from dead organisms.

Figure 7 *The kingdom Animalia contains many different organisms, such as the bald eagle.*

Quick Lab

Fossils and Branching Diagrams

Try this activity to learn how you can study a fossil and include it in a branching diagram with modern organisms.

7.3.d
7.7.d

▶ Try It!

1. The image on the right is a photo of a fossil of an organism called an archaeopteryx.

2. Create a simple list of characteristics that describe the archaeopteryx.

3. Construct a branching diagram of the animal kingdom. Include fish, amphibians, reptiles, birds, and apes in the branching diagram. (Hint: Among these organisms, fish evolved earliest. Amphibians formed the next group, and they were followed by reptiles and then birds. Among these organisms, apes are the most recent group.)

4. Consider the characteristics of each group of organisms. Decide where the archaeopteryx would fit in your branching diagram, and add it to your diagram.

▶ Think About It!

5. Using your branching diagram, how can you tell that the archaeopteryx is extinct?

6. Which kinds of organisms are more recent than the archaeopteryx? Which kinds of organisms evolved before the archaeopteryx?

🕐 15 min

Quick Lab

Teacher Notes

In this activity, students learn how to include a fossil into a branching diagram they have created. Students should classify the fossil based on their observation of the fossil's characteristics, such as the feathers and a lizard-shaped or dinosaur-shaped head (covers standard 7.3.d).

Answers

2. Sample answer: The archaeopteryx has a backbone, legs, and wings with feathers.

3.–4.

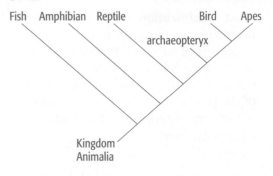

Strange Organisms

Classifying organisms is often not easy. Like an animal, some plants can eat other organisms to obtain nutrition. Some protists can use photosynthesis as plants do and move around as animals do. The animal kingdom also includes some members that might surprise you, such as corals.

The red cup sponge in **Figure 8** is also an animal. Sponges are usually considered the simplest animals. They lack sense organs, and most of them cannot move. Scientists used to classify sponges as plants. But sponges cannot make their own food. They must eat other organisms to get nutrients, which is one reason that sponges are classified as animals.

Figure 8 *This red cup sponge is a simple animal.*

SECTION Review

7.1.a, 7.3.d

Summary

- Most biologists recognize three domains: Archaea, Bacteria, and Eukarya.
- As scientists discover new organisms, classification systems are changed to include the characteristics of those new organisms.
- Archaea can live in extreme environments. Bacteria live almost everywhere else. All prokaryotes are members of the domain Archaea or the domain Bacteria.
- Domain Eukarya is made up of four kingdoms: Protista, Fungi, Plantae, and Animalia. All members of Eukarya are eukaryotes.

Using Vocabulary

1 Write an original definition for *Archaea* and *Bacteria*.

Understanding Concepts

2 **Identifying** Describe one characteristic of the domain Eukarya and one characteristic of each kingdom in the domain Eukarya.

Critical Thinking

3 **Applying Concepts** What do all of the organisms from the three domains have in common?

4 **Making Inferences** A branching diagram shows an unusual group of organisms on a branch between birds and mammals. What could you tell about when this unusual group of organisms evolved?

5 **Applying Concepts** You have discovered a new prokaryote. It lives deep within the crust of Earth, which is an extreme environment that has little air or food. Into which domain would you classify this organism? Explain.

Math Skills

6 **Making Calculations** If a certain bacterium divides every 30 min, when will there be more than 1,000 bacteria?

Challenge

7 **Identifying Relationships** Very hot water gushes out of formations on the sea floor called black smokers. Scientists have discovered many new kinds of organisms around black smokers. Why are scientists using a classification system to group these organisms?

8 **Applying Concepts** To get nutrients, the Venus' flytrap uses photosynthesis and traps and digests insects. Its cells have cell walls. Into which kingdom would you place this organism? What makes this organism unusual in this kingdom?

Internet Resources

For a variety of links related to this chapter, go to www.scilinks.org
Topic: Kingdoms
SciLinks code: HY71397

⏱ **15 min**

5. The branch with archaeopteryx at its tip does not reach the top of the diagram.

6. Birds and apes evolved more recently than the archaeopteryx evolved. Fish, amphibians, and reptiles evolved before the archaeopteryx.

🗀 Differentiated Datasheets
A **BASIC**, B **GENERAL**, C **ADVANCED**

Section Resources

🗀 Directed Reading
A **BASIC** (Also in Spanish), B **GENERAL**

🗀 Interactive Reader and Study Guide

🗀 Section Quiz **GENERAL** (Also in Spanish)

🗀 Section Review **GENERAL** (Also in Spanish)

🗀 Vocabulary and Section Summary
A **BASIC** (Also in Spanish), B **GENERAL**

Also editable on the Holt Lab Generator CD-ROM

Teacher Notes

In this activity, students use the shared derived characteristics of several life-forms to create their own branching diagram. The activity also requires students to include the fossil of a life-form in their branching diagram (covers standards 7.3.d and 7.7.d).

Time Required

One 45-minute class period

Lab Ratings

EASY ——————————— HARD

Teacher Prep 🧪
Student Set-Up 🧪
Concept Level 🧪🧪🧪
Clean Up 🧪

Preparation Notes

Some students may have greater success at this lab if they are given photocopied cut outs of the life-forms that they can manipulate. Be sure that students understand that changes in the complexity of groups of organisms are likely to be linear. Thus, in deciding which life-forms came first and which life-forms came later, students may logically assume that life-forms evolved from having fewer body segments to having more body segments.

Skills Practice Lab

OBJECTIVES

Observe the characteristics of different life-forms.

Identify how life-forms can be grouped based on their characteristics.

Construct a branching diagram.

MATERIALS

- paper
- pencil

7.3.d Students know how to construct a simple branching diagram to classify living groups of organisms by shared derived characteristics and how to expand the diagram to include fossil organisms.

Investigation and Experimentation
7.7.d Construct scale models, maps, and appropriately labeled diagrams to communicate scientific knowledge (e.g., motion of Earth's plates and cell structure).

Grouping Life-Forms by Their Characteristics

You are a crew member and a biologist on the USS *Adventure*. The USS *Adventure* has been on a 5-year mission to collect life-forms and fossils from outside the solar system. On the voyage back to Earth, your ship went through a meteor shower. The meteor shower damaged several of the rooms containing the alien life-forms and the fossils that you collected. Now, there are only two undamaged rooms in your starship for the life-forms. Assuming that life-forms with similar characteristics can live safely together, use observable characteristics to group the life-forms into these two rooms.

Procedure

1. Make a data table similar to the one below for all of the life-forms shown.

2. Fill in the columns about the shared derived characteristics of the life-forms based on your observations. (Remember that shared derived characteristics are characteristics that two or more life-forms share with their most recent common ancestor.) Use your observations to divide the life-forms and the remaining fossil into two main groups.

3. Fill in the last column of your table with the room assignments for each life-form.

4. Make a branching diagram based on the characteristics that you have recorded in the table. (Hint: Start with Life-form 1 at the base of the branching diagram. Because you have life-forms in two compartments, you are likely to have two branches splitting off from Life-form 1.) Also, include the fossil of Life-form 7 in the branching diagram.

Life-form Characteristics			
Life-form	Number of body segments	Number of antennae	Room assignment
1	DO NOT WRITE IN BOOK		
2			
3			

Lab Resources

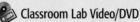

📁 Differentiated Datasheets
   A **BASIC**, B **GENERAL**, C **ADVANCED**

📹 Classroom Lab Video/DVD

Holt Lab Generator CD-ROM

Search for any lab by topic, standard, difficulty level, or time. Edit any lab to fit your needs, or create your own labs. Use the Lab Materials QuickList software to customize your lab materials list.

5 In deciding the order in which life-forms evolved, use the information about the number of body segments or the number of antennae. For example, life-forms that have many body segments may have evolved more recently than life-forms that have fewer body segments.

6 The USS *Adventure* makes one more stop on the way home. On planet X437, you discover another interesting life-form—the CC9, which is shown below. Based on your previous group ing of life-forms, decide if you can include CC9 in one of the rooms for the trip to Earth.

Life-form 1

Life-form 2

Life-form 3

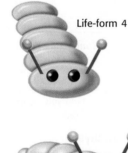
Life-form 4

Life-form 5

Life-form 6

Fossil of life-form 7

CC9

Analyze the Results

7 **Identifying Patterns**   Describe the life-forms in room 1. How are they similar? How are they different?

8 **Identifying Patterns**   Describe the life-forms in room 2. Are they similar to each other? How do they differ from the life-forms in room 1?

9 **Interpreting Information**   To which life-forms is the fossil related? (Hint: Use your branching diagram.)

Draw Conclusions

10 **Applying Conclusions**   In which room did you place life-form CC9? How did you decide?

11 **Making Inferences**   What other characteristics could you use to make a branching diagram of these life-forms? Would the use of other information change the branching diagram? What difficulties can using other information cause for scientists?

Big Idea Question

12 **Identifying Patterns**   How do you group living and extinct organisms? How do branching diagrams show evolutionary relationships?

Analyze the Results

7. Sample answer: Life-forms in room 1 have more than one repeating body segment. The shapes of these repeating body segments differ between life-forms.

8. Sample answer: The body of each life-form in room 2 is shaped differently. The bodies of life-forms in room 2 are similar to each other because they are not divided into repeating body segments. The life-forms in room 2 differ from the life-forms in room 1 because of the number of repeating body segments.

9. The fossil of life-form 7 shows that the body of life-form 7 is not divided into repeating body segments. Therefore, life-form 7 is likely to be most closely related to life-form 2 and life-form 5.

Draw Conclusions

10. Sample answer: I placed life-form CC9 in room 2 because the body of life-form CC9 is not divided into repeating body segments.

11. Sample answer: Other characteristics that might have been used to classify these different life-forms include the number and kind of eyes the life-forms have, whether or not the life-forms have legs, and whether or not the life-forms have mouths. Using different characteristics would change the branching diagram. It would be hard for scientists to decide which characteristics to use and the scientists might not agree with each other.

Big Idea Question

12. Living organisms and extinct organisms can be grouped based on their shared derived characteristics. Branching diagrams show the relationships between living organisms and extinct organisms along a timeline.

Procedure

4.   Life-form 3   Life-form 4   Life-form 6   Life-form 2   Life-form CC9   Fossil of Life-form 7   Life-form 5

Life-form 1

Sushma Kashyap, MSc
Alvarado Intermediate School
Rowland Heights, California

Teacher Notes

This activity asks students to use the appropriate writing style for scientific reports. To help students understand the differences in writing styles, use actual examples from a newspaper article, a scientific journal article, and an excerpt from a fictional story. Depending on the abilities of your students, you might ask some students to bring in their own research on the plesiosaur. You may wish to provide other students with photocopies of articles from the Internet, magazines, or science journals that they can use to write the report.

Answers to You Try It!

4. Accept all reasonable answers. Students should be able to articulate whether their report is objective.

5. Sample answer: I assumed that all of the information that I collected was accurate. My conclusions may be wrong if the information that I used is inaccurate.

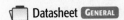 Datasheet **GENERAL**

Also editable on the Holt Lab Generator CD-ROM

Science Skills Activity

| Scientific Methods | Research | Data Analysis | Models, Maps & Diagrams |

 Investigation and Experimentation
7.7.e Communicate the steps and results from an investigation in written reports and oral presentations.

Communicating Through Written Reports

▶ Tutorial

After completing an investigation, scientists record and communicate the steps they followed as well as the results of their investigation. Communicating this information can be in the form of a written report. Use the following instructions to write a report based on the steps and results of an investigation.

① Gathering Information   First, gather the information that you collected during your investigation.

② Organizing Findings   Then, organize your information. Your report should have the following parts:
- title
- introduction
- paragraph(s) on materials and methods used
- discussion of your findings and conclusions
- list of the sources of information used

③ Communicating Findings
- In the introductory paragraph, describe the question that you want to answer.
- In the materials and methods section, describe the steps you followed, the facts that you collected, and any observations that you made during the investigation.
- In the discussion section, explain what you learned from your research. Make sure to state whether or not you found an answer to your question.

④ Applying Concepts   The style of writing in scientific reports is different from the writing in opinion columns in newspapers or mystery stories. Writing in science must be *objective*. Objective writing is writing that includes only facts. Inferences are only included if there is enough evidence. Review your report to make sure that your writing is objective.

▶ You Try It!

Procedure

Choose an extinct organism that interests you. Check with your teacher about your subject. Conduct research to find out about this organism. Write a report on your findings.

① Designing Questions   Think of a question that would help you learn about the fossils related to the organism you chose. For example, "Where and when did the Plesiosaur live?"

② Conducting Research   Use library resources and the Internet to find information about the organism you chose.

③ Communicating Findings   Use the Tutorial to help you organize and communicate your findings.

Analysis

④ Applying Concepts   Is your report objective? Explain your position.

⑤ Evaluating Sources   All of your conclusions were based on the information that you found in your research. What did you assume about the information that you found? What kinds of problems may arise from using sources that may not be accurate?

Universal Access · Differentiated Instruction

Special Education Students

Research Report Outline   For students with special needs, writing an entire research report may be too difficult. Simplify the task in the following ways:
1. Since the objective of the activity is to learn the steps of writing a report, provide students with the research information.
2. Give students this outline to follow:

  I. Title

 II. Introduction
  - Question

III. Materials and methods used (Provide this information to students so that they know where the research was found.)
  - Steps followed
  - Facts collected
  - Observations

IV. Discussion of findings
  - What was learned
  - Was the answer found?

 V. List of sources

LS Logical

Chapter Summary

The Big Idea Organisms can be classified into groups based on their characteristics.

Section

1 Sorting It All Out

Key Concept An eight-level classification system and branching diagrams are two basic tools that scientists use to study living and extinct organisms.

- Scientists use classification to study organisms and how organisms are related to each other.
- The eight levels of classification are the domain, kingdom, phylum, class, order, family, genus, and species.
- Each organism that has been described is given a scientific name.
- Branching diagrams show relatedness between living and extinct organisms over time.

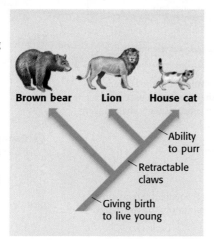

Brown bear Lion House cat

Ability to purr

Retractable claws

Giving birth to live young

Branching diagrams are useful when studying organisms.

2 Domains and Kingdoms

Key Concept All organisms can be classified into three domains based on their shared derived characteristics.

- Classification systems change as greater numbers of different organisms are described.
- All prokaryotes are divided into one of two domains, domain Archaea or domain Bacteria.
- All eukaryotes are classified into the domain Eukarya, which is divided into four kingdoms.

These giant sequoias are in the domain Eukarya and the kingdom Plantae.

Vocabulary

classification p. 332
taxonomy p. 333

Archaea p. 339
Bacteria p. 339
Eukarya p. 340
Protista p. 340
Fungi p. 340
Plantae p. 341
Animalia p. 342

Chapter Summary

SUPER SUMMARY

Have students connect the major concepts in this chapter through an interactive Super Summary. Visit go.hrw.com and type in the keyword HY7CLSS to access the Super Summary for this chapter.

Identifying Roots

Etymology Have students use a dictionary to discover the history of the vocabulary words *Archaea* and *Bacteria*. (The term *Archaea* comes from the Greek word *arkhaios*, which means "ancient." The term *Bacteria* is derived from the Greek word *bakterium*, which means "small staff" or "small rod.") **LS** Verbal

Focus on Reading

Expanding Summaries Have students read the bulleted chapter summary points presented on this page. Ask students to match each point in the chapter summary to the bulleted section summary points at the end of each section. Then, using what they have learned, ask students to write one sentence describing each section of this chapter in their own words. **LS** Verbal/Logical

Review Resources

- Reinforcement Worksheet **BASIC**
- Critical Thinking Worksheet **ADVANCED**
- Chapter Review **GENERAL** (Also in Spanish)
- Standards Review Workbook (Also in Spanish)
- Study Guide A **BASIC** (Also in Spanish), B **GENERAL**

Assessment Resources

- Chapter Tests A **BASIC**, B **GENERAL** (Also in Spanish), C **ADVANCED**
- Standards Assessment **GENERAL**

Chapter Review 7.1.a, 7.3.d

Assignment Guide

Section	Questions
1	1, 5–8, 10–12, 17–18, 20
2	2–4, 9, 13–14, 16, 19, 21–25

Answers

Using Vocabulary

1. b **7.3.d** (supporting)

2. Archaea **7.3.d** (supporting)

3. Animalia **7.3.d** (supporting)

4. prokaryotes **7.1.a** (mastering)

Understanding Concepts

5. a **7.3.d** (supporting)

6. a

7. Sample answer: Each species is unique, and scientific names make it possible for scientists all over the world to know specifically which organism is being discussed without the confusion of common names. **7.3.d** (supporting)

8. Taxonomists classify organisms based on the shared derived characteristics of the organisms. **7.3.d** (supporting)

9. no; A bacterium is a prokaryote because it does not have a nucleus. **7.1.a** (supporting), **7.3.d** (mastering)

10. lemur **7.3.d** (mastering)

11. chimpanzee **7.3.d** (mastering)

12. no; Lemurs branched off between points A and B. **7.3.d** (mastering)

Organize

Booklet Review the FoldNote that you created at the beginning of the chapter. Add to or correct the FoldNote based on what you have learned.

Using Vocabulary

❶ **Academic Vocabulary** In the sentence "Scientists classify organisms based on their shared derived characteristics," what does the word *derived* mean?
   a. caused by
   b. inherited from
   c. rare
   d. common

Complete each of the following sentences by choosing the correct term from the word bank.

   Archaea   prokaryotes
   eukaryotes   Animalia

❷ Prokaryotes that live in extreme environments are in the domain ___.

❸ Complex multicellular organisms that can usually move around and respond to their environment are in the kingdom ___.

❹ Although ___ are very similar, they are divided into two domains in part because they can live in extremely different environments.

Understanding Concepts

Multiple Choice

❺ How do scientists classify organisms?
   a. by grouping the organisms by their characteristics
   b. by giving the organisms many common names
   c. by deciding whether the organisms are useful
   d. by using only existing categories of classification

❻ The scientific name for the European white water lily is *Nymphaea alba*. To which genus does this plant belong?
   a. *Nymphaea*
   b. *alba*
   c. water lily
   d. alba lily

Short Answer

❼ **Identifying** Why is the use of scientific names important in biology?

❽ **Evaluating** What kind of evidence is used by modern taxonomists to classify organisms based on evolutionary relationships?

❾ **Demonstrating** Is a bacterium a type of eukaryote? Explain your answer.

INTERPRETING GRAPHICS Use the branching diagram of selected primates below to answer the next three questions.

Lemur   Baboon   Chimpanzee   Human

D — Bipedal, language
C — Much larger brain
B — Color vision
A — Binocular vision, opposable thumbs

❿ **Identifying** Which primate is the closest relative to the common ancestor of all primates?

⓫ **Evaluating** Which primate shares the most characteristics with humans?

⓬ **Demonstrating** Do both lemurs and humans have the characteristics listed at point D? Explain your answer.

Writing Skills

13. Answers may vary; accept all reasonable responses. Students should be able to articulate that not all organisms are either plants or animals. Some students may even point out that some organisms have characteristics of both plants and animals, and therefore could not be classified as either a plant or an animal. **7.3.d** (exceeding)

Writing Skills

13 **Writing Persuasively** In the past, scientists classified organisms as either plants or animals. Why doesn't that classification system work? Make sure to use examples to support your position.

Critical Thinking

14 **Concept Mapping** Use the following terms to create a concept map: *domain, kingdom, fern, lizard, Animalia, Fungi, algae, Protista, Plantae,* and *mushroom.*

15 **Analyzing Methods** Explain how the levels of classification depend on the similarities and differences between organisms.

16 **Identifying Relationships** What characteristic do all of the members of the four kingdoms in the domain Eukarya share?

17 **Applying Concepts** You have discovered the fossil of an organism that has a tail, gills, and legs. What steps would you take to figure out where this fossil would fit on a branching diagram that contains, fish, amphibians, reptiles, birds and mammals?

18 **Making Inferences** Sometimes, the branches in a branching diagram stop at dead ends. These dead ends may not reach the top of the diagram. What can you tell about the organisms shown at the end of these branches? Explain.

19 **Identifying Relationships** All organisms are made up of cells. Prokaryotes are made up of single cells but are divided into two domains. Describe a way in which you could determine the domain in which to classify a prokaryote.

20 **Expressing Opinions** Sam has discovered a new organism that has some strange features. He has decided to create a new phylum for this organism. Do you think that this is the correct way to classify this organism? Explain your position.

INTERPRETING GRAPHICS Use the photo below to answer the next three questions.

21 **Evaluating Data** Describe two basic characteristics of the organism in the photo.

22 **Identifying Relationships** Using the characteristics of the organism in the photo, can you decide whether this organism is a fish, a reptile, a bird, an animal, or a plant? Explain.

23 **Expressing Opinions** What other kinds of information could help you decide how to classify the organism in the photo?

Math Skills

24 **Making Conversions** Many prokaryotes live near deep-sea hydrothermal vents. The water coming out of the vents can be hotter than 536°F. Just a few meters away from the vent, the water temperature can be as cool as 35.6°F. Calculate the range of temperatures (in degrees Celsius), in which the prokaryotes live. (Hint: Convert both temperatures into degrees Celsius first.)

Challenge

25 **Identifying Relationships** The kingdom Protista is made up of single-celled organisms and multicellular organisms. These organisms are classified into the kingdom Protista because they do not fit into the other kingdoms. Explain why this characteristic makes kingdom Protista unusual when compared to other kingdoms?

18. Sample answer: The organism is probably extinct and no other organisms have been found that seem to have developed from the extinct organism. **7.3.d** (mastering)

19. Sample answer: One way to determine into which domain a prokaryote should be classified is to know what type of environment the prokaryote lives in. **7.3.d** (mastering)

20. Sample answer: no; Sam should first find out if there are other organisms with similar characteristics to determine whether the new organism may be related to other organisms. **7.3.d** (exceeding)

Interpreting Graphics

21. Sample answer: The organism has long, leafy appendages and a tail. **7.3.d** (supporting)

22. Sample answer: I think this organism is an animal because it has a mouth and a tail. However, I can't see enough characteristics to decide what kind of animal it is. **7.3.d** (mastering)

23. Sample answer: Other useful information might include where the organism lives, how the organism breathes, and how the organism moves. **7.3.d** (mastering)

Math Skills

24. The difference is 278°C;
536°F = 5/9 × (536 − 32) = 280°C;
35.6°F = 5/9 × (35.6 − 32) = 2°C;
280°C − 2°C = 278°C

Challenge

25. Sample answer: Members in each of the other kingdoms share characteristics that allow them to be grouped together. Kingdom Protista is unusual because it's members are grouped together not because they have characteristics in common but because they d not fit in the other kingdoms. **7.3.d** (exceeding)

Critical Thinking

14. An answer to this exercise can be found at the end of this book. **7.3.d** (supporting)

15. Sample answer: Each level of classification groups organisms according to the characteristics that they share. At broader levels of classification, such as domain and kingdom, members of the group share fewer characteristics than they do at more specific levels, such as family and genus. **7.3.d** (supporting)

16. Sample answer: All members of the four kingdoms in the domain Eukarya are made up of eukaryotic cells. The DNA of these organisms are found in the nucleus in their cells. **7.1.a** (mastering)

17. Sample answer: I would study the characteristics of the fossil and compare them to what I know about fish, amphibians, reptiles, birds, and mammals. Then, I would determine which group of organisms the fossil is most closely related to and determine the fossil's place on the branching diagram. **7.3.d** (mastering)

Chapter Review Standards Guide			
	Supporting	Mastering	Exceeding
7.1.a	9	4, 16, 19, 25	
7.3.d	1–3, 5, 7–8, 14–15, 21	9–12, 17–19, 22–23	13, 20, 25

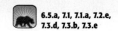
Teacher Notes

To provide practice under more realistic testing conditions, give students 20 min to answer all of the questions in this assessment.

Answer Key

Question Number	Correct Answer
1	B
2	D
3	B
4	C
5	B
6	C
7	B
8	D
9	A
10	C
11	C
12	B
13	B
14	D
15	A

Standards Guide

	Supporting	Mastering	Exceeding
6.5.a		14	
7.1		1	
7.1.a		11	
7.2.e		13	
7.3.b		15	
7.3.d	2–5	6–10	
7.3.e			12

📁 Standards Assessment **GENERAL**

📁 Teacher Notes for Standards Assessment contain a longer Assessment Doctor and Diagnostic Teaching Tips.

REVIEWING ACADEMIC VOCABULARY

1 In the sentence "The nucleus of a human cell is visible only with a microscope," what does the word *visible* mean?

A hidden

B observable

C separable

D driven

2 Which of the following words means "to build something by putting parts together"?

A adapt

B interpret

C display

D construct

3 In the sentence "The function of a branching diagram is to show how different kinds of organisms are related to each other," what does the word *function* mean?

A a relationship between mathematical sets

B a specialized activity of a tool or system

C a characteristic that depends upon another

D a social gathering or formal ceremony

4 Which of the following sets of words best completes the following sentence: The scientific name *Tyrannosaurus rex* ___ two Greek words that mean "tyrant lizard".

A derives into

B is derived with

C is derived from

D derives on

REVIEWING CONCEPTS

5 Classification is a tool that is used to study living and extinct organisms. Which of the following are levels in this system?

A living and nonliving

B families, genera, and species

C endangered and not endangered

D land, marine, and freshwater organisms

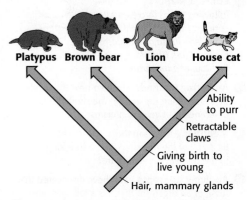

Platypus   Brown bear   Lion   House cat

Ability to purr
Retractable claws
Giving birth to live young
Hair, mammary glands

6 The branching diagram above shows similarities and differences between four mammals. Which of the following mammals has retractable claws?

A only the brown bear

B only the house cat

C the lion and the house cat

D the platypus and the brown bear

7 A scientist discovers a fossil of a new mammal that was an immediate ancestor of the brown bear. How would this fossil be shown in a branching diagram?

A It's name would be italicized.

B It's name would be placed on a branch leading to the brown bear.

C It's name would be placed at the tip of a new branch next to the brown bear.

D It's name would appear at the base of a branching diagram showing all bears.

➕ ASSESSMENT DOCTOR

Question 1: The correct answer is B. *Observable* and *visible* are interchangeable in most sentences. They both refer to things that can be seen. The details of a human cell can only be seen or observed with a microscope.

Question 2: The correct answer is D. *Construct* means "to build something by putting parts together."

Question 3: The correct answer is B. *Function* in this sentence means that the branching diagram is "a specialized activity of a tool or system."

Question 4: The correct answer is C. The scientific name *Tyrannosaurus rex* is derived from two Greek words.

Question 5: The correct answer is B. Families, genera, and species are levels in this system of classification.

Question 6: The correct answer is C. Both the lion and the house cat have retractable claws.

Question 7: The correct answer is B. An immediate ancestor of the brown bear would be placed on the branch leading directly to the brown bear.

8 Scientists today use an eight-level classification system. Who developed the original system on which the current classification system is based?

A the Chicabo people

B Oliver Zompro

C Michael Fay

D Carolus Linnaeus

9 The fossil of an organism is found near a hot spring. This single-celled organism has a cell wall and no nucleus. Into which of the following groups would you classify this organism?

A domain Archaea

B kingdom Plantae

C kingdom Protista

D kingdom Fungi

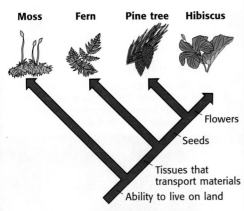

Moss   Fern   Pine tree   Hibiscus

Flowers

Seeds

Tissues that transport materials

Ability to live on land

10 The branching diagram above shows the relationships between four groups of plants. According to the diagram, which group of plants is the oldest?

A hibiscus

B fern

C moss

D pine tree

REVIEWING PRIOR LEARNING

11 Which of the following statements about cells is true?

A Some organisms have no cells.

B All cells make their own food.

C All cells function similarly.

D All cells have a nucleus.

12 Which of the following events is most likely to lead to the extinction of the largest number of species?

A a hurricane   C a flood

B an ice age   D a war

13 An algal cell's DNA is found

A in a loose loop within the cell.

B in long strands called *chromatin*.

C in the cytoplasm outside the nucleus.

D in the cell's endoplasmic reticulum.

14 Energy flows through the biosphere

A from decomposers to producers to consumers to sunlight.

B from sunlight to animals to producers.

C from sunlight through animals to plants.

D from sunlight through producers to consumers.

15 Darwin developed the following theory: Organisms that have heritable characteristics that are best suited to the organisms' environment survive and pass those characteristics on to their offspring more successfully than organisms that are not well suited to the environment do. What is this theory called?

A natural selection

B natural extinction

C genetic homogeneity

D uniformitarianism

Standards Assessment

Question 8: The correct answer is D. Linnaeus developed a system for classifying organisms. The classification system scientists use today is based on Linnaeus's system.

Question 9: The correct answer is A. A single-celled organism that has a cell wall and no nucleus and is found near a hot spring is likely an archaeon and therefore should be classified into the domain Archaea.

Question 10: The correct answer is C. The moss is the oldest organism because it is at the tip of the first branch that evolved from the main branch.

Question 11: The correct answer is C. Cells perform some basic functions similarly in all organisms. For example, all cells make proteins.

Question 12: The correct answer is B. An ice age would most likely lead to the extinction of the largest number of species.

Question 13: The correct answer is B. Algal DNA, like that of all eukaryotes, is found in the nucleus in long strands called chromatin.

Question 14: The correct answer is D. Energy enters the biosphere as sunlight. Plants convert the energy into chemical energy. The energy passes to consumers that eat the plants.

Question 15: The correct answer is A. This theory is called natural selection. Environmental and ecological conditions "select" certain characteristics of organisms for survival and reproduction.

Weird Science

Discussion

Tell students that one adaptation that allows fish to eat fruit is large, flat molars. Then ask students if they know what other animals have flat molars, and what those animals usually eat.

(Rodents such as mice and squirrels have flat molars. They eat seeds and grass. Rabbits and hoofed animals, such as deer and cows, also have flat molars, and they eat grass and other plants. Omnivores, such as bears, have molars like humans. They eat fruit, seeds, plants, and some meat.) **LS** **Verbal/ Logical**

Scientific Discoveries

ACTIVITY

Some species of black coral are very popular among collectors, who harvest the coral to make crafts and jewelry. As a result, the populations of these coral species have been severely depleted. Have students research other coral species that may be threatened or endangered because they are collected and used to make other products. Have students debate the issue of harvesting coral species. One side should be in favor of harvesting coral while the other should be in favor of protecting coral. **LS** **Verbal/ Interpersonal**

Science in Action

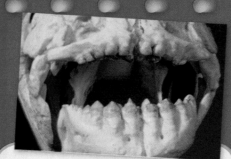

Weird Science

Fish That Eat Fruit

Have you ever thought about fish teeth? You probably know what shark teeth look like. So, you shouldn't be surprised that fish teeth are usually very different from your own teeth. But take a look at the fish shown above. This fish is *frugivorous* (froo JIV uh ruhs), which means that it eats fruit. Some frugivorous fishes live in the Amazon River in Brazil. Parts of the Amazon River basin flood for much of the year, which causes the water level to rise and spread under fruit trees. Fruit falls from the trees into the water, so these fishes have evolved to eat fruit. Eating fruit requires teeth that can bite and chew, just like human teeth. So, these fishes' teeth have evolved into a form that is similar to human teeth!

Math ACTIVITY

Suppose the water level in a river rose 8 m during a flood. At this time, only 4 m of a 16 m tall tree is above water. What was the original depth of the river before it was flooded? Record your work in your **Science Journal**.

Scientific Discoveries

A New Species of Black Coral

Milton Love from the University of California has recently discovered a new species of black coral. The black coral grows between 91 m deep (about 300 ft) and 221 m deep (about 725 ft) in the Channel Islands in California. Love named the coral *Antipathes dendochristos*. *Antipathes* is the genus name for black corals, which were once thought to help fight diseases (*anti* means "against" and *pathos* means "disease"). Love chose the specific name *dendochristos* (a Greek word for Christmas tree) because the live corals look like red or white decorated Christmas trees. Black corals are black only when they die and their black skeletons become exposed.

Language Arts ACTIVITY

Give the newly discovered species of black coral a nickname. Write a short essay in your **Science Journal** about why you chose that particular name for the coral.

Answer to Math Activity

The original depth of the river equals the tree's height (16 m) minus the height above the water (4 m) minus the amount the water rose (8m). So, the original depth of the river was 4 m.

Answer to Language Arts Activity

Nicknames may vary, but all essays should provide clear reasoning for the nickname chosen. Students should recognize that nicknames for organisms are often derived from an organism's location or a unique characteristic of the organism.

People in Science

Michael Fay

Crossing Africa Finding and classifying wild animals takes a great deal of perseverance. Just ask Michael Fay, who spent 15 months crossing 2,000 miles of uninhabited rain forest in the Congo River Basin of West Africa. He used video, photography, and old-fashioned note taking to record the types of animals and vegetation that he encountered along the way.

To find and classify wild animals, Fay often had to think like an animal. When coming across a group of monkeys swinging high above him in the emerald green canopy, Fay would greet the monkeys with his imitation of the crowned eagle's high-pitched, whistling cry. When the monkeys responded with their own distinctive call, Fay could identify exactly what species they were and would jot it down in one of his 87 waterproof notebooks. Fay also learned other tricks, such as staying downwind of an elephant to get as close to the elephant as possible. He could then identify its size, its age, and the length of its tusks.

Social Studies ACTIVITY

Many organizations around the world are committed to helping preserve biodiversity. Conduct some Internet and library research to find out about an organization that works to keep species safe from extinction. Record your work in your **Science Journal.** Then, create a poster that describes the organization and some of the species that the organization protects.

Internet Resources

- To learn more about careers in science, visit www.scilinks.org and enter the SciLinks code HY70225.
- To learn more about these Science in Action topics, visit go.hrw.com and type in the keyword HY7CLSF.
- Check out articles related to this chapter by visiting go.hrw.com. Just type in the keyword HY7CLSC.

People in Science

ACTIVITY

Have students conduct Internet research on Michael Fay and "Megatransect," the official name of his exploration. Once students have found a Web site that traces Fay's route, have them trace this route along a map or a globe. Then, have students research some of the national parks that have been created since Fay's trip, such as the Wonga-Wongué, the Ogooué Wetlands, and Mont Iboundji. Students could then choose a particular national park and draw their own map of the area. Maps should include pictures and information about the plants and animals that live in the region. **LS Visual/Logical**

Answer to Social Studies Activity

Answers may include groups such as the World Wildlife Fund, the Nature Conservancy, and Conservation International, which all work to preserve biodiversity around the world. Groups such as these help protect many animals and habitats and raise public awareness about the importance of preserving biodiversity.

UNIT 5

TIMELINE

Structure and Function in Plants and Animals

Have you ever been to a botanical garden or zoo? If so, you have some idea of how many types of animals—from tiny insects to massive whales—are found on Earth. You may have noticed that an organism's shape, size, or appearance help it survive in the environment in which the organism lives. In this unit, you will learn about many types of plants and animals. This timeline shows some developments in the study of plants and animals.

1580

Prospero Alpini discovers that plants have both male structures and female structures.

1775

J. C. Fabricius develops a system for the classification of insects.

1960

Jane Goodall, an English zoologist, begins her research on chimpanzees in Tanzania.

1610
Galileo Galilei uses a compound microscope to study insect anatomy.

1761
The first veterinary school is founded in Lyons, France.

1763
Joseph Kolreuter studies orchid pollination and discovers that both parent plants contribute traits to the offspring.

1838
Matthias Schleiden discovers that all plant tissue is made up of cells.

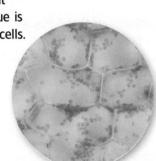

1882
Research on the ship *The Albatross* helps increase our knowledge of marine life.

1935
Francis B. Sumner studies the protective coloration of fish.

1983
The U.S. Space Shuttle *Challenger* is launched. Sally Ride, the first American woman in space, is on board.

1987
The last wild California condor is captured in an effort to save the species from extinction.

1998
The collection of a flower of the species *Smithatris supraneeana* leads to the discovery of a new genus of ginger.

Standards Course of Study

The elements listed in the Standards Course of Study provide a base for presenting, supporting, and assessing the California Grade 7 Science Standards. Use this Standards Course of Study as a base for planning your lessons.

Why Teach
Introduction to Plants

This chapter was designed to cover the California Grade 7 Science Standards about plants (7.1.b, 7.1.d, 7.2.a, 7.5.a, and 7.5.f). It follows a chapter about the classification of living things. This chapter describes the variety and importance of plants on Earth. It also describes the ways in which plants and animals rely on one another.

After they have completed this chapter, students will begin a chapter about plant processes.

 California Standards

Focus on Life Sciences

7.1.b Students know the characteristics that distinguish plant cells from animal cells, including chloroplasts and cell walls.

7.1.d Students know that mitochondria liberate energy for the work that cells do and that chloroplasts capture sunlight energy for photosynthesis.

7.2.a Students know the differences between the life cycles and reproduction methods of sexual and asexual organisms.

7.5.a Students know plants and animals have levels of organization for structure and function, including cells, tissues, organs, organ systems, and the whole organism.

7.5.f Students know the structures and processes by which flowering plants generate pollen, ovules, seeds, and fruit.

Investigation and Experimentation

7.7.c Communicate the logical connection among hypotheses, science concepts, tests conducted, data collected, and conclusions drawn from the scientific evidence.

7.7.d Construct scale models, maps, and appropriately labeled diagrams to communicate scientific knowledge (e.g., motion of Earth's plates and cell structure).

Chapter Pacing

Getting Started **45 min** pp. 358–359
The Big Idea Plants have several common characteristics and can be classified by their structures. **7.5.a, 7.7.c**

Section 1 What Is a Plant? **60 min** pp. 360–363
Key Concept Most plants perform photosynthesis, reproduce, and share some physical characteristics. **7.1.b, 7.1.d, 7.5.a**

Section 2 Seedless Plants **60 min** pp. 364–367
Key Concept Seedless plants do not produce seeds but are well adapted for reproduction and survival. **7.2.a, 7.5.a, 7.7.c**

Section 3 Seed Plants **60 min** pp. 368–373
Key Concept Seed plants produce seeds and are categorized as gymnosperms or angiosperms. **7.2.a, 7.5.f, 7.7.c**

Section 4 Structures of Seed Plants **90 min** pp. 374–381
Key Concept Seed plants are made up of roots and shoots. Each part carries out functions for the seed plant.

   7.5.a, 7.5.f, 7.7.c

Wrapping Up **180 min** pp. 382–391

  7.5.a, 7.5.f, 7.7.d

Basic Learners

TE Nonvascular or Vascular?, p. 362
TE Identifying Stems, p. 376
📁 Reinforcement Worksheet
📁 Chapter Test A
📁 Differentiated Datasheets A for Labs and Activities ■
📁 Study Guide A ■

Advanced Learners/GATE

TE Seed Plant Posters, p. 368
TE Leaves to Scale, p. 384
📁 Critical Thinking Worksheet
📁 Chapter Test C
📁 Differentiated Datasheets C for Labs and Activities ■

Key

SE Student Edition
TE Teacher's Edition

□ Chapter Resource File
📖 Workbook
🖥 Transparency

💿 CD or CD-ROM
*   Datasheet or blackline master available

■ Also available in Spanish

All resources listed below are also available on the One-Stop Planner.

Teach

SE Explore Activity Observing Plant Growth, p. 359* ■

🖥 **Bellringer**
💿 **PowerPoint® Resources**
SE Quick Lab Cell Walls and Wilting, p. 361* ■
🖥 L48 The Main Groups of Plants

🖥 **Bellringer**
💿 **PowerPoint® Resources**
🖥 L49 Moss Life Cycle; Fern Life Cycle
SE Quick Lab Moss Mass, p. 365* ■

🖥 **Bellringer**
💿 **PowerPoint® Resources**
SE Quick Lab Dissecting Seeds, p. 369* ■
🖥 L50 Life Cycle of a Pine Tree

🖥 **Bellringer**
💿 **PowerPoint® Resources**
🖥 L51 Structures of a Root
🖥 L52 Cross-Section of an Herbaceous Root; Cross-Section of a Woody Root
🖥 L53 Structure of a Leaf
SE Quick Lab How Do the Parts of a Plant Work Together?, p. 379* ■
🖥 L54 Structure of a Flower

SE Model-Making Lab Build a Flower, pp. 382–383* ■

Practice

SE Organize Activity Pyramid, p. 358

SE Section Review, p. 363* ■

SE Section Review, p. 367* ■

SE Section Review, p. 373* ■

SE Section Review, p. 381* ■

SE Science Skills Activity Constructing Scale Diagrams, p. 384* ■
🖥 **Concept Mapping***
SE Chapter Review, pp. 386–387* ■

Assess

□ **Chapter Pretest**

SE Standards Checks, pp. 360, 362
TE Standards Focus, p. 362
□ **Section Quiz** ■

SE Standards Check, p. 365
TE Standards Focus, p. 366
□ **Section Quiz** ■

SE Standards Checks, pp. 368, 369, 371, 372
TE Standards Focus, p. 372
□ **Section Quiz** ■

SE Standards Checks, pp. 375, 376, 379, 380
TE Standards Focus, p. 380
□ **Section Quiz** ■

SE Standards Assessment, pp. 388–389*
□ **Chapter Tests A, B ■, C**
📖 **Standards Review Workbook** ■

Resources for Universal Access • Differentiated Instruction

English Learners
TE Activity, p. 360
TE Re-Assess, p. 362
TE Using the Figure, pp. 369, 370
TE Pronunciation Guide, p. 370
TE Group Activity, pp. 375, 378
TE Proper Pronunciation, p. 378
TE Science Homophones, p. 380
□ Vocabulary and Section Summary A ■, B

□ Section Quizzes ■
□ Chapter Tests A, B ■
□ Differentiated Datasheets A, B, and C for Labs and Activities ■
📖 Study Guide A ■
📖 Multilingual Glossary

Struggling Readers
TE Ferns, p. 366
TE Reading Data Tables, p. 384

Special Education Students
TE What Is a Plant?, p. 360
TE Plant Uses, p. 367
TE Gymnosperm or Angiosperm?, p. 372
TE Watching the Speaker, p. 374

To help plan your lessons, refer to the On Course Mapping Instruction booklet.

Visual Resources

CHAPTER STARTER TRANSPARENCY

This Really Happened!

A lone scientist trudges through a remote rain forest. Peering into a steep, narrow canyon, he notices something unusual. On closer inspection, he discovers that it is a species of tree that has survived from the days when *Tyrannosaurus rex* and *Velociraptor* walked the Earth! No, this isn't a scene out of *Jurassic Park*. This really happened in an Australian rain forest in 1994. The scientist's name was David Noble. He discovered a tree species that dates back to the Cretaceous period, between 144 million and 65 million years ago.

The trees, called Wollemi pines, have large, bladelike leaves and knobby brown bark. They grow as tall as 35 m, and their trunks can grow as wide as 1 m.

Since the discovery of the trees, scientists at the Royal Botanic Gardens in Sydney, Australia, have been planting seeds of the Wollemi pines and growing seedlings. Soon Wollemi pines will be made available to gardeners so they can transform their yards into their own Cretaceous parks.

BELLRINGER TRANSPARENCIES

Section: What Is a Plant?
Compare plant cells to animal cells by making two lists. First, list the characteristics that are unique to plant cells. Then, list the characteristics that are shared by plant cells and animal cells.

Write your lists in your **science journal**.

Section: Seedless Plants
Which of the following groups of seedless plants produce sperm and egg cells that fuse during fertilization?

mosses liverworts
hornworts ferns
club mosses

Write your answer in your **science journal**.

TEACHING TRANSPARENCIES

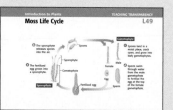
The Main Groups of Plants — L48

Life Cycle of a Pine Tree — L50

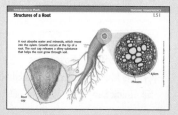
Moss Life Cycle — L49

Structures of a Root — L51

TEACHING TRANSPARENCIES

Cross-Section of an Herbaceous Root — L52

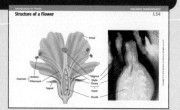
Structure of a Flower — L54

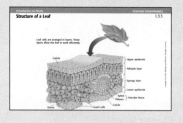
Structure of a Leaf — L53

A Food Chain — E83

LINK TO EARTH SCIENCE

STANDARDS REVIEW TRANSPARENCIES

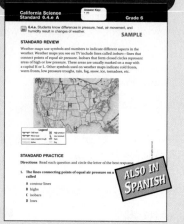

California Science Standard 6.4.e A — Grade 6

6.4.e. Students know differences in pressure, heat, air movement, and humidity result in changes of weather.

SAMPLE

STANDARD REVIEW
Weather maps use symbols and numbers to indicate different aspects in the weather. Weather maps you see on TV include lines called isobars—lines that connect points of equal air pressure. Isobars that form closed circles represent areas of high or low pressure. These areas are usually marked on a map with a capital H or L. Other symbols used on weather maps indicate cold fronts, warm fronts, low pressure troughs, rain, fog, snow, ice, tornadoes, etc.

STANDARD PRACTICE
Directions Read each question and circle the letter of the best response.

1. The lines connecting points of equal air pressure on a map are called
   A contour lines
   B highs
   C isobars
   D lows

ALSO IN SPANISH

CONCEPT MAPPING TRANSPARENCY

Use the following terms to complete the concept map below:
angiosperms, vascular, plants, sporophyte, nonvascular, pollen, gametophyte, xylem

Planning Resources

PARENT LETTER

SAMPLE

Dear Parent,

Your son's or daughter's science class will soon begin exploring the chapter entitled "The Nature of Physical Science." In this chapter, students will learn about how the scientific method applies to the world of physical science and the role of physical science in the world. By the end of the chapter, students should demonstrate a clear understanding of the chapter's main ideas and be able to discuss the following topics:

1. the role of questions in the process of investigation (Section 1)
2. how applying science saves lives and benefits the environment (Section 1)
3. careers that rely on science (Section 1)
4. the steps used in scientific methods (Section 2)
5. how scientific methods are used to answer questions and solve problems (Section 2)
6. the importance of safety precautions in the laboratory (Section 3)
7. examples of safety equipment and when to use them (Section 3)
8. how safety symbols are used to make laboratories safer (Section 3)

Questions to Ask Along the Way

You can help your child learn about these topics by asking interesting questions as he or she progresses through the chapter. For example, you may wish to ask your son or daughter the following questions:

What are some surprising careers that use science?
What is a characteristic of a good hypothesis?
What is the first step to take if an accident happens?

ALSO IN SPANISH

TEST ITEM LISTING

SAMPLE

Holt California Physical Science
Chapter 6 Introduction to Atoms
Test Item Listing
Multiple choice

1. The smallest particle into which an element can be divided and still have the properties of that element is called a(n)
   a. nucleus. c. atom.
   b. electron. d. neutron.
   ANS: C DIF: 1 REF: 1 OBJ: 1 STO: 8.3.a KEY: atom
   MSC: SQ 1.1

2. What particle did J. J. Thomson discover?
   a. neutron
   b. electron
   c. atom
   d. proton
   ANS: B DIF: 1 REF: 1 OBJ: 1 STO: 8.3.a KEY: electron
   SQ 1.2

3. How would you describe the nucleus?
   a. dense, positively charged
   b. mostly empty space, positively charged
   c. tiny, negatively charged
   d. dense, negatively charged
   ANS: A DIF: 1 REF: 1 OBJ: 2 STO: 8.3.a KEY: nucleus MSC:
   SQ 1.3

4. Where are electrons likely to be found?
   a. in the nucleus
   b. in electron clouds
   c. mixed throughout an atom
   d. in definite paths
   ANS: B DIF: 1 REF: 1 OBJ: 2 STO: 8.3.a KEY: electron MSC:
   SQ 1.4

5. Dalton believed that
   a. atoms of the same element are exactly alike.
   b. most, but not all, substances are made of atoms.
   c. atoms of different elements are the same.
   d. atoms can be divided.
   ANS: A DIF: 1 REF: 2 OBJ: 1 STO: 8.3.a KEY: atom
   MSC: SQ 1.5

6. Every atom of a given element has the same number of
   a. protons.
   b. neutrons.
   c. electrons.
   d. isotopes.
   ANS: A DIF: 1 REF: 2 OBJ: 2 STO: 8.3.a KEY: atom

ALSO IN SPANISH

One-Stop Planner® CD-ROM

This CD-ROM package includes all of the resources shown here and the following time-saving tools:

- **Lab Materials QuickList Software**
- **Customizable Lesson Plans** Correlated to the California Science Standards
- **Holt Calendar Planner**
- **PowerPoint® Resources**
- **Printable Worksheets**
- **ExamView® Test Generator** Correlated to the California Science Standards
- **Holt PuzzlePro®**
- **Interactive Teacher's Edition**

For a correlation of each lab or activity to the **California Science Standards,** see pages T22–T27.

Meeting Individual Needs

DIRECTED READING A

BASIC / ALSO IN SPANISH

DIRECTED READING B

Directed Reading B — SAMPLE

Section: Body Organization
A STABLE INTERNAL ENVIRONMENT

1. The maintenance of a stable internal environment in the body is

CELLS, TISSUES, AND ORGANS

GENERAL

VOCABULARY AND SECTION SUMMARY A

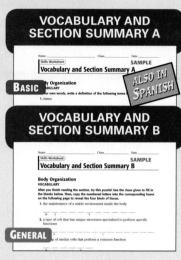

BASIC / ALSO IN SPANISH

VOCABULARY AND SECTION SUMMARY B

Vocabulary and Section Summary B — SAMPLE

Body Organization
VOCABULARY

GENERAL

REINFORCEMENT

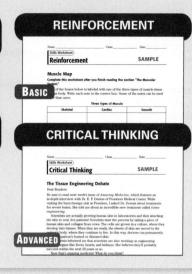

BASIC

CRITICAL THINKING

Critical Thinking — SAMPLE

The Tissue Engineering Debate

Dear Readers:

ADVANCED

INTERACTIVE READER AND STUDY GUIDE

MULTILINGUAL GLOSSARY

Labs and Activities

DIFFERENTIATED DATASHEETS FOR EXPLORE ACTIVITY, QUICK LABS, AND CHAPTER LAB

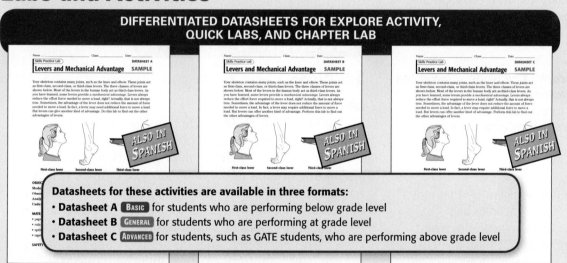

Levers and Mechanical Advantage — DATASHEET A / DATASHEET B / DATASHEET C — SAMPLE

First-class lever / Second-class lever / Third-class lever

Datasheets for these activities are available in three formats:
- **Datasheet A** BASIC for students who are performing below grade level
- **Datasheet B** GENERAL for students who are performing at grade level
- **Datasheet C** ADVANCED for students, such as GATE students, who are performing above grade level

DATASHEET FOR SCIENCE SKILLS ACTIVITY

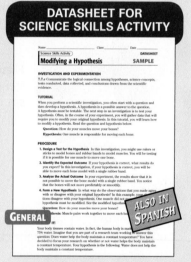

Modifying a Hypothesis — DATASHEET — SAMPLE

INVESTIGATION AND EXPERIMENTATION

GENERAL

Reviews and Assessments

SECTION REVIEWS

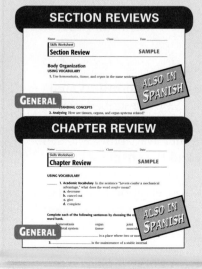

GENERAL / ALSO IN SPANISH

CHAPTER REVIEW

Chapter Review — SAMPLE

USING VOCABULARY

GENERAL / ALSO IN SPANISH

CHAPTER PRETEST

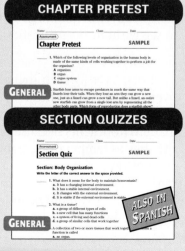

GENERAL / ALSO IN SPANISH

SECTION QUIZZES

Section Quiz — SAMPLE

Section: Body Organization

GENERAL / ALSO IN SPANISH

CHAPTER TEST A

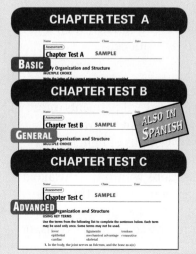

BASIC

CHAPTER TEST B

Chapter Test B — SAMPLE

GENERAL / ALSO IN SPANISH

CHAPTER TEST C

Chapter Test C — SAMPLE

ADVANCED / ALSO IN SPANISH

STANDARDS ASSESSMENT

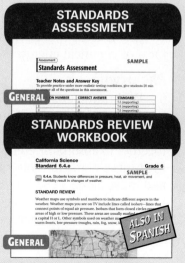

Standards Assessment — SAMPLE

Teacher Notes and Answer Key

GENERAL

STANDARDS REVIEW WORKBOOK

California Science Standard 6.4.e — SAMPLE — Grade 6

STANDARD REVIEW

GENERAL / ALSO IN SPANISH

This Teacher Background explains science concepts, principles, and theories that appear in the chapter. Use the information on these pages to refresh or enhance your understanding of the topics covered.

Section 1

What Is a Plant?

Plant Cells

Plant cells are similar to all other eukaryotic cells in structure and function but have several key structures that make them unique. Some of these structures are shown in **Figure A.** Plant cells have cell walls, made of the complex carbohydrate cellulose imbedded in proteins such as lignin. Some plant cells have two cell walls, with the secondary cell wall being much thicker and stronger than the primary cell wall. This secondary cell wall serves as an additional supportive structure in large woody plants.

Figure A *Cell walls, a large central vacuole, and chloroplasts are structures that make a plant cell different from animal cells.*

Plants also have large *vacuoles* (fluid-filled sacs) that may take up 90% of the cell space. These vacuoles help give structure to the plant and store metabolic products and wastes. Plants also contain chloroplasts. Chlorophyll, found in chloroplasts, is the green pigment responsible for converting the sun's energy into chemical energy (glucose) that can be used by the plant and plant-eating organisms. Like other eukaryotic cells, plant cells contain mitochondria to carry out cellular respiration. The mitochondria convert the glucose into adenosine triphosphate (ATP), a form of chemical energy used by plant cells.

Photosynthesis

Within the chloroplasts are flattened disks called thylakoids, which contain pigments. Several pigments, most importantly chlorophyll a and chlorophyll b, work together to absorb different wavelengths of light. When light hits a pigment molecule, electrons become excited and move along a chain of reactions within the thylakoid membrane. Water molecules are important in this reaction, as they are the source of additional electrons needed to maintain the chain reaction. The chain of reactions, or

"light reactions," converts light energy to chemical energy in the form of ATP and the reduced form of nicotinamide adenine dinucleotide phosphate (NADPH). These phosphorous-containing molecules provide energy for carbon fixation, during which carbon atoms are removed from carbon dioxide and recombined into sugars and other organic compounds. Carbon fixation occurs outside the thylakoids, in the lumen. The two processes of photosynthesis, separated in location and time, can be combined and simplified with the following equation:

$$CO_2 + H_2O + \text{light energy} \Rightarrow (CH_2O) + O_2$$

This equation is the reverse of cellular respiration, during which glucose and oxygen are used to release energy within the mitochondria, and carbon dioxide and water are produced as by-products. Mitochondria liberate energy through cellular respiration so that cells may do work, while chloroplasts capture sunlight energy for photosynthesis.

Section 2

Seedless Plants

Life Cycles

All plants have a life cycle that consists of an alternation of generations. In fact, plants' sexual reproduction depends upon this alternation of generations. In the alternating generations, a haploid gametophyte, which has only one set of chromosomes, produces the gametes, or eggs and sperm. When united, these gametes result in the diploid sporophyte, which has two sets of chromosomes. The sporophyte goes on to produce spores, which in turn develop into the gametophyte, and the cycle repeats itself. In nonvascular plants, such as mosses and liverworts, the gametophyte is the larger, more conspicuous generation. In both seedless and seed-producing vascular plants, the sporophyte is larger and more conspicuous, while the gametophyte may be impossible to see without magnification.

Bryophytes

Bryophytes, which include mosses, hornworts, and liverworts, make up more than 15,000 described species worldwide. Various species tend to be restricted to particular environments because of water availability and sensitivities to temperature, light, and the chemical composition of the soil. Thus, bryophytes are good indicator species for ecologists and conservation biologists. These experts can characterize an environment by identifying the bryophytes present in an area.

Ferns

Fern sporophytes are photosynthetic and live independently of the gametophyte, unlike the sporophytes of nonvascular plants, which are generally non-photosynthetic and live almost like parasites on the dominant gametophyte. See the fern life cycle illustrated in **Figure B.** The fern gametophyte shown here is actually much smaller than the sporophyte. Ferns and other seedless vascular plants produce rhizomes. Under ideal conditions, these rhizomes allow the plants to spread rapidly. In this way, areas are colonized by asexual reproduction rather than sexual reproduction, which requires the formation of a gametophyte. While ferns do not make seeds, they are adapted to a wider range of environmental conditions than nonvascular plants are.

Figure B *The gametophyte of a fern is smaller than and lives independently of the sporophyte.*

Section 3

Seed Plants

Pollination Versus Fertilization

In seed-producing plants, pollination and fertilization are two related but distinct events. Pollination occurs when pollen grains land on the sticky fluid secreted between the scales of the female cone (as in conifers), or when pollen grains land on the sticky surface of the stigma (as in angiosperms). Fertilization occurs when the sperm cell within a pollen grain unites with the egg cell. In pines, the events of pollination and fertilization can be separated by 15 months. In flowering plants, pollination and fertilization are separated by a matter of days or even hours.

Double Fertilization

Angiosperm seeds develop a bit differently than gymnosperm seeds do, although both contain an embryo and stored food at maturity. In angiosperms, the pollen grain (or microgametophyte) contains two sperm cells, both of which "fertilize" cells within the embryo sac (megagametophyte). One sperm fuses with the egg to produce a zygote, which develops into the plant embryo. The other sperm fuses with the polar nuclei, which are left over from the meiotic divisions that led to the formation of the egg. This second fusion results in rapid cell division and formation of the endosperm, the nutrient-rich material that makes up the bulk of the mature seed. The endosperm nourishes the young plant as it germinates and begins to grow.

Section 4

Structures of Seed Plants

Help from Fungi

As shown in **Figure C,** the tiny root hairs on the roots of plants greatly increase the absorptive surface area of the roots and increase the uptake of water and nutrients. But even the hairs have "hairs" to increase the surface area even further. These hairs are actual fungal hyphae, and more than 80% of plant species have these hyphae. A vast network of fungal threads, also called hyphae, helps plants absorb water and nutrients such as phosphorus. Some plants, such as many orchids, cannot live without this network of hyphae. Other plants would grow much more slowly without them. In return, the fungal hyphae use the sugars produced by the plant as a food source. In fact, just as some plants cannot live without the fungi, some of the fungi are completely dependent on the plants. These symbiotic relationships are called *mycorrhizae,* which means "fungus root."

Figure C *Root hairs and symbiotic fungi increase the ability of roots to absorb water and nutrients.*

Improving Comprehension

Use the Graphic Organizer on this page of the Student Edition to introduce the topics that are covered in this chapter, to summarize the chapter material, or to show students how to make a Venn diagram.

Teaching Tips

• Explain to students that a Venn diagram is ideal for showing the similarities and differences between two or three topics.

• Explain to students that because it requires the topics to have both shared and unique characteristics, a Venn diagram has a more limited use than other comparison organizers, such as a comparison table, do.

LS Logical

Improving Comprehension

Graphic Organizers are important visual tools that can help you organize information and improve your reading comprehension. The Graphic Organizer below is called a *Venn diagram*. Instructions for creating other types of Graphic Organizers are located in the **Study Skills** section of the Appendix.

How to Make a Venn Diagram

❶ Draw a diagram like the one shown below. Draw one circle for each topic. Make sure that each circle partially overlaps the other circles.

❷ In each circle, write a topic that you want to compare with the topics in the other circles.

❸ In the areas of the diagram where circles overlap, write the characteristics that the topics in the overlapping circles share.

❹ In the areas of the diagram where circles do not overlap, write the characteristics that are unique to the topic of the particular circle.

When to Use a Venn Diagram

A Venn diagram is a useful tool for comparing two or three topics in science. A Venn diagram shows which characteristics the topics share and which characteristics are unique to each topic. Venn diagrams are ideal when you want to illustrate relationships in a pair or small group of topics. As you read, look for topics that have both shared and unique characteristics, and draw a Venn diagram that shows how the topics are related.

Seed Plants
• produce seeds
• gametophytes are dependent on sporophyte
• do not need water to reproduce sexually
• grouped into gymnosperms and angiosperms

• carry out photosynthesis
• reproduce sexually and asexually
• have a two-stage lifecycle
• have qualities that are useful for humans

Seedless Plants
• need water to reproduce sexually
• gametophytes live independently of sporophyte
• divided into two groups: vascular and nonvascular

You Try It!

This Reading Strategy can also be used within the chapter that you are about to read. Practice making your own *Venn diagram* as directed in the Reading Strategies for Section ❷ and Section ❸. Record your work in your **Science Journal**.

Using Other Graphic Organizers

Students can practice using a variety of Graphic Organizers while reading this chapter. The following Graphic Organizers may also be useful in this chapter:

A **spider map** can be used to describe plant characteristics, discussed in Section 1.

An **idea wheel** can be used to organize ideas about angiosperms, discussed in Section 3. An **idea wheel** can also be used to organize details about the structure of seed plants, discussed in Section 4.

Instructions for creating these Graphic Organizers are located on pages 583–591 of the Appendix.

Unpacking the Standards

The information below "unpacks" the standards by breaking them down into basic parts. The higher-level, academic vocabulary is highlighted and defined to help you understand the language of the standards. "What It Means" restates the standards as simply as possible.

California Standard	Academic Vocabulary	What It Means
7.1.b Students know the characteristics that distinguish plant cells from animal cells, including chloroplasts and cell walls.		Plant cells have some unique structures that make plant cells different from animal cells. These structures include chloroplasts and a cell wall.
7.1.d Students know that mitochondria **liberate** energy for the work that cells do and that chloroplasts capture sunlight **energy** for photosynthesis.	**liberate** (LIB uhr ᴀʏᴛ) to release; to set free **energy** (EN uhr jee) the capacity to do work	Mitochondria release energy from sugar to power the cell's life processes. Chloroplasts turn energy from the sun into sugars and oxygen.
7.2.a Students know the differences between the life **cycles** and reproduction **methods** of **sexual** and asexual organisms.	**cycle** (SIE kuhl) a repeating series of changes **method** (METH uhd) a way of doing something **sexual** (SEK shoo uhl) having to do with sex	You must know how the life cycles of living things that reproduce sexually differ from the life cycles of living things that reproduce asexually. You must also explain how these ways of reproducing differ.
7.5.a Students know plants and animals have levels of organization for **structure** and **function,** including cells, tissues, organs, organ systems, and the whole organism.	**structure** (STRUHK chuhr) the arrangement of the parts of a whole **function** (FUHNGK shuhn) use or purpose	Plants and animals are made of smaller parts which are organized by shape and purpose. These layers of organization include cells, tissues, organs, organ systems, and the whole organism.
7.5.f Students know the **structures** and **processes** by which flowering plants **generate** pollen, ovules, seeds, and fruit.	**process** (PRAH sᴇs) a set of steps, events, or changes **generate** (JEN uhr ᴀʏᴛ) to bring about; to produce	You must know the parts of flowering plants and the ways by which those parts make pollen, ovules, seeds, and fruit.

Unpacking the Standards

Use the following information with the *What It Means* in the Student Edition to help students understand why studying each standard is important.

Why It Matters
Plants and animals are the organisms with which people interact the most.
To understand digestion and the need to eat and breathe at the macro level, students must understand where their food originates at a cellular level and how their cells make use of this food.
Students should be aware of the variety of ways in which organisms reproduce.
Multicellular organisms, including humans, function because their cells are organized at many levels. Each subsequent level of organization has unique properties that the prior level of organization does not have.
Most forms of life on Earth depend on plants to convert solar energy into a usable source of energy that supports life. Flowering plants are the most common type of plants on Earth.

Word Parts

Students will be able to understand a wide variety of words once they learn meanings of common prefixes and suffixes and understand how these prefixes and suffixes are used to modify word roots. Use this activity to help students learn about prefixes, suffixes, and word roots.

Prefix	Definition	Root	Definition
a–	not	**gymn**	naked
non–	not	**sperm**	seed

Practice Instruct students to use the table to write definitions for the following terms: *nonvascular plant, gymnosperm,* and *asexual plant.*

(*nonvascular plant:* a plant that does not have vascular tissue or specialized conducting tissues; *gymnosperm:* a woody, vascular seed plant whose seeds are "naked," or not enclosed by an ovary or fruit; *asexual plant:* a plant that does not reproduce sexually)

Chapter Overview

Tell students that this chapter will help them learn about plants. The chapter describes the four main groups of plants. The chapter also discusses the structures of flowering plants.

MISCONCEPTION ALERT

Plant Food

Identify It! Ask students, "Where do plants get their food?" Students may think that plants obtain all of their food energy from the soil.

Correct It! Tell students that although soil contains minerals, it is not a plant's source of food energy. Tell students to imagine a potted plant, and ask "If plants get their food from the soil, what will happen to the soil as the plant grows?" (Sample answer: The soil would disappear.) Ask the students if they have ever known soil to disappear in a potted plant. Tell them that plants use energy from the sun to make their own food from water and carbon dioxide. Because plants can produce their own food, they are known as "producers." Have students conduct an experiment in which they periodically measure the amount of soil in a potted plant over the course of a day or two. Students will find that there is no change in the amount of soil.

Assess It! Ask students to explain how plants get the food that they need to survive. Have each student create a drawing of a plant, labeling the sources of various materials used by the plant.

Introduction to Plants

The Big Idea Plants have several common characteristics and can be classified by their structures.

California Standards

Focus on Life Sciences

7.1 All living organisms are composed of cells, from just one to many trillions, whose details usually are visible only through a microscope. (Section 1)

7.2 A typical cell of any organism contains genetic instructions that specify its traits. Those traits may be modified by environmental influences. (Sections 2 and 3)

7.5 The anatomy and physiology of plants and animals illustrate the complementary nature of structure and function. (Sections 1, 2, 3, and 4)

Investigation and Experimentation

7.7 Scientific progress is made by asking meaningful questions and conducting careful investigations. (Science Skills Activity)

Math

7.1.1 Mathematical Reasoning

English–Language Arts

7.1.3 Reading
7.2.4 Writing

About the Photo

This picture looks alien, but it is very much of this Earth. This buttercup stem has been magnified so that individual cells can be seen. Some of the cells in this plant stem contain green chloroplasts, the organelles responsible for capturing sunlight for the process of photosynthesis.

Organize

Pyramid

Before you read the chapter, create the FoldNote entitled "Pyramid." Label the sides of the pyramid with "Nonvascular plants," "Seedless vascular plants," and "Seed plants." As you read the chapter, define each kind of plant, and write characteristics of each kind of plant on the appropriate side of the pyramid.

Instructions for creating FoldNotes are located in the Study Skills section on p. 579 of the Appendix.

California Standards Alignment

Focus on Life Sciences

7.1.b Students know the characteristics that distinguish plant cells from animal cells, including chloroplasts and cell walls. **pp. 360–361, 363, 386–387, 389**

7.1.d Students know that mitochondria liberate energy for the work that cells do and that chloroplasts capture sunlight energy for photosynthesis. **pp. 360, 363, 386–388**

7.2.a Students know the differences between the life cycles and reproduction methods of sexual and asexual organisms. **pp. 364, 365–368, 371–373, 386–388**

7.5.a Students know plants and animals have levels of organization for structure and function, including cells, tissues, organs, organ systems, and the whole organism. **pp. 359, 362–365, 367, 374–378, 381, 383, 386–389**

7.5.f Students know the structures and processes by which flowering plants generate pollen, ovules, seeds, and fruit **pp. 368–369, 372–373, 379–383, 383–387, 389**

Investigation and Experimentation

7.7.c Communicate the logical connection among hypotheses, science concepts, tests conducted, data collected, and conclusions drawn from the scientific evidence. **pp. 359, 365, 369, 379**

7.7.d Construct scale models, maps, and appropriately labeled diagrams to communicate scientific knowledge (e.g., motion of Earth's plates and cell structure). **pp. 382–384**

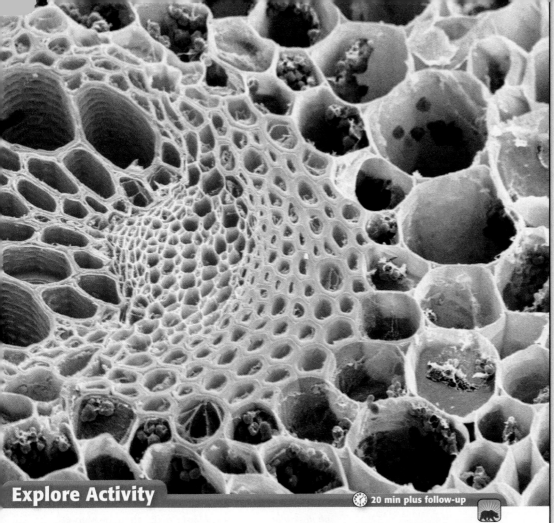

Teacher Notes

This activity has students observe the change in the structures of a seed as it grows into a plant (covers standards 7.5.a and 7.7.c). Cut off the neck of each bottle before distributing bottles to students. Soaking the seeds overnight in advance will decrease the number of days until germination.

Materials for Each Group

- aluminum foil
- bean seeds (3–4)
- soda bottle, clear plastic, with neck cut off, 2 L
- potting soil, moist
- water, 60 mL

Safety Caution

Some students—particularly those who suffer from allergies or have open cuts—may wish to wear protective gloves while handling the soil and seeds. Remind students to wash their hands when they are finished with the activity.

Answers

6. Answers may vary. Students may report that not all of their seeds grew.

7. Answers may vary. Germination times vary depending on the type of seeds used, temperature, and soil moisture.

8. Sample answer: The seed contains stored food that is used for energy to grow.

Differentiated Datasheets
A **BASIC**, B **GENERAL**, C **ADVANCED**

Also editable on the
**Holt Lab Generator
CD-ROM**

Explore Activity

20 min plus follow-up

Observing Plant Growth

When planting a garden, you bury seeds and water them. What happens to the seeds below the soil? How do seeds grow into plants?

Procedure

1. Fill a clear **2 L soda bottle** to within 8 cm of the top with **moist potting soil.** Your teacher will have already cut off the neck of the bottle.

2. Press **three or four bean seeds** into the soil and against the wall of the bottle. Add enough additional potting soil to cover the seeds.

3. Cover the sides of the bottle with **aluminum foil** to keep out light. Leave the top of the bottle uncovered.

4. Water the seeds with about **60 mL of water,** or water them until the soil is moist. Add more water when the soil dries out. **7.5.a 7.7.c**

5. Place the bottle in an area that receives sunshine. Check on your seeds each day for 10 days, and record your observations.

Analysis

6. How many seeds grew?

7. How long did the seeds take to start growing?

8. From where did the seeds most likely get the energy to grow?

Math Standards

Mathematical Reasoning 7.1.1 Analyze problems by identifying relationships, distinguishing relevant from irrelevant information, identifying missing information, sequencing and prioritizing information, and observing patterns. **p. 387**

Number Sense 7.1.1 Read, write, and compare rational numbers in scientific notation (positive and negative powers of 10) with approximate numbers using scientific notation. **p. 373**

English–Language Arts Standards

Reading 7.1.3 Clarify word meaning through the use of definition, example, restatement, or contrast. **p. 360**

Writing 7.2.4 Write narrative, expository, persuasive, and descriptive texts. **p. 387**

This Really Happened!

A lone scientist trudges through a remote
rain forest. Peering into
canyon, he notices s
On closer inspection,
it is a species of tre
from the days when
and Velociraptor walk
No, this isn't a sc
Park. This really happen
rain forest in 1994. Th
was David Noble. He
species that dates bac
period, between 144
million years ago.
The trees, called Wollemi pines, have
large, bladelike leaves and knobby brown
bark. They grow as tall as 35 m, and their

Chapter Starter Transparency
Use this transparency to help students
begin thinking about the world of plants.

Preteach

Reviewing Prior Knowledge

Read one of the vocabulary words for this section aloud. Before students read the definition of the term in the book, ask them to explain what they think the term means. Repeat this exercise for each of the other vocabulary words.

Bellringer

Have students focus on standard 7.1.b by asking them to compare plant cells to animal cells. Have students indicate characteristics that are unique to plant cells, as well as characteristics that are shared by both plant cells and animal cells. (Only plant cells contain chloroplasts and have rigid cell walls. Both cell types are small and contain many organelles, including mitochondria, nuclei, and ribosomes.)

Bellringer Transparency

Motivate

ACTIVITY

Baby Powder Cuticle Have students work in groups of four. Give each group 15 g of baby powder, an eyedropper, and water. Tell students that all but one member of the group should coat the palms of their hands with baby powder. Instruct the remaining member of the group to place a few drops of water on his or her classmates' hands and to record any observations. Explain that a plant's cuticle forms a similar barrier to keep the plant from losing moisture. **LS Kinesthetic** Co-op Learning

---

SECTION
1

What You Will Learn

- All plants share four main characteristics.
- Photosynthesis is a process that occurs in the chloroplasts of plant cells.
- Plant cells have some structures that animal cells do not have.
- Plants reproduce sexually and asexually.

Why It Matters

Plants supply most of the oxygen on Earth and use energy from the sun to make food.

Vocabulary

- nonvascular plant
- vascular plant
- gymnosperm
- angiosperm

READING STRATEGY

Brainstorming The main idea of this section is that all plants share certain characteristics and can be classified in groups. Brainstorm words and phrases related to the characteristics and classification of plants. Record your work in your **Science Journal.**

7.1.b Students know the characteristics that distinguish plant cells from animal cells, including chloroplasts and cell walls.
7.1.d Students know that mitochondria liberate energy for the work that cells do and that chloroplasts capture sunlight energy for photosynthesis.
7.5.a Students know plants and animals have levels of organization for structure and function, including cells, tissues, organs, organ systems, and the whole organism.

Figure 1 *Chlorophyll makes the leaves of this plant green. Chlorophyll allows plants to make their own food by capturing energy from sunlight.*

What Is a Plant?

Key Concept   Most plants perform photosynthesis, reproduce, and share some physical characteristics.

▶ Imagine spending a day without plants. It would be impossible to make bread and most other foods. Almost all food is made from plants or from animals that eat plants!

Plant Characteristics

Plants come in many different shapes and sizes. So, what do cactuses, water lilies, ferns, redwoods, and all other plants have in common? Almost all plants share certain characteristics.

Cuticles

Most plants live on land and need sunlight to live. But why don't plants dry out? Plants are protected by a cuticle. A *cuticle* is a waxy layer that coats most of the surfaces of plants that are exposed to air. The cuticle keeps plants from drying out. Plant cuticles vary in thickness depending on where the plants live. Plants that live in dry climates have thicker cuticles than plants that live in more humid climates do.

Photosynthesis

Look at **Figure 1.** Do you know why this plant is green? Plant cells contain chlorophyll. *Chlorophyll* is a green pigment that captures energy from sunlight. Chlorophyll is found in chloroplasts. Chloroplasts are organelles that are found only in plant cells and some protist cells. Animal cells do not have chloroplasts. Chloroplasts capture energy from sunlight to make food from carbon dioxide and water. This process is called *photosynthesis.* Because plants make their own food, they are called *producers.*

Standards Check   List an organelle that only plant cells have, and describe its role in a plant cell. **7.1.b, 7.1.d**

Universal Access • Differentiated Instruction

Special Education Students

What Is a Plant?   Personalizing information can make it easier for some students to understand. As you begin discussing what is and is not a plant, point out that plants are an important part of a healthy diet. Ask students to make a list of foods that they have eaten in the last two days. Make a large two-column chart on the board with the headings *Plants* and *Non-Plants.* Ask

students to write their foods in the appropriate columns on the chart, but not to add any items that others have already added. If some students cannot write their foods on the board, have them form small groups with other students in the class. Ask each group to consolidate their food lists and send one person to the board to write on the chart. **LS Visual/Kinesthetic**

Figure 2 Some Structures of a Photosynthetic Plant Cell

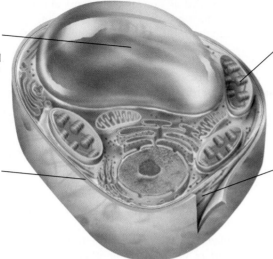

Large Central Vacuole A vacuole stores water, helps support the cell, and plays a role in many other cell functions.

Chloroplast Chloroplasts contain chlorophyll. Chlorophyll captures energy from the sun. Plants use this energy to make food.

Cell Wall The cell wall surrounds the cell membrane. The cell wall supports and protects the plant cell.

Cell Membrane The cell membrane surrounds a plant cell and lies beneath the cell wall.

Cell Walls

How do plants stay upright? They do not have skeletons like many animals do. Instead, plant cells are surrounded by a rigid cell wall. The cell wall lies outside the cell membrane, as **Figure 2** shows. Carbohydrates and other materials in the cell wall form a hard material. Cell walls support and protect the plant cell. Some plant cells also have a secondary cell wall that forms after the cell is mature. When this wall has formed, a plant cell cannot grow larger.

Reproduction

Plants have two stages in their life cycle—the sporophyte (SPOH ruh FIET) stage and the gametophyte (guh MEET uh FIET) stage. In the sporophyte stage, plants make spores. In a suitable environment, such as damp soil, some spores may grow. These new plants are called *gametophytes*.

During the gametophyte stage, female gametophytes produce eggs. Male gametophytes produce sperm. Eggs and sperm are sex cells. For a new plant to be produced, a sperm must fertilize an egg. This type of reproduction is called sexual reproduction. The fertilized egg will eventually grow into a sporophyte, and the cycle will begin again. During the sporophyte and gametophyte stages, the plant can be very different sizes. Most plants are also able to reproduce asexually.

Quick Lab

Cell Walls and Wilting

7.1.b

The vacuole and cell wall in plant cells work together to provide a plant with structure. Try this activity to find out how!

1. Take a **small piece of old celery,** and place it in a **beaker** with **colored water.**
2. Record the amount of water in the beaker.
3. Leave the setup overnight.
4. Describe any changes that occurred to the celery and to the volume of the water.
5. Describe how the structure of the plant cell is responsible for the change that you observed.

🕐 **15 min plus follow-up**

Quick Lab

🕐 **15 min**

Teacher Notes

This activity reinforces standard 7.1.b by showing the function of organelles that are unique to plant cells such as the cell wall and large, central vacuole. Leave the celery out the night before the activity to make the stalks "thirstier." Shortly before the activity, cut the bottom end of each stalk.

Materials for Each Group

- beaker, 100 mL
- food coloring
- celery stalk, small, old
- water, 50 mL

Safety Caution

Remind students to review all safety cautions and icons before beginning this activity.

Answers

4. The celery is more rigid and colored by the dye.
5. The large central vacuole and cell wall make a plant cell rigid. The plant cells became rigid as the celery absorbed the water from the beaker.

📋 **Differentiated Datasheets**
A **BASIC**, B **GENERAL**, C **ADVANCED**

Also editable on the Holt Lab Generator CD-ROM

Assess

1. How is a plant's size related to its method of transporting water and nutrients? (Sample answer: Nonvascular plants rely on diffusion, which is efficient only in small plants. Vascular plants have conducting tissues, which enable the plant to be very large.) **7.5.a**

2. How do plants stay upright? (The rigid structure of plants' cell walls allows plants to stay upright.) **7.1.b**

3. What is chlorophyll? Describe its role in plants. (Chlorophyll is a green pigment found in the chloroplasts of plants. Chlorophyll captures energy from sunlight.) **7.1.d**

Reteach

Plant Structures Specialized for Functions Ask students to describe the ways that plant structures are well-suited for their specialized functions. (Sample answer: plant cells are surrounded by rigid cell walls to provide support; plant cells contain vacuoles to store water and help support the cell.) **LS** Logical **7.5.a**

Re-Assess

Interview Have students interview one another about the characteristics that are common to all plants. Have students ask each other, "How do plants make their own food?" "What is the purpose of the cuticle?" "What are gametophytes and sporophytes, and what roles do they play in a plant's life cycle?" **LS** Verbal
Co-op Learning **7.1.d, 7.5.a**

Teaching Transparency:
L48 The Main Groups of Plants

---

nonvascular plant (nahn VAHS kyuh luhr PLANT) a plant that lacks specialized conducting tissues and true roots, stems, and leaves

vascular plant (VAHS kyuh luhr PLANT) a plant that has specialized tissues that conduct materials from one part of the plant to another

gymnosperm (JIM noh SPUHRM) a woody, vascular seed plant whose seeds are not enclosed by an ovary or fruit
 Wordwise The root *gymn-* means "naked." The root *-sperm* means "seed."

angiosperm (AN jee oh SPUHRM) a flowering plant that produces seeds within a fruit
 Wordwise The root *angi-* means "vessel."

Plant Classification

Plants can be classified into four groups. First, they are classified as nonvascular plants and vascular plants. Vascular plants are further divided into three groups—seedless plants, nonflowering seed plants, and flowering seed plants.

Nonvascular Plants

Mosses, liverworts, and hornworts are nonvascular plants. A **nonvascular plant** is a plant that does not have specialized tissues to move water and nutrients through the plant. Nonvascular plants depend on diffusion to move materials from one part of the plant to another. Diffusion is possible because nonvascular plants are small. If nonvascular plants were large, the cells of the plants would not get enough water and nutrients.

Vascular Plants

In the same way that the human body has special tissues to move materials through the body, so do many plants. A plant that has tissues to deliver water and nutrients from one part of the plant to another is called a **vascular plant.** These tissues are called *vascular tissues.* Vascular tissues can move water and nutrients to any part of a plant. So, vascular plants can be almost any size.

Vascular plants are divided into three groups—seedless plants and two types of seed plants. Seedless vascular plants include ferns, horsetails, and club mosses. Nonflowering seed plants are called **gymnosperms.** Flowering seed plants are called **angiosperms.** The four main groups of plants are shown in **Figure 3.**

Standards Check What is vascular tissue? **7.5.a**

| **Figure 3** | **The Main Groups of Plants** |

Nonvascular plants	Vascular plants		
Mosses, liverworts, and hornworts	Seedless plants	Seed plants	
	Ferns, horsetails, and club mosses	Nonflowering	Flowering
		Gymnosperms	Angiosperms

Wordwise

Review the definition of *gymnosperm* and *angiosperm,* and point out that the root *gymn-* means "naked", the root *angi-* means "vessel" and the root *-sperm* means "seed." Then, ask students what the terms *gymnasium, angiogenesis,* and *spermatogenesis* mean. (*gymnasium:* a large room used for various indoor sports; *angiogenesis:* the formation and differentiation of blood vessels; *spermatogenesis:* the process of male gamete formation.)
LS Logical

Universal Access · Differentiated Instruction

Basic Learners

Nonvascular or Vascular? Help students relate nonvascular and vascular plants to the plants that they are familiar with. Ask students to bring in three actual plants or three pictures of familiar plants. Have them do research to find out if these plants are nonvascular or vascular and why. **LS** Verbal

The Origin of Plants

Imagine that you traveled back in time about 440 million years. The Earth seems like a strange, bare, and unfriendly place. For one thing, no plants live on land. So, where did plants come from?

Look at **Figure 4**. The photo on the left shows a green alga. The photo on the right shows a fern. The green alga may look like a plant, such as a fern, but the green alga is not a plant.

Green algae lack structures that are present in some plants, such as specialized tissues. But green algae and plants have many similarities. Green algae cells and plant cells have the same kind of chlorophyll. They have similar cell walls. Green algae and plants make their own food through photosynthesis. Both store energy in the form of starch. Also, green algae have a two-stage life cycle. Because of these similarities, most scientists think that green algae and plants share a common ancestor.

Figure 4 *The similarities between a modern green alga (left) and plants, such as ferns (right), suggest that both may have originated from an ancient species of green algae.*

SECTION Review

 7.1.b, 7.1.d, 7.5.a

Summary

- All plants make their own food and have cuticles, cells walls, and a two-stage life cycle.

- Plants are first classified into two groups: nonvascular plants and vascular plants. Vascular plants are further divided into seedless plants, gymnosperms, and angiosperms.

- Similarities between green algae and plants suggest that they have a common ancestor.

Understanding Concepts

1. **Listing** What are four characteristics that all plants share?

2. **Comparing** What is the relationship between chlorophyll and chloroplasts?

3. **Analyzing** Describe the plant life cycle.

Critical Thinking

4. **Making Inferences** One difference between plant cells and animal cells is that animal cells lack cell walls. What is the function of the cell wall?

5. **Applying Concepts** Imagine an environment that is very dry and receives a lot of sunlight. Water is found deep below the soil. Which of the four groups of plants could survive in this environment? Explain your answer.

INTERPRETING GRAPHICS Use the diagram below to answer the next question.

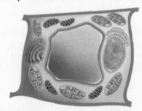

6. **Identifying Relationships** Which structures in the cell above are found only in plant cells? What do each of these structures do in the cell?

Internet Resources

For a variety of links related to this chapter, go to www.scilinks.org

Topic: Plant Characteristics; How Are Plants Classified?
SciLinks code: HY71158; HY70763

---

5. Sample answer: Vascular plants could live in a dry environment because they have tissues for transporting water and nutrients. However, seedless vascular plants need moisture, so only ferns, gymnosperms and angiosperms could live in this environment.

6. The chloroplast, cell wall, and large central vacuole are found only in the plant cell. The chloroplast performs photosynthesis. The cell wall gives structure to plant cells. The large central vacuole stores water and nutrients, and gives structure to the plant cell. **7.1.b** (mastering), **7.1.d** (mastering)

Section Review Standards Guide

	Supporting	Mastering	Exceeding
7.1.b		4, 6	
7.1.d		2, 6	1
7.5.a	1		

Answer to Standards Check

Vascular tissue is specialized tissue that moves water and nutrients to any part of a vascular plant. **7.5.a** (mastering)

Answers to Section Review

1. Sample answer: Plants make their own food, have a cuticle, have cells with cell walls, and have a two-stage life cycle. **7.1.d** (exceeding), **7.5.a** (supporting)

2. Chlorophyll is the pigment that is found in chloroplasts. Chlorophyll collects and stores the energy in sunlight. Chloroplasts use this energy during the process of photosynthesis. **7.1.d** (mastering)

3. Sample answer: Plants make spores in the sporophyte stage. The spores grow into gametophytes. Female gametophytes produce eggs. Male gametophytes produce sperm, which fertilize the eggs. A fertilized egg grows into a sporophyte.

4. The role of a plant cell wall is to provide structure to plant cells. **7.1.b** (mastering)

Section Resources

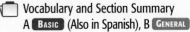

- Directed Reading A **BASIC** (Also in Spanish), B **GENERAL**

- Interactive Reader and Study Guide

- Section Quiz **GENERAL** (Also in Spanish)

- Section Review **GENERAL** (Also in Spanish)

- Vocabulary and Section Summary A **BASIC** (Also in Spanish), B **GENERAL**

Preteach

Reviewing Prior Knowledge

Ask student volunteers to read the red and blue heads in this section aloud. Then, ask students what they think the section is about. Finally, ask students what they already know about seedless plants, including mosses, liverworts, ferns, and club mosses.

🔔 Bellringer

Have students focus on standard 7.2.a by asking them to identify which of the following plants produce sperm and egg cells that fuse during fertilization: mosses, hornworts, liverworts, ferns, and club mosses. (All of these plants produce sperm and egg cells that fuse during fertilization. The union of these gametes results in the sporophyte stage of the plant life cycle.)

📽 Teaching Transparency:
L49 Moss Life Cycle; Fern Life Cycle

Motivate

ACTIVITY

Identifying Plant Parts Before students read this section, let them view a moss and a fern. Ask students to compare the two plants. (Sample answer: The moss is much smaller than the fern.) Ask students to identify the sporophyte and gametophyte. (Help students to identify the sporophyte and gametophyte. The most familiar form of moss is the gametophyte, while the most familiar form of fern is the sporophyte.)
LS Visual

SECTION 2

What You Will Learn

- Nonvascular plants do not have specialized vascular tissues.
- Seedless vascular plants have specialized vascular tissues.
- Seedless plants reproduce sexually and asexually, but they need water to reproduce.
- Seedless plants have two stages in their life cycle.

Why It Matters

Seedless plants play many roles in the environment, including helping to form soil and preventing erosion.

Vocabulary

- rhizoid
- rhizome

READING STRATEGY

Graphic Organizer In your **Science Journal,** create a Venn Diagram that compares vascular plants and nonvascular plants.

rhizoid (RIE ZOYD) a rootlike structure in nonvascular plants that holds the plants in place and helps plants get water and nutrients

---

Seedless Plants

Key Concept Seedless plants do not produce seeds but are well adapted for reproduction and survival.

▶ When you think of plants, you probably think of plants, such as trees and flowers, that make seeds. But two groups of plants don't make seeds. The two groups of seedless plants are nonvascular plants and seedless vascular plants.

Nonvascular Plants

Mosses, liverworts, and hornworts do not have vascular tissue to transport water and nutrients. Each cell of the plant must get water from the environment or from a nearby cell. So, nonvascular plants usually live in places that are damp. Also, nonvascular plants are small. They grow on soil, the bark of trees, and rocks. Mosses, liverworts, and hornworts don't have true stems, roots, or leaves. They do, however, have structures that carry out the activities of stems, roots, and leaves.

Mosses

Large groups of mosses cover soil or rocks with a mat of tiny green plants. Mosses have leafy stalks and rhizoids. A **rhizoid** is a rootlike structure that holds nonvascular plants in place. Rhizoids help the plants get water and nutrients. As you can see in **Figure 1,** mosses have two stages in their life cycle. During the gametophyte stage, a sperm must travel through a thin film of water to fertilize an egg. This is sexual reproduction. Mosses can also reproduce asexually.

Figure 1 Moss Life Cycle

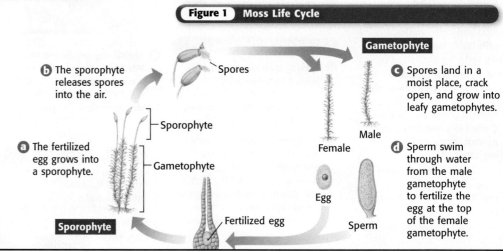

b The sporophyte releases spores into the air.

Spores

a The fertilized egg grows into a sporophyte.

Sporophyte

Gametophyte

Sporophyte

Fertilized egg

Gametophyte

c Spores land in a moist place, crack open, and grow into leafy gametophytes.

Male

Female

Egg

Sperm

d Sperm swim through water from the male gametophyte to fertilize the egg at the top of the female gametophyte.

Homework

Moss Hunt Mosses are common but often overlooked plants. Have students "hunt" for mosses around the school, their homes, or nearby parks. If possible, students should use magnifying lenses to make detailed sketches of the mosses that they find. Ask students to note environmental factors that may affect the mosses that they find, such as shade, water, and other plants. Have students compare their findings in class to see how many different mosses were found, and if there are any patterns as to where each type can be found. **LS** Kinesthetic

Liverworts and Hornworts

Like mosses, liverworts and hornworts are small, nonvascular plants that usually live in damp places. The life cycles of liverworts and hornworts are similar to the life cycle of mosses. The gametophytes of liverworts can be leafy and mosslike or broad and flattened. Hornworts also have broad, flattened gametophytes. Both liverworts and hornworts have rhizoids.

The Importance of Nonvascular Plants

Nonvascular plants have an important role in the environment. They are usually the first plants to live in a new environment, such as newly exposed rock. When these nonvascular plants die, they decompose to help form a thin layer of soil. New plants can grow in this soil. More nonvascular plants may grow and hold the soil in place. This reduces soil erosion. Some animals eat nonvascular plants. Other animals use these plants for nesting material.

Peat mosses are important to humans. Peat mosses grow in bogs and other wet places. This peat can be dried and burned as a fuel. Peat mosses are also used in potting soil.

Seedless Vascular Plants

Seedless vascular plants include, ferns, horsetails, and club mosses. Ancient seedless vascular plants grew very tall. For example, club mosses grew to 40 m tall in ancient forests! Today, ferns, horsetails, and club mosses are usually much smaller. **Figure 2** shows modern club mosses.

Because they have vascular tissue, seedless vascular plants are often larger than nonvascular plants. Vascular tissue is specialized to transport water to all of the cells in a plant.

Standards Check How does vascular tissue help plants? 7.5.a

Figure 2 *Club mosses are seedless vascular plants.*

7.2.a Students know the differences between the life cycles and reproduction methods of sexual and asexual organisms.

7.5.a Students know plants and animals have levels of organization for structure and function, including cells, tissues, organs, organ systems, and the whole organism.

Quick Lab

Moss Mass   7.2.a   7.7.c

1. Determine the mass of a small sample of **dry sphagnum moss.**
2. Observe what happens when you put a small piece of the moss in **water.** Predict what will happen if you put the entire sample in water.
3. Place the moss sample in a **large beaker of water** for 10 to 15 minutes.
4. Remove the wet moss from the beaker, and determine the mass of the moss.
5. How much mass did the moss gain? Compare your result with your prediction.
6. How is water important to the reproduction of moss?

🕐 **20 min**

Teach

Connection To
Real World

Sphagnum Moss
Sphagnum moss was used during World War I as a dressing for wounds. Its hollow cells enable it to absorb up to 20 times its own weight in fluid. Sphagnum moss was also once used for diapers, oil lamp wicks, and bedding. Have students research how sphagnum moss is used today. (Sample answer: Sphagnum moss is used as protection for plants during shipping and for potting material.) Have students make posters describing their findings.
LS Visual

MISCONCEPTION ALERT

The Size of Club Mosses
Some students may have seen club mosses in the forest and thought they were young pine trees. Club mosses do resemble tiny conifer saplings, and are sometimes called "fairy pines" or "princess pines." Emphasize to students that mature club mosses do not make cones or seeds and do not grow more than 20 cm or so.

Answer to Standards Check

Vascular tissue transports water and nutrients to parts of the plant.
7.5.a (mastering)

Quick Lab

🕐 **20 min**

Teacher Notes

This activity reinforces that moss relies on water for sexual reproduction (covers standard 7.2.a). It may be helpful to use a dry beaker of predetermined mass.

Materials for Each Group
- balance or scale
- beaker, large
- sphagnum moss, dry
- water

Safety Caution
Remind students to review all safety cautions and icons before beginning this activity.

Answers

5. Results may vary. Students should include a statement about how the actual result compared to their predictions.

6. Water is needed so that sperm can reach and fertilize eggs. Therefore, water is needed for sexual reproduction.

 Differentiated Datasheets
A **BASIC**, B **GENERAL**, C **ADVANCED**

Also editable on the Holt Lab Generator CD-ROM

Close

Standards Focus

This **Standards Focus** provides you with a quick way to **assess, reteach,** and **re-assess** one or more concepts in the section.

**Assess**

1. Why is a damp environment so critical to the success of nonvascular plants? (Nonvascular plants lack extensive root systems and vascular tissue. Water is absorbed directly through cells. Also, the sperm require water to swim to the eggs.) **7.2a, 7.5.a**

2. What is the role of a rhizoid, and how is it different from a rhizome? (Rhizoids perform the functions of roots in nonvascular plants. They are fibrous and root-like. A rhizome is an underground stem that produces leaves, shoots, and roots.) **7.5.a**

Reteach

Plant Life Cycles   Help students review the life cycles of mosses and ferns. Ask volunteers to come up to the board individually and diagram a single step in the life cycle of each type of plant. **LS** Visual **7.2.a**

Re-Assess

Organizational Chart   Have students make a Venn diagram that describes the differences and similarities between the nonvascular plants and the seedless vascular plants discussed in this section. Have students present their diagrams to the class. **LS** Logical/ Visual **7.2.a, 7.5.a**

Teaching Transparency: L49 Moss Life Cycle; Fern Life Cycle

---

rhizome (RIE zOHM) a horizontal, underground stem that produces new leaves, shoots, and roots

Ferns

Ferns grow in many places, from the cold Arctic to warm, humid tropical forests. Many ferns are small plants. But some tropical tree ferns grow as tall as 24 m. Most ferns have a rhizome. A **rhizome** is an underground stem from which new leaves and roots grow. At first, fern leaves, or fronds, are tightly coiled. These fronds look like the end of a violin, or fiddle. So, they are called *fiddleheads*. You are probably most familiar with the leafy fern sporophyte. The fern gametophyte is a tiny plant about half the size of one of your fingernails. The fern gametophyte is green and flat. It is usually shaped like a tiny heart. The life cycle of ferns is shown in **Figure 3.** Ferns and other seedless vascular plants have two stages in their life cycle. Like mosses, ferns rely on water for sexual reproduction. Also, like mosses, ferns are also able to reproduce asexually.

Horsetails and Club Mosses

Modern horsetails can be as tall as 8 m. But many horsetails are smaller. They usually grow in wet, marshy places. Their stems are hollow and contain silica. The silica gives horsetails a gritty texture. In fact, early American pioneers used horsetails to scrub pots and pans. Club mosses grow in woodlands. Unlike mosses, club mosses have vascular tissue. Horsetails, club mosses, and ferns have similar life cycles.

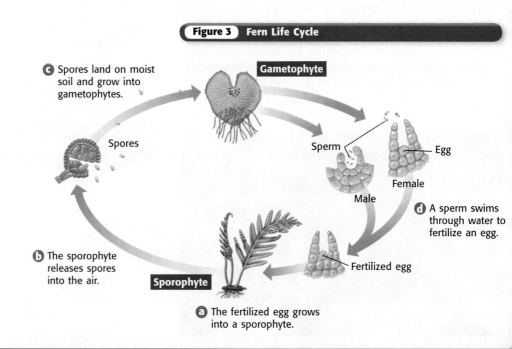

Figure 3   Fern Life Cycle

c Spores land on moist soil and grow into gametophytes.

Gametophyte

Spores

Sperm

Egg

Female

Male

d A sperm swims through water to fertilize an egg.

b The sporophyte releases spores into the air.

Sporophyte

Fertilized egg

a The fertilized egg grows into a sporophyte.

Universal Access • Differentiated Instruction

Struggling Readers

Ferns   Explain to students how to review the key parts of sentences. Tell students that if they do not understand part of a sentence, they should stop and look up the information that they need or ask for help. Ask students to look at the first sentence under the head "Ferns." Ask them to explain the phrases "in the cold Arctic" and "warm, humid tropical rain forests." (Sample answer: the very cold areas of the north end of Earth; forests that are near the equator) Ask volunteers to point out these two areas on a map or globe. **LS** **Verbal/Kinesthetic**

The Importance of Seedless Vascular Plants

Seedless vascular plants play important roles in the environment. Ferns, horsetails, and club mosses help form soil. They also help prevent soil erosion. In rocky areas, ferns can play a role in the formation of communities. After lichens and mosses create a layer of soil, ferns may take over. Ferns add to soil depth, which allows other plants to grow.

Ferns and some club mosses are popular houseplants. The fiddleheads of some ferns can be cooked and eaten. Young horsetail shoots and their roots are also edible. Horsetails are used in some dietary supplements, shampoos, and skin-care products.

Seedless vascular plants that lived and died about 300 million years ago are among the most important to humans living today. The remains of these ancient ferns, horsetails, and club mosses formed coal and oil. Coal and oil are fossil fuels that humans mine from Earth's crust. Coal and oil are called fossil fuels because they formed from plants that lived long ago. Humans rely on coal and oil for energy.

INTERNET ACTIVITY

Weird and Wonderful Plants

What is your favorite plant? What do you like about it most? Tell your classmates all about it. Go to **go.hrw.com,** and type in the keyword HY7PL1W.

SECTION Review

7.2.a, 7.5.a

Summary

Nonvascular plants include mosses, liverworts, and hornworts.

Seedless vascular plants include ferns, horsetails, and club mosses.

Most plants have a two-stage life cycle and reproduce both sexually and asexually.

The rhizoids and rhizomes of seedless plants prevent erosion by holding soil in place. The remains of seedless vascular plants that lived and died about 300 million years ago formed coal.

Understanding Concepts

1 Listing What are four important roles of seedless plants in the environment?

2 Identifying Describe six kinds of seedless plants.

3 Analyzing What is the relationship between coal and seedless vascular plants?

Critical Thinking

4 Making Inferences Imagine a very damp area. Mosses cover the rocks and trees in this area. Liverworts and hornworts are also very abundant. What might happen if the area dries out? Explain your answer.

5 Applying Concepts Modern ferns, horsetails, and club mosses are smaller than they were millions of years ago. Why might these plants be smaller?

6 Making Comparisons Compare the life cycle of mosses with the life cycle of ferns.

INTERPRETING GRAPHICS Use the image below to answer the next question.

7 Identifying Relationships Identify the structure shown above. What role does this structure play in reproduction?

Internet Resources

For a variety of links related to this chapter, go to www.scilinks.org
Topic: Seedless Plants
SciLinks code: HY71368

Answers to Section Review

1. Sample answer: Some seedless plants help form soil. Others help establish communities of living things. Some seedless plants are popular houseplants. The remains of seedless plants that lived long ago formed coal and oil, which are major energy sources for humans.

2. Answers should include accurate descriptions of mosses, liverworts, hornworts, ferns, horsetails, and club mosses. **7.2.a** (mastering)

3. Sample answer: The remains of seedless vascular plants formed coal.

4. Sample answer: If this area were to dry out, the seedless plants growing there would have a difficult time surviving and may die out completely. None of the plants listed would be able to reproduce without water. **7.2.a** (exceeding)

5. These plants may be smaller because most places are drier than they were millions of years ago. Without abundant moisture, these plants would find it more difficult to reproduce and support a large size. **7.2.a** (supporting)

6. Answers may vary. Sample answer: Both mosses and ferns have a two-stage life cycle. The fern gametophyte is very small, while the moss gametophyte is a larger plant. **7.2.a** (mastering)

7. Sample answer: The image above shows a portion of a fern sporophyte. This structure is releasing spores, which may combine with a female fern gametophyte. **7.5.a** (mastering), **7.2.a** (mastering)

Section Review Standards Guide			
	Supporting	Mastering	Exceeding
7.2.a	5	2, 6, 7	4
7.5.a		7	

Universal Access · Differentiated Instruction

Special Education Students

Plant Uses For a student with behavior problems, have him or her to go to the board and create a Venn diagram (two overlapping circles). Have the student label the three parts of the diagram "only nonvascular," "only seedless vascular," and "both nonvascular and seedless vascular." Ask the class to give examples of why nonvascular plants are important. (Sample answer: nesting material; some are used as fuel, and in potting soil.) Have the student at the board write these ideas in the appropriate area of the diagram. Have students repeat this process for seedless vascular plants. (Sample answer: Some types are used in dietary supplements, shampoos, and skin-care products; some ancient types became coal.) Finally, have the class give examples of the similar roles nonvascular and vascular plants play in the environment. (Sample answer: Both types of plants form soil, contribute to new plant growth, and reduce soil erosion by holding soil in place.) **LS Visual/Kinesthetic**

Section Resources

Directed Reading
A **BASIC** (Also in Spanish), B **GENERAL**

Interactive Reader and Study Guide

Section Quiz **GENERAL** (Also in Spanish)

Section Review **GENERAL** (Also in Spanish)

Vocabulary and Section Summary
A **BASIC** (Also in Spanish), B **GENERAL**

Preteach

Reviewing Prior Knowledge

Tell students that a key concept in this section is pollination. Ask students to draw a picture of a situation in which pollination is occurring.

Bellringer

To help the class focus on standard 7.5.f, ask students to use the following terms to explain how they think flowering plants make seeds: *pollen, flower, seeds,* and *eggs.* Students may create drawings to help them present their ideas. (Sample answer: Flowers produce pollen, which fertilizes eggs to produce seeds.)

📦 Bellringer Transparency

Motivate

Discussion

Gymnosperms Many students are already familiar with conifers such as pine trees, but may become confused when the term *gymnosperm* is introduced. Encourage students to list some of the characteristics of pine trees. (Sample answers: Pine trees stay green all year; they have thin, needle-shaped leaves; they produce cones instead of fruit.) Emphasize to students that even though this section provides additional information about gymnosperms, students already know a great deal about them. **LS Verbal**

Answer to Standards Check

Seed plants produce seeds. In seed plants, the gametophyte and sporophyte never live independently of one another. The sperm of seed plants does not rely on water to reach and fertilize the egg of seed plants. **7.2.a** (exceeding), **7.5.f** (supporting)

What You Will Learn

- Seed plants differ from seedless plants in three main ways.
- A seed is composed of a young plant, a food source, and an outer coating.
- Gymnosperms and angiosperms have different patterns of sexual reproduction.
- Gymnosperms and angiosperms are economically and environmentally important.

Why It Matters

Humans use seed plants as a source of food and as a source of clothing and construction materials.

Vocabulary

- pollen
- pollination

READING STRATEGY

Graphic Organizer In your **Science Journal,** create a Venn Diagram that compares various characteristics of the two groups of vascular plants that produce seeds.

pollen (PAHL uhn) the tiny granules that contain the male gametophytes of seed plants

---

Seed Plants

Key Concept Seed plants produce seeds and are categorized as gymnosperms or angiosperms.

▶ Think about the seed plants that you use during the day. You likely use dozens of seed plants, from the food you eat to the paper you write on. The two groups of vascular plants that produce seeds are gymnosperms and angiosperms. Gymnosperms are trees and shrubs that do not have flowers or fruit. Angiosperms have flowers and seeds that are protected by fruit.

Characteristics of Seed Plants

Like seedless plants, seed plants have a life cycle that alternates between two stages. But seed plants, such as the plant in **Figure 1,** differ from seedless plants in the following ways:

- Seed plants produce seeds. Seeds nourish and protect young sporophytes.
- Unlike the gametophytes of seedless plants, the gametophytes of seed plants do not live independently of the sporophyte. The gametophytes of seed plants are tiny. The gametophytes form within the reproductive structures of the sporophyte.
- The sperm of seedless plants need water to swim to the eggs of female gametophytes. The sperm of seed plants do not need water to reach an egg. Sperm form inside tiny structures called **pollen.** Pollen can be transported by wind or by animals.

These three characteristics of seed plants allow them to live just about anywhere. For this reason, seed plants are the most common plants on Earth today.

Standards Check **List three characteristics that seed plants share.**
🐻 **7.2.a, 7.5.f**

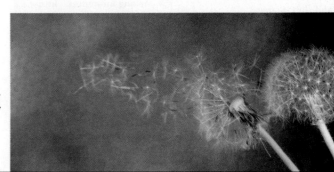

Figure 1 *Dandelion fruits, which each contain a seed, are spread by wind.*

Universal Access · Differentiated Instruction

Advanced Learners/GATE
Materials for Each Group

- colored markers
- pictures of the interiors and exteriors of various seeds
- poster board

Seed Plant Posters Divide the class into groups of three. Ask each group to create a poster showing examples of seeds from 10 different seed plants. Encourage groups to include both interior and exterior views of each seed. **LS Visual/Kinesthetic**

Quick Lab

Teacher Notes

This lab introduces students to the basic structure of seeds and reinforces standard 7.5.f. Use the large lima bean seeds that are sold for use in gardens.

Materials for Each Group

- eyedropper
- iodine
- lima bean seed
- toothpick
- water

Safety Caution

Remind students to wear lab coats or aprons, as iodine stains clothing.

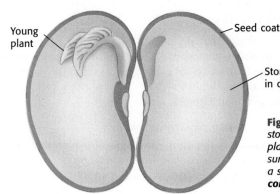

Young plant

Seed coat

Stored food in cotyledon

Figure 2 *A seed contains stored food and a young plant, or sporophyte. A seed is surrounded and protected by a seed coat.* **Why do seeds contain stored food?**

The Structure of Seeds

A seed forms after fertilization, when sperm and eggs are joined. A seed is made up of three parts, as **Figure 2** shows. The first part is a young plant, or the sporophyte. The second part is stored food. It is often found in the *cotyledons* (KAHT uh LEED uhnz), or the seed leaves of the young plant. Finally, a seed coat surrounds and protects the young plant.

Seed plants have some advantages over seedless plants. For example, when a seed begins to grow, the young plant uses the food stored in the seed. The spores of seedless plants don't have stored food to help a new plant grow. Another advantage of seed plants is that seeds can be spread by animals. The spores of seedless plants are usually spread by wind. Animals often spread seeds more efficiently than the wind spreads spores.

7.2.a Students know the differences between the life cycles and reproduction methods of sexual and asexual organisms.
7.5.f Students know the structures and processes by which flowering plants generate pollen, ovules, seeds, and fruit.

Standards Check After which process does a seed form? **7.2.a**

Quick Lab

Dissecting Seeds

1. Draw a **lima bean seed.** Then, soak the lima bean seed in **water** overnight.
2. Remove the seed from the water. Draw what you see.
3. The seed will likely look wrinkly. This is the seed coat. Use a **toothpick** to gently remove the seed coat from the lima bean seed.
4. Gently separate the halves of the lima bean seed. Draw and label what you see.
5. With gloves on, place a drop of **iodine** on one half of the lima bean. Describe what happens.

6. What structures did you see after you split the lima bean seed in half? How do these structures rely on one another?
7. Iodine changes from a rusty red color to dark blue in the presence of starch. Explain what the iodine test indicated about the seed.
8. What part of the seed do you think provides the lima bean plant with the energy to grow?

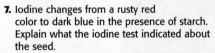

7.5.f
7.7.c

🕐 **15 min**

🕐 **15 min**

Answers

5. Before the iodine was added, the sporophyte could be seen. After the iodine was added, a large portion of the seed was colored black.

6. When the seed was split in half, I could see the sporophyte, or young plant, the cotyledon, where the food is stored, and the seed coat. The food in the cotyledon is necessary for the young plant to grow. The seed coat protects the plant.

7. The iodine test indicated that starch is present in the seed.

8. Starch is the part of the seed that provides the lima bean plant with the energy to grow.

📁 **Differentiated Datasheets**
A **BASIC**, B **GENERAL**, C **ADVANCED**

Also editable on the Holt Lab Generator CD-ROM

Using the Figure
Some Common Gymnosperms
Have students work in pairs. Ask students to examine the examples of gymnosperms on this page. Students should take turns summarizing the information in the figure aloud. If the person who is listening finds the information confusing or needs clarification, he or she should have the reader pause. **Ⓛ Verbal**
Co-op Learning

CONNECTION ACTIVITY
Earth Science

Growth Rings Geochronology, the interpretation and dating of the geologic record, includes dendrochronolgy, which is the study of trees' growth rings. Bristlecone pines have been particularly useful in dendrochronology because many of these trees are very old. Ask interested students to research how scientists date trees and use them for geochronology. Ask students to present their findings to the class. **Ⓛ Verbal**

Homework

Our Wooded World Ask students to note all the wood products that they use or see during the course of a day. Remind them to include paper and cardboard products as well. Ask students to share their answers with the class the following day. Then, have students determine whether each product was made from the wood of conifers (gymnosperms) or hardwoods (angiosperms). (Most building products and paper will be from conifers. Furniture, doors, cabinetry, tool handles, and charcoal will likely be hardwoods.) **Ⓛ Visual/Verbal**

Gymnosperms

Seed plants that do not have flowers or fruit are called *gymnosperms*. Gymnosperm seeds are usually protected by a cone. The four groups of gymnosperms are conifers, ginkgoes, cycads, and gnetophytes (NEE toh FIETS). You can see some gymnosperms in **Figure 3.**

The Importance of Gymnosperms

Conifers are the most economically important gymnosperms. People use conifer wood for building materials and paper products. Pine trees produce a sticky fluid called *resin*. Resin is used to make soap, turpentine, paint, and ink. Some conifers produce an important anticancer drug. Some gnetophytes produce anti-allergy drugs. Conifers, cycads, and ginkgoes are popular in gardens and parks.

Figure 3 **Examples of Gymnosperms**

◀ **Conifers** The conifers, such as this ponderosa pine, are the largest group of gymnosperms. There are about 630 species of conifers. Most conifers are evergreens that keep their needle-shaped leaves all year. Conifer seeds develop in cones.

◀ **Ginkgoes** Today, there is only one living species of ginkgo, the ginkgo tree. Ginkgo seeds are not produced in cones. The seeds have fleshy seed coats and are attached directly to the branches of the tree.

◀ **Cycads** The cycads were more common millions of years ago. Today, there are only about 140 species of cycads. These plants grow in the Tropics. Like conifer seeds, cycad seeds develop in cones.

◀ **Gnetophytes** About 70 species of gnetophytes, such as this joint fir, exist today. Many gnetophytes are shrubs that grow in dry areas. The seeds of most gnetophytes develop in cones.

Universal Access • Differentiated Instruction

English Learners
Pronunciation Guide Discuss with the class that the letter *g* has different pronunciations in the English language. Write these headings on the board (without the answers): hard *g* (g), as in *go* (the first *g* in gingkoes, gardens, group, evergreen, and grow); soft *g* (j), as in *gym* (gymnosperms, allergy, largest); *N* (ng) as in *king* (building). Usually *g* is hard before other consonants and the letters *o, u,* and *a,* and soft before *e, y,* and *i.* Remind students that sometimes a *g* is silent as in *gnat.* Ask students to find words on this page that contain the letter *g* and sort them into the different categories; note: the middle sound in *gingkoes* is *N.* **Ⓛ Visual/Auditory**

Figure 4 The Life Cycle of a Pine Tree

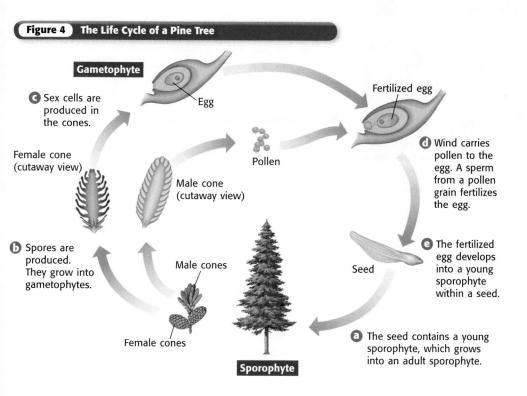

Gametophyte

c Sex cells are produced in the cones.

Egg

Female cone (cutaway view)

Pollen

Male cone (cutaway view)

Fertilized egg

d Wind carries pollen to the egg. A sperm from a pollen grain fertilizes the egg.

b Spores are produced. They grow into gametophytes.

Male cones

Female cones

Seed

e The fertilized egg develops into a young sporophyte within a seed.

a The seed contains a young sporophyte, which grows into an adult sporophyte.

Sporophyte

Life Cycle of Gymnosperms

The gymnosperms that are most familiar to you are probably the conifers. The word *conifer* comes from two words that mean "cone-bearing." Conifers have two kinds of cones—male cones and female cones. The spores from each kind of cone develop into tiny gametophytes.

The male gametophytes of gymnosperms are found in pollen. Pollen grains contain sperm. The female gametophytes produce eggs. Wind carries pollen from the male cones to the female cones. This transfer of pollen from the male to the female is called **pollination.** Pollination occurs during sexual reproduction.

Sperm from pollen fertilize the eggs of the female cone. A fertilized egg develops into a young sporophyte within the female cone. The sporophyte is surrounded by a seed. Eventually, the seed is released. Some cones release seeds right away. Other cones release seeds under special circumstances, such as after forest fires. If conditions are right, the seed will grow. The life cycle of a pine tree is shown in **Figure 4.**

pollination (PAWL uh NAY shuhn) the transfer of pollen from the male reproductive structures to the female structures of seed plants

Standards Check Describe the life cycle of gymnosperms. 7.2.a

Answer to Standards Check

Gymnosperms begin life as a seed. The seed grows into an adult sporophyte. The sporophyte produces male and female cones. The male cones produce sperm, which fertilize the eggs formed in the female cones. The fertilized eggs form seeds and the cycle begins once again. **7.2.a** (mastering)

SCIENCE **HUMOR**

Q: What do you call people who buy a lot of books on gardening?

A: good weeders

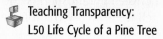
Teaching Transparency: L50 Life Cycle of a Pine Tree

Discussion

Good Fires Ask students what factors they think are necessary for a gymnosperm to germinate. (Sample answer: air, sunlight, water, and soil) Tell students that the cones of jack pines only open in the extreme heat of a fire. Explain that jack pines were once numerous, but are now less common. Ask students to explain why there are fewer jack pines today. (Sample answer: Today, many forest fires are put out, especially those that are near towns and housing developments.) Tell students that the Kirtland's warbler nests only in young jack pines. Then, ask students what they think has happened to the warbler's population. (Sample answer: If there are fewer jack pines, then there are probably fewer Kirtland's warblers.) **LS Verbal**

MISCONCEPTION ALERT

Fruit Types Students may think that fruits are always sweet and juicy foods. Tell students that many fruits have dry, hard shells; papery wings; or prickly coverings. Then, have students research and give an example of each of the following types of fruits: samara, legume, capsule, and achene. (Sample answer: Samaras are helicopter-like fruits, such as those produced by maples. Legumes are seeds within a pod, such as soybeans. Capsules have seed-holding compartments, such as the fruits of the eucalyptus. Achenes are one-seeded fruits that often have a papery shell, such as those found in sunflowers.) **LS Logical**

Standards Focus

This **Standards Focus** provides you with a quick way to **assess, reteach,** and **re-assess** one or more concepts in the section.

Assess

1. How are gymnosperms and angiosperms different from each other? (Sample answer: Angiosperms have flowers for reproduction and fruits to protect the seeds. Gymnosperms often have gametophytes and seeds enclosed in cones.) **7.2.a, 7.5.f**

2. What does pollen contain, and why does pollen increase the likelihood of fertilization? (Pollen contains sperm. The pollen can deliver the sperm to the egg without water via the wind or animals.) **7.2.a, 7.5.f**

Reteach

Seed Plants Write the following words on the board: *gymnosperms, angiosperms, monocots,* and *eudicots.* Ask students to give an example and description of each. **LS Verbal 7.2.a, 7.5.f**

Re-Assess

Concept Mapping Have students organize the following terms into a concept map: *seed plants, gymnosperms, angiosperms, flowers, fruits, conifers, cycads, monocots, eudicots, gnetophytes,* and *ginkgoes.* **LS Logical/Visual 7.2.a, 7.5.f**

Figure 5 *This bee is on its way to another squash flower, where it will leave some of the pollen it is carrying.*

Angiosperms

Vascular plants that produce flowers and fruits are called *angiosperms.* Angiosperms are the most abundant plants today. There are about 300,000 species of angiosperms. Angiosperms can be found in almost every land ecosystem.

Reproduction in Angiosperms

Flowers are the reproductive structures of angiosperms. Some angiosperms depend on the wind for pollination. But others have flowers that attract animals. As **Figure 5** shows, when animals visit different flowers, the animals may carry pollen from flower to flower.

Fruits surround seeds. Some fruits and seeds have structures that help the wind carry them short or long distances. Other fruits attract animals that eat the fruits. The animals discard the seeds away from the plant. Some fruits, such as burrs, are carried from place to place by sticking to the fur of animals.

Standards Check Why do angiosperms have flowers and fruits? **7.5.f**

Two Kinds of Angiosperms

Most angiosperms are divided into two classes—monocots and eudicots. The two classes differ in the number of cotyledons, or seed leaves, their seeds have. Monocot seeds have one cotyledon. Grasses, orchids, onions, lilies, and palms are monocots. Eudicot seeds have two cotyledons. Eudicots include roses, cactuses, sunflowers, peanuts, and peas. Other differences between monocots and eudicots are shown in **Figure 6.**

Figure 6 Two Classes of Angiosperms

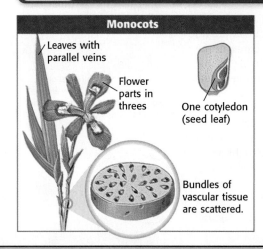

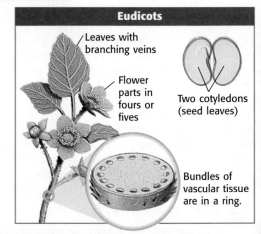

Monocots
- Leaves with parallel veins
- Flower parts in threes
- One cotyledon (seed leaf)
- Bundles of vascular tissue are scattered.

Eudicots
- Leaves with branching veins
- Flower parts in fours or fives
- Two cotyledons (seed leaves)
- Bundles of vascular tissue are in a ring.

Universal Access · Differentiated Instruction

Special Education Students

Gymnosperm or Angiosperm? Some students may have difficulty keeping different terms and their meanings straight. To help these students remember the difference between gymnosperms and angiosperms, tell them to use the following mnemonic: "Jim has no fruit, but Ann has fruit." Have students draw a picture of a boy who has some food, but no fruit and a picture of a girl holding a big bowl of fruit. Tell students to label the shirt of the boy in their drawing *Jim* and the shirt of the girl in their drawing *Ann.* Have students write the following sentence under their drawing of Jim: *Gymnosperms have no fruit or flowers.* Then, have students write this sentence under their drawing of Ann: *Angiosperms have fruits and flowers.* **LS Visual/Verbal**

The Importance of Angiosperms

Flowering plants provide many land animals with the food they need to survive. A field mouse that eats seeds and berries is using flowering plants directly as food. An owl that eats a field mouse is using flowering plants indirectly as food. Flowering plants are also a food source for the insects that pollinate them.

People use flowering plants in many ways. Major food crops, such as corn, wheat, and rice, are flowering plants. Some flowering plants, such as oak trees, are used for building materials. Flowering plants, such as cotton and flax, are used to make clothing and rope. Flowering plants are also used to make medicines, rubber, and perfume oils.

SECTION Review

7.2.a, 7.5.f

Summary

- Seeds nourish the young sporophyte of seed plants. Seed plant gametophytes rely on the sporophyte. Also, they do not need water for fertilization.

- Sexual reproduction occurs in gymnosperms when sperm from the male cone fertilizes the eggs of the female cone. The embryo develops within the female cone, which then releases seeds.

- Flowers are the reproductive structures of angiosperms. Wind and animals help angiosperms reproduce.

- Many organisms rely on seed plants for food. Humans have many uses for seed plants.

Understanding Concepts

1. **Describing** What are two advantages of seed plants?

2. **Comparing** How are the gametophytes of seed plants different from the gametophytes of seedless plants?

3. **Identifying** Describe the structure of seeds.

4. **Identifying** When does fertilization occur during the gymnosperm life cycle?

5. **Comparing** How are angiosperms and gymnosperms similar to one another?

Critical Thinking

6. **Making Inferences** How do angiosperms use flowers and fruits to reproduce?

7. **Applying Concepts** An angiosperm lives in a dense rain forest and close to the ground. It receives little wind. Several herbivores (animals that eat plants) live in this area of the rain forest. What are some ways the plant can ensure its seeds are carried throughout the forest?

INTERPRETING GRAPHICS Use the image below to answer the next question.

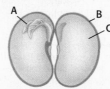

8. **Identifying Relationships** In the seed above, describe how part A relies on parts B and C for its survival.

Math Skills

9. **Making Calculations** About 330,000 species of plants have been discovered. Approximately 300,000 of those species are angiosperms. What percentage of plants are NOT angiosperms?

Internet Resources

For a variety of links related to this chapter, go to www.scilinks.org
Topic: Plants with Seeds; Plants of California
SciLinks code: HY71168; HY7C03

---

6. Sample answer: Flowers attract pollinators, which carry pollen to the flowers. Fruits surround the seeds, but fruits also attract animals or stick to animals' fur. Being eaten and sticking to fur both help to spread seeds. Some fruits have structures that help the wind carry them. **7.2.a** (mastering), **7.5.f** (exceeding)

7. Sample answer: The plant does not get much wind to spread its seeds, so it probably relies on animals to spread its seeds. Because there are herbivores in the area, the plant may have fruits to attract the animals. The animals could eat the fruits and spread the seeds. **7.5.f** (supporting), **7.2.a** (supporting)

8. Part A, the sporophyte, relies on part B, the seed coat, for protection. Part A relies on part C, the stored food source, for energy when it begins to grow. **7.5.f** (mastering)

9. $330{,}000 - 300{,}000 = 30{,}000$ plants; $30{,}000 \div 330{,}000 \times 100 = 9.1\%$

Section Review Standards Guide			
	Supporting	Mastering	Exceeding
7.2.a	4, 7	2, 6	
7.5.f	1, 5, 7	3, 8	6

Answer to Standards Check

Flowers help angiosperms reproduce by attracting pollinators. Fruits form a protective coating around seeds and allow seeds to be transported to new locations by animals, wind, or water. **7.5.f** (mastering)

Answers to Section Review

1. Seed plants nourish young plants with food that is stored in the seed. Seeds can also be dormant. **7.5.f** (supporting)

2. The gametophytes of seed plants are protected in the reproductive structures of the sporophyte. The gametophytes of seedless plants are separate structures. **7.2.a** (mastering)

3. Sample answer: Seeds are made up of three parts. The first part is the young plant. The second part is the stored food. The third part is the seed coat, which surrounds and protects the young plant. **7.5.f** (mastering)

4. Sexual reproduction occurs when pollen from male cones fertilizes eggs that were formed in the female cones. **7.2.a** (supporting)

5. Gymnosperms and angiosperms are both seed plants. **7.5.f** (supporting)

Section Resources

- Directed Reading A **BASIC** (Also in Spanish), B **GENERAL**

- Interactive Reader and Study Guide

- Section Quiz **GENERAL** (Also in Spanish)

- Section Review **GENERAL** (Also in Spanish)

- Vocabulary and Section Summary A **BASIC** (Also in Spanish), B **GENERAL**

Reviewing Prior Knowledge

Review standard 7.5.f with students. Ask students to summarize the standard in their own words. Then, have students draw a diagram of a flower and label how each part of the flower functions.

Bellringer

Have students focus on standard 7.5.a by asking them to name some functions that plants need to be able to carry out. (Sample answer: get water, food, reproduce) Then, have students think about the different parts of a plant and match each function to a part of the plant that might carry out this function. (Sample answer: The root system anchors the plant in the soil, obtains water and minerals, and stores food energy. The shoot system provides structure, carries out photosynthesis, and stores materials. The reproductive system ensures continued survival of the plant species.)

📋 Bellringer Transparency

Motivate

Discussion

Roots Bring several plants to class. Gently remove each plant from its pot and show the roots to the class. Ask students to identify whether each plant has a taproot system or a fibrous root system. Point out any structures that are not roots but are found underground, such as tubers and bulbs (modified stems). Then, ask students to list three functions of roots. (Sample answer: Roots supply plants with water and dissolved minerals. Roots hold plants securely in the soil. Roots store surplus food.)

LS Verbal

SECTION
4

Structures of Seed Plants

Key Concept Seed plants are made up of roots and shoots. Each part carries out functions for the seed plant.

What You Will Learn

- Seed plants have roots and shoots that allow for water and nutrient uptake and provide support.
- Leaves capture light energy for photosynthesis and provide a surface for gas exchange.
- Flowers are the reproductive structures for angiosperms.

Why It Matters

A seed plant's survival relies on both underground and above ground parts.

Vocabulary

- xylem
- stamen
- phloem
- pistil
- sepal
- ovary
- petal
- ovule

READING STRATEGY

Outlining In your **Science Journal,** create an outline of the section. Use the headings from the section in your outline.

xylem (ZIE luhm) the type of tissue in vascular plants that provides support and conducts water and nutrients from the roots

phloem (FLOH em) the tissue that conducts food in vascular plants

▶ Just like the human body, a plant has different parts that carry out many functions. Plants have roots, shoots, and reproductive structures. A plant's roots and shoots supply the plant with what it needs to survive. The roots are often found underground. The shoot includes stems and leaves. It is often found above ground.

The vascular tissues of the root and shoot are connected. There are two kinds of vascular tissue—xylem and phloem. **Xylem** is vascular tissue that transports water and minerals through the plant. Xylem moves materials from the roots to the shoots. **Phloem** is vascular tissue that transports food molecules to all parts of a plant. Xylem and phloem are found in all parts of vascular plants.

Roots

Most roots are underground, as **Figure 1** shows. Many people do not realize how extensive root systems can be. For example, a corn plant that is 2.5 m tall can have roots that grow 2.5 m deep and 1.2 m out and away from the stem!

Root Functions

The following are the three main functions of roots:

- Roots absorb water and dissolved minerals from the soil. The water and minerals are transported by the xylem to the shoots.
- Roots hold plants securely in the soil.
- Roots store surplus food made during photosynthesis. The food is produced in the leaves. Then, it is transported in the phloem to the roots. In the roots, the surplus food is usually stored as sugar or starch.

Onion **Dandelion** **Carrots**

Figure 1 *The roots of these plants absorb and store water and minerals.*

Universal Access • Differentiated Instruction

Special Education Students

Watching the Speaker Students with hearing impairments can better understand speech if they can watch the mouth of the person who is speaking. When presenting key points about this section to the class, position yourself so that students with hearing impairments have an unblocked view of your mouth. Consider which student seating positions and teaching positions might benefit hearing-impaired students the most. In group discussions, consider placing all chairs in a circle so that students with hearing impairments can see all the students' mouths. **LS** Visual

---

Root Structure

The structures of a root are shown in **Figure 2.** The layer of cells that covers the surface of roots is called the *epidermis.* Some cells of the epidermis extend from the root. These cells, or *root hairs,* increase the surface area of the root. This surface area helps the root absorb water and minerals. After water and minerals are absorbed by the epidermis, they diffuse into the center of the root, where the vascular tissue is located.

Roots grow longer at their tips. A group of cells called the *root cap* protects the tip of a root. The root cap produces a slimy substance. This substance makes it easier for the root to push through soil as it grows.

Root Systems

There are two kinds of root systems—taproot systems and fibrous root systems. A taproot system has one main root, or a taproot. The taproot grows downward. Many smaller roots branch from the taproot. Taproots can reach water deep underground. Eudicots and gymnosperms usually have taproot systems.

A fibrous root system has several roots that spread out from the base of a plant's stem. The roots are usually the same size. Fibrous roots usually get water from close to the soil surface. Monocots usually have fibrous roots.

Standards Check What are two types of root systems? 🐻 **7.5.a**

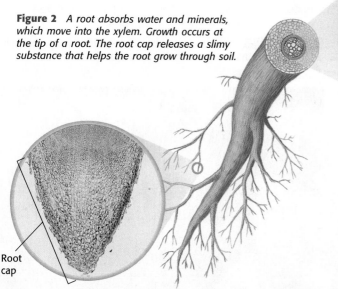

Figure 2 *A root absorbs water and minerals, which move into the xylem. Growth occurs at the tip of a root. The root cap releases a slimy substance that helps the root grow through soil.*

Root cap

Xylem

Phloem

Practice with Percentages

The table gives an estimate of the number of species in each plant group. What percentage of plant species do not produce seeds?

Plant Species	
Plant group	**Number of species**
Mosses, liverworts, and hornworts	16,000
Ferns, horsetails, and club mosses	12,200
Gymnosperms	840
Angiosperms	300,000

Teach

Group Activity

Materials for Each Group

- bags, plastic, resealable (4)
- ruler, metric
- seeds, 4 varieties (1 seed of each variety)
- towels, paper (4)
- water

Root Growth Have students work in groups of four. Tell students to fold each paper towel in quarters, placing a seed in the middle fold of each towel. Students should then moisten the paper towel thoroughly, taking care that the towel does not become dripping wet. Tell students to place the wet paper towel in a plastic bag and seal the bag. Each day for the next week, have students measure the length of the roots that develop and note any changes in the roots' appearance. Students should moisten the paper towel as needed during the week. Ask students to make a table of their measurements. Then, ask students the following questions: "What did you notice about the appearance of your roots as they grew?" (Students may notice that the roots grew root hairs or became more numerous. Some students may also note that the tips of the roots seemed slimy.) "Which of your seeds grew the fastest?" (Answers may vary.) At the end of the experiment, consider asking students to plant their seeds in potting soil to see how the roots continue to develop. **LS Kinesthetic Co-op Learning**

📦 Teaching Transparency: L51 Structures of a Root

Answer to Math Practice

about 9.0% (16,000 + 12,200 = 28,200 species of seedless plants; 16,000 + 12,200 + 840 + 300,000 = 329,040 total plant species; 28,200/329,040 × 100 = 8.6%)

Answer to Standards Check

Two types of root systems are tap and fibrous root systems. **7.5.a** (supporting)

Stem Functions Have students draw pictures that illustrate the functions of stems. Tell them to write captions for each illustration.
LS Visual/Verbal

CONNECTION ACTIVITY
History

Using Stems Many large aquatic grasses are called *reeds*. After their stems are harvested and dried, they can be used to construct many useful products. For thousands of years, arrows, pens, baskets, musical instruments, furniture, and houses have been made out of reeds. Building boats from reeds is an ancient craft that is still practiced in some regions where reeds are plentiful. Ancient Egyptian buildings include friezes of oceangoing ships made of reeds. In the 1960s, a Norwegian explorer named Thor Heyerdahl had a reed ship built to see if such a vessel could weather an ocean voyage. His ship was called *Ra II*. Have students research Heyerdahl and the *Ra II*. Ask interested students to make a model of Heyerdahl's reed vessel.
LS Kinesthetic

Answer to Standards Check

A herbaceous stem is one that is soft, thin, and flexible. Sample answer: Poppies have herbaceous stems.
7.5.a (supporting)

Teaching Transparency:
L52 Cross-Section of an Herbaceous Root; Cross-Section of a Woody Root

Figure 3 *The stem, or trunk, of this valley oak keeps the tree upright, which helps leaves get sunlight for photosynthesis.*

Stems

Stems vary greatly in shape and size. Stems are usually located above ground. However, many plants have underground stems. The trunk of the valley oak in **Figure 3** is a stem.

Stem Functions

A stem connects a plant's roots to its leaves and reproductive structures. A stem also has the following functions:

- Stems support the plant body. Leaves are arranged along stems. This arrangement helps leaves get sunlight for photosynthesis. Stems hold up reproductive structures, like flowers, which helps pollinators, such as bees, find the flowers.
- Stems transport materials between the root system and the leaves and reproductive structures. Xylem carries water and dissolved minerals from the roots to the leaves and other shoot parts. Phloem carries the food made during photosynthesis to roots and other parts of the plant.
- Some stems store materials. For example, the stems of cactuses and some trees are adapted for water storage.

Herbaceous Stems

Many plants have stems that are soft, thin, and flexible. These stems are called *herbaceous stems* (huhr BAY shuhs STEMZ). Examples of plants that have herbaceous stems include wildflowers, such as clovers and poppies. Many crops, such as beans, tomatoes, and corn, have herbaceous stems. A cross section of an herbaceous stem is shown in **Figure 4.**

Standards Check What is an herbaceous stem? Give an example of a plant that has an herbaceous stem. **7.5.a**

Figure 4 *Buttercups are just one plant that has herbaceous stems. Wildflowers and many vegetables have soft, thin, and flexible stems.*

Phloem

Xylem

Universal Access • Differentiated Instruction

Basic Learners

Identifying Stems Make sure that students can identify the stems of different kinds of plants. Show students pictures of plants or take them on a nature walk to view live plants. Include plants such as dandelions, tomato plants, raspberry bushes, oak trees, cacti, vines, and palm trees. Ask volunteers to identify the stems of each type of plant. **LS** Visual

Growth ring

Phloem

Xylem

Figure 5 *Some plants, such as these trees, have woody stems. Plants that have woody stems usually live for many years. People can use growth rings to estimate the age of a plant.*

Woody Stems

Trees and shrubs have rigid stems made of wood and bark. These stems are called *woody stems*. **Figure 5** shows a cross section of a woody stem. Trees or shrubs that live in areas with cold winters have a growing period during the spring and summer. These plants have a dormant period during the winter. At the beginning of each growing period, large xylem cells are produced. As fall approaches, the plants produce smaller xylem cells, which appear darker. In the fall and winter, the plants stop producing new cells. The cycle begins again the next spring. A ring of dark cells surrounding a ring of light cells makes up a growth ring.

Leaves

Leaves vary greatly in shape. They may be round, narrow, heart-shaped, or fan-shaped. Leaves also vary in size. The raffia palm has leaves that may be six times longer than you are tall. The leaves of duckweed, a tiny aquatic plant, are so small that several of the leaves can fit on your fingernail. **Figure 6** shows a poison ivy leaf. Leaf size, shape, and thickness can change based on the environment in which the plant lives.

Leaf Functions

The main function of leaves is to make food for the plant. Chloroplasts in the cells of leaves capture energy from sunlight. The leaves also absorb carbon dioxide from the air. The leaves use the captured energy to make food, or sugar, from carbon dioxide and water.

Figure 6 *The leaves of poison ivy are very distinctive. They make food to help the plant survive.*

Group Activity

Materials for Each Group
- books, heavy
- leaves
- newspapers
- notebook or index cards
- paper towels
- tape, transparent

Safety Caution

Tell students to avoid plants such as poison oak during this activity. You may want to show students pictures of poisonous plants that are common in your area.

Leaf Collecting Challenge students to see how many different types of leaves they can collect. Students should press the leaves for a few days after collecting them. They can do this by placing each leaf between two paper towels and adding several sheets of newspaper on each side. Then, students should stack heavy books on top of the leaf and papers. When the leaves are flat and dry, have students tape them to index cards or to the pages of a notebook. Have students use reference books to identify the names of the plants from which they collected the leaves. Have students label each leaf with the plant's common and scientific names, the date, and the location where the leaf was found.

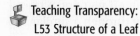 **Kinesthetic**

Teaching Transparency:
L53 Structure of a Leaf

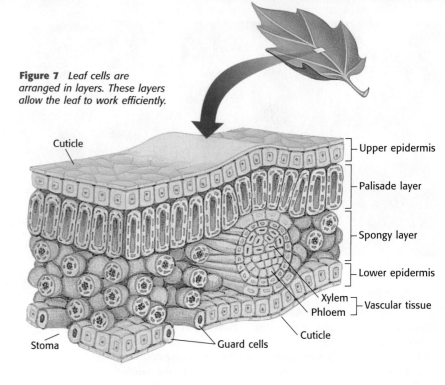

Figure 7 *Leaf cells are arranged in layers. These layers allow the leaf to work efficiently.*

Cuticle — Upper epidermis — Palisade layer — Spongy layer — Lower epidermis — Xylem — Phloem — Vascular tissue — Cuticle — Guard cells — Stoma

SCHOOL to HOME

Looking at Leaves
Leaves are many shapes and sizes. They are also arranged on a stem in many ways. Walk around your home. In your **Science Journal**, sketch the leaves of the plants you see. Notice the arrangement of the leaves on the stem, the shapes of the leaves, and the veins in the leaves. Use a ruler to measure the size of the leaves.

Leaf Structure

The structure of leaves, shown in **Figure 7,** is related to their main function—photosynthesis. A cuticle covers the outer surfaces of a leaf. The cuticle prevents the leaf from losing water. A single layer of cells, the epidermis, lies beneath the cuticle. Light passes through the epidermis. Tiny openings in the epidermis, called *stomata* (singular, *stoma*), let carbon dioxide enter the leaf. Guard cells open and close the stomata.

Most photosynthesis takes place in the middle of a leaf. This part of a leaf often has two layers. Cells in the upper layer, the palisade layer, contain many chloroplasts. Photosynthesis takes place in the chloroplasts. Carbon dioxide moves freely in the space between the cells of the second layer, the spongy layer. Xylem and phloem are also found in the spongy layer.

Leaf Adaptations

Some leaves have functions other than photosynthesis. For example, the leaves of many cactuses are modified as spines. These spines keep animals from eating the cactuses. The leaves of another plant, the sundew, are modified to catch insects. Sundews grow in soil that does not contain enough nitrogen to meet the plants' needs. By catching and digesting insects, a sundew is able to get the nitrogen that it needs to survive.

Universal Access · Differentiated Instruction

English Learners

Proper Pronunciation Tell students that if they are unsure how to pronounce a word, they should determine the correct pronunciation rather than making up their own. Point out that knowing how a word sounds will help them recognize and understand it, and that changing incorrect pronunciation later is often difficult. Tell students that three ways to find out the correct pronunciation of a word are to look in a glossary in the back of the book, look in a dictionary, and ask the teacher. Ask students to find at least one word on these two pages that they are unsure how to pronounce. Have them verify the pronunciation and then share with the class what tactic they used to determine the correct pronunciation. **Verbal/Auditory**

Flowers

Most people admire the beauty of flowers, but why do plants have flowers? Flowers are structures of sexual reproduction for flowering plants. Flowers come in many shapes, colors, and fragrances. Brightly colored and fragrant flowers usually rely on animals for pollination. Other flowers look and smell like rotting meat. These flowers attract flies. The flies pollinate the flowers. Plants that lack brightly colored flowers and fragrances, such as grasses, depend on the wind to spread pollen.

Many flowers also produce nectar. Nectar is a fluid that contains sugar. Nectar attracts birds and insects. These animals move from flower to flower and drink the nectar. As they do so, they often carry pollen to the flowers.

Sepals and Petals

Flowers may have the following basic parts: sepals, petals, stamens, and one or more pistils. Flowers that have all four basic parts are called *perfect flowers*. Flowers that have sepals, petals, and stamens are male flowers. And flowers that have sepals, petals, and one or more pistils are female flowers.

Sepals are modified leaves that make up the outermost ring of flower parts and protect the bud. Sepals are often green like other leaves. Sepals cover and protect the flower while it is a bud. As the blossom opens, the sepals fold back. Then, the petals can unfold and become visible. **Petals** are broad, flat, thin leaflike parts of a flower. Petals vary in color and shape. Petals attract insects or other animals to the flower. Animals help plants reproduce by carrying pollen from flower to flower.

sepal (SEE puhl) in a flower, one of the outermost rings of modified leaves that protect the flower bud

petal (PET uhl) one of the usually brightly colored leaf-shaped parts that make up one of the rings of a flower

Standards Check What is a perfect flower? 7.5.f

Quick Lab

How Do the Parts of a Plant Work Together?

1. Obtain a **potted plant** from your teacher.
2. Water the plant until the soil is damp to the touch.
3. Record the mass of the potted plant.
4. Place the plant in a **large, resealable bag.** Seal the bag.
5. Record the appearance of the plant and bag.
6. For the next week, record your observations of the plant without removing it from the plastic bag.

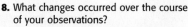

7. At the end of one week, remove the plant from the plastic bag. Record the final mass of the potted plant.

7.5.a
7.7.c

8. What changes occurred over the course of your observations?
9. Draw a picture of your plant. Label the different parts of the plant. How did these parts work together during the week that you observed the plant?
10. What do you think happened to make the mass of the plant change?

⏲ **20 min plus follow-up**

Quick Lab

⏲ **20 min**

Teacher Notes

This activity helps reinforce the importance of specialized tissue to the function of an entire organism (covers standard 7.5.a). It also supports a discussion of photosynthesis. Have students make predictions about what will happen to the plant while it is sealed in the bag. Make sure that students determine the final mass of the plant after it is removed from the bag.

Materials for Each Group
• bag, large, resealable • plant, potted • water

Safety Caution

Remind students to review all safety cautions and icons before beginning this activity.

Answers

8. Answers may vary but might include that moisture gathered on the inside of the bag and that the plant was still alive at the end of one week.

9. Drawings should include roots, leaves, and stems. Students should describe how the roots, stems, and other parts of the plant worked together.

10. The mass of the plant may have changed because water was transferred from the soil into the plant.

📋 **Differentiated Datasheets**
A **BASIC**, B **GENERAL**, C **ADVANCED**

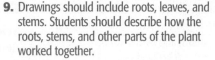
Also editable on the **Holt Lab Generator CD-ROM**

Connection To
Earth Science

Electromagnetic Spectrum
Photosynthesis is the process by which plants convert light energy to chemical energy. The light energy that plants use is only a small part of the electromagnetic spectrum. Help students understand that plants use the visible-light portion of the electromagnetic spectrum for photosynthesis. **LS** Visual

Discussion

Attracting Pollinators Ask students what they know about the role of flowers. Have students read the material on flowers and consider how the following factors make flowers successful in the plant world: color, shape, and smell. (Sample answers: The color of a flower may attract insects. The shape of a flower may be adapted for a specific pollinator, such as a hummingbird. Or, the shape may help the flower use the wind to spread pollen. The fragrance of a flower is designed to attract pollinators. For example, some flies are drawn to flowers that smell like rotting meat.) **LS** Verbal

Answer to Standards Check

A perfect flower is a flower with both male and female structures.

Standards Focus

This **Standards Focus** provides you with a quick way to **assess**, **reteach**, and **re-assess** one or more concepts in the section.

 **Assess**

1. Why do some plants have brightly colored flowers while other plants do not? (Sample answer: Plants with brightly colored flowers usually attract animals for pollination. Plants without brightly colored flowers usually rely on the wind for pollination.) **7.5.f**

2. Describe the two types of root systems and give examples of each type. (Sample answer: A taproot has one main root. Carrots have a taproot. Fibrous root systems include many roots of a similar size that grow from the base of the stem. Onions have fibrous roots.) **7.5.a**

Reteach

Flower Parts Ask student volunteers to describe a flower part and to draw that part on the board. Continue until students have drawn a complete flower. **LS** Visual **7.5.f**

Re-Assess

Eating Plants Have students list some of the plant ingredients in a salad. (Sample answer: lettuce, tomato, cucumber, carrot, cabbage, broccoli, alfalfa sprouts, and garbanzo beans) Then, ask students to identify the part of the plant that is eaten in each case. (Sample answer: Lettuce and cabbage are leaves. Tomato and cucumber are fruits. Carrots are roots. Broccoli florets are flower buds. Alfalfa sprouts are roots, stems, and leaves. Garbanzo beans are seeds.) **LS** Visual **7.5.a**

Teaching Transparency:
L54 Structure of a Flower

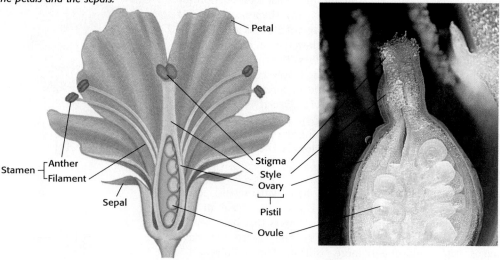

Figure 8 *The stamens, which produce pollen, and the pistil, which produces eggs, are surrounded by the petals and the sepals.*

Petal

Stamen — Anther
— Filament

Sepal

Stigma
Style
Ovary

Pistil

Ovule

stamen (STAY muhn) the male reproductive structure of a flower that produces pollen and consists of an anther at the tip of a filament

pistil (PIS til) the female reproductive part of a flower that produces seeds and consists of an ovary, style, and stigma

ovary (OH vuh ree) in flowering plants, the lower part of a pistil that produces eggs in ovules

ovule (AHV yool) a structure in the ovary of a seed plant that contains an embryo sac and that develops into a seed after fertilization

Stamens and Pistils

As **Figure 8** shows, the stamens of flowers are usually found just above the petals. A **stamen** is the male reproductive structure of flowers. Each stamen has a thin stalk called a *filament*. The filament is topped by an anther. Anthers are saclike structures that produce pollen, the male gametophyte.

The center of most flowers contains one or more pistils. A **pistil** is the female reproductive structure of flowers. The tip of the pistil is called the *stigma*. Pollen grains collect on stigmas, which are often sticky or feathery. The long, slender part of the pistil is the style. The rounded base of a pistil that contains one or more ovules is called the **ovary**. Each **ovule** contains an egg. When the egg is fertilized, the ovule develops into a seed. The ovary develops into a fruit.

Standards Check Describe stamens and pistils. Which are the female parts of a flower? the male parts of a flower? **7.5.f**

The Importance of Flowers

Flowers help plants reproduce. Humans also use flowers for many things. Roses and many other flowers are used for floral arrangements. Some flowers, such as artichokes, broccoli, and cauliflower, can be eaten. Other flowers, such as hibiscus and chamomile flowers, are used to make tea. Flowers used as spices include cloves and saffron. Flowers are also used in perfumes, lotions, and shampoos.

Universal Access · Differentiated Instruction

English Learners

Science Homophones Point out to students who are learning English that the English language includes many homophones, which are words that sound alike but are spelled differently. On the board, make a vertical list of the following words: *bass, cede, flour, four, mail, pistol, tee,* and *won.* Ask students to find a homophone for each word on the board by looking in the text on this page. (base, seed, flower, for, male, pistil, tea, and one) Have volunteers come up to the board and write the appropriate homophone next to each word. Then, have students write in their **Science Journals** the definitions for both words in each set of homophones. **LS** Verbal/Kinesthetic

SECTION Review

 7.5.a, 7.5.f

Summary

- Roots supply plants with water and dissolved minerals. Roots support and anchor plants. Roots also store surplus food made during photosynthesis.

- Stems support the body of a plant. They allow transport of materials between the roots and shoots. Some stems store materials, such as water.

- A leaf has a thin epidermis on its upper and lower surfaces. The epidermis allows sunlight to pass through to the center of the leaf.

- Most photosynthesis takes place in the palisade layer of a leaf. The spongy layer of a leaf allows the movement of carbon dioxide and contains the xylem and phloem.

- Flowers are the reproductive structures of angiosperms. They may have four parts: sepals, petals, stamens, and one or more pistils.

- The pistil is usually located in the center of the flower. The ovary of a pistil contains ovules, which contain eggs. When the eggs are fertilized, ovules develop into seeds and the ovary becomes a fruit.

Using Vocabulary

1. Write an original definition for *xylem*, *phloem*, *stamen*, and *pistil*.

2. Use *sepal*, *petal*, *pistil*, and *ovary* in separate sentences.

Understanding Concepts

3. **Identifying** Which flower structure produces pollen?

4. **Identifying** What part of a leaf allows carbon dioxide to enter?

5. **Comparing** Compare xylem and phloem.

6. **Describing** Describe the internal structure of a leaf.

7. **Listing** What are three functions of stems?

8. **Identifying** Briefly describe the two types of stems.

Critical Thinking

9. **Making Inferences** Describe two kinds of root systems. How does the structure of each system help the roots perform their three functions?

10. **Applying Concepts** Pampas grass flowers are found at the top of tall stems, are light-colored, and are unscented. Explain how pampas grass flowers are most likely pollinated.

INTERPRETING GRAPHICS Use the image below to answer the next question.

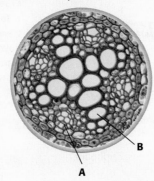

A

B

11. **Analyzing Processes** Describe how parts A and B work together to keep a plant alive. What would happen if one part stopped functioning?

Challenge

12. **Making Inferences** Flowers and some animals, especially insects, have influenced one another in the way they have evolved. Develop a hypothesis about how flowers may have changed because of their relationship with bees.

Internet Resources

For a variety of links related to this chapter, go to www.scilinks.org
Topic: Structure of Seed Plants
SciLinks code: HY71467

6. Accept all reasonable answers that describe a leaf's structure. **7.5.a** (mastering)

7. Sample answer: Stems support the plant body, transport materials between the root and shoot systems, and store materials. **7.5.a** (mastering)

8. Herbaceous stems are soft, thin, and flexible. Woody stems are rigid and made of wood and bark. **7.5.a** (supporting)

9. Accept all reasonable answers that describe the functions of tap roots compared to fibrous roots. **7.5.a** (mastering)

10. Sample answer: Pampas grass flowers are probably pollinated by the wind. They don't have brightly colored petals to attract pollinators. Also, because pampas grass flowers are at the top of a tall stem, it is likely that they would be caught by the wind. **7.5.f** (supporting)

11. Sample answer: The xylem and phloem shown in the image work together to make sure that all parts of a vascular plant get the water and nutrients they need to live. If one part stopped functioning, the whole plant would suffer. **7.5.a** (exceeding)

12. Sample answer: Flowers that attract pollinators are able to produce seeds. These seeds have plant embryos that share the characteristics of the parent plants. Insects impact what plant characteristics are passed to the next generation because they carry the pollen, which contains sperm, to the female parts of the flower. **7.5.f** (exceeding)

Section Review Standards Guide			
	Supporting	**Mastering**	**Exceeding**
7.5.a	1, 4, 8	5, 6, 7, 9	11
7.5.f	1, 2, 10	3	12

Answer to Standards Check

Stamens are the male part of a flower. Stamens have an anther and a filament. Pistils are the female part of a flower. The pistil is made of a stigma, style, and ovary. **7.5.f** (mastering)

Answers to Section Review

1. Sample answer: Xylem transports water and minerals. Phloem transports food molecules. A stamen is the male reproductive part of a flower. A pistil is the female reproductive structure of a flower. **7.5.a** (supporting), **7.5.f** (supporting)

2. Sample answer: A flower bud is protected by sepals. The petals of a flower attract pollinators. The pistil of a flower is often found at the center of the flower. The ovary of a flower protects the ovules and develops into a fruit. **7.5.f** (supporting)

3. The anther produces pollen. **7.5.f** (mastering)

4. The stoma of a leaf allows carbon dioxide to enter. **7.5.a** (supporting)

5. Sample answer: Xylem transports water and minerals from a plant's roots to its shoots. Phloem transports food molecules throughout the plant. **7.5.a** (mastering)

Section Resources

- Directed Reading A **BASIC** (Also in Spanish), B **GENERAL**

- Interactive Reader and Study Guide

- Section Quiz **GENERAL** (Also in Spanish)

- Section Review **GENERAL** (Also in Spanish)

- Vocabulary and Section Summary A **BASIC** (Also in Spanish), B **GENERAL**

Model-Making Lab

Model-Making Lab

Teacher Notes

This lab has students model flowers. By building and then comparing their models, students are able to understand the structures of flowers and how flowers function as the reproductive structures of angiosperms (covers standards 7.5.a, 7.5.f, and 7.7.d).

Time Required

One 45-minute class period

Lab Ratings

EASY ——————→ HARD

Teacher Prep 🧪
Student Set-Up 🧪🧪
Concept Level 🧪🧪
Clean Up 🧪

Materials

The materials listed on the student page are enough for one student or one group of students.

Safety Caution

Remind students to review all safety cautions and icons before beginning this activity.

Preparation Notes

You may wish to build your own model before class or to have on hand several models created by other students. Examining appropriate models can help students generate ideas for their own models.

OBJECTIVES

Build a model of a flower.

Explain how the model represents an actual flower.

Describe the basic parts of a flower.

MATERIALS

- art materials, such as colored paper, pipe cleaners, beads, and yarn
- card, index, 3 × 5 in.
- glue
- recycled items, such as paper plates and cups, yogurt containers, wire, string, buttons, cardboard, and bottles
- scissors
- tape

SAFETY

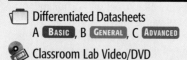

7.5.a Students know plants and animals have levels of organization for structure and function, including cells, tissues, organs, organ systems, and the whole organism.
7.5.f Students know the structures and processes by which flowering plants generate pollen, ovules, seeds, and fruit.
Investigation and Experimentation
7.7.d Construct scale models, maps, and appropriately labeled diagrams to communicate scientific knowledge (e.g., motion of Earth's plates and cell structure).

Build a Flower

Scientists often make models in the laboratory. Models help scientists understand processes and structures. Models are especially useful when scientists are trying to understand processes that are too small to be seen easily, such as pollination, or processes that are too large to be examined in a laboratory, such as the growth of a tree. Models also make it possible to examine the structures of objects, such as flowers.

In this activity, you will use your creativity and your understanding of the structure of a flower to make a model of a flower from recycled materials and art supplies. Remember, a perfect flower is a flower that has both male and female reproductive organs.

Procedure

1. Your teacher will assign to you one of the flowers in this lab. Draw and label the flower that you are assigned.

2. Decide which materials you will use to represent each flower part. Then, build a three-dimensional model of the flower. The model that you build should contain each of the parts present in your flower. Flowers may contain the following parts: stem, sepals, petals, stamens (anther and filament), and pistil (stigma, style, and ovary).

Perfect Flower

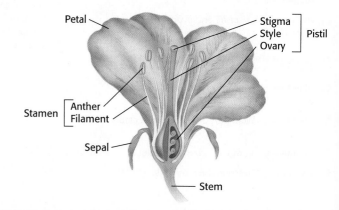

Lab Resources

📁 Differentiated Datasheets
A **BASIC**, B **GENERAL**, C **ADVANCED**

💿 Classroom Lab Video/DVD

🔴 **Holt Lab Generator CD-ROM**

Search for any lab by topic, standard, difficulty level, or time. Edit any lab to fit your needs, or create your own labs. Use the Lab Materials QuickList software to customize your lab materials list.

3 After you build your model, draw a key for your flower model on an index card. Label each of the structures represented on your flower.

Analyze the Results

4 Organizing Data List the structures of a flower, and explain the function of each part.

5 Identifying Patterns What is the outermost part of your flower? the innermost part of your flower?

6 Analyzing Data How are your flower model and an actual flower alike? How are they different?

Draw Conclusions

7 Drawing Conclusions How might your flower attract pollinators? What modifications could you make to your flower to attract a greater number of pollinators?

8 Evaluating Models Is your model an accurate representation of a flower? Why or why not?

9 Making Predictions Compare your flower model with the other two kinds of flowers. How do male and female flowers differ? Why might plants have male and female flowers instead of perfect flowers?

Big Idea Question

10 Identifying Relationships While plants share many characteristics, plants also differ in a variety of ways. For example, flowers are not the only structures that plants use for reproduction. Create a table that lists the different kinds of plants and lists their similarities and differences.

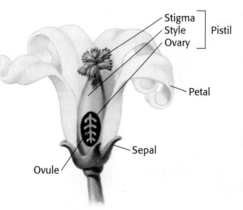

Male Flower
- Anther
- Filament } Stamen
- Petal
- Sepal

Female Flower
- Stigma
- Style } Pistil
- Ovary
- Petal
- Sepal
- Ovule

---

5. sepals; pistil

6. Sample answer: My flower model and an actual flower have the same parts: sepals, petals, stamens, and pistils. Unlike real flowers, however, my flower cannot be pollinated, nor can it produce seeds.

Draw Conclusions

7. Sample answer: My flower will attract pollinators because it has bright petals. I could give my flower a fragrance to attract more pollinators.

8. Sample answer: My flower model is an accurate visual representation of a real flower, but it does not function the way a real flower does. My model looks like a flower, but it cannot be pollinated or fertilized.

9. Male and female flowers have different reproductive parts. A plant may have male and/or female flowers instead of perfect flowers so that offspring have parents that are not as closely related to one another.

Big Idea Question

10. Answers may vary. In their tables, students should include information about at least three different plant types with which they are familiar. Students should also include in their tables any information that they have about the root, stem, and reproductive structures of their chosen plant types.

Analyze the Results

4. petal: the often colorful leaf-shaped part of the flower that attracts pollinators

sepal: the modified leaves that form the base of the flower and that enclose and protect the bud before the flower opens

stem: the main stalk of the plant from which leaves, flowers, and fruits develop; water and nutrients move through the stem between the leaves and roots

pistil: the female reproductive structure of the flower

stigma: the upper tip of the pistil, which receives the pollen

style: the stalklike part of the pistil between the stigma and ovary

ovary: the enlarged part of the pistil in which ovules are formed

stamen: the male reproductive structure of the flower

anther: the saclike structure at the top of the stamen, which produces pollen

filament: the threadlike part of the stamen that holds the anther

Gayle Van Fossen
George Leyva
Intermediate School
San Jose, California

Teacher Notes

This activity enhances students' knowledge of the parts of a leaf. Students will construct a scale diagram of the cross section of a leaf (covers standard 7.7.d). You may wish to have several examples of scale diagrams and models on hand to share with students, such as maps, blueprints, and model cars.

Answers to You Try It!

1. Students should construct scale diagrams based on the following scale measurements:

Parts of lilac leaf cross-section	Actual measurement	To scale measurement
Upper epidermis	24 μm	2.4 cm
Palisade layer	64 μm	6.4 cm
Spongy layer	124 μm	12.4 cm
Lower epidermis	20 μm	2.0 cm
Diameter of vein	40 μm	4.0 cm

2. The upper epidermis may be thicker than the lower epidermis because the upper epidermis is exposed to more sunlight and environmental conditions that could harm the leaf.

3. The upper epidermis is the part of the leaf that is exposed to sunlight. It must protect the inner parts of the leaf from direct sunlight.

4. The palisade layer of the leaf, where most photosynthesis occurs, is not as thick as the spongy layer but is thicker than any other layer of the leaf.

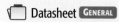 Datasheet GENERAL

Also editable on the Holt Lab Generator CD-ROM

Science Skills Activity

| Scientific Methods | Research | Data Analysis | Models, Maps & Diagrams |

Investigation and Experimentation
7.7.d Construct scale models, maps, and appropriately labeled diagrams to communicate scientific knowledge.

Constructing Scale Diagrams

▶ Tutorial

A scale diagram accurately represents the proportions of an object. A scale diagram must indicate the scale that was used to create the diagram. The scale explains how measurement is represented by each unit on the diagram. The following procedure explains how to construct scale diagrams.

Procedure

❶ Determine the actual size of the object. You may be able to measure the object if it is big enough, or you may have to do research to find its size.

❷ Determine the scale. Large objects, such as sequoia trees, may be represented by diagrams or models by using the following scale: 1 cm = 1 m. A model of a sequoia that is 75 m tall would be 7.5 cm tall.

❸ Determine the scale. Small objects, such as cells, may be represented by diagrams or models that have the following scale: 1 cm = 5 μm. A model of a human red blood cell that has a diameter of 7 μm would have a diameter of 7 cm.

❹ After you determine the scale, apply it consistently to every measurement you take of the object. A data table similar to **Table 1** may be helpful when creating your diagram or model.

Table 1	Scale Conversions of a Sequoia	
	Actual measurement	**Scale measurement**
Height of sequoia tree	75 m	7.5 cm
Diameter of sequoia trunk	11 m	1.1 cm
Height of first branch from ground	40 m	4.0 cm
Diameter of largest branch	2 m	0.2 cm

Scale: 1 cm = 1 m

▶ You Try It!

In this activity, you will construct a scale diagram of a leaf. The measurements for a lilac leaf are provided in **Table 2**.

Table 2	Scale Conversions of a Lilac Leaf	
Parts of lilac leaf cross section	**Actual measurement**	**Scale measurement**
Upper epidermis	24 μm	
Palisade layer	64 μm	
Spongy layer	124 μm	
Lower epidermis	20 μm	
Diameter of vein	40 μm	

Scale: 1 cm = 10 μm

Procedure

❶ Complete **Table 2** to determine the measurements that you would use to construct a scale diagram of a lilac leaf.

❷ Using your measurements and the cross section of a leaf in Section 4, create a scale diagram of a leaf cross section.

Analysis

❸ **Analyzing** Why might the upper epidermis and lower epidermis be different sizes?

❹ **Evaluating** Use **Table 2** to discuss other differences in the parts of the leaf. For example, what do you notice about the part of the leaf that performs photosynthesis? Is it larger than or smaller than the other parts of the leaf?

Universal Access · Differentiated Instruction

Struggling Readers

Reading Data Tables Tell students that when reading a table, they should read the parts of the table in the following order:

1. title
2. column headings
3. row headings
4. key, if provided
5. data

Tell students that only after they have read the first four parts of a table and understood what the data in the table represents, should they read the data. Ask volunteers to demonstrate the steps with **Table 1**.
LS Verbal

Advanced Learners/GATE

Leaves to Scale You may extend the You Try It! activity to challenge advanced learners. Invite students to determine the measurements for a scale diagram with the following scale: 10 cm = 10 μm. Have the students use the scale to create a new scale diagram of the lilac leaf cross section.
LS Logical/Kinesthetic

Chapter Summary

The Big Idea
Plants have several common characteristics and can be classified by their structures.

Section

Vocabulary

① What Is a Plant?

Key Concept Most plants perform photosynthesis, reproduce, and share some physical characteristics.

- All plants share four main characteristics.
- Photosynthesis is a process that occurs in the chloroplasts of plant cells.
- Plants cells have some structures that animal cells do not have.
- Plants reproduce sexually and asexually.

A plant cell is different from an animal cell.

nonvascular plant p. 362

vascular plant p. 362

gymnosperm p. 362

angiosperm p. 362

② Seedless Plants

Key Concept Seedless plants do not produce seeds but are well adapted for reproduction and survival.

- Nonvascular plants do not have specialized vascular tissues.
- Seedless vascular plants have specialized vascular tissues.
- Seedless plants reproduce sexually and asexually, but they need water to reproduce.
- Seedless plants have two stages in their life cycle.

Seedless plants have a two-stage life cycle.

rhizoid p. 364
rhizome p. 366

③ Seed Plants

Key Concept Seed plants produce seeds and are categorized as gymnosperms or angiosperms.

- Seed plants differ from seedless plants in three main ways.
- A seed is composed of a young plant, a food source, and an outer coating.
- Gymnosperms and angiosperms have different patterns of sexual reproduction.
- Gymnosperms and angiosperms are economically and environmentally important.

The structure of a seed protects a plant embryo.

pollen p. 368
pollination p. 371

④ Structures of Seed Plants

Key Concept Seed plants are made up of roots and shoots. Each part carries out functions for the seed plant.

- Seed plants have root and shoot systems that allow for water and nutrient uptake and provide support.
- Leaves capture sunlight energy for photosynthesis and provide a surface for gas exchange.
- Flowers are the reproductive structures for angiosperms.

Leaves are one specialized stucture in a seed plant.

xylem p. 374
phloem p. 374
sepal p. 379
petal p. 379
stamen p. 380
pistil p. 380
ovary p. 380
ovule p. 380

Review Resources

- Reinforcement Worksheet **BASIC**
- Critical Thinking Worksheet **ADVANCED**
- Chapter Review **GENERAL** (Also in Spanish)
- Standards Review Workbook (Also in Spanish)
- Study Guide A **BASIC** (Also in Spanish), B **GENERAL**

Assessment Resources

- Chapter Tests A **BASIC**, B **GENERAL** (Also in Spanish), C **ADVANCED**
- Standards Assessment **GENERAL**

Chapter Summary

SUPER SUMMARY

Have students connect the major concepts in this chapter through an interactive Super Summary. Visit go.hrw.com and type in the keyword HY7PL1S to access the Super Summary for this chapter.

Identifying Roots

The Root Phyton The Greek root word *phyton* means "plant," and it appears several times in this chapter. *Sporphyte* is the plant life stage that produces spores, and *gametophyte* is the plant life stage that produces gametes. Have students work in pairs to discover the meanings of the following words based on the root *phyton: epiphyte* (epiphyte: plant living on top of another plant), *xerophyte* (xerophyte: plant adapted for a dry habitat), *phytoplankton* (phytoplankton: tiny floating plants and algae), *phytotoxin* (phytotoxin: poison derived from plants). **LS** Verbal

Focus on Speaking

Native Californians Ask students to work with a partner to prepare a presentation about a plant that is native to California. Students should share the research and presentation responsibilities and should present their findings in the form of a poster or other visual aid. Ask students to include the following information in their presentations: a description of the plant, common and scientific names for the plant, where the plant is found in California, the plant's habitat, the environmental importance of the plant, and the plant's economic value. **LS** Verbal/Interpersonal

Chapter Review  7.1.b, 7.1.d, 7.2.a, 7.5.a, 7.5.f

Assignment Guide

Section	Questions
1	6, 11–14, 24, 28
2	4
3	8, 15
4	2–3, 5, 7, 9–10, 16–23, 25–26

Answers

Using Vocabulary

1. In this sentence, characteristics refers to the many structures with specific functions that plants have.

2. stamen **7.2.a** (mastering)

3. Xylem **7.5.a** (supporting)

4. rhizome **7.5.a** (supporting)

5. pollen **7.5.f** (mastering)

6. nonvascular plant **7.5.a** (supporting)

7. Phloem **7.5.a** (supporting)

Understanding Concepts

8. a **7.5.f** (supporting)

9. d **7.5.a** (supporting)

10. a **7.5.a** (supporting)

11. Plant cells have cell walls, a large central vacuole, and chloroplasts, and are able to perform the process of photosynthesis. **7.1.b** (mastering)

12. nonvascular plants, seedless vascular plants, gymnosperms, and angiosperms

13. Accept all reasonable answers. The purpose of a chloroplast is to capture sunlight energy and perform the process of photosynthesis. Life on Earth would be different if there were no chloroplasts because photosynthesis would not take place and plants would not make food or sugar. Most nonphotosynthetic organisms rely on plants. **7.1.d** (mastering)

14. Sample answer: Plants and green algae have many similarities, so scientists think that they are related. Both have the same kind of chlorophyll and cell walls. Both store food in the form of starch, and both have a two-stage life cycle.

Organize

Pyramid Review the FoldNote that you created at the beginning of the chapter. Add to or correct the FoldNote based on what you have learned.

Using Vocabulary

1 **Academic Vocabulary** In the sentence "Most plants share some physical characteristics," what does the word *characteristics* mean?

Complete each of the following sentences by choosing the correct term from the word bank.

pistil	rhizoid
vascular plant	rhizome
xylem	phloem
pollen	stamen
nonvascular plant	

2 A ___ is the male part of a flower.

3 ___ is a specialized tissue that transports water and nutrients through a plant.

4 An underground stem that produces new leaves and roots is called a ___.

5 The male gametophytes of flowers are contained in structures called ___.

6 A ___ does not have specialized tissues for transporting water.

7 ___ is a specialized tissue that transports food through a plant.

Understanding Concepts

Multiple Choice

8 Which of the following statements about angiosperms is NOT true?
  a. Their seeds are protected by cones.
  b. They produce seeds.
  c. They provide animals with food.
  d. They have flowers.

9 Which of the following statements about roots is true?
  a. Roots supply water and nutrients.
  b. Roots anchor and support a plant.
  c. Roots store surplus food.
  d. All of the above

10 In which part of a leaf does most photosynthesis take place?
  a. palisade layer   c. xylem
  b. phloem   d. epidermis

Short Answer

11 **Listing** What are four ways in which plant cells differ from animal cells?

12 **Listing** What are the four main groups of plants?

13 **Identifying** What is the function of a chloroplast? How would life on Earth be different if plant cells did not have chloroplasts?

14 **Concluding** Why do scientists think green algae and plants have a common ancestor?

15 **Comparing** What are the differences between the sporophyte and gametophyte stages of the life cycle of moss?

16 **Evaluating** How are seedless plants, gymnosperms, and angiosperms important to the environment?

17 **Analyzing** What are two advantages that seeds have over spores?

INTERPRETING GRAPHICS Use the cross section of the woody stem below to answer the next question.

18 **Identifying** What is the age of the tree in the diagram?

15. Accept all reasonable answers. **7.2.a** (mastering)

16. Sample answer: Nonvascular plants are often the first plants to live in a new environment. They form a thin layer of soil; seedless vascular plants add to this layer. Seedless plants also prevent erosion. Gymnosperms are often found in gardens and parks, and angiosperms provide most of the food that animals need to survive.

17. Sample answer: When the young plant begins to grow, it can use the stored food in the seed. Spores do not have stored food to help a plant grow. Another advantage is that seeds can be spread by animals, while spores are spread by wind. Animals spread seeds more efficiently than the wind spreads spores. **7.2.a** (supporting), **7.5.f** (supporting)

18. 10 years

19. d, anther **7.5.f** (mastering)

20. b, ovary **7.5.f** (mastering)

21. c, sepal **7.5.f** (mastering)

Writing Skills

22. Accept all reasonable responses. **7.5.a** (mastering)

INTERPRETING GRAPHICS Use the diagram below to answer the next three questions.

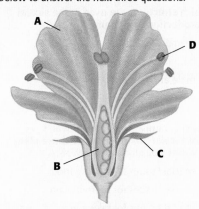

19 **Identifying** Which letter corresponds to the structure in which pollen is produced? What is the name of this structure?

20 **Identifying** Which letter corresponds to the structure that contains the ovules? What is the name of this structure?

21 **Identifying** Which letter corresponds to the structure that protects the flower bud? What is the name of this structure?

Writing Skills

22 **Writing Persuasively** Write a short essay that compares stems, leaves, and roots in terms of their structure and function in vascular plants.

Critical Thinking

23 **Concept Mapping** Use the following terms to create a concept map: *flowers, pollen, stamens, ovaries, pistils, stigmas, filaments, anthers, ovules, petals,* and *sepals.*

24 **Making Comparisons** Imagine that a seed and a spore are beginning to grow in a deep, dark crack in a rock. Which of the two is more likely to grow into an adult plant? Explain your answer.

25 **Identifying Relationships** Grass flowers do not have strong fragrances or bright colors. How might these characteristics be related to the way by which grass flowers are pollinated?

26 **Analyzing Ideas** Plants that are pollinated by wind produce more pollen than plants that are pollinated by animals do. Why might wind-pollinated plants produce more pollen?

27 **Applying Concepts** A scientist discovered a new plant. The plant has vascular tissue and produces seeds. It has brightly colored and strongly scented flowers. It also has sweet fruits. Based on this information, which of the four main types of plants did the scientist discover? How is the plant most likely pollinated? How does the plant most likely spread its seeds?

Math Skills

28 **Solving Problems** A peach tree produces 127 peaches. If 32% of the peach tree blossoms were fertilized, how many flowers were originally produced by the peach tree?

Challenge

29 **Evaluating Data** Choose three different kinds of plants. Prepare a table that illustrates the structures that the plants have in common and the structures that differ from plant to plant. Using this table, determine whether or not a mushroom is a plant. Explain your conclusion.

27. Sample answer: The plant is an angiosperm because it has flowers and fruit. Because the plant has brightly colored and strongly scented flowers, it is likely pollinated by animals. The fruits are sweet, so they are likely to be eaten by animals, and the seeds are dispersed elsewhere by the animals. **7.5.a** (supporting), **7.5.f** (exceeding)

Math Skills
28. $127 = 32\%\ x$; $127 = 0.32x$; $x = 127 \div 0.32 = 397$ flowers

Challenge
29. Accept all reasonable answers. **7.5.a** (mastering), **7.5.f** (mastering), **7.1.d** (supporting), **7.1.b** (supporting)

Chapter Review Standards Guide			
	Supporting	**Mastering**	**Exceeding**
7.1.b	29	11	
7.1.d	29	13	
7.2.a	17, 24	2, 15, 23	
7.5.a	3, 4, 6, 7, 9, 10, 27	22, 29	
7.5.f	8, 17, 24, 25, 26	5, 19, 20, 21, 29	27

Critical Thinking

23. An answer to this exercise can be found at the end of this book.

24. Sample answer: The seed is more likely to grow than the spore is. Because spores do not have stored food, the new plant must begin photosynthesis right away. But the spore and seed are in a deep, dark crack, so the spore is not getting any light for photosynthesis. Because the seed has stored food, the plant can grow in the crack without light for photosynthesis. **7.2.a** (supporting), **7.5.f** (supporting)

25. Sample answer: If grass flowers had bright petals and strong fragrances, they would likely be pollinated by animals. However, because grass flowers do not have these characteristics, they are most likely pollinated by the wind. **7.5.f** (supporting)

26. Sample answer: Animals pollinate plants by traveling from one plant to another. However, the wind may not blow from one plant to another, so wind-pollinated plants produce more pollen. Producing more pollen increases the chance that pollen will be blown onto the female structures of wind-pollinated plants' flowers. **7.5.f** (supporting)

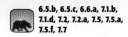
Standards Assessment

Teacher Notes

To provide practice under more realistic testing conditions, give students 20 min to answer all of the questions in this assessment.

Answer Key	
Question Number	Correct Answer
1	D
2	D
3	B
4	A
5	C
6	D
7	C
8	B
9	A
10	B
11	D
12	C
13	B
14	C
15	D
16	A

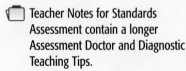

Standards Guide			
	Supporting	Mastering	Exceeding
5.2.a		13	
6.5.b			15
6.5.c		14	
6.6.a		16	
7.1.b		12	
7.1.d	3		
7.2	1		
7.2.a		5	
7.5	4		
7.5.a	2, 8	6, 11	10
7.5.f		9, 10	
7.7		7	

☐ Standards Assessment GENERAL

☐ Teacher Notes for Standards Assessment contain a longer Assessment Doctor and Diagnostic Teaching Tips.

REVIEWING ACADEMIC VOCABULARY

1 Which of the following words means "to change"?

A eliminate

B replace

C explain

D modify

2 In the sentence "The main function of a leaf is photosynthesis," what does the word *function* mean?

A part

B system

C form

D use

3 In the sentence "Molecules in the cell store energy and liberate it as the energy is needed for cells to do work," what does the word *liberate* mean?

A absorb

B release

C capture

D expand

4 Which of the following words is the closest in meaning to the word *illustrate*?

A show

B legend

C sequence

D characteristic

REVIEWING CONCEPTS

5 Which structures are used in the sexual reproduction of a conifer?

A sexual and asexual spores

B herbaceous and woody stems

C male and female cones

D xylem and phloem tissues

6 Mosses, hornworts, and liverworts are nonvascular plants. What do these plants lack that vascular plants have?

A special tissues for making food

B special tissues for reproduction

C special tissues for taking in water and nutrients

D special tissues for moving water through the plant

7 Which of the following questions can you answer by counting the growth rings on the tree trunk above?

A What kind of a tree is it?

B How tall did the tree grow?

C How old is the tree?

D What caused the tree to die?

✚ ASSESSMENT DOCTOR

Question 1: The corect answer is D. The word *modify* means to change in minor ways.

Question 2: The correct answer is D. In this sentence, *function* means use. Photosynthesis is the main use a leaf performs.

Question 3: The correct answer is B. *Liberate* means release, or let out.

Question 4: The correct answer is A. The word *illustrate* is closest in meaning to *show*.

Question 5: The correct answer is C. The reproduction of a pine tree requires both female and male cones, which may or may not grow on the same tree.

Question 6: The correct answer is D. Vascular plants have special structures for moving water through the plant. Nonvascular plants do not.

Question 7: The correct answer is C. You can calculate the ago of a treeby counting the number of growth rings on a cross section of a tree's trunk.

8 Which structures produce most of the food that a plant needs to survive?

A roots

B leaves

C stems

D flowers

9 What are seed plants that produce flowers or fruit called?

A angiosperms

B gymnosperms

C vascular plants

D conifers

10 Which of the following are structures found in a flower?

A xylem and phloem

B sepals and stamen

C chloroplasts and stomata

D fiddleheads and fronds

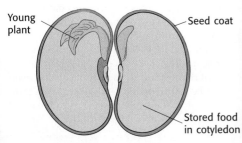

Young plant — Seed coat — Stored food in cotyledon

11 In the image above, what is the function of the seed coat?

A It produces the chloroplasts needed for photosynthesis.

B It eventually forms the adult plant.

C It contains stored food to nourish the young sporophyte.

D It protects the young plant while the seed is dormant.

REVIEWING PRIOR LEARNING

12 Which characteristics distinguish plant cells from animal cells?

A stamen and pistils

B nuclei and cytoplasm

C cell walls and chloroplasts

D pollination and photosynthesis

13 Which plant cell organelle captures and stores sunlight energy for photosynthesis?

A mitochondrion

B chloroplast

C chromosome

D lysosome

14 Which of the following organisms is the decomposer in the food web?

A fern

B vulture

C fungi

D squirrel

15 Which web shows how energy transfers between organisms on Earth?

A sun → plant → plant → animal

B sun → animal → animal → animal

C sun → plant → sun → animal

D sun → plant → animal → animal

16 What is a hypothesis?

A an explanation that can be tested

B a prediction that someone has made

C an experiment that can be performed

D a conclusion based on observation

Standards Assessment

Weird Science

Background

One might attribute the Methuselah Tree's long life to ideal growing conditions, but nothing could be further from the truth. The subalpine bristlecone (*Pinus longaeva*) lives in the White Mountains at or near the timberline, above which no trees can grow. The ancient trees receive only 30 cm of precipitation each year, mostly in the form of snow. The growing season is condensed to just six weeks of summer, and the soil is primarily dolomite, a type of limestone. However, factors that can adversely affect much younger trees, such as fires and competition from other plants, are usually absent from the bristlecones' habitat. Bristlecones are also uniquely adapted against insects, fungi, and draught.

Science, Technology, and Society

ACTiViTY

Researching Plant Poaching

Ask students to research plant poaching in your area. Have them identify which plants are being stolen and why, as well as any steps being taken to control poaching. Ask students to contact local park managers or state and federal natural resource agencies, such as the National Park Service. Other sources of information include the Internet, newspapers, and magazines. Students should make posters about their findings; posters should include pictures of the plants that poachers steal and a description of the plants' habitats.

Science in Action

Weird Science

The World's Oldest Known Tree

Long before Egyptians began building the pyramids at Giza, a seedling took root in the White Mountains in California. More than 4,000 years later, that bristlecone pine tree—known as the Methuselah (muh THOO zuh luh) Tree—is still alive.

The Methuselah Tree is a living history book. Its rings tell a story about volcanic eruptions, drought, and forest fires. A tree's growth appears as a series of rings or layers in the cross section of the tree's trunk. By studying these rings, scientists are able to learn about the changes in the climate that occurred during the life of the tree.

Social Studies ACTiViTY

Research the major events have happened in the lifetime of the Methuselah Tree. Make a timeline that shows these events. Include your work in your **Science Journal.**

Science, Technology, and Society

Plant Poachers

Imagine that you are walking through a swamp. The swamp is full of life. You are surrounded by trees, vines, and water lilies. You can hear frogs singing and mosquitoes buzzing. Then, you notice a ghost orchid hanging from a tree branch. The flower of this orchid looks like a ghost or like a white frog leaping. For some people, this orchid is worth stealing. These people, called *plant poachers,* steal orchids and other plants from the wild. Many plant species and natural areas are threatened by plant theft.

Math ACTiViTY

A plant poacher stole 100 plants from a nature preserve. The poacher planned to sell each plant for $50 but was caught and fined $300 for each stolen plant. What is the difference between the total fine and the total amount of money the plant poacher would have made by selling the plants? Record your work in your **Science Journal.**

Answer to Social Studies Activity

Students' timelines may include the following world events: the building of the Great Cheops Pyramid in Giza; the founding and fall of Rome; the beginnings of democracy in Athens; the beginnings of Christianity, Buddhism, and Islam; the teachings of Confucius; the building of the Great Wall of China; the Persian Wars; and the fall of the Greek empire.

Answer to Math Activity

$25,000 (100 × $50 = $5,000; 100 × $300 = $30,000; $30,000 − $5,000 = $25,000)

Paul Cox

Ethnobotanist Paul Cox is an ethnobotanist. He travels to remote places to look for plants that can help treat diseases. He seeks the advice of native healers in his search. In Samoan cultures, the healer is one of the most valued members of the community. In 1984, Cox met a 78-year-old Samoan healer named Epenesa. Epenesa understood human anatomy, and she dispensed medicines with great accuracy.

After Cox spent months observing Epenesa, she gave him her treatment for yellow fever. Cox brought the yellow-fever remedy to the United States. In 1986, researchers at the National Cancer Institute found that the plant contains a virus-fighting chemical called *prostratin,* which may have potential as a treatment for AIDS.

When two of the Samoan healers that Cox observed died in 1993, generations of medical knowledge was lost with them. The healers' deaths show the urgency of recording this knowledge before all of the healers are gone. Cox and other ethnobotanists work hard to gather knowledge from healers before their knowledge is lost.

Language Arts ACTIVITY

Imagine that you are a healer. Write a letter to an ethnobotanist describing some of the plants you use to treat diseases. Record your work in your **Science Journal.**

Internet Resources

- To learn more about careers in science, visit **www.scilinks.org** and enter the SciLinks code HY70225.
- To learn more about these Science in Action topics, visit go.hrw.com and type in the keyword HY7PL1F.
- Check out articles related to this chapter by visiting go.hrw.com. Just type in the keyword HY7PL1C.

Careers

Background

Some biologists estimate that there are 235,000 species of flowering plants in the world. Of these, less than half of 1% have been studied for their potential medicinal properties. Because there are so many plant species, ethnobotanists need efficient strategies to find the plants that are most likely to have medicinal value. One strategy used by ethnobotanists is to assume that if native people use a local plant for medicine, then the plant probably has some medicinal value. Many ethnobotanists seek out native healers or shamans. In doing so, ethnobotanists hope to acquire the knowledge that the healers or shamans have accumulated over the years. With this knowledge, the researchers can then decide which plants they should collect and study.

Some of the most useful drugs developed from plants used by indigenous peoples include aspirin, which reduces pain and inflammation; codeine, which decreases pain and suppresses coughs; and quinine, which combats malaria.

Answer to Language Arts Activity

In their letters, students should demonstrate an understanding of how important native healers are to ethnobotanists. Students should also demonstrate an understanding of the fact that although native cultures may seem primitive, the knowledge that many native healers have is actually very sophisticated. In some cases, this knowledge may rival that of modern medicine.

The elements listed in the Standards Course of Study provide a base for presenting, supporting, and assessing the California Grade 7 Science Standards. Use this Standards Course of Study as a base for planning your lessons.

Why Teach
Plant Processes

This chapter was designed to cover the California Grade 7 Science Standards about plant processes (7.1.b, 7.1.d, 7.1.f, 7.2.a, 7.5.a, and 7.5.f). It follows a chapter that introduced the variety and importance of plants. This chapter describes plant processes, such as photosynthesis, which have shaped life on Earth.

After they have completed this chapter, students will begin a chapter about animals.

 California Standards

Focus on Life Sciences

7.1.b Students know the characteristics that distinguish plant cells from animal cells, including chloroplasts and cell walls.

7.1.d Students know that mitochondria liberate energy for the work that cells do and that chloroplasts capture sunlight energy for photosynthesis.

7.1.f Students know that as multicellular organisms develop, their cells differentiate.

7.2.a Students know the differences between the life cycles and reproduction methods of sexual and asexual organisms.

7.5.a Students know plants and animals have levels of organization for structure and function, including cells, tissues, organs, organ systems, and the whole organism.

7.5.f Students know the structures and processes by which flowering plants generate pollen, ovules, seeds, and fruit.

Investigation and Experimentation

7.7.a Select and use appropriate tools and technology (including calculators, computers, balances, spring scales, microscopes, and binoculars) to perform tests, collect data, and display data.

7.7.c Communicate the logical connection among hypotheses, science concepts, tests conducted, data collected, and conclusions drawn from the scientific evidence.

Chapter Pacing

Getting Started
The Big Idea Like all living things, plants need nourishment, reproduce, and respond to stimuli.

 45 min
pp. 394–395

 7.1.f, 7.5.a

Section ❶ Photosynthesis
Key Concept Plants make food during photosynthesis and use the energy in the food during cellular respiration.

 60 min
pp. 396–399

7.1.b, 7.1.d, 7.7.c

Section ❷ Reproduction of Flowering Plants
Key Concept Flowering plants reproduce sexually and asexually.

 60 min
pp. 400–403

 7.2.a, 7.5.f, 7.7.c

Section ❸ Plant Development and Responses
Key Concept Plants develop differently than animals do. Also, plants respond to stimuli in a variety of ways.

 60 min
pp. 404–409

 7.1.f, 7.5.a

Wrapping Up

 180 min
pp. 410–419

 7.1.b, 7.1.d, 7.7.a, 7.7.c

Basic Learners	Advanced Learners/GATE
TE Types of Data, p. 412	TE Asexual Reproduction, p. 403
Reinforcement Worksheet	TE Displaying Data, p. 412
Chapter Test A	Critical Thinking Worksheet
Differentiated Datasheets A for Labs and Activities ■	Chapter Test C
Study Guide A ■	Differentiated Datasheets C for Labs and Activities ■

Key

SE Student Edition
TE Teacher's Edition

📄 Chapter Resource File
📓 Workbook
📰 Transparency

💿 CD or CD-ROM
* Datasheet or blackline master available

■ Also available in Spanish

All resources listed below are also available on the One-Stop Planner.

Teach

SE Explore Activity Observing Structure and Function in Plants, p. 395* ■

📰 **Bellringer**
💿 **PowerPoint® Resources**
📰 L55 Structure of Chloroplast
📰 L56 Photosynthesis
📰 L57 Gas Exchange in Plants
SE Quick Lab Measuring Gas Exchange in Plants, p. 398* ■

📰 **Bellringer**
💿 **PowerPoint® Resources**
📰 L58 Pollination and Fertilization
📰 L59 Seed Production
📰 L60 Three Structures for Asexual Reproduction
SE Quick Lab Plant Cuttings, p. 402* ■

📰 **Bellringer**
💿 **PowerPoint® Resources**
📰 L61 African Violet Leaf and Cell Differentiation
SE Quick Lab Observing the Effects of Ethylene, p. 405* ■

SE Skills Practice Lab Food Factory Waste, pp. 410–411* ■

Practice

SE Organize Activity Booklet, p. 394

SE Section Review, p. 399* ■

SE Section Review, p. 403* ■

SE Section Review, p. 409* ■

SE Science Skills Activity Selecting Tools to Display Data, p. 412* ■
📰 **Concept Mapping***
SE Chapter Review, pp. 414–415* ■

Assess

📄 **Chapter Pretest**

SE Standards Checks, pp. 396, 399
TE Standards Focus, p. 398
📄 **Section Quiz** ■

SE Standards Checks, pp. 400, 401, 402
TE Standards Focus, p. 402
📄 **Section Quiz** ■

SE Standards Checks, pp. 404, 406, 407
TE Standards Focus, p. 408
📄 **Section Quiz** ■

SE Standards Assessment, pp. 416–417*
📄 **Chapter Tests A, B ■, C**
📓 **Standards Review Workbook** ■

Resources for Universal Access • Differentiated Instruction

English Learners

TE Using the Figure, pp. 397, 407
TE Food Chains, p. 399
TE Demonstration, pp. 400, 404
TE Group Activity, p. 405
📄 Vocabulary and Section Summary A ■, B
📄 Section Quizzes ■
📄 Chapter Tests A, B ■
📄 Differentiated Datasheets A, B, and C for Labs and Activities ■
📓 Study Guide A ■
📓 Multilingual Glossary

Struggling Readers

TE Reading Strategy, p. 400
TE Plant Reading, p. 408

Special Education Students

TE Photosynthesis Summary, p. 396
TE Seeds and Fruits, p. 401
TE Plants Terms, p. 404
TE Plant Acts, p. 406
TE Data Tables, p. 413

To help plan your lessons, refer to the On Course Mapping Instruction booklet.

Visual Resources

CHAPTER STARTER TRANSPARENCY

BELLRINGER TRANSPARENCIES

TEACHING TRANSPARENCIES

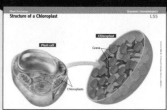

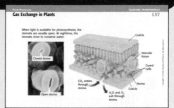

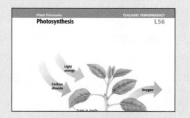

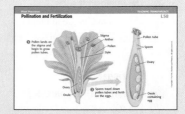

TEACHING TRANSPARENCIES

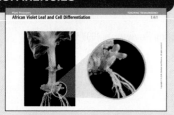

STANDARDS REVIEW TRANSPARENCIES

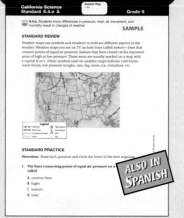

CONCEPT MAPPING TRANSPARENCY

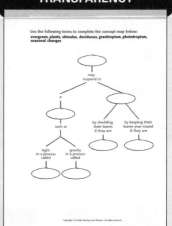

Planning Resources

PARENT LETTER

Dear Parent,

Your son's or daughter's science class will soon begin exploring the chapter entitled "The Nature of Physical Science." In this chapter, students will learn about how the scientific method applies to the world of physical science and the role of physical science in the world. By the end of the chapter, students should demonstrate a clear understanding of the chapter's main ideas and be able to discuss the following topics:

1. the role of questions in the process of investigation (Section 1)
2. how applying science saves lives and benefits the environment (Section 1)
3. careers that rely on science (Section 1)
4. the steps used in scientific methods (Section 2)
5. how scientific methods are used to answer questions and solve problems (Section 2)
6. the importance of safety precautions in the laboratory (Section 3)
7. examples of safety equipment and when to use them (Section 3)
8. how safety symbols are used to make laboratories safer (Section 3)

Questions to Ask Along the Way

You can help your child learn about these topics by asking interesting questions as he or she progresses through the chapter. For example, you may wish to ask your son or daughter the following questions:

What are surprising careers that rely on science?

What is a characteristic of a good hypothesis?

What is the first step to take if an accident happens?

TEST ITEM LISTING

One-Stop Planner® CD-ROM

This CD-ROM package includes all of the resources shown here and the following time-saving tools:

- **Lab Materials QuickList Software**
- **Customizable Lesson Plans** Correlated to the California Science Standards
- **Holt Calendar Planner**
- **PowerPoint® Resources**

- **Printable Worksheets**
- **ExamView® Test Generator** Correlated to the California Science Standards
- **Holt PuzzlePro®**
- **Interactive Teacher's Edition**

Meeting Individual Needs

DIRECTED READING A

Skills Worksheet
Directed Reading A — SAMPLE

Section: Body Organization
A STABLE INTERNAL ENVIRONMENT

Write the letter of the correct answer in the space provided.

BASIC

ALSO IN SPANISH

DIRECTED READING B

Skills Worksheet
Directed Reading B — SAMPLE

Section: Body Organization
A STABLE INTERNAL ENVIRONMENT

1. The maintenance of a stable internal environment in the body is

CELLS, TISSUES, AND ORGANS

GENERAL

VOCABULARY AND SECTION SUMMARY A

Skills Worksheet
Vocabulary and Section Summary A — SAMPLE

Body Organization

your own words, write a definition of the following terms.

BASIC

ALSO IN SPANISH

VOCABULARY AND SECTION SUMMARY B

Skills Worksheet
Vocabulary and Section Summary B — SAMPLE

Body Organization
VOCABULARY

After you finish reading the section, try this puzzle! Use the clues given to fill in the blanks below. Then, copy the numbered letters into the corresponding boxes on the following page to reveal the four kinds of tissue.

1. the maintenance of a stable environment inside the body

2. a type of cell that has unique structures specialized to perform specific functions

GENERAL

REINFORCEMENT

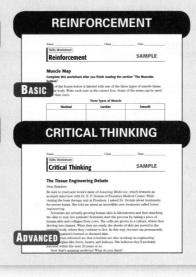

Skills Worksheet
Reinforcement — SAMPLE

Muscle Map
Complete this worksheet after you finish reading the section "The Muscular System."

of the bones below is labeled with one of the three types of muscle tissue body. Write each note in the correct box. Some of the notes can be used than once.

Three Types of Muscle		
Skeletal	Cardiac	Smooth

BASIC

CRITICAL THINKING

Skills Worksheet
Critical Thinking — SAMPLE

The Tissue Engineering Debate

Dear Readers:

Be sure to read next week's issue of *Amazing Medicine*, which features an in-depth interview with Dr. E. P. Dermis of Frontiers Medical Center. While visiting the burn therapy unit at Frontiers, I asked Dr. Dermis about treatments for severe burns. She told me about an incredible new treatment called *tissue engineering*.

Scientists are actually growing human skin in laboratories and then attaching the skin to real, live patients! Scientists start the process by taking a piece of human skin and collagen from cows. The cells are grown in a culture, where they develop into tissues. When they are ready, the sheets of skin are moved to the patient's body, where they continue to live. In this way, doctors can permanently patient's burned or diseased skin.

mis informed me that scientists are also working on engineering organs like livers, hearts, and kidneys. She believes they'll probably succeed within the next 20 years or so.

Now that's amazing medicine! What do you think?

ADVANCED

INTERACTIVE READER AND STUDY GUIDE

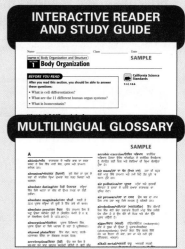

Name ___ Class ___ Date ___
CHAPTER 1 | Body Organization and Structure
Body Organization — SAMPLE

BEFORE YOU READ
After you read this section, you should be able to answer these questions:

• What is cell differentiation?
• What are the 11 different human organ systems?
• What is homeostasis?

California Science Standards 7.1.f, 7.5.b

MULTILINGUAL GLOSSARY

SAMPLE

A

Labs and Activities

DIFFERENTIATED DATASHEETS FOR EXPLORE ACTIVITY, QUICK LABS, AND CHAPTER LAB

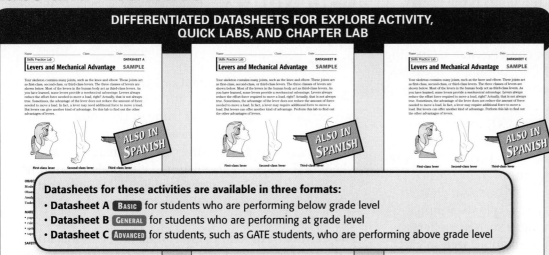

Skills Practice Lab — DATASHEET A
Levers and Mechanical Advantage — SAMPLE

Your skeleton contains many joints, such as the knee and elbow. These joints act as first-class, second-class, or third-class levers. The three classes of levers are shown below. Most of the levers in the human body act as third-class levers. As you have learned, some levers provide a mechanical advantage. Levers always reduce the effort force needed to move a load, right? Actually, that is not always true. Sometimes, the advantage of the lever does not reduce the amount of force needed to move a load. In fact, a lever may require additional force to move a load. But levers can offer another kind of advantage. Do this lab to find out the other advantages of levers.

First-class lever   Second-class lever   Third-class lever

ALSO IN SPANISH

OBJE
Mod
Obse
Anal
Unde

MATE
• pap
• rule
• spri
• tape

SAFET

Skills Practice Lab — DATASHEET B
Levers and Mechanical Advantage — SAMPLE

Your skeleton contains many joints, such as the knee and elbow. These joints act as first-class, second-class, or third-class levers. The three classes of levers are shown below. Most of the levers in the human body act as third-class levers. As you have learned, some levers provide a mechanical advantage. Levers always reduce the effort force required to move a load, right? Actually, that is not always true. Sometimes, the advantage of the lever does not reduce the amount of force needed to move a load. In fact, a lever may require additional force to move a load. But levers can offer another kind of advantage. Perform this lab to find out the other advantages of levers.

First-class lever   Second-class lever   Third-class lever

ALSO IN SPANISH

Skills Practice Lab — DATASHEET C
Levers and Mechanical Advantage — SAMPLE

Your skeleton contains many joints, such as the knee and elbow. These joints act as first-class, second-class, or third-class levers. The three classes of levers are shown below. Most of the levers in the human body act as third-class levers. As you have learned, some levers provide a mechanical advantage. Levers always reduce the effort force required to move a load, right? Actually, that is not always true. Sometimes, the advantage of the lever does not reduce the amount of force needed to move a load. In fact, a lever may require additional force to move a load. But levers can offer another kind of advantage. Perform this lab to find out the other advantages of levers.

First-class lever   Second-class lever   Third-class lever

ALSO IN SPANISH

> **Datasheets for these activities are available in three formats:**
> • **Datasheet A** BASIC for students who are performing below grade level
> • **Datasheet B** GENERAL for students who are performing at grade level
> • **Datasheet C** ADVANCED for students, such as GATE students, who are performing above grade level

DATASHEET FOR SCIENCE SKILLS ACTIVITY

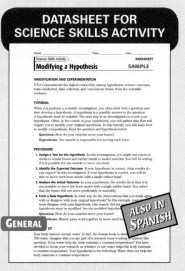

Science Skills Activity — DATASHEET
Modifying a Hypothesis — SAMPLE

INVESTIGATION AND EXPERIMENTATION
7.7.c Communicate the logical connection among hypotheses, science concepts, tests conducted, data collected, and conclusions drawn from the scientific evidence.

TUTORIAL
When you perform a scientific investigation, you often start with a question and then develop a hypothesis. A hypothesis is a possible answer to the question. A hypothesis must be testable. The next step in an investigation is to test your hypothesis. Often, in the course of your experiment, you will gather data that will require you to modify your original hypothesis. In this tutorial, you will learn how to modify a hypothesis. But the question and hypothesis below.

Question: How do muscles move your bones?
Hypothesis: One muscle is responsible for moving each bone.

PROCEDURE

1. **Design a Test for the Hypothesis** In this investigation, you might use rulers or sticks to model bones and rubber bands to model muscles. You will be testing if it is possible for one muscle to move one bone.

2. **Identify the Expected Outcome** If your hypothesis is correct, what results do you expect? In this investigation, if your hypothesis is correct, you will be able to move each bone model with a single rubber band.

3. **Analyze the Actual Outcome** In your experiment, the results show that it is not possible to move the bone model with a single rubber band. You notice that the bone will not move predictably or smoothly.

4. **Form a New Hypothesis** In what way do the observations that you made agree with or disagree with your original hypothesis? In this example, your observations disagree with your hypothesis. One muscle did not move the bone, so your hypothesis must be modified. See the modified hypothesis

Question: How do your muscles move your bones?
Hypothesis: Muscle pairs work together to move each bone

ALSO IN SPANISH

IT!

Your body tissues contain water. In fact, the human body is made 70% water. Imagine that you are part of a research team working to answer this question: Does water help the body maintain a constant temperature? You have decided to focus your research on whether or not water helps the body maintain a constant temperature. Your hypothesis is the following: Water does not help the body maintain a constant temperature.

GENERAL

Reviews and Assessments

SECTION REVIEWS

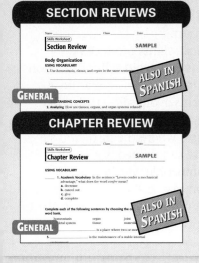

Skills Worksheet
Section Review — SAMPLE

Body Organization
USING VOCABULARY

1. Use *homeostasis*, *tissue*, and *organ* in the same sentence.

ALSO IN SPANISH

ANDING CONCEPTS

2. **Analyzing** How are tissues, organs, and organ systems related?

GENERAL

CHAPTER REVIEW

Skills Worksheet
Chapter Review — SAMPLE

USING VOCABULARY

1. **Academic Vocabulary** In the sentence "Levers confer a mechanical advantage," what does the word *confer* mean?
a. decrease
b. cancel out
c. give
d. complete

Complete each of the following sentences by choosing the co___ word bank.

homeostasis   organ   joint
letal system   tissue   muscle

3. ___ is a place where two or more ___

GENERAL

ALSO IN SPANISH

CHAPTER PRETEST

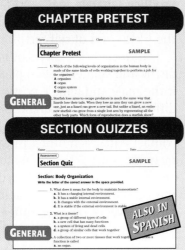

Assessment
Chapter Pretest — SAMPLE

ly Organization and Structure

1. Which of the following levels of organization in the human body is made of the same kinds of cells working together to perform a job for the organism?
A organism
B organ
C organ system
D tissue

Starfish lose arms to escape predators in much the same way that lizards lose their tails. When they lose an arm they can grow a new one, just as a lizard can grow a new tail. But unlike a lizard, an entire new starfish can grow from a single lost arm by regenerating all the other body parts. Which form of reproduction does a starfish show?

GENERAL

SECTION QUIZZES

Assessment
Section Quiz — SAMPLE

Section: Body Organization
Write the letter of the correct answer in the space provided.

1. What does it mean for the body to maintain homeostasis?
a. It has a changing internal environment.
b. It has a stable internal environment.
c. It changes with the external environment.
d. It is stable if the external environment is stable

2. What is a tissue?
a. a group of different types of cells
b. a new cell that has many functions
c. a system of living and dead cells
d. a group of similar cells that work together

ALSO IN SPANISH

GENERAL

CHAPTER TEST A

Assessment
Chapter Test A — SAMPLE

ly Organization and Structure
MULTIPLE CHOICE

Write the letter of the correct answer in the space provided.

BASIC

CHAPTER TEST B

Assessment
Chapter Test B — SAMPLE

Organization and Structure
MULTIPLE CHOICE

Write the letter of the correct answer in the space provided.

GENERAL

ALSO IN SPANISH

CHAPTER TEST C

Assessment
Chapter Test C — SAMPLE

Organization and Structure

USING KEY TERMS

Use the terms from the following list to complete the sentences below. Each term may be used once only. Some terms may not be used.

lever   ligaments   tendons
epithelial   mechanical advantage   connective
cardiac   skeletal

1. In the body, the joint serves as fulcrum, and the bone is a(n)

ADVANCED

STANDARDS ASSESSMENT

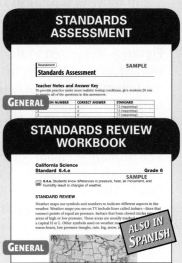

Assessment
Standards Assessment — SAMPLE

Teacher Notes and Answer Key
To provide practice under more realistic testing conditions, give students 20 min to answer all of the questions in this assessment.

ON NUMBER	CORRECT ANSWER	STANDARD
	A	7.5 (supporting)
3	A	7.6 (supporting)
3	B	7.5 (supporting)

GENERAL

STANDARDS REVIEW WORKBOOK

California Science Standard 6.4.e — Grade 6

6.4.e. Students know differences in pressure, heat, air movement, and humidity result in changes of weather.

STANDARD REVIEW

Weather maps use symbols and numbers to indicate different aspects in the weather. Weather maps you see on TV include lines called *isobars*—lines that connect points of equal air pressure. Isobars that form closed circles represent areas of high or low pressure. These areas are usually marked with a capital H or L. Other symbols used on weather maps warm fronts, low pressure troughs, rain, fog, snow, s

GENERAL

ALSO IN SPANISH

This Teacher Background explains science concepts, principles, and theories that appear in the chapter. Use the information on these pages to refresh or enhance your understanding of the topics covered.

Section 1

Photosynthesis

Saving Water During Photosynthesis

The first set of photosynthetic reactions require water, which is split to provide electrons to the electron transport chain. The electron transport chain begins when sunlight excites electrons within chlorophyll molecules into a higher energy state. A chain of reactions produces a concentration gradient of protons, which drives the synthesis of ATP. This molecule, along with NADPH (formed in the electron chain reactions) is the energy source used to combine carbon atoms from CO_2 into organic compounds, such as glucose.

In hot weather, plants must conserve water. Opening the stomata lets in the needed CO_2, but it also releases water vapor. To adapt to photosynthesis in hot and/or arid conditions, many warm region plants create a four-carbon compound at relatively low CO_2 concentrations instead of forming the typical six-carbon compound of the standard photosynthetic pathway. Because this process requires less carbon, the stomata can be opened for shorter periods, thus saving water. Plants that create the four-carbon compounds are called C_4 plants. Familiar C_4 plants include warm weather grasses such as crabgrass, corn, and sugar cane. Another adaptation, seen in cacti, is to open the stomata only at night.

Absorption and Pigments

In order to capture as much energy from the light spectrum as possible, chloroplasts contain a number of pigments within the individual disks of the grana. Use **Figure A** to explain to students that grana look like stacked coins. These "coins" are actually stacks of thylakoid membranes and it is these membranes which contain pigments. Each different kind of pigment within the thylakoid membranes absorbs a certain portion of the light spectrum and reflects non-absorbed wavelengths. The primary pigment is chlorophyll a, which absorbs light in the red and blue-violet wavelengths and reflects green. Although chlorophyll a is the only pigment directly involved in photosynthesis, other pigments, known as accessory pigments, contribute the energy they absorb to chlorophyll a. Chlorophyll b, for example,

absorbs blue-green light. The carotenoids are yellow, orange, and brown pigments that absorb green light. These accessory pigments are masked in healthy leaves, but may be visible in fruits or in leaves in which chlorophyll a has broken down.

Figure A *Chloroplasts consist of an outer membrane and stacks of inner membranes that form grana.*

Section 2

Reproduction of Flowering Plants

Flower Morphology

Flowers are plant adaptations that increase the likelihood of out-crossing. Unlike self-fertilization, out-crossing is reproduction through the combination of an egg and sperm from *two* individuals. Out-crossing produces greater genetic diversity and increases the likelihood of species survival in a changing environment.

Angiosperms have several other adaptations that further increase the likelihood of out-crossing. Dioecious (from the Greek for "two houses") plants show one such adaptation. In dioecious species, such as willows, an individual plant produces only male (staminate) or only female (pistillate) flowers. So, fertilization in dioecious plants always involves at least two individuals. Similarly, some monoecious species, including oaks and birches, produce separate male and female flowers on the same plant. The distance between the flowers helps decrease the likelihood of self-fertilization.

However, the flowers of most plants produce both pistils and stamens. Such plants can avoid self-fertilization if the male and female portions of the flower mature at different rates. Some angiosperms avoid self-fertilization by producing anthers and stigmas that cannot come in contact with each other. In cases where the pistil and stamen of complete flowers mature simultaneously, the ova and sperm are genetically incompatible within flowers of the same individual. Pollination may still occur within the same flower or between different flowers on the same plant, but viable seeds do not develop.

Pollen Grains

The pollen grain, which is the male gametophyte, or microgametophyte, contains just two cells: the generative cell and the tube cell. The generative cell divides to become two sperm cells. When the pollen grain germinates, the tube cell causes the pollen tube to grow through the style to deliver the two sperm cells to the ovule, as shown in **Figure B.**

Use this figure to help students understand the difference between pollination and fertilization. Pollination is the transfer of pollen from anthers to stigmas. However, fertilization cannot occur until the tube cell grows through the style and the sperm cells reach the ovules. One of the sperm cells fertilizes the egg, while the other sperm cell is involved in forming the endosperm, or nutrient storage tissue for the seed.

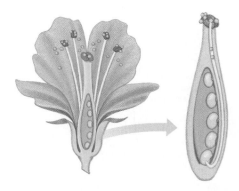

Figure B *Pollen grains contain sperm cells that fertilize eggs within a stigma.*

Ovules and Double Fertilization

At maturity, the angiosperm ovule contains the embryo sac. This structure, which is the female gametophyte, or mega-gametophyte, contains eight nuclei plus seven cells. Two of the nuclei, found near the center of the central cell and known as the polar nuclei, receive one of the sperm from the pollen grain. This union produces a $3n$ (containing three sets of chromosomes) cell that develops into the large endosperm tissue that the developing embryo will use. Of the remaining six cells in the ovule, only one is fertilized as the egg; the others break down once one egg is fertilized. Because there are two cell fusions (the fertilizations of the central cells and the egg cell), the process is considered a double fertilization. This process is unique to angiosperms.

Seed Dormancy

Dormancy (from *dormire*, Latin for "to sleep") is an important survival adaptation in which the developing embryo is prevented from further growth. The resumption of growth and development is called germination. Many plant seeds must experience a period of cold before they can germinate. This exposure to cold, called *stratification*, ensures that a newly mature seed will not germinate in the fall, when approaching winter temperatures could kill the seedling. Other seeds have a thick seed coat that will not allow water to penetrate until damaged by the acid of an animal's digestive system. This specialized coat helps ensure dispersal, and the animal's feces ensure a nutrient-rich germination site.

Under dry conditions, some dormant seeds can remain viable for decades, even centuries. Dormancy is broken when enzymes become activated within the seed and convert stored starches into simple sugars for the developing embryo.

Section 3
Plant Development and Responses

Hormones and Differentiation

Knowledge of the effects of plant hormones on cell differentiation has allowed researchers and plant breeders to take advantage of plant cell *totipotency,* or the ability of a single cell to provide all the genetic information needed to develop into an entire individual. Breeders have used hormones to propagate genetically manipulated plants with unique features as well as certain rare plants that are difficult to breed. Plants produced in this way are genetic replicas, or clones, of the parent plant from which tissue samples were taken.

Breeders have employed several methods with the same result. In one method, they apply the plant hormone cytokinin to unorganized parenchyma tissue (called *callus*) to cause shoots to develop. They then treat these shoots with the hormone auxin to cause root tissue to develop. The new plant structures respond to light (phototropism) and gravity (gravitropism) and quickly organize themselves into tiny plants, which can then be transferred to soil.

13 Chapter Preview

Chapter Preview

📁 Chapter Pretest
Use the Chapter Pretest in the Chapter Resource File to determine the prior knowledge of your students. The Test Doctors and diagnostic teaching tips in the Teacher Notes pages will help you tailor your instruction to your students' specific needs.

Improving Comprehension

Use the Graphic Organizer on this page of the Student Edition to introduce the topics that are covered in this chapter, to summarize the chapter material, or to show students how to make an idea wheel.

Teaching Tips

• Explain to students that an idea wheel is most useful when the categories contain details that are not analogous or when the details require more space than other classification organizers permit.

• Explain to students that an idea wheel is useful for organizing topics that include figurative details, such as sketches, equations, and graphs.

LS Logical

Improving Comprehension

Graphic Organizers are important visual tools that can help you organize information and improve your reading comprehension. The Graphic Organizer below is called an *idea wheel*. Instructions for creating other types of Graphic Organizers are located in the **Study Skills** section of the Appendix.

How to Make an Idea Wheel

❶ Draw a circle. Draw a larger circle around the first circle. Divide the ring between the circles into sections by drawing lines from one circle to the other across the ring. Divide the ring into as many sections as you want.

❷ Write a main idea or topic in the smaller circle. Label each section in the ring with a category or characteristic of the main idea.

❸ In each section of the ring, include details that are unique to the topic.

When to Use an Idea Wheel

An idea wheel is an effective type of visual organization in which ideas in science can be divided into categories or parts. It is also a useful way to illustrate characteristics of a main idea or topic. As you read, look for topics that are divided into ideas or categories, that can be organized around an idea wheel.

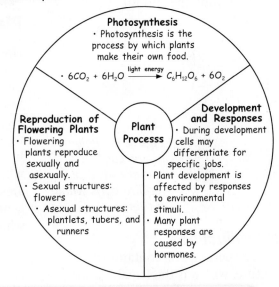

Photosynthesis
• Photosynthesis is the process by which plants make their own food.
• $6CO_2 + 6H_2O \xrightarrow{\text{light energy}} C_6H_{12}O_6 + 6O_2$

Plant Process

Development and Responses
• During development cells may differentiate for specific jobs.
• Plant development is affected by responses to environmental stimuli.
• Many plant responses are caused by hormones.

Reproduction of Flowering Plants
• Flowering plants reproduce sexually and asexually.
• Sexual structures: flowers
• Asexual structures: plantlets, tubers, and runners

You Try It!

This Reading Strategy can also be used within the chapter that you are about to read. Practice making your own *idea wheel* as directed in the Reading Strategies for Section ❷ and Section ❸. Record your work in your **Science Journal.**

Using Other Graphic Organizers

Students can practice using a variety of Graphic Organizers while reading this chapter. The following Graphic Organizers may also be useful in this chapter:

A **concept map** can be used to show the connections between concepts relating to photosynthesis, discussed in Section 1.

A **process chart** can be used to show the process of fertilization, described in Section 2.

A **cause-and-effect map** can be used to show how environmental stimuli affect the production and role of hormones in plants, discussed in Section 3.

Instructions for creating these Graphic Organizers are located on pp. 583–591 of the Appendix.

Unpacking the Standards

The information below "unpacks" the standards by breaking them down into basic parts. The higher-level, academic vocabulary is highlighted and defined to help you understand the language of the standards. "What It Means" restates the standards as simply as possible.

Unpacking the Standards

Use the following information with the *What It Means* in the Student Edition to help students understand why studying each standard is important.

California Standard	Academic Vocabulary	What It Means	Why It Matters
7.1.b Students know the characteristics that distinguish plant cells from animal cells, including chloroplasts and cell walls.		Plant cells have some unique structures that make plant cells different from animal cells. These structures include chloroplasts and a cell wall.	Plants and animals are the organisms with which people interact the most.
7.1.d Students know that mitochondria **liberate** energy for the work that cells do and that chloroplasts capture sunlight **energy** for photosynthesis.	**liberate** (LIB uhr AYT) to release; to set free **energy** (EN uhr jee) the capacity to do work	Mitochondria release energy from sugar to power the cell's life processes. Chloroplasts turn energy from the sun into sugars and oxygen.	To understand digestion and the need to eat and breathe at the macro level, students must understand where their food originates at a cellular level and how their cells make use of this food.
7.1.f Students know that as multicellular organisms develop, their cells **differentiate**.	**differentiate** (DIF uhr EN shee AYT) to become specialized in structure and function	As a living thing that is made of more than one cell grows, the structure of its cells change so that the cells perform specific jobs.	Differentiation allows multicellular organisms to accomplish the tasks of living efficiently. It also explains the presence of many types of cells.
7.2.a Students know the differences between the life **cycles** and reproduction **methods** of **sexual** and asexual organisms.	**cycle** (SIE kuhl) a repeating series of changes **method** (METH uhd) a way of doing something **sexual** (SEK shoo uhl) having to do with sex	You must know how the life cycles of living things that reproduce sexually differ from the life cycles of living things that reproduce asexually. You must also explain how these ways of reproducing differ.	Students should be aware of the variety of ways in which organisms reproduce.
7.5.a Students know plants and animals have levels of organization for **structure** and **function,** including cells, tissues, organs, organ systems, and the whole organism.	**structure** (STRUHK chuhr) the arrangement of the parts of a whole **function** (FUHNGK shuhn) use or purpose	Plants and animals are made of smaller parts which are organized by shape and purpose. These layers of organization include cells, tissues, organs, organ systems, and the whole organism.	Multicellular organisms, including humans, function because their cells are organized at many levels. Each subsequent level of organization has unique properties that the prior level of organization does not have.
7.5.f Students know the **structures** and **processes** by which flowering plants **generate** pollen, ovules, seeds, and fruit.	**process** (PRAH ses) a set of steps, events, or changes **generate** (JEN uhr AYT) to bring about; to produce	You must know the parts of flowering plants and the ways by which those parts make pollen, ovules, seeds, and fruit.	Most forms of life on Earth depend on plants to convert solar energy into a usable source of energy that supports life. Flowering plants are the most common type of plants on Earth.

Words with Multiple Meanings

Words that have both common and scientific meanings can be confusing to students. The following table identifies some of those words that are used in this chapter.

Term	Common meaning	Scientific meaning
product	something available for sale (for example, a computer product)	a substance that forms in a chemical reaction
reaction	a response to a stimulus	the process by which one or more substances change to produce one or more different substances

Practice Draw this table on the board. Fill in the words, but not the definitions. Have students write down what they think the words mean. Then, write the correct meanings of the words in the table on the board, and ask students to write sentences that demonstrate the meaning of each word. (Oxygen, a *product* of photosynthesis, is released and used by animals and plants to complete life processes. Photosynthesis is the *reaction* in which plants make their own food.)

Chapter Overview

Tell students that this chapter will help them learn about photosynthesis, reproduction in flowering plants, and plant responses to the environment. The chapter describes pollination, fertilization, asexual reproduction, and tropisms in plants.

MISCONCEPTION //// ALERT \\\\

Plant Food

Identify it! Students may think that plants do not use food to grow. Ask students, "How do plants grow?" Students may know that plants perform photosynthesis without realizing that plants depend on the food they make through the process.

Correct it! Tell students that plant cells, just like their own cells, need energy from glucose sugar to carry out all the cellular activities involved in living and growing. Tell students that the distinction between consumers (such as people) and producers (such as plants) is that consumers need to eat (consume) food for energy, while producers make (produce) their food. Explain that plants use carbon dioxide and water to make their food, and that they use oxygen to break down and use the food.

Assess it! Ask students to explain why plants need *both* carbon dioxide and oxygen. (Plants need carbon dioxide to make sugars during photosynthesis. Plants need oxygen to break down these sugars for energy during cellular respiration.)

13
Plant Processes

The Big Idea

Like all living things, plants need nourishment, reproduce, and respond to stimuli.

 California Standards

Focus on Life Sciences

7.1 All living organisms are composed of cells, from just one to many trillions, whose details usually are visible only through a microscope. (Sections 1 and 3)

7.2 A typical cell of any organism contains genetic instructions that specify its traits. Those traits may be modified by environmental influences. (Section 2)

7.5 The anatomy and physiology of plants and animals illustrate the complementary nature of structure and function. (Sections 2 and 3)

Investigation and Experimentation

7.7 Scientific progress is made by asking meaningful questions and conducting careful investigations. (Science Skills Activity)

Math

7.1.1 Algebra and Functions
7.1.2 Mathematical Reasoning

English–Language Arts

7.1.3 Reading
7.2.4 Writing

About the Photo

The plant in this photo is a Venus' flytrap. Those red and green spiny pads are its leaves. Like other plants, Venus' flytraps depend on photosynthesis to get energy. Unlike most plants, the Venus' flytrap gets important nutrients, such as nitrogen, by capturing and digesting insects or other small animals.

Organize

Booklet

Before you read this chapter, create the FoldNote entitled "Booklet." On the front cover, title the booklet "Plant processes." Label the pages of the booklet with "Photosynthesis," "Flowering plants," "Sexual reproduction," "Asexual reproduction," "Plant development," and "Tropism." As you read the chapter, write what you learn about each topic on the appropriate page of the booklet.

Instructions for creating FoldNotes are located in the Study Skills section on p. 580 of the Appendix.

 California Standards Alignment

Focus on Life Sciences

7.1.b Students know the characteristics that distinguish plant cells from animal cells, including chloroplasts and cell walls. **pp. 396, 399, 410–411, 414–416**

7.1.d Students know that mitochondria liberate energy for the work that cells do and that chloroplasts capture sunlight energy for photosynthesis. **pp. 396–399, 410–411, 414–416**

7.1.f Students know that as multicellular organisms develop, their cells differentiate. **pp. 395, 404, 407, 409, 414–416**

7.2.a Students know the differences between the life cycles and reproduction methods of sexual and asexual organisms. **pp. 400, 402–403, 414–417**

7.5.a Students know plants and animals have levels of organization for structure and function, including cells, tissues, organs, organ systems, and the whole organism. **pp. 395, 405–406, 409, 414–415, 417**

7.5.f Students know the structures and processes by which flowering plants generate pollen, ovules, seeds, and fruit. **pp. 400–403, 414–417**

Investigation and Experimentation

7.7.a Select and use appropriate tools and technology (including calculators, computers, balances, spring scales, microscopes, and binoculars) to perform tests, collect data, and display data. **p. 412**

7.7.c Communicate the logical connection among hypotheses, science concepts, tests conducted, data collected, and conclusions drawn from the scientific evidence. **pp. 398, 402, 410–411**

Students will investigate the direction of plant growth (covers standards 7.1.f, and 7.5.a). To minimize light's effect, students should rotate the cups every day. Be sure that students keep the paper towels moist throughout the activity. After the plants have grown for several days, have students turn their cups upside down to further emphasize the effect of gravity on plant growth.

Materials for Each Group
- corn seeds (5–6)
- cup, clear plastic, medium-sized
- marker
- paper towels
- water

Answers
6. Students should observe that the shoots of all the germinating seeds grow upward, or away from the force of gravity, no matter what the original orientation of the seeds was.

7. The shoots grew upward because plants grow away from the force of gravity.

 Differentiated Datasheets
A **BASIC**, B **GENERAL**, C **ADVANCED**

Also editable on the
**Holt Lab Generator
CD-ROM**

Explore Activity 🕙 10 min plus follow-up

Observing Structure and Function in Plants

If you plant seeds in such a way that their "tops" face different directions, will all of their stems grow upward? Do this activity to find the answer.

Procedure

1. Pack **slightly moistened paper towels** into a **clear, medium-sized plastic cup.**

2. Place **five or six corn seeds** between the side of the cup and the paper towels. Equally space the seeds around the cup. Point the tip of each seed in a different direction.

3. Use a **marker** to draw arrows on the outside of the cup to show the direction in which each seed tip is pointing.

4. Place the cup in a well-lit location for 1 week. Keep the seeds moist by adding **water** to the paper towels as needed.

5. After 1 week, observe the seeds. Record the direction in which each stem grew.

7.1.f
7.5.a

Analysis

6. In which direction did each of your shoots grow?

7. Why do you think that your stems grew in the direction that they did?

Math Standards

Algebra and Function 7.1.1 Use variables and appropriate operations to write an expression, an equation, an inequality, or a system of equations or inequalities that represents a verbal description (e.g., three less than a number, half as large as area A). **pp. 403, 409, 415**

Mathematical Reasoning 7.1.2 Formulate and justify mathematical conjectures based on a general description of the mathematical question or problem posed. **pp. 399, 407**

English–Language Arts Standards

Reading 7.1.3 Clarify word meaning through the use of definition, example, restatement, or contrast. **p. 396**

Writing 7.2.4 Write persuasive compositions which (a) State a clear position or perspective in support of a proposition or proposal; (b) Describe the points in support of the proposition, employing well-articulated evidence; (c) Anticipate and address reader concerns and counterarguments. **p. 415**

Strange but True!

📖 **Chapter Starter Transparency**
Use this transparency to help students begin thinking about plant processes.

SECTION 1

Preteach

Reviewing Prior Knowledge

Tell students that a main idea of this chapter is photosynthesis. Ask students to brainstorm words or phrases related to photosynthesis. Ask students to identify why the words they have chosen are related to photosynthesis.

 **Bellringer**

Ask students to focus on standard 7.1.d by answering the following questions: Where do you get the energy you need to stay alive? (Students will likely answer that they get their energy from the foods that they eat.) What organelle is responsible for releasing energy within your cells? (mitochondria) Do all organisms on Earth get their energy from the same source as you do? (All organisms except producers must consume food for energy. Producers are able to capture energy from the sun to make their own food. All organisms use mitochondria to release the energy in food.) **LS** Verbal

🗃 Bellringer Transparency

Motivate

Discussion

Food and Energy Before students begin reading this section, ask them the following questions:

Where do the animals that we eat get their energy? (Those animals eat plants or eat other animals that eat plants.) Where do plants get their energy? (Plants get energy from sunlight.) Explain to students that plants use sunlight energy to make their own food through *photosynthesis*. **LS** Verbal

Answer to Standards Check

The chloroplasts capture sunlight energy. This organelle is not found in animal cells. **7.1.b** (mastering), **7.1.d** (mastering)

SECTION 1

Photosynthesis

Key Concept Plants make food during photosynthesis and use the energy in the food during cellular respiration.

What You Will Learn

● Chloroplasts capture sunlight energy for photosynthesis.
● Photosynthesis is the process by which most plants make food.
● Mitochondria release the energy that cells use to do work.
● Cellular respiration allows living things, including plants, to use the products of photosynthesis.

Why It Matters

Most living things depend on the products of photosynthesis.

Vocabulary

• photosynthesis
• chlorophyll
• cellular respiration
• stoma
• transpiration

READING STRATEGY

Brainstorming The main idea of this section is that photosynthesis is a complicated but important process. Brainstorm words and phrases related to photosynthesis. Record your work in your **Science Journal.**

▶ Plants do not have lungs. But like you, plants need air. Air contains oxygen, carbon dioxide, and other gases. Your body needs oxygen, and plants need oxygen. But what other gas is important to plants?

If you guessed *carbon dioxide*, you are correct. Plants use carbon dioxide for photosynthesis. **Photosynthesis** is the process by which plants make their own food. Plants capture energy from sunlight during photosynthesis. This energy is used to make the sugar glucose, $C_6H_{12}O_6$, from carbon dioxide, CO_2, and water, H_2O.

Capturing Light Energy

Plant cells have organelles called *chloroplasts* (KLAWR uh PLASTS), shown in **Figure 1.** Chloroplasts are the parts of plant cells that capture energy from sunlight for photosynthesis. Two membranes surround each chloroplast. Inside the chloroplast, another membrane forms stacks called *grana* (GRAY nuh). Grana contain **chlorophyll,** a green pigment that absorbs light energy. Because it reflects the green wavelengths of sunlight, chlorophyll looks green. Every green part of a plant looks green because of the presence of chloroplasts and the pigment chlorophyll.

Standards Check What organelle captures energy from sunlight? Is this organelle present in animal cells? 🐘 **7.1.b, 7.1.d**

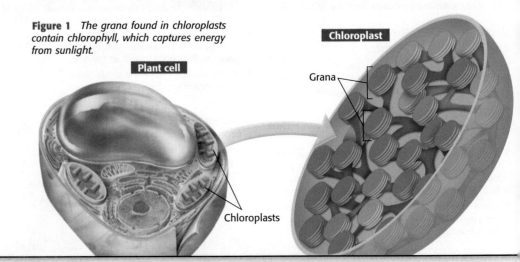

Figure 1 The grana found in chloroplasts contain chlorophyll, which captures energy from sunlight.

Plant cell

Chloroplast

Grana

Chloroplasts

Universal Access · Differentiated Instruction

Special Education Students

Photosynthesis Summary For some students, a reachable goal is to learn one main idea for each subheading. Help students with this process by discussing the information under each subheading and then writing a simple summary sentence on the board for them to copy and study. (Sample answers for Section 1: Photosynthesis is the way plants make food. Plants get energy from the sun to use in photosynthesis. Plants use the energy from the sun to make a kind of sugar. Plants then break down the sugar, use its energy and oxygen, and give off carbon dioxide and water during cellular respiration. Carbon dioxide, oxygen, and water move in and out of the plants, and when more water is lost through the leaves than enters the plant through the roots, the plant wilts. Animals get the oxygen their cells need because oxygen is a byproduct of photosynthesis.) **LS** Visual

Making Sugar

The light energy captured by chlorophyll is used to help form glucose molecules. Glucose is a simple sugar that plants use for food. In turn, plant cells give off oxygen gas, O_2. Photosynthesis is a complicated process made up of many steps. But it can be summarized by the following chemical equation:

$$6CO_2 + 6H_2O \xrightarrow{\text{light energy}} C_6H_{12}O_6 + 6O_2$$

Six molecules of carbon dioxide and six molecules of water are needed to form one molecule of glucose and six molecules of oxygen. **Figure 2** shows where plants get the materials for photosynthesis.

Getting Energy from Sugar

Glucose molecules store energy. Plant cells use this energy for their life processes. Mitochondria release the energy stored in glucose, which plant cells use to do work. To get energy, mitochondria in plant cells break down glucose and other food molecules in a process called **cellular respiration.** During this process, plant cells use oxygen and give off carbon dioxide and water. Excess glucose is converted into another sugar called *sucrose* or is stored as starch.

photosynthesis (FOHT oh SIN thuh sis) the process by which plants, algae, and some bacteria use sunlight, carbon dioxide, and water to make food

chlorophyll (KLAWR uh FIL) a green pigment that captures light energy for photosynthesis

cellular respiration (SEL yoo luhr RES puh RAY shuhn) the process by which cells use oxygen to produce energy from food

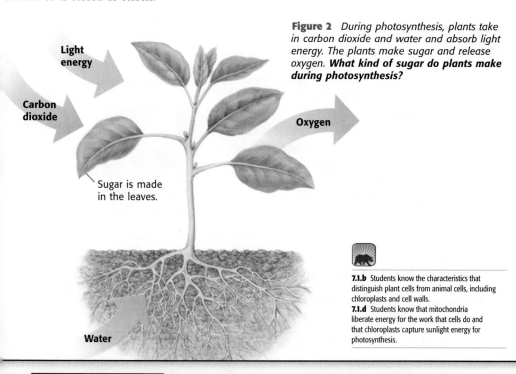

Figure 2 *During photosynthesis, plants take in carbon dioxide and water and absorb light energy. The plants make sugar and release oxygen.* **What kind of sugar do plants make during photosynthesis?**

Light energy

Carbon dioxide

Oxygen

Sugar is made in the leaves.

Water

7.1.b Students know the characteristics that distinguish plant cells from animal cells, including chloroplasts and cell walls.
7.1.d Students know that mitochondria liberate energy for the work that cells do and that chloroplasts capture sunlight energy for photosynthesis.

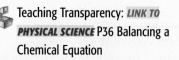
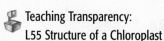
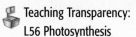

Standards Focus

This **Standards Focus** provides you with a quick way to **assess, reteach,** and **re-assess** one or more concepts in the section.

Assess

1. What molecules do plants use to make sugar? (carbon dioxide and water) **7.1.d**

2. What substances enter and exit through the stomata? (Carbon dioxide enters through the stomata. Oxygen and water exit through the stomata.) **7.1.b, 7.1.d**

3. Why is the oxygen that is a byproduct of photosynthesis so important? (Animals and plants use the oxygen produced by photosynthesis during cellular respiration.) **7.1.b, 7.1.d**

Reteach

Definitions Have students read the definitions of *photosynthesis, cellular respiration,* and *transpiration* aloud and then rewrite each definition in their own words.
LS Verbal **7.1.d**

Re-Assess

Guarding the Guard Cells
Have students imagine that it is their job to open and close the guard cells of the stomata. Ask them to describe the appearance and location of the guard cells, as well as the materials they let in and the materials they let out.
LS Verbal **7.1.d**

Teaching Transparency:
L57 Gas Exchange in Plants

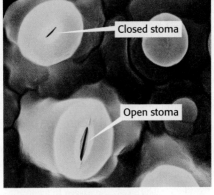

Figure 3 *When light is available for photosynthesis, the stomata are usually open. At nighttime, the stomata close to conserve water.*

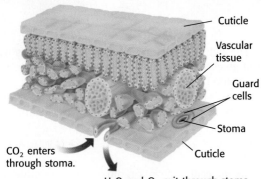

CO₂ enters through stoma.

H₂O and O₂ exit through stoma.

Cuticle
Vascular tissue
Guard cells
Stoma
Cuticle

stoma (STOH muh) one of many openings in a leaf or a stem of a plant that enable gas exchange to occur (plural, *stomata*)

transpiration (TRAN spuh RAY shuhn) the process by which plants release water vapor into the air through stomata

Gas Exchange

A waxy cuticle covers much of the above-ground outer surfaces of a plant. The cuticle protects the plant from water loss. How does a plant get carbon dioxide through this barrier? Carbon dioxide enters the plant's leaves through stomata (singular, *stoma*). A **stoma** is an opening in the epidermis and cuticle of a leaf. Each stoma is surrounded by two *guard cells.* The guard cells act like double doors by opening and closing the stoma. Stomata are shown in **Figure 3.**

When stomata are open, carbon dioxide enters the leaf. The oxygen produced during photosynthesis exits the leaf through the stomata. Water vapor also exits the leaf in this way. The loss of water through leaves is called **transpiration.** Most of the water absorbed by a plant's roots replaces the water lost during transpiration. Sometimes, the amount of water lost through a plant's leaves is greater than the amount of water absorbed by the plant's roots. As a result, the plant wilts.

Quick Lab

Measuring Gas Exchange in Plants

1. Obtain **4 jars** from your teacher. Label two of the jars with your last name and the letter *A.* Label the other 2 jars with your last name and the letter *B.*

2. Fill each jar with **bromothymol-blue (BTB) solution.**

3. Place a **small piece of elodea** in one of the jars labeled "A" and one of the jars labeled "B."

4. Carefully place the lids on the jars so that no air bubbles form.

5. Place the two jars labeled "A" in a dark place.

6. Place the two jars labeled "B" in a sunny place.

7. The next day, observe your jars. Record your observations.

8. When it turns yellow, BTB indicates the presence of carbon dioxide. Use this fact to explain what happened inside the jars.

9. What role did the jars without elodea play in this experiment?

7.1.d
7.7.c

⏱ **15 min plus follow-up**

Quick Lab

Teacher Notes

This activity has students investigate the gases released by plants (covers standards 7.1.d and 7.7.c). Make sure students do not have air bubbles trapped in their sealed jars. The bromothymol blue solution should not be too concentrated. It should be medium to light blue when students begin the experiment. *Elodea* is a rootless water plant available in aquarium or pet supply stores.

Materials for Each Group
• Bromothymol blue solution
• *Elodea,* small piece
• jars, with lids (4)

Safety Caution
Remind students to review all safety icons and cautions before beginning this activity.

The Importance of Photosynthesis

Plants and other photosynthetic organisms, such as some bacteria and many protists, form the base of nearly all food chains on Earth. An example of one food chain is shown in **Figure 4.** During photosynthesis, plants store light energy as chemical energy. Some animals use this chemical energy when they eat plants. Other animals get energy from plants indirectly. These animals eat animals that eat plants. Most organisms could not survive without photosynthetic organisms.

Plants, animals, and most other organisms depend on cellular respiration to get energy. Cellular respiration requires oxygen. Oxygen is a byproduct of photosynthesis. So, photosynthesis provides the oxygen that animals and plants need for cellular respiration.

Standards Check What are two ways in which the products of photosynthesis are important? **7.1.d**

Figure 4 *Mice depend on plants for food. In turn, cats get energy from mice.*

Answers to Section Review

1. Chloroplasts capture sunlight energy and perform photosynthesis. Mitochondria perform cellular respiration. **7.1.d** (mastering)

2. Photosynthesis produces glucose and oxygen. Oxygen is used during cellular respiration to release energy from glucose and other food molecules. **7.1.d** (exceeding)

3. Gases enter and exit plants through stomata. **7.1.d** (supporting)

4. Sample answer: The structure shown is a chloroplast. Without chloroplasts, cells would not be able to make their own food or produce oxygen gas. **7.1.b** (exceeding), **7.1.d** (mastering)

5. Answers may vary. Without photosynthetic organisms, many animals would starve. Also, without photosynthetic organisms there may not be enough oxygen available for cellular respiration.

6. Answers may vary. Animals cannot perform photosynthesis because they do not have chloroplasts and cannot capture sunlight energy. Animals rely on plants for food and oxygen. **7.1.b** (mastering)

7. 72 carbon dioxide molecules and 72 water molecules (6 × 12 = 72 molecules)

SECTION Review

7.1.b, 7.1.d

Summary

- Chloroplasts and mitochondria are important organelles in plant cells.

- During photosynthesis, plants use energy from sunlight, carbon dioxide, and water to make glucose and oxygen.

- Plants get energy from food by cellular respiration, which uses oxygen and releases carbon dioxide and water.

- Transpiration, or the loss of water through the leaves of plants, occurs when stomata are open.

Understanding Concepts

① **Describing** What do chloroplasts and mitochondria do?

② **Comparing** What is the relationship between cellular respiration and photosynthesis?

③ **Identifying** How do plants take in and give off gases?

Critical Thinking

INTERPRETING GRAPHICS Use the image below to answer the next question.

④ **Predicting Consequences** What would happen if the structure above was not present in plant cells?

⑤ **Predicting Consequences** Predict what might happen if plants and other photosynthetic organisms disappeared.

⑥ **Applying Concepts** Why are animals not able to perform photosynthesis? In what ways do animals depend on plants?

Math Skills

⑦ **Solving Problems** Plants use 6 carbon dioxide molecules and 6 water molecules to make 1 glucose molecule. How many carbon dioxide and water molecules are needed to make 12 glucose molecules?

Internet Resources

For a variety of links related to this chapter, go to www.scilinks.org
Topic: Photosynthesis
SciLinks code: HY71140

⚫ Section Review Standards Guide			
	Supporting	Mastering	Exceeding
7.1.b		6	4
7.1.d	3	1, 4	2

Universal Access · Differentiated Instruction

English Learners

Food Chains In English, ask students to write three examples of individual food chains that end with people. Tell students to begin by thinking of something they like to eat and to think backward to the sun. Tell them to make sure at least one of their food chains includes a minimum of three items other than people. (Sample answer: sun–plant–pond snail–fish–people) Have students share their food chains with the class. **LS Verbal**

Reviewing Prior Knowledge

Ask students to draw a series of pictures to show the life cycle of a flowering plant. Have students focus on the roles played by flowers, fruits, and seeds. Ask students to include captions to explain their drawings and the roles played by various plant parts.

 Bellringer

Have students focus on standard 7.5.f by completing the following sentences:

I think pollination occurs when ____.

I think fertilization occurs when ____.

(Sample answer: Pollination occurs when a pollen grain lands on the female flower parts (stigma). Fertilization occurs when a sperm unites with an egg.)

 Bellringer Transparency

Demonstration

Parts of a Flower Show students a variety of fresh flowers and ask them to compare the flowers. Point out the stamens, stigmas, petals, and sepals in each flower. Remove the petals and then shake the flower over paper. Ask students to identify the powder on the paper. (pollen) Explain that pollen contains the flower's male reproductive cells. (Pollen can stain skin and clothing. You may wish to wear protective gloves. Also, students may have allergies to pollen so be sure to inquire about student allergies.)
LS Visual

 Teaching Transparency:
L58 Pollination and Fertilization

SECTION 2

What You Will Learn

- After pollination, sexual reproduction in flowering plants occurs when an egg is fertilized by a sperm.
- Seeds form from fertilized ovules. The ovary of a flower becomes a fruit.
- In the proper conditions, seeds can sprout and develop into plants.
- Flowering plants can reproduce asexually.

Why It Matters

Flowering plants and their reproductive structures provide food for many organisms.

Vocabulary

- dormant

READING STRATEGY

Graphic Organizer In your **Science Journal**, create an Idea Wheel about the stages of sexual reproduction in a flowering plant.

7.2.a Students know the differences between the life cycles and reproduction methods of sexual and asexual organisms.

7.5.f Students know the structures and processes by which flowering plants generate pollen, ovules, seeds, and fruit.

Sexual reproduction in plants occurs when sperm found in pollen fertilizes an egg. **7.2.a** (mastering)

READING STRATEGY

Anticipation Guide Before students read this page, ask them to predict the difference between pollination and fertilization. Then, ask students to read the page to find out if their predictions were accurate.
LS Verbal

Reproduction of Flowering Plants

Key Concept   Flowering plants reproduce sexually and asexually.

▶ Imagine you are standing in a field of wildflowers. You're surrounded by bright colors and sweet fragrances. You can hear bees buzzing from flower to flower. Flowering plants are the largest and most diverse group of plants. Their success is partly due to their flowers. Flowers are structures for sexual reproduction. In sexual reproduction, an egg is fertilized by a sperm.

Fertilization

The fertilization of flowering plants takes place within the flower. *Pollination* occurs when pollen, which carries sperm, is moved from anthers to stigmas. Usually, wind or animals move pollen from one flower to another flower. After pollen lands on the stigma, a tube grows from each pollen grain. The tube grows through the style to an ovule. Ovules are found inside the ovary. Each ovule contains an egg. Sperm from the pollen grain move down the pollen tube and into an ovule. Fertilization occurs when a sperm fuses with the egg inside an ovule. **Figure 1** shows pollination and fertilization.

Standards Check   Describe sexual reproduction in plants. **7.2.a**

Figure 1   **Pollination and Fertilization**

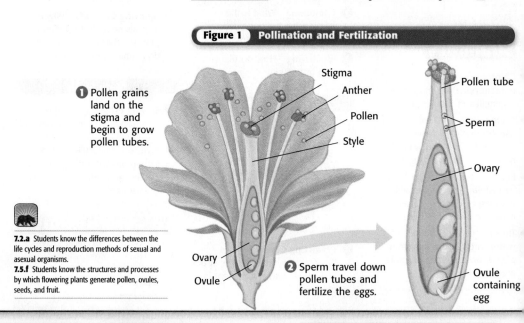

❶ Pollen grains land on the stigma and begin to grow pollen tubes.

Stigma
Anther
Pollen
Style
Ovary
Ovule

Pollen tube
Sperm
Ovary
Ovule containing egg

❷ Sperm travel down pollen tubes and fertilize the eggs.

 SCIENCE HUMOR

Q: What did the angry plant say to her parents?

A: Leaf me alone!

Figure 2 Seed Production

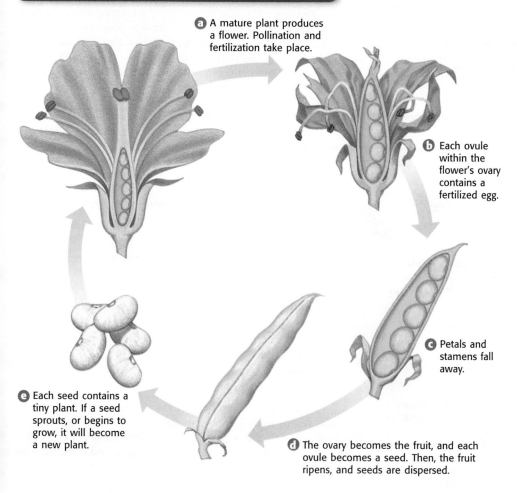

ⓐ A mature plant produces a flower. Pollination and fertilization take place.

ⓑ Each ovule within the flower's ovary contains a fertilized egg.

ⓒ Petals and stamens fall away.

ⓓ The ovary becomes the fruit, and each ovule becomes a seed. Then, the fruit ripens, and seeds are dispersed.

ⓔ Each seed contains a tiny plant. If a seed sprouts, or begins to grow, it will become a new plant.

From Flower to Fruit

After fertilization takes place, the ovule develops into a seed. The seed contains a tiny, undeveloped plant, called an *embryo*. The ovary surrounding the ovule becomes a fruit, as **Figure 2** shows.

As it swells and ripens, a fruit protects its developing seeds. **Figure 3** shows a common fruit. Fruits often help a plant spread its seeds. Many fruits are edible. Animals may eat these fruits. Then, the animals discard the seeds away from the parent plant. Fruits such as burrs are spread when they get caught in an animal's fur. And some fruits are carried by the wind.

Standards Check Where do seeds and fruit come from? 🐻 **7.5.f**

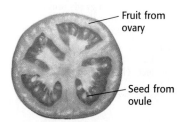

Fruit from ovary

Seed from ovule

Figure 3 *Tomatoes develop from a flower's ovary and ovules.*

Teach

CONNECTION ACTiViTY
Art

Flowers in Art Have students find examples of flowers and fruit created by artists and illustrators throughout time. You may want to show students reproductions of works by Pierre Redoute, Claude Monet, or Georgia O'Keefe to encourage their interest in this activity. Ask students to create their own fruit or flower art.

MISCONCEPTION ALERT

Not All Flowers are Perfect Students may think that all plants have flowers with all of the parts illustrated on the opening page of this section. Point out that this flower shows all of the parts for illustrative purposes. Show students examples of various flowers to demonstrate that some flowers lack petals or have colorful sepals instead of petals. In some plants, flowers have only male parts or only female parts.

Answer to Standards Check

Seeds come from fertilized eggs. Fruit form from the ovaries of flowers whose ovules have become fertilized.
7.5.f (mastering)

 Teaching Transparency:
L59 Seed Production

Universal Access • Differentiated Instruction

Special Education Students

Seeds and Fruits Some students have a difficult time making connections between what they see in textbooks and what they see in their daily lives. Ask students to look at **Figure 2** and ask them where they have seen seeds that look like those marked "e." (Sample answers: in chili, in soup, in salads, when planting the garden) Ask students to look at **Figure 3.** Ask them to think about a tomato and ask how the seeds of a tomato feel different from the ovary of a tomato. (Sample answer: The seeds are surrounded by soft, watery tissue. The ovary is the solid flesh of the tomato.) **LS** Visual/Logical

Standards Focus

This **Standards Focus** provides you with a quick way to **assess**, **reteach**, and **re-assess** one or more concepts in the section.

Assess

1. _____ happens when a sperm joins with an egg. (fertilization) **7.5.f**

2. How do sexual and asexual reproduction differ in plants? (Sexual reproduction requires a sperm and an egg to unite to form an embryo that is genetically related to, but different from, the parent plants. In asexual reproduction, plants produce individuals genetically identical to themselves without the union of an egg and a sperm.) **7.2.a**

Reteach

Drawing Flowers   Have students draw a flower and label its anthers, stigmas, style, ovary, and ovule. Students should also draw the steps of pollination and fertilization. **LS** Visual **7.2.a, 7.5.f**

Re-Assess

Concept Map   Have students create a concept map using the following terms: *pollen, pollination, fertilization, egg, sexual reproduction, asexual reproduction, plantlets, tubers,* and *runners.* **LS** Visual

---

Answer to Standards Check

plantlets, tubers, and runners
7.2.a (mastering)

 Teaching Transparency:
L60 Three Structures for Asexual Reproduction

---

dormant (DAWR muhnt) describes the inactive state of a seed or other plant part when conditions are unfavorable to growth

Quick Lab

Plant Cuttings   **7.2.a** **7.7.c**

1. Get an **African violet leaf** from your teacher. Create a sketch of the leaf.

2. Place the leaf in a **cup of soil** so that the tip of the leaf is above the soil.

3. Water the plant, and place it in a sunny location. Predict what will happen.

4. If the soil feels dry, water the plant as needed for three days. Record your observations.

5. On the fourth day, carefully take the leaf out of the soil. Use water to gently remove the soil from the leaf. Sketch the leaf.

6. How is the leaf different? What is happening to the leaf cells of this plant?

⏱ **15 min plus follow-up**

From Seed to Plant

Once a seed is fully developed, the embryo inside the seed stops growing. If the conditions are not favorable for growth, the seed may become **dormant,** or inactive. Dormant seeds often survive long periods of drought or freezing temperatures. Some seeds need extreme conditions, such as cold winters or forest fires, to break their dormancy.

When seeds are dropped or planted in a suitable environment, the seeds sprout. To sprout, most seeds need water, air, and warm temperatures. Each plant species has an ideal temperature at which most of its seeds begin to grow. For many plants, the ideal temperature for growth is about 27°C (80.6°F). **Figure 4** shows the *germination,* or sprouting, of a bean seed.

Other Methods of Reproduction

Flowering plants can also reproduce asexually. But they do not need flowers to do so. Instead, a new plant grows from one of the plant parts, such as a stem or root. The following are three examples of structures plants use to reproduce asexually:

- **Plantlets**   Tiny plants grow along the edges of a plant's leaves. These plantlets fall off and grow on their own.
- **Tubers**   Underground stems, or tubers, can produce new plants after a dormant season.
- **Runners**   Above-ground stems from which new plants can grow are called *runners.*

Figure 5 shows examples of these three structures. A plant that results from sexual reproduction is genetically related to both parents. But a new plant that grows from the plantlet, tuber, or runner of another plant is genetically identical to that plant.

Standards Check   What are three structures that plants use to reproduce asexually?  **7.2.a**

Figure 4   *Seeds grow into new plants. First, the roots begin to grow. Then, the shoot grows up through the soil.*

Quick Lab

⏱ **15 min plus follow-up**

Teacher Notes

This activity introduces asexual reproduction in plants (covers standards 7.2.a and 7.7.c). You may wish to leave some leaves in the soil for a longer period than specified by this lab and let students continue their observations. Be sure that the surface of the leaves remain dry.

Materials for Each Group
- cup   • water
- leaf, African violet plant
- soil, potting

Answers

6. Answers may vary. Students should notice that the African violet leaf has begun to form roots on the edge of the leaf that is below soil.

 Differentiated Datasheets
A **BASIC**, B **GENERAL**, C **ADVANCED**

Also editable on the Holt Lab Generator CD-ROM

Figure 5 Three Structures for Asexual Reproduction

Kalanchoe plants produce **plantlets** along the edges of their leaves. The plantlets eventually fall off and root in the soil to grow on their own.

A potato is a **tuber,** or underground stem. The "eyes" of potatoes are buds that can grow into new plants.

The strawberry plant produces **runners,** or stems that grow horizontally along the ground. Buds along the runners take root and grow into new plants.

SECTION Review

7.2.a, 7.5.f

Summary

In the sexual reproduction of flowering plants, a sperm fertilizes an egg.

After fertilization, seeds and fruit form. The seeds may sprout into new plants.

A dormant seed can survive drought and freezing temperatures. Some seeds need extreme conditions to break their dormancy.

Some plants use plantlets, tubers, or runners to reproduce asexually.

Understanding Concepts

1 Comparing How are pollination and fertilization related?

2 Identifying Which part of a flower develops into a fruit? into a seed?

3 Concluding Why do some seeds become dormant?

4 Describing How do plants reproduce asexually?

Critical Thinking

5 Identifying Relationships When may asexual reproduction be important for the survival of some flowering plants?

6 Analyzing Ideas Sexual reproduction produces more genetic variety than asexual reproduction does. Why is variety important?

7 Making Inferences What do flowers and runners have in common? How do they differ?

Math Skills

8 Using Equations A seed sprouts when the temperature is 27°C. If the temperature starts at 20°C and rises 1.5°C each week, how many weeks will the seed take to sprout?

Challenge

9 Predicting Consequences How might the world be different if the ovaries of fertilized plants no longer developed into fruits?

Internet Resources

For a variety of links related to this chapter, go to www.scilinks.org
Topic: Reproduction of Plants
SciLinks code: HY71295

Answers to Section Review

1. Pollination may lead to fertilization because during pollination pollen is transferred to the female parts of flowers. Fertilization occurs when the sperm in pollen fertilize the plant eggs found in ovules. **7.2.a** (supporting), **7.5.f** (exceeding)

2. ovary; ovule **7.2.a** (exceeding), **7.5.f** (mastering)

3. Sample answer: Seeds become dormant to survive unfavorable conditions, such as long periods of drought and freezing temperatures. Some seeds need extreme conditions, such as cold winters or forest fires, to break their dormancy. **7.2.a** (exceeding), **7.5.f** (exceeding)

4. Sample answer: Plants reproduce asexually through one of three types of structures: plantlets,

tubers, or runners. Plantlets are tiny plants that grow along the edges of a plant's leaves, fall to the ground, and grow on their own. Tubers are underground stems that can produce new plants. Runners are aboveground stems from which new plants can grow. **7.2.a** (mastering)

5. Sample answer: A flowering plant produces seeds, but conditions may not be favorable for the seeds to grow. However, these same conditions may not affect asexual reproduction, so the plant can continue reproducing in this way. Also, if there are no pollinators in an area, sexual reproduction would be difficult for some plants. So, these plants may reproduce asexually. **7.2.a** (mastering)

6. Sample answer: Genetic variety may improve the ability of the plant to survive. For example, the offspring produced by asexual reproduction have the same weaknesses that the parent plant does. The offspring of sexual reproduction differ from a parent plant and may survive unfavorable conditions that would have affected the parent plant. **7.2.a** (exceeding)

7. Sample answer: Both flowers and runners are used for reproduction, but flowers are involved in sexual reproduction, whereas runners are used for asexual reproduction. **7.2.a** (mastering), **7.5.f** (mastering)

8. in about 5 weeks (27 °C − 20 °C = 7 °C; 7 °C ÷ 1.5 °C/week = 4.7 weeks)

9. Fruits are a source of nutrition for many organisms and the basis of food webs. Organisms dependent on fruits might not survive. Also, many plants would lose an effective way of spreading their seeds. **7.5.f** (exceeding)

Section Review Standards Guide

	Supporting	Mastering	Exceeding
7.2.a	1	4–5, 7	2–3, 6
7.5.f		2, 7	1, 3, 9

Section Resources

- Directed Reading A BASIC (Also in Spanish), B GENERAL
- Interactive Reader and Study Guide
- Section Quiz GENERAL (Also in Spanish)
- Section Review GENERAL (Also in Spanish)
- Vocabulary and Section Summary A BASIC (Also in Spanish), B GENERAL

Preteach

Reviewing Prior Knowledge

Have students consider the fact that plants appear to grow in certain directions. Then, have students list reasons why a plant would benefit from growing towards light and in the opposite direction of the force of gravity. (Sample answers: Plants growing away from the force of gravity and toward light have a better chance of receiving more sunlight because they may be taller than their competitors.)

 Bellringer

Tell students that this section likely contains a lot of new information. Ask students to focus on standard 7.1.f by making their best guess about how plants are able to change the way they grow when the amount of light or the amount of water changes. (Sample answer: Changes in the environment can cause certain cells to make more or less of certain hormones. These hormones can change the way cells grow.)

🗂 Bellringer Transparency

Motivate

Demonstration

Carnivorous Plants Bring to class a *Mimosa pudica* or a Venus' flytrap. Show students how the leaves of the plant respond when they are touched. Tell your students that not all plant responses are as easy to observe, but that plants continually respond to their environments. Note: The leaves will need time to recover before they will react again to stimuli. **LS** Visual

Answer to Standards Check

When a cell differentiates, it becomes specialized to do a certain job. **7.1.f** (mastering)

SECTION 3

What You Will Learn

- Some plant cells are able to differentiate throughout the life of the plant.
- Hormones cause a plant to develop in response to certain stimuli.
- Plants may grow toward some stimuli and away from others.

Why It Matters

Environmental stimuli can affect the structures and functions in plants.

Vocabulary

- stimulus
- tropism

READING STRATEGY

Graphic Organizer In your **Science Journal,** create an Idea Wheel that describes plant tropisms.

stimulus (STIM yoo luhs) anything that causes a reaction or change in an organism or any part of an organism

Figure 1 *The cells in this African violet leaf are differentiating into stem cells and root cells.*

7.1.f Students know that as multicellular organisms develop, their cells differentiate.
7.5.a Students know plants and animals have levels of organization for structure and function, including cells, tissues, organs, organ systems, and the whole organism.

Plant Development and Responses

Key Concept Plants develop differently than animals do. Also, plants respond to stimuli in a variety of ways.

▶ *Development* is the process by which an organism increases in ability or skill. Development is different from growth. *Growth* refers to an increase in size. During development, the cells of an organism become *differentiated*. In other words, each kind of cell is specialized to perform a specific function.

Plant Development

As a baby bird develops, its cells differentiate and become fixed in their development. So, the bird's cells lose the ability to differentiate into other kinds of cells. Most animal cells differentiate only once.

But some cells of some plants can differentiate many times as the plants develop. **Figure 1** shows an African violet leaf. Cells at the edge of this leaf are differentiating into root cells and stems cells. This process is one way some plants reproduce asexually. Many animals cannot reproduce asexually.

A plant's development can be affected by an environmental stimulus. A **stimulus** (plural, *stimuli*) is anything that causes a reaction or change in an organism. Plants do not see or react to stimuli, such as weather or light, in the same way that animals do. Many of a plant's responses to stimuli are caused by hormones. A *hormone* is a chemical that causes cells to react in certain ways. Hormones may cause certain plant cells to differentiate in response to stimuli.

Standards Check What happens when a cell differentiates? **7.5.a**

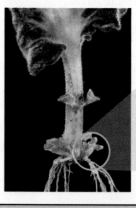

Universal Access • Differentiated Instruction

Special Education Students

Plant Terms Students with hearing impairments tend to have language delay issues. For this reason, they often do not have the level of vocabulary that their peers have and will need additional help understanding some terms when they come to them in the text. In this section, some words that might require support include the following:
p. 404—organism, asexually, environmental stimuli; p. 405—accumulate, stems and shoots, aging, tissues, dormant; p. 406—gravity; p. 407—seasonal, mature; p. 408—chlorophyll, pigments, cuticle. Determine which words your students need to study, and ask students to create riddles for each of them. Have them exchange their riddles and answer each other's riddles. Make sure they understand that their riddles should include definitions of the words. (Sample answer: I am made up of differentiated cells that develop into tissues and organs.–organism)
LS Verbal/Interpersonal

Plant Hormones

There are many groups of plant hormones. These hormones cause specific changes in plants.

Role of Hormones in Plants

Hormones play important roles in each stage of a plant's life cycle. Stimuli, such as the amount of light or water present in the environment or the temperature of the environment, change how much of a particular hormone is made in the cells of a plant. In turn, the concentrations of individual plant hormones change how and where a plant grows. For example, you may have noticed that plants grow toward light. The tendency of a plant to grow toward light is caused by a group of plant hormones called *auxins*. Auxins accumulate on the shaded side of a plant's stem, which makes the cells on that side *elongate*, or increase in length.

Use of Hormones in Agriculture

Some plant hormones are very useful in agriculture. A plant hormone called *ethylene* is used to ripen fruits, such as bananas and tomatoes, that are picked before they are ripe. Gibberellins are another group of plant hormones that are very useful in agriculture. The effect of gibberellins can be seen in **Figure 2.**

Figure 2 *A gibberellin was applied to the Thompson seedless grapes on the left. They are larger than the normal Thompson seedless grapes on the right.*

Quick Lab

Observing the Effects of Ethylene

In this experiment, you will use a ripe apple to observe how ethylene affects plants.

▶ **Try It!**

1. Place a **small plant** in a **large jar.** Tightly close the lid.
2. Place a **small plant** and an **apple** in a **second jar.** Tightly close the lid.
3. Observe the jars. Record your observations.
4. Place the jars in a well-lit place.
5. Observe the jars each day for a week. Record your observations.

7.5.a

▶ **Think About It!**

6. Describe any changes in the plants. Which plant changed the most?
7. A ripe apple releases ethylene gas. Using your observations, describe how ethylene may affect a plant?

⏱ **10 min/day for 6 days**

Quick Lab

⏱ **10 min/day for 6 days**

Teacher Notes

This activity has students test the effects of ethylene on plants (covers standard 7.5.a). Have students water the plants well before sealing, and leave the jars sealed for the duration of the week. Do not place the jars in direct sunlight. This may cause wilting.

Materials for Each Group
• apple
• jars, large, with lids, (2)
• plants, matching, small, (2)
• water

Safety Caution

Remind students to review all safety cautions and icons before beginning this activity.

Answers

6. Answers may vary. Students may notice that the plant in the jar with the apple will have yellowed leaves or may have lost leaves.
7. Answers may vary. Students may hypothesize that ethylene causes plants to age or die.

📋 Differentiated Datasheets
A **BASIC**, B **GENERAL**, C **ADVANCED**

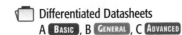
Teach

Group ACTiViTy

Materials for Each Group
• cups (2)
• plant cuttings (2)
• rooting hormone
• soil
• water

Safety Caution
Be certain to have students wear protective eyewear and gloves during this activity. Also, have students clean their lab stations carefully when finished.

Rooting Hormones   Give each group two similar plant cuttings, including stem and leaves. Have students dip one of the cuttings into a commercially prepared rooting hormone mix. Then, ask students to set both of their cuttings into the cups filled with moist soil. Tell students the rooting hormones are auxins, which stimulate growth. Have students keep their soil moist. After one week, have them examine each cutting for signs of root growth, and record their results.

LS Kinesthetic Co-op Learning

Connection To
Real Life

Controlling Ethylene   The old phrase "one bad apple spoils the whole bunch" refers to the effect of ethylene released by ripening and rotting fruit. This released ethylene causes nearby fruit to ripen more quickly. So, to keep fruits from spoiling, fruit growers, handlers, and sellers try to limit their fruit's exposure to ethylene. Or, to force unripe fruit to ripen, they may expose the green fruit to ethylene gas.

📦 Teaching Transparency:
L61 African Violet Leaf and Cell Differentiation

Teach, continued

Connection To Earth Science

Plants Grown in Zero Gravity

Past experiments in space showed that without light or gravity to induce organized growth, plants grew in random directions. So researchers were surprised when a type of moss grown in space showed a distinct spiral pattern. The spiral pattern is believed to be the result of the radial growth pattern of moss, which allows moss to grow outward in all directions.

Wordwise

Other Tropisms Ask students to research two types of *tropisms* other than gravitropism and phototropism. In addition, have students make up tropisms by adding their own prefix, such as "quesotropism" (growth in the direction of cheese). Let students try to guess the meaning of each other's created and real tropisms. (Thigmotropism is directional growth in response to touch, as seen in vines, roots, and tendrils. Hydrotropism is directional growth in response to water.) **LS Verbal/Logical**

tropism (TROH PIZ uhm) growth of all or part of an organism in response to an external stimulus, such as light

Wordwise The root *trop-* means "to turn." Other examples are *Tropics*, *phototropism*, and *gravitropism*.

INTERNET ACTIVITY

Biographies of Biologists

How do biologists become famous? Write the biography of an interesting biologist. Go to **go.hrw.com,** and type in the keyword HY7PL2W.

Plant Tropisms

What happens when you get really cold? Do your teeth chatter? Do you shiver? What other reactions do you have to environmental stimuli? When it rains, you may go inside or get an umbrella. But, how do plants respond to stimuli?

Some plants respond to environmental stimuli by growing in particular directions. Growth in response to a stimulus is called a **tropism.** Tropisms are either positive or negative. Plant growth toward a stimulus is a positive tropism. Plant growth away from a stimulus is a negative tropism. Plant tropisms are caused by the concentrations of certain hormones in plants. These concentrations are affected by environmental stimuli.

Light

What happens if a houseplant is getting light from only one direction, such as through a window? The shoot tips probably bend toward the light. Bending toward the light is a positive tropism. A change in the direction of the growth of a plant in response to light is called *phototropism* (foh TAH troh PIZ uhm). The result of phototropism is shown in **Figure 3.** A shoot bends because cells on one side of the shoot grow longer than cells on the other side of the shoot. You read earlier that the plant hormone auxin plays a role in phototropism.

Standards Check What happens to the cells of a plant's shoots when the plant gets light from only one direction? **7.5.a**

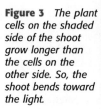

Figure 3 *The plant cells on the shaded side of the shoot grow longer than the cells on the other side. So, the shoot bends toward the light.*

Universal Access · Differentiated Instruction

Special Education Students

Plant Acts Students who have trouble sitting for long periods of time need a chance to move around. Ask students to physically act out plant tropisms. Have students act as plants that are growing tall and straight with their bodies being stems and their arms being leaves. Shine a light source on them (raise window shade or act it out).

Tell students to act as a plant would naturally act. (Students should bend their bodies and arms towards the light.) Ask students to sit in their chairs and slouch as if they are plants that have been knocked over. Ask them to respond like a knocked-over plant. (Students should direct their torsos, heads, and arms upwards.) **LS Kinesthetic**

Figure 4 Gravitropism

To grow away from the pull of gravity, this plant has grown upward.

This plant has recently been upside down.

Gravity

Gravity can also cause a change in the direction in which a plant is growing. This change is called *gravitropism* (GRAV i TROH PIZ uhm). The effect of gravitropism is demonstrated by the plants in **Figure 4.** A few days after a plant is placed on its side or turned upside down, the direction in which its roots and shoots are growing changes. Most shoot tips have negative gravitropism. They grow upward, away from the center of Earth. In contrast, most root tips have positive gravitropism. Roots grow downward, toward the center of Earth. Gravitropism is also known as *geotropism*.

Seasonal Responses

What would happen if a plant living in an area that has very cold winters flowered in December? Could the plant successfully produce seeds and fruits? Probably not. The plant's flowers would likely freeze and die. So, the flowers would never produce mature seeds.

Plants can respond to the change of seasons because they are affected by the change in the length of the day. For example, as fall and winter approach, the days get shorter, and the nights get longer. The opposite happens when spring and summer approach.

Standards Check Why must plants respond to seasonal changes?
7.1.f

Bending by Degrees

Suppose a plant has a positive phototropism and bends toward light at a rate of 0.3° per minute. In how many hours will the plant bend 90°? Record your work in your **Science Journal.**

MISCONCEPTION ALERT

Negative Tropisms Aren't Bad Tell students that negative and positive tropisms do not indicate good or bad, but merely indicate direction. *Positive* here means "toward the stimulus" and *negative* means "away from the stimulus." Have students create a list of other cases where the words "positive" and "negative" are used without judgment, such as the positive and negative terminals of a battery.

Cultural Awareness

Harvest Festivals Many ancient and traditional cultures have festivals during harvest time, often in the fall. Ask interested students to research a harvest festival. Have students write a magazine article about their findings.

Using the Figure
Positive and Negative Tropisms
Have students look closely at the photos of the bending plants on this page and the preceding page. Point out that after a few days, the leaves of the plants in the photos grew toward light or away from the force of gravity. Roots are not affected by light but do grow toward the force of gravity. Ask students to label these tropisms as positive or negative. (Growth toward a stimulus is a positive tropism, while growth away from a stimulus is a negative tropism. Growth by shoots toward light and growth by roots toward gravity are positive tropisms. The growth of shoots away from gravity is a negative tropism.)
LS Verbal/Visual

Homework
Investigating Plant Growth
Have students research how the lifespan of a plant is measured in terms of one-year growing seasons. Ask students to describe the life cycles of the plants in each of the following categories, and to give common garden examples of each:

- annuals (complete life cycle in one growing season; corn, marigolds, beans, and sunflowers)
- biennials (complete life cycle in two growing seasons; hollyhocks, foxgloves, carrots, onions)
- perennials (plants that live for more than two years; trees, roses, asparagus, and irises)

Encourage students to include drawings that illustrate the timing when each plant begins to grow, produces seeds, and dies. **LS** Verbal/Visual

Answer to Math Practice
5 hours (90° ÷ 0.3°/min = 300 min; 300 min ÷ 60 min/h = 5 h)

Answer to Standards Check
Sample answer: If plants couldn't detect seasonal changes, they might produce flowers or fruit when these structures might freeze and die. **7.1.f** (exceeding)

Close

Standards Focus

This **Standards Focus** provides you with a quick way to **assess, reteach,** and **re-assess** one or more concepts in the section.

Assess

1. What happens when a plant cell differentiates? (When plant cells differentiate, their structure becomes specialized for a specific function or job.) **7.1.f**

2. What would happen to a plant that tipped over but remained rooted? What type of tropism does this represent? (The shoots of the plant would begin bending upright in response to gravity. This is an example of negative gravitropism. The roots of the plant would bend downward in the same direction of the force of gravity, through positive gravitropism.) **7.1.f, 7.5.a**

**Reteach**

Organizing Information Write the following heads on the board: "Plant Development," "Phototropism," "Gravitropism," and "Seasonal Responses." Ask student volunteers to add information under the appropriate head. [LS] **Verbal/Logical 7.1.f, 7.5.a**

**Re-Assess**

Seasonal Changes Have students write a short article about how plants change in response to seasonal environmental changes. Ask students to use plants and trees native to California in their examples. [LS] **Verbal 7.1.f, 7.5.a**

Answer to School-to-Home Activity

Students' models should illustrate an understanding of how Earth's orbit and tilt affect the amount of sunlight that an area receives at a particular time of year.

Earth's Orbit and the Seasons

The seasons are caused by Earth's tilt and Earth's orbit around the sun. Research how Earth's orbit determines the seasons. With a parent or guardian, make a model of the Earth's orbit around the sun to illustrate your findings.

Figure 5 Amount of Pigment Based on Season

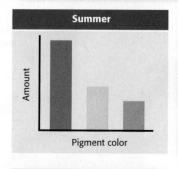

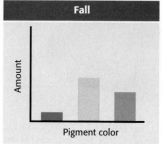

Length of Day

The difference between the length of the nights and the length of the days is an important environmental stimulus for many plants. This stimulus can cause plants to begin reproducing. For example, some plants flower in fall or in winter. At this time, nights are long. These plants are called *short-day plants*. Poinsettias are short-day plants. Chrysanthemums are also short-day plants. Other plants flower in spring or early summer, when nights are short. These plants are called *long-day plants*. Clover, spinach, and lettuce are examples of long-day plants.

Seasons and Leaf Color

As **Figure 5** shows, the leaves of some trees may change color before the leaves fall off. As fall approaches, green chlorophyll breaks down. Then, orange or yellow pigments in the leaves are revealed. These pigments were always present in the leaves. But green chlorophyll hid the pigments. This change is most common in *deciduous trees* (dee SIJ oo uhs TREEZ). These trees lose all of their leaves at about the same time each year. Maple, oak, and elm trees are deciduous trees. The plant hormones auxin and ethylene are involved in this process.

Universal Access • Differentiated Instruction

Struggling Readers

Plant Reading Tell students that before starting to read a two-page spread, they should skim the pages to get a general idea about the content. Tell them to look at the pictures, subheadings, and specially marked words on these two pages. Then, ask volunteers to answer the following questions:

1. What do you think the bar graph and the trees show? (Sample answer: the green pigment in trees decreases in fall)

2. What does length of day have to do with flowering plants? (Sample answer: The length of day helps most plants determine when to flower and germinate.)

3. Which of the subheadings goes with **Figure 5**? (Seasons and Leaf Color)

4. What kinds of trees do not lose their leaves? (evergreens) [LS] **Visual/Verbal**

Seasons and Leaf Loss

All trees lose their leaves. Some trees, such as pines, shed some of their leaves year-round so that some leaves are always on the tree. These trees are called *evergreen trees*. Evergreen trees have leaves that are often covered with a thick cuticle. This cuticle protects the leaves from cold and dry weather.

Deciduous trees lose all of their leaves at about the same time each year. In colder areas, deciduous trees usually lose their leaves before winter begins. In warmer climates that have wet and dry seasons, deciduous trees lose their leaves before the dry season. The loss of leaves helps plants survive low temperatures or long periods without rain.

SECTION Review

7.1.f, 7.5.a

Summary

- Some plant cells are able to differentiate many times in the lifetime of the plant.
- There are many groups of plant hormones. Plant hormones can affect a plant's growth and development.
- A growth in response to a stimulus is called a tropism. Tropisms are positive or negative.
- Plants react to light, gravity, and the change of seasons.
- Short-day plants flower when nights are long. Long-day plants flower when nights are short.

Understanding Concepts

1 **Describing** How do light and gravity affect plants?

2 **Evaluating** Describe an advantage of having cells that can differentiate many times.

Critical Thinking

INTERPRETING GRAPHICS Use the image below to answer the next question.

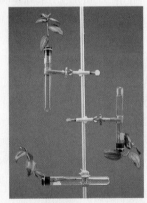

3 **Making Inferences** Describe the tropism that is shown in the picture above. What is causing the plants to grow this way?

4 **Making Inferences** Many evergreen trees live in areas with long, cold winters. Why do you think that these evergreen trees keep their leaves all year?

5 **Analyzing Ideas** Some short-day plants bloom during the winter. If cold weather reduces the chances that a plant will produce seeds, where do you think that these short-day plants are likely to be found?

Math Skills

6 **Using Equations** It must be dark for 70% of a 24 hour period before a certain plant will bloom. For how long will there be daylight on the day that this plant blooms?

Internet Resources

For a variety of links related to this chapter, go to www.scilinks.org
Topic: Plant Tropisms; Plant Growth
SciLinks code: HY71166; HY71159

---

5. Answers may vary. These short-day plants are likely found in areas that don't have cold winters.
   7.1.f (supporting), **7.5.a** (exceeding)

6. 7.2 h (100% − 70% = 30%; 24 h ÷ 0.3 = 7.2 h)

Section Review Standards Guide

	Supporting	Mastering	Exceeding
7.1.f	5	2	1
7.5.a	3–4		5

Answers to Section Review

1. Sample answer: Plant shoots usually grow toward light. Plant shoots grow in the opposite direction of the force of gravity, and plant roots grow in the same direction of the force of gravity. **7.1.f** (exceeding)

2. Some plant cells are able to differentiate more than once in the course of a plant's life. This means that some plants can form roots when needed from certain stem and leaf tissue. **7.1.f** (mastering)

3. Gravitropism is shown in the image. The plant is growing in the opposite direction of the force of gravity. Hormones regulate this response. **7.1.f** (exceeding), **7.5.a** (supporting)

4. Answers may vary. If the trees live in areas that have long winters, the growing season is likely too short for the trees to make all new leaves each year. So, the trees keep their leaves year round to conduct photosynthesis during the winter. **7.5.a** (supporting)

Section Resources

- Directed Reading
  A **BASIC** (Also in Spanish), B **GENERAL**
- Interactive Reader and Study Guide
- Section Quiz **GENERAL** (Also in Spanish)
- Section Review **GENERAL** (Also in Spanish)
- Vocabulary and Section Summary
  A **BASIC** (Also in Spanish), B **GENERAL**

Teacher Notes

This lab has students determine the rate of oxygen produced by an *Elodea* plant (covers standards 7.1.b, 7.1.d, and 7.7.c).

Time Required

One 45-minute class period and about 5 minutes per day for 5 days

Lab Ratings

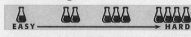

EASY	→		HARD

Teacher Prep 🧪🧪
Student Set-Up 🧪🧪🧪
Concept Level 🧪🧪🧪
Clean Up 🧪🧪

Materials

The materials listed on the student page include enough supplies for one student or one group of students. *Elodea* (commonly known as waterweed) is a common aquarium plant and can be found at most pet stores. To make a 5% solution of baking soda and water, add water to 5 g of baking soda until the volume is 100 mL.

Safety Caution

Remind students to review all safety cautions and icons before beginning this activity.

Preparation Notes

You may want to have students practice placing the test tube over the inverted funnel using just water before they do so with the baking-soda solution. It may take two or three tries to get the test tube over the funnel stem without letting any air into the tube. Say, "First, be sure that you have the *Elodea* in place under the funnel. Then, fill the test tube with the solution and place your thumb tightly over the opening so that air cannot get in. Submerge your thumb and the top of the test tube. Once the top of the tube is under water, you can remove your thumb from the opening of the test tube and maneuver the test tube over the stem of the funnel."

Skills Practice Lab

OBJECTIVES

Measure the amount of gas that photosynthesis produced over time.

Draw a graph of the amount of gas produced versus time.

MATERIALS

- baking soda and water solution, 5% (500 mL)
- beaker (600 mL)
- elodea sprigs, 20 cm long (2 to 3)
- funnel
- gloves, protective
- ruler, metric
- test tube

SAFETY

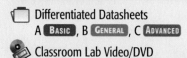

7.1.b Students know the characteristics that distinguish plant cells from animal cells, including chloroplasts and cell walls.
7.1.d Students know that mitochondria liberate energy for the work that cells do and that chloroplasts capture sunlight energy for photosynthesis.

Investigation and Experimentation
7.7.c Communicate the logical connection among hypotheses, science concepts, tests conducted, data collected, and conclusions drawn from the scientific evidence.

Food Factory Waste

Plants use photosynthesis to make food. Photosynthesis produces oxygen gas. Humans and many other organisms cannot live without this oxygen. Oxygen is necessary for cellular respiration. In this activity, you will determine the rate of oxygen production for an elodea plant.

Procedure

1. Add 450 mL of baking soda and water solution to a beaker.

2. Put two or three sprigs of elodea in the beaker. The baking soda will produce the carbon dioxide which the elodea needs for photosynthesis.

3. Place the wide end of the funnel over the elodea. The small end of the funnel should be pointing up. The elodea and the funnel should be completely covered by the solution.

4. Fill a test tube with the remaining solution of baking soda and water. Place your thumb over the end of the test tube, and turn the test tube upside down. Make sure that no air enters the test tube. Hold the opening of the test tube under the solution. Place the test tube over the small end of the funnel. Try not to let any solution out of the test tube.

Lab Resources

📋 **Differentiated Datasheets**
A BASIC, B GENERAL, C ADVANCED

📹 **Classroom Lab Video/DVD**

💿 **Holt Lab Generator CD-ROM**

Search for any lab by topic, standard, difficulty level, or time. Edit any lab to fit your needs, or create your own labs. Use the Lab Materials QuickList software to customize your lab materials list.

5 Place the beaker setup in a well-lit area.

6 Prepare a data table similar to the one below.

Amount of Gas Present in the Test Tube

Days of exposure to light	Total amount of gas present (mm)	Amount of gas produced per day (mm)
0		
1		
2	DO NOT WRITE	
3	IN BOOK	
4		
5		

7 If no air entered the test tube, record that 0 mm of gas was in the test tube before the plant was exposed to light. If air got into the tube while you were placing the tube, measure the height of the column of air in the test tube in millimeters. Measure the gas in the test tube from the middle of the curve on the bottom of the upside-down test tube to the level of the solution. Record this number in the first row.

8 As described in the previous step, measure the amount of gas in the test tube each day for the next 5 days. Record your measurements in the second column of your data table.

9 Calculate the amount of gas produced each day. Subtract the amount of gas present on the previous day from the amount of gas present on the current day. Record these amounts in the third column of your data table.

Analyze the Results

10 **Constructing Graphs**   Make a graph similar to the one below. Based on your measurements, your graph should show the amount of gas produced versus time.

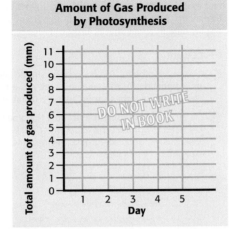

Amount of Gas Produced by Photosynthesis

11 **Describing Events**   Use your graph to determine what happened to the amount of gas in the test tube.

Draw Conclusions

12 **Interpreting Information**   Write the equation for photosynthesis. Then, relate each part of your experiment to a part of the equation.

Big Idea Question

13 **Defending Conclusions**   Most plants perform photosynthesis to make food. In order to perform photosynthesis, plants need water. How does the cuticle covering the leaves of a pine tree help the tree perform photosynthesis in a cold and dry environment?

Analyze the Results

10. Students' graphs should show a gradual increase in the amount of gas in the test tube.

11. Sample answer: The amount of gas in the test tube increased over time.

Draw Conclusions

12. $6CO_2 + 6H_2O + \text{light energy} \rightarrow C_6H_{12}O_6 + 6O_2$. CO_2 is carbon dioxide, which comes from the baking soda-and-water solution. H_2O is water, also found in the baking soda-and-water solution. Light energy comes from the sun. $C_6H_{12}O_6$ is glucose, and O_2 is oxygen. Glucose and oxygen are products of photosynthesis. The *Elodea* stores the glucose and releases the oxygen that is then captured in the test tube.

Big Idea Question

13. Answers may vary. Cuticles on leaves prevent the pine tree from losing moisture. The small surface area of the leaves helps to prevent water loss. And, leaves remain green all year so that the tree can continue to absorb sunlight energy.

Gayle Van Fossen
George V. Leyva
Intermediate School
San Jose, California

Scientific Methods	Research	Data Analysis	Models, Maps & Diagrams

Investigation and Experimentation

7.7.a Select and use appropriate tools and technology (including calculators, computers, balances, spring scales, microscopes, and binoculars) to perform tests, collect data, and display data.

Teacher Notes

The tutorial gives students a question "Does ice exist at room temperature?" and a hypothesis to explain the question "Ice melts at room temperature." This activity covers standard 7.7.a. Have students think about their own observations. Ask them to develop a question and hypothesis based on something they are curious about from their own lives.

Answers to You Try It!

1. This data is numerical.

2. Answers may vary. Students should suggest both technology such as graphing software and non-technological tools.

3. Answers may vary. Students may choose to display data in a data table or in a graph.

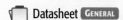 Datasheet GENERAL

Also editable on the Holt Lab Generator CD-ROM

Selecting Tools to Display Data

▶ Tutorial

Scientists ask many questions about the natural world. They conduct experiments to find answers. A scientist must choose the correct equipment and tools in order to perform the experiment and display the data gathered. It is very important to display data in a way that is easy to understand.

Procedure

❶ Write a hypothesis. The hypothesis should offer an explanation for the question that you are asking. The hypothesis must also be testable.

❷ List all of the equipment and tools that you will need to conduct the experiment, make observations, and record data. Perform the experiment.

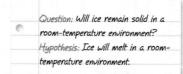
Question: Will ice remain solid in a room-temperature environment?
Hypothesis: Ice will melt in a room-temperature environment.

Time Vs. Temperature

Time (min)	Temperature (°C)
0	25
1	23
2	22
3	21.5
4	19

❸ Examine the data that you collected. Numerical data can be displayed in tables and graphs, as the table above. Nonnumerical data, such as descriptions, can be displayed in maps, illustrations, and videos.

❹ Use the format that you have chosen to display your data as clearly and accurately as possible. Be sure to include labels and units of measurement where necessary.

▶ You Try It!

Procedure

Imagine that you are examining the relationship between the surface area of a leaf and the rate at which photosynthesis occurs. Using three leaves from the same plant, you measured the amount of water each leaf loses through transpiration. Because each leaf is roughly the same size, you covered half of the surface of one leaf and a quarter of the surface of another leaf with white paper. Use the data listed below to answer the following questions.

Data from Experiment:
Full Leaf - 0.4 g
Half Leaf - 0.3 g
Quarter Leaf - 0.1 g

Analysis

❶ **Describing** Is this data numerical or non-numerical?

❷ **Listing** What tools would you use to display this data? What technology could help you display this data?

❸ **Modeling** Make a sketch of how you would display this data. Be sure to include all labels and units of measurement if necessary.

Universal Access · Differentiated Instruction

Basic Learners

Types of Data Some students may not understand that numerical data includes numbers and non-numerical data is given in words. Write the following data on the board: 1. Joe is 5′3″, Clyde is 5′7″, and Ella is 4′8″. (numerical) 2. Joe is taller than Ella. (non-numerical) 3. Clyde grew a lot last summer. (non-numerical) Ask students to identify each as numerical or nonnumerical data. **LS** Logical

Advanced Learners/GATE

Displaying Data Have students conduct an experiment comparing plants treated with fertilizer and plants treated with a growth hormone. Be sure to have control plants and enough experimental plants to ensure results. Allow plants to grow for several weeks under controlled conditions. After they have collected their data, have students design and produce a display of their results. **LS** Logical/Visual

Chapter Summary

The Big Idea
Like all living things, plants need nourishment, reproduce, and respond to stimuli.

Section		Vocabulary

① Photosynthesis

Key Concept Plants make food during photosynthesis and use energy in the food during cellular respiration.

- Chloroplasts capture sunlight energy for photosynthesis.
- Photosynthesis is the process by which most plants make food.
- Mitochondria release the energy that cells use to do work.
- Cellular respiration allows living things, including plants, to use the products of photosynthesis.

Gases produced during plant processes are exchanged through the leaves of plants.

photosynthesis p. 396
chlorophyll p. 396
cellular respiration p. 397
stoma p. 398
transpiration p. 398

② Reproduction of Flowering Plants

Key Concept Flowering plants reproduce sexually and asexually.

- After pollination, sexual reproduction in flowering plants occurs when an egg is fertilized by a sperm.
- Seeds form from fertilized ovules. The ovary of a flower becomes a fruit.
- In the proper conditions, seeds can sprout and develop into plants.
- Flowering plants can reproduce asexually.

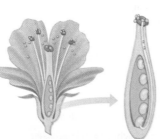

The ovary of a flower contains eggs that can be fertilized.

dormant p. 402

③ Plant Development and Responses

Key Concept Plants develop differently than animals do. Also, plants respond to stimuli in a variety of ways.

- Some plant cells are able to differentiate throughout the life of the plant.
- Hormones cause a plant to develop in response to certain stimuli.
- Plants may grow toward some stimuli and away from others.

This plant is growing toward light because of the plant hormone auxin.

stimulus p. 404
tropism p. 406

Universal Access · Differentiated Instruction

Special Education Students

Data Tables Because the data is numerical, most students will indicate that they could present this data in a data table. However, students with visual impairments are not likely to conclude this because they would not be able to create or read the table. Guide such students in creating a table using Braille labels. Even though they might need help to create the table, they can review it later. **LS Kinesthetic**

Review Resources

- Reinforcement Worksheet **BASIC**
- Critical Thinking Worksheet **ADVANCED**
- Chapter Review **GENERAL** (Also in Spanish)
- Standards Review Workbook (Also in Spanish)
- Study Guide A **BASIC** (Also in Spanish), B **GENERAL**

Assessment Resources

- Chapter Tests A **BASIC**, B **GENERAL** (Also in Spanish), C **ADVANCED**
- Standards Assessment **GENERAL**

Chapter Summary

SUPER SUMMARY

Have students connect the major concepts in this chapter through an interactive Super Summary. Visit go.hrw.com and type in the keyword HY7PL2S to access the Super Summary for this chapter.

Identifying Prefixes

Word Match Have students match the prefix *photo-* (meaning "light") with the proper suffix for each of the following definitions: process of making food using sunlight for energy (photosynthesis); directional growth of plant in response to light (phototropism). **LS Verbal**

Focus on Speaking

Talk Show Have students work in pairs. Assign one of the three chapter sections to each pair. Have them work together to develop a set of questions and answers as the characters: "talk show host" and "expert guest." Make sure they cover the key concepts and relate the material to the standards addressed in their section. Have students present their interviews to the class. **LS Verbal/Interpersonal**

Chapter Review

 7.1.b, 7.1.d, 7.1.f,
7.2.a, 7.5.a, 7.5.f

Assignment Guide

Section	Questions
1	2, 4–6, 8–9, 18, 20, 25–26
2	7, 11–12, 15–17, 19, 24, 28
3	3, 10, 13–14, 21–23, 27

Answers

Using Vocabulary

1. c

2. transpiration

3. tropism

4. Chlorophyll **7.1.d** (supporting)

5. cellular respiration **7.1.d** (mastering)

6. stoma **7.5.a** (supporting)

7. dormant

8. Photosynthesis **7.1.d** (supporting)

Understanding Concepts

9. b **7.5.a** (supporting)

10. b **7.1.f** (supporting)

11. c **7.2.a** (mastering)

12. a **7.5.f** (mastering)

13. Short-day plants bloom when nights are long, during the fall and winter. Long-day plants bloom when nights are short, during the spring and summer. **7.1.f** (supporting)

14. The shoots would bend upward, in the opposite direction of the force of gravity, while the roots would bend downward, in the same direction of the force of gravity. **7.1.f** (supporting)

15. Pollination happens when pollen is transferred from the anthers to the stigma. After the pollen lands on the stigma, a tube grows from each pollen grain. The tube grows through the style to an ovule. A sperm travels down the tube and fertilizes an egg in the ovule. **7.5.f** (mastering), **7.2.a** (mastering)

16. water, air, and warm temperatures **7.5.f** (exceeding)

17. After the egg is fertilized, the ovule forms a seed. The ovary becomes a fruit, which protects the seed or seeds. **7.5.f** (mastering)

Organize

Booklet Review the FoldNote that you created at the beginning of the chapter. Add to the Fold-Note or correct it based on what you have learned.

Using Vocabulary

1 **Academic Vocabulary** In the sentence "As multicellular organisms develop their cells differentiate," what does the word <u>differentiate</u> mean?
a. migrate
b. grow
c. become different in structure and function
d. change orientation and location in the organism

Complete each of the following sentences by choosing the correct term from the word bank.

stoma	photosynthesis
dormant	cellular respiration
tropism	chlorophyll
transpiration	

2 The loss of water from leaves is called ___.

3 A plant's response to light or gravity is called a ___.

4 ___ is a green pigment found in plant cells.

5 To get energy from the food made during photosynthesis, mitochondria in the cells of plants use the process of ___.

6 A ___ is an opening in the epidermis and cuticle of a leaf.

7 An inactive seed is ___.

8 ___ is the process by which plants make their own food.

Understanding Concepts

Multiple Choice

9 During gas exchange in plants,
a. carbon dioxide exits the leaf while oxygen and water enter the leaf.
b. oxygen and water exit the leaf while carbon dioxide enters the leaf.
c. carbon dioxide and water enter the leaf while oxygen exits the leaf.
d. carbon dioxide and oxygen enter the leaf while water exits the leaf.

10 Plants often respond to light from one direction by
a. bending away from the light.
b. bending toward the light.
c. wilting.
d. None of the above

11 Which of the following is NOT a structure that plants use to reproduce asexually?
a. a runner
b. a tuber
c. a flower
d. a plantlet

INTERPRETING GRAPHICS Use the image below to answer the next question.

12 What is the purpose of the structure shown above?
a. reproduction
b. water absorption
c. food storage
d. gas exchange

18. Answers may vary. Photosynthesis is the process by which plants make glucose. Photosynthesis uses carbon dioxide and water and produces oxygen. Cellular respiration is the process by which plants get energy from glucose and other food molecules. Cellular respiration uses oxygen and gives off carbon dioxide and water. **7.1.d** (mastering)

Short Answer

13 **Comparing** Describe the relationship between short-day plants and long-day plants.

14 **Analyzing** How do potted plants respond to gravity when they are placed on their sides?

15 **Describing** What happens during the pollination and fertilization of flowering plants?

16 **Listing** What three things do seeds need in order to sprout?

17 **Describing** How do fruits and seeds form from flowers?

18 **Comparing** Describe the relationship between photosynthesis and cellular respiration.

Writing Skills

19 **Writing Persuasively** Write a short essay that compares sexual and asexual reproduction in plants. Demonstrate which form of reproduction is the most advantageous.

Critical Thinking

20 **Concept Mapping** Use the following terms to create a concept map: *plants, cellular respiration, light energy, photosynthesis, chemical energy, carbon dioxide,* and *oxygen*.

21 **Analyzing Ideas** Most plant shoots have positive phototropism. Plant roots have positive gravitropism. What are the benefits of each of these characteristics?

22 **Applying Concepts** Describe the advantages of a plant whose cells can differentiate more than one time, such as the cells of an African violet.

23 **Making Inferences** Imagine that someone discovers a new flowering plant. The plant has yellow flowers and underground stems. How could this plant reproduce asexually?

24 **Predicting Consequences** What would happen to a plant if its stem were the main surface for gas exchange?

INTERPRETING GRAPHICS Use the image below to answer the next question.

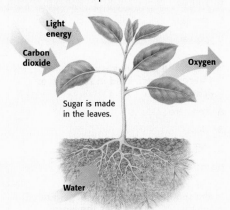

Light energy
Carbon dioxide
Oxygen
Sugar is made in the leaves.
Water

25 **Identifying Relationships** The blue arrows in the diagram above show gas exchange in the plant. How is the intake of carbon dioxide related to the release of oxygen?

Math Skills

26 **Using Calculations** Right before winter break, you accidently knocked over a plant in the school greenhouse . The plant has a negative gravitropism, which means that the plant grows away from gravity. This plant grows away from gravity at a rate of 0.1° per hour. After how many days will the plant be growing perpendicular to the ground?

Challenge

27 **Analyzing Relationships** Animals depend on plants in many ways. But, plants also depend on animals. Describe how plants rely on animals. Be sure to include information about plant reproduction and food production.

22. A plant, such as an African violet, has advantages because some of its cells are able to differentiate many times in the course of the plant's life. Tissue on the African violet's stems or leaves can form roots which may help the plant survive if the root structure is killed in an adult plant. **7.1.f** (mastering)

23. Answers may vary. Underground stems, such as tubers, can grow into new plants, so the plant likely reproduces asexually in this way. **7.2.a** (mastering)

24. If the stem were the main surface for gas exchange, stems would have to be bigger so that the plant would get carbon dioxide and could get rid of enough oxygen. Also, plants with woody stems would not be able to survive. **7.1.d** (exceeding), **7.5.a** (exceeding)

25. The intake of carbon dioxide is related to the release of oxygen because during photosynthesis a plant uses carbon dioxide and produces oxygen. **7.1.d** (exceeding)

Math Skills

26. 0.1°/hr × *x* hr = 90°; *x* hr = 90°/0.1°/hr = 900 hours; 900 hrs = 37.5 days

Challenge

27. Accept all reasonable answers. Students should describe how animals are involved in pollination and the dispersal of seeds. Also, students may mention that plants rely on the carbon dioxide that animals exhale for the process of photosynthesis. **7.1.b** (supporting), **7.1.d** (supporting), **7.5.f** (exceeding)

	Chapter Review Standards Guide		
	Supporting	**Mastering**	**Exceeding**
7.1.b	27		
7.1.d	4, 8, 27	5, 18	20, 24–25
7.1.f	10, 13–14	22	
7.2.a		11, 23	19
7.5.a	6, 9		21, 24
7.5.f		12, 15, 17	16, 27

Writing Skills

19. Accept all reasonable answers. Students should be able to demonstrate that in certain circumstances, sexual reproduction is favorable for plants because it increases the variety in any given species of plant and increases the chance that that species could survive changes in its habitat. Also, students should be able to demonstrate that in other circumstances, asexual reproduction is favorable for plants because it allows plants to continue reproducing when circumstances may not be favorable for the fertilization of eggs by sperm. **7.2.a** (exceeding)

Critical Thinking

20. An answer to this exercise can be found at the end of the book. **7.1.d** (exceeding)

21. Sample answer: Positive phototropism can ensure that plant shoots get the sunlight that they need for photosynthesis. The positive gravitropism of plant roots ensures that the roots can reach water. **7.5.a** (exceeding)

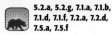
Teacher Notes

To provide practice under more realistic testing conditions, give students 20 min to answer all of the questions in this assessment.

Answer Key

Question Number	Correct Answer
1	D
2	C
3	C
4	A
5	B
6	C
7	B
8	C
9	A
10	D
11	D
12	C
13	B
14	D
15	A

Standards Guide

	Supporting	Mastering	Exceeding
5.2.e		12	
5.2.g		13	
7.1.b			5
7.1.d	1	7	
7.1.f	2		
7.2.a		6	8
7.2.d		14	
7.5.a		10, 15	
7.5.f	3–4	9, 11	

Standards Assessment GENERAL

Teacher Notes for Standards Assessment contain a longer Assessment Doctor and Diagnostic Teaching Tips.

REVIEWING ACADEMIC VOCABULARY

1 Which of the following words is the closest in meaning to the word *energy*?

A work

B source

C increase

D power

2 Which of the following words means "to become specialized in structure or function"?

A separate

B classify

C differentiate

D merge

3 In the sentence "The biologist generated many results," what does the word *generated* mean?

A produced energy through a chemical process

B formed a geometrical figure on a curve

C brought into existence

D created offspring

4 Choose the appropriate form of the word *structure* for the following sentence: Plants are _____ to generate energy from sunlight.

A structured

B structural

C structure

D structurally

REVIEWING CONCEPTS

5 Why do most plants look green?

A The chlorophyll in plants captures green light for photosynthesis.

B The chlorophyll in plants reflects wavelengths of green light.

C The chloroplasts in plants are surrounded by two green membranes.

D The chloroplasts in plants make green sugar during photosynthesis.

6 When plants reproduce using plantlets, tubers, or runners, what is true of their offspring?

A They inherit characteristics from both parents.

B Their stems will grow horizontally along the ground.

C They are genetically identical to the parent plant.

D Their seeds will remain dormant through the winter.

7 In the image above, what does the blue arrow represent?

A Sugar is made in the leaves from light energy and CO_2.

B Oxygen is released from the plant as a waste product.

C The plant takes in water to help make glucose molecules.

D Carbon dioxide is absorbed through the plant's leaves.

➕ ASSESSMENT DOCTOR

Question 1: The correct answer is D. *Power* and *energy* are synonymous. They both refer to the ability or capacity to do something.

Question 2: The correct answer is C. *Differentiate* means "to change to a specialized form or function." In multicellular plants and animals, cells differentiate to perform different functions.

Question 3: The correct answer is C. The biologist brought many results into existence. *Generate* in this sentence means "to bring into existence."

Question 4: The correct answer is A. This sentence is missing an adverb. *Structured* is the past participle of the verb *structure*, which can also be used as an adjective. *Structural* is also an adjective. *Structure* can act as a verb or a noun. The adverb *structurally* is the form of *structure* that fits this sentence, because it modifies the adjective *equipped*. Plants are structurally equipped to create energy from sunlight.

Question 5: The correct answer is B. Most plants look green because their chlorophyll reflects wavelengths of green light and absorbs wavelengths of other colors of light.

8 What must happen for sexual reproduction to occur in flowering plants?

A Plantlets must fall from the parent.

B The fruit of the plant must be edible.

C An egg must be fertilized by a sperm.

D Pollen must be produced.

9 Pollination occurs in angiosperms when

A pollen moves from anthers to stigmas.

B the ovule develops into a seed.

C the ovary becomes the fruit.

D sperm moves down the pollen tube.

10 A stoma is one of a plant's

A systems.

B cells.

C tissues.

D organs.

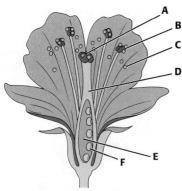

11 At which point in the above diagram do you find the flower's ovary?

A point A

B point B

C point C

D point D

REVIEWING PRIOR LEARNING

12 What structure in vascular plants carries food throughout the plant?

A xylem

B cuticle

C phloem

D rhizome

13 The chemical equation for cellular respiration is shown below.

$$C_6H_{12}O_6 + 6O_2 \longrightarrow 6CO_2 + 6H_2O$$

What happens on the right side of the arrow?

A Sugar is produced.

B Carbon dioxide and water are produced.

C 6 carbon atoms combine with 6 oxygen atoms.

D Carbon dioxide and oxygen are produced.

14 Two pea plants with purple flowers produce an offspring with white flowers. Which of the following is most likely true?

A The trait for white flowers was passed through self-pollination.

B Both parents had dominant alleles for white flowers.

C The offspring of these parents was a first-generation pea plant.

D Both parents had recessive alleles for white flowers.

15 Which of the following is a shared characteristic of all living things?

A made of one or more cells

B are consumers in the ecosystem

C have nuclei which contain DNA

D perform sexual reproduction

Standards Assessment

Question 6: The correct answer is C. The offspring of plants that use plantlets, tubers, or runners to reproduce will be genetically identical to the parent plant. These plants reproduce asexually and so do not have two parents or seeds.

Question 7: The correct answer is B. At point E, oxygen is released from the plant as a waste product after photosynthesis. Sugar is made at point C. The plant takes in water at point D. Carbon dioxide is absorbed at point A.

Question 8: The correct answer is C. In order for sexual reproduction to occur in flowering plants, an egg must be fertilized by a sperm.

Question 9: The correct answer is A. Pollination occurs when pollen moves from the anthers of a flower to the stigmas of a flower. Fertilization rather than pollination occurs when sperm moves down the pollen tube. Fertilization leads to the development of a plant's fruit and seeds.

Question 10: The correct answer is D. A stoma is an organ made up of two guard cells.

Question 11: The correct answer is D. The ovary is found at point D. The stigma is shown at point A. Pollen is found at point B. An ovule is shown at point C.

Question 12: The correct answer is C. The phloem is the tissue that carries food made through photosynthesis throughout the plant. The xylem carries water and minerals from the roots to the leaves. The cuticle protects the leaves. Rhizomes are underground fern stems.

Question 13: The correct answer is B. During cellular respiration, carbon dioxide ($6CO_2$) and water ($6H_2O$) are expelled from the cell. Nothing is expelled from the lungs during cellular respiration. Waste is expelled from the cells.

Question 14: The correct answer is D. Both parents must have had recessive alleles for white flowers for an offspring to have white flowers.

Question 15: The correct answer is A. All living things have cells. All living things also have DNA, although it is not contained in a nucleus in prokaryotes.

Scientific Debate

ACTIVITY

Have an ecologist or a landscaper come to the classroom and talk to your class about how to plan, plant, and take care of a native plant garden. Then, have students research and design a native plant garden. After students design their gardens, consider choosing one of the designs and having the class plant the garden in the schoolyard or on an empty lot. Be sure to get the appropriate permission before planting the garden. Your community may already have native plant gardens that your class can visit for inspiration.

Weird Science

Background

The corpse flower, or titan arum (*Amorphophallus titanium*), generates heat to disperse malodorous sulfuric compounds across a great distance. This metabolic burning of the plant's stored carbohydrates uses up an enormous amount of energy. This is one reason why the titan arum seldom blooms—in the wild, it may bloom only three to four times within 40 years.

Science in Action

Scientific Debate

Are Exotic Species Helpful or Harmful?

Have you visited the coast of California? If so, you may have seen large eucalyptus trees. You may be surprised to know that those trees are *exotic species*. An exotic species is an organism that is not native to the place where it lives. Eucalyptus trees were brought to California to be planted in people's yards and gardens. Since then, eucalyptus trees have spread to other areas. Exotic species often take over areas. Exotic species may compete with native species. Sometimes, exotic species keep native species from surviving. But in urban areas, exotic species are sometimes the only plants that will grow.

Social Studies ACTIVITY

Research an exotic species. Find out where the exotic species came from and what effect it is having on the environment. Write about your findings in your **Science Journal**.

Weird Science

What's That Smell?

Imagine that you are walking through a tropical rain forest. You're surrounded by green—green leaves, green vines, and green trees. You can hear monkeys and birds calling to one another. When you touch the plants nearby, they are wet from a recent rain shower. But what's that horrible smell? You don't see any rotting garbage, but you do see a huge flower spike. As you get closer, the smell gets stronger. Then, you realize the flower is what smells so bad! The flower is called a *corpse flower*. The corpse flower is just one plant that uses bad odors to attract pollinators.

Math ACTIVITY

A corpse flower sprouts and grows to a maximum height of 2.35 m in 28 days. In centimeters, what is the average growth of the corpse flower per day? Record the answer and your work in your **Science Journal**.

Answer to Social Studies Activity

Students may be surprised to discover that many of the plants that they are familiar with are exotic species. Some of these plants include dandelion, white clover, Scotch broom, and gorse. Students should recognize that exotic species can have an adverse effect on native species.

Answer to Math Activity

8.4 cm per day (2.35 m $\times$ 100 cm/m = 235 cm; 235 cm $\div$ 28 days = 8.4 cm/day)

Nalini Nadkarni

Canopy Scientist As a child, Nalini Nadkarni loved to climb trees. She still does. Nadkarni is a biologist who studies the forest canopy. The canopy is the uppermost layer of the trees. It includes leaves, twigs, and branches and the air among them. Far above the ground, the canopy is home to plants, birds, insects, and other animals.

Canopy science was a new field of study when Nadkarni started her research 20 years ago. Because most canopies are tall, few scientists visited them. Most field biologists did their research with both feet planted firmly on the ground. Today, scientists know that the canopy is an important habitat for wildlife.

Nadkarni tells others about the importance of forests. As she puts it, "I can have a real impact in raising public awareness of the need to save forests." Nadkarni has invited artists and musicians to visit the canopy. "In my job, I try to understand the science of the canopy, but artists and musicians help capture the aesthetic value of the canopy."

Language Arts ACTiViTY

Imagine that you are a canopy scientist. Then, write a creative story about something that you would like to study in the canopy. Write your story in your **Science Journal**.

Internet Resources

- To learn more about careers in science, visit **www.scilinks.org** and enter the SciLinks code HY70225.

- To learn more about these Science in Action topics, visit **go.hrw.com** and type in the keyword HY7PL2F.

- Check out articles related to this chapter by visiting **go.hrw.com**. Just type in the keyword HY7PL2C.

Answer to Language Arts Activity
Students should recognize the interdisciplinary nature of canopy science. They will likely come up with many different ideas involving different disciplines.

The elements listed in the Standards Course of Study provide a base for presenting, supporting, and assessing the California Grade 7 Science Standards. Use this Standards Course of Study as a base for planning your lessons.

Why Teach

Introduction to Animals

This chapter was designed to cover the California Grade 7 Science Standards about structure and function in the bodies of animals (7.1.f, 7.2.a, 7.5.a, 7.5.b, 7.5.c, and 7.5.g). It follows a chapter about plant processes. These plant processes provide the nutrients and the energy necessary for most animal life. This chapter introduces students to the various groups of animals on Earth and the animals' strategies for reproduction and survival.

After they have completed this chapter, students will begin a chapter about human body organization and structure.

California Standards

Focus on Life Sciences

7.1.f Students know that as multicellular organisms develop, their cells differentiate.

7.2.a Students know the differences between the life cycles and reproduction methods of sexual and asexual organisms.

7.5.a Students know plants and animals have levels of organization for structure and function, including cells, tissues, organs, organ systems, and the whole organism.

7.5.b Students know organ systems function because of the contributions of individual organs, tissues, and cells. The failure of any part can affect the entire system.

7.5.c Students know how bones and muscles work together to provide a structural framework for movement.

7.5.g Students know how to relate the structures of the eye and ear to their functions.

Investigation and Experimentation

7.7.a Select and use appropriate tools and technology (including calculators, computers, balances, spring scales, microscopes, and binoculars) to perform tests, collect data, and display data.

7.7.d Construct scale models, maps, and appropriately labeled diagrams to communicate scientific knowledge (e.g., motion of Earth's plates and cell structure).

Chapter Pacing

Getting Started — 45 min — pp. 422–423
The Big Idea Animals have many unique characteristics to perform their life functions.
 7.5.a, 7.7.a

Section 1 What Is an Animal? — 90 min — pp. 424–429
Key Concept Animals are made up of many cells. Animals consume other organisms to get the energy they need to grow, survive, and reproduce.
7.1.f, 7.2.a, 7.5.a, 7.5.b, 7.5.c

Section 2 The Animal Kingdom — 90 min — pp. 430–437
Key Concept Animals are a diverse group of organisms that have adaptations to live in water and on land.
 7.5.a

Section 3 Invertebrates — 90 min — pp. 438–443
Key Concept Invertebrates do not have backbones, but they do have other structures to perform their life functions.
7.2.a, 7.5.a, 7.5.b, 7.5.g

Section 4 Vertebrates — 90 min — pp. 444–449
Key Concept All vertebrates have a backbone, which supports other specialized body structures and functions.
 7.1.f, 7.2.a, 7.5.a, 7.5.b, 7.5.c, 7.5.g

Wrapping Up — 180 min — pp. 450–459
7.5.a, 7.5.c, 7.7.a, 7.7.d

Basic Learners

TE Coral Report, p. 424
TE Mollusks, p. 433
TE Symmetry, p. 438
TE Distribution Map, p. 452
⬜ Reinforcement Worksheet
⬜ Chapter Test A
⬜ Differentiated Datasheets A for Labs and Activities ■
⬜ Study Guide A ■

Advanced Learners/GATE

TE Differentiation, p. 426
TE Comparing Structure and Function, p. 436
TE Making Digestive Tracts, p. 440
TE Population Size, p. 452
⬜ Critical Thinking Worksheet
⬜ Chapter Test C
⬜ Differentiated Datasheets C for Labs and Activities ■

Teach

SE Explore Activity Observing Animal Characteristics, p. 423* ■

🖨 **Bellringer**
💿 **PowerPoint® Resources**
🖨 L62 Organs of a Shark
🖨 L63 Symmetry in Animal Body Plans
SE Quick Lab Differentiating Blood Cells, p. 427* ■

🖨 **Bellringer**
💿 **PowerPoint® Resources**
🖨 L64 Makeup of the Animal Kingdom
SE Quick Lab Grouping Organisms by Characteristics, p. 431* ■

🖨 **Bellringer**
💿 **PowerPoint® Resources**
SE Quick Lab Seeing Like an Insect, p. 441* ■
🖨 L65 Nervous Systems in Invertebrates
🖨 L66 The Stages of Complete Metamorphosis
🖨 L67 Incomplete Metamorphosis

🖨 **Bellringer**
💿 **PowerPoint® Resources**
SE Quick Lab Amplifying Sound, p. 447* ■
🖨 L68 Nervous Systems in Vertebrates

SE Skills Practice Lab Structure and Function of Bone, pp. 450–451*

Practice

SE Organize Activity Two-Panel Flip Chart, p. 422

SE Section Review, p. 429* ■

SE Section Review, p. 437* ■

SE Section Review, p. 443* ■

SE Section Review, p. 449* ■

SE Science Skills Activity Constructing Distribution Maps, p. 452* ■
📓 **Concept Mapping***
SE Chapter Review, pp. 454–455* ■

Assess

🗁 **Chapter Pretest**

SE Standards Checks, pp. 425, 427, 428
TE Standards Focus, p. 428
🗁 **Section Quiz** ■

SE Standards Checks, pp. 431, 432, 434, 436
TE Standards Focus, p. 436
🗁 **Section Quiz** ■

SE Standards Checks, pp. 438, 439, 440, 442
TE Standards Focus, p. 442
🗁 **Section Quiz** ■

SE Standards Checks, pp. 445, 446, 447, 448
TE Standards Focus, p. 448
🗁 **Section Quiz** ■

SE Standards Assessment, pp. 456–457*
🗁 **Chapter Tests A, B ■, C**
📓 **Standards Review Workbook** ■

Resources for Universal Access • Differentiated Instruction

English Learners

TE Group Activity, pp. 424, 426, 432, 433, 440, 446
TE Using the Headings, p. 425
TE Using the Figure, pp. 426, 430, 435, 444
TE Demonstration, pp. 430, 444
TE Finding Cartilage, p. 435
TE Hard Cs, p. 438
🗁 Vocabulary and Section Summary A ■, B

🗁 Section Quizzes ■
🗁 Chapter Tests A, B ■
🗁 Differentiated Datasheets A, B, and C for Labs and Activities ■
📓 Study Guide A ■
📓 Multilingual Glossary

Struggling Readers

TE Reading Strategy, pp. 427, 432, 434, 440, 446
TE Subheadings, p. 430
TE Bilateral and Radial Symmetry, p. 434
TE Conquering Subheadings, p. 440
TE Vertebrate Body Coverings, p. 445

Special Education Students

TE Finding Personal Vertebrae, p. 434
TE Invertebrates and Vertebrates, p. 439
TE Understanding Opposites, p. 444
TE Grid Intersections, p. 453

To help plan your lessons, refer to the On Course Mapping Instruction booklet.

Visual Resources

CHAPTER STARTER TRANSPARENCY

Strange but True!

BELLRINGER TRANSPARENCIES

Section: What Is an Animal?
What is the best material for washing a car – a cotton rag, a scratch pad, or an animal skeleton?

Explain your answer in your **science journal**.

Section: The Animal Kingdom
Brainstorm examples of how an organ or organ system in an animal helps the animal live in its environment.

Write your thoughts in your **science journal**.

TEACHING TRANSPARENCIES

Organs of a Shark — L62

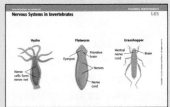
Makeup of the Animal Kingdom — L64

Symmetry in Animal Body Plans — L63

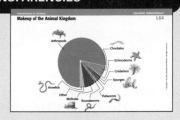
Nervous Systems in Invertebrates — L65

TEACHING TRANSPARENCIES

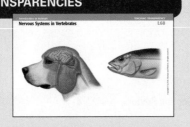
The Stages of Complete Metamorphosis — L66

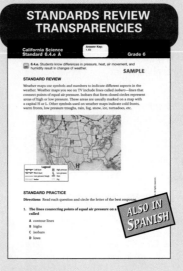
Nervous Systems in Vertebrates — L68

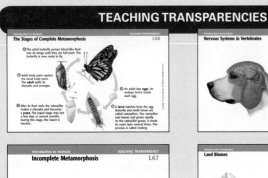
Incomplete Metamorphosis — L67

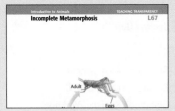

Land Biomes — E86
LINK TO EARTH SCIENCE

STANDARDS REVIEW TRANSPARENCIES

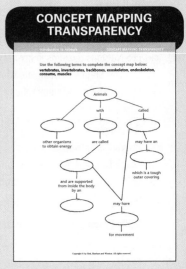

California Science Standard 6.4.e A — Grade 6
Answer Key: 1. B1

6.4.e. Students know differences in pressure, heat, air movement, and humidity result in changes of weather.

SAMPLE

STANDARD REVIEW

STANDARD PRACTICE

Directions Read each question and circle the letter of the best response.

1. The lines connecting points of equal air pressure on a map are called

A contour lines
B highs
C isobars
D lows

ALSO IN SPANISH

CONCEPT MAPPING TRANSPARENCY

Use the following terms to complete the concept map below: vertebrates, invertebrates, backbones, exoskeleton, endoskeleton, consume, muscles

Planning Resources

PARENT LETTER

SAMPLE

Dear Parent,

Your son's or daughter's science class will soon begin exploring the chapter entitled "The Nature of Physical Science." In this chapter, students will learn about how the scientific method applies to the world of physical science and the role of physical science in the world. By the end of the chapter, students should demonstrate a clear understanding of the chapter's main ideas and be able to discuss the following topics:

1. the role of questions in the process of investigation (Section 1)
2. how applying science saves lives and benefits the environment (Section 1)
3. careers that rely on science (Section 1)
4. the steps used in scientific methods (Section 2)
5. how scientific methods are used to answer questions and solve problems (Section 2)
6. the importance of safety precautions in the laboratory (Section 3)
7. examples of safety equipment and when to use them (Section 3)
8. how safety symbols are used to make laboratories safer (Section 3)

Questions to Ask Along the Way

You can help your child learn about these topics by asking interesting questions as he or she progresses through the chapter. For example, you may wish to ask your son or daughter the following question:

What are some surprising careers that use science?

What is a characteristic of a good hypothesis?

What is the first step to take if an accident happens?

ALSO IN SPANISH

TEST ITEM LISTING

SAMPLE

Holt California Physical Science
Chapter 6 Introduction to Atoms
Test Item Listing
Multiple choice

1. The smallest particle into which an element can be divided and still have the properties of that element is called a(n)
   a. nucleus.   c. atom.
   b. electron.   d. neutron.
   ANS: C   DIF: 1   REF: 1   OBJ: 2   STO: 8.3.a   KEY: atom
   MSC: SQ.1.1

2. What particle did J. J. Thomson discover?
   a. neutron   c. electron
   b. electron   d. atom
   c. atom
   d. proton
   ANS: B   DIF: 1   REF: 1   OBJ: 2   STO: 8.3.a   KEY: electron   MSC: SQ.1.2

3. How would you describe the nucleus?
   a. dense, positively charged
   b. mostly empty space, positively charged
   c. tiny, negatively charged
   d. dense, negatively charged
   ANS: A   DIF: 1   REF: 1   OBJ: 2   STO: 8.3.a   KEY: nucleus   MSC: SQ.1.3

4. Where are electrons likely to be found?
   a. in the nucleus
   b. in electron clouds
   c. mixed throughout an atom
   d. in definite paths
   ANS: B   DIF: 1   REF: 1   OBJ: 2   STO: 8.3.a   KEY: electron   MSC: SQ.1.4

5. Dalton believed that
   a. atoms of the same element are exactly alike.
   b. most, but not all, substances are made of atoms.
   c. atoms of different elements are the same.
   d. atoms can be divided.
   ANS: A   DIF: 1   REF: 1   OBJ: 1|2   STO: 8.3.a   KEY: atom

6. Every atom of a given element has the same number of
   a. protons.   c. neutrons.
   b. neutrons.   d. isotopes.
   c. Electrons
   d. isotopes
   ANS: A   DIF: 1   REF: 2   OBJ: 1   STO: 8.3.a   KEY:

ALSO IN SPANISH

👆 One-Stop Planner® CD-ROM

This CD-ROM package includes all of the resources shown here and the following time-saving tools:

- **Lab Materials QuickList Software**
- **Customizable Lesson Plans** Correlated to the California Science Standards
- **Holt Calendar Planner**
- **PowerPoint® Resources**

- **Printable Worksheets**
- **ExamView® Test Generator** Correlated to the California Science Standards
- **Holt PuzzlePro®**
- **Interactive Teacher's Edition**

Meeting Individual Needs

DIRECTED READING A

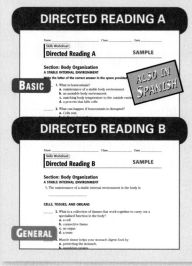

Directed Reading A — SAMPLE

Section: Body Organization
A STABLE INTERNAL ENVIRONMENT

BASIC

ALSO IN SPANISH

DIRECTED READING B

Directed Reading B — SAMPLE

Section: Body Organization
A STABLE INTERNAL ENVIRONMENT

GENERAL

VOCABULARY AND SECTION SUMMARY A

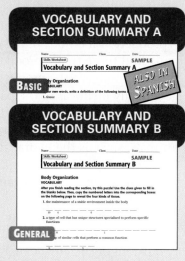

Vocabulary and Section Summary A — SAMPLE

BASIC

ALSO IN SPANISH

VOCABULARY AND SECTION SUMMARY B

Vocabulary and Section Summary B — SAMPLE

Body Organization
VOCABULARY

GENERAL

REINFORCEMENT

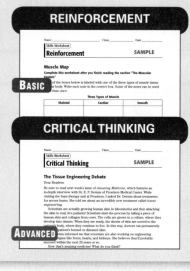

Reinforcement — SAMPLE

Muscle Map

BASIC

CRITICAL THINKING

Critical Thinking — SAMPLE

The Tissue Engineering Debate

ADVANCED

INTERACTIVE READER AND STUDY GUIDE

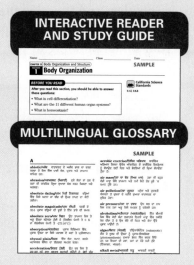

Body Organization — SAMPLE

GENERAL

MULTILINGUAL GLOSSARY

SAMPLE

Labs and Activities

DIFFERENTIATED DATASHEETS FOR EXPLORE ACTIVITY, QUICK LABS, AND CHAPTER LAB

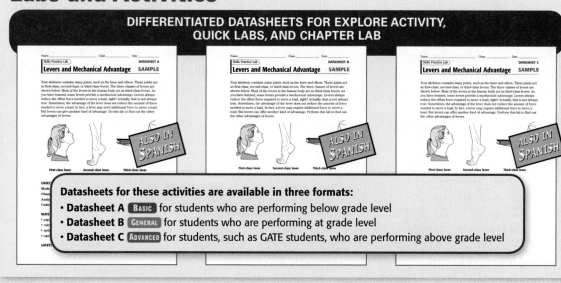

Levers and Mechanical Advantage — DATASHEET A SAMPLE

Levers and Mechanical Advantage — DATASHEET B SAMPLE

Levers and Mechanical Advantage — DATASHEET C SAMPLE

ALSO IN SPANISH

Datasheets for these activities are available in three formats:
- **Datasheet A** *BASIC* for students who are performing below grade level
- **Datasheet B** *GENERAL* for students who are performing at grade level
- **Datasheet C** *ADVANCED* for students, such as GATE students, who are performing above grade level

DATASHEET FOR SCIENCE SKILLS ACTIVITY

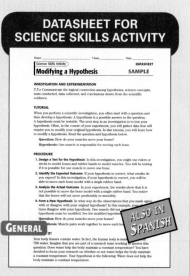

Modifying a Hypothesis — DATASHEET SAMPLE

INVESTIGATION AND EXPERIMENTATION

GENERAL

ALSO IN SPANISH

Reviews and Assessments

SECTION REVIEWS

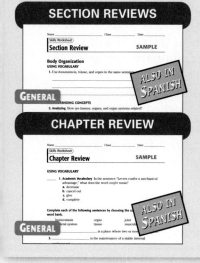

Section Review — SAMPLE

Body Organization
USING VOCABULARY

GENERAL

ALSO IN SPANISH

CHAPTER REVIEW

Chapter Review — SAMPLE

USING VOCABULARY

GENERAL

CHAPTER PRETEST

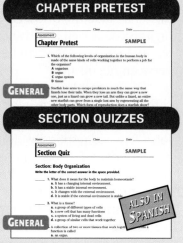

Chapter Pretest — SAMPLE

GENERAL

SECTION QUIZZES

Section Quiz — SAMPLE

Section: Body Organization

GENERAL

ALSO IN SPANISH

CHAPTER TEST A

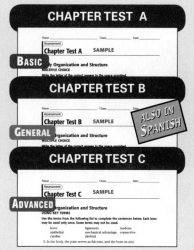

Chapter Test A — SAMPLE

BASIC

CHAPTER TEST B

Chapter Test B — SAMPLE

GENERAL

ALSO IN SPANISH

CHAPTER TEST C

Chapter Test C — SAMPLE

ADVANCED

STANDARDS ASSESSMENT

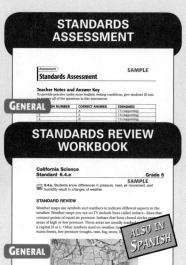

Standards Assessment — SAMPLE

Teacher Notes and Answer Key

GENERAL

STANDARDS REVIEW WORKBOOK

California Science
Standard 6.4.e — Grade 6
SAMPLE

STANDARD REVIEW

GENERAL

ALSO IN SPANISH

For a correlation of each lab or activity to the California Science Standards, see pages T22–T27.

This Teacher Background explains science concepts, principles, and theories that appear in the chapter. Use the information on these pages to refresh or enhance your understanding of the topics covered.

Section 1

What Is an Animal?

Cellular Differentiation and Organization in Animals

As multicellular organisms develop, their cells differentiate. In most multicellular organisms, the mature organism develops from a single fertilized cell. The process by which cells specialize is known as *differentiation.* In animals, cells that have the ability to differentiate or specialize into many cell types are called *pluripotent* cells. Pluripotent cells in animals are called stem cells. During differentiation, cells undergo structural changes in order to be able to perform specialized functions when the cells are mature. These changes include changes in size, shape, metabolic activity, signal responsiveness, and gene expression. As a result of cell specialization, most multicellular organisms have several levels of structural organization for structure and function within the organism: cells, tissues, organs, and organ systems.

As differentiation takes place, specialized cells that perform the same function work together as tissues. Examples of tissues include muscle tissue, epithelial tissue, connective tissue, and nervous tissue. A 10-day-old mouse embryo, like the one shown in **Figure A,** already has specialized cells that are working together in tissues. Stem cells are not only found in developing organisms, but also in adult organisms. Adult stem cells may reproduce daily to form specialized cells. For example, in humans, red blood cells develop from blood stem cells. Adult stem cells have also been found in human bone marrow and skin.

Figure A *The results of cellular differentiation and growth can be seen in a 10-day mouse embryo.*

Reproduction in Animals

Animals can reproduce either asexually or sexually. There are significant differences in the life cycles and reproduction methods of organisms that reproduce asexually and those that reproduce sexually. Asexual reproduction results in the production of an organism that is genetically identical to the parent organism. Forms of asexual reproduction include budding and fragmentation. Budding is most often seen in plants. However some animals, such as the hydra, also reproduce by budding. Fragmentation occurs in organisms such as corals, molds, and some worms. Some organisms can reproduce both asexually and sexually.

Sexual reproduction is more complex than asexual reproduction and requires the combination of DNA from two parent organisms. Sexual reproduction also requires two types of cell division, meiosis and mitosis. Gametes, or sex cells, are produced during meiosis, a process by which the genetic material of a parent cell is halved. The resulting sex cell is ready to combine with another gamete of a different sex. When two gametes from opposite sexes merge, the genetic information from each sex cell combines, and the result is an offspring that is genetically different from either parent organism. Methods of sexual reproduction and fertilization vary greatly between different kinds of organism. However, most animals primarily reproduce by sexual reproduction.

Section 2

The Animal Kingdom

Biological Classification

The history of biological classification is quite complex. The characteristics of organisms and how these characteristics are used in classification has changed largely due to scientific advancements. These advancements include the discovery and study of more and more organisms, as well as advances in the studies of DNA technology, evolution, and evolutionary relationships between organisms.

The earliest known method of biological classification is the work of Aristotle, who classified organisms based on their medium of movement or transportation. Later, John Ray was responsible for a great taxonomical advancement. Ray began classifying organisms according to their similarities and differences as determined through observation. Carolus Linnaeus was responsible for the introduction of binomial nomenclature, which helped significantly in the identification of organisms.

Today, organisms are classified mainly by their evolutionary relationships, which are based on observable and genetic similarities and differences. These relationships can be displayed in branching diagrams, as **Figure B** shows. Due to advances in evolutionary studies, cladistics has become the most accepted method for classifying organisms. This method includes arranging organisms in a specialized branching diagram, or *cladogram*. These advances have also lead to the development and wide acceptance of the domain system of classification. However, some scientists still use the older five-kingdom classification system.

Figure B
Sponges were the first kind of animals to evolve.

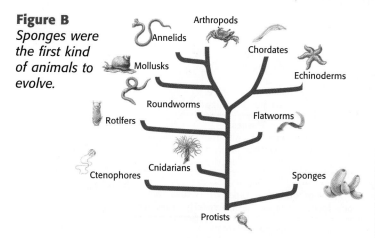

Kingdom Animalia

Members of the animal kingdom share many unique characteristics that separate them from the members of other kingdoms. Most fundamentally, animals are eukaryotic, multicellular, and heterotrophic. Additionally, animal cells do not have cell walls. Animals also have specialized structures to perform specialized functions. As animals develop, their cells differentiate, giving rise to specialized cells that form tissues, organs, and organ systems. These specialized structures and organ systems allow for a variety of functions, such as movement, digestion, and the sensory functions of the nervous system.

Section 3

Invertebrates

Invertebrate Nervous Systems

Invertebrate animals have nervous systems of varying complexity, which directly relate to the organism's sensory functions and abilities. Some animals, such as the hydra, have a very simple mechanism for the detection of movement and touch. The hydra has a *nerve net,* which is a group of separate but connected neurons.

Jellyfish also have a nerve net, as well as specialized structures called *rhopalia,* which have receptors to detect light and chemicals, maintain balance, and sense touch.

Flatworms have a nerve net in which neurons are connected by long nerve cords. Flatworms also have structures called *auricles,* which project from the side of the head region. Auricles are receptive to chemicals and aid in the detection of food. Structures called *ocelli* form eyespots and allow the flatworm to detect light.

Some insects, such as the grasshopper, have both a brain and a pair of eyes. The brain interprets sensory information and helps with movement. Insects have compound eyes that contain several units called *ommatidia.* Each ommatidium has an individual lens that detects a small part of the insect's visual field. Many ommatidia work together in the compound eye to form an image.

Section 4

Vertebrates

Structure and Function in Vertebrates

Vertebrates are characterized by a number of features, such as the presence of a backbone. The backbone is responsible for the internal support of the organism, as well as the protection of the spinal cord.

Vertebrates also have a well-developed head, in which a bony skull protects the brain. Vertebrates have a number of highly specialized organs that work together in organ systems to perform necessary life functions. The heart is a specialized organ that pumps blood and nutrients throughout the body through a system of arteries, capillaries, and veins. The mammalian heart has four chambers that work together to pump blood. Amphibians and most reptiles have a three-chambered heart, and fish have a two-chambered heart. Birds also have a four-chambered heart but many scientists consider the bird heart more closely related evolutionarily to the reptilian heart than to the mammalian heart.

Internet Resources

SciLinks is maintained by the National Science Teachers Association to provide you and your students with interesting, up-to-date links that will enrich your classroom presentation of the chapter.

Visit **www.scilinks.org** and enter the SciLinks code for more information about the topic listed.

Topic: Animals of California
SciLinks code: HY7C02

Topic: Sponges; Echinoderms
SciLinks code: HY71443; HY70458

Topic: Vertebrates and Invertebrates
SciLinks code: HY71603

Topic: Vertebrates
SciLinks code: HY71602

Improving Comprehension

Use the Graphic Organizer on this page of the Student Edition to introduce the topics that are covered in this chapter, to summarize the chapter material, or to show students how to make a pyramid chart.

Teaching Tips

- Make sure that students understand the meaning of *hierarchy*.

- Explain how the shape of the pyramid suggests that the bottom of the pyramid is the broadest level and the top is the most specific level.

LS Logical

Improving Comprehension

Graphic Organizers are important visual tools that can help you organize information and improve your reading comprehension. The Graphic Organizer below is called a *pyramid chart*. Instructions for creating other types of Graphic Organizers are located in the **Study Skills** section of the Appendix.

How to Make a Pyramid Chart

➊ Draw a triangle that is divided into sections like the one shown below. Draw as many sections as you need to draw.

➋ Draw a box to the left of the triangle, as shown in the example. Write the topic of your pyramid chart in the box.

➌ In each section of your triangle, write information about the topic in the appropriate level of the pyramid.

When to Use a Pyramid Chart

A pyramid chart is used to organize information in a hierarchy of magnitude or detail. As the shape of the pyramid suggests, the pyramid's bottom level contains information that is largest in terms of magnitude and broadest, or least specific, in terms of detail. As you read about science, look for information that you can organize into a hierarchy.

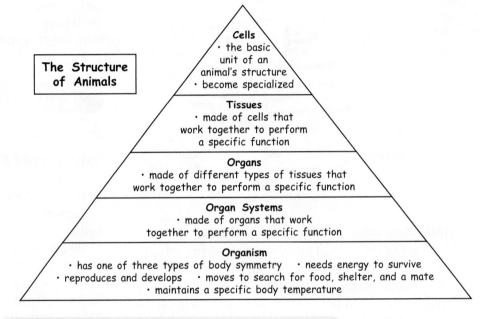

The Structure of Animals

Cells
- the basic unit of an animal's structure
- become specialized

Tissues
- made of cells that work together to perform a specific function

Organs
- made of different types of tissues that work together to perform a specific function

Organ Systems
- made of organs that work together to perform a specific function

Organism
- has one of three types of body symmetry
- needs energy to survive
- reproduces and develops
- moves to search for food, shelter, and a mate
- maintains a specific body temperature

You Try It!

This Reading Strategy can also be used within the chapter that you are about to read. Practice making your own *pyramid chart* as directed in the Reading Strategy for Section ➋. Record your work in your **Science Journal**.

Using Other Graphic Organizers

Students can practice using a variety of Graphic Organizers while reading this chapter. The following Graphic Organizers may also be useful in this chapter.

An **idea wheel** can be used to organize details about animal characteristics, discussed in Section 1.

Combination notes can be used to take notes about invertebrate body symmetry, described in Section 3.

A **process chart** can be used to describe the processes of vertebrate digestive systems, discussed in Section 4.

A **comparison table** can be used to compare qualities of invertebrates and vertebrates, discussed in Section 3 and Section 4.

Instructions for creating these Graphic Organizers are located on pp. 583–591 of the Appendix.

Unpacking the Standards

The information below "unpacks" the standards by breaking them down into basic parts. The higher-level, academic vocabulary is highlighted and defined to help you understand the language of the standards. "What It Means" restates the standards as simply as possible.

Unpacking the Standards

Use the following information with the *What It Means* in the Student Edition to help students understand why studying each standard is important.

California Standard	Academic Vocabulary	What It Means	Why It Matters
7.2.a Students know the differences between the life **cycles** and reproduction **methods** of **sexual** and asexual organisms.	**cycle** (SIE kuhl) a repeating series of changes **method** (METH uhd) a way of doing something **sexual** (SEK shoo uhl) having to do with sex	You must know how the life cycles of living things that reproduce sexually differ from the life cycles of living things that reproduce asexually. You must also explain how these ways of reproducing differ.	Students should be aware of the variety of ways in which organisms reproduce.
7.5.a Students know plants and animals have levels of organization for **structure** and **function**, including cells, tissues, organs, organ systems, and the whole organism.	**structure** (STRUHK chuhr) the arrangement of the parts of a whole **function** (FUHNGK shuhn) use or purpose	Plants and animals are made of smaller parts which are organized by shape and purpose. These layers of organization include cells, tissues, organs, organ systems, and the whole organism.	Multicellular organisms, including humans, function because their cells are organized at many levels. Each subsequent level of organization has unique properties that the prior level of organization does not have.
7.5.b Students know organ systems **function** because of the **contributions** of **individual** organs, tissues, and cells. The failure of any part can **affect** the entire system.	**function** (FUHNGK shuhn) to work **contribution** (KAHN truh BYOO shuhn) a part given toward a whole **individual** (IN duh VIJ oo uhl) being a single, separate entity; particular **affect** (uh FEKT) to change; to have an effect on; to influence	An organ system is able to work because of the work that each of its smaller parts (organs, tissues, and cells) does. If any part of an organ system fails to work well, the entire system is changed.	Organ systems within an organism are interrelated. When one part of a multicellular organism fails to perform its function, the entire organism is affected.
7.5.c Students know how bones and muscles work together to provide a **structural framework** for movement.	**structural** (STRUHK chuhr uhl) having to do with the arrangement of the parts of a whole **framework** (FRAYM WUHRK) a basic structure that supports something	Bones and muscles work together to make a system of support that allows the body to move.	Students should know that the skeletal and muscular systems function in cooperation with one another.
7.5.g Students know how to relate the **structures** of the eye and ear to their **functions.**		You must know how the shapes of the eye and the ear are related to the roles of these parts in the body.	Understanding the relationship between structure and function in eyes and ears helps scientists heal damaged eyes and ears.

The following identifies other standards that are covered in this chapter and where you can go to see them unpacked: **7.1.f** (Chapter 4)

Word Parts

Students will be able to understand a wide variety of words once they learn the meanings of common prefixes and suffixes and understand how these prefixes and suffixes are used to modify word roots. Use this activity to help students learn about prefixes, suffixes, and word roots.

Practice Have students use the prefixes and roots in the table to form four words. Then, have students define each word.

(*endotherm:* an organism that can maintain its own body temperature despite changes in the temperature of its environment; *exotherm:* an organism that maintains its body temperature by relying on the temperature of its environment; *endoskeleton:* a skeleton that supports the body from the inside of the body; *exoskeleton:* a skeleton that supports the body from outside of the body)

Prefix	Definition	Root	Definition
endo-	in, within, inside of	**skeleton**	a structure that supports a body
exo-	out, outside of	**therm**	having to do with heat

Chapter Overview

This chapter introduces the different types of invertebrate and vertebrate animals and their characteristics. The chapter also explores the animal body structure, how animals get energy, and how animals reproduce and develop.

14

Introduction to Animals

The Big Idea Animals have many unique characteristics to perform their life functions.

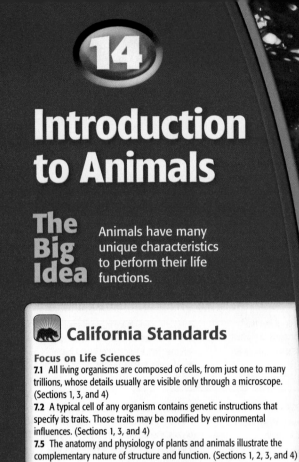

California Standards

Focus on Life Sciences
7.1 All living organisms are composed of cells, from just one to many trillions, whose details usually are visible only through a microscope. (Sections 1, 3, and 4)
7.2 A typical cell of any organism contains genetic instructions that specify its traits. Those traits may be modified by environmental influences. (Sections 1, 3, and 4)
7.5 The anatomy and physiology of plants and animals illustrate the complementary nature of structure and function. (Sections 1, 2, 3, and 4)

Investigation and Experimentation
7.7 Scientific progress is made by asking meaningful questions and conducting careful investigations. (Science Skills Activity)

Math
7.1.2 Number Sense
7.4.2 Algebra and Functions

English–Language Arts
7.1.3 Reading
7.2.2 Writing

About the Photo

Many marine bird species are found on the California coast, including the booby. This bird can spot a fish in the water from as high as 15 m (50 ft). With the fish in sight, the booby power dives beak first and closes its wings only just before it hits the water. It may not resurface for several seconds.

Organize

Two-Panel Flip Chart

Before you read this chapter, create the FoldNote entitled "Two-Panel Flip Chart." Write "Invertebrates" on one flap of the two-Panel Flip chart and "Vertebrates" on the other flap. As you read the chapter, write the characteristics of invertebrates and vertebrates under the appropriate flaps.

Instructions for creating FoldNotes are located in the Study Skills section on p. 582 of the Appendix.

California Standards Alignment

Focus on Life Sciences

7.1.f Students know that as multicellular organisms develop, their cells differentiate. **pp. 427, 429, 448–449, 455–457**

7.2.a Students know the differences between the life cycles and reproduction methods of sexual and asexual organisms. **pp. 427, 429, 442–443, 448–449, 454–457**

7.5.a Students know plants and animals have levels of organization for structure and function, including cells, tissues, organs, organ systems, and the whole organism. **pp. 423, 425–437, 439–451, 454–457**

7.5.b Students know organ systems function because of the contributions of individual organs, tissues, and cells. The failure of any part can affect the entire system. **pp. 425, 428–429, 440–441, 443, 445–447, 449, 454–456**

7.5.c Students know how bones and muscles work together to provide a structural framework for movement. **pp. 428–429, 445, 449–451, 454–456**

7.5.g Students know how to relate the structures of the eye and ear to their functions. **pp. 441, 443, 447, 449, 455–457**

Investigation and Experimentation

7.7.a Select and use appropriate tools and technology (including calculators, computers, balances, spring scales, microscopes, and binoculars) to perform tests, collect data, and display data. **pp. 423, 450–451**

7.7.d Construct scale models, maps, and appropriately labeled diagrams to communicate scientific knowledge (e.g., motion of Earth's plates and cell structure). **p. 452**

Teacher Notes

In this activity, students will choose tools to observe animals and make connections between animals that look very different but have the same basic needs (covers standards 7.5.a and 7.7.a).

Materials for Each Group

You will need to approve the tools each student selects.

Safety Caution

Remind students to review all safety cautions and icons before beginning this activity. Tell students to exercise caution around wild or unfamiliar animals, and remind students never to handle wild or unfamiliar animals.

Answers

3. Answers may vary, but should include information on the appearance of each animal and each animal's activities.

4. Answers may vary, but should include descriptions of the differences between the two kinds of animals.

5. Answers may vary, but students should identify how the animals move and the structures that the animals use to move.

6. Answers may vary. Students may not be able to locate the "mouth" of an animal such as a worm. Encourage students who cannot determine what an animal eats to conduct research on the animal's diet, eating habits, and how it finds or catches food.

Differentiated Datasheets
A **BASIC**, B **GENERAL**, C **ADVANCED**

Also editable on the Holt Lab Generator CD-ROM

Explore Activity

Observing Animal Characteristics

You don't have to travel far to see interesting animals. If you look closely, you can find many animals nearby. In this activity, you will observe the characteristics of two different animals. **Caution:** Always be careful around wild or unfamiliar animals, because they may bite or sting. Do not handle wild animals or any animals that are unfamiliar to you.

Procedure

1. Go outside, and find **two different kinds of animals** to observe.

2. Without disturbing the animals, watch them quietly for a few minutes from a distance. You may want to use **binoculars** or a **magnifying lens.**

3. Write down everything that you notice about each animal. Do you know what kind of animal each is? Where did you find them? What do they look like? What are they doing? You may want to draw a picture of them.

Analysis

4. Compare the two animals that you studied. Do they look alike? Identify their body parts.

5. How do the animals move? What structures are they using to help them move?

6. Can you tell what each animal eats? What characteristics of each animal help it find or catch food?

Math Standards

Number Sense 7.1.2 Add, subtract, multiply, and divide rational numbers (integers, fractions, and terminating decimals) and take positive rational numbers to whole-number powers. **pp. 437, 443**

Algebra and Functions 7.4.2 Solve multistep problems involving rate, average speed, distance, and time or a direct variation. **p. 455**

English–Language Arts Standards

Reading 7.1.3 Clarify word meaning through the use of definition, example, restatement, or contrast. **pp. 424, 430, 438, 444**

Writing 7.2.2 Write responses to literature: (a) Develop interpretations exhibiting careful reading, understanding, and insight; (b) Organize interpretations around several clear ideas, premises, or images from the literary work; (c) Justify interpretations through sustained use of examples and textual evidence. **p. 455**

Strange but True!

In 1995, researchers in Germany made a computer chip that could send signals to a single nerve cell in a living leech. Even more amazing, the leech's nerve cell could send signals back to the computer chip. What is so amazing about having a "mind link" with a leech? The answer may surprise you.

In the United States alone, accidents result in more than 10,000 spinal-cord injuries a year. In severe cases, a person can lose muscle control, particularly in the arms and legs. But what does this have to do with leeches?

Giant leeches from South America, like the one shown here on the scientist's arm, have only a few nerve cells. By studying leech nerves, biologists are learning how to communicate directly with nerve cells.

The scientists hope that communicating with leech nerves using a computer chip will one day help them communicate with human nerve cells. In the future, people with spinal-cord injuries may be able to use computers to communicate with the nerve cells in their bodies and move their muscles.

Scientists still have [...] but who would have [...] a promising breakthro[...] animal that doesn't e[...] backbone?

Chapter Starter Transparency
Use this transparency to help students begin thinking about invertebrates and how they might one day be used to help people with spinal cord injuries.

Preteach

Reviewing Prior Knowledge

Ask student volunteers to read the red and blue heads in the section aloud. Then, ask students what they think the section is about. Finally, ask students what they already know about multicellular organisms and how the levels of organization within an organism relates to animals.

 Bellringer

To help students focus on standard 7.5.a, ask them, "What is the best material to use for washing a car—a cotton rag, a scratch pad, or an animal skeleton? Why?" (Students may say that the cotton rag is the best material because it is soft.) Tell students that genuine sponges—the ones that some people use for washing cars—are actually skeletons of sponges that have been dried out. Although there are thousands of sponge species, fewer than 20 of them have any commercial value.

⬛ Bellringer Transparency

Motivate

Group ACTIVITY

Animal Diversity In groups, have students write down two examples of each of the following: animals that crawl, animals that fly, animals that do not have bones, animals that live in the soil, and animals that live in the ocean. Answers should be specific. For example, an answer should be "a praying mantis" rather than "an insect." As each group shares its answers with the class, others should cross out matches on their own lists. How many animals did they think of? That's diversity! ⬛ Interpersonal

---

What You Will Learn

- Animals are multicellular organisms.
- Animals have specialized cells, tissues, organs, and organ systems.
- Animals have seven basic characteristics.

Why It Matters

The characteristics of animals allow them to adapt to their environment.

Vocabulary

- coelom
- consumer
- differentiation

READING STRATEGY

Brainstorming The main idea of this section is that all animals share certain characteristics. Brainstorm words and phrases related to the characteristics of animals. Record your work in your **Science Journal**.

What Is an Animal?

Key Concept Animals are made up of many cells. Animals consume other organisms to get the energy they need to grow, survive, and reproduce.

▶ What do you think of when you hear the word *animal*? You may think of your dog or cat. You may also think about giraffes or black bears. But would you think of a sponge? Some natural sponges that people use when showering are the remains of an animal. Animals come in many shapes and sizes. Some have four legs and fur, but most do not. Some are too small to be seen without a microscope, and others are bigger than a school bus.

Animal Characteristics

Sponges, worms, penguins, and lions are all animals. But until about 200 years ago, most people thought sponges were plants. And worms don't look like penguins or lions. Some different kinds of organisms are shown in **Figure 1**. The feather star has many flexible arms that it uses to trap food. The coral has a rigid skeleton that is attached to a hard surface. Fish move their bodies to swim from place to place. So, are all of these organisms animals? And what determines whether an organism is an animal, a plant, or something else? There is no simple answer. But all animals share characteristics that set them apart from all other organisms.

Figure 1 *Most of the organisms in this picture are animals.*

Feather star · Fish · Coral

Universal Access · Differentiated Instruction

Basic Learners

Coral Report Have students study one particular animal in detail so that they can understand its physical structure. Studying one animal will help students recognize the common characteristics that all animals share. Help students understand animal characteristics by having them research the characteristics of stony corals. Then, have the students design a poster that diagrams the anatomy of one kind of stony coral. Tell students to include in their poster the characteristics that classify stony corals as animals. ⬛ Visual

---

Multicellular Makeup

Like all organisms, animals are made up of cells. Unlike plant cells, animal cells do not have cell walls. Animal cells are surrounded by only cell membranes. All animals are made up of many cells and are therefore *multicellular* organisms. In animals, all of the cells work together to perform the life functions of the animal.

Organization in Animals

Animals have different levels of structural organization in their bodies. Each cell in a multicellular organism does not perform every life function of the organism. Instead, a specific kind of cell can specialize to perform a specific function. For example, muscle cells in an animal help the animal move. Groups of the same kinds of cells that work together form *tissues*. For example, muscle cells form muscle tissue.

When different kinds of tissues work together to perform a specific function for the organism, these tissues form an *organ*. The heart, lungs, and kidneys are organs. When a group of organs work together to perform a specific function, the organs form an *organ system*. Each organ system has a unique job that is important to the survival of the whole organism. The failure of any organ system may lead to the death of the organism. The shark shown in **Figure 2** has organ systems that allow the shark to digest food, pump blood, and sense the environment.

Standards Check What would happen to the shark if its heart failed? **7.5.b**

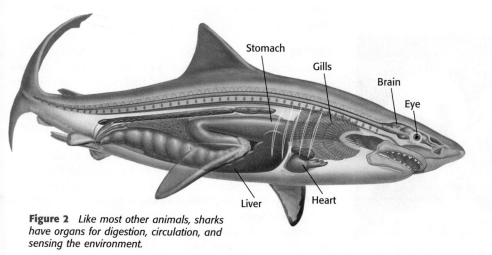

Figure 2 *Like most other animals, sharks have organs for digestion, circulation, and sensing the environment.*

Labels on Figure 2: Stomach, Gills, Brain, Eye, Liver, Heart

7.1.f Students know that as multicellular organisms develop, their cells differentiate.
7.2.a Students know the differences between the life cycles and reproduction methods of sexual and asexual organisms.
7.5.a Students know plants and animals have levels of organization for structure and function, including cells, tissues, organs, organ systems, and the whole organism.
7.5.b Students know organ systems function because of the contributions of individual organs, tissues, and cells. The failure of any part can affect the entire system.
7.5.c Students know how bones and muscles work together to provide a structural framework for movement.

Teach

Homework

Research Sharks Have interested students choose a type of shark to research and write a short report about. In the report, students should describe the shark's range, habitat, and food sources. They should also include how the shark obtains food, avoids predators, and affects people. Have students include one unusual fact about their chosen shark. **LS** Verbal

Homework

Body Organization The human body has trillions of cells, thousands of different tissues, numerous organs, and 11 major organ systems. Help students understand the levels of organization in the human body by having students list specific cells, tissues, and organs in a particular organ system. Allow students to use this text, the Internet, or other books to complete this assignment. (Sample answer for respiratory system: alveolus cell [cell], alveolus sac [tissue], and lung [organ].)

Answer to Standards Check

If the shark's heart failed, its ability to pump blood through its body would also fail. As a result, the shark would die. **7.5.b** (mastering)

Teaching Transparency: L62 Organs of a Shark

Universal Access · Differentiated Instruction

English Learners

Using the Headings English learners may have an easier time understanding the text when they know what to expect. As a group, read a heading and discuss its meaning. Tell students they can change a heading into a question and then read the paragraph to search for the answer. (For example; What are animal characteristics?) Then, have a volunteer read the text under the heading aloud. Discuss how the heading relates to the text. Address the entire section in this manner. (Sample answer for first paragraph on p. 424: Meaning of heading—Animal characteristics refer to how animals look and what some of their actions are. How the heading relates to the text—The paragraph is about characteristics that determine whether an organism is an animal or not.) Encourage students to use this strategy regularly to improve their comprehension of the text. **LS** Visual/Logical

Determining Symmetry Divide the class into cooperative groups of three or four students. Give each group a small rectangular hand mirror and copies of simple top-view drawings of a butterfly and a sea urchin. Challenge students to use the mirror to demonstrate that the butterfly has bilateral symmetry and that the sea urchin has radial symmetry.

LS Kinesthetic Co-op Learning

Using the Figure

Making Sense of Symmetry

Have students study the three animals in **Figure 3**. Discuss where these animals live and how they move. Tell students that bilateral symmetry is an advantage for animals that are highly mobile because this type of symmetry allows for streamlined movement. Radial symmetry is an advantage for animals that live attached to a substratum. Ask students to examine the organisms pictured in the figure, and have them explain why the statement about the advantages of bilateral and radial symmetry is true. **LS** Verbal

Homework

Researching Reproduction

Have interested students choose one form of asexual reproduction discussed in this section and create a poster describing at least three animals that reproduce in this way. Encourage students to include in their poster pictures and diagrams that show how each animal reproduces. **LS** Visual

 Teaching Transparency:
L63 Symmetry in Animal Body Plans

Figure 3 Symmetry in Animal Body Plans

This tortoise has **bilateral symmetry**. The two sides of its body mirror each other. On each side of its body, the tortoise has one eye, one ear, and two legs.

This sea star has **radial symmetry**. Its body is organized around the center, like spokes on a wheel.

This sponge is **asymmetrical**. You cannot draw a straight line to divide its body into two or more equal parts. Its body is not organized around a center.

coelom (SEE luhm) a body cavity that contains the internal organs

consumer (kuhn SOOM uhr) an organism that eats other organisms or organic matter

Body Plans

Animal bodies have two basic types of *symmetry*. Symmetry can be bilateral (bievLAT uhr uhl) or radial (RAY dee uhl). Animals that have no symmetry are asymmetrical (AY suh ME tri kuhl). Most animals have bilateral symmetry. **Figure 3** shows an example of each type of symmetry.

Another basic characteristic of a body plan is whether or not it has a *coelom*. A **coelom** is a body cavity that surrounds and protects many organs, such as the heart. Many animals have coeloms.

Getting Energy

All organisms need energy to survive. Plants can make their own food to get the energy that they need to live. Unlike plants however, animals cannot make their own food. Animals get energy by consuming other organisms or parts and products of other organisms. Therefore, animals are *consumers*. A **consumer** is an organism that feeds on other organisms to meet its energy needs. One way in which animals differ from plants is that animals are consumers. Although there are a few exceptions, most plants do not feed on other organisms.

Animals eat many kinds of foods. As **Figure 4** shows, pandas eat bamboo. Spiders eat other animals. Mosquitoes drink blood. Butterflies drink nectar from flowers. Also, some animals eat more than one kind of food. For example, the black bear eats both fruits and other animals.

Figure 4 Pandas eat about 13.6 kg of bamboo every day.

Answer to Standards Check

Cells that will perform different functions develop different structures. **7.1.f** (exceeding)

Reproduction

Animals make more animals like themselves through reproduction. Some animals reproduce asexually. In *asexual reproduction,* a parent has offspring that are genetically identical to the parent. For example, hydras can reproduce by budding. In *budding,* part of an organism develops into a new organism. As the new organism develops, it breaks off from the parent. Another kind of asexual reproduction is called *fragmentation.* In fragmentation, parts of an organism break off and then develop into new individuals.

Most animals reproduce sexually. In *sexual reproduction,* offspring are formed when sex cells from two parent combine. The female parent produces sex cells called *eggs.* The male parent produces sex cells called *sperm.* When an egg's nucleus and a sperm's nucleus join in a process called *fertilization,* the first cell of a new organism is formed.

Wordwise asexual reproduction
The prefix *a-* means "not."

differentiation (DIF uhr EN shee AY shuhn) the process in which the structure and function of the parts of an organism change to enable specialization of those parts

Development

A fertilized egg cell divides into many cells to form an *embryo* (EM bree OH). An embryo is one of the early stages of development of an organism, such as the mouse embryo shown in **Figure 5.**

As a multicellular organism develops, its cells become specialized through *differentiation.* **Differentiation** is the process by which cells that will perform different functions develop different structures. For example, some nerve cells grow very long, to carry electrical signals from your spine to your feet.

Standards Check What happens during differentiation? 🐻 **7.1.f**

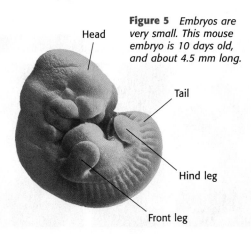

Figure 5 *Embryos are very small. This mouse embryo is 10 days old, and about 4.5 mm long.*

Head
Tail
Hind leg
Front leg

Quick Lab

Differentiating Blood Cells

1. Examine the **slide of the red bone marrow smear.**

2. Notice the different kinds of blood cells in the smear. Sketch a red blood cell and a white blood cell.

3. All blood cells differentiate from the same kind of cell called a blood stem cell. Examine the sketch of a *blood stem cell* made by your teacher.

4. Make a **flip book animation** that shows how one of the blood cells that you sketched developed from the blood stem cell.

7.1.f

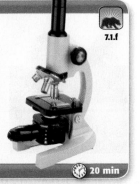

🕐 **20 min**

Quick Lab

🕐 **20 min**

Teacher Notes

In this activity, students explore the different structures of red blood cells and white blood cells as the result of differentiation (covers standard 7.1.f). Explain to students that all blood cells form from a special type of cell called a hematopoietic stem cell.

Materials for Each Group
- flipbook animation
- red bone marrow smear
- slide

Safety Caution

Remind students to review all safety cautions and icons before beginning this activity.

Answers

2. Sketches should show round, concave red blood cells; large, irregularly-shaped white blood cells.

3. Point out the differences between the stem cell and the cells in the students' sketches.

📋 Differentiated Datasheets A **BASIC**, B **GENERAL**, C **ADVANCED**

Also editable on the Holt Lab Generator CD-ROM

READING STRATEGY

Reading Organizer After students read the material about reproduction and development in animals, have them construct a concept map using the following terms: *asexual reproduction, sexual reproduction, budding, fragmentation, sex cells, egg, sperm, fertilization, embryo,* and *differentiation.* **LS** Visual

Wordwise

Etymology Review with students the meaning of the term *asexual reproduction.* Tell students that the word *asexual* contains the Greek prefix *a-,* which means "not." Ask students how the meaning of this prefix relates to the meaning of *asexual.* (Asexual reproduction is reproduction in which there is only one parent and the offspring is genetically identical to the parent. Asexual reproduction does not involve two organisms, as sexual reproduction does; therefore, the term asexual reproduction literally means, "not sexual reproduction.")

MISCONCEPTION ALERT

Endotherms Some students may be confused about the ways in which endotherms control their body temperature. Explain to students that endotherms can regulate their body temperature by performing activities such as warming themselves in the sun. They can also rely on their internal systems for temperature regulation. Ask students how body temperature is regulated in humans. Ask students to select a specific type of endotherm and research how that type of endotherm regulates its body temperature. Have students write a paragraph describing their findings. **LS** Verbal

Close

Standards Focus

This **Standards Focus** provides you with a quick way to **assess, reteach,** and **re-assess** one or more concepts in the section.

**Assess**

1. A cell that will perform a specialized function undergoes ____ to develop specialized structures. (differentiation) **7.1.f**

2. If one of a frog's organ systems, such as the digestive system, fails, what might happen to the frog? (The frog may die.) **7.5.a**

3. What type of reproduction is budding? (asexual reproduction) **7.2.a**

Reteach

Animal Traits Have students create a chart comparing the traits of the animals discussed in this section. Students' charts should have the following column headings: Organ Systems, Body Plan, Getting Energy, Reproduction and Development, Movement, and Maintaining Body Temperature. Have students choose at least three animals discussed in this section and use each animal name as a row heading in the chart. Then, have students fill in the chart using their textbooks and other research materials, such as the Internet or an encyclopedia.
LS Visual **7.2.a, 7.5.a**

Re-Assess

Animal Examples Have students write a summary of the characteristics shared by all animals. Tell them not to repeat the boldface paragraph headings in the text. Instead, students must explain each characteristic by first giving an example. (Sample answer: Monkeys run, climb, and swing in trees. Animals move.) **LS** Verbal **7.2.a, 7.5.a**

Movement

Nearly all animals move to search for food, shelter, or mates. **Figure 6** shows some of the different ways in which animals move. Some animals can move from place to place only at certain stages of their life. For example, a young sea anemone finds its food as it drifts in ocean currents. When a sea anemone is older, it will swim to the ocean floor and attach itself there. As an adult, a sea anemone cannot move around and must wait for food to come within reach of its tentacles, as **Figure 6** shows.

Most movement in animals is possible because of muscle cells. By contracting and relaxing, groups of muscle cells work together to help an animal move. For example, a parrot flies because the muscles that are attached to its breast bone and bones in its wings contract and relax.

Standards Check How do muscle cells allow a parrot to fly? **7.5.a, 7.5.c**

Figure 6 How Animals Move

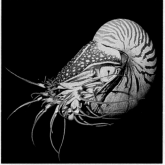

Anemone catching food **Nautilus swimming** **Fish swimming**

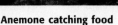

Caterpillar crawling **Moth flying** **Parrot flying** **Gibbon walking**

Answer to Standards Check

The parrot can fly because the muscles that are attached to its breast bone and to the bones in its wings contract and relax. These muscles are made up of muscle cells that work together. **7.5.a** (exceeding), **7.5.c** (mastering)

Maintaining Body Temperature

To function well, all animals need to maintain their bodies within a specific range of temperatures. Birds and mammals maintain their own body temperatures by using some of the energy released by chemical reactions. These kinds of animals are called *endotherms* (EN doh THURMZ).

Animals that rely on their environment to maintain their body temperature are called *ectotherms* (EK toh THURMZ). Some ectotherms have developed different behaviors to control their body temperatures. For example, some lizards sit in the sun to warm themselves in the morning before they hunt. When the weather gets too hot, the lizard may burrow underground to stay cool.

SECTION Review

7.1.f, 7.2.a, 7.5.a, 7.5.b, 7.5.c

Summary

- All animals are multicellular organisms. Specialized cells in animals are organized into tissues, organs, and organ systems.

- Most animals have bilateral symmetry or radial symmetry. Some are asymmetrical.

- Animals consume other organisms to get energy.

- Animals reproduce asexually or sexually.

- As an embryo develops, its cells differentiate.

- Animals move in many ways.

- Animals that maintain their own body temperature are endotherms. Animals that rely on their environment to maintain their body temperature are ectotherms.

Using Vocabulary

1 Write an original definition for *embryo* and *consumer*.

Understanding Concepts

2 **Identifying** What is differentiation?

3 **Describing** Starting at the level of the cell, describe the levels of structural organization in animals.

Critical Thinking

4 **Making Comparisons** What are the two main kinds of reproduction in animals? How do the kinds of reproduction differ?

5 **Identifying Relationships** A fish tank contains water, chemicals, fish, snails, algae, and gravel. Which of these items are alive? Which of these items are animals? Why are some of the living organisms not classified as animals?

6 **Making Inferences** Could a parrot fly if it did not have muscle cells? Explain.

INTERPRETING GRAPHICS The graph shows body temperatures of organism A and organism B and shows the ground temperature. Use the graph below to answer the next two questions.

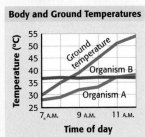

Body and Ground Temperatures

7 **Evaluating Data** How do the body temperatures of the two organisms change as the ground temperature changes?

8 **Making Inferences** Which organism is probably an ectotherm? Which organism is probably an endotherm? Explain.

Internet Resources

For a variety of links related to this chapter, go to www.scilinks.org
Topic: Animals of California
SciLinks code: HY7C02

---

5. Fish, snails, and algae are alive. The fish and the snails are animals. Algae are not classified as animals because they cannot move around on their own and can perform photosynthesis.

6. A parrot could not fly if it did not have muscle cells because muscles are made up of muscle cells; muscles are required to contract and relax to move the wing and support flight. **7.5.a** (exceeding), **7.5.b** (exceeding), **7.5.c** (mastering)

7. The body temperature of organism A increases as the ground temperature increases. The body temperature of organism B stays the same regardless of the ground temperature.

8. Organism A is probably an ectotherm because its body temperature changes with its environment. Organism B is probably an endotherm because it is able to maintain a steady body temperature regardless of the ground temperature.

Section Review Standards Guide

	Supporting	Mastering	Exceeding
7.1.f			2
7.2.a		4	
7.5.a		3	6
7.5.b			6
7.5.c		6	

Answers to Section Review

1. Sample answer: An organism is called an embryo during the early stages of its development. A consumer is an organism that obtains energy and nutrients from other organisms.

2. Sample answer: Differentiation is the process by which cells specialize and develop the structures needed to perform specific functions. **7.1.f** (exceeding)

3. Cells that perform the same function and work together form tissues. Different kinds of tissues work together to perform specific functions in an organ. Organs work together to perform specific functions in an organ system. Organ systems perform important functions for the life of the organism. **7.5.a** (mastering)

4. The two main kinds of reproduction are asexual reproduction and sexual reproduction. Asexual reproduction requires only a single individual and results in offspring that are genetically identical to the parent. In sexual reproduction, offspring are formed when the genetic information of two parents combine. **7.2.a** (mastering)

Section Resources

- Directed Reading A **BASIC** (Also in Spanish), B **GENERAL**

- Interactive Reader and Study Guide

- Section Quiz **GENERAL** (Also in Spanish)

- Section Review **GENERAL** (Also in Spanish)

- Vocabulary and Section Summary A **BASIC** (Also in Spanish), B **GENERAL**

Preteach

Reviewing Prior Knowledge

Review standard 7.5.a with students. Ask students to summarize the standard in their own words. Then, ask students to predict how the standard may apply to this section.

 Bellringer

Have students focus on standard 7.5.a by asking them to brainstorm examples of how an organ or organ system in an animal helps the animal live in its environment. (Sample answer: A fish has gills which allow it to breathe in water.)

Bellringer Transparency

Motivate

Demonstration

Sponge Expansion Place a thin, dry slice of a natural sponge under a microscope. Allow students to examine the spongin fiber network. Next, add a few drops of water to the sponge, and have students re-examine the slice. Students should see how the the fibers take up the water (the fibers will swell slightly) and how the water moves into the spaces between the fibers. **LS** Visual

Using the Figure

Pie Graphs Use the pie graph shown in **Figure 1** to discuss animal diversity. Ask students whether invertebrates or vertebrates form the larger proportion of the animal kingdom. (invertebrates) Then, ask students to which group they think humans belong. (chordates) Answer to caption question: arthropods. **LS** Visual/Logical

Teaching Transparency:
L64 Makeup of the Animal Kingdom

What You Will Learn

- The animal kingdom is made up of many different kinds of animals.
- Animals can be divided into two main groups: invertebrates and vertebrates.
- Each group of animals has unique characteristics.

Why It Matters

Studying the characteristics of an animal will help you understand how the animal survives in its environment.

Vocabulary

- invertebrate
- exoskeleton
- vertebrate
- endoskeleton

READING STRATEGY

Graphic Organizer In your **Science Journal**, make a Pyramid Chart that ranks the invertebrates discussed in this section by levels of complexity.

The Animal Kingdom

Key Concept Animals are a diverse group of organisms that have adaptations to live in water and on land.

▶ Both eagles and butterflies have wings. Are eagles and butterflies closely related because they both have wings? The answer is no. Butterflies are insects, and eagles are birds. Insects, birds, and other animals show great diversity in body structure and function, as well as in how and where they live.

Animal Diversity

Scientists have named more than 1 million species of animals. Many species that exist have not yet been discovered and named. Some scientists estimate that more than 3 million species of animals live on Earth. Some of these animals are becoming extinct before they have been discovered or described.

Animals that have been discovered and described have been placed into groups. Placing animals into groups makes it easier to study all of the different kinds of animals. The pie graph in **Figure 1** shows the proportions of the main groups of animals in the animal kingdom.

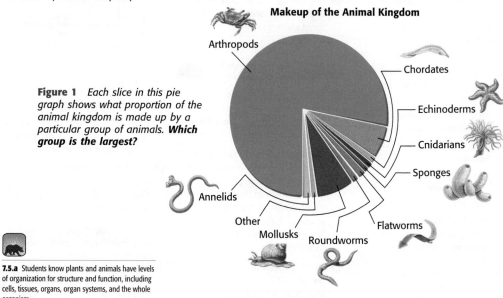

Makeup of the Animal Kingdom

Arthropods · Chordates · Echinoderms · Cnidarians · Sponges · Flatworms · Roundworms · Mollusks · Other · Annelids

Figure 1 *Each slice in this pie graph shows what proportion of the animal kingdom is made up by a particular group of animals.* **Which group is the largest?**

7.5.a Students know plants and animals have levels of organization for structure and function, including cells, tissues, organs, organ systems, and the whole organism.

Universal Access · Differentiated Instruction

Struggling Readers

Subheadings Tell students to take clues from subheadings. Point out that the phrase "Invertebrate Characteristics" on p. 431 is a main heading and that the word "Sponges" is a sub-heading in smaller font under "Invertebrate Characteristics." Show readers that this means they can make the statement, "Sponges are a type of invertebrate." Tell students to look through the rest of the section and make similar statements based on the other headings that they see. (Sample answers: Sponges, cnidarians, flatworms, roundworms, mollusks, annelids, arthropods, and echinoderms are all invertebrates. Fish, amphibians, reptiles, birds, and mammals are all vertebrates.) **LS** Verbal/Logical

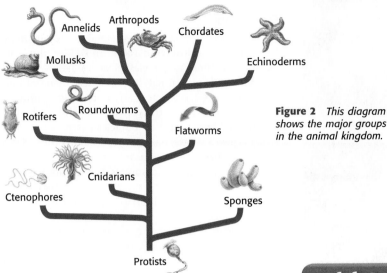

Labels on diagram: Annelids, Arthropods, Chordates, Mollusks, Echinoderms, Rotifers, Roundworms, Flatworms, Cnidarians, Ctenophores, Sponges, Protists

Figure 2 *This diagram shows the major groups in the animal kingdom.*

Classification

Scientists organize animals into groups based on the animals' characteristics and evolutionary relationships. In the past, scientists grouped animals based on only structural characteristics, such as symmetry. Today, scientists also use DNA to place animals into groups. **Figure 2** shows groups of animals and how they are related to each other. All animals, except for most of the members of chordates, are known as *invertebrates*.

Invertebrate Characteristics

Most of the animals on Earth are invertebrates. An **invertebrate** is an animal that does not have a backbone. In fact, invertebrates do not have any bones. Insects, snails, jellyfish, and worms are all examples of invertebrates. Invertebrates can be found living in every environment on Earth. Sponges are some of the simplest invertebrates.

Sponges

Most sponges live in the ocean. Sponges have an asymmetrical body plan. A sponge is a mass of specialized cells that is held together by a jelly-like material. Tiny, glassy structures in the sponge also provide support. The body of a sponge has many tubes and thousands of small holes or *pores*. A sponge sweeps water through the pores into the tubes. In the tubes, specialized cells filter and digest food particles from the water. Sponges reproduce asexually by fragmentation and sexually.

Standards Check Describe the body of a sponge. **7.5.a**

Quick Lab

Grouping Organisms by Characteristics **7.5.a**

1. On a **sheet of paper**, write a list of six organisms from this chapter.

2. Divide the organisms into two groups based on one characteristic. Record the animals in each group.

3. Divide each group into two new groups based on a different characteristic. Keep a record of the animals in each group.

4. Repeat step 3 until there is only one animal in a group.

5. Exchange your list with another student, and try to figure out the characteristics the student used to divide his or her list of organisms.

⏱ **15 min**

invertebrate (in VUHR tuh brit) an animal that does not have a backbone

---

Quick Lab ⏱ 15 min

Teacher Notes

In this activity, students classify organisms based on the organisms' characteristics (covers standard 7.5.a). Discuss with the class how observable characteristics are a product of an organism's levels of structural organization. When compiling the initial list, students should select a diversity of animals.

Materials for Each Group
• sheet of paper

Answers

Answers may vary depending on the list of organisms the students choose to explore. Students should be able to articulate their reasons for their choices.

📋 **Differentiated Datasheets**
A **Basic**, B **General**, C **Advanced**

Also editable on the
Holt Lab Generator CD-ROM

Teach

CONNECTION ACTIVITY
Real World

Helpful Sponges Sponges have few predators. The sharp spicules and tough fibers in the bodies of sponges discourage fish and other aquatic organisms from eating sponges. Many sponges also produce toxic chemicals that deter predators and keep other sponges from growing too close. A chemical produced by a Caribbean sponge, *Cryptothethya crypta*, was one of the first marine chemicals to be used in chemotherapy. Currently, many other chemicals produced by sponges are being tested as anti-cancer and antiviral drugs. Have students use the Internet to research other modern uses for chemicals produced by sponges. **LS** Verbal

Discussion

Classification Diagrams
Launch a class discussion about the diagram shown in **Figure 2.** Ask students how this diagram compares to the branching diagrams that they learned about in Chapter 11. Ask students what the different branches on this diagram represent. (Each branch of the diagram represents a difference in characteristics. Animals grouped together before a branch in the diagram share similar characteristics. This diagram is different from the branching diagrams in Chapter 11 because all of the groups of organisms that are still living today are not lined up at the top of the diagram.)

Answer to Standards Check

Sponges have asymmetrical body plans. Sponges are a mass of specialized cells that are held together by a jelly-like material. Tiny, glassy structures also provide the sponge with support. **7.5.a** (exceeding)

Mnemonics To help students remember the two different body plans of cnidarians, provide them with the following mnemonics. Write the words *medusa* and *polyp* on the board. Point out that the word *medusa* contains the letter *d* and that this form of a cnidarian has tentacles that hang **d**own from the animal's body. Then, point out that the word *polyp* contains the letter *p*, and that this form of a cnidarian has tentacles that project u**p** from the animal's body.

LS Verbal

Group ACTiViTY

Observing Hydras Obtain live hydras and water fleas (*Daphnia*) from a biological supply house. Distribute the hydras in water-filled specimen dishes. Have pairs of students study the hydras under a dissecting microscope. Add a few water fleas to each dish, and have students observe how hydras use their tentacles to capture and subdue prey. Encourage students to draw the hydras and to record their observations of how hydras move and manipulate captured prey into their mouths. **LS** Visual

ACTiViTY

Blood Flukes Schistosomiasis is an infectious disease caused by blood flukes of the genus *Schistosoma*. About 200 million people are afflicted by schistosomiasis worldwide. Encourage students to research the *Schistosoma* blood fluke and schistosomiasis. As a class, create a bulletin-board display describing and illustrating the blood fluke's complex life cycle, the symptoms of schistosomiasis, and the steps that can be taken to reduce the chance of infection. **LS** Visual/Verbal

Figure 3 *This jellyfish has a medusa body form. It floats in ocean currents and traps prey with its tentacles.*

exoskeleton (EKS oh SKEL uh tuhn) a hard, external, supporting structure

Wordwise The prefix *exo-* means "outside" or "external." Another example is *exotic.*

Figure 4 *This flatworm has a head with eyespots and sensory lobes. This kind of flatworm is often about 15 mm long.*

Cnidarians

Cnidarians are also invertebrates, but they are more complex than sponges. Most cnidarians (ni DER ee uhnz) live in the ocean. The three major classes of cnidarians are hydrozoans (HIE droh ZOH uhnz), jellyfish, and sea anemones and corals.

Cnidarians have one of two radially symmetrical body plans—the *medusa* or the *polyp* form. The medusa is a cup or bell-shaped body that has tentacles extending from it. The jellyfish **Figure 3** shows, has the medusa body form. Sea anemones and corals have medusa body forms when they are young, or *larvae.* As adults, sea anemones and corals have polyp body forms. Polyps attach to hard surfaces at the base of the cup. The tentacles of the animal then extend into the water. Specialized stinging cells, called *cnidocytes* (NEE doh siets), are located on the tentacles. Cnidocytes are used to stun and capture prey. Many cnidarians reproduce by sexual reproduction. Some cnidarians can also reproduce by budding or fragmentation.

Standards Check Describe two cnidarian body plans. **7.5.a**

Flatworms

Flatworms are the simplest worms. Many flatworms live in water, while some live in damp soils. Other flatworms are parasites. A parasite is an organism that invades and feeds on the body of another organism. For example, tapeworms are parasites that live in the intestines of humans.

Flatworms have more-complex bodies than sponges or cnidarians do. Flatworms have flat bodies that are bilaterally symmetrical. The flatworm, as **Figure 4** shows, has a clearly defined head with eyespots, which are sensitive to light. Flatworms reproduce both sexually and by fragmentation.

Roundworms

Unlike flatworms, roundworms have a coelom and are cylindrical, like spaghetti. Roundworms also have bilateral symmetry. Most roundworms are little more than 2 cm long. They live in freshwater habitats, in damp soils, and as parasites in the tissues and body fluids of other animals. Some roundworms eat tiny organisms. Other roundworms break down dead organisms and make soils more fertile.

Eyespot

Sensory lobe

Answer to Standards Check

Cnidarians have two kinds of body forms, a medusa form and a polyp form. The medusa has a cup or bell-shaped body with tentacles hanging down from it. The cup of the polyp attaches to a hard surface and allows the tentacles to stick up into the water.

7.5.a (exceeding)

Wordwise

What's Outside? Review the definition of *exoskeleton,* and point out that the prefix *exo-* means "outside," or "external" as does the prefix *ecto-*. Then ask students, what the terms *ectoderm, ectothermic,* and *ectoplasm* mean. (An *ectoderm* is an outer cellular membrane; an *ectothermic* animal is a cold-blooded animal, which means it relies on its external environment for body temperature regulation; *ectoplasm* is the outer layer of a cell's cytoplasm.) **LS** Logical

Mollusks

Snails, slugs, clams, oysters, squids, and octopuses are mollusks. Although most mollusks live in the ocean, some live in fresh water. Others live on land. Mollusks have a specialized tissue called a *mantle*. The mantle secretes the shell of snails, clams, and oysters. Mollusks also have a muscular foot. Snails use the foot to move. In squids, such as the one in **Figure 5,** and in octopuses, the foot has evolved into tentacles. Squids and octopuses use their tentacles to capture prey, such as fish. Mollusks that do not have tentacles feed differently. Clams and oysters filter food from the water. Snails and slugs feed on plants and break down dead organisms. Mollusks reproduce sexually.

Figure 5 *The squid is a mollusk that moves by forcing water out of its mantle.*

Annelids

Annelids live in the ocean and on land. Annelids have round, bilaterally symmetrical bodies. Because annelids are made up of repeating compartments, or segments, annelids are also called *segmented worms*. Leeches are annelids that suck blood. Earthworms, such as the worm in **Figure 6,** break down dead organisms as they burrow through soil. Marine annelids eat mollusks and small animals. Each annelid has both male and female sex organs. But individuals cannot fertilize themselves. Individuals fertilize each other to reproduce sexually.

Arthropods

Arthropods are the most diverse group in the animal kingdom. Arthropods have bilaterally symmetry and a strong, external armor called an **exoskeleton.** The exoskeleton provides defense against predators. The exoskeleton also prevents the animal from drying out in the air and in the sun. Insects, such as the bumblebee in **Figure 7,** are a familiar group of arthropods that live on land. Insects' bodies are clearly divided into a head, thorax, and abdomen. Millipedes, centipedes, and arachnids, such as spiders, and scorpions are also arthropods. Arthropods that live in the water include crab and shrimp. Most arthropods are either males or females and reproduce sexually.

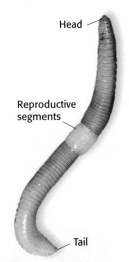

Head

Reproductive segments

Tail

Figure 6 *Except for the head, tail, and reproductive segments, all of the segments of this common garden earthworm are identical.*

Figure 7 *The bumblebee has two antennae, two wings, six legs, a head, a thorax, and an abdomen.*

Sea Star Hypotheses Display an example of an echinoderm, such as a sea star. In their **Science Journal,** students should draw the echinoderm and write a brief hypothesis of what it eats, how it moves, and where it most likely lives. Discuss students' answers before beginning the section. **LS** Verbal

Echinoderm Metamorphosis
Most adult echinoderms are sessile or move slowly over the sea floor. But echinoderm larvae are able to swim a little, and with the help of ocean currents, often travel great distances before they settle and metamorphose into adults. Ask students why it is an advantage for echinoderm larvae to have bilateral symmetry and for adults to have radial symmetry.

📖 READING STRATEGY

Making Outlines Have students use headings in the text to create an outline of the material on vertebrate characteristics. Under each heading, have students list details about each type of vertebrate discussed in this section.
LS Logical/Verbal

Answer to Standards Check

Lancelets differ from vertebrates because lancelets do not have backbones as vertebrates do. **7.5.a** (exceeding)

Figure 8 *Sea urchins are common in kelp forests along the coast of California.*

vertebrate (VUHR tuh brit) an animal that has a backbone

endoskeleton (EN doh SKEL uh tuhn) an internal skeleton made of bone and cartilage

Figure 9 *Lancelets are one of the few marine organisms grouped as chordates. A lancelet has a notochord but does not have a backbone.*

Echinoderms

Echinoderms (ee KIE noh DUHRMZ) are invertebrates that live in the ocean and include sea stars, sea urchins, and sand dollars. The name *echinoderm* means "spiny skinned." Echinoderms, such as the sea urchins in **Figure 8,** have an exoskeleton covered in bumps and spines. Echinoderms have bilateral symmetry as larvae but have radial symmetry as adults. They also have a unique system of canals filled with water called the *water vascular system* (WAWT uhr VAS kuh luhr SIS tuhm). The water vascular system uses water pumps to help the animals move, eat, breathe, and sense the environment. Most echinoderms feed by scavenging and filtering food out of the water. However, many sea stars prey on mollusks, such as clams.

Echinoderms usually reproduce sexually. For fertilization to take place, males release sperm into the water and females release eggs into the water. Larvae are formed when the sperm fertilizes the eggs. Some sea stars can regenerate a whole individual from an arm that is cut off. This is a form of asexual reproduction.

Vertebrate Characteristics

Vertebrates belong to the phylum Chordata. Members of this phylum are called *chordates* (KAWR DAYTS). Lancelets (LANS lits), such as the one shown in **Figure 9,** and tunicates (TOO ni kits) are also chordates. All chordates share some characteristics, such as a *notochord*, during their life cycle. The notochord is a stiff but flexible rod that supports the body of the animal.

As a vertebrate develops, the notochord is replaced by a backbone. **Vertebrates** are animals that have backbones. The backbone is a strong but flexible column of individual bony units called *vertebrae* (VUHR tuh BRAY). The backbone is a part of the endoskeleton of a vertebrate. An **endoskeleton** is an internal skeleton that supports the body of the animal and provides a place for muscles to attach. Muscles that are attached to the endoskeleton allow the animal to move.

Less than 5% of the known animal species are vertebrates. Vertebrates are divided into five main groups: fishes, amphibians, reptiles, birds, and mammals. Vertebrates can live in water and on land. Some vertebrates feed on only plants or on only animals. Some feed on both plants and animals. Vertebrates are either male or female and reproduce mainly by sexual reproduction.

Standards Check How do lancelets differ from vertebrates? **7.5.a**

Universal Access · Differentiated Instruction

Special Education Students

Finding Personal Vertebrae Make sure students realize that they have vertebrae and know how to find them. Ask students to stand up. Have them put one hand at the center base of their skulls and feel the bumpy bones. Then, have them place the other hand at their center backs below their waists and feel their bumpy bones. Then, have them move their two hands towards each other along their spines feeling the bumpy bones as they go. **LS** Kinesthetic

Struggling Readers

Bilateral and Radial Symmetry Make sure students understand the terms *bilateral* and *radial symmetry*. Place the following items on a table where students can see them: a silk daisy (stemless), a glove, and a water bottle. Ask students to write a sentence explaining why each of the three items has bilateral, radial, or no symmetry. **LS** Visual/Verbal

Fish

More than half of the species of vertebrates are fish. The oldest recognizable vertebrates that appeared nearly 500 million years ago were small, odd-looking fish without jaws. Today, there are two small groups of jawless fishes. All other fishes can be divided into two main groups: the *cartilaginous fish* and the *bony fish*. Cartilaginous fish have a skeleton made of a flexible tissue called *cartilage*. This group includes sharks and stingrays. All other fish have a bony skeleton. Bony fish, such as the Garibaldi in **Figure 10,** are found in marine and freshwater environments around the world.

Figure 10 *This Garibaldi, is a bony fish that is commonly found in the kelp forests along the coast of California.*

Amphibians

Most modern amphibians live near fresh water because their eggs and larvae need water to survive. Salamanders, frogs, toads, and caecilians are amphibians. Adult frogs, such as the frog shown in **Figure 11,** and toads do not have tails. Frogs and toads have long hind legs used for hopping and swimming. Adult salamanders have tails, and most have legs equal in size to the tail. Like frogs, some salamanders live completely in the water. However, others spend their lives on land and return to water only to reproduce. Caecilians are tropical amphibians that live under logs and in burrows. All amphibians have thin skins that must be moist. Most amphibians have an aquatic larval stage in their life cycle. In the larval stage, a frog is called a tadpole.

Figure 11 *The Pacific Tree frog can be found in western North America, including California.* **By studying this photo, can you tell which part of its life cycle this frog has reached?**

Reptiles

Reptiles live nearly anywhere on land because they do not need water to lay their eggs. Reptile eggs are protected from drying out by membranes and a shell. Some reptiles, such as turtles, alligators, and snakes can also live in water. Some reptiles feed on plants. Other reptiles feed on insects and other arthropods. Some reptiles, such as the snake in **Figure 12,** eat other vertebrates. Reptiles mainly reproduce sexually.

Figure 12 *Both the caiman and the snake are reptiles. The caiman and the snake share many characteristics, such as tails and scaly skins.*

Close

Standards Focus

This **Standards Focus** provides you with a quick way to **assess, reteach,** and **re-assess** one or more concepts in the section.

Assess

1. How do sponges obtain and digest food? (A sponge sweeps water through the pores into the tubes in the sponge's body. Then, specialized cells filter and digest food particles from the water.) **7.5.a**

2. What function does the mantle serve in a mollusk? (The mantle secretes the shell of a mollusk.) **7.5.a**

3. What is an endoskeleton? (an internal skeleton which supports the body of the animal) **7.5.a**

Reteach

Light as a Feather Help students focus on standard 7.5.a by providing groups of students with a wing feather, a paper clip, a small scale, and a meterstick. Tell groups to weigh the feather and the paper clip. Next, tell the class to let group members take turns dropping the feather and the paper clip from a height of 1 m. Challenge groups to discuss how the fall of the feather differs from the fall of the paper clip and how feather shape plays a role in bird flight. **LS** Visual/ Logical **7.5.a**

Re-Assess

Making Comparisons Have students choose one invertebrate and one vertebrate discussed in this section. Then, ask students to make a chart describing how the method that each animal uses to move helps the animal survive in its environment. Tell students to use the following column headings in their chart: "Type of Animal" (invertebrate or vertebrate), "Method of Movement," and "How Method Helps the Animal Survive." **LS** Visual **7.5.a**

Figure 13 *The California brown pelican can live on land and on water. Pelicans feed on fish.*

Birds

Some birds live on land. Others live in the water. Birds such as the pelican in **Figure 13** live on land and on the water. Birds share many characteristics with reptiles, such as similar structures in their feet. But birds also have unique characteristics. For example, birds are the only living animals that have feathers. Feathers are important for maintaining body temperature. Feathers also help shape the body and the wings for flying. Some birds, such as the penguin, no longer use their wings to fly. The penguin uses its wings to swim. Birds such as the ostrich and emu do not fly but have unique characteristics that help them run. All birds reproduce by sexual reproduction.

Standards Check List two reasons that feathers are important? **7.5.a**

Mammals

All of the approximately 5,000 species of mammals share certain characteristics. For example, all mammals have hair, and all female mammals can produce milk for their young. Some members of the three main groups of mammals are shown in **Figure 14.** The echidna is a monotreme. Monotremes lay eggs that have shells. Kangaroos and opossums are marsupials or "pouched mammals." Marsupials give birth to embryos. The embryos continue to develop in their mother's pouch. The sea otter is a placental mammal, which means that is has placenta in its uterus. The *placenta* is an organ through which nutrients and wastes are exchanged between the mother and developing offspring. All mammals reproduce by sexual reproduction.

Figure 14 **Examples of Three Kinds of Mammals**

Echidna (monotreme)	Kangaroo (marsupial)	Sea Otter (placental mammal)

Universal Access · Differentiated Instruction

Advanced Learners/GATE

Comparing Structure and Function

Have students compare the differences in structure and function of various animals by displaying the endoskeletons of a sea urchin or a sea star, a model or an image of a shark skeleton, and a model or an image of another vertebrate animal, such as a mouse or a bird. Then, have students discuss how these skeletons are different from each other in structure and function. **LS** Visual/Verbal

ACTIVITY

Where Animals Live Use the teaching transparency titled "Land Biomes" to tell students how animals that live in different biomes are adapted to their biome. Have each student research the conditions in and the animals of a biome by using the Internet or library resources. Then, have each student make a list of eight clues to help the rest of the students guess his or her animal and its biome.

 Teaching Transparency: *LINK TO EARTH SCIENCE* E86 Land Biomes

Summary

- The animal kingdom can be divided into two main groups: invertebrates and vertebrates. Invertebrates do not have backbones. Vertebrates have backbones.
- Sponges, cnidarians, flatworms, roundworms, mollusks, annelids, arthropods, and echinoderms are groups of invertebrates.
- Fish, amphibians, reptiles, birds, and mammals are groups of vertebrates.
- Invertebrate bodies can be asymmetrical, radially symmetrical, or bilaterally symmetrical. Some invertebrates have different body symmetries at different stages in their life cycle.
- Most vertebrate bodies have bilateral symmetry.
- Many invertebrates reproduce by asexual reproduction and sexual reproduction. Most vertebrates reproduce only by sexual reproduction.

Using Vocabulary

1. Write an original definition for *exoskeleton*.

2. Use the following terms in the same sentence: *invertebrate and vertebrate,* and *placenta*.

Understanding Concepts

3. **Describing** Describe the kinds of cnidarian body forms and cnidarian stinging cells.

4. **Identifying** Name two characteristics that are found in mollusks.

5. **Comparing** What are two main differences between a sponge and a roundworm?

6. **Identifying** Identify one similarity and one difference between vertebrates and other chordates.

7. **Classifying** Into what group would you classify a female organism that is covered in fur and that provides milk for its young?

Critical Thinking

8. **Applying Concepts** Explain why adult amphibians have to live near water or in a very wet habitat.

INTERPRETING GRAPHICS Use the two diagrams below to answer the next two questions.

9. **Making Comparisons** What kind of skeleton does the organism in (a) have? What kind of skeleton does the organism in (b) have?

10. **Identifying Relationships** Could you classify these two organisms as an invertebrate or a vertebrate based on only the kind of the skeleton they have? Explain.

Math Skills

11. **Making Calculations** A bird that weighs 15 g eats 10 times its weight in food in a week. Calculate how much food the bird eats in a day.

Challenge

12. **Analyzing Relationships** What is the relationship between the kind of eggs reptiles produce and where reptiles can live?

5. Sample answer: Two main differences between sponges and roundworms are that sponges are asymmetrical and do not have a coelom, while roundworms are bilaterally symmetrical and do have a coelom. **7.5.a** (exceeding)

6. All chordates, including vertebrates, have a notochord but only vertebrates have a backbone. **7.5.a** (exceeding)

7. I would classify a female organism that is covered in fur and provides milk for its young as a mammal. **7.5.a** (exceeding)

8. Adult amphibians have to live near water or in a very wet habitat because their eggs and larvae need water or a very wet habitat. Adult amphibians also need to keep their skin moist. **7.5.a** (exceeding)

9. The organism in (a) has an exoskeleton. The organism in (b) has an endoskeleton. **7.5.a** (exceeding)

10. yes; I could classify these organisms as vertebrates or invertebrates based on the kind of skeleton they have because I can see whether or not they have a backbone. **7.5.a** (exceeding)

11. 21.4 g/day;
15 g × 10 = 150 g in a week;
150 g ÷ 7 days in a week = 21.4 g/day **7.5.a** (exceeding)

12. Reptiles can live nearly anywhere on land because they do not have to lay their eggs in water or in a very moist place. Reptile eggs have special characteristics that prevent them from drying out on land. **7.5.a** (exceeding)

	Section Review Standards Guide		
	Supporting	Mastering	Exceeding
7.5.a			3–12

Answer to Standards Check

Feathers are important in maintaining the bird's body temperature and in helping to shape the body and wings for flying. **7.5.a** (exceeding)

Answers to Section Review

1. Sample answer: An exoskeleton is a hard, supportive outer covering of an invertebrate.

2. Sample answer: All animals that have placentas are known as vertebrates because they each have a backbone unlike an invertebrate, which does not have a backbone.

3. Cnidarians have two kinds of radially symmetrical body plans, the medusa form and the polyp form. The medusa is a cup or bell-shaped body with tentacles that extend into the water. The polyp is attached to a hard surface at the base of the cup so that its tentacles extend upwards and into the water. Cnidocytes are specialized stinging cells in the tentacles that are used to stun and capture prey. **7.5.a** (exceeding)

4. Sample answer: Mollusks have a specialized tissue called a mantle that secretes the shell of a mollusk. Some mollusks also have a muscular foot with which they are able to move. **7.5.a** (exceeding)

Section Resources

- Directed Reading A **BASIC** (Also in Spanish), B **GENERAL**

- Interactive Reader and Study Guide

- Section Quiz **GENERAL** (Also in Spanish)

- Section Review **GENERAL** (Also in Spanish)

- Vocabulary and Section Summary A **BASIC** (Also in Spanish), B **GENERAL**

Preteach

Reviewing Prior Knowledge

Read one of the vocabulary words for the section aloud. Before students read the definition in the book, ask them to explain what they think the word means. Repeat for the other vocabulary words.

 Bellringer

Have students focus on standard 7.2.a by asking them if they think that most invertebrates reproduce sexually or asexually.

(most invertebrates reproduce sexually, but some reproduce asexually)

🗂 Bellringer Transparency

Motivate

Discussion

Discussing Invertebrates

Launch a class discussion about invertebrates by asking students the following questions:

• What is an invertebrate? (an animal that does not have a backbone)

• What is your favorite invertebrate? (Answers may vary.)

• What special characteristics help your favorite invertebrate survive? (Answers may vary.)

Answer to Standards Check

no; I would not expect an animal with radial symmetry to have a head because it only has a top and a bottom, whereas animals that have a head have bilateral symmetry and therefore have a top, bottom, front (where there is a head), and a back. **7.5.a** (exceeding)

What You Will Learn

● Invertebrates have many specialized structures that perform specialized functions.

● Organ systems perform basic life functions in some invertebrates.

● Invertebrates have many methods for reproduction and development.

Why It Matters

Studying the characteristics of invertebrates will help you understand how the same life function may be performed in different ways.

Vocabulary

• segment
• open circulatory system
• closed circulatory system
• metamorphosis

READING STRATEGY

Outlining In your **Science Journal**, create an outline of the section. Use the headings from the section in your outline.

Invertebrates

Key Concept Invertebrates do not have backbones, but they do have other structures to perform their life functions.

▶ Humans and snakes have them, but octopuses and butterflies don't. What are they? Backbones! Most animals do not have backbones. These animals are called *invertebrates*.

Invertebrate Characteristics

Invertebrates can be found in nearly every environment on Earth. Invertebrates also have many different shapes and sizes. For example, grasshoppers, clams, earthworms, and jellyfish are all invertebrates. Some invertebrates have heads, and others do not. Some invertebrates eat food through their mouths. Others absorb food particles through their tissues.

The structures of invertebrates show how well adapted invertebrates are to their environment. For example, insects have different kinds of wings that help them fly. Some invertebrates have legs that help them burrow through the ground. Others have strong bodies that help them swim. But all invertebrates are similar because they do not have backbones.

Body Symmetry

Invertebrate bodies have one of two kinds of symmetry or no symmetry at all. Sponges have irregular shapes and are therefore asymmetrical. Jellyfish have radial symmetry. In animals that have radial symmetry, many lines can be drawn through the center of the body. Each line divides the animal into opposite, or mirror images. Animals that have radial symmetry have only a top and a bottom.

Most invertebrates have "two sides," or bilateral symmetry. A body with bilateral symmetry can be divided into two parts by one vertical line. A line through the middle of the body divides the body into nearly equal right and left halves. Animals with bilateral symmetry have a top and bottom, as well as a front end and a back end. The development of a head is only seen in organisms with bilateral symmetry, such as in the sea hare seen in **Figure 1**.

Standards Check Would you expect an animal with radial symmetry to have a head? Explain. 🐻 **7.5.a**

Figure 1 *The* Aplysia californica *is a species of sea hare. This mollusk has bilaterally symmetry.*

Universal Access • Differentiated Instruction

Basic Learners

Symmetry Have students create clay models of three invertebrate animals each with different symmetry. Once students have completed their models, have them use a plastic knife to divide the models into equal parts. Once students try to divide the asymmetrical model into equal parts, they will understand how an asymmetrical body plan is different from radial and bilateral body plans. **LS** Visual

English Learners

Hard Cs Point out to students that the pronunciation of the letter *c* within a word can cause some confusion. As a group, find the following words containing at least one *c* on these two pages and discuss whether or not the pronunciation of the *c* is hard or soft in each word. (p. 438: structures, octopuses, characteristics, clams, circulatory, backbones, asymmetrical, vertical; p. 439: sections, insect, muscles, protection, coverings, because, contract) **LS** Visual/Auditory

Figure 2 Segmentation in Invertebrate Bodies

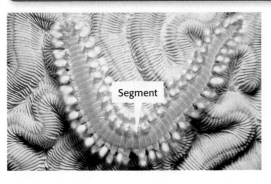

Abdomen

Thorax

Head

Segment

Segmentation

The bodies of many animals are divided into sections or **segments.** The body of the marine worm shown in **Figure 2** has many nearly equal segments. The body of the insect shown in **Figure 2** has three unequal segments. The insect has a head, a thorax, and an abdomen. Segmentation in the body has many advantages. For example, each segment in an earthworm has a set of muscles that help the earthworm push through soil.

Support of the Body

Invertebrate bodies need support and protection. **Figure 3** shows three invertebrates that have different kinds of support. The body of a sponge is supported by a jelly-like material and tiny, glassy structures. Other invertebrates have tough outer coverings. For example, round worms have thick skins, and lobsters have exoskeletons. These coverings are also important because muscles that are attached to these coverings contract and relax to help invertebrates move.

Standards Check Why are outer coverings important for movement in animals? 🐻 **7.5.a**

segment (SEG muhnt) any part of a larger structure, such as the body of an organism, that is set off by natural or arbitrary boundaries

7.2.a Students know the differences between the life cycles and reproduction methods of sexual and asexual organisms.

7.5.a Students know plants and animals have levels of organization for structure and function, including cells, tissues, organs, organ systems, and the whole organism.

7.5.b Students know organ systems function because of the contributions of individual organs, tissues, and cells. The failure of any part can affect the entire system.

7.5.g Students know how to relate the structures of the eye and ear to their functions.

Figure 3 Support in Invertebrate Bodies

Paired Summarizing Divide the class into pairs, and have the pairs read silently about the respiratory and circulatory systems, the digestive and excretory systems, and the nervous systems of invertebrates. Then, have one student in each pair summarize each heading of the text. The other student in the pair should listen to the summary and should point out any inaccuracies or ideas that were left out. Allow students to refer to the text as needed. **LS** Verbal

Homework

Poster Project Have interested students research the open circulatory system of a mollusk. Then, have the students create a poster that includes an example of a mollusk and a diagram of its open circulatory system. The poster should describe how the open circulatory system functions. Have students present their posters to the class. **LS** Visual/Verbal

Group ACTIVITY

Earthworm Digestion Divide the class into groups of four or five students, and have each group research the digestive system of an earthworm. Each group should draw a diagram of the earthworm's digestive system and add labels to the diagram describing the process of digestion in an earthworm. Have the groups share their diagrams with the class. **LS** Verbal/Visual
Co-op Learning

Answer to Standards Check

If an insect's tracheae became clogged, the insect would die because it would not be able to take in oxygen and expel carbon dioxide. **7.5.b** (mastering)

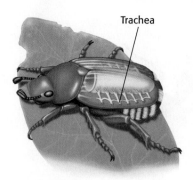

Figure 4 *This beetle moves air into its body and out of its body through small holes along the sides of its body.*

INTERNET ACTIVITY

Human Metamorphosis
How would you help a friend who turned into a larva? Using pictures, describe the changes that your friend would go through. Go to **go.hrw.com,** and type in the keyword HY7INVW.

Respiratory and Circulatory Systems

All animals need oxygen to live. Animals take oxygen into their bodies and release carbon dioxide from their bodies through respiration. Respiration is performed by the *respiratory system* (RES puhr uh TAWR ee SIS tuhm). In lobsters, gills are the main organs that perform respiration. In insects, such as the beetle in **Figure 4,** a network of tubes inside the body, called *tracheae* (TRAY kee EE), performs respiration.

Oxygen, carbon dioxide, and nutrients must be moved or circulated throughout the body. The *circulatory system* transports many substances in a fluid called *blood*. Most mollusks have an **open circulatory system.** In open circulatory systems, blood moves through open spaces in the body. Invertebrates, such as annelids, have a **closed circulatory system.** In closed circulatory systems, blood moves through tubes that form a closed loop.

Standards Check What would happen to an insect if its tracheae became clogged? 🐾 **7.5.b**

Digestive and Excretory Systems

Animals obtain the energy they need by digesting food. Digestion is performed by the *digestive system*. Food is digested as it is consumed and broken down. Any remaining material is expelled from the body. Invertebrates have relatively simple digestive systems. The mouth and anus form two ends of a tube called a *digestive tract*. The snail shown in **Figure 5** has a stomach and other specialized areas along the digestive tract.

As cells in the body use up nutrients, wastes are formed. The *excretory system* (EKS kruh TAWR ee SIS tuhm) eliminates these wastes from cells with any excess water. In many invertebrates, the digestive tract also eliminates this kind of waste. Other invertebrates have separate excretory systems. These systems have specialized organs to eliminate excess water and waste from cells.

Figure 5 *The digestive system in the snail is made up of a digestive tract that has four parts: a mouth, a stomach, an intestine, and an anus.*

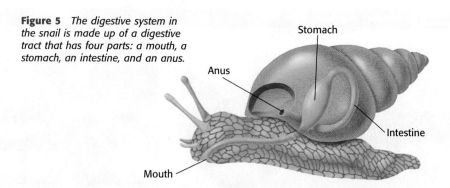

Universal Access · Differentiated Instruction

Advanced Learners/GATE

Making Digestive Tracts Some students learn best when they can learn additional information on their own. Ask such students to choose an invertebrate with a simple digestive tract. Then, have students research the animals' digestive tract construction and create a three-dimensional model of the tract. Give students time to share their creations with the class. **LS** Verbal/Kinesthetic

Struggling Readers

Conquering Subheadings Remind struggling readers that subheadings can be their reading and studying guides as long as they make sure they understand them. Ask students to place sticky notes in their books and to write simplified definitions of the two subheadings on this page.
(Sample answers: Breathing and blood systems; Food movement in and out of the body) **LS** Verbal

Figure 6 Examples of Invertebrate Nervous Systems

Hydra

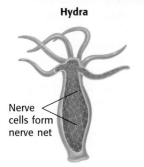

Nerve cells form nerve net

Flatworm

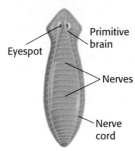

Eyespot

Primitive brain

Nerves

Nerve cord

Grasshopper

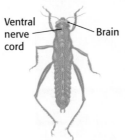

Ventral nerve cord

Brain

Nervous Systems

The *nervous system* is specialized for receiving and sending electrical signals that control all of the functions of the body. **Figure 6** shows examples of the nervous systems of three invertebrates. Many nervous systems have a specialized area called the *brain*. The brain acts as the control center. Nervous systems also have specialized areas called *sense organs*. Sense organs collect information, such as sound and light, from outside and inside the body. For example, eyes are organs that sense light. When light enters the eye, signals are sent to the brain. The brain interprets the signals as an image.

open circulatory system
(OH puhn SUHR kyuh luh TAWR ee SIS tuhm) a circulatory system in which the circulatory fluid is not contained entirely within vessels

closed circulatory system
(KLOHZD SUHR kyuh luh TAWR ee SIS tuhm) a circulatory system in which the heart circulates blood through a network of vessels that form a closed loop

Quick Lab

Seeing Like an Insect

Insects have a compound eye made up of repeating units. Each unit has its own lens.

7.5.g

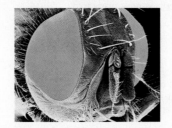

▶ Try It!

1. Use a **ruler** to draw a grid with dimensions of about 10 cm × 10 cm on a **sheet of tracing paper.** The grid lines should be separated by 0.5 cm.

2. Place the **grid** over a **black-and-white image.** Secure the grid with **tape.**

3. Note the relative amount of black ink that shows through in each box.

4. Use a **black marker** to fill in the grid boxes that are on top of an area that is mostly black. Don't fill in the grid boxes that are above squares that are mostly white.

▶ Think About It!

5. Remove your grid, and examine it from across the room. Describe what you see?

6. What part of the activity mimicked the repeating units in the eye of an insect?

7. How might the curve of the insect eye further change how an insect sees images?

⏱ **20 min**

Quick Lab

⏱ **20 min**

Teacher Notes

In this activity, students explore how insects see images (covers standard 7.5.g). Emphasize that the eyes need light for sight. When light enters the eye, signals are transmitted to the brain. The brain then interprets these signals as an image.

Materials for Each Group

- grid
- paper, tracing
- tape
- marker, black
- ruler

Answers

5. Answers may vary according to the picture provided.

6. The squares of the grid mimicked the repeating units in the eye of an insect.

7. The images would also be more curved.

📋 Differentiated Datasheets
A **BASIC**, B **GENERAL**, C **ADVANCED**

Also editable on the Holt Lab Generator CD-ROM

MISCONCEPTION ALERT

Compound Eyes Some students may have misconceptions about how an insect detects images. Students may think that an insect detects the same image with each repeating unit in the eye, therefore seeing multiple images of the same subject. Each repeating unit actually detects only one part of the entire image. The parts of the image detected by each repeating unit allows the insect to see a single whole image. Have interested students conduct further research on the compound eye. Ask them to draw a diagram on a piece of poster board of how the compound eye works. Have students present their completed posters to the rest of the class. **LS** Visual/Verbal

Teaching Transparency:
L65 Nervous Systems in Invertebrates

SCIENCE HUMOR

When you breathe, you inspire! When you don't breathe, you expire!

Close

Standards Focus

This **Standards Focus** provides you with a quick way to **assess, reteach,** and **re-assess** one or more concepts in the section.

Assess

1. What is metamorphosis? (a period of rapid change in which an organism develops into the adult form) **7.2.a**

2. What might happen if a grasshopper became blind? (Sample answer: The grasshopper may not be able to find food and would eventually die.) **7.5.b**

3. What body system is the brain a part of? (the nervous system) **7.5.a, 7.5.b**

Reteach

Life Cycles Have students choose an invertebrate discussed in this section and create a poster of the animal's life cycle. **LS** Visual **7.2.a**

Re-Assess

Invertebrate Encounters Have students write a narrative in which they describe a walk along a rocky ocean shore or through a tropical rain forest. Tell students to research and describe how at least a dozen different invertebrates sense their environment on the rocky ocean shore or in the rain forest. Some students may wish to create illustrations or collages to accompany their narratives. **LS** Verbal **7.5.a, 7.5.b**

Teaching Transparency: L66 The Stages of Complete Metamorphosis

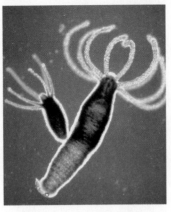

Figure 7 *Hydra reproduce by asexual reproduction. The offspring look similar to and are genetically identical to the parent.*

metamorphosis (met uh MAWR fuh sis) a process in the lifecycle of many animals during which a rapid change from the immature organism to the adult takes place

Reproduction and Development

Many invertebrates reproduce asexually. One kind of asexual reproduction is called *budding*. Budding happens when a part of the parent organism develops into a new organism. The new organism then pinches off from the parent and lives independently. The hydra, shown in **Figure 7**, reproduces by budding. The new hydra is genetically identical to its parent. Fragmentation is a second kind of asexual reproduction. In fragmentation, parts of an organism break off and then develop into a new individual that is identical to the original organism. Certain organisms, such as flatworms called *planaria,* reproduce by fragmentation.

Complete Metamorphosis

Many insects reproduce sexually and lay eggs. As an insect hatches from an egg and develops, the insect changes form through a process called **metamorphosis.** Most insects go through a complex change called *complete metamorphosis.* As shown in **Figure 8,** complete metamorphosis has four main stages: egg, larva, pupa (PYOO puh), and adult. Butterflies, beetles, flies, bees, wasps, and ants go through this change.

Standards Check Compare the life cycle of a hydra with the life cycle of a butterfly. **7.2.a**

Figure 8 The Stages of Complete Metamorphosis

e The adult butterfly pumps blood-like fluid into its wings until they are full-sized. The butterfly is now ready to fly.

d Adult body parts replace the larval body parts. The **adult** splits its chrysalis and emerges.

c After its final molt, the caterpillar makes a chrysalis and becomes a **pupa.** The pupal stage may last a few days or several months. During this stage, the insect is inactive.

a An adult lays **eggs.** An embryo forms inside each egg.

b A **larva** hatches from the egg. Butterfly and moth larvae are called *caterpillars.* The caterpillar eats leaves and grows rapidly. As the caterpillar grows, it sheds its outer layer several times. This process is called *molting.*

Answer to Standards Check

A hydra reproduces by budding, which is a form of asexual reproduction. A part of the parent hydra develops into a new individual and pinches off from the parent. A butterfly reproduces by sexual reproduction and undergoes complete metamorphosis during its life cycle. A caterpillar hatches from an egg and develops into a pupa. The pupa metamorphoses into an adult. **7.2.a** (mastering)

Incomplete Metamorphosis

Grasshoppers and cockroaches are two kinds of insects that go through *incomplete metamorphosis.* Incomplete metamorphosis is less complicated than complete metamorphosis. As shown in **Figure 9,** incomplete metamorphosis has three main stages: egg, nymph, and adult. Some nymphs shed their exoskeleton several times in a process called *molting.* An insect in the nymph stage looks very much like an adult insect. But a nymph does not have wings and is smaller than an adult. Through molting, the nymph develops into an adult.

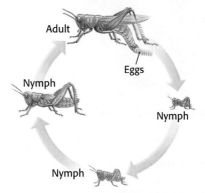

Figure 9 *The grasshopper nymphs look like smaller versions of the adult.*

Understanding Concepts

1 **Describing** Explain why respiration is important. Be sure to include an example of an invertebrate respiratory system.

2 **Comparing** How is the support in the body of a sponge different from the support in the body of an insect?

3 **Identifying** How do invertebrates remove wastes that are produced by cells in their bodies?

4 **Comparing** In the life cycle of a grasshopper, what are two main differences between nymphs and adults?

5 **Inferring** If an animal has a head, which kind of body symmetry would you expect the animal to have?

Critical Thinking

6 **Analyzing Processes** Describe metamorphosis in the life cycle of a butterfly and in the life cycle of a grasshopper.

7 **Making Comparisons** Compare an open circulatory system and a closed circulatory system.

8 **Expressing Opinions** Why are earthworms in a different group than roundworms? Explain.

9 **Applying Concepts** Why can't insects see in complete darkness?

Math Skills

10 **Making Calculations** A sea urchin lost 12 of its 178 spines in a storm. What percentage of its spines does the sea urchin still have?

Challenge

11 **Applying Concepts** If the head of an insect became stuck underwater, would the insect drown? Explain your answer.

12 **Making Inferences** What other body part do invertebrates that have ears or noses have?

Internet Resources

For a variety of links related to this chapter, go to www.scilinks.org
Topic: Sponges; Echinoderms
SciLinks code: HY71443; HY70458

---

7. In an open circulatory system, the blood moves through open spaces in the body. In a closed circulatory system, blood moves through tubes that form a closed loop. **7.2.b** (supporting)

8. Earthworms are in a different group than roundworms because earthworms are segmented, while roundworms are not segmented. **7.5.a** (supporting)

9. Insects cannot see in complete darkness because there is no light entering their eyes. **7.5.g** (mastering)

10. 93.3%;
$178 - 12 = 166;$
$166 \times 100 = 93.3\%$

11. no; The insect would not drown because it takes in oxygen through the holes in the sides of its body and not through its head. **7.5.b** (mastering)

12. Invertebrates that have noses and ears must also have a head. **7.2.a** (exceeding)

Section Review Standards Guide			
	Supporting	**Mastering**	**Exceeding**
7.2.a	4, 6, 8		12
7.5.a			2, 5
7.5.b	7	1, 3, 11	
7.5.g		9	

Teaching Transparency:
L67 Incomplete Metamorphosis

Answers to Section Review

1. Respiration is important because all animals must perform respiration to live. Respiration is the process in which oxygen is taken into the body and carbon dioxide is released from the body. In insects, oxygen moves through holes in the sides of insects' bodies into a network of tubes called tracheae. **7.5.b** (mastering)

2. The body of a sponge is supported by jelly-like material and tiny, glassy structures, whereas the body of an insect is supported by a tough exoskeleton. **7.5.a** (exceeding)

3. Insects remove the wastes produced by their cells through their excretory systems. **7.5.b** (mastering)

4. Two main differences between nymphs and adults in the life cycle of a grasshopper are that nymphs do not have wings like adults do and nymphs are smaller than adults are. **7.2.a** (supporting)

5. I would expect an animal that had a head to have bilateral body symmetry. **7.5.a** (exceeding)

6. Butterflies undergo complete metamorphosis, which has four stages: egg, larva, pupa, and adult. Butterfly larvae and butterfly pupae look very different from adult butterflies. Grasshoppers undergo incomplete metamorphosis, which has three stages: egg, nymph, and adult. Grasshopper nymphs look like smaller adults. **7.2.a** (supporting)

Section Resources

- Directed Reading
A **BASIC** (Also in Spanish), B **GENERAL**

- Interactive Reader and Study Guide

- Section Quiz **GENERAL** (Also in Spanish)

- Section Review **GENERAL** (Also in Spanish)

- Vocabulary and Section Summary
A **BASIC** (Also in Spanish), B **GENERAL**

Section 3 • Invertebrates **443**

SECTION 4

Preteach

Reviewing Prior Knowledge

Ask student volunteers to read the red and blue heads in the section aloud. Then, ask students what they think the section is about. Finally, ask students what they already know about how vertebrates differ from invertebrates.

 **Bellringer**

Have students review standard 7.5.c by asking them to write a brief paragraph describing how they think the bones and muscles of vertebrates relate to how these animals move.

Bellringer Transparency

Motivate

Demonstration

Identifying Backbones Extract a skeleton from an owl pellet. Ask students to find the backbone in the skeleton. Students may understand the structure of vertebrae better if they are able to manipulate the parts of the skeleton to see how the vertebrae interlock. (Have students wear gloves if necessary.) **LS Kinesthetic**

Using the Figure

Body Coverings in Vertebrates Have students study **Figure 2.** Then, ask students to discuss, in groups or as a class, the advantages that each type of body covering provides the animals shown in the figure. If the discussion occurs in groups, have each group make a list of the advantages of each type of body covering. Then, have each group present its lists to the class. **LS Interpersonal**

SECTION 4

What You Will Learn

- Vertebrates have an endoskeleton that provides support and protection.
- Vertebrates have organ systems that perform life functions.
- Nearly all vertebrates reproduce by only sexual reproduction.

Why It Matters

The characteristics of vertebrates show how vertebrates have adapted to living in their environment.

Vocabulary

- cartilage
- small intestine
- large intestine

READING STRATEGY

Outlining In your **Science Journal**, create an outline of the section. Use the headings from the section in your outline.

7.1.f Students know that as multicellular organisms develop, their cells differentiate.
7.2.a Students know the differences between the life cycles and reproduction methods of sexual and asexual organisms.
7.5.a Students know plants and animals have levels of organization for structure and function, including cells, tissues, organs, organ systems, and the whole organism.
7.5.b Students know organ systems function because of the contributions of individual organs, tissues, and cells. The failure of any part can affect the entire system.
7.5.c Students know how bones and muscles work together to provide a structural framework for movement.
7.5.g Students know how to relate the structures of the eye and ear to their functions.

Figure 1 *This frog has bilateral symmetry.*

Vertebrates

Key Concept All vertebrates have a backbone, which supports other specialized body structures and functions.

You may have seen a dinosaur skeleton at a museum. You have probably also seen many fish. Have you ever thought about what these animals might have in common with each other? These animals have backbones, which makes them vertebrates.

Vertebrate Characteristics

Vertebrates live in the oceans, in freshwater, and on land. Vertebrates swim, crawl, burrow, hop, run, and fly. Like many invertebrates, vertebrates have organ systems to perform their life functions. However, vertebrates also have features that other organisms do not have. For example, only vertebrates have a backbone, which is part of a skeleton that is made of bone. Bone is a special type of very hard tissue that is found only in vertebrates.

Vertebrates also have a well-developed head that is protected by a skull. The skull is made of either cartilage or bone. **Cartilage** is a flexible material made of cells and proteins. The skeletons of all embryos are made of cartilage. But as most vertebrates grow, the cartilage is replaced by the much harder bone.

Body Symmetry

All vertebrates, such as the frog in **Figure 1,** are bilaterally symmetrical. In vertebrates, the head is distinct from the rest of the body. A bilaterally symmetrical body has at least four main parts. For example, the upper body surface, or back, is the *dorsal* side. The lower surface or belly is the *ventral* side. The head is in the front, or *anterior* of the body. The tail is in the back, or *posterior* of the body.

Universal Access · Differentiated Instruction

Special Education Students

Understanding Opposites Ask students what the opposite of "up" is. (down) Ask students what the opposite of front is. (back) Draw a simple animal on the board. Write the word "dorsal" near the animal's back. Ask a volunteer to add the opposite of dorsal in the correct location. (the word "ventral" should be added near the animal's belly) Write the word "anterior" near the animal's head. Ask a volunteer to add the opposite of anterior in the correct location. (the word "posterior" should be added near the animal's tail.) **LS Visual/Verbal**

Figure 2 Body Coverings in Vertebrates

Scales   Feathers   Fur   Skin

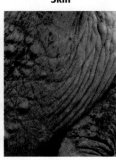

Body Coverings

The body of a vertebrate is covered by skin. One function of skin is to protect the body from the external environment. The skin of vertebrates varies in structure. For example, reptiles, such as the chameleon in **Figure 2,** and most fish are covered in small, thin plates called *scales*. However, fish scales have a different structure than reptile scales do. The scales of fish are also covered in a slippery fluid called *mucus* (MYOO kuhs), while the scales of reptiles are dry. The skin of amphibians is also covered in mucus and functions in part as a respiratory organ. Feathers on birds and the hair and fur on mammals help keep the organisms' body temperatures stable. Some body coverings display colors and patterns that allow vertebrates to hide from predators.

Support of the Body

The body of a vertebrate is supported by an endoskeleton. **Figure 3** shows the endoskeleton of a bird. The three main parts of an endoskeleton are the skull, the backbone, and the limb bones. The skull surrounds and protects the brain of the vertebrate. The backbone is made up of many vertebrae. Vertebrae surround and protect the spinal cord. Limb bones, such as leg bones, are an important part of movement in vertebrates. Bones provide a place for muscles to attach. As muscles contract and relax, the bones move. For example, in arms and in legs, pairs of muscles work together to move the limb. Vertebrates need large bones and muscles for support and movement on land.

Standards Check Describe the three main parts of an endoskeleton. 🔲 **7.5.c**

cartilage (KAHRT uhl ij) a flexible and strong connective tissue

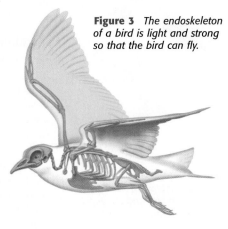

Figure 3 *The endoskeleton of a bird is light and strong so that the bird can fly.*

Figure 4   **Respiratory Systems in Vertebrates**

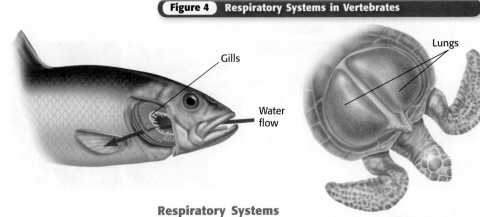
Gills

Water flow

Lungs

ACTIVITY

Underwater Breathing Some students may be interested in learning more about the way in which fish breathe underwater. Have interested students research how fish use their gills to breathe, or remove oxygen from the water. Encourage students to create a presentation or a poster describing this process.  Verbal/Visual

Group ACTIVITY

Frog Skit Have students perform a skit that describes the circulatory system of a frog. Each student in the group should play a different "part" in the system. During the skit, the students should introduce themselves and describe their function in the circulatory system of a frog. Then, the group should demonstrate how each part of the circulatory system works together to distribute blood throughout the body of the frog. ⓁⓈ Verbal/Kinesthetic

📖 READING STRATEGY

Reading Organizer To help students understand and organize the material discussing the respiratory, circulatory, digestive, excretory, and nervous systems of vertebrates, have them create flash cards describing each system. Students should write the name of the system on one side of the flash card and the basic characteristics of the system on the other side of the card.
ⓁⓈ Verbal

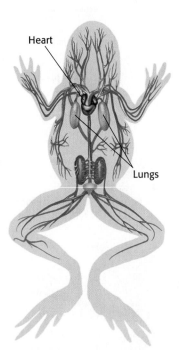

Heart

Lungs

Figure 5 *The frog has a closed circulatory system. The arteries are shown in red, and the veins are shown in blue.*

Respiratory Systems

Like invertebrates, vertebrates have a respiratory system to perform respiration. **Figure 4** shows the two kinds of respiratory systems in vertebrates. The main respiratory organs in vertebrates are either lungs or gills. These organs have many blood vessels that provide the organs with a steady blood supply. In fish, water flows into the mouth and over the gills. Oxygen from the water moves across the gills and into the bloodstream. At the same time, carbon dioxide moves from the bloodstream, across the gills, and into the water.

In vertebrates that live on land, respiratory organs must be protected from drying out. Therefore, the main respiratory organs are inside the body. Lungs are sacs that are kept moist by the body's fluids. The internal surface of the lungs is made up of small pockets that increase the area available for the exchange of oxygen and carbon dioxide.

Circulatory Systems

Vertebrates have a closed circulatory system made up of blood, vessels, and a pump. Blood is pushed through the vessels by a pump, or *heart*. Vessels that carry blood away from the heart are called *arteries*. Vessels that carry blood to the heart are called *veins*. Arteries are connected to veins by a network of *capillaries*. Capillaries are the smallest blood vessels in the body. **Figure 5** shows the circulatory system of a frog.

In land vertebrates, the heart first pumps the blood to the lungs or gills. In lungs or gills, oxygen moves into the blood. At the same time, carbon dioxide moves out of the body from the blood. Then, the oxygen-rich blood returns to the heart and is pumped to the rest of the body. The circulatory system also transports nutrients and other substances around the body.

Standards Check Describe how the circulatory system and the respiratory system in a vertebrate work together. 🔊 **7.5.b**

Answer to Standards Check

The heart is part of the circulatory system. The heart pumps blood to the lungs, which are part of the respiratory system. Oxygen moves through the lungs and into the blood. At the same time, carbon dioxide moves from the blood, through the lungs and out of the body. The oxygen-rich blood travels back to the heart and is then pumped to the rest of the body. **7.5.b** (exceeding)

Digestive and Excretory Systems

Vertebrates have digestive systems to break down food. The digestive system is made up of a long tube called the *digestive tract*. Some vertebrates, such as fish and snakes, swallow their food whole. Other vertebrates crush or chew their food before swallowing. Food passes from the mouth to the stomach. Acids and other chemicals in the stomach turn the food into a kind of soup. This soup then moves into the next part of the digestive tract, an organ called the **small intestine.** Blood vessels in the small intestine absorb nutrients. Then, the materials move into an organ called the **large intestine.** The large intestine absorbs excess water and converts undigested material into feces.

Some cell activities result in the formation of nitrogen compounds, such as ammonia. Ammonia diffuses into the blood and is removed from the body by the excretory system. In mammals, the liver converts ammonia into urea. Then, the *kidneys* filter urea from the blood. Urea is then combined with excess water to form urine, which is expelled from the body.

Nervous Systems

In the nervous system of a vertebrate, the brain is part of the spinal cord. The brain is an organ that serves as the main control center of the body. Nerves from the spinal cord branch throughout the body. Nerves carry impulses between the brain and the body. For example, when a sound reaches the ear, the ear sends an impulse through *sensory nerves* and the spinal cord, to the brain. To make the body react, the brain interprets the impulses and sends command impulses throughout the body through *motor nerves*.

The brain of a fish is much smaller than the brain of a dog, as **Figure 6** shows. Animals that have larger brains depend more on learning than on instinct. Learning is a behavior that changes the reaction of an animal based on new experiences.

Standards Check Describe what happens when a sound reaches the ear. 🐻 **7.5.g**

Figure 6 Nervous Systems in Vertebrates

Quick Lab 👓 ✂

Amplifying Sound
🐻 7.5.g

1. Roll a **sheet of paper** into a loose cone.
2. Wrap the smaller open end of the cone around the stem of a **funnel.** Use **tape** to secure the shape of the cone.
3. Place the funnel over an ear.
4. Move the cone towards a faint sound and then away from the sound. How does the sound change?
5. Make a new cone with several sheets of paper. Repeat step 4. How does the size of the cone affect what you hear?

⏱ 15 min

small intestine
(SMAWL in TES tuhn) the organ between the stomach and the large intestine where most of the breakdown of food happens and most of the nutrients from food are absorbed

large intestine (LAHRJ in TES tuhn) the wider and shorter portion of the intestine that removes water from mostly digested food and that turns the waste into semisolid feces, or stool

---

CONNECTION ACTIVITY
Math

Shark Teeth *Carcharodon megalodon* shark teeth can be as long as 16.8 cm. Based on the shark's tooth length, scientists estimate that this Miocene-era shark was probably 16 m long, which is about twice as long as today's great white shark. Ask students to imagine that they have discovered some shark teeth with the following lengths: 33.6 cm, 67.2 cm, and 8.4 cm. Have students use ratios to estimate the sizes of the sharks that these teeth came from. (32 m, 64 m, and 8 m)
LS **Logical**

MISCONCEPTION ALERT

Body Systems Students may understand that vertebrate animals have several organ systems, but they may be confused as to how all of the organ systems work together. Explain to students that the brain is part of the nervous system. The brain is the organ that is responsible for sending signals to all of the other organ systems so that they function properly. The brain works with the other parts of the nervous system to send these signals. After explaining this concept to students, ask them to write a few sentences in their **Science Journal** describing how organ systems function due to the contribution of other organ systems, individual organs, tissues, and cells. LS **Logical/Verbal**

Answer to Standards Check

When a sound reaches the ear, the ear sends an impulse through sensory nerves and the spinal cord, to the brain. **7.5.g** (mastering)

📽 Teaching Transparency:
L68 Nervous Systems in Vertebrates

Quick Lab ⏱ 15 min

Teacher Notes
In this activity, students will experiment with characteristics that affect hearing (covers standard 7.5.g). The large opening of ear trumpets captures sound waves and "funnels" them to the smaller end of the tube. There, the sound waves exit the tube and enter the ear.

Materials for Each Student
• funnel
• paper
• tape

Safety Caution
Remind students to review all safety cautions and icons before beginning this activity.

Answers
4. The sound should be loudest when the cone is positioned directly towards the sound.
5. The larger the cone, the more easily and clearly a sound is heard.

📋 Differentiated Datasheets
A **BASIC**, B **GENERAL**, C **ADVANCED**

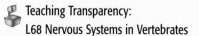
Also editable on the Holt Lab Generator CD-ROM

Standards Focus

This **Standards Focus** provides you with a quick way to **assess, reteach,** and **re-assess** one or more concepts in the section.

Assess

1. What are the main respiratory organs in vertebrates? (lungs or gills) **7.5.a**

2. Which of the following is NOT a function of the digestive system?

a. to digest food

b. to remove wastes

c. to break down food

d. to get oxygen

Reteach

Levels of Organization

Most complex multicellular organisms are maintained by organ systems, which, are made up of organs. Organs are made up of cooperating tissues, and tissues are made up of cells. Instruct students to create a series of drawings. Students should begin by drawing an animal. They should then zoom in on an organ system within the animal, an organ within the organ system, a tissue within the organ, and finally, a cell within the tissue. ⒮ Visual **7.5.a**

Re-Assess

Modeling Organ Systems Have interested students select an animal and make a model of an organ system found in that animal. Students can make their models out of clay or papier-mâché, and various materials such as wire, tape, and tubing. Have students present their models to the class. In their presentation, students should explain how the organ system works and describe any characteristics that make the organ system unique to the animal. ⒮ Visual **7.5.a, 7.5.b**

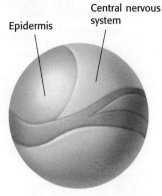

Figure 7 Parts of a frog embryo are beginning to differentiate into the kind of cells they will become.

Reproduction and Development

Most vertebrates reproduce by sexual reproduction. Fertilization happens when the nucleus of a sperm cell fuses with the nucleus of an egg cell. A fertilized egg cell divides many times as it becomes a multicellular embryo. As the embryo develops, its cells differentiate. Differentiation is the process in which cells become specialized. For example, cells that will perform different functions, such as skin cells and blood cells, will develop different structures. **Figure 7** shows the differentiation of some tissues of a frog embryo.

In most fish and amphibians, larvae hatch in the water and live on their own. These larvae behave similarly to adults. However, larvae cannot reproduce. Eventually, the larvae metamorphose into adults.

Reptiles, birds, and mammals do not have a larval stage in their lifecycle. The eggs of reptiles, birds, and mammals are protected by special membranes. The eggs of reptiles, birds, and some mammals also have a shell. Eggs that have shells are laid on land. Most mammals do not lay eggs, and the embryo develops in the female until the offspring is born. **Figure 8** shows the embryos of vertebrates during early stages of their development. Embryos of different species are similar to each other at early stages of development. Embryos begin to look more like the adults of their own species as they develop. Offspring of reptiles, birds, and mammals look similar to adults when they are born. These offspring gradually develop into adults.

Standards Check Why do cells in a developing embryo undergo differentiation? **7.1.f**

Figure 8 The Embryos of Different Vertebrates

Fish   Reptile   Bird

Answer to Standards Check

Cells in an embryo undergo differentiation as they specialize, developing different structures to perform different functions. **7.1.f** (mastering)

Parental Care

Some vertebrates do not care for their young. The female simply lays the eggs and leaves. These animals lay hundreds of eggs, so at least a few offspring will survive. Many fish species and reptile species guard the nest until the eggs hatch. Afterward, the offspring are left on their own. Birds and mammals are very different. Birds and mammals have only a few offspring at a time. Therefore, birds and mammals spend a lot of time and energy feeding and protecting their offspring. The fish shown in **Figure 9** is unusual because it cares for its offspring after they hatch. The parent fish holds its offspring in its mouth to protect them as they develop. Parental care increases the chances of offspring surviving.

Figure 9 *This fish will hold its offspring in its mouth to protect them from predators.*

8. An egg becomes fertilized when the nucleus of a sperm cell fuses with the nucleus of an egg cell. This is sexual reproduction because it requires two sex cells from two different parents. **7.2.a** (mastering)

9. Sample answer: Gravity and the ability to maintain a large skeleton are two of the factors that might limit the maximum body size that land vertebrates can grow to. **7.5.c** (exceeding)

10. Larger ears may be better able to hear a sound than smaller ears can because larger ears are able to capture more sound waves than smaller ears can. **7.5.g** (exceeding)

SECTION Review

 7.1.f, 7.2.a, 7.5.a, 7.5.b, 7.5.c, 7.5.g

Summary

- Skin protects the body from the environment. Skin of vertebrates may be covered in scales, feathers, or fur.
- Most vertebrates have an endoskeleton made of bone. The endoskeleton provides support, protection, and a place for muscles to attach.
- Major organs systems of vertebrates are the respiratory system, circulatory system, digestive system, excretory system, nervous system, and reproductive system.
- Cells of embryos differentiate and specialize as the embryo develops.
- The amount of parental care given to offspring varies among species of vertebrates.

Understanding Concepts

1. **Demonstrating** How do different kinds of cells develop in an embryo?

2. **Describing** Describe the structure of the backbone and what it provides the vertebrate body.

3. **Identifying** What kind of circulatory system do vertebrates have?

INTERPRETING GRAPHICS Use the graph below to answer the next two questions.

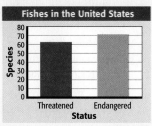

Fishes in the United States

4. **Evaluating** How many fish species in the United States are endangered?

5. **Calculating** What is the total number of endangered and threatened fish species in the United States?

Critical Thinking

6. **Making Comparisons** How does gas exchange in gills differ from gas exchange in lungs?

7. **Applying Concepts** What is an advantages and a disadvantage of depositing a large number of eggs?

8. **Applying Concepts** How does an egg become fertilized? Is this sexual or asexual reproduction? Explain your answer.

Challenge

9. **Making Inferences** What factors might limit the maximum body size to which land vertebrates can grow?

10. **Applying Concepts** Why might large ears be better able to hear a sound than small ears?

Internet Resources

For a variety of links related to this chapter, go to www.scilinks.org

Topic: Vertebrates
SciLinks code: HY71602

Section Review Standards Guide

	Supporting	Mastering	Exceeding
7.1.f		1	
7.2.a		8	7
7.5.a		6	2–3
7.5.b	6		
7.5.c		2	9
7.5.g			10

Answers to Section Review

1. Different kinds of cells develop in an embryo through the process of differentiation. **7.1.f** (mastering)

2. The backbone is made up of many vertebrae that surround and protect the spinal cord. The backbone also supports the body. **7.5.a** (exceeding), **7.5.c** (mastering)

3. Vertebrates have closed circulatory systems. **7.5.a** (exceeding)

4. There are 71 species of fish that are endangered in the United States.

5. There are 133 species of fish that are threatened or endangered in the United States.

6. Gas exchange in the gills differs from gas exchange in the lungs because the oxygen is removed directly from the water by the gills whereas, oxygen is removed from the air in the lungs. **7.5.a** (mastering), **7.5.b** (supporting)

7. An advantage of depositing a large number of eggs is that a larger percentage of the offspring may survive. A disadvantage of depositing a large number of eggs is that the parent cannot provide much parental care for so many offspring, which would further increase the chances of survival of the offspring. **7.2.a** (exceeding)

Section Resources

- Directed Reading A **BASIC** (Also in Spanish), B **GENERAL**
- Interactive Reader and Study Guide
- Section Quiz **GENERAL** (Also in Spanish)
- Section Review **GENERAL** (Also in Spanish)
- Vocabulary and Section Summary A **BASIC** (Also in Spanish), B **GENERAL**

Teacher Notes

In this lab, students will identify and compare the densities of three kinds of animal bones. This activity will help students understand how a bone's density is related to its function (covers standards 7.5.a and 7.5.c). In this lab, students will also consider the suitability of the equipment needed to conduct the activity (covers standard 7.7.a).

Time Required

One 45-minute class period

Lab Ratings

EASY ——————————→ HARD

Teacher Prep 🔬🔬🔬🔬
Student Set-Up 🔬🔬
Concept Level 🔬🔬🔬
Clean Up 🔬

Materials

The materials listed on the student page are enough for two students.

Safety Caution

Remind students to review all safety cautions and icons before beginning this lab activity. Students should use caution when working with a length of stiff wire.

Preparation Notes

Collect and prepare sets of bone samples in advance. Once classroom sets are prepared, they can be easily stored and reused.

For the chicken bone, leg bones will work best. For the fish bone, try to obtain three to four connected vertebrae of a swordfish or large tuna. For added safety, make sure that the spines are cut off. For the beef bone, marrow bones or broad sections of beef, lamb, or pork bone will all work well. Prepared beef bones sold as chew toys for dogs will also work. Make sure that the bones will fit into the graduated cylinder that students will use.

To prepare the bones, boil them in water. As they cook, the muscle and other soft tissues will loosen. Let the bones cool, and use a knife to scrape off any leftover tissue. Boil the bones again. After they cool, scrape off any remaining meat. If you dry the bones outdoors, make sure that pets or other animals will not find them.

Structure and Function of Bone

The structure of each body part of an organism is related to the function of that body part. For example, animals depend on specialized body parts for movement. Animals contract and relax muscles that are attached to bones in order to move. Some animals have legs, wings, or fins to move around. In vertebrates, most movement is the result of bones and muscles working together. Bones that support a lot of weight are thick and heavy, such as in elephants. Bones that do not support a lot of weight are light, such as in the wings of birds.

You have already learned that the bones of vertebrates have many similarities. In this activity, you will compare the bones of a mammal, a bird, and a fish. Through this activity, you will learn how differences in the structure of different bones relates to the function of these bones.

Ask a Question

1. Lets ask, "Are the bones of animals that walk more dense than the bones of animals that swim or of animals that fly?"

Form a Testable Hypothesis

2. To change the question into a testable hypothesis, you may come up with the following: "There are no differences in density between the bones of animals that walk, swim, or fly."

Procedure

3. Create a table like the one below to record the measurements for each kind of bone.

Bone Measurements			
Kind of bone	Mass of bone (g)	Volume of bone (cm³)	Density of bone (g/cm³)
Mammal bone			
Chicken bone			
Fish bone			

DO NOT WRITE IN BOOK

OBJECTIVES

Determine the density of three kinds of animal bones.

Compare the bone of a mammal, a fish, and a bird.

Identify the relationship between the structure of the bone and the function of the bone.

MATERIALS

- balance, laboratory
- beef bone
- chicken bone
- fish bone
- graduated cylinder, large
- string
- wire

SAFETY

7.5.a Students know plants and animals have levels of organization for structure and function, including cells, tissues, organs, organ systems, and the whole organism.

7.5.c Students know how bones and muscles work together to provide a structural framework for movement.

Investigation and Experimentation

7.7.a Select and use appropriate tools and technology (including calculators, computers, balances, spring scales, microscopes, and binoculars) to perform tests, collect data, and display data.

Lab Resources

 Differentiated Datasheets
A **BASIC**, B **GENERAL**, C **ADVANCED**

 Classroom Lab Video/DVD

Holt Lab Generator CD-ROM

Search for any lab by topic, standard, difficulty level, or time. Edit any lab to fit your needs, or create your own labs. Use the Lab Materials QuickList software to customize your lab materials list.

4 Use a balance to determine the mass of a mammal bone. Record this value in your table.

5 Fill a graduated cylinder about 3/4 full with water. Note the water level in the cylinder. (Note: 1 mL = 1 cm³)

6 Tie a string around the beef bone. Gently lower it into the cylinder. When the bone is completely submerged, note the new water level.

7 Determine the volume of the bone, by subtracting the initial water level in the graduated cylinder from the water level when the bone was submerged. Record you finding in your table.

8 Calculate the density of this bone by dividing the bone's mass by its volume. Record this value in grams per centimeter cubed (g/cm³) in you table.

9 Repeat steps 4–8 using a chicken bone and a fish bone. If a bone floats, you will need to hold it under the surface of the water by using a length of wire.

Analyze the Results

10 **Analyzing Results** Which bones sank? Which bones floated?

11 **Evaluating Results** Which bone was the most dense? Which bone was the least dense?

Draw Conclusions

12 **Drawing Conclusions** Did you prove or disprove the hypothesis?

13 **Applying Results** What can you assume about the muscles that are needed to move these bones?

14 **Making Inferences** What other factors may affect the characteristics of the muscles required to move these bones?

15 **Making Inferences** How is the density of the different bones related to how the organisms move? How is the density of the different bones related to where the organism lives?

16 **Applying Conclusions** If an organism that was the size of a whale lived on land, what kind of bones would the organism have? What kind of muscles would the animal need to move those bones?

Big Idea Question

17 **Identifying Relationships** Describe how the structure of a bone is related to a life function of the animal. Make sure to include examples in your answer.

15. The mammal bone is more dense than the bird bone or fish bone because the bone of a mammal, such as a cow, must support a greater weight then that of a bird or of a fish. The bone of a bird is less dense than the bone of a mammal because it needs to be both strong and light enough for the bird to fly. Fish bones are the least dense because fish bones do not have to support the weight of the fish's body in the same way that the bones of land animals do. The bones of a fish must be light and flexible so that the fish can swim without sinking.

16. If an animal as large as a whale lived on land, it would have to have very large, dense bones and large muscles attached to the bones to move the bones. Large, dense bones would be needed to support the weight of the body and the muscles would have to be strong enough to move the bones.

Big Idea Question

17. Accept all reasonable answers. Students should be able to articulate the reasons for their examples based on considerations, such as the weight being supported and the type of movement required.

Analyze the Results

10. Answers may vary. The chicken bone and the beef bone are most likely to sink. Although fish bones are the least dense, some fish bones may also sink.

11. The beef bone is the most dense. The fish bone is the least dense.

Draw Conclusions

12. Sample answer: My original hypothesis was disproved.

13. Larger muscles are needed to move the denser and heavier bones.

14. The size and shape of the muscles would be different relative to the bone and according to how the muscle is involved in movement. For example, larger muscles are required for an animal to fly than for an animal with similar-sized bones to walk.

Kelly Sullivan
Harry M. Marsh
Junior High School
Chico, California

Teacher Notes

This activity walks students through how to create a map of the distribution of a species of organisms (covers standard 7.7.d). Students may find it easier to perform this activity if a large sheet of graph paper or a piece of poster board is available for them to draw the map on. Have students include the table describing the distribution of the Red beetle on their poster board. This will help them visually relate the table to the distribution map that they have drawn.

Materials
- paper, white
- pencils, colored
- ruler

Answers to You Try It!

2. Students' distribution map should resemble the following:

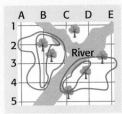

3. The highest numbers of Red beetles are found along the edge of the river. This information would be useful if this beetle were becoming extinct because steps could be taken to protect the areas along the edge of the river. This would help maintain these areas for the Red beetle.

Datasheet **GENERAL**

Also editable on the Holt Lab Generator CD-ROM

Science Skills Activity

| Scientific Methods | Research | Data Analysis | Models, Maps & Diagrams |

Investigation and Experimentation
7.7.d Construct scale models, maps, and appropriately labeled diagrams to communicate scientific knowledge (e.g., motion of Earth's plates and cell structure).

Constructing Distribution Maps

▶ Tutorial

Procedure

Use the following instructions to construct the distribution map of a specific population of organisms.

❶ **Organizing** A labelled grid has been placed on top of a map. Use **Table 1** to write the number of goats that were found at each intersection.

Analysis

❷ **Evaluating** Draw a line around the intersections that have at least one goat.

❸ **Evaluating** In another color, draw a second line around the intersections that have at least 10 goats.

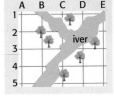

Table 1	Distribution of Mountain Goats
Intersection	**Population Size**
1B	1
2B	20
2C	2
2D	25
3B	1
3C	30
3D	3
4D	40
5C	1
5D	1

▶ You Try It!

Procedure

Use the map and the data table below to construct a distribution map of a population of rare red beetles.

❶ **Organizing** Redraw the map shown here. Use **Table 2** to write the number of beetles that are found at each intersection.

Analysis

❷ **Evaluating** Draw a line around the intersections that have at least one beetle. In another color, draw a second line around the intersections that have at least 10 beetles.

❸ **Inferring** Use the map to identify where the beetle is found. How might this information be helpful if the beetle were becoming extinct?

Table 2	Distribution of Red Beetles
Intersection	**Population Size**
2A	1
2B	30
3B	5
3D	20
3E	3
4B	40
4C	30
4D	4

Universal Access · Differentiated Instruction

Advanced Learners/GATE

Population Size Ask students to think about how the data for the distribution map in this activity were collected. Then, have the students research methods, such as the mark and recapture method that scientists use when determining population size. Have students present their findings in a short report. Reports should include a description of the method and an example of how the method is used in scientific experimentation. **LS Verbal**

Basic Learners

Distribution Map After dividing the classroom into three rows and three columns, put labels on the walls marking columns A, B, and C and rows 1, 2, and 3. Create a "Distribution of Students" table and a map with a grid on the board. Have students determine how many of them are closest to each of the nine intersections when they are seated. Record this information in the table. Then, have students transfer this information onto the map. **LS Logical/Kinesthetic**

Chapter Summary

The Big Idea Animals have many unique characteristics to perform their life functions.

Section | Vocabulary

1 What Is an Animal?

Key Concept Animals are made up of many cells. Animals consume other organisms to get the energy they need to grow, survive, and reproduce.

- Animals are multicellular organisms.
- Animals have specialized cells, tissues, organs, and organ systems.
- Animals have seven basic characteristics.

coelom p. 426
consumer p. 426
differentiation p. 427

2 The Animal Kingdom

Key Concept Animals are a diverse group of organisms that have adaptations to live in water and on land.

- The animal kingdom is made up of many different kinds of animals.
- Animals can be divided into two main groups: invertebrates and vertebrates.
- Each group of animals has unique characteristics.

invertebrate p. 431
exoskeleton p. 433
vertebrate p. 434
endoskeleton p. 434

3 Invertebrates

Key Concept Invertebrates do not have backbones, but they do have other structures to perform their life functions.

- Invertebrates have many specialized structures that perform specialized functions.
- Organ systems perform basic life functions in some invertebrates.
- Invertebrates have many methods for reproduction and development.

segment p. 439
open circulatory system p. 440
closed circulatory system p. 440
metamorphosis p. 442

4 Vertebrates

Key Concept All vertebrates have a backbone, which supports other specialized body structures and functions.

- Vertebrates have an endoskeleton that provides support and protection.
- Vertebrates have organ systems that perform life functions.
- Nearly all vertebrates reproduce by only sexual reproduction.

cartilage p. 444
small intestine p. 447
large intestine p. 447

Universal Access · Differentiated Instruction

Special Education Students

Grid Intersections The concept of grid intersections may be confusing for some students. Give each student a large, five-column by five-row grid on a piece of paper. Assign letters A–E to the columns, and numbers 1–5 to the rows. Ask students to put their finger on the 4 and slide their finger along the line until they are right below the D. Explain that where the D line and the 4 line meet is called 4D. Ask students to put Xs at the following points on the grid: 2B, 4C, 3C, 4D, 2D, and 4B. Then, ask them to put small circles around the Xs at 2B and 2D. Have students put a small square around the X at 3C. Then, direct students to connect the Xs at 4B, 5C, and 4D, in that order, with a curved line. (Students should have created a smiling face.) **LS** Visual/Auditory

Chapter Summary

SUPER SUMMARY

Have students connect the major concepts in this chapter through an interactive Super Summary. Visit go.hrw.com and type in the keyword HY7AMLS to access the Super Summary for this chapter.

Identifying Roots

Etymology Have students use a dictionary to find the roots of the terms *consumer, invertebrate, metamorphosis,* and *intestine.* (*Consumer* is derived from the Latin word *consumere,* which means, "to use up, eat, waste." *Invertebrate* is derived from the Latin prefix *in–,* which means "not," and the Latin word *vertebra,* which means "joint." The term *metamorphosis* is derived from the Greek roots *meta,* which means "change," and *morphe,* which means "form." Finally, the term *intestine* is derived from the Latin word *intestina,* which means "internal" or "inward.") **LS** Verbal

Focus on Writing

Connecting Concepts Ask students to write two or three paragraphs explaining the connection between the Big Idea of this chapter and the Key Concepts of each section. Remind students that they should write in complete sentences and use examples to explain their ideas. **LS** Logical

Review Resources

- Reinforcement Worksheet **BASIC**
- Critical Thinking Worksheet **ADVANCED**
- Chapter Review **GENERAL** (Also in Spanish)
- Standards Review Workbook (Also in Spanish)
- Study Guide A **BASIC** (Also in Spanish), B **GENERAL**

Assessment Resources

- Chapter Tests A **BASIC**, B **GENERAL** (Also in Spanish), C **ADVANCED**
- Standards Assessment **GENERAL**

Assignment Guide

Section	Questions
1	9, 12, 23
2	2–4, 17, 19
3	5–6, 10–11, 13–15, 21–22
4	1, 7–8, 16, 18, 20, 24–29

Answers

Using Vocabulary

1. differentiation

2. An endoskeleton provides support from the inside of the body. An exoskeleton provides support from the outside of the body. **7.5.a** (supporting)

3. An invertebrate is an animal that does not have a backbone. A vertebrate is an animal that does have a backbone. **7.5.a** (exceeding)

4. In asexual reproduction, a single parent produces a genetically identical offspring. In sexual reproduction, the sex cells from two parents fuse to develop into an offspring. **7.2.a** (supporting)

Understanding Concepts

5. b **7.5.a** (exceeding)

6. d **7.5.a** (exceeding)

7. a **7.5.b** (mastering)

8. b **7.5.b** (supporting)

9. The seven basic characteristics that most animals have are as follows: All animals are made up of cells; most animals have levels of structural organization in their bodies; animal bodies either have one of two kinds of symmetry or no symmetry at all; animals consume other organisms to get the energy that they need to live; animals reproduce and develop; most animals are able to move around; animals need to maintain the temperature of their body within a specific range of temperatures.

10. Insects that develop into adults from nymphs undergo incomplete metamorphosis because the nymphs are already very similar in structure to adults. **7.2.a** (exceeding)

Organize

Two-Panel Flip Chart Review the FoldNote that you created at the beginning of the chapter. Add to or correct the FoldNote based on what you have learned.

Using Vocabulary

1. **Academic Vocabulary** Which word best completes the following sentence: "Through ___ the cells in a developing embryo specialize to develop into different kinds of cells."

For each pair of terms, explain how the meanings of the terms differ.

2. *endoskeleton* and *exoskeleton*

3. *invertebrate* and *vertebrate*

4. *asexual reproduction* and *sexual reproduction*

Understanding Concepts

Multiple Choice

5. The sea urchin's body is organized around the organism's center, like the spokes on a wheel. What kind of symmetry does the sea urchin have?
   a. bilateral
   b. radial
   c. asymmetrical
   d. unilateral

6. Members of which of the following groups of invertebrates have segmented bodies?
   a. mollusks
   b. sea anemones
   c. roundworms
   d. arthropods

7. What would happen if the gills of a fish stopped working?
   a. The fish would probably die.
   b. The fish would make its own oxygen.
   c. The fish would make more carbon dioxide.
   d. The fish would not be able to maintain its body temperature.

8. Which of the following is NOT a function of the endoskeleton?
   a. The endoskeleton provides a place for muscles to attach.
   b. The endoskeleton supports the body from the outside of the body.
   c. The endoskeleton supports the body from the inside of the body.
   d. The endoskeleton protects the organs of the body.

Short Answer

9. **Listing** List the seven basic characteristics of animals.

10. **Inferring** Some insects develop from nymphs into adults. What kind of metamorphosis do these insects undergo? Explain.

11. **Comparing** How does fragmentation in sponges differ from reproduction in reptiles?

12. **Listing** What are the levels of structural organization in the body of a shark?

INTERPRETING GRAPHICS The picture below shows a member of the animal kingdom. Use the picture to answer the next three questions.

13. **Identifying** Name the body segments labeled a, b, and c.

14. **Identifying** To which segment are the legs of this animal attached?

15. **Analyzing** Into which group you would classify this animal? Explain.

11. Fragmentation in sponges is a form of asexual reproduction because it only requires one parent, whereas reptiles reproduce sexually, which requires two parents. **7.2.a** (mastering)

12. Sample answer: The simplest level of structural organization in a shark is a cell. A group of similar cells that work together and perform a similar function forms a tissue. A group of tissues working together to perform a specific function forms an organ. A group of organs working together to perform a life function forms an organ system. Many organ systems work together to keep the shark alive. **7.5.a** (mastering)

13. a is the head; b is the thorax; c is the abdomen **7.5.a** (exceeding)

14. The legs of the animal are attached to the thorax.

15. I would classify this animal as an arthropod because it is an insect and it has an exoskeleton. **7.5.a** (exceeding)

Writing Skills

16. Explaining Ideas What is the relationship between bones and muscles? Describe how these two kinds of structures help vertebrates move around.

Critical Thinking

17. Concept Mapping Use the following terms to create a concept map: *vertebrates, bilateral symmetry, fish, sponge, radial symmetry, sea urchin, sexual reproduction, asymmetrical, asexual reproduction,* and *invertebrates*.

18. Identifying Relationships Why are vertebrates classified as chordates?

19. Making Comparisons Describe three groups of mammals and how they differ.

20. Predicting Consequences If differentiation in an embryo is stopped, predict what is likely to happen to the embryo. Explain.

21. Analyzing Methods Could you identfy the entire life cycle of an animal by studying only the adult forms of that animal? Explain.

22. Analyzing Relationships How do the eyes of a dog help the dog fetch a ball?

23. Predicting Consequences Cats are endotherms, and geckos are ectotherms. Describe what would happen to a cat and a gecko if they were caught in a snowstorm.

24. Making Inferences A bird may have only two or three offspring at a time. A sea turtle may lay 100 eggs at a time. Which of these two organisms is more likely to provide its offspring with more parental care?

25. Making Comparisons Compare the circulatory system in an insect with a fish.

INTERPRETING GRAPHICS The graph below shows the kinds of amphibians that are threatened or endangered in the United States. Use the graph to answer the next two questions.

Threatened and Endangered Amphibian Species in the United States

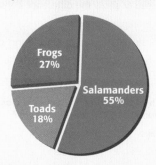

Frogs 27%
Salamanders 55%
Toads 18%

26. Making Conversions If the total number of threatened and endangered amphibian species in the United States is 22, how many more species of salamanders are threatened or endangered than species of frogs and toads?

27. Making Inferences What do you expect to happen to the percentage of toads in the pie graph as endangered toad species become extinct?

Math Skills

28. Making Calculations All of the females in a boar population produce exactly 10 offspring during their lifetime. What percentage of each female's offspring must survive so that the number of individuals in the population remains constant?

Challenge

29. Making Inferences On land, only animals that have endoskeletons become very large. Why are vertebrates on land larger than invertebrates on land?

22. When light enters a dog's eyes, signals are sent to the dog's brain. The brain interprets the signals as an image. The brain then sends signals to the body of the dog so that it can fetch the ball. **7.5.g** (mastering)

23. Unlike the cat, the gecko will die because it will not be able to maintain its body temperature within the range of temperatures that it needs to live.

24. The bird is more likely to provide parental care for its young. **7.1.f** (exceeding)

25. The fish has a closed circulatory system, while the insect has an open circulatory system. **7.5.b** (mastering)

26. About two more salamander species are threatened or endangered than are species of frogs and toads together.

27. The percentage of toads in the pie graph will decrease as endangered toad species become extinct.

Math Skills

28. Twenty percent of each female's offspring would need to survive to replace each male and female parent and keep the population size constant.

Challenge

29. On land, vertebrates are larger than invertebrates are because the vertebrate skeleton can support a larger body than the invertebrate systems can support. **7.5.c** (exceeding)

Chapter Review Standards Guide			
	Supporting	Mastering	Exceeding
7.1.f			20, 24
7.2.a	4	11	2, 10, 19, 21
7.5.a		12	3, 5, 6, 13, 15, 18–19
7.5.b	8	7, 25	
7.5.c		16	29
7.5.g		22	

Writing Skills

16. Sample answer: Many muscles are attached to bones. As these muscles contract and relax, the muscles move the bones, allowing the animal to move around. **7.5.c** (mastering)

Critical Thinking

17. An answer to this exercise can be found at the end of this book.

18. Vertebrates are classified as chordates because vertebrates have a notochord at some point in their development. **7.5.a** (exceeding)

19. Three groups of mammals are monotremes, which lay eggs; marsupials, which have a pouch in which embryos develop; and placental mammals, which have a placenta in their uterus. **7.2.a** (exceeding), **7.5.a** (exceeding)

20. If differentiation in an embryo is stopped, the embryo will die because the cells will be unable to specialize and perform the specific life functions. **7.1.f** (exceeding)

21. no; I could not learn about the life cycle of an animal by studying only the adult forms of the animal. The animal might have very different body forms in the other stages of its life cycle. **7.2.a** (exceeding)

Standards Assessment

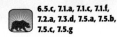

6.5.c, 7.1.a, 7.1.c, 7.1.f,
7.2.a, 7.3.d, 7.5.a, 7.5.b,
7.5.c, 7.5.g

Teacher Notes

To provide practice under more realistic testing conditions, give students 20 min to answer all of the questions in this assessment.

Answer Key

Question Number	Correct Answer
1	D
2	A
3	B
4	C
5	C
6	B
7	D
8	B
9	C
10	A
11	A
12	D
13	A
14	B
15	D
16	A
17	A

Standards Guide

	Supporting	Mastering	Exceeding
6.5.c		17	
7.1.a		15	
7.1.c		14	
7.1.f		1, 11	
7.2.a	2	6, 12	
7.3.d		16	
7.5.a	5, 10, 13	7	
7.5.b	3		
7.5.c	4, 9		
7.5.g		8	10

📋 Standards Assessment **GENERAL**

📋 Teacher Notes for Standards Assessment contain a longer Assessment Doctor and Diagnostic Teaching Tips.

REVIEWING ACADEMIC VOCABULARY

1 In the sentence "As multicellular organisms develop, their cells differentiate into specialized cells," what does the word *differentiate* mean?

- **A** to see or show the difference between
- **B** to multiply more rapidly
- **C** to calculate a mathematical function
- **D** to become specialized for specific functions

2 Which of the following words is closest in meaning to the word *methods*?

- **A** ways
- **B** actions
- **C** orders
- **D** sets

3 In the sentence "The failure of an organ can affect the entire organ system," what does the word *affect* mean?

- **A** move emotionally
- **B** act upon or have an effect upon
- **C** infect or damage with disease
- **D** assume a particular form

4 Which of the following words means "a structure for supporting something"?

- **A** construction
- **B** house
- **C** framework
- **D** plane

5 Choose the appropriate form of the word for the following sentence: Organ systems are made up of ___ cells, tissues, and organs.

- **A** individually
- **B** individuate
- **C** individual
- **D** individualize

REVIEWING CONCEPTS

6 Which of the following is a method of asexual reproduction?

- **A** monotreme
- **B** budding
- **C** segmentation
- **D** metamorphosis

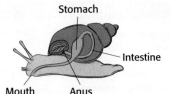

Stomach
Intestine
Mouth
Anus

7 In the image of the snail above, which organ system is shown?

- **A** the respiratory system
- **B** the nervous system
- **C** the circulatory system
- **D** the digestive system

8 How do the eyes of a dragonfly help the dragonfly catch its prey?

- **A** Specialized cells in the eyes send signals to the bones in the dragonfly's wings.
- **B** The brain interprets the signals sent by the dragonfly's eyes as images to identify the location of the prey.
- **C** The dragonfly's eyes have receptors on their surface to locate the prey.
- **D** The nerve cells in the dragonfly's eyes interpret the location of the prey.

9 Which of the following is a difference between invertebrates and vertebrates?

- **A** Vertebrates have exoskeletons, and invertebrates have endoskeletons.
- **B** Invertebrates reproduce only asexually, and vertebrates reproduce only sexually.
- **C** Vertebrates have a backbone, while invertebrates do not.
- **D** Invertebrates have bilateral symmetry, while vertebrates have radial symmetry.

 ASSESSMENT DOCTOR

Question 1: The correct answer is D. When cells differentiate, they become specialized for specific functions.

Question 2: The correct answer is A. *Methods* and *ways* are synonyms that both mean "means or manners of doing or achieving goals."

Question 3: The correct answer is B. In this sentence, *affect* means "act upon or have an effect upon." The failure of an organ can act upon or have an effect upon the entire organ system.

Question 4: The correct answer is C. A framework is a structure for supporting something. The bones and muscles provide a framework that makes movement possible.

Question 5: The correct answer is C. Organ systems function with the help of individual cells, tissues, and organs. The sentence was missing an adjective, and *individual* is an adjective.

Question 6: The correct answer is B. Budding is a form of asexual reproduction during which a piece of an organism develops into a new organism and then pinches off from the parent. The offspring of asexual reproduction are identical to the parent organism.

10 What type of body symmetry does a sea urchin have?

A radial

B skeletal

C bilateral

D asymetrical

11 Which of the following statements about vertebrate embryos is true?

A As embryos develop, their cells become specialized to perform different functions.

B All vertebrate embryos develop fins before becoming adults.

C Cell differentiation occurs only after the birth of a vertebrate.

D Even as embryos, vertebrates look much like the adults of the species.

12 Most vertebrates reproduce sexually. When does fertilization occur in sexual reproduction?

A when a male animal releases sperm and a female animal releases eggs

B when part of an organism breaks off and begins to grow independently

C when the cells of the embryo begin to differentiate and become specialized

D when the nucleus of a sperm cell fuses with the nucleus of an egg cell

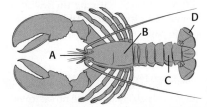

13 In the diagram of a lobster shown above, which segment of the lobster's body is labeled B?

A the thorax

B the abdomen

C the head

D the nerves

REVIEWING PRIOR LEARNING

14 What does the statement "All animals are eukaryotes," mean?

A It means that all animals live on land.

B It means that all of the DNA of an animal is located in the nuclei of the cells of the animal.

C It means that all animals have closed circulatory systems.

D It means that all animal bodies have coeloms.

15 Which of the following is an example of similar cell function in different animals?

A The wings of a bat and the flippers of a dolphin look similar.

B Animals have a variety of coverings, including skin, scales, and fur.

C Sea anemone larvae have medusa body forms but are polyps as adults.

D Nerve cells carry impulses throughout the body in both a tortoise and a chicken.

16 What role does an earthworm play in the transfer of energy in the food web of an ecosystem?

A decomposer

B consumer

C producer

D scavenger

17 What characteristics might a fossil that was classified into the animal kingdom have?

A The fossilized organism had bones.

B The fossilized organism had structures identified as cell walls.

C The fossil is of a single-celled organism.

D The fossilized organism had root structures.

Standards Assessment

Question 12: The correct answer is D. Fertilization takes place when the nucleus of a sperm cell fuses with the nucleus of an egg cell forming a zygote that has a complete complement of DNA.

Question 13: The correct answer is A. The thorax is the middle segment of the lobster's body. The bodies of many lobsters are segmented into three parts: the head, the thorax, and the abdomen.

Question 14: The correct answer is B. "All animals are eukaryotes" refers to the fact that the cells of all animals are eukaryotic. Eukaryotic cells have a membrane-bound nucleus within which the DNA is located.

Question 15: The correct answer is D. Nerve cells in both a tortoise and a chicken carry impulses throughout the body. This is the only choice that shows the same type of cell functioning similarly in different animals.

Question 16: The correct answer is A. Earthworms are decomposers, which means that they get energy from breaking down materials from dead organisms. Waste products from earthworms return nutrients to the soil, and producers are able to use these nutrients for their growth.

Question 17: The correct answer is A. An organism in the animal kingdom is likely to have bones and is not likely to have cell walls around their cells or roots which are characteristics of plants. Also, all members of the animal kingdom are multicellular organisms.

Question 7: The correct answer is D. The digestive system of the snail includes the mouth, the stomach, the intestine, and the anus. The organs of the digestive system are specialized to break down food, absorb its nutrients, and expel waste from the body.

Question 8: The correct answer is B. When the dragonfly sees prey, the eyes signal the brain to tell the muscles to fly after its prey. Dragonflies have very large compound eyes with many lenses. Their keen eyesight and strong wings make them successful predators.

Question 9: The correct answer is C. Vertebrates have bony structures called vertebrae that make up the backbone of their endoskeleton. Invertebrates do not have backbones.

Question 10: The correct answer is A. The sea star's body has radial symmetry, which means that its body is organized around a center, like spokes on a wheel. Animals with radial symmetry do not have heads.

Question 11: The correct answer is A. As an embryo grows, its cells become specialized to perform different functions. These specialized cells group to form tissues, organs, and organ systems that will allow the animal to grow and survive.

Science in Action

Science, Technology, and Society

Discussion

The History of Leeches in Medicine   Tell students that for centuries, physicians used leeches to remove blood from patients in a process called *bloodletting*. Physicians thought that an excess of blood in the body was responsible for several illnesses, including headaches, fevers, and heart disease, and that the leeches would remove the bad blood from a patient's body. Point out that this idea was discredited in the late 1800s. Ask students to brainstorm how people may have realized that illnesses were not caused by excess blood in the body. Discuss how science depends on challenging old ideas and testing new ideas.

Weird Science

Background

In 1934, scientists brought 22 lyrebirds to the island of Tasmania to protect the birds from extinction. Lyrebirds have spread throughout the island; their number is now estimated to be 8,200. Some people are concerned about the impact that lyrebirds are having on the island. People enjoy the presence of lyrebirds and their songs. However, some people note that lyrebirds are changing Tasmanian forest ecosystems.

Science, Technology, and Society

Leeches to the Rescue

Bloodsucking leeches may sound scary, but they could save your toes! Leeches are used in operations to reattach lost limbs, fingers, or toes. During these operations, doctors can reconnect arteries, but not small veins, which are more delicate. As a result, blood flow in the limb, finger, or toe is impaired. The tissues may become swollen with blood. If this happens, the tissues of the reattached parts die. But if leeches suck the extra blood from the reattached part, the tissues can remain healthy until the veins grow back.

Math **ACTIVITY**

Measure the widest and narrowest parts of the leech in the photo. Calculate how many times larger the wide part is than the narrow part. Which end of the leech do you think is the head? Why do you think so? Record your work in your **Science Journal.**

Weird Science

Sounds of the Lyrebird

Imagine that you are hiking in an Australian forest. You hear many different bird calls, beaks snapping, and wings rustling. There must be many species of birds around, right? Not if a lyrebird is nearby—all of those sounds could be coming from just one bird! The lyrebird imitates the songs of other birds. In fact, lyrebirds can imitate almost any sound they hear. Many Australians have heard lyrebirds singing the sounds of chainsaws, car engines, and dog barks. According to stories, a lyrebird once confused timbermill workers when it sang the sound of the mill's whistle and caused the workers to quit for the day.

Language Arts **ACTIVITY**

A lyrebird's ability to imitate noises could lead to a lot of humorous confusion for people who hear its songs. Think about how lyrebirds could mimic human-made sounds and cause confusion for the people nearby. Then, write a short story in your **Science Journal** about the situation.

Answer to Math Activity

The widest part of the leech is about 2.7 cm and the narrowest part of the leech is about 0.5 cm. Thus, 2.7 cm ÷ 0.5 cm = 5.4. The wide part is about 5.4 times wider than the narrowest part. Accept all reasonable answers as to which end of the leech is the head. Two important parts of the answer are that the student may use the measurements as a basis for an answer and that the student demonstrates some rational basis for the answer.

Answer to Language Arts Activity

Students' stories should detail a specific and realistic scenario in which lyrebirds' vocal impersonations can cause confusion.

Careers

George Matsumoto

Marine Biologist Dr. George Matsumoto is a marine biologist at the Monterey Bay Aquarium in California. A seventh-grade snorkeling class first sparked his interest in ocean research. Since then, he has studied the oceans by snorkeling, scuba diving, using research vessels, using remotely operated vehicles (ROVs), and using deep-sea submersibles. On the Johnson Sea Link submersible, he traveled to 1,000 m (3,281 ft) below sea level!

Marine biology is a field in which there are many strange and wonderful creatures. Matsumoto focuses on marine invertebrates, particularly the delicate animals called comb jellies. Comb jellies are also called *ctenophores* (TEN uh FAWRZ), which means "comb-bearers." Ctenophores have eight rows of cilia that look like the rows of a comb. These cilia help ctenophores move through the water. Some ctenophores glow when they are disturbed. By studying ctenophores and similar marine invertebrates, Matsumoto and other marine scientists can learn about the ecology of ocean communities.

Social Studies ACTIVITY

One kind of ctenophore from the United States took over both the Black Sea and the Sea of Azov by eating small fish. This left little food for bigger fish and thus changed the ecosystem and ruined the fisheries. Write a paragraph in your **Science Journal** about how Matsumoto's work as a marine biologist could help solve problems like this one.

Internet Resources

- To learn more about careers in science, visit www.scilinks.org and enter the SciLinks code HY70225.

- To learn more about these Science in Action topics, visit go.hrw.com and type in the keyword HY7AMLF.

- Check out articles related to this chapter by visiting go.hrw.com. Just type in the keyword HY7AMLC.

Answer to Social Studies Activity

Sample answer: Marine biologists who study ctenophores could think of ways to control the population of the foreign ctenophores that were disrupting the Black Sea and the Sea of Azov ecosystems. For example, marine biologists like Matsumoto may be able to develop ways to reduce the ctenophore populations by protecting natural ctenophore predators that live in the Black Sea and the Sea of Azov. Marine biologists might also develop ways to stop the transfer of ctenophores from the United States to the Black Sea and the Sea of Azov.

Human Body Systems

Like a finely tuned machine, your body is made up of many systems that work together. Your lungs take in oxygen. Your brain reacts to things you see, hear, and smell and sends signals through your nervous system that cause you to react to those things. Your digestive system converts the food you eat into energy that the cells of your body can use. And those are just a few things that your body can do!

In this unit, you will study the systems of your body. You'll discover how the parts of your body work together.

Around
3000 BCE
Ancient Egyptian doctors are the first to study the human body scientifically.

1824
Jean Louis Prevost and Jean Batiste Dumas prove that sperm is essential for fertilization.

1766
Albrecht von Haller determines that nerves control muscle movement and that all nerves are connected to the spinal cord or to the brain.

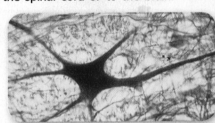

1940
During World War II in Italy, Rita Levi-Montalcini is forced to leave her work at a medical school laboratory because she is Jewish. She sets up a laboratory in her bedroom and studies the development of the nervous system.

Around 500 BCE
Indian surgeon Susrata performs operations to remove cataracts.

1492
Christopher Columbus lands in the West Indies.

1543
Andreas Vesalius publishes the first complete description of the structure of the human body.

1616
William Harvey discovers that blood circulates and that the heart acts as a pump.

1893
Daniel Hale Williams, an African American surgeon, becomes the first person to repair a tear in the pericardium, the sac around the heart.

1922
Frederick Banting, Charles Best, and John McLeod discover insulin.

1930
Karl Landsteiner receives a Nobel Prize for his discovery of the four human blood types.

1982
Dr. William DeVries implants an artificial heart in Barney Clark.

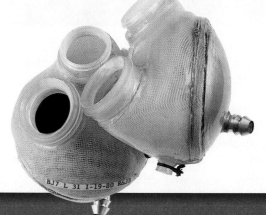

1998
The first successful hand transplant is performed in France.

2001
Drs. Laman A. Gray, Jr. and Robert D. Dowling at Jewish Hospital in Louisville, Kentucky, implant the first self-contained mechanical human heart.

The elements listed in the Standards Course of Study provide a base for presenting, supporting, and assessing the California Grade 7 Science Standards. Use this Standards Course of Study as a base for planning your lessons.

Why Teach

Body Organization and Structure

This chapter was designed to cover the California Grade 7 Science Standards about structure and function and how structure and function apply to the human body (7.1.f, 7.5.a, 7.5.b, 7.5.c, 7.6.h, and 7.6.i). This chapter describes the levels of organization in the human body as well as the relationship between structure and function in human body parts with an emphasis on bones and muscles. This chapter also details the important relationship of bones and muscles in the human body.

After they have completed this chapter, students will begin a chapter about the human circulatory system.

California Standards

Focus on Life Sciences

7.1.f Students know that as multicellular organisms develop, their cells differentiate.

7.5.a Students know plants and animals have levels of organization for structure and function, including cells, tissues, organs, organ systems, and the whole organism.

7.5.b Students know organ systems function because of the contributions of individual organs, tissues, and cells. The failure of any part can affect the entire system.

7.5.c Students know how bones and muscles work together to provide a structural framework for movement.

7.6.h Students know how to compare joints in the body (wrist, shoulder, thigh) with structures used in machines and simple devices (hinge, ball-and-socket, and sliding joints).

7.6.i Students know how levers confer mechanical advantage and how the application of this principle applies to the musculoskeletal system.

Investigation and Experimentation

7.7.c Communicate the logical connection among hypotheses, science concepts, tests conducted, data collected, and conclusions drawn from the scientific evidence.

7.7.d Construct scale models, maps, and appropriately labeled diagrams to communicate scientific knowledge (e.g., motion of Earth's plates and cell structure).

Chapter Pacing

Getting Started **45 min** pp. 464–465

The Big Idea The human body is composed of major systems that have differing functions, but all of the systems work together to maintain homeostasis.

7.5.c, 7.6.h, 7.7.d

Section ❶ Body Organization **60 min** pp. 466–471

Key Concept The human body functions because of the contributions of cells, tissues, organs, and organ systems.

7.1.f, 7.5.a, 7.5.b, 7.7.d

Section ❷ The Skeletal System **60 min** pp. 472–475

Key Concept The skeletal system is an organ system. The functions of the skeletal system include support, protection, movement, and the production of blood cells.

7.5.a, 7.5.c, 7.6.h, 7.7.c

Section ❸ The Muscular System **60 min** pp. 476–481

Key Concept The muscular system is an organ system. The skeletal and muscular systems work together to provide a structural framework for movement.

7.5.a, 7.5.c, 7.6.i

Wrapping Up **180 min** pp. 482–491

7.6.j, 7.7.c, 7.7.d

Basic Learners

TE Key Term Review, p. 469
TE Modifying a Hypothesis as a Class, p. 484
⬜ Reinforcement Worksheet
⬜ Chapter Test A
⬜ Differentiated Datasheets A for Labs and Activities ■
⬜ Study Guide A ■

Advanced Learners/GATE

TE Skeletal System Dysfunction, p. 475
TE Classifying Exercises, p. 480
TE Additional Hypotheses, p. 484
⬜ Critical Thinking Worksheet
⬜ Chapter Test C
⬜ Differentiated Datasheets C for Labs and Activities ■

Teach

SE Explore Activity How Do Your Legs Bend?, p. 465* ■

📦 **Bellringer**
💿 **PowerPoint® Resources**
📦 L69 Structure of the Stomach
📦 L70 Organ Systems
SE Quick Lab Modeling the Stomach, p. 470* ■

📦 **Bellringer**
💿 **PowerPoint® Resources**
📦 L71 The Skeleton
📦 L72 Three Human Body Joints
SE Quick Lab Pickled Bones, p. 474*

📦 **Bellringer**
💿 **PowerPoint® Resources**
📦 L73 A Pair of Muscles
📦 L74 Levers in the Human Body
SE Quick Lab How Do Levers Work?, p. 479* ■

SE Skills Practice Lab Levers and Mechanical Advantage, pp. 482–483* ■

Practice

SE Organize Activity Table Fold, p. 464

SE Section Review, p. 471* ■

SE Section Review, p. 475* ■

SE Section Review, p. 481* ■

SE Science Skills Activity Modifying a Hypothesis, p. 484* ■
📦 **Concept Mapping***
SE Chapter Review, pp. 486–487* ■

Assess

📁 **Chapter Pretest**

SE Standards Checks, pp. 467, 468, 470
TE Standards Focus, p. 470
📁 **Section Quiz** ■

SE Standards Checks, pp. 473, 474
TE Standards Focus, p. 474
📁 **Section Quiz** ■

SE Standards Checks, pp. 477, 479, 480
TE Standards Focus, p. 480
📁 **Section Quiz** ■

SE Standards Assessment, pp. 488–489*
📁 **Chapter Tests A, B** ■, **C**
📓 **Standards Review Workbook** ■

Resources for Universal Access · Differentiated Instruction

English Learners
TE Demonstration, pp. 473, 477, 478
TE Using the Figure, p. 473
TE Visualizing Joints, p. 475
TE Group Activity, p. 476
📁 Vocabulary and Section Summary A ■, B

📁 Section Quizzes ■
📁 Chapter Tests A, B ■
📁 Differentiated Datasheets A, B, and C for Labs and Activities ■
📓 Study Guide A ■
📓 Multilingual Glossary

Struggling Readers
TE Reading Strategy, pp. 467, 478
TE Visual Aids for Levers, p. 478

Special Education Students
TE Body Tissue Clues, p. 466
TE Body System Cooperation, p. 468
TE Finding Bones in the Body, p. 472
TE Muscle Pairs, p. 476
TE Demonstration, p. 484

To help plan your lessons, refer to the On Course Mapping Instruction booklet.

Visual Resources

CHAPTER STARTER TRANSPARENCY

BELLRINGER TRANSPARENCIES

TEACHING TRANSPARENCIES

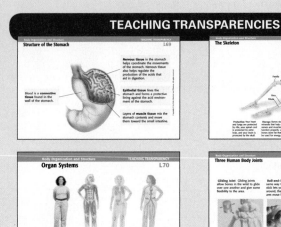

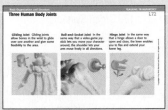

TEACHING TRANSPARENCIES

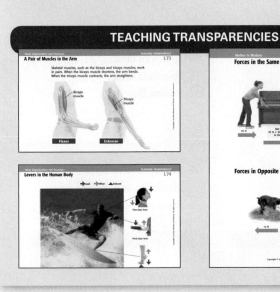
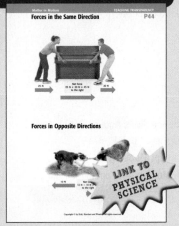

STANDARDS REVIEW TRANSPARENCIES

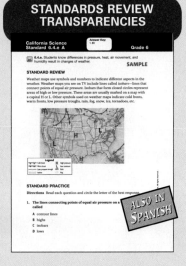

CONCEPT MAPPING TRANSPARENCY

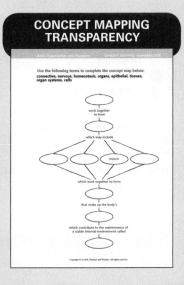

Planning Resources

PARENT LETTER

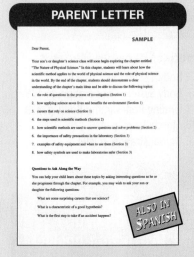

TEST ITEM LISTING

One-Stop Planner® CD-ROM

This CD-ROM package includes all of the resources shown here and the following time-saving tools:

- **Lab Materials QuickList Software**
- **Customizable Lesson Plans** Correlated to the California Science Standards
- **Holt Calendar Planner**
- **PowerPoint® Resources**
- **Printable Worksheets**
- **ExamView® Test Generator** Correlated to the California Science Standards
- **Holt PuzzlePro®**
- **Interactive Teacher's Edition**

Meeting Individual Needs

DIRECTED READING A

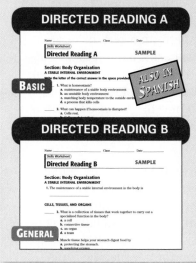

Name _____ Class _____ Date ____
Skills Worksheet
Directed Reading A   SAMPLE

Section: Body Organization
A STABLE INTERNAL ENVIRONMENT

BASIC
Write the letter of the correct answer in the space provided.

_____ 1. What is homeostasis?
   a. maintenance of a stable body environment
   b. an unstable body environment
   c. matching body temperature to the outside environment
   d. a process that kills cells

_____ 2. What can happen if homeostasis is disrupted?
   a. Cells rest.

ALSO IN SPANISH

DIRECTED READING B

Name _____ Class _____ Date ____
Skills Worksheet
Directed Reading B   SAMPLE

Section: Body Organization
A STABLE INTERNAL ENVIRONMENT

1. The maintenance of a stable internal environment in the body is

CELLS, TISSUES, AND ORGANS

2. What is a collection of tissues that work together to carry out a
   specialized function in the body?
   a. a cell
   b. connective tissue
   c. an organ
   d. a team

3. Muscle tissue helps your stomach digest food by
   a. protecting the stomach.
   b. supplying oxygen.

GENERAL

VOCABULARY AND SECTION SUMMARY A

Name _____ Class _____ Date ____
Skills Worksheet
Vocabulary and Section Summary A   SAMPLE

Body Organization
VOCABULARY

BASIC
In your own words, write a definition of the following terms

1. tissue

ALSO IN SPANISH

VOCABULARY AND SECTION SUMMARY B

Name _____ Class _____ Date ____
Skills Worksheet
Vocabulary and Section Summary B   SAMPLE

Body Organization
VOCABULARY

After you finish reading the section, try this puzzle! Use the clues given to fill in
the blanks below. Then, copy the numbered letters into the corresponding boxes
on the following page to reveal the four kinds of tissue.

1. the maintenance of a stable environment inside the body

2. a type of cell that has unique structures specialized to perform specific
   functions

GENERAL   _____ of similar cells that perform a common function

REINFORCEMENT

Name _____ Class _____ Date ____
Skills Worksheet
Reinforcement   SAMPLE

BASIC

Muscle Map
Complete this worksheet after you finish reading the section "The Muscular System."

of the boxes below is labeled with one of the three types of muscle tissue
than once. Write each note in the correct box. Some of the notes can be used
than once.

Three Types of Muscle

Skeletal	Cardiac	Smooth

CRITICAL THINKING

Name _____ Class _____ Date ____
Skills Worksheet
Critical Thinking   SAMPLE

ADVANCED

The Tissue Engineering Debate
Dear Readers:
Be sure to read next week's issue of *Amazing Medicine,* which features an
in-depth interview with Dr. E. P. Dennis of Frontiers Medical Center. While
visiting the burn therapy unit at Frontiers, I asked Dr. Dennis about treatments
for severe burns. She told me about an incredible new treatment called *tissue
engineering.*
Scientists are actually growing human skin in laboratories and then attaching
the skin to real, live patients! Scientists start the process by taking a piece of
human skin and collagen from cows. The cells are grown in a culture, where they
develop into tissues. When they are ready, the sheets of skin are moved to the
patient's body, where they continue to live. In this way, doctors can permanently
patient's burned or diseased skin.
_____ is informed me that scientists are also working on engineering
organs like livers, hearts, and kidneys. She believes they'll probably
succeed within the next 20 years or so.
Now that's amazing medicine! What do you think?

INTERACTIVE READER AND STUDY GUIDE

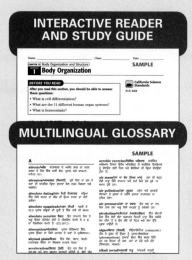

Name _____ Class _____ Date ____
CHAPTER to Body Organization and Structure
Body Organization   SAMPLE

BEFORE YOU READ

California Science Standards
7.1.f, 7.6.b

After you read this section, you should be able to answer
these questions:
• What is cell differentiation?
• What are the 11 different human organ systems?
• What is homeostasis?

MULTILINGUAL GLOSSARY

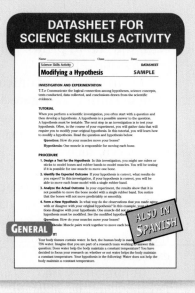

SAMPLE

A
abiotic/ ...
abrasion/ ...
absolute dating/ ...
absolute magnitude/ ...
absolute zero/ ...
absorption/ ...
abyssal plain/ ...
acceleration/ ...

aerobic exercise/ ...
air pollution/ ...
air pressure/ ...
alcoholism/ ...
algae/ ...
alkali metal/ ...

Labs and Activities

DIFFERENTIATED DATASHEETS FOR EXPLORE ACTIVITY, QUICK LABS, AND CHAPTER LAB

Name _____ Class _____ Date ____
Skills Practice Lab   DATASHEET A
Levers and Mechanical Advantage   SAMPLE

Your skeleton contains many joints, such as the knee and elbow. These joints act
as first-class, second-class, or third-class levers. The three classes of levers are
shown below. Most of the levers in the human body act as third-class levers. As
you have learned, some levers provide a mechanical advantage. Levers always
reduce the effort force needed to move a load, right? Actually, that is not always
true. Sometimes, the advantage of the lever does not reduce the amount of force
needed to move a load. In fact, a lever may need additional force to move a load.
But levers can also offer another kind of advantage. Do this lab to find out the other
advantages of levers.

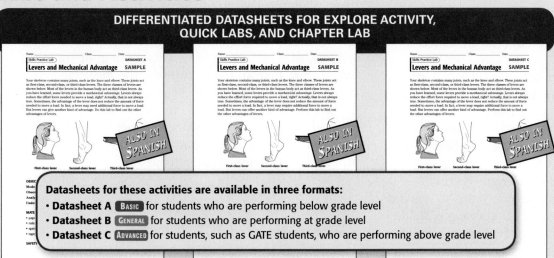

First-class lever   Second-class lever   Third-class lever

OBJECTIVE
Mode...
Obser...
Analy...
Unde...

MATE
• pape...
• rule...
• spri...
• tape...

SAFET...

Name _____ Class _____ Date ____
Skills Practice Lab   DATASHEET B
Levers and Mechanical Advantage   SAMPLE

Your skeleton contains many joints, such as the knee and elbow. These joints act
as first-class, second-class, or third-class levers. The three classes of levers are
shown below. Most of the levers in the human body act as third-class levers. As
you have learned, some levers provide a mechanical advantage. Levers always
reduce the effort force required to move a load, right? Actually, that is not always
true. Sometimes, the advantage of the lever does not reduce the amount of force
needed to move a load. In fact, a lever may need additional force to move a
load. But levers can offer another kind of advantage. Perform this lab to find out
the other advantages of levers.

First-class lever   Second-class lever   Third-class lever

ALSO IN SPANISH

Name _____ Class _____ Date ____
Skills Practice Lab   DATASHEET C
Levers and Mechanical Advantage   SAMPLE

Your skeleton contains many joints, such as the knee and elbow. These joints act
as first-class, second-class, or third-class levers. The three classes of levers are
shown below. Most of the levers in the human body act as third-class levers. As
you have learned, some levers provide a mechanical advantage. Levers always
reduce the effort force required to move a load, right? Actually, that is not always
true. Sometimes, the advantage of the lever does not reduce the amount of force
needed to move a load. In fact, a lever may need additional force to move a
load. But levers can offer another kind of advantage. Perform this lab to find out
the other advantages of levers.

First-class lever   Second-class lever   Third-class lever

ALSO IN SPANISH

Datasheets for these activities are available in three formats:
• **Datasheet A** BASIC for students who are performing below grade level
• **Datasheet B** GENERAL for students who are performing at grade level
• **Datasheet C** ADVANCED for students, such as GATE students, who are performing above grade level

DATASHEET FOR SCIENCE SKILLS ACTIVITY

Name _____ Class _____ Date ____
Science Skills Activity   DATASHEET
Modifying a Hypothesis   SAMPLE

INVESTIGATION AND EXPERIMENTATION
7.7.c Communicate the logical connection among hypotheses, science concepts,
tests conducted, data collected, and conclusions drawn from the scientific
evidence.

TUTORIAL
When you perform a scientific investigation, you often start with a question and
then develop a hypothesis. A hypothesis is a possible answer to the question.
A hypothesis must be testable. The next step in an investigation is to test your
hypothesis. Often, in the course of your experiment, you will gather data that will
require you to modify your original hypothesis. In this tutorial, you will learn how
to modify a hypothesis. Read the question and hypothesis below.
Question: How do your muscles move your bones?
Hypothesis: One muscle is responsible for moving each bone.

PROCEDURE
1. Design a Test for the Hypothesis In this investigation, you might use rulers or
sticks to model bones and rubber bands to model muscles. You will be testing
if it is possible for one muscle to move one bone.
2. Identify the Expected Outcome If your hypothesis is correct, what results do
you expect? In this investigation, if your hypothesis is correct, you will be
able to move each bone model with a single rubber band.
3. Analyze the Actual Outcome In your experiment, the results show that it is
not possible to move the bone model with a single rubber band. You notice
that the bones will not move predictably or smoothly.
4. Form a New Hypothesis In what way do the observations that you made agree
with or disagree with your original hypothesis? In this example, your observations disagree with your hypothesis. One muscle did not move a bone, so the
hypothesis must be modified. The modified hypothesis ...
Question: How do your muscles move your bones?
thesis: Muscle pairs work together to move your bones.

Your body tissues contain water. In fact, the human body is made up of about
70% water. Imagine that you are part of a research team working to answer this
question. Does water help the body maintain a constant temperature? You have
decided to focus your research on whether or not water helps the body maintain
a constant temperature. Your hypothesis is the following: Water does not help the
body maintain a constant temperature.

GENERAL

ALSO IN SPANISH

Reviews and Assessments

SECTION REVIEWS

Name _____ Class _____ Date ____
Skills Worksheet
Section Review   SAMPLE

Body Organization
USING VOCABULARY

1. Use *homeostasis, tissue,* and *organ* in the same sentence.

GENERAL

ALSO IN SPANISH

UNDERSTANDING CONCEPTS
2. **Analyzing** How are tissues, organs, and organ systems related?

CHAPTER REVIEW

Name _____ Class _____ Date ____
Skills Worksheet
Chapter Review   SAMPLE

USING VOCABULARY

1. **Academic Vocabulary** In the sentence "Levers confer a mechanical
advantage," what does the word *confer* mean?
   a. decrease
   b. cancel out
   c. give
   d. remove

Complete each of the following sentences by choosing the c_____ from the
word bank.

_____ organ _____ organ
_____ systems   tissue   muscle

3. _____ is a place where two or mo_____

GENERAL

ALSO IN SPANISH

CHAPTER PRETEST

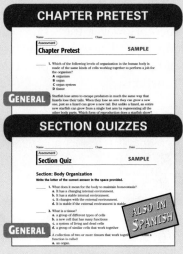

Name _____ Class _____ Date ____
Assessment
Chapter Pretest   SAMPLE

1. Which of the following levels of organization in the human body is
made of the same kinds of cells working together to perform a job for
the organism?
   A organism
   B organ
   C organ system
   D tissue

GENERAL
2. Starfish lose arms to escape predators in much the same way that
lizards lose their tails. When they lose an arm, they grow a new
one, just as a lizard can grow a new tail. But unlike a lizard, an entire
new starfish can grow from a single lost arm by regenerating all the
other body parts. Which form of reproduction does a starfish show?

ALSO IN SPANISH

SECTION QUIZZES

Name _____ Class _____ Date ____
Assessment
Section Quiz   SAMPLE

Section: Body Organization
Write the letter of the correct answer in the space provided.

_____ 1. What does it mean for the body to maintain homeostasis?
   A. It has an unstable internal environment.
   B. It has a stable internal environment.
   C. It changes with the external environment.
   D. It is stable if the external environment is stable.

_____ 2. What is a tissue?
   A. a group of different types of cells
   B. a new cell that has many functions
   C. a system of living and dead cells
   D. a group of similar cells that work together

GENERAL

ALSO IN SPANISH

CHAPTER TEST A

Name _____ Class _____ Date ____
Assessment
Chapter Test A   SAMPLE

BASIC

Body Organization and Structure
MULTIPLE CHOICE
Write the letter of the correct answer in the space provided.

CHAPTER TEST B

Name _____ Class _____ Date ____
Assessment
Chapter Test B   SAMPLE

GENERAL

Body Organization and Structure
MULTIPLE CHOICE
Write the letter of the correct answer in the space provided.

ALSO IN SPANISH

CHAPTER TEST C

Name _____ Class _____ Date ____
Assessment
Chapter Test C   SAMPLE

ADVANCED

Body Organization and Structure
USING KEY TERMS
Use the terms from the following list to complete the sentences below. Each term
may be used only once. Some terms may not be used.

lever   ligaments   tendons
epithelial   mechanical advantage connective
cardiac   skeletal

1. In the body, the joint serves as fulcrum, and the bone is the a(n)

STANDARDS ASSESSMENT

Name _____ Class _____ Date ____
Assessment
Standards Assessment   SAMPLE

GENERAL

Teacher Notes and Answer Key
To provide practice under more realistic testing conditions, give students 20 min
to answer all of the questions in this assessment.

ON NUMBER	CORRECT ANSWER	STANDARD
		7.5 (supporting)
2		7.6 (supporting)
3	B	7.5 (supporting)

STANDARDS REVIEW WORKBOOK

California Science
Standard 6.4.e   Grade 6
                        SAMPLE
6.4.e. Students know differences in pressure, heat, air movement, and
humidity result in changes of weather.

STANDARD REVIEW
Weather maps use symbols and numbers to indicate different aspects of the
weather. Weather maps you see on TV include lines called *isobars*—lines that
connect points of equal air pressure. Isobars that form closed circles with
areas of high or low pressure. These areas are usually marked with
a capital H or L. Other symbols used on weather maps represent
warm fronts, low pressure troughs, rain, fog, snow, i_____

GENERAL

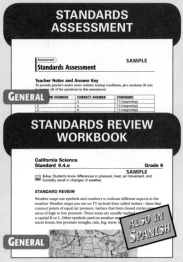

ALSO IN SPANISH

This Teacher Background explains science concepts, principles, and theories that appear in the chapter. Use the information on these pages to refresh or enhance your understanding of the topics covered.

Section 1

Body Organization

Cellular Differentiation

As multicellular organisms develop, their cells differentiate. Most mature multicellular organisms begin as a single fertilized cell. In mammals, the fertilized cell develops through several stages of cell division. After the first several cycles of cell division, cells begin to specialize, giving rise to cells that have a particular function. The process by which cells specialize is known as *differentiation.*

In plants and animals, cells that have the ability to differentiate or specialize into many cell types are called *pluripotent* cells. In animals, these cells are called *stem* cells, whereas in plants, pluripotent cells are called *meristematic* cells.

For an example of differentiation in the development of an organism, see **Figure A** which shows four types of cells that are all derived from a single fertilized cell. Differentiation allows for cells to specialize into a specific type of cell, such as a muscle cell, nerve cell, blood cell, or an epithelial cell.

During differentiation, cells undergo structural changes of all aspects to enable them to perform specific functions. These changes include changes in size, shape, metabolic activity, signal responsiveness, as well as gene expression.

In humans, stem cells are developed within the first few days after fertilization. Once a sperm cell has fertilized an egg cell, the fertilized cell undergoes several cycles of cell division. After about four days, the cells begin to differentiate and form a *blastocyst.* A blastocyst has an outer layer of cells that form a hollow sphere. Inside the sphere resides a small group of cells known as the *inner cell mass.* The inner cell mass eventually differentiates to form almost every cell in the human body.

The cells of the inner cell mass are pluripotent and undergo specialization to form different types of stem cells. The resulting stem cells, which are programmed to develop into specific cells that perform a certain function, are referred to as *multipotent* cells. Examples of multipotent stem cells include blood stem cells and skin stem cells. Blood stem cells give rise to white blood cells, red blood cells, or platelets. Skin stem cells give rise to different types of skin cells.

Levels of Organization

Plants and animals have structural and functional levels of organization. This hierarchy of organizational development derives from the process of cellular differentiation. As differentiation takes place, specialized cells group together to form tissues, highly-specialized groups of cells that work together to perform a specific function. Examples of tissue include muscle tissue, epithelial tissue, connective tissue, and nervous tissue. Groups of tissue work together to form specialized organs, such as the heart or the lungs. At the next level of body organization, specialized organs work together to form organ systems, such as the cardiovascular system or the digestive system. Like all organ systems, the digestive system results from the joint effort of several organs, including the stomach, large intestine, and small intestine. All of the body's organ systems work together to carry out the functions of the whole organism. If one system fails, all other organ systems are affected.

Section 2

The Skeletal System

Joints

Specialized joints, such as the ball-and-socket joints or hinges used in every aspect of modern life from artificial hips to car doors, are considered a technological advancement. However, these types of simple machines are present in nature. The way in which joints function is an example of how physical concepts underlie biological structures and functions.

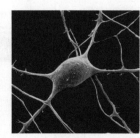
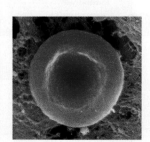
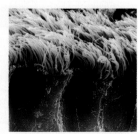

Figure A *Cell differentiation produces different cell types.*

A joint is the point at which two bones meet or make contact. Joints allow for smooth movement and for structural support of the organism. Joints can be classified by both structure and function.

Structurally, joints can be classified as fibrous, cartilaginous, or synovial. Fibrous joints are the points at which bones are connected by fibrous connective tissue. Bones connected by cartilage are cartilaginous joints. Synovial joints are the points at which bones make contact but create a space known as a synovial cavity, which is filled with synovial fluid.

Functionally, joints can be classified as synarthrosis joints, amphiarthrosis joints, or diarthrosis joints. Synarthrosis joints provide little or no movement, amphiarthrosis joints provide limited movement, and diarthrosis joints provide a variety of movements.

The types of joints discussed in this section include diarthrosis joints. These are synovial joints that also have cartilage to protect the surfaces of the bones at the joint. Diarthrosis joints, shown in **Figure B,** are classified by shape and include gliding joints (found in the wrist), hinge joints (found in the elbow and knee), pivot joints (found in the elbow), and ball-and-socket joints (found in the hip).

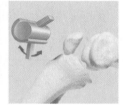

Figure B *The structure of different types of joints allows for different types of movement.*

Section 3

The Muscular System

Three Types of Muscle

The three types of muscle that are found in the human body are skeletal muscle, smooth muscle, and cardiac muscle. Skeletal muscle is muscle tissue that covers the bones of the body, gives the body tone and shape, and is responsible for body movement. Skeletal muscle action can be voluntary or involuntary. Smooth muscle is found in the walls of organs, such as the stomach, lungs, and intestines. Smooth muscle action is involuntary and responsible for basic body functions, such as digesting food and expelling wastes from the body. Cardiac muscle is found only in the heart and performs involuntary muscle action.

The structure of skeletal muscle is directly related to its function. Muscle tissue is composed of muscle cells, which are also referred to as muscle fibers. A skeletal muscle is a bundle of muscle fibers, each of which is a single cell with many nuclei. Muscle fibers are long, rod-shaped cells that are actually bundles of smaller components called myofibrils. Myofibrils are composed of two kinds of myofilaments: thick filaments and thin filaments. These filaments contain actin and myosin, two molecules that allow for contraction. Myofilaments are arranged in a striated fashion, and thick and thin myofilmaments slide over one another during muscle contraction.

A muscle is either relaxed or contracted. The myofilaments in a relaxed muscle overlap each other slightly. When a nerve impulse stimulates a muscle fiber, the muscle's myofilaments slide over each other until they overlap completely. The muscle becomes shorter and fatter and is said to be contracted.

Muscles Occur in Pairs

Muscles can contract in only one direction. Therefore, muscles almost always work in pairs. For example, as shown in **Figure C,** the biceps muscle contracts to bend the arm at the elbow but is unable to straighten the arm. Similarly, the opposing triceps muscle, which cannot bend the arm, contracts to straighten it again. The two muscles work together to allow for a range of motion of the arm.

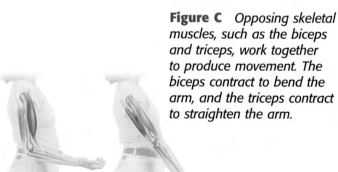

Figure C *Opposing skeletal muscles, such as the biceps and triceps, work together to produce movement. The biceps contract to bend the arm, and the triceps contract to straighten the arm.*

Internet Resources

SciLinks is maintained by the National Science Teachers Association to provide you and your students with interesting, up-to-date links that will enrich your classroom presentation of the chapter.

Visit **www.scilinks.org** and enter the SciLinks code for more information about the topic listed.

Topic: Tissues and Organs
SciLinks code: HY71530

Topic: Body Systems
SciLinks code: HY70184

Topic: Muscular System
SciLinks code: HY71008

Topic: Skeletal System
SciLinks code: HY71399

Improving Comprehension

Graphic Organizers are important visual tools that can help you organize information and improve your reading comprehension. The Graphic Organizer below is called a *comparison table*. Instructions for creating other types of Graphic Organizers are located in the **Study Skills** section of the Appendix.

Improving Comprehension

Use the Graphic Organizer on this page of the Student Edition to introduce the topics that are covered in this chapter, to summarize the chapter material, or to show students how to make a comparison table.

Teaching Tips

- Explain to students that they may want to read the source information for a comparison table twice—once to determine the general characteristics that they want to compare and once to fill in the table.

- Explain to students that comparison tables allow for broader, more general comparisons than some other comparison organizers do. For example, unlike a Venn diagram, a comparison table does not need to contain both shared and unique characteristics.

- Encourage students to use the comparison table as a quick and efficient form of notes.

LS Logical

How to Make a Comparison Table

1 Draw a table like the one shown below. Draw as many columns and rows as you want to draw.

2 In the top row, write the topics that you want to compare.

3 In the left column, write the general characteristics that you want to compare. As you read the chapter, fill in the characteristics for each topic in the appropriate boxes.

When to Use a Comparison Table

A comparison table is useful when you want to compare the characteristics of two or more topics in science. Organizing information in a table helps you compare several topics at one time. In a table, all topics are described in terms of the same list of characteristics, which helps you make a thorough comparison. As you read, look for topics whose characteristics you may want to compare in a table.

	Skeletal System	Muscular System
Parts	• bones, cartilage, connective tissue	• muscles
Structure	• Bone is made of connective tissue and minerals. • Compact bone is rigid and dense bone tissue. • Spongy bone is bone tissue that has open spaces.	• Smooth muscle is in the digestive tract and in the walls of blood vessels. • Cardiac muscle is in the heart. • Skeletal muscle is attached to bones.
Function	• Some bones protect organs. • Bones store minerals that help nerves and muscles function. • Bones provide the body with structure. • Some bones make blood cells.	• Muscles let a person move. • Voluntary action is action that can be controlled. (skeletal) • Involuntary action is action that cannot be controlled. (smooth, cardiac, or skeletal) • Muscles often work in pairs.

You Try It!

This Reading Strategy can also be used within the chapter that you are about to read. Practice making your own *comparison table* as directed in the Reading Strategies for Section **1** and Section **2**. Record your work in your **Science Journal**.

Using Other Graphic Organizers

Students can practice using a variety of Graphic Organizers while reading this chapter. The following Graphic Organizers may also be useful in this chapter.

A **pyramid chart** can be used to describe body organization, discussed in Section 1.

Combination notes can be used to take notes about the three classes of levers, described in Section 2.

Instructions for creating these Graphic Organizers are located on pp. 583–591 of the Appendix.

Unpacking the Standards

The information below "unpacks" the standards by breaking them down into basic parts. The higher-level, academic vocabulary is highlighted and defined to help you understand the language of the standards. "What It Means" restates the standards as simply as possible.

Unpacking the Standards

Use the following information with the *What It Means* in the Student Edition to help students understand why studying each standard is important.

California Standard	Academic Vocabulary	What It Means	Why It Matters
7.5.a Students know plants and animals have levels of organization for **structure** and **function**, including cells, tissues, organs, organ systems, and the whole organism.	**structure** (STRUHK chuhr) the arrangement of the parts of a whole **function** (FUHNGK shuhn) use or purpose	Plants and animals are made of smaller parts which are organized by shape and purpose. These layers of organization include cells, tissues, organs, organ systems, and the whole organism.	Multicellular organisms, including humans, function because their cells are organized at many levels. Each subsequent level of organization has unique properties that the prior level of organization does not have.
7.5.b Students know organ systems **function** because of the **contributions** of **individual** organs, tissues, and cells. The failure of any part can **affect** the entire system.	**function** (FUHNGK shuhn) to work **contribution** (KAHN truh BYOO shuhn) a part given toward a whole **individual** (IN duh VIJ oo uhl) being a single, separate entity; particular **affect** (uh FEKT) to change; to have an effect on; to influence	An organ system is able to work because of the work that each of its smaller parts (organs, tissues, and cells) does. If any part of an organ system fails to work well, the entire system is changed.	Organ systems within an organism are interrelated. When one part of a multicellular organism fails to perform its function, the entire organism is affected.
7.5.c Students know how bones and muscles work together to provide a **structural framework** for movement.	**structural** (STRUHK chuhr uhl) having to do with the arrangement of the parts of a whole **framework** (FRAYM wuhrk) a basic structure that supports something	Bones and muscles work together to make a system of support that allows the body to move.	Students should know that the skeletal and muscular systems function in cooperation with one another.
7.6.h Students know how to compare joints in the body (wrist, shoulder, thigh) with **structures** used in machines and simple **devices** (hinge, ball-and-socket, and sliding joints).	**device** (di VIES) a piece of equipment made for a specific use	You must be able to compare places in the body where two or more bones meet, such as wrists, shoulders, and thighs, with structures used in simple machines, such as hinge, ball-and-socket, and sliding joints.	Some joints allow the human body to move. One can understand how levers work by studying how simple machines such as doorknobs and video-game joysticks work.
7.6.i Students know how levers **confer** mechanical advantage and how the application of this **principle** applies to the musculoskeletal system.	**confer** (kuhn FUHR) to give **principle** (PRIN suh puhl) basic law, rule, or belief	You must know how levers can reduce the amount of force required to perform a task or can increase the speed of a motion. You must also know how levers are part of the muscular and skeletal systems of the human body.	Many movable human joints also function as levers. Understanding the function of a lever allows one to understand the principles that affect the function of the human body.

The following identifies other standards that are covered in this chapter and where you can go to see them unpacked: **7.1.f** (Chapter 18)

Words with Multiple Meanings

Words that have both common and scientific meanings can be confusing to students. The following table identifies some of those words that are used in this chapter.

Term	Common meaning	Scientific meaning
organ	a musical instrument similar to a piano	a collection of tissues that carries out a specialized function of the body
tissue	a soft, absorbent piece of paper	a group of similar cells that perform a common function

Practice Have students define the following words: *organ* and *tissue*. Then, give students the definitions for the scientific meanings of these terms. (These definitions can be found in the glossary of this book.) Have students write sentences that use the common meanings of these words. Then, have students write sentences that use the scientific meanings of the words.

Chapter Overview

Tell students that this chapter will help them learn about human body systems. In particular, the chapter will introduce students to general body organization, the skeletal system, and the muscular system.

Homeostasis

Identify It! Students may be confused about the concept of *homeostasis,* the state in which a stable environment is maintained inside the body or inside a cell. Ask students, to describe how they know that they are thirsty. Ask students to identify what parts of their body are involved in recognizing thirst.

Correct It! Tell students that all of the systems in the body work together to alert the brain of the need for water. Because the body constantly uses water to perform different functions, water must be constantly replenished in order for the body to maintain a stable environment, or homeostasis. So, even if a person drank plenty of water today, he or she will still need water tomorrow.

Assess It! To asses students' understanding of homeostasis, ask students to write a paragraph in their **Science Journal** describing what happens if a person's body temperature becomes too high or too low. (A person may begin to sweat if his or her body temperature is too high or begin to shiver if it is too low.)

Body Organization and Structure

The Big Idea The human body is composed of major systems that have differing functions, but all of the systems work together to maintain homeostasis.

California Standards

Focus on Life Sciences

7.1 All living organisms are composed of cells, from just one to many trillions, whose details usually are visible only through a microscope. (Sections 1 and 2)

7.5 The anatomy and physiology of plants and animals illustrate the complementary nature of structure and function. (Sections 1, 2, and 3)

7.6 Physical principles underlie biological structures and functions. (Sections 2 and 3)

Investigation and Experimentation

7.7 Scientific progress is made by asking meaningful questions and conducting careful investigations. (Science Skills Activity)

Math

7.1.1 Algebra and Functions

English–Language Arts

7.1.3 Reading
7.2.5 Writing

About the Photo

Lance Armstrong has won the Tour de France seven times. These victories are especially remarkable because he was diagnosed with cancer in 1996. But with medicine to treat the cancer and hard work, he grew strong enough to win one of the toughest racing events.

Organize

Table Fold

Before you read this chapter, create the FoldNote entitled "Table Fold." Label the columns of the table with "Example," and "Function." Label the rows with "Levels of organization," "Joints," and "Levers." As you read the chapter, write an example and the function of each example under the appropriate column.

Instructions for creating FoldNotes are located in the Study Skills section on p. 582 of the Appendix.

California Standards Alignment

Focus on Life Sciences

7.1.f Students know that as multicellular organisms develop, their cells differentiate. **pp. 467, 471, 487–489**

7.5.a Students know plants and animals have levels of organization for structure and function, including cells, tissues, organs, organ systems, and the whole organism. **pp. 466–473, 475–476, 480–481, 486–489**

7.5.b Students know organ systems function because of the contributions of individual organs, tissues, and cells. The failure of any part can affect the entire system. **pp. 468, 470–471, 486–488**

7.5.c Students know how bones and muscles work together to provide a structural framework for movement. **pp. 465, 473–476, 481, 486–489**

7.6.h Students know how to compare joints in the body (wrist, shoulder, thigh) with structures used in machines and simple devices (hinge, ball-and-socket, and sliding joints). **pp. 465, 474–475, 486–488**

7.6.i Students know how levers confer mechanical advantage and how the application of this principle applies to the musculoskeletal system. **pp. 478–479, 481–483, 486–488**

Investigation and Experimentation

7.7.c Communicate the logical connection among hypotheses, science concepts, tests conducted, data collected, and conclusions drawn from the scientific evidence. **pp. 473, 484**

7.7.d Construct scale models, maps, and appropriately labeled diagrams to communicate scientific knowledge (e.g., motion of Earth's plates and cell structure). **pp. 465, 470, 472–473**

Teacher Notes

This activity models bone and muscle interactions (covers standards 7.5.c, 7.6.h, and 7.7.d). Each group will need two crayons. You may substitute sticks for the crayons, but the sticks need to be of even diameter.

Materials for Each Group

- crayon, 2 pieces
- masking tape
- modeling clay
- paper clips, 2
- twine, 2 pieces

Answers

6. Answers may vary. Most students will find that the T-shape moves in the direction of pull.

7. The twine represents muscle.

8. The T-shape represents bone.

9. Answers may vary. Bones provide a frame for muscle to work against. Muscles attach to bones and make bones move.

10. Answers may vary. Accept all reasonable responses. Most students will note that a hinge joint allows back-and-forth movement.

Differentiated Datasheets
A **BASIC**, B **GENERAL**, C **ADVANCED**

Also editable on the Holt Lab Generator CD-ROM

Explore Activity

How Do Your Legs Bend?

Use simple materials to model a joint in the body. Then, observe how muscles and bones work together.

Procedure

1. Make a T-shaped figure by **using two pieces of crayon.** Wrap the entire T-shaped figure with **masking tape.**

2. Shape **modeling clay** into a socket in which the short end of the T-shaped figure will be able to move freely. The socket is the base of your model.

3. Insert **two half-opened paper clips** into opposite sides of the base.

4. Tie **two pieces of twine** to the tip of the long end of the T-shaped figure. Thread one piece of twine through each of the paper clips.

5. Insert the short end of the T-shaped figure into the socket. Pull one piece of twine and then the other. Repeat this motion.

**7.5.c
7.6.h
7.7.d**

Analysis

6. What happens when you pull each piece of twine?

7. Does the twine represent muscle or bone?

8. Does the T shape represent muscle or bone?

9. How do muscles and bones work together to produce movement?

10. You have just created a model of a hinge joint. Your knee is one example of a hinge joint. Describe the motion permitted by a hinge joint.

Math Standards

Algebra and Function 7.1.1 Use variables and appropriate operations to write an expression, an equation, an inequality, or a system of equations or inequalities that represents a verbal description (e.g., three less than a number, half as large as area A). **pp. 475, 479, 481**

English–Language Arts Standards

Reading 7.1.3 Clarify word meaning through the use of definition, example, restatement, or contrast. **p. 476**

Writing 7.2.5 Write summaries of reading materials: (a) Include the main ideas and most significant details; (b) Use the student's own words, except for quotations; (c) Reflect underlying meaning, not just the superficial details. **p. 487**

Chapter Starter Transparency
Use this transparency to help students begin thinking about human body systems.

Body Organization

Key Concept The human body functions because of the contributions of cells, tissues, organs, and organ systems.

Preteach

Reviewing Prior Knowledge

Tell students that a key idea of this chapter is homeostasis. Ask students to describe what they already know about homeostasis. Tell students that the word *homeostasis* comes from the Greek prefix *homeo-*, which means "same" and the Greek suffix *-stasis*, which means "stationary" or "still."

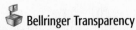 Bellringer

To have students focus on standards 7.5.a and 7.5.b, write the following on the board: *respiratory system, muscular system, digestive system, cardiovascular system,* and *endocrine system.* Then, write the following functions: *to pump blood, to enable movement, to send out chemical messages, to absorb oxygen,* and *to break down food.* Ask students to match each organ system with its correct function. (The respiratory system absorbs oxygen. The muscular system enables movement. The digestive system breaks down food. The cardiovascular system pumps blood. The endocrine system sends out chemical messages.)

Bellringer Transparency

Motivate

Discussion

Levels of Organization Before students read this section, ask them what they know about levels of organization within an organism. (Students may explain that cells are the building blocks of organisms.) Then, ask students how they think cells make up different body parts, such as organs and bones. Discuss how similar cells group together to perform different functions and form tissues, which in turn form different body structures. **LS** Logical/Verbal

What You Will Learn

- The levels of organization in the human body include cells, tissues, organs, organ systems, and the organism.
- Human cells are differentiated to perform specific jobs in the body.
- There are 11 human organ systems.
- Organ systems work together to maintain homeostasis. The failure of one organ system affects the entire body.

Why It Matters

The failure of any part of an organ system may lead to the failure of the entire system or organism.

Vocabulary

- tissue
- organ

READING STRATEGY

Graphic Organizer In your **Science Journal,** make a Comparison Table that compares the composition, function, and location of epithelial tissue, nervous tissue, muscle tissue, and connective tissue in the body.

Your body contains approximately 100 trillion cells and more than 100 kinds of cells. How do all of those cells work together? The body has different levels of organization: cells, tissues, organs, organ systems, and the whole organism. **Figure 1** shows four kinds of tissues. Tissues are one level of organization in the human body.

A Stable Internal Environment

Elements in each level of organization, whether in the cell, tissue, or organ level, work with other parts of the body to maintain a stable environment. *Homeostasis* is the maintenance of a stable environment inside the body. For example, the temperature outside your body changes, but your internal temperature remains close to 37°C. When homeostasis is not maintained, most cells do not function properly and may die.

Cells, Tissues, and Organs

Your cells must do many jobs to maintain homeostasis. But each of your cells does not have to do all jobs. Just as each person on a soccer team has a role during a game, each cell in your body plays a part in maintaining homeostasis.

Figure 1 **Four Kinds of Tissue**

Epithelial tissue covers and protects underlying tissue. When you look at the surface of your skin, you see epithelial tissue. The cells form a continuous sheet.

Nervous tissue sends electrical signals through the body. It is found in the brain, nerves, and sense organs.

Universal Access • Differentiated Instruction

Special Education Students

Body Tissue Clues Many students can retain information better if they create a visual image. Have students work in groups of four. Give each group a sheet of poster board. Have students divide the poster board into four sections and draw memory clues to help them remember the four kinds of body tissue. **LS** Visual/Interpersonal

Figure 2 Examples of Differentiated Body Cells

Muscle cells have proteins that are specialized for contraction.

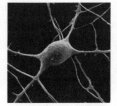

Neurons are nerve cells. Most neurons are long and thin.

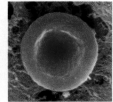

Red blood cells have no nucleus but contain a special pigment that picks up oxygen.

Epithelial cells have many jobs. They are found in skin and the linings of your organs.

Cells Form Tissues

Most cells in your body are *differentiated*. A differentiated cell is a cell that has unique structures that are specialized to perform specific functions in the body. **Figure 2** shows four kinds of differentiated cells. The function of each cell is related to the cell's structure. For example, the muscle cell has special proteins that allow the cell to shorten in length. This structure of the muscle cell allows the cell to contract. Thus, many muscle cells working together can cause an organism to move.

Your cells are organized into groups. A group of similar cells working together forms a **tissue.** Your body has four main kinds of tissue. The four kinds of tissue are shown in **Figure 1.**

Standards Check What is a differentiated cell? **7.1.f**

tissue (TISH oo) a group of similar cells that perform a common function

7.1.f Students know that as multicellular organisms develop, their cells differentiate.
7.5.a Students know plants and animals have levels of organization for structure and function, including cells, tissues, organs, organ systems, and the whole organism.
7.5.b Students know organ systems function because of the contributions of individual organs, tissues, and cells. The failure of any part can affect the entire system.

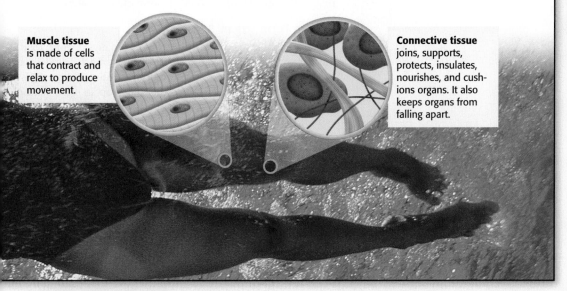

Muscle tissue is made of cells that contract and relax to produce movement.

Connective tissue joins, supports, protects, insulates, nourishes, and cushions organs. It also keeps organs from falling apart.

MISCONCEPTION ALERT

Organ Systems Working Together

Some students may not realize that all of the body's organ systems work together. To clarify this misconception, ask three student volunteers to stand in front of the class. Then, give each student one of three signs: Cardiovascular System, Respiratory System, and Nervous System. Have students touch each other's shoulders to represent the concept that all three organ systems work together. Then, have the student with the Cardiovascular System sign step away from the other students. Ask the class what will happen to the two other systems if the cardiovascular system fails. (The body will no longer be able to provide blood to all of the other organs, so the lungs in the respiratory system will not be able to function and the brain, which is part of the nervous system, will not be able to send signals to the rest of the body.)

CONNECTION ACTIVITY
History

Organ Transplants The first human heart transplant was performed in Cape Town, South Africa on December 3, 1967 by Dr. Christian Barnard and a team of 30 physicians. Have interested students research when other organs, such as kidneys, livers, and lungs, were first transplanted. Have students write a short report about their findings.
LS Visual

Debate

Transplant Ethics Thousands of people in the United States are waiting for organ transplants. The average cost of an organ transplant is $120,000. Encourage students to research and debate the ethical issues surrounding transplants. The following are suggested topics:

• Should transplants happen at all?

• Who should get a transplant?

• Should a child receive a transplant before an older person does?

• Where do most organs donated for transplants come from?

LS Logical/Interpersonal

Answer to Standards Check

The stomach helps a person digest his or her food by working with other organs, such as the small and large intestines, in the digestive system.
7.5.a (mastering)

Teaching Transparency:
L69 Structure of the Stomach

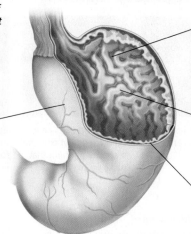

Figure 3 *The stomach is an organ. The four kinds of tissue work together so that the stomach can carry out digestion.*

Nervous tissue in the stomach helps coordinate the movements of the stomach. Nervous tissue also helps regulate the production of the acids that aid in digestion.

Blood is a **connective tissue** found in the wall of the stomach.

Epithelial tissue lines the stomach and forms a protective lining against the acid environment of the stomach.

Layers of **muscle tissue** mix the stomach contents and move them toward the small intestine.

organ (AWR guhn) a collection of tissues that carry out a specialized function of the body

Tissues Form Organs

One kind of tissue alone cannot do all of the things that several kinds of tissue working together can do. Two or more tissues working together form an **organ.** The stomach, shown in **Figure 3,** uses the four kinds of tissue to carry out digestion. Another organ, the heart, is made of muscle tissue, connective tissue, and epithelial tissue (EP i THEE lee uhl TISH oo).

Organs, such as the heart, can perform jobs that the tissues, which make up the organ, cannot perform on their own. The heart pumps blood throughout the body. None of the tissues that make up the heart could perform this job alone.

Organs Form Organ Systems

Your stomach does a lot to help you digest your food. But the stomach does not do it all. Your stomach works with other organs, such as the small and large intestines, to digest your food. Organs that work together make up an *organ system.* Your stomach is part of the digestive system. In another organ system called the nervous system, the brain, spinal cord, nerves, sense organs, and receptors work together. Each organ helps the nervous system control body movements.

Organ systems also perform jobs that organs alone cannot perform. In an organ system, each organ is specialized to perform part of the organ system's job. Each human organ system has a unique function. The human body's 11 organ systems are shown in **Figure 4.**

Standards Check Describe how the stomach functions as part of an organ system. **7.5.a**

Universal Access • Differentiated Instruction

Special Education Students

Body System Cooperation Kinesthetic activities offer learning opportunities that are equally available to students with and without vision and hearing impairments. Give body system signs to 10 students (exclude the reproductive system). The signs will help students remember who represents which system. Have the 10 students stand in a circle and step forward if his or her system is involved in the following activities: snoring (respiratory and muscular), sweating (lymphatic and integumentary), jumping in fear (muscular, skeletal, nervous, and endocrine), drinking (muscular, digestive, and urinary), eating an apple (digestive and muscular), running (muscular, skeletal, circulatory, cardiovascular, and respiratory). You may want to tell students that some body systems, such as the nervous system and the endocrine system, play a role in nearly all of the body's functions. **LS** Verbal/Kinesthetic

Figure 4 Organ Systems

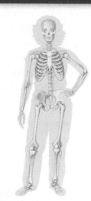

Integumentary System Your skin, hair, and nails protect the tissue that lies beneath them.

Muscular System Your muscular system works with the skeletal system to help you move.

Skeletal System Your bones provide a frame to support and protect your body parts.

Cardiovascular System Your heart pumps blood through all of your blood vessels.

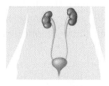

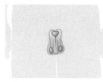

Respiratory System Your lungs absorb oxygen and release carbon dioxide.

Urinary System Your urinary system removes wastes from the blood and regulates your body's fluids.

Male Reproductive System The male reproductive system produces and delivers sperm.

Female Reproductive System The female reproductive system produces eggs and nourishes and protects the fetus.

Nervous System Your nervous system receives and sends electrical messages throughout your body.

Digestive System Your digestive system breaks down the food you eat into nutrients that your body can absorb.

Lymphatic System The lymphatic system returns leaked fluids to blood vessels and helps get rid of bacteria and viruses.

Endocrine System Your glands send out chemical messages. Ovaries and testes are part of this system.

Homework

Poster Project Have interested students choose one of the organ systems on this page and research how the organ system works. Students should create a poster that describes the organ system. Encourage students to be creative in their poster design by including a labeled drawing of the organs that make up the organ system and a written description of how the organs work together as a system. Tell students to explain clearly which activities the system is responsible for. **LS** Visual

Teaching Transparency: L70 Organ Systems

Universal Access · Differentiated Instruction

Basic Learners

Key Term Review Many students can benefit from a review of key terms. Ask students to use ten words in this section to write science-related clues and use a piece of graph paper to create unanswered crossword puzzles. Then, have students trade papers and complete each other's crossword puzzles. **LS** Logical/Interpersonal

Standards Focus

This **Standards Focus** provides you with a quick way to **assess, reteach,** and **re-assess** one or more concepts in the section.

Assess

Ask students whether the following statements are true or false.

1. In humans, all cells are identical. (false) **7.1.f**

2. Plants and animals have similar levels of organization, such as cells, tissues, organs, and organ systems. (true) **7.5.a**

3. The failure of any part of an organ system may lead to the failure of the whole organism. (true) **7.5.b**

Reteach

Organizing Information

To help students understand and identify the major organ systems of the body, have them make a table with the following headings: "Name of organ system," "Function(s)," and "Main organs." Have students complete the table to review the information presented in this section. **LS** Visual **7.5.a, 7.5.b**

Re-Assess

Organ Systems In their **Science Journal,** have students describe three of the organ systems introduced in this section. Have them describe the functions and primary organs of each system and include drawings of each system. **LS** Verbal **7.5.a**

Answer to Standards Check

The respiratory system uses the lungs to get oxygen into the body; the cardiovascular system picks up oxygen in the lungs and transports it to other parts of the body. **7.5.b**

Organ Systems Working Together

Your body's major organ systems work together to maintain homeostasis. For example, the cardiovascular system, which includes the heart, blood, and blood vessels, works with the respiratory system, which includes the lungs. The cardiovascular system picks up oxygen from the lungs and carries the oxygen to cells in the body. These cells produce carbon dioxide, which is returned to the respiratory system by the cardiovascular system. Then, the respiratory system expels the carbon dioxide.

Standards Check How does the cardiovascular system work with the respiratory system in the human body? **7.5.b**

Interdependence of Organ Systems

Some organs perform jobs that are important to more than one organ system. For example, the pancreas is an organ that produces fluids for digestion. But the pancreas is also part of the endocrine system. If the pancreas became damaged, the damage would affect both the digestive and endocrine systems. Therefore, the failure of one organ may affect more than one organ system. The failure of one organ may even affect the entire organism.

Quick Lab

Modeling the Stomach

Creating a model of the stomach can help you understand how this organ functions. The model will also help you understand how each tissue contributes to the function of the organ.

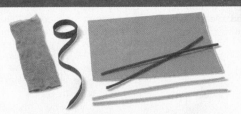

7.5.a
7.5.b
7.7.d

▶ **Try It!**

1. Collect some **art supplies** from your teacher.

2. Use the diagram of the stomach in **Figure 3** to decide which material to use for each type of tissue.

3. Make a table that lists each material and what each material represents in the model.

4. Make a sketch of your model, and label the different tissues. Then, construct a model of a stomach.

▶ **Think About It!**

5. Describe the role of each tissue that makes up the stomach.

6. How do the materials in your model represent the role of each tissue?

7. Change your model so that it does not have any muscle tissue. Describe what happened.

8. What can the stomach do that the tissues alone cannot do?

⏱ 25 min

Quick Lab

Teacher Notes

Students model the organization of an organ made of various tissue types (covers standards 7.5.a, 7.5.b, and 7.7.d).

Materials for Each Group
• art supplies (such as felt, pipe cleaners, ribbon, knee length nylons with feet cut out)

Safety Caution

Remind students to review all safety cautions and icons before beginning this activity.

Answers

5. Connective tissue holds the stomach together. Nervous tissue coordinates the movements of the stomach. Epithelial tissue forms a barrier between the stomach and the rest of the body. Muscle tissue mixes the food and moves it toward the small intestine.

6. Accept all reasonable answers. Students should list the materials they used and what each material represents.

7. Using their models, students should be able to see that without muscle tissue, the stomach

When Systems Fail

To maintain homeostasis, the body's organ systems must function properly and work together. When one part of an organ system fails to perform its roles in the body, the entire organism is affected and may die. The entire organism is affected because all of the processes needed for life are divided between the body's organ systems. Each organ system is specialized and thus performs a certain job. For example, the cardiovascular system transports nutrients and other substances throughout the entire body. Without the cardiovascular system, cells, tissues, and organs would not get the nutrients they need to function. No other organ system is able to do this job.

INTERNET ACTIVITY

Humans in Space
What are the effects of zero gravity and space travel on the human body systems? Go to **go.hrw.com,** and type in the keyword HY7BD1W to find out!

SECTION Review

7.1.f, 7.5.a, 7.5.b

Summary

- A human has many levels of organization.
- Most human cells are differentiated in structure for specific functions, or jobs, within the body.
- A group of cells that work together is a tissue. Tissues form organs. Organs that work together form organ systems.
- There are four kinds of tissue in the human body.
- There are 11 organ systems in the human body.
- Organ systems work together to help the body maintain homeostasis.

Using Vocabulary

1. Use *homeostasis, tissue,* and *organ* in the same sentence.

Understanding Concepts

2. **Analyzing** How are tissues, organs, and organ systems related?

3. **Listing** Name the 11 organ systems.

4. **Concluding** Are the organs in an organ system able to do the same jobs as the organ system? Explain.

5. **Describing** What happens when a cell becomes differentiated?

6. **Evaluating** How are organ systems related to one another?

Critical Thinking

7. **Applying Concepts** Tanya went to a restaurant and ate a hamburger. Describe how Tanya used five organ systems to eat and digest her hamburger.

8. **Predicting Consequences** Predict what might happen if the human body did not have specialized cells, tissues, organs, and organ systems to maintain homeostasis.

Math Skills

9. **Making Calculations** The human skeleton has 206 bones. The human skull has 22 bones. What percentage of human bones are skull bones?

Challenge

10. **Making Inferences** What would happen if the muscle tissue in your body suddenly stopped working? Which organ systems would be affected? How would each system be affected?

Internet Resources

For a variety of links related to this chapter, go to www.scilinks.org
Topic: Tissues and Organs; Body Systems
SciLinks code: HY71530; HY70184

---

5. When a cell differentiates, it becomes specialized to do a certain job. **7.1.f** (mastering)

6. All of the organ systems in your body work together to maintain homeostasis. **7.5.a** (mastering), **7.5.b** (mastering)

7. Answers may vary. The nervous system sends messages to Tanya's muscular system to bite into the hamburger. Tanya's jaws, which are part of the skeletal system, help grind up the food. The food moves into Tanya's stomach, which is part of her digestive system. The digestive system breaks down the food, and the cardiovascular system picks up nutrients from the digestive system and carries them throughout the body. **7.5.b** (exceeding)

8. Answers may vary. The body would be unable to maintain homeostasis because the cells of the body would have too many jobs to do. The cells likely would not be able to do all of these jobs. **7.5.a** (exceeding), **7.5.b** (exceeding)

9. about 11% (22 bones ÷ 206 bones × 100 = 10.7%)

10. Answers may vary. Your body would be unable to move. Most of your major organ systems would fail because muscle tissue is necessary for a person to eat, digest food, move, and pump blood throughout the body. **7.5.b** (mastering)

Section Review Standards Guide			
	Supporting	**Mastering**	**Exceeding**
7.1.f		5	
7.5.a	3	1, 2, 4, 6	8
7.5.b		2, 4, 6, 10	7, 8

⏱ **25 min**

would just be a bag. It wouldn't be able to mix or move the food.

8. The stomach is able to perform part of digestion. One tissue alone could not do all of the stomach's jobs. For example, epithelial tissue would not be able to move food, nervous tissue would not be able to hold the food in one place and protect the body from the stomach's acidic environment.

Differentiated Datasheets
A **BASIC**, B **GENERAL**, C **ADVANCED**

Also editable on the Holt Lab Generator CD-ROM

Answers to Section Review

1. Sample answer: Homeostasis is maintained by cells, tissues, and organs. **7.5.a** (mastering)

2. Sample answer: Tissues form organs and organs form organ systems. **7.5.a** (mastering), **7.5.b** (mastering)

3. integumentary system, muscular system, skeletal system, cardiovascular system, respiratory system, urinary system, reproductive system, nervous system, digestive system, lymphatic system, endocrine system **7.5.a** (supporting)

4. no; Each organ in an organ system does a different job, but they work together as a system. **7.5.a** (mastering), **7.5.b** (mastering)

Section Resources

📋 **Directed Reading**
A **BASIC** (Also in Spanish), B **GENERAL**

📋 **Interactive Reader and Study Guide**

📋 **Section Quiz** **GENERAL** (Also in Spanish)

📋 **Section Review** **GENERAL** (Also in Spanish)

📋 **Vocabulary and Section Summary**
A **BASIC** (Also in Spanish), B **GENERAL**

Preteach

Reviewing Prior Knowledge

Review standard 7.1.f with your students. Ask students how they think this standard may apply to this section. Tell students that the word *differentiate* means "to become different or distinct." Ask students how the meaning of this term helps explain how differentiated cells make up tissues.

 Bellringer

Have students focus on standard 7.5.c by asking them to brainstorm problems that they would have if they had no bones. (Students should understand that they would have no defined structure and no means of mobility. Students may conclude that they would be unable to perform simple functions, such as using their hands to pick up a pencil and that their internal organs would not be protected.)

Bellringer Transparency

Motivate

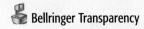 ACTIVITY

Locating Bones Review with students that the skeletal system supports the body and protects delicate body parts. Encourage students to press the skin in various parts of their body to feel their bones. Ask students to describe any parts of their body where they cannot feel their bones. (Answers may vary but should include the abdomen, nose, and ears.) As you point to various parts of the body, ask students what organs the bones protect. (Sample answers: The skull protects the brain. The ribs protect the heart and lungs.)
LS Kinesthetic/Visual

Teaching Transparency:
L71 The Skeleton

What You Will Learn

- The skeletal system includes bones, cartilage, and connective tissue.
- Bones have four important functions in the body. Bones are structured to perform these functions.
- Three human body joints are gliding, ball and socket, and hinge.

Why It Matters

The functions of the skeletal system play a role in maintaining the body's homeostasis.

Vocabulary

- skeletal system
- joint

READING STRATEGY

Graphic Organizer In your **Science Journal,** make a Comparison Table that compares various types of joints.

Figure 1 *The human skeleton is made of many bones. These bones serve many important functions in the body including the production of blood cells, protection, and support.*

The Skeletal System

Key Concept The skeletal system is an organ system. The functions of the skeletal system include support, protection, movement, and the production of blood cells.

▶ You may think that your bones are dry and brittle. But they are alive and active. Bones, cartilage, and the connective tissue that holds bones together make up your **skeletal system.**

Bones

The adult human skeleton, shown in **Figure 1,** has 206 bones. Bones help support and protect parts of your body. They work with your muscles so that you can move. Bones also help your body maintain homeostasis by storing minerals and making blood cells. The skeletal system has the following functions:

- Some bones protect organs. For example, your heart and lungs are protected by the ribs.
- Bones store minerals that help your nerves and muscles function properly. Long bones store fat that can be used as energy.
- Skeletal muscles pull on bones to produce movement. Without bones, you would not be able to sit, stand, or run.
- Some of your bones make blood cells. *Marrow* is a special material found in these bones. Marrow makes blood cells.

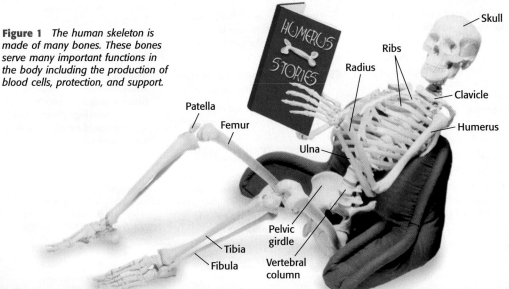

Universal Access • Differentiated Instruction

Special Education Students

Finding Bones in the Body

Personalizing information is one way to help students with special needs gain a better understanding. Have students point to their own bodies to identify the location of each of the labeled bones in **Figure 1.** LS **Kinesthetic**

SCIENCE HUMOR

Q: Why didn't the skeleton cross the road?

A: It didn't have the guts.

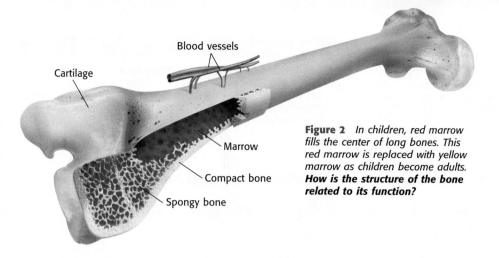

Cartilage
Blood vessels
Marrow
Compact bone
Spongy bone

Figure 2 *In children, red marrow fills the center of long bones. This red marrow is replaced with yellow marrow as children become adults.* **How is the structure of the bone related to its function?**

Bone Structure

A bone may seem lifeless. But a bone is a living organ that is made of several different tissues. Bone is made of connective tissue and minerals. These minerals are deposited by living cells called *osteoblasts* (AHS tee oh BLASTS).

If you look inside a bone, you will notice two kinds of bone tissue. If the bone tissue does not have any visible open spaces, it is called *compact bone*. Compact bone is rigid and dense. Tiny canals within compact bone contain small blood vessels. Bone tissue that has many open spaces is called *spongy bone*. Spongy bone provides most of the strength and support for a bone because it is able to absorb shock easily.

As you read earlier, some bones contain a tissue called marrow. There are two types of marrow. Red marrow produces both red and white blood cells. Yellow marrow, which is found in the central cavity of long bones, stores fat. **Figure 2** shows a cross section of a long bone.

Standards Check How does the structure of bones provide support?
 7.5.c

Bone Growth

Do you know that most of your skeleton used to be soft and rubbery? Most bones start out as a flexible tissue called *cartilage*. When you were born, you did not have much true bone. But as you grew, most of the cartilage was replaced by bone. During childhood, most bones still have growth plates of cartilage. These growth plates provide a place for bones to continue to grow.

Feel the end of your nose. Or bend the top of your ear. These areas are two places where cartilage is never replaced by bone. These areas stay flexible.

skeletal system (SKEL i tuhl SIS tuhm) the organ system whose primary function is to support and protect the body and to allow the body to move

7.5.a Students know plants and animals have levels of organization for structure and function, including cells, tissues, organs, organ systems, and the whole organism.
7.5.c Students know how bones and muscles work together to provide a structural framework for movement.
7.6.h Students know how to compare joints in the body (wrist, shoulder, thigh) with structures used in machines and simple devices (hinge, ball-and-socket, and sliding joints).

MISCONCEPTION ALERT

Bones are Alive Many students may have the misconception that all tissue must be soft or spongy, rather than hard and sturdy. Identify any misconceptions by asking students the following questions: What are bones made of? (Students may answer that bones are made of hard materials.) Does blood flow through your bones? (Some students may answer no.) Explain to students that bones are made of living

tissues, and blood flows through these tissues to maintain bone health. Using a cross section of a bone obtained from a butcher, show the class the open spaces within the bone, as well as the hollow center. Explain to students that the spaces allow for blood flow and the hollow inside is where marrow tissue is found.
LS Visual

Figure 3 Three Joints in the Human Body

Gliding Joint Gliding joints allow bones in the wrist to glide over one another and give some flexibility to the area.

Ball-and-Socket Joint In the same way that a video-game joystick lets you move your character around, the shoulder lets your arm move freely in all directions.

Hinge Joint In the same way that a hinge allows a door to open and close, the knee enables you to flex and extend your lower leg.

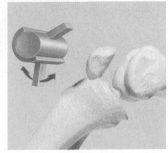

Standards Focus

This **Standards Focus** provides you with a quick way to **assess, reteach,** and **re-assess** one or more concepts in the section.

Assess

1. What is the difference between compact bone and spongy bone? (Sample answer: Compact bone has no visible, open spaces. Spongy bone has many visible spaces.) **7.1.f**

2. Where in the body are ball-and-socket joints found? (hip and shoulder) Where are hinge joints found? (knee) Where are gliding joints found? (wrist and ankle) **7.6.h**

Reteach

Organizing Information Have students create a chart that describes each of the joints shown on this page. In their charts, students should describe the joint, give an example of the joint from the body, and give an example of the same type of joint found in everyday objects, such as a door hinge or video-game joysticks. **LS** Visual **7.6.h**

Re-Assess

Bone Essays Have students write an essay about bones. Essays should address what bones do, how they are specialized, and how they are joined. **LS** Verbal

joint (JOYNT) a place where two or more bones meet

Joints

A place where two or more bones meet is called a **joint.** Your joints allow your body to move when your muscles contract. Some joints, such as fixed joints, allow little or no movement. Many of the joints in the skull are fixed joints. Other joints, such as your shoulder, allow a lot of movement. Joints can be classified based on how the bones in a joint move. Three joints are shown in **Figure 3.**

Your shoulder is a ball-and-socket joint. Ball-and-socket joints are similar to video-game joysticks. A ball-and-socket joint allows a bone to move up, down, forward, backward, and in a complete circle. A hinge joint allows less movement. The hinge joint that joins your thigh and lower leg allows the knee to bend in one direction. This joint is similar to some door hinges. Gliding joints, also called sliding joints, allow the bones in the wrist and the bones in the foot to glide over one another.

Standards Check How is a door hinge similar to the joint in your knee? **7.6.h**

The Structure of Joints

Joints are often placed under a great deal of stress. But joints can withstand a lot of wear and tear because of their structure. Joints are held together by *ligaments* (LIG uh muhnts). Ligaments are strong elastic bands of connective tissue. They connect the bones in a joint. Also, cartilage covers the ends of many bones. Cartilage helps cushion the area in a joint where bones meet.

Quick Lab

Pickled Bones

7.5.a
7.7.c

1. Place a **clean chicken bone** in a **jar of vinegar.**

2. After 1 week, remove the bone and rinse it with **water.**

3. Describe the changes that you can see or feel.

4. How has the bone's strength changed?

5. What did the vinegar remove?

6. How would this change in the bone's structure change the bone's function in the chicken's body?

⏱ 15 min

Answer to Standards Check

The hinge joint of a door and the hinge joint in the knee are similar because they allow motion in only one direction. **7.6.h** (mastering)

📦 Teaching Transparency:
L72 Three Human Body Joints

Quick Lab

⏱ 15 min

Teacher Notes

This lab demonstrates the structure of bones (covers standards 7.5.a and 7.7.c). Remember to use a jar with a lid to prevent the liquid from evaporating.

Materials for Each Group
• chicken bone, clean
• jar of vinegar

Safety Caution

Remind students to review all safety cautions and icons before beginning this lab activity.

Answers

3. Accept all reasonable answers.

4. Sample answer: The bone has become more flexible.

5. Sample answer: The vinegar dissolved the hard minerals in the leg bone.

6. Answers may vary. The bone has become weaker. Because it is no longer rigid, it will not be able to provide the support and protection it once did.

📄 Differentiated Datasheets
A **BASIC**, B **GENERAL**, C **ADVANCED**

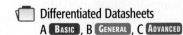
Also editable on the
Holt Lab Generator
CD-ROM

Skeletal System Injuries and Diseases

Sometimes, parts of the skeletal system are injured. As **Figure 4** shows, bones may be fractured, or broken. Joints can also be injured. A dislocated joint is a joint in which one or more bones have been moved out of place. Another joint injury, called a *sprain,* happens if a ligament is stretched too far or torn.

There are also diseases of the skeletal system. *Osteoporosis* (AHS tee OH puh ROH sis) is a disease in which the bones become less dense. Bones become weak and break more easily. Age and poor eating habits can make it more likely for people to develop osteoporosis. Other bone diseases affect the marrow or make bones soft. A disease that affects the joints is called *arthritis* (ahr THRIET is). Arthritis is painful. Joints may swell or stiffen. As they get older, some people are more likely to have some types of arthritis.

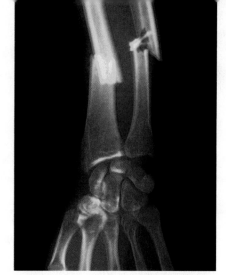

Figure 4 *This X ray shows that the two bones of the forearm have been fractured, or broken.*

SECTION Review

7.5.a, 7.5.c, 7.6.h

Summary

- The skeletal system includes bones, cartilage, and the connective tissue that connects bones.
- Bones protect the body, store minerals, allow movement, and make blood cells.
- A joint is a place where two or more bones meet.
- Skeletal system injuries include fractures, dislocations, and sprains. Skeletal system diseases include osteoporosis and arthritis.

Understanding Concepts

1. **Listing** What parts make up the skeletal system?

2. **Describing** What are four functions of bones?

3. **Summarizing** Name three joints, and describe the range of motion they allow.

Critical Thinking

INTERPRETING GRAPHICS Use the image below to answer the next question.

4. **Identifying Relationships** How is the object related to your skeletal system?

5. **Identifying Relationships** How do bones provide a structure for muscles to move?

6. **Predicting Consequences** What might happen if children's bones didn't have growth plates made of cartilage?

Math Skills

7. **Using Equations** A broken bone usually heals in about six weeks. A mild sprain takes one-third as long to heal. How many days does a mild sprain take to heal?

Internet Resources

For a variety of links related to this chapter, go to www.scilinks.org
Topic: Skeletal System
SciLinks code: HY71399

Answers to Section Review

1. The skeletal system includes bones, cartilage, and the connective tissue that connects bones. **7.5.a** (mastering), **7.5.c** (supporting)

2. Bones protect the body, store minerals, allow movement, and make blood cells. **7.5.c** (supporting)

3. Sample answer: Gliding joints allow the bones to glide over one another. Ball-and-socket joints allow a bone to move up, down, forward, backward, and in a complete circle. A hinge joint allows motion in one direction. **7.6.h** (mastering)

4. Answers may vary. The object pictured is a hinge joint. Two rigid plates are joined together at a point. The structure is able to bend at the place where the plates join. Hinge joints in the human body, such as the knee joint, work this way too. **7.6.h** (mastering)

5. Answers may vary. Bones provide a structure for muscles to move that is rigid and does not bend when muscles contract. Muscles attach to bones. **7.5.c** (mastering)

6. Sample answer: Growth plates are places where bones continue to grow. If children did not have growth plates, their bones would not continue to grow. **7.5.c** (exceeding)

7. 14 days (6 weeks × 7 days/week = 42 days; 42 days × 1/3 = 14 days)

Section Review Standards Guide

	Supporting	Mastering	Exceeding
7.5.a		1	8
7.5.c	1, 2	5	6
7.6.h		3, 4	

Universal Access · Differentiated Instruction

English Learners

Visualizing Joints Help students understand key words related to the joints by visualizing the act of gliding, the movement of a ball in a socket, and an opening and closing hinge. Tell them to close their eyes and think of a skater gliding on ice, a pitcher rotating a ball in his glove, a door opening and closing. Then, tell them to look at the diagrams in this section and focus on the names for the joints.

LS Verbal/Kinesthetic

Advanced Learners/GATE

Skeletal System Dysfunction Researching diseases or injuries of the skeletal system may enhance students' understanding of the structure and function of the skeletal system. Have interested students research either osteoporosis or arthritis. Then, have students report on how the disease affects the skeletal system and what can be done to prevent the disease, control it, or ease its symptoms.

LS Verbal/Logical

Section Resources

- Directed Reading A **BASIC** (Also in Spanish), B **GENERAL**
- Interactive Reader and Study Guide
- Section Quiz **GENERAL** (Also in Spanish)
- Section Review **GENERAL** (Also in Spanish)
- Vocabulary and Section Summary A **BASIC** (Also in Spanish), B **GENERAL**

Reviewing Prior Knowledge

Review standard 7.5.c with your students. Ask students to summarize the standard in their own words. Have interested students use their own bodies to demonstrate to the class how they think bones and muscles work together to provide movement. Then, ask students to predict how that standard may apply to this section.

Bellringer

To have students focus on standard 7.5.c, write the following on the board: "List at least five parts of your body that you use to drink a glass of water." (Sample answer: fingers, hands, arm, lips, and tongue) Remind students that all of the parts that they use, including the eyes that they use to see the glass, are controlled by muscles.

Bellringer Transparency

Motivate

 Group ACTIVITY

Poster Project   Have students create a poster illustrating the three types of muscle. Students should include information about where each muscle type is found, what it looks like, and whether it is involuntary or voluntary. Have students present their posters to the class. LS Verbal/Visual

---

The Muscular System

Key Concept   The muscular system is an organ system. The skeletal and muscular systems work together to provide a structural framework for movement.

What You Will Learn

● There are three kinds of muscle tissue: cardiac, smooth, and skeletal.
● Bones and muscles work together to form levers, which increase the mechanical advantage of most movements.
● The two kinds of exercise include resistance exercise and aerobic exercise.

Why It Matters

Most muscular movement in the human body occurs because bones and muscles work together.

Vocabulary

• muscular system
• lever
• mechanical advantage

READING STRATEGY

Asking Questions   Read this section silently. In your **Science Journal,** write down questions that you have about this section. Discuss your questions in a small group.

▶ Your heart is a muscle. Muscles make you breathe. And muscles hold you upright. If all of your muscles rested at the same time, you would collapse. The **muscular system** is made up of the muscles that let you move.

Kinds of Muscle

Figure 1 shows the three kinds of muscle in your body. *Smooth muscle* is found in the digestive tract and in the walls of blood vessels. *Cardiac muscle* is found only in your heart. *Skeletal muscle* is attached to your bones and helps you move. Skeletal muscle also helps protect your inner organs.

Muscle action can be voluntary or involuntary. Muscle action that is under your control is *voluntary*. Muscle action that is not under your control is *involuntary*. Smooth muscle and cardiac muscle are involuntary muscles. Skeletal muscles can be both voluntary and involuntary muscles. For example, you can blink your eyes anytime you want to. But your eyes will also blink automatically.

Figure 1   Three Kinds of Muscle

Skeletal muscle enables bones to move.

Smooth muscle moves food through the digestive system.

Cardiac muscle pumps blood around the body.

Universal Access · Differentiated Instruction

Special Education Students

Muscle Pairs   Have students act out the diagram in **Figure 2** so that students with visual impairments can learn the concept of muscles working in pairs. Pair students with visual impairments with students without visual impairments. Have students use their own arms to demonstrate the con-cept to each other. Students with visual impairments may have to use the sense of touch to understand what the other students is demonstrating. Have students with visual impairments listen to the explanation once before they try to demonstrate and explain the process.
LS Verbal/Interpersonal

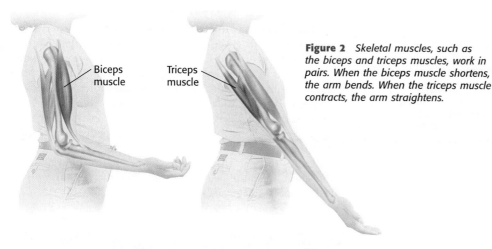

Biceps muscle

Triceps muscle

Figure 2 *Skeletal muscles, such as the biceps and triceps muscles, work in pairs. When the biceps muscle shortens, the arm bends. When the triceps muscle contracts, the arm straightens.*

Movement

Skeletal muscles are responsible for hundreds of movements. You can see many of these movements by watching a dancer or even someone smiling or frowning. When you want to move, signals travel from your brain to your skeletal muscle cells. The muscle cells then contract, or get shorter. Mitochondria in muscle cells provide energy for the cells to contract.

Muscles Attach to Bones

Strands of tough connective tissue connect your skeletal muscles to your bones. These strands of tissue are called *tendons.* When a muscle that connects two bones gets shorter, the bones are pulled closer to each other. For example, tendons attach the biceps muscle to a bone in your shoulder and to a bone in your forearm. When the biceps muscle shortens, your forearm bends toward your shoulder. The combination of skeletal muscles and bones working together is sometimes called the *musculoskeletal system.*

Muscles Work in Pairs

Your skeletal muscles often work in pairs to produce smooth, controlled motions. Usually, one muscle in the pair bends part of the body. The other muscle straightens part of the body. A muscle that bends part of your body is called a *flexor.* A muscle that straightens part of your body is an *extensor.* As shown in **Figure 2,** the biceps muscle of the arm is a flexor. The triceps muscle of the arm is an extensor.

Standards Check Describe how skeletal muscles work in pairs.
 7.5.c

muscular system (MUHS kyoo luhr SIS tuhm) the organ system whose primary function is movement and flexibility

7.5.a Students know plants and animals have levels of organization for structure and function, including cells, tissues, organs, organ systems, and the whole organism.
7.5.c Students know how bones and muscles work together to provide a structural framework for movement.
7.6.i Students know how levers confer mechanical advantage and how the application of this principle applies to the musculoskeletal system.

READING STRATEGY

Paired Summarizing Group students into pairs and have them read silently about levers in the human body. Then, have one student summarize how muscles and bones in the human body act as levers and define the three classes of levers. The other student should listen to the retelling and should point out any inaccuracies or ideas that were left out. Allow students to refer to the text as needed. **LS** Verbal

Connection To Physical Science

Levers Tell students that levers are the simplest kind of machine. Levers allow people to apply, increase, and change the direction of force. Ask students to think of examples of simple levers they use everyday. **LS** Verbal

Demonstration

Levers in the Body To help students understand how bones and muscles act together as levers in the human body, visually demonstrate the three classes of levers. Ask three student volunteers to stand at the front of the classroom. To demonstrate a first class lever, have one volunteer lift his or her head. Point out to the class the location of the fulcrum, and ask the class to identify where the force is being applied or changed. Repeat the demonstration for a second class (toes and feet) and a third class lever (arm). **LS** Visual/Kinesthetic

Teaching Transparency:
L74 Levers in the Human Body

lever (LEV uhr) a simple machine that consists of a bar that pivots at a fixed point called a *fulcrum*

mechanical advantage (muh KAN i kuhl ad VANT ij) a number that tells you how many times a machine multiplies force

Levers in the Human Body

The action of a muscle pulling on a bone often works like a type of simple machine called a lever. A **lever** is a rigid bar that pivots at a fixed point known as a *fulcrum*. Any force applied to the lever is called the *effort force*. A force that resists the motion of the lever, such as the downward force exerted by a weight on the bar, is called the *load*. **Figure 3** shows the action of three types of levers in the human body. In your body, the rigid bar is a bone. The effort force is supplied by muscles. And the fulcrum at which the bone pivots, is a joint.

Levers increase the amount of work that can be done by the effort force applied to a load. This increase in work is called **mechanical advantage.**

Figure 3 Levers in the Human Body

→ Load   → Effort   ▲ Fulcrum

First-class lever

Third-class lever

Second-class lever

Universal Access · Differentiated Instruction

Struggling Readers

Visual Aids for Levers Encourage struggling readers to draw pictures when a picture can help to clarify the information in the text. Ask students to draw in their **Science Journals** one of each kind of lever (first class, second class, and third class) and to label its parts. **LS** Logical

Three Classes of Levers

As **Figure 3** shows, there are three classes of levers. First-class and second-class levers increase the amount of force applied to a load. Third-class levers increase the speed of the motion. The class of a lever is determined by the location of the fulcrum, load, and effort force.

In a *first-class lever,* the fulcrum is between the effort force and the load. First-class levers work like a car jack or seesaw. To lift a load, a downward effort force must be applied to the other end of the lever. There are few first-class levers in the body. The joint in your neck acts as the fulcrum in a first-class lever that lifts your head. The effort force is supplied by the muscles at the back of your neck.

In a *second-class lever,* the load is between the fulcrum and the effort force. Second-class levers allow you to use less effort force than the force exerted by the load. Second-class levers work like a shovel. There are also few second-class levers in the body. The action of rising onto your toes represents the action of a second-class lever.

The effort force in a *third-class lever* is between the fulcrum and the load. Third-class levers increase the distance through which the load is moved. Third-class levers work like a dolly that is used to carry heavy boxes. Most movable joints in the human body work like third-class levers. You use a third-class lever to lift your textbook. Your elbow is the fulcrum, and the biceps muscle in your upper arm provides the effort force.

Standards Check Give an example of a lever in the body. 🐻 **7.6.i**

Mechanical Advantage

Force is measured using the SI unit called a newton (N). Use the equation below to answer the questions that follow.

mechanical advantage = force applied to load ÷ effort force

If a second-class lever in your body has a mechanical advantage of 8. What is the effort force applied to a load of 40 N? Where is this lever in your body?

Quick Lab

How Do Levers Work?

You can use simple materials to model how levers in the human body work.

1. Draw a table like the one below.

Class of lever	Sketch of model	Human body sketch
First		
Second	*DO NOT WRITE IN BOOK*	
Third		

2. Use a **meterstick, small wooden block,** and **100 g weight,** to build a lever from each class. Refer to **Figure 3** as needed.

6.7.i

3. Sketch each of your models in your table.
4. Which part of the human body moves like each class of lever? Sketch this body part in the table that you created.
5. How does the location of the fulcrum change the action of the lever?
6. What advantage does each class of lever provide?

🕐 **25 min**

Quick Lab

🕐 **25 min**

Teacher Notes

Models will demonstrate the action of levers (covers standard 7.6.i).

Materials for Each Group
- meterstick
- weight, 100 g
- textbook
- wooden block, small

Safety Caution

Remind students to review all safety cautions and icons before beginning this activity.

Answers

4. Accept all reasonable answers. Student answers may reflect the examples shown in Figure 3.
5. The location of the fulcrum changes the amount of effort force needed to lift or move the load.
6. Answers may vary. Students may refer to the structure of the human body or the kind of movements that humans commonly perform.

 Differentiated Datasheets
A **BASIC**, B **GENERAL**,
C **ADVANCED**

Also editable on the Holt Lab Generator CD-ROM

Standards Focus

This **Standards Focus** provides you with a quick way to **assess, reteach,** and **re-assess** one or more concepts in the section.

Assess

1. Give one example of how muscles and joints in your body can increase the distance through which a force is exerted. (Sample answer: The arm bones and muscles make a third-class lever that increases the work that can be done by the arm.) **7.6.i**

Reteach

How the Body Moves Separate the class into two groups. Have one group design a demonstration showing at least two examples of how the body can act as a lever. Have the second group design a demonstration showing how bones and muscles work together to provide a framework for movement in the body. Finally, have the two groups perform their demonstrations for the class.

LS Interpersonal/Verbal **7.5.c, 7.6.i**

Re-Assess

Venn Diagram Have students create a Venn Diagram showing an example of how bones and muscles work together and how they can be affected if either is not functioning properly.

LS Logical **7.5.c**

Wordwise

Aero- Words Relate that the root *aero* means "air." Ask students to use this information to write a definition for *aerobic*. Then, ask students to think of other words that begin with *aero-* and to write simple definitions for each. (Sample answers: aerodynamic, aerobe, aeronautics)

LS Verbal

Figure 4 *This girl (left) is strengthening her heart and improving her endurance by doing aerobic exercise. This boy (right) is doing resistance exercise to build strong muscles.*

SCHOOL to HOME

Power in Pairs

Ask a parent or guardian to sit in a chair and to place a hand palm up under the edge of a table. Tell your parent to apply gentle upward pressure. Feel the front and back of your parent's upper arm. Next, ask your parent to push down on top of the table. Feel your parent's arm again. What did you notice about the muscles in your parent's arm when he or she was pressing up? pushing down?

ACTIVITY

Wordwise aerobic
The root *aero-* means "air."

Use It or Lose It

What happens when someone wears a cast for a broken arm? Skeletal muscles around the broken bone become smaller and weaker. The muscles weaken because they are not exercised. Exercised muscles are stronger and larger. Strong muscles can help other organs, too. For example, contracting muscles squeeze blood vessels. These muscle contractions help move blood back to the heart.

Certain exercises can give muscles more strength and endurance. More endurance lets muscles work longer without getting tired. Two kinds of exercise can increase muscle strength and endurance. They are resistance exercise and aerobic exercise. You can see an example of each kind in **Figure 4.**

Standards Check How can exercise benefit organ systems? **7.5.a**

Resistance Exercise

Resistance exercise is a great way to strengthen skeletal muscles. During resistance exercise, people work against the resistance, or weight, of an object. Some resistance exercises, such as curl-ups, use your own weight for resistance.

Aerobic Exercise

Steady, moderately intense activity is called *aerobic exercise*. Jogging, cycling, skating, swimming, and walking are aerobic exercises. This kind of exercise can increase muscle strength. However, aerobic exercise mostly strengthens the heart and increases endurance.

Any exercise program should be started slowly. Starting slowly will help prevent you from getting hurt. You should also warm up for exercise by stretching.

Universal Access · Differentiated Instruction

Advanced Learners/GATE

Classifying Exercises Ask students to create a list of 25 resistance activities and a second list of 25 aerobic activities. Tell students that they can use both standard exercises and non-exercise activities. (Sample answers: resistance—leg pushes, knee curls, push ups, pull ups, forcing a door to open, playing tug of war; aerobic—dancing, mowing lawn, washing windows, painting a wall, running, swimming) Have students combine their lists to create one list with no duplicates. Allow time for students to share their final list.

LS Verbal/Logical

Muscle Injury

A *strain* is an injury in which a muscle or tendon is over-stretched or torn. Strains often happen because a muscle has not been warmed up by stretching or it has been overworked. If a tendon is injured, the body cannot repair it before the next exercise session. So, the tendon becomes inflamed. This condition is called *tendinitis*. Often, a long rest is needed for it to heal.

Some people try to make their muscles stronger by taking drugs called *anabolic steroids* (an uh BAHL ik STER OYDZ). Anabolic steroids cause long-term health problems. They can damage the heart, liver, and kidneys. If taken before the skeleton is mature, anabolic steroids can cause bones to stop growing.

SECTION Review

 7.5.a, 7.5.c, 7.6.i

Summary

- The three kinds of muscle tissue are smooth muscle, cardiac muscle, and skeletal muscle.

- Skeletal muscles work in pairs. Skeletal muscles contract to move bones.

- Muscles and bones work together to form levers.

- There are three classes of levers in the human body. Levers work to provide some advantage to body movements.

- First- and second-class levers increase the amount of force applied to a load. Third-class levers increase the speed of the motion.

- Strains are injuries that affect muscles and tendons. Tendinitis affects tendons.

Using Vocabulary

1. Write an original definition for *muscular system*.

Understanding Concepts

2. **Comparing** Describe three kinds of muscle.

3. **Listing** Name two kinds of exercise.

4. **Summarizing** What is a lever?

5. **Analyzing** What are the roles of bones and muscles in levers?

Critical Thinking

6. **Applying Concepts** Describe the muscle action needed to pick up a book. Include flexors and extensors in your description. Also, include a description of the kind of lever action used.

7. **Analyzing Ideas** What is the difference between a voluntary muscle action and an involuntary muscle action? Do bones and muscles work together differently in voluntary muscle actions when compared to involuntary muscle actions?

INTERPRETING GRAPHICS Use the image below to answer the next question.

8. **Identifying Relationships** Describe how the muscles and bones in this soccer player are working together to move the soccer ball. How are levers involved in this action?

Math Skills

9. **Using Equations** If Trey can do one curl-up every 2.5 s, about how long will it take him to do 35 curl-ups?

Internet Resources

For a variety of links related to this chapter, go to www.scilinks.org
Topic: Muscular System
SciLinks code: HY71008

---

6. Sample answer: An extensor in the back of my arm straightens out my arm as I reach for the book. Flexors in my hand let me close my fingers on the book, and a flexor in my arm bends my arm as I pick up the book. The arm acts as a third-class lever. **7.5.c** (exceeding), **7.6.i** (exceeding)

7. Answers may vary. A voluntary muscle action is an action that you control. Skeletal muscles generally perform voluntary muscle action. Involuntary muscle action is generally performed by smooth and cardiac muscles. yes; Involuntary muscle action and voluntary muscle actions usually involve different interactions of muscles and bones.

8. Answers may vary. Muscles are attached to the bones of this soccer player. When the muscles shorten or contract, they cause movement. Levers are involved in this movement because the leg kicking the soccer ball is an example of a third-class lever. The knee is the fulcrum, the muscles in the upper leg and behind the knee provide the effort force, and the foot is the load. **7.5.c** (mastering), **7.6.i** (mastering)

9. 87.5s (35 curl-ups × 2.5 s per curl-up = 87.5s)

Section Review Standards Guide

	Supporting	Mastering	Exceeding
7.5.a		1	
7.5.c	2	5, 7	6
7.6.i		4–5, 7	6

Answer to Standards Check

Exercise increases the circulation of blood to the tissues of the body. It also helps strengthen muscle tissue. Muscle tissue is a part of most organ systems in the human body. **7.5.a** (exceeding)

Answers to Section Review

1. Sample answer: The muscular system is the group of muscles that allow people to move. **7.5.a** (mastering)

2. Sample answer: Smooth muscle is found in the digestive tract and in the walls of blood vessels. Cardiac muscle is found only in the heart. Skeletal muscle is attached to bones for movement. **7.5.c** (supporting)

3. Two kinds of exercise are resistance exercise and aerobic exercise.

4. A lever is a rigid bar that pivots at a fixed point, known as a fulcrum. **7.6.i** (mastering)

5. Sample answer: Bones are the rigid bars, the muscles supply the input force, and joints act as fulcrums. **7.5.c** (mastering), **7.6.i** (mastering)

Section Resources

- Directed Reading A **BASIC** (Also in Spanish), B **GENERAL**
- Interactive Reader and Study Guide
- Section Quiz **GENERAL** (Also in Spanish)
- Section Review **GENERAL** (Also in Spanish)
- Vocabulary and Section Summary A **BASIC** (Also in Spanish), B **GENERAL**

Levers and Mechanical Advantage

Teacher Notes

This lab explores how the joints function in the levers of the human body (covers standards 7.6.i and 7.7.d). To introduce the activity, you may wish to demonstrate the action of first-, second-, and third-class levers. Have the students identify the applied force, fulcrum, and load. If available, display a variety of bone joints.

Time Required

One 45-minute class period

Lab Ratings

Teacher Prep 🗴🗴
Student Set-Up 🗴
Concept Level 🗴🗴🗴🗴
Clean Up 🗴

Materials

The materials listed on the student page are enough for groups of two students.

Safety Caution

Remind students to review all safety cautions and icons before beginning this lab activity. Remember hand safety and the ease at which a finger can be pinched by the falling ruler or wood block. Make sure that the paper clips are securely attached to the ruler. Goggles may help prevent eye injury in the event of a paper clip pulling away from the ruler. Encourage students to lift the ruler to a preselected height at each step.

OBJECTIVES

Model the action of a lever in the human body.

Observe how the placement of force affects a lever.

Analyze a model to understand the action of a lever in a joint.

Understand the advantages and disadvantages of levers.

MATERIALS

- paper clips
- ruler (marked in centimeters)
- spring scale
- tape, masking

SAFETY

7.6.i Students know how levers confer mechanical advantage and how the application of this principle applies to the musculoskeletal system.

Investigation and Experimentation
7.7.d Construct scale models, maps, and appropriately labeled diagrams to communicate scientific knowledge (e.g., motion of Earth's plates and cell structure).

Preparation Notes

Before starting this activity, you'll need to select a spring scale that best matches the observed weight of the ruler. Make sure that the paper clips are securely fastened to the ruler. Demonstrate the paper clip bend and its secure attachment to the ruler. Heavier wooden rulers work best. With appropriate modification, a yardstick can also serve as a lever arm.

Levers and Mechanical Advantage

Your skeleton contains many joints, such as the knee and elbow. These joints act as first-class, second-class, or third-class levers. The three classes of levers are shown below. Most of the levers in the human body act as third-class levers. As you have learned, some levers provide a *mechanical advantage*. Levers always reduce the effort force required to move a load, right? Actually, that is not always true. Sometimes, the advantage of the lever does not reduce the amount of force needed to move a load. In fact, a lever may require additional force to move a load. But levers can offer another kind of advantage. Perform this lab to find out the other advantages of levers.

First-class lever   Second-class lever   Third-class lever

Procedure

1. Copy the data table below onto a sheet of paper.

Levers Data Table

	Trial 1	Trial 2	Trial 3
30 cm			
15 cm			
3 cm			

2. Open three paper clips to form a right-angle bend in each paper clip.

3. Tape one paper clip to the surface of a ruler at the 30 cm mark. Make sure that the loop of the paper clip is upright.

Lab Resources

Differentiated Datasheets
A BASIC, B GENERAL, C ADVANCED

Classroom Lab Video/DVD

Holt Lab Generator CD-ROM

Search for any lab by topic, standard, difficulty level, or time. Edit any lab to fit your needs, or create your own labs. Use the Lab Materials QuickList software to customize your lab materials list.

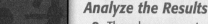

4. Tape a second paper clip to the ruler at the 15 cm mark. Tape the third paper clip at the 3 cm mark.

5. Tape the end of the ruler to a table. Make sure that you tape the end closest to the 3 cm mark. Attach the ruler so that it forms a joint with the table.

6. Attach the spring scale to the paper clip positioned at the 30 cm mark. Using the spring scale, lift the ruler from the table. In your data table, record the amount of force needed to lift the ruler. Repeat this step two more times.

7. Attach the spring scale to the paper clip positioned at the 15 cm mark. Using the spring scale, lift the ruler from the table. In your data table, record the amount of force needed to lift the ruler. Repeat this step two more times.

8. Attach the spring scale to the paper clip positioned at the 3 cm mark. Using the spring scale, lift the ruler from the table. In your data table, record the amount of force needed to lift the ruler. Repeat this step two more times.

Analyze the Results

9. Recognizing Patterns The tape that attached the ruler to the table represented your elbow. The table represented your upper arm. What part of your body did the ruler represent?

10. Analyzing Data Which paper clip position, 30 cm, 15 cm, or 3 cm, required the greatest force to raise the ruler?

11. Analyzing Data When you performed step 7, which paper clip position on the ruler moved the farthest distance?

Draw Conclusions

12. Making Predictions If each paper clip represented the point at which your muscle attaches to your lower arm bones, which paper clip position would require you to do the least amount of work when lifting an object?

13. Applying Concepts In your elbow joint, the muscle that does the kind of lifting modeled in this lab is attached close to the joint. In fact, in the model used, the muscle would be attached to the bone at the 3 cm mark. Does this placement provide the best mechanical advantage for lifting your arm? Explain your answer.

Big Idea Question

14. Making Predictions If the lever action of a joint does not reduce the amount of force needed to lift a load, what other advantage might be provided by this joint? Use the model to determine the advantage of this joint when comparing the joint with the other kinds of joints.

Analyze the Results

9. The ruler represented the forearm. At the skeletal level, it represented the ulna and radius bones. The paper clip represented the site where the lifting muscle (biceps) was attached to the forearm bones.

10. The amount of required force was greatest at the 3 cm position. The amount of required force was least at the 30 cm position.

11. The part on the ruler that moved the farthest was its tip end. It was the point most distant from the joint.

Draw Conclusions

12. The paper clip at the 30 cm mark requires the least amount of work to lift.

13. no; The 3 cm mark required a greater amount of force to lift the ruler.

Big Idea Question

14. The applied force causes an increase in the distance that the far end of the lever arm moves. So, if a muscle contracts only a centimeter, the end of the lever arm may move six centimeters. If you consider this movement over time, it means that the end of the arm can move six times faster than the speed of the muscle contraction. Faster speeds can help an animal catch prey or escape from predators.

Kelly Sullivan
Harry M. Marsh
Junior High School
Chico, California

Science Skills Activity

Teacher Notes

In the tutorial, students are asked to develop a hypothesis, design a test for the hypothesis, and then to modify the hypothesis (covers standard 7.7.c). Ask students to develop a hypothesis based on something they are curious about from their own lives. With their own hypothesis, they may be better able to test and modify the hypothesis.

Answers to You Try It!

2. New hypothesis: Water helps regulate the temperature of an object.

3. Answers may vary. Sample answer: Yes, I will need to see if water can help regulate the temperature of objects. The original experiment only showed me what would work in one situation.

4. Answers may vary. Modifying a hypothesis after experimentation allows scientists to continue investigating something they are interested in even after the experiment has shown that the original explanations were not accurate.

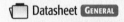 Datasheet GENERAL

Also editable on the Holt Lab Generator CD-ROM

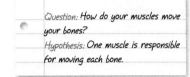

| Scientific Methods | Research | Data Analysis | Models, Maps & Diagrams |

Investigation and Experimentation
7.7.c Communicate the logical connection among hypotheses, science concepts, tests conducted, data collected, and conclusions drawn from the scientific evidence.

Modifying a Hypothesis

▶ Tutorial

When you perform a scientific investigation, you often start with a question and then develop a hypothesis. A hypothesis is a possible answer to the question. A hypothesis must be testable. The next step in an investigation is to test your hypothesis. Often, in the course of your experiment, you will gather data that will require you to modify your original hypothesis. In this tutorial, you will learn how to modify a hypothesis. Read the question and hypothesis below.

> Question: How do your muscles move your bones?
> Hypothesis: One muscle is responsible for moving each bone.

Procedure

① **Design a Test for the Hypothesis** In this investigation, you might use rulers or sticks to model bones and rubber bands to model muscles. You will be testing if it is possible for one muscle to move one bone.

② **Identify the Expected Outcome** If your hypothesis is correct, what results do you expect? In this investigation, if your hypothesis is correct, you will be able to move each bone model with a single rubber band.

③ **Analyze the Actual Outcome** In your experiment, the results show that it is not possible to move the bone model with a single rubber band. You notice that the bones will not move predictably or smoothly.

④ **Form a New Hypothesis** In what way do the observations that you made agree with or disagree with your original hypothesis? In this example, your observations disagree with your hypothesis. One muscle did not move the bone. The hypothesis must be modified. See the modified hypothesis below.

> Question: How do your muscles move your bones?
> Hypothesis: Muscle pairs work together to move each bone.

▶ You Try It!

Your body tissues contain water. In fact, the human body is made up of about 75% water. Imagine that you are part of a research team working to answer this question: Does water help the body maintain a constant temperature? You have decided to focus your research on whether or not water helps the body maintain a constant temperature. Your hypothesis is the following: Water does not help the body maintain a constant temperature.

Procedure

① Complete steps 1 and 2 from the tutorial above.

Analysis

② **Applying Concepts** If you were to test your hypothesis, the results would disagree with the expected results. You would conclude that the temperature of objects that are surrounded by water or objects that are mostly made of water would remain fairly constant. Based on this information, modify the original hypothesis.

③ **Analyzing Methods** Will you need to change the original experiment to test the new hypothesis? Why or why not?

④ **Expressing Opinions** Why is it important that scientists modify their hypotheses?

Universal Access · Differentiated Instruction

Special Education Students

Demonstration Some students may benefit from a demonstration of how to use the rulers or sticks and rubber bands in Tutorial Procedure steps 1 and 2. **LS** Visual

Advanced Learners/GATE

Additional Hypotheses Some students may want to test additional hypotheses. Have them test both the modified hypothesis in the "Tutorial" and their modified hypotheses in "You Try It." **LS** Logical

Basic Learners

Modifying a Hypothesis as a Class
Some students may better grasp the concept of modifying a hypothesis if this activity is performed as a class with a directed discussion. To do this, have the class suggest a few different ways to test the hypothesis proposed in the activity. Then, choose one test, perform the test as a class, and analyze the hypothesis in a group discussion. **LS** Verbal

Chapter Summary

The Big Idea The human body is composed of major systems that have differing functions, but all of the systems work together to maintain homeostasis.

Section

Vocabulary

① Body Organization

Key Concept The human body functions because of the contributions of cells, tissues, organs, and organ systems.

- The levels of organization in the human body include cells, tissues, organs, organ systems, and the organism.
- Human cells are differentiated to perform specific jobs in the body.
- There are 11 human organ systems.
- Organ systems work together to maintain homeostasis. The failure of one organ system affects the entire body.

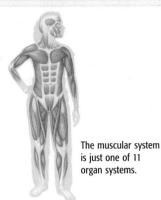

The muscular system is just one of 11 organ systems.

tissue p. 467
organ p. 468

② The Skeletal System

Key Concept The skeletal system is an organ system. The functions of the skeletal system include support, protection, movement, and the production of blood cells.

- The skeletal system includes bones, cartilage, and connective tissue.
- Bones have four important functions in the body. Bones are structured to perform these functions.
- Three human body joints are gliding, ball and socket, and hinge.

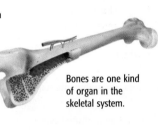

Bones are one kind of organ in the skeletal system.

skeletal system p. 472
joint p. 474

③ The Muscular System

Key Concept The muscular system is an organ system. The skeletal and muscular systems work together to provide a structural framework for movement.

- There are three kinds of muscle tissue: cardiac, smooth, and skeletal.
- Bones and muscles work together to form levers, which increase the mechanical advantage of most movements.
- The two kinds of exercise include resistance exercise and aerobic exercise.

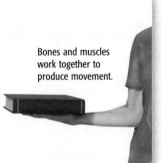

Bones and muscles work together to produce movement.

muscular system p. 476
lever p. 478
mechanical advantage p. 478

Chapter Summary

SUPER SUMMARY

Have students connect the major concepts in this chapter through an interactive Super Summary. Visit go.hrw.com and type in the keyword HY7BD1S to access the Super Summary for this chapter.

Identifying Roots

Etymology Have students use a dictionary to discover the history of the following key terms: *organ, skeletal,* and *muscular.* (The term *organ* comes from the Latin word *organum,* which means "tool," or "instrument." The term *skeletal* is derived from the Greek word *skeletos,* which means "dried up." Students may be surprised to find that the term *muscular* is derived from the Latin word *musculus,* which means "mouse.") **LS** Verbal

Focus on Reading

Extending Summaries Have students read through the summary points of one section of this chapter. Then, ask students to make an outline of the section using the summary points as main headings. Finally, allow students to compare their expanded summaries with each other. **LS** Verbal/Interpersonal

Review Resources

- 🗒 Reinforcement Worksheet **BASIC**
- 🗒 Critical Thinking Worksheet **ADVANCED**
- 🗒 Chapter Review **GENERAL** (Also in Spanish)
- 📓 Standards Review Workbook (Also in Spanish)
- 📓 Study Guide A **BASIC** (Also in Spanish), B **GENERAL**

Assessment Resources

- 🗒 Chapter Tests A **BASIC**, B **GENERAL** (Also in Spanish), C **ADVANCED**
- 🗒 Standards Assessment **GENERAL**

Chapter Review

7.1.f, 7.5.a, 7.5.b,
7.5.c, 7.6.h, 7.6.i

Assignment Guide

Section	Questions
1	3, 4, 6, 10, 17, 26, 28
2	2, 5, 9, 11–14, 16, 18, 22–24
3	1, 7–8, 15, 19–21, 25

Answers

Using Vocabulary

1. c

2. joint **7.5.c** (supporting)

3. Homeostasis **7.5.b** (supporting)

4. organ **7.5.a** (mastering), **7.5.b** (supporting)

5. skeletal system **7.5.c** (supporting)

Understanding Concepts

6. c **7.5.a** (mastering)

7. c **7.5.c** (supporting)

8. d **7.5.c** (supporting)

9. Sample answer: The skeletal system includes the bones, cartilage, and connective tissue whose primary function is to support the body. The skeletal system protects organs, stores minerals, allows movement, and produces blood cells. **7.5.a** (supporting), **7.5.b** (supporting), **7.5.c** (supporting)

10. Sample answer: The muscular system and the skeletal system work together to produce movement in the human body. The muscular system includes skeletal muscles that are attached to bones in the skeletal system. When skeletal muscles contract, they pull on bones that act as levers to move parts of the human body. **7.5.a** (mastering), **7.5.b** (mastering)

11. injuries: fractures, dislocations, and sprains; diseases: osteoporosis and arthritis **7.5.c** (supporting)

12. Sample answer: Aerobic exercise is steady, moderately intense activity that improves endurance. During resistance exercise, skeletal muscles are strengthened by working against resistance, or weight.

13. Joints allow the body to move when muscles contract.
    7.6.h (mastering)

Organize

Table Fold Review the FoldNote that you created at the beginning of the chapter. Add to or correct the FoldNote based on what you have learned.

Using Vocabulary

1 **Academic Vocabulary** In the sentence "Levers confer a mechanical advantage," what does the word *confer* mean?
   a. decrease
   b. cancel out
   c. give
   d. complete

Complete each of the following sentences by choosing the correct term from the word bank.

homeostasis	organ
joint	skeletal system
tissue	muscular system

2 A(n) ___ is a place where two or more bones meet.

3 ___ is the maintenance of a stable internal environment.

4 A(n) ___ is made up of two or more tissues working together.

5 The ___ supports and protects the body, stores minerals, and allows movement.

Understanding Concepts

Multiple Choice

6 Which of the following lists of the levels of organization shows the way in which the body is organized?
   a. cells, organs, organ systems, tissues
   b. tissues, cells, organs, organ systems
   c. cells, tissues, organs, organ systems
   d. cells, tissues, organ systems, organs

7 Which muscle tissue can be both voluntary and involuntary?
   a. smooth muscle
   b. cardiac muscle
   c. skeletal muscle
   d. All of the above

8 Which of the following statements about muscles is true?
   a. They work in pairs.
   b. They can be voluntary or involuntary.
   c. They become stronger if exercised.
   d. All of the above

Short Answer

9 **Analyzing** Describe the skeletal system, and list four functions of bones.

10 **Summarizing** Give an example of how organ systems work together.

11 **Listing** Name three injuries and two diseases that affect the skeletal system.

12 **Comparing** How are aerobic exercise and resistance exercise related?

13 **Evaluating** What is the role of joints in the human body?

INTERPRETING GRAPHICS Use the image below to answer the next two questions.

14 **Describing** How are this boy's muscles and bones working together to produce movement?

15 **Classifying** In the image, what class of levers is at work?

14. Answers may vary. The bones are providing a structure against which the muscles can contract and relax. According to how they are connected to the bones of the body, some muscles straighten the bones and others bend the bones. **7.5.c** (mastering)

15. Mostly third-class levers are at work in the image shown. **7.6.i** (mastering)

Writing Skills

16. Accept all reasonable answers. **7.5.c** (mastering), **7.6.h** (mastering), **7.6.i** (mastering)

Critical Thinking

17. An answer to this exercise can be found at the end of the book.
    7.5.a (mastering)

18. Sample answer: Leg bones are long and skinny, while skull bones are thin and wide. Many skull bones are curved. Leg bones enable walking and standing, while skull bones are designed to protect the brain. **7.5.c** (supporting)

Writing Skills

16 **Communicating Concepts** Create a brochure that describes the relationship between human body levers and joints. Include information about the relationship of muscles and bones to these concepts.

Critical Thinking

17 **Concept Mapping** Use the following terms to create a concept map: *tissues, muscle tissue, connective tissue, cells, organ systems, organs, epithelial tissue,* and *nervous tissue.*

18 **Making Comparisons** Compare the shapes of the bones of the human skull with the shapes of the bones of the human leg. How do the shapes differ? Why are the shapes important?

INTERPRETING GRAPHICS Use the image below to answer the next three questions.

19 **Identifying Relationships** What class of levers is shown in the image?

20 **Analyzing Processes** How does this human body lever work?

21 **Making Inferences** How would the motion shown in the image be different if the lever was replaced by a second-class lever?

22 **Making Inferences** How does your muscular system rely on the health and functions of your skeletal system?

23 **Making Inferences** Imagine that you are building a robot. Your robot will have a skeleton that is similar to a human skeleton. If the robot needs to be able to move a limb in all directions, what kind of joint would be needed? Explain your answer.

24 **Analyzing Ideas** Human bones are dense and are often filled with marrow. But many bones of birds are hollow. Why might birds have hollow bones?

25 **Identifying Relationships** Why might some muscles fail to work properly if a bone is broken?

26 **Analyzing Ideas** Why are red blood cells called differentiated cells? What happens to a cell when it becomes differentiated?

Math Skills

INTERPRETING GRAPHICS Use the table below to answer the next question.

Number of Sit-ups Vs. Time

	30 s	60 s	120 s
Martin	10	20	35
Midori	9	19	38
Maria	11	18	36

27 **Analyzing Data** Use the data in the table above to create a graph. Be sure to include all of the appropriate labels.

Challenge

28 **Identifying Relationships** Describe how the muscular and skeletal organ systems maintain homeostasis. What would happen if the skeletal system no longer functioned properly?

---

22. Weak or broken bones do not provide good places for muscles to flex against. Also, the skeletal system stores minerals that are important for the function of the muscular system. **7.5.a** (supporting), **7.5.b** (mastering), **7.5.c** (mastering)

23. Sample answer: The robot would need a ball-and-socket joint. A ball-and-socket joint allows movement in all directions. **7.6.h** (mastering)

24. Sample answer: Dense bones that are filled with marrow weigh more than hollow bones do. Because most birds fly, they need lighter bones. So, birds' bones are hollow. **7.5.c** (exceeding)

25. Sample answer: If a bone is broken, flexors or extensors likely will not work properly. These muscles will not be able to pull on a bone in the way that they do when a bone is not broken. Also, damage to the area where the muscle attaches may affect the ability of the muscle to pull on the bone. **7.5.c** (mastering)

26. Red blood cells are called differentiated cells because they are specialized to perform certain tasks or jobs. When a cell becomes differentiated, it is able to do one or a few jobs very well but unable to perform the jobs of other specialized cells. **7.1.f** (mastering)

Math Skills

27. Accept all reasonable answers. Students should label the axes. They should also have a title for their graph.

Challenge

28. Accept all reasonable answers. Students should include information about how bones in the skeletal system store minerals and muscles in the digestive system help make nutrients available for the body. **7.5.b** (mastering), **7.5.a** (mastering), **7.5.c** (mastering)

---

19. The action of using a tennis racket is a third-class lever. **7.6.i** (mastering)

20. Answers may vary. Effort force comes from the contraction of the muscle that is attached to the bones. The fulcrum is the joint, or place where the bones meet. The load is the object or body part that is being moved. **7.6.i** (mastering)

21. Answers may vary. Students should state that if the third-class lever was replaced by a second-class lever, the results would differ. To represent a second-class lever, the head of the tennis racket would be the fulcrum and the effort force would be applied by hand and arm muscles at the handle of the tennis racket in order to hit the tennis ball somewhere in the middle of the tennis racket. A second-class lever would not be as advantageous as a third-class lever would be in this scenario. **7.6.i** (exceeding)

Chapter Review Standards Guide

	Supporting	Mastering	Exceeding
7.1.f		26	
7.5.a	9, 22	4, 6, 10, 17, 28	
7.5.b	3–4, 9	10, 22, 28	
7.5.c	2, 5, 7–9, 11, 18	14, 16, 22, 25, 28	24
7.6.h		13, 16, 23	
7.6.i		15–16, 19–20	21

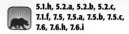
Standards Assessment

Teacher Notes

To provide practice under more realistic testing conditions, give students 20 min to answer all of the questions in this assessment.

Answer Key

Question Number	Correct Answer
1	A
2	A
3	B
4	B
5	D
6	C
7	B
8	C
9	C
10	D
11	A
12	D
13	B
14	B
15	C
16	C
17	B

Standards Guide

	Supporting	Mastering	Exceeding
5.1.h		14	
5.2.a		15	
5.2.b		16	
5.2.c		17	
7.1.f	5		12
7.5	1, 3		
7.6	2		
7.5.a		7	13
7.5.b			8
7.5.c		9, 10	11
7.6.h		6	
7.6.i	4		

☐ Standards Assessment GENERAL

☐ Teacher Notes for Standards Assessment contain a longer Assessment Doctor and Diagnostic Teaching Tips.

REVIEWING ACADEMIC VOCABULARY

1 In the sentence "Human body systems have a complementary relationship," what does the word *complementary* mean?

A supporting each other

B competing against each other

C unrelated to each other

D replacing each other

2 Which of the following sets of words is closest in meaning to the word *underlie*?

A to form the foundation of

B to take the place of

C to take care of

D to stand in the way of

3 In the sentence "Each major system of the body serves a different function," what does the word *function* mean?

A position

B purpose

C variable

D gathering

4 Which of the following words is the closest in meaning to the word *principle*?

A idea

B rule

C hypothesis

D situation

5 In the sentence "As multicellular organisms develop, their cells differentiate," what does the word *differentiate* mean?

A to show the differences between

B to merge two different things

C to recognize a difference between

D to become different from each other

REVIEWING CONCEPTS

6 Which kind of joint allows the most movement in different directions?

A gliding joint

B hinge joint

C ball-and-socket joint

D sliding joint

7 How are tissue and organs related in the body?

A Organs are surrounded by tissue.

B Organs are made up of tissue.

C Tissue contains one or more organs.

D Tissue and organs work independently.

8 The body's cells, tissues, and organs work together to maintain homeostasis. What is the goal of homeostasis?

A to keep the body physically active

B to keep the body free of disease

C to maintain a stable internal environment

D to remove and replace dead tissue

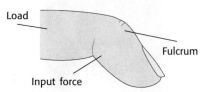

Load

Fulcrum

Input force

9 What kind of lever is shown in the illustration above?

A a first-class lever

B a second-class lever

C a third-class lever

D a fourth-class lever

Question 1: The correct answer is A. A complementary relationship is one in which one part supports or completes the other.

Question 2: The correct answer is A. An idea that underlies a principle forms the foundation for that principle.

Question 3: The correct answer is B. The systems of the body each serve a different purpose or function.

Question 4: The correct answer is B. A principle is a rule or law that underlies a system of ideas.

Question 5: The correct answer is D. As multicellular organisms develop, their cells differentiate, or become different from each other.

Question 6: The correct answer is C. A ball-and-socket joint, such as the one in the shoulder, allows a limb to move freely in all directions.

Question 7: The correct answer is B. All organs are made up of two or more types of tissue.

Question 8: The correct answer is C. Homeostasis is the state of stability maintained inside the body, no matter what the conditions outside the body. Structures at all levels in an organism contribute to homeostasis.

10 Which of the following must occur for the forearm to move toward the shoulder?

A The forearm muscle must contract.

B The shoulder muscle must contract.

C The triceps muscle must contract.

D The biceps muscle must contract.

11 Which of the following helps cushion the area in a joint where bones meet?

A cartilage

B muscle tissue

C blood vessels

D marrow

12 How is the structure of muscle cells different from that of other cells?

A Muscle cells are organized into groups that work together.

B Muscle cells contain a special pigment that picks up oxygen.

C Muscle cells are shaped for the transfer of electrical impulses.

D Muscle cells contain special proteins that allow them to contract.

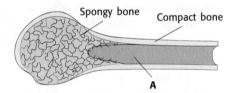

Spongy bone   Compact bone

A

13 What does point A represent in the diagram above?

A osteoblasts

B marrow

C cartilage

D blood vessels

REVIEWING PRIOR LEARNING

14 The human body is composed of just a few elements. Which element is most abundant in the body?

A carbon

B oxygen

C hydrogen

D nitrogen

15 Which organ system is responsible for transporting oxygen to each cell?

A the digestive system

B the nervous system

C the circulatory system

D the endocrine system

16 How do the heart and lungs work together to replace oxygen in the blood?

A Blood enters the lungs, where it is filled with oxygen, and then the blood is sent to the heart.

B Blood fills with oxygen in the heart, and then the lungs remove carbon dioxide.

C The heart pumps blood into the lungs, where it is then filled with oxygen.

D The heart removes carbon dioxide from the blood, and then the lungs fill it with oxygen.

17 What is the first step in the process of digestion?

A passing food into the small intestine

B chewing food in the mouth

C breaking down food in the stomach

D absorbing molecules of food into the blood

Standards Assessment

ASSESSMENT DOCTOR

Question 9: The correct answer is C. A finger, like most of the levers in the body, is an example of a third-class lever. The fulcrum is the joint, the effort force is the tendon where the muscle attaches to the bone, and the load is the finger itself.

Question 10: The correct answer is D. The elbow bends and the forearm moves toward the shoulder when the biceps muscle contracts.

Question 11: The correct answer is A. Cartilage cushions the area where bones and joints meet.

Question 12: The correct answer is D. Muscle cells contain special proteins that allow them to contract.

Question 13: The correct answer is B. The inside of a bone is filled with marrow, which produces red and white blood cells.

Question 14: The correct answer is B. The human body is composed primarily of oxygen.

Question 15: The correct answer is C. Transporting oxygen throughout the body is the role of the circulatory system.

Question 16: The correct answer is C. The heart pumps blood into the lungs, which replenish oxygen and remove carbon dioxide.

Question 17: The correct answer is B. Chewing food is the first step in the digestive process. Teeth and saliva begin the process of breaking down food.

Science in Action

Scientific Discoveries

Background

Engineering microelectronic devices that may help reverse major disabilities, such as blindness, is an example of biomimetrics. Biomimetrics is an area of biotechnology in which technology is used to mimic natural biological systems. Scientists involved in biomimetric research have seen their efforts come full circle. Initially, they used advanced microelectronic technology to build devices that mimic biological systems, and now they are taking what they have learned about the biology and using this knowledge to build better devices.

Science, Technology, and Society

ACTiVITY

Have students model having a prosthetic hand by using a spring clothespin to pick up papers, hold a pencil to write their name, and tie their shoes. Have them discuss how it feels, and have them try to imagine what having an artificial hand would be like. Then, ask students to brainstorm ways that they might improve their "prosthetic hand" (the clothespin). **LS Kinesthetic**

Science in Action

Scientific Discoveries

Engineering Inspired by Nature

What can a cockroach contribute to engineering and science? The answer is nothing, right? Well, that's wrong! Cockroaches, as well as many other organisms, provide models for scientists and engineers. These scientists synthesize new materials that have structures and functions related to materials found in nature. For example, researchers in the California Institute for Quantitative Biomedical Research (QB3) have developed a new prosthesis. Instead of replacing a leg or arm, this prosthesis provides vision and is based on the structure of human eyes. This prosthesis could bring vision to many.

Math ACTiVITY

One out of every 4,000 people loses the ability to see because special cells in the eye stop functioning properly. In a city that has a population of 750,000, how many people are blind in this way? Record your work in your **Science Journal.**

Science, Technology, and Society

Beating the Odds

Sometimes, people are born without limbs or lose limbs in accidents. Many of these people have prostheses (prahs THEE SEEZ), or human-made replacements for the body parts. Until recently, many of these prostheses made it difficult for many people to participate in physical activities, such as sports. But new designs have led to lighter, more comfortable prostheses that move the way that a human limb does. These new designs have allowed athletes that have physical disabilities to compete at higher levels.

Social Studies ACTiVITY

Research the use of prostheses throughout history. Create a timeline showing major advances in prosthesis use and design.

Answer to Math Activity

1/4000 = 0.00025;

0.00025 × 750,000 = 187.5 blind people

Answer to Social Studies Activity

Students' timelines should display an understanding of how modern technology has improved prosthesis design. Timelines should include the use of wooden prostheses, expand into the use of metal and the development of plastics and other synthetics in prosthesis construction, and discuss modern ergonomic designs.

Careers

Zahra Beheshti

Physical Therapist A physical therapist is a licensed professional who helps people recover from injuries by using hands-on treatment instead of medicines. Dr. Zahra Beheshti is a physical therapist at the Princeton Physical Therapy Center in New Jersey. She often helps athletes who suffer from sports injuries.

After an injury, a person may go through a process called *rehabilitation* to regain the use of the injured body part. The most common mistake made by athletes is that they play sports before completely recovering from injuries. Dr. Beheshti explains, "Going back to their usual pre-injury routine could result in another injury."

Dr. Beheshti also teaches patients about preventing future sports injuries. "Most injuries happen when an individual engages in strenuous activities without a proper warm-up or cool-down period." Being a physical therapist is rewarding work. Dr. Beheshti says, "I get a lot of satisfaction when treating patients and seeing them regain their function and independence and return to their normal life."

Language Arts ACTiViTy

Interview a physical therapist who works in or near your community. Write a newspaper article about the therapist that you interview in your **Science Journal**.

Internet Resources

- To learn more about careers in science, visit www.scilinks.org and enter the SciLinks code HY70225.

- To learn more about these Science in Action topics, visit go.hrw.com and type in the keyword HY7BD1F.

- Check out articles related to this chapter by visiting go.hrw.com. Just type in the keyword HY7BD1C.

The elements listed in the Standards Course of Study provide a base for presenting, supporting, and assessing the California Grade 7 Science Standards. Use this Standards Course of Study as a base for planning your lessons.

Why Teach

Circulation and Respiration

This chapter was designed to cover the California Grade 7 Science Standards about the human circulatory and respiratory systems (7.5.a, 7.5.b, and 7.6.j). It follows a chapter that introduced the human organ systems and the relationship between structure and function that can be observed in the human body. This chapter describes the structures of the circulatory and respiratory systems along with the functions of these structures. It also describes the physical principles that underlie the function of these systems.

After they have completed this chapter, students will begin a chapter about the human integumentary and nervous systems.

 California Standards

Focus on Life Sciences

7.5.a Students know plants and animals have levels of organization for structure and function, including cells, tissues, organs, organ systems, and the whole organism.

7.5.b Students know organ systems function because of the contributions of individual organs, tissues, and cells. The failure of any part can affect the entire system.

7.6.j Students know that contractions of the heart generate blood pressure and that heart valves prevent backflow of blood in the circulatory system.

Investigation and Experimentation

7.7.b Use a variety of print and electronic resources (including the World Wide Web) to collect information and evidence as part of a research project.

7.7.c Communicate the logical connection among hypotheses, science concepts, tests conducted, data collected, and conclusions drawn from the scientific evidence.

7.7.d Construct scale models, maps, and appropriately labeled diagrams to communicate scientific knowledge (e.g., motion of Earth's plates and cell structure).

 Chapter Pacing

Getting Started
🕐 **45 min** pp. 494–495
The Big Idea The human body has organ systems that transport gases, nutrients, and wastes.
🐻 7.6.j, 7.7.d

Section 1 **The Cardiovascular System**
🕐 **90 min** pp. 496–501
Key Concept The cardiovascular system circulates blood, gases, and nutrients throughout your body.
🐻 7.5.a, 7.5.b, 7.6.j

Section 2 **Blood**
🕐 **45 min** pp. 502–507
Key Concept Blood transports many things through the body, including oxygen, nutrients, wastes, heat, immune system cells, and hormones.
🐻 7.5.a, 7.5.b, 7.6.j, 7.7.d

Section 3 **The Respiratory System**
🕐 **45 min** pp. 508–511
Key Concept The respiratory system is responsible for taking in oxygen and releasing carbon dioxide.
🐻 7.5.a, 7.5.b

Wrapping Up
🕐 **180 min** pp. 512–521
🐻 7.5.a, 7.5.b, 7.7.b, 7.7.c

Basic Learners
TE Blood Vessel Poster, p. 498
TE Blood Model, p. 503
TE Giving Directions, p. 511
TE Check Along the Way, p. 514
📄 Reinforcement Worksheet
📄 Chapter Test A
📄 Differentiated Datasheets A for Labs and Activities ■
📱 Study Guide A ■

Advanced Learners/GATE
TE Pacemaker, p. 497
TE Mapping Cardiovascular Diseases, p. 501
TE White Blood Cells, p. 502
TE Blood Types, p. 506
📄 Critical Thinking Worksheet
📄 Chapter Test C
📄 Differentiated Datasheets C for Labs and Activities ■

Key

SE Student Edition
TE Teacher's Edition

📄 Chapter Resource File
📘 Workbook
📦 Transparency

💿 CD or CD-ROM
*   Datasheet or blackline master available

■ Also available in Spanish

All resources listed below are also available on the One-Stop Planner.

Teach

SE Explore Activity Modeling a Valve, p. 495* ■

📦 **Bellringer**
💿 **PowerPoint® Resources**
📦 L75 The Heart
📦 L76 The Flow of Blood Through the Heart
📦 L77 The Flow of Blood Through the Body
SE Quick Lab Vessel Blockage, p. 500* ■

📦 **Bellringer**
💿 **PowerPoint® Resources**
SE Quick Lab Modeling Blood Pressure, p. 504* ■
📦 L78 Mixing Blood

📦 **Bellringer**
💿 **PowerPoint® Resources**
📦 L79 The Respiratory System
📦 L80 The Lungs
📦 L81 The Role of Blood in Respiration
SE Quick Lab Replicate Respiration, p. 510* ■

SE Skills Practice Lab Carbon Dioxide in Respiration, pp. 512–513* ■

Practice

SE Organize Activity Four-Corner Fold, p. 494

SE Section Review, p. 501* ■

SE Section Review, p. 507* ■

SE Section Review, p. 511* ■

SE Science Skills Activity Evaluating Resources for Research, p. 514* ■
📦 **Concept Mapping***
SE Chapter Review, pp. 516–517* ■

Assess

📄 **Chapter Pretest**

SE Standards Checks, pp. 496, 498, 500, 501
TE Standards Focus, p. 500
📄 **Section Quiz** ■

SE Standards Checks, pp. 502, 503, 504, 506
TE Standards Focus, p. 506
📄 **Section Quiz** ■

SE Standards Checks, pp. 509, 511
TE Standards Focus, p. 510
📄 **Section Quiz** ■

SE Standards Assessment, pp. 518–519*
📄 **Chapter Tests A, B ■, C**
📘 **Standards Review Workbook** ■

Resources for Universal Access • Differentiated Instruction

English Learners
TE Less is More, p. 497
TE Using the Figure, pp. 497, 505
TE Group Activity, p. 499
TE Respiration Game, p. 509
📄 Vocabulary and Section Summary A ■, B

📄 Section Quizzes ■
📄 Chapter Tests A, B ■
📄 Differentiated Datasheets A, B, and C for Labs and Activities ■
📘 Study Guide A ■
📘 Multilingual Glossary

Struggling Readers
TE Cardiovascular Vocabulary, p. 496
TE Reading Strategy, pp. 498, 503
TE Sticky Words, p. 505
TE Silent Letters, p. 508

Special Education Students
TE Memory Cues, p. 499
TE Blood Cell Jobs, p. 502
TE Knowing What You Know, p. 511
TE Alternate Research Topics, p. 514

To help plan your lessons, refer to the On Course Mapping Instruction booklet.

Visual Resources

CHAPTER STARTER TRANSPARENCY

BELLRINGER TRANSPARENCIES

TEACHING TRANSPARENCIES

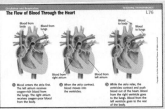
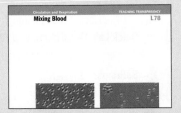

TEACHING TRANSPARENCIES

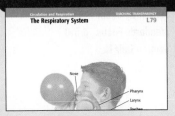
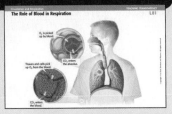

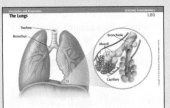

STANDARDS REVIEW TRANSPARENCIES

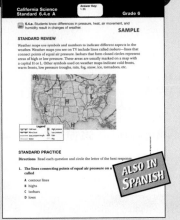

CONCEPT MAPPING TRANSPARENCY

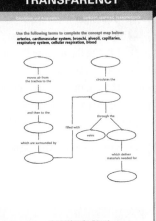

Planning Resources

PARENT LETTER

TEST ITEM LISTING

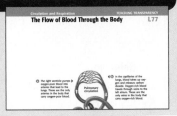

One-Stop Planner® CD-ROM

This CD-ROM package includes all of the resources shown here and the following time-saving tools:

- **Lab Materials QuickList Software**
- **Customizable Lesson Plans** Correlated to the California Science Standards
- **Holt Calendar Planner**
- **PowerPoint® Resources**

- **Printable Worksheets**
- **ExamView® Test Generator** Correlated to the California Science Standards
- **Holt PuzzlePro®**
- **Interactive Teacher's Edition**

Meeting Individual Needs

DIRECTED READING A
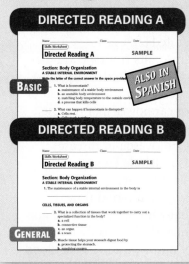
BASIC

Directed Reading A — SAMPLE

Section: Body Organization
A STABLE INTERNAL ENVIRONMENT

ALSO IN SPANISH

DIRECTED READING B
BASIC

Directed Reading B — SAMPLE

Section: Body Organization
A STABLE INTERNAL ENVIRONMENT

GENERAL

VOCABULARY AND SECTION SUMMARY A

BASIC

Vocabulary and Section Summary A — SAMPLE

ALSO IN SPANISH

VOCABULARY AND SECTION SUMMARY B
GENERAL

Vocabulary and Section Summary B — SAMPLE

Body Organization
VOCABULARY

REINFORCEMENT
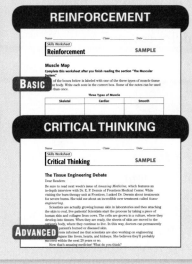
BASIC

Reinforcement — SAMPLE

Muscle Map

CRITICAL THINKING
ADVANCED

Critical Thinking — SAMPLE

The Tissue Engineering Debate

INTERACTIVE READER AND STUDY GUIDE

Body Organization — SAMPLE

BEFORE YOU READ

MULTILINGUAL GLOSSARY
SAMPLE

Labs and Activities

DIFFERENTIATED DATASHEETS FOR EXPLORE ACTIVITY, QUICK LABS, AND CHAPTER LAB

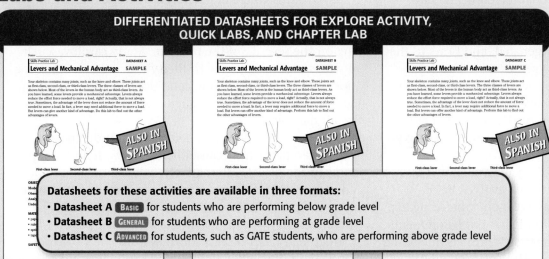

Levers and Mechanical Advantage — DATASHEET A / SAMPLE

Levers and Mechanical Advantage — DATASHEET B / SAMPLE

Levers and Mechanical Advantage — DATASHEET C / SAMPLE

ALSO IN SPANISH

Datasheets for these activities are available in three formats:
- **Datasheet A** BASIC for students who are performing below grade level
- **Datasheet B** GENERAL for students who are performing at grade level
- **Datasheet C** ADVANCED for students, such as GATE students, who are performing above grade level

DATASHEET FOR SCIENCE SKILLS ACTIVITY
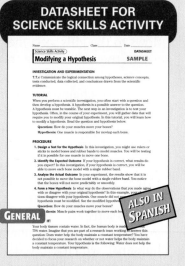

Modifying a Hypothesis — DATASHEET / SAMPLE

INVESTIGATION AND EXPERIMENTATION

TUTORIAL

PROCEDURE

GENERAL

ALSO IN SPANISH

Reviews and Assessments

SECTION REVIEWS
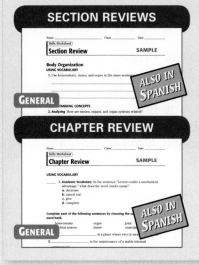

Section Review — SAMPLE

Body Organization
USING VOCABULARY

ALSO IN SPANISH

GENERAL

CHAPTER REVIEW

Chapter Review — SAMPLE

USING VOCABULARY

ALSO IN SPANISH

GENERAL

CHAPTER PRETEST
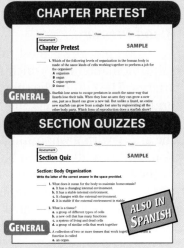

Chapter Pretest — SAMPLE

GENERAL

SECTION QUIZZES
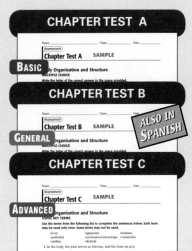

Section Quiz — SAMPLE

Section: Body Organization

ALSO IN SPANISH

GENERAL

CHAPTER TEST A
BASIC

Chapter Test A — SAMPLE

Body Organization and Structure
MULTIPLE CHOICE

CHAPTER TEST B
GENERAL

Chapter Test B — SAMPLE

Organization and Structure
MULTIPLE CHOICE

ALSO IN SPANISH

CHAPTER TEST C
ADVANCED

Chapter Test C — SAMPLE

Organization and Structure
USING KEY TERMS

ALSO IN SPANISH

STANDARDS ASSESSMENT
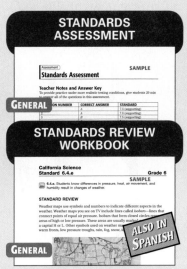

Standards Assessment — SAMPLE

Teacher Notes and Answer Key

GENERAL

STANDARDS REVIEW WORKBOOK

California Science
Standard 6.4.e — Grade 6 SAMPLE

STANDARD REVIEW

GENERAL

ALSO IN SPANISH

This Teacher Background explains science concepts, principles, and theories that appear in the chapter. Use the information on these pages to refresh or enhance your understanding of the topics covered.

Section 1

The Cardiovascular System

The Diverse Structure of the Heart

Like all mammals, humans have four-chambered hearts, which include two atria and two ventricles. However, the structure of the heart differs in other organisms. For example, both cartilaginous fishes (Chondrichthyes: sharks, rays, and skates) and bony fishes (Osteichthyes: about 30,000 species) have two-chambered hearts. And, amphibians have three-chambered hearts.

Organisms that have two-chambered hearts have only one circuit of blood flow. In fishes, only deoxygenated blood flows through the heart. This blood then flows to the gills, becomes oxygenated, and flows to the rest of the body, where the oxygen is used. The deoxygenated blood then returns to the heart. Organisms that have three-chambered hearts have two circuits of blood flow, like humans do. However, the three-chambered heart allows some mixing of the oxygenated and deoxygenated blood.

An evolutionary relationship is illustrated by the structure of the heart. Fishes, which evolved before amphibians and mammals, have two-chambered hearts. Amphibians, which evolved after fishes but before mammals, have three-chambered hearts. Mammals (including humans), which evolved after both fishes and amphibians, have four-chambered hearts. The human circulatory system is shown in **Figure A.** You may wish to have students redraw this figure to help them identify the four chambers and learn about the two types of circulation.

Figure A *Mammals have a four-chambered heart, which allows for oxygenated blood to stay separated from deoxygenated blood.*

Cardiovascular Problems

Failure of any organ of the cardiovascular system can result in death. In fact, cardiovascular diseases are the leading cause of death in the United States.

Cardiovascular disease often results from a combination of hereditary and lifestyle factors. A sedentary lifestyle, poor eating habits, and experiencing a great deal of stress can all increase the risk of cardiovascular disease. Incorporating healthy lifestyle changes, especially at a young age, can prevent many cardiovascular diseases.

Cardiovascular problems also include congenital defects of the heart. For example, the aortic heart valve normally has three flaps to ensure that blood flow is properly regulated. An individual who has a bicuspid aortic valve defect has an aortic valve that has only two flaps. As a result, the valve may narrow and restrict blood flow, or blood may flow backwards from the aorta into the heart when the heart is not contracting. Individuals that have this congenital defect may not experience symptoms until they become adults.

Treatment of a cardiovascular problem varies depending on the severity of the problem. Many cardiovascular diseases can be treated with lifestyle changes and medication, but other more severe conditions require surgery, such as valve replacement, stents, or arterial bypasses to repair damage.

Many congenital heart defects are not diagnosed. This often happens because there are few, if any, symptoms of the defect. Alternatively, a defect may be minor enough so that it does not require treatment. Otherwise, surgery may be performed to correct the problem. Advances in fetal surgery have also made it possible to correct fetal heart defects in the womb.

Section 2

Blood

Blood Pressure

Blood pressure is most frequently measured using a sphygmomanometer, which measures pressure within arteries. The cuff of the sphygmomanometer is inflated until the brachial artery in the arm is completely blocked. As the cuff is gradually released, blood reenters the artery with a whooshing sound (also known as a Korotkoff sound) that can be heard using a stethoscope. At the first Korotkoff sound, the first blood pressure measurement (systolic pressure) is recorded. The pressure in the cuff is gradually lowered until no swooshing sound is heard, and at that time, another measurement is taken. This measurement is diastolic pressure. Blood pressure is measured in millimeters of mercury and is written as a ratio between systolic and diastolic pressure (for example, 120/70 mm Hg).

Blood Disorders

Hemophilia is an inherited disease that results in bleeding for longer periods of time compared to people without hemophilia. Hemophilia is caused by a low level or complete absence of a clotting factor in the blood. Hemophilia can also develop when the body produces antibodies that block clotting factors. Hemophilia cannot be cured, but transfusions and intravenous clotting-factor replacement can be used to stem bleeding.

As shown in **Figure B,** normal red blood cells are round and concave. However, in the inherited sickle cell disease, red blood cells are sickle-shaped due to an abnormal variant of hemoglobin. The sickle shape of these blood cells can result in the blockage of blood flow as the cells pass through small blood vessels. Sickled cells are more fragile than normal RBCs are, and thus have shorter lifetimes in circulation. The rapid loss of these cells leads to a shortage of RBCs. Sickle cell disease leads to a number of serious problems, including heart failure, brain damage, and kidney failure. There is no cure for sickle cell disease, but individuals who have the disease can be treated with drugs and blood transfusions.

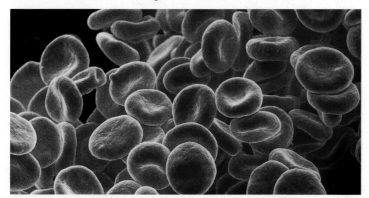

Figure B   *Normal red blood cells are round and concave.*

Section 3

The Respiratory System

The Pathway of Air

Air usually enters the respiratory system through the nose, where it is filtered by hairs, warmed, and humidified. The nasal cavity joins with the pharynx. Both food and air pass through the pharynx. When food is

swallowed, the larynx moves up, which causes the epiglottis to cover the trachea. This keeps food from entering the trachea and subsequently causing asphyxiation. The larynx is supported by cartilage and contains the vocal cords, which produce sound when air passes over them.

Air passes from the larynx into the trachea. Like the larynx, the trachea is supported by cartilage. The trachea branches into two bronchi, each of which leads to a lung. In turn, the bronchi split into bronchioles, which branch off into smaller and smaller tubes within the lungs. The bronchioles lead to millions of tiny air sacs called alveoli.

The bronchi, bronchioles, and alveoli are lined with epithelial tissue. This epithelium is covered with tiny cilia and mucus, both of which serve to protect the body from pathogens and particulates. Alveoli give the lungs a total surface area of about 100 m^2, which facilitates the exchange of oxygen and carbon dioxide between the air and the blood. Without this surface area, the body would not be able to undergo sufficient gas exchange.

The Mechanics of Breathing

Mammals breathe by negative pressure breathing, which is a process that pulls air into the lungs rather than pushing it into the lungs. The action of the diaphragm and the intercostal muscles changes the volume of the chest cavity, which results in inhalation or exhalation. When the contraction of the intercostal muscles and the diaphragm increase chest cavity volume, air enters the lungs due to the difference in air pressure between the outside of the body (higher pressure) and the inside of the body (lower pressure). When the diaphragm and intercostal muscles relax, the process is reversed—the volume within the lungs decreases, and the pressure pushes air out of the lungs.

Internet Resources

SciLinks is maintained by the National Science Teachers Association to provide you and your students with interesting, up-to-date links that will enrich your classroom presentation of the chapter.

Visit **www.scilinks.org** and enter the SciLinks code for more information about the topic listed.

Topic: The Cardiovascular System
SciLinks Code: HY70221

Topic: Cardiovascular Problems
SciLinks Code: HY70220

Topic: Blood
SciLinks Code: HY70175

Topic: Blood Donations
SciLinks Code: HY70178

Topic: The Respiratory System
SciLinks Code: HY71307

Topic: Respiratory Disorders
SciLinks Code: HY71306

Improving Comprehension

Use the Graphic Organizer on this page of the Student Edition to introduce the topics that are covered in this chapter, to summarize the chapter material, or to show students how to make a Venn diagram.

Teaching Tips

• Explain to students that a Venn diagram is ideal for showing the similarities and differences between two or three topics.

• Explain to students that because it requires the topics to have both shared and unique characteristics, a Venn diagram has a more limited use than other comparison organizers, such as a comparison table, do.

LS Logical

Improving Comprehension

Graphic Organizers are important visual tools that can help you organize information and improve your reading comprehension. The Graphic Organizer below is called a *Venn diagram*. Instructions for creating other types of Graphic Organizers are located in the **Study Skills** section of the Appendix.

How to Make a Venn Diagram

1 Draw a diagram like the one shown below. Draw one circle for each topic. Make sure that each circle partially overlaps the other circles.

2 In each circle, write a topic that you want to compare with the topics in the other circles.

3 In the areas of the diagram where circles overlap, write the characteristics that the topics in the overlapping circles share.

4 In the areas of the diagram where circles do not overlap, write the characteristics that are unique to the topic of the particular circle.

When to Use a Venn Diagram

A Venn diagram is a useful tool for comparing two or three topics in science. A Venn diagram shows which characteristics the topics share and which characteristics are unique to each topic. Venn diagrams are ideal when you want to illustrate relationships in a pair or small group of topics. As you read, look for topics that have both shared and unique characteristics, and draw a Venn diagram that shows how the topics are related.

Cardiovascular System
• supplies nutrients to cells and removes wastes
• is made up of heart, blood, and blood vessels
• carries heat and hormones throughout the body

• is an organ system
• is necessary for cellular gas exchange
• is essential to the proper functioning of the entire organism

Respiratory System
• is responsible for taking in oxygen and releasing carbon dioxide
• includes the nose, mouth, pharynx, larynx, trachea, lungs, bronchi, diaphragm, and mouth
• makes breathing possible

You Try It!

This Reading Strategy can also be used within the chapter that you are about to read. Practice making your own *Venn diagram* as directed in the Reading Strategy for Section **1**. Record your work in your **Science Journal.**

Using Other Graphic Organizers

Students can practice using a variety of Graphic Organizers while reading this chapter. The following Graphic Organizers may also be useful in this chapter.

A **comparison table** can be used to compare the different types of blood vessels, discussed in Section 1.

A **cause-and-effect map** can be used to describe the possible causes and effects of atherosclerosis, discussed in Section 1.

An **idea wheel** can be used to organize details about the components of blood, described in Section 2.

A **process chart** can be used to describe the process of cellular respiration, described in Section 3.

Instructions for creating these Graphic Organizers are located on pp. 583–591 of the Appendix.

Unpacking the Standards

The information below "unpacks" the standards by breaking them down into basic parts. The higher-level, academic vocabulary is highlighted and defined to help you understand the language of the standards. "What It Means" restates the standards as simply as possible.

California Standard	Academic Vocabulary	What It Means
7.5.a Students know plants and animals have levels of organization for **structure** and **function,** including cells, tissues, organs, organ systems, and the whole organism.	**structure** (STRUHK chuhr) the arrangement of the parts of a whole **function** (FUHNGK shuhn) use or purpose	Plants and animals are made of smaller parts which are organized by shape and purpose. These layers of organization include cells, tissues, organs, organ systems, and the whole organism.
7.5.b Students know organ systems **function** because of the **contributions** of **individual** organs, tissues, and cells. The failure of any part can **affect** the entire system.	**function** (FUHNGK shuhn) to work **contribution** (KAHN truh BYOO shuhn) a part given toward a whole **individual** (IN duh VIJ oo uhl) being a single, separate entity; particular **affect** (uh FEKT) to change; to have an effect on; to influence	An organ system is able to work because of the work that each of its smaller parts (organs, tissues, and cells) does. If any part of an organ system fails to work well, the entire system is changed.
7.6.j Students know that contractions of the heart **generate** blood pressure and that heart valves prevent backflow of blood in the circulatory system.	**generate** (JEN uhr AYT) to bring about, to produce	The heart generates blood pressure by contracting, or squeezing, regularly. Valves in the heart keep blood flowing in one direction in the body.

Unpacking the Standards

Use the following information with the *What It Means* in the Student Edition to help students understand why studying each standard is important.

Why It Matters
Multicellular organisms, including humans, function because their cells are organized at many levels. Each subsequent level of organization has unique properties that the prior level of organization does not have.
Organ systems within an organism are interrelated. When one part of a multicellular organism fails to perform its function, the entire organism is affected.
The heart is structured so that it produces a one-way flow of blood through the human body. Valves are important structures for this function.

Academic Vocabulary

Standards that are covered in this chapter may contain academic terms that are unfamiliar to students. The following table identifies some of the academic terms used in this chapter and their meanings.

Term	Definition
function	to work
generate	to bring about, produce
structure	the arrangement of the parts of a whole

Practice Draw this table on the board. Fill in the words, but not the definitions. Have students write down what they think the words mean. Then, write the correct meanings of the words in the table on the board, and ask students to write sentences that demonstrate the meaning of each word. (Bones *function* as a supportive framework for the body. If our class can *generate* enough money, we can go on a field trip. The *structure* of the building was weakened during the earthquake.)

Chapter Overview

This chapter describes how different parts of the body work together in the cardiovascular and respiratory systems. The chapter also examines how problems of the cardiovascular and respiratory systems can affect the entire organism.

MISCONCEPTION ALERT

Breathing and Respiration

Identify It! Some students may not recognize the difference between breathing, cellular respiration, and respiration. Ask students to identify which of these processes brings oxygen into the body and removes carbon dioxide from the body. (breathing) Then, ask them to identify the type of respiration that uses oxygen and produces carbon dioxide. (cellular respiration) Finally, ask students to relate which process involves inspiration, expiration, and cellular activities. (respiration)

Correct It! Have students illustrate the processes of breathing, cellular respiration, and respiration.

Assess It! Ask students to write a short paragraph that describes the relationship between respiration, breathing, and cellular respiration. Students who have successfully overcome the misconception will accurately describe the relationship between the three processes.

16

Circulation and Respiration

The Big Idea

The human body has organ systems that transport gases, nutrients, and wastes.

California Standards

Focus on Life Sciences

7.5 The anatomy and physiology of plants and animals illustrate the complementary nature of structure and function. (Sections 1, 2, and 3)
7.6 Physical principles underlie biological structures and functions. (Sections 1 and 2)

Investigation and Experimentation

7.7 Scientific progress is made by asking meaningful questions and conducting careful investigations. (Science Skills Activity)

Math

6.2.1 Algebra and Functions
7.1.1 Mathematical Reasoning

English–Language Arts

7.2.3 Reading
7.2.4 Writing

About the Photo

Your cardiovascular system is made up of the heart, blood vessels, and blood. This picture is a colored scanning electron micrograph of red blood cells (disk shaped), white blood cells (rounded), and cell fragments called *platelets* (small green fragments). Blood transports gases such as oxygen and carbon dioxide.

Organize

Four-Corner Fold

Before you read this chapter, create the FoldNote entitled "Four-Corner Fold." Label each flap of the four-corner fold with "Cardiovascular system," "Blood," "Blood pressure," and "Respiratory system." As you read the chapter, add details about each topic under the appropriate flap.

Instructions for creating FoldNotes are located in the Study Skills section on p. 581 of the Appendix.

California Standards Alignment

Focus on Life Sciences

7.5.a Students know plants and animals have levels of organization for structure and function, including cells, tissues, organs, organ systems, and the whole organism. **pp. 496–513, 516–519**

7.5.b Students know organ systems function because of the contributions of individual organs, tissues, and cells. The failure of any part can affect the entire system. **pp. 496–504, 506–513, 516–519**

7.6.j Students know that contractions of the heart generate blood pressure and that heart valves prevent backflow of blood in the circulatory system. **pp. 495–498, 500–501, 504, 507, 516–519**

Investigation and Experimentation

7.7.b Use a variety of print and electronic resources (including the World Wide Web) to collect information and evidence as part of a research project. **p. 514**

7.7.c Communicate the logical connection among hypotheses, science concepts, tests conducted, data collected, and conclusions drawn from the scientific evidence. **pp. 512–513**

7.7.d Construct scale models, maps, and appropriately labeled diagrams to communicate scientific knowledge (e.g., motion of Earth's plates and cell structure). **pp. 495, 504**

Math Standards

Algebra and Functions 6.2.1 Convert one unit of measurement to another (e.g., from feet to miles, from centimeters to inches). **pp. 501, 506, 517**

Explore Activity

 ⏱ 15 min

Teacher Notes

In this activity, students will create a model of a one-way valve (covers standards 7.6.j and 7.7.d). Cardboard tubes from paper towel rolls are ideal to use as models of blood vessels. Otherwise, you can make tubes by rolling up sheets of paper. Suggest that students add the marbles slowly. Otherwise, a rush of marbles might tear or dislodge the paper cone.

Materials for Each Group

• bowl
• marbles (handful)
• paper (1 sheet)
• scissors
• tape
• tube, cardboard, from paper towel roll OR a second sheet of paper and tape

Safety Caution

Remind students to review all safety cautions and icons before beginning this activity.

Answers

5. Sample answer: The paper cone worked like a one-way valve. It allowed the marbles to move in only one direction through the tube.

6. Sample answer: When the marbles are put into the wide end of the cone first, the flaps spread apart. This permits movement of the marbles through the valve. When the marbles are put in the narrow end of the cone first, the flaps collapse inward and seal the passageway.

7. Sample answer: Within the heart, valves direct the flow of blood, preventing blood from flowing backward. In the veins, valves prevent the blood from ebbing backward.

📋 Differentiated Datasheets
A **BASIC**, B **GENERAL**, C **ADVANCED**

Also editable on the Holt Lab Generator CD-ROM

Explore Activity 🥽 ✂️

⏱ 15 min

Modeling a Valve

In this activity, you will create a model of a valve that allows material to flow in only one direction. Similar valves in the heart and in certain large blood vessels prevent blood from flowing in the wrong direction.

Procedure

1. Roll a **sheet of paper** into a cone, and secure it with a piece of **tape.** The diameter of the wide part of the cone should be 7 cm. Use **scissors** to create several slits that extend outward from the point of the cone so that you make a series of paper flaps.

2. Insert the point of the cone into one end of a **cardboard tube.** Secure the tube in place with tape. Place a **bowl** beneath the open end of the tube.

3. Hold the tube with the cone positioned at the top. Pour a **handful of marbles** into the tube.

4. Turn the tube upside down so that the cone is at the bottom. Pour the marbles into the tube.

7.6.j
7.7.d

Analysis

5. How did the paper cone affect the movement of the marbles?

6. Describe how this model valve works.

7. Why do you think valves are needed in the heart?

Mathematical Reasoning 7.1.1 Analyze problems by identifying relationships, distinguishing relevant from irrelevant information, identifying missing information, sequencing and prioritizing information, and observing patterns. **pp. 507, 511**

English–Language Arts Standards

Reading 7.1.3 Clarify word meaning through the use of definition, example, restatement, or contrast. **p. 496**

Writing 7.2.4 Write persuasive compositions: (a) State a clear position or perspective in support of a proposition or proposal; (b) Describe the points in support of the proposition, employing well-articulated evidence; (c) Anticipate and address reader concerns and counterarguments. **p. 517**

Circulation and Respiration   CHAPTER STARTER

This Really Happened!

The human heart is normally a very dependable organ. It may beat more than 100,000 times per day for a person's entire life. During this time it pumps millions of liters of blood through the body. When there is a serious problem, shown above right is one of the more recent test models. Its mass is about 680 g—only a little heavier than a real human heart. Newer test models are even smaller and lighter. These artificial hearts have special sensors and micro-

Chapter Starter Transparency
Use this transparency to help students begin thinking about the heart and lungs.

SECTION
1

Preteach

Reviewing Prior Knowledge

Tell students that the term *cardiovascular* contains the Greek root *kardia* and the Latin root *vasculum,* which mean "heart" and "vessel," respectively. Have students use this information to define the term *cardiovascular system.* (Sample answer: the body system that includes the heart and the vessels leading to and from it)

 Bellringer

Have students focus on standard 7.5.b by asking them to identify some of the organs and structures that work with the heart. (Sample answers: blood, blood vessels) Ask students to predict what might happen if the heart stopped working. (Sample answer: Cells would not get the materials that they need to survive.)

Bellringer Transparency

Motivate

Discussion

Cardiovascular System Skit

Students can perform a skit that demonstrates the flow and function of blood. Assign some students the role of blood cells and other students the role of blood vessels. Have the "blood vessels" stand in rows, with no more than three in each row. Then, give the "blood cells" slips of colored paper that represent oxygen and nutrients. Give the students playing "blood vessels" objects representing waste products. Direct the "blood cells" to walk in a circle through the "blood vessels" and exchange objects with them to depict the exchange of oxygen and nutrients with waste products.
LS Kinesthetic

What You Will Learn

- The cardiovascular system is made up of the heart, three types of blood vessels, and blood.
- Contractions of the heart pump blood throughout the entire body.
- Cardiovascular problems include atherosclerosis, high blood pressure, strokes, heart attacks, and heart failure.

Why It Matters

Learning about the cardiovascular system helps you understand how organ systems in the human body work together.

Vocabulary

- cardiovascular system
- artery
- capillary
- vein
- pulmonary circulation
- systemic circulation

READING STRATEGY

Graphic Organizer In your **Science Journal,** create a Venn Diagram that compares systemic circulation and pulmonary circulation.

cardiovascular system
(KAR dee OH VAS kyoo luhr SIS tuhm) a collection of organs that transport blood throughout the body

7.5.a Students know plants and animals have levels of organization for structure and function, including cells, tissues, organs, organ systems, and the whole organism.
7.5.b Students know organ systems function because of the contributions of individual organs, tissues, and cells. The failure of any part can affect the entire system.
7.6.j Students know that contractions of the heart generate blood pressure and that heart valves prevent backflow of blood in the circulatory system.

The Cardiovascular System

Key Concept The cardiovascular system circulates blood, gases, and nutrients throughout your body.

▶ When you hear the word *heart,* what do you think of first? Many people think of love. But the heart is much more than a symbol of love. Your heart is an amazing pump.

The heart is an organ that is part of your cardiovascular system. The word *cardio* means "heart," and the word *vascular* means "blood vessel." The blood vessels—arteries, capillaries, and veins—carry blood pumped by the heart. The cardiovascular system is sometimes called the *circulatory system* because it circulates materials around the body.

Your Cardiovascular System

Your heart, blood, and blood vessels make up your **cardiovascular system.** Your *heart* is an organ made mostly of cardiac muscle tissue. When the heart *contracts,* or squeezes, pressure is created. This pressure moves blood throughout your body. **Figure 1** shows your heart, major arteries, and major veins.

The cardiovascular system helps maintain *homeostasis,* a state of stable internal conditions. The cardiovascular system supplies oxygen and nutrients to cells and removes wastes from cells. It also carries heat and chemical signals called *hormones* throughout the body.

Standards Check What are the main parts of the cardiovascular system? **7.5.a**

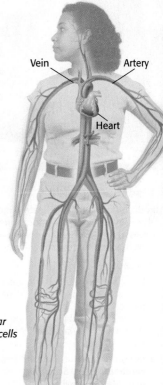

Vein   Artery

Heart

Figure 1 *The cardiovascular system carries blood to the cells in your body.*

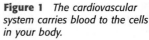

Universal Access · Differentiated Instruction

Struggling Readers

Cardiovascular Vocabulary Tell students to fold a piece of paper in half lengthwise. Have them scan Section 1 and list the boldfaced and italicized terms on the left half of the piece of paper. Tell students to leave a blank line after each term. On the right side of the paper, students should write the definition of each term. Make sure that students realize that they will find the definitions within the text. Remind them that boldfaced terms are defined in the margins and that italicized terms are defined in context either before or after the word in the text. **LS Verbal**

The Heart

Your heart is a muscular organ that is about the size of your fist. It is almost in the center of your chest. Like hearts of all mammals, your heart has a left side and a right side that are separated by a thick wall. The right side of the heart pumps oxygen-poor blood to the lungs. The left side pumps oxygen-rich blood to the body. As you can see in **Figure 2,** each side has an upper chamber and a lower chamber. Each upper chamber is called an *atrium* (plural, *atria*). Each lower chamber is called a *ventricle*.

Flaplike structures called *valves* are found between the atria and ventricles. Valves are also found where some large blood vessels attach to the heart. As blood moves through the heart, the valves close and produce the "lub-dub, lub-dub" sound of a beating heart. Valves prevent blood from going backward. **Figure 3** shows the flow of blood through the heart.

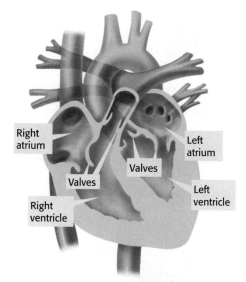

Right atrium

Left atrium

Valves

Valves

Right ventricle

Left ventricle

Figure 2 *The heart pumps blood through blood vessels. The vessels carrying oxygen-rich blood are shown in red. The vessels carrying oxygen-poor blood are shown in blue.*

Figure 3 The Flow of Blood Through the Heart

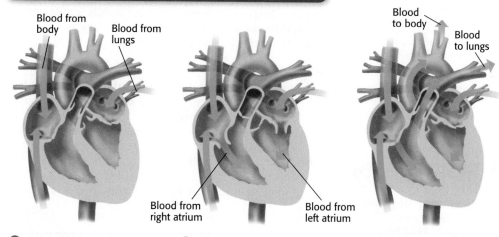

Blood from body

Blood from lungs

Blood to body

Blood to lungs

Blood from right atrium

Blood from left atrium

❶ Blood enters the atria first. The left atrium receives oxygen-rich blood from the lungs. The right atrium receives oxygen-poor blood from the body.

❷ When the atria contract, blood moves into the ventricles.

❸ While the atria relax, the ventricles contract and push blood out of the heart. Blood from the right ventricle goes to the lungs. Blood from the left ventricle goes to the rest of the body.

Universal Access · Differentiated Instruction

Advanced Learners/GATE

Pacemaker Many advanced students benefit from the opportunity to study a concept or structure in detail. Have students research the sinoatrial node, which initiates the contraction of the atria, and the atrioventricular node, which initiates the contraction of the ventricles. Have students explain to the class how these nodes control the heartbeat. Encourage students to create visual aids to accompany their oral presentations. **LS** Verbal/Visual

English Learners

Less Is More Some students might be confused about the words *atria* and *atrium.* Explain that *atrium* is singular and the shorter word *atria* is plural. Ask students to look at the first text block in **Figure 2.** At each instance when the word *atria* or *atrium* appears, ask students to identify whether the word is singular or plural. **LS** Verbal/Logical

---

Teach

Using the Figure

Left Versus Right Have students examine **Figure 2.** Ask students to explain why the left atrium is on the right side in the figure. (The illustration shows the anterior portion of the heart, so when the heart is oriented in the body, the left atrium is on the left side of the body.) Then, divide the class into pairs. Have pairs of students face each other and take turns indicating their partner's left index finger and their own left index finger. You can also provide pairs with a labeled illustration of the heart, allowing each student to hold the drawing in front of his or her chest so that the other student can see that the left ventricle is located on the left side of the body. **LS** Visual

Teaching Transparency:
L75 The Heart

Connection To Math

Blood Volume Tell students that their heart beats about 100,800 times each day and pumps about 70 mL of blood with each beat (the volume of blood moved per beat is called the *stroke volume*). Ask students to calculate how many liters of blood the heart pumps in one hour. (100,800 beats/d ÷ 24 h/d = 4,200 beats/h; 4,200 beats/h × 70 mL ÷ 1,000 mL/L = 294 L/h) Show students a one-, two-, or three-L soda bottle to illustrate the size of a liter. **LS** Logical

Teaching Transparency:
L76 The Flow of Blood Through the Heart

Answer to Standards Check

The main parts of the cardiovascular system are the heart, blood, arteries, veins, and capillaries. **7.5.a** (supporting)

Teach, *continued*

Anticipation Guide Before students read this page, ask them the following questions:

1. Which type of blood vessel has the thinnest walls? (capillaries)

2. Which type of blood vessel carries blood back to the heart? (veins)

3. Which type of blood vessel is used to measure blood pressure? (arteries)

Have students evaluate their answers after they read the page.
LS Logical

MISCONCEPTION ALERT

The Color of Blood Some students may think that deoxygenated blood is blue because veins, which frequently carry deoxygenated blood, are often illustrated in blue. To help students overcome this misconception, give them an illustration of blood circulation in which the blood vessels that carry oxygenated blood are colored bright red (the actual color of oxygenated blood) and blood vessels that carry deoxygenated blood are colored dark red (the actual color of deoxygenated blood). Ask students to compare this illustration to the ones in the book. Tell students that blood vessels under the skin appear dark because of the layers of fat and skin over the vessels.

Answer to Standards Check

Arteries carry blood away from the heart and branch into capillaries. Capillaries are tiny blood vessels that allow the exchange of gases and nutrients between cells and blood. Capillaries join back together to form veins. Veins are blood vessels that carry blood back to the heart. **7.5.a** (supporting)

Figure 4 *Large arteries branch into smaller arteries, which branch into capillaries. Capillaries join small veins, which join to form large veins.*

artery (ART uhr ee) a blood vessel that carries blood away from the heart to the body's organs

capillary (CAP uh LEYR ee) a tiny blood vessel that allows an exchange between blood and cells in tissue

vein (VAYN) in biology, a vessel that carries blood to the heart

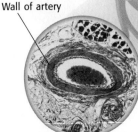

INTERNET ACTIVITY

William Harvey Biography
Why is William Harvey famous? Write about the life and work of William Harvey in your **Science Journal**. Go to **go.hrw.com,** and type in the keyword HY7BD2W.

Blood Vessels

Blood travels throughout your body in hollow tubes called *blood vessels*. The three types of blood vessels—arteries, capillaries, and veins—are shown in **Figure 4.**

Arteries

A blood vessel that carries blood away from the heart is an **artery.** Arteries have thick walls, which contain a layer of smooth muscle. Each heartbeat pumps blood into your arteries at high pressure. Artery walls stretch and are usually strong enough to stand the pressure. Your *pulse* is caused by the rhythmic contractions of the heart pumping blood into arteries.

Capillaries

Nutrients, oxygen, and other substances must leave blood and get to your body's cells. Carbon dioxide and other wastes leave body cells and are carried away by blood. A **capillary** is a tiny blood vessel that allows exchanges between body cells and blood. The exchanges can take place because capillary walls are only one cell thick. Capillaries are so narrow that blood cells must pass through them in single file. Most cells in the body are no more than three or four cells away from a capillary.

Veins

After leaving capillaries, blood enters veins. A **vein** is a blood vessel that carries blood back to the heart. As blood travels through veins, valves found in large veins keep the blood from flowing backward. When skeletal muscles contract, they squeeze nearby veins and help push blood toward the heart.

Standards Check How do the three types of blood vessels work together? 🐻 **7.5.a**

Universal Access · Differentiated Instruction

Basic Learners

Blood Vessel Poster Provide students with poster board, various thicknesses of yarn or string, and tape or glue. Have students work in small groups to make a poster that illustrates the three types of blood vessels. Students should use the yarn or string to illustrate the relative size of each type of blood vessel. (Students should use the thicker yarn or string for arteries and veins and the thinner yarn or string for capillaries.) To extend the activity, provide students with red and blue yarn, and have them use the colored yarn to illustrate blood vessels that carry oxygenated and deoxygenated blood. **LS** Visual/Kinesthetic

---

Two Types of Circulation

Where does blood get the oxygen to deliver to your body? From your lungs! Your heart contracts and pumps blood to the lungs. Here, carbon dioxide leaves the blood and oxygen enters the blood. The oxygen-rich blood then flows back to the heart. This circulation of blood between your heart and lungs is called **pulmonary circulation.**

The oxygen-rich blood returning to the heart from the lungs is then pumped to the rest of the body. The circulation of blood between the heart and the rest of the body is called **systemic circulation.** Both types of circulation are shown in **Figure 5.**

pulmonary circulation
(PUL muh NER ee SUHR kyoo LAY shuhn) the flow of blood from the heart to the lungs and back to the heart through the pulmonary arteries, capillaries, and veins

systemic circulation
(sis TEM ik SUHR kyoo LAY shuhn) the flow of blood from the heart to all parts of the body and back to the heart

Figure 5 The Flow of Blood Through the Body

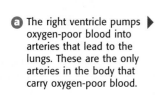
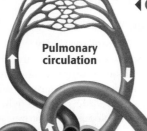
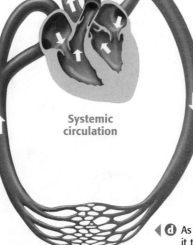

a The right ventricle pumps oxygen-poor blood into arteries that lead to the lungs. These are the only arteries in the body that carry oxygen-poor blood.

b In the capillaries of the lungs, blood takes up oxygen and releases carbon dioxide. Oxygen-rich blood travels through veins to the left atrium. These are the only veins in the body that carry oxygen-rich blood.

Pulmonary circulation

Systemic circulation

c The heart pumps oxygen-rich blood from the left ventricle into arteries and then into capillaries.

e Oxygen-poor blood travels back to the heart and is delivered into the right atrium by two large veins.

d As blood travels through capillaries, it transports oxygen, nutrients, and water to the cells of the body. At the same time, waste materials and carbon dioxide are carried away.

Universal Access • Differentiated Instruction

Special Education Students

Memory Cues Help students remember the functions of pulmonary circulation and systemic circulation using the following memory cues:

Pulmonary circulation **pulls** oxygen from the lungs into the blood.

Systemic circulation brings blood to all the **systems** in the body. ⬛ **Auditory**

Teaching Transparency:
L77 The Flow of Blood Through the Body

Group Activity

Circulate! In class, set up an obstacle course that is based on the flow of blood through the body. Divide the class into teams for a relay race. The race should start in the left ventricle, go through the aorta, head to the muscles, travel back to the right atrium, then go to the right ventricle, move through the pulmonary artery to the lungs, and finally end at the left atrium. The next relay runner on the team should start in the left ventricle. Students should carry a red balloon when they are in the parts of the circulatory system that carry oxygenated blood and carry a blue balloon in the parts of the system that carry deoxygenated blood.

Safety Caution: Remind students to warm up before exercising. ⬛ **Kinesthetic**

Activity

Viewing Blood Vessels Set up microscope stations with prepared slides of an artery and a vein. Have students view the slides and match them with the descriptions of the arteries and veins in the textbook. Have students sketch what they see under the microscope and write descriptive words beside each sketch. ⬛ **Visual**

Homework

Poster Project Have students make a poster showing a diagram of the heart. Remind students to label each chamber of the heart properly and to use arrows to indicate the flow of blood. Tell students that they can also include diagrams of the lungs and other parts of the body to show how blood flows to and from the heart. ⬛ **Visual**

Standards Focus

This **Standards Focus** provides you with a quick way to **assess, reteach,** and **re-assess** one or more concepts in the section.

Assess

1. What happens when heart muscle cells don't get enough blood? (heart attack) **7.5.b**

2. In which type of blood vessel is blood pressure measured? (arteries) **7.6.j**

3. Which type of muscle tissue makes up the heart? (cardiac muscle tissue) **7.5.a**

Reteach

Owner's Guide Have students make an owner's guide for their cardiovascular system. In their guides, students should describe the structures and functions of the cardiovascular system, as well as problems of the cardiovascular system. Encourage students to include illustrations in their guides.
LS Verbal/Visual **7.5.a, 7.5.b, 7.6.j**

Re-Assess

Spider Map Ask students to create a spider map that has the term "cardiovascular system" as the main concept. Instruct students to fill in the map with at least eight other key terms, secondary terms, and concepts from the section. **LS** Verbal **7.1.a**

Answer to Standards Check

High blood pressure can lead to blood vessels rupturing or becoming blocked. If the damaged blood vessels are located in the brain, brain cells will not receive enough oxygen. Without oxygen, the brain cells may die and cause a stroke. **7.5.b** (mastering), **7.6.j** (exceeding)

Quick Lab

Vessel Blockage 🐻 **7.5.b**

1. Connect **4 or 5 straws** together by taping them end to end with **clear tape.**

2. Tape a **tissue** to the side of your desk so that the tissue hangs. Blow through your long straw so that the tissue moves.

3. Tightly wrap a **small piece of wire** around one section of your straw. Blow through your straw, and try to make the tissue move. How does this blockage affect the function of the straw?

4. How does this activity relate to atherosclerosis?

5. How might the failure of one blood vessel in the body affect the rest of the organism?

⏱ **10 min**

Cardiovascular Problems

More than just your heart and blood vessels are at risk if you have cardiovascular problems. Your whole body may be harmed. Cardiovascular problems can be caused by smoking, high levels of cholesterol in the blood, stress, physical inactivity, or heredity. Eating a healthy diet and getting plenty of exercise can lower the risk of having cardiovascular problems.

Atherosclerosis

Heart diseases are the leading cause of death in the United States. One major cause of heart diseases is a cardiovascular disease called *atherosclerosis* (ATH uhr OH skluh ROH sis). Atherosclerosis happens when cholesterol (kuh LES tuhr AWL) and other lipids build up inside blood vessels. This buildup causes the blood vessels to become narrower and less elastic. **Figure 6** shows a blocked pathway through an artery. When an artery that supplies blood to the heart becomes blocked, the person may have a heart attack.

High Blood Pressure

Atherosclerosis may be caused in part by hypertension. *Hypertension* is abnormally high blood pressure. The higher the blood pressure is, the greater the risk of cardiovascular problems is. For example, high blood pressure can cause a stroke. A *stroke* happens when a blood vessel in the brain becomes blocked or ruptures. As a result, that part of the brain receives no oxygen. Without oxygen, brain cells die. High blood pressure can also cause other cardiovascular problems, such as heart attacks and heart failure.

Standards Check How can high blood pressure lead to a stroke? 🐻 **7.5.b, 7.6.j**

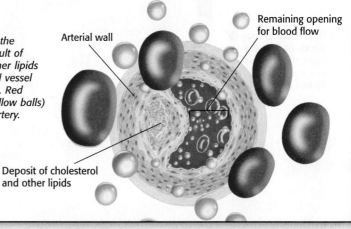

Figure 6 *This illustration shows the narrowing of an artery as the result of lipid deposits. Cholesterol and other lipids (yellow) build up inside the blood vessel walls and block the flow of blood. Red blood cells and lipid particles (yellow balls) are shown moving through the artery.*

Arterial wall

Remaining opening for blood flow

Deposit of cholesterol and other lipids

Quick Lab ⏱ **10 min**

Teacher Notes

This activity will help students understand how a blockage in a blood vessel can affect the whole organism (covers standard 7.5.b).

Materials for Each Group

- facial tissue
- straws (4 or 5)
- tape, clear
- wire, small piece

Safety Caution

Remind students to review all safety cautions and icons before beginning this activity.

Answers

3. Sample answer: The blockage does not allow much air, if any, through the straws.

4. Atherosclerosis is also a blockage. It prevents blood from moving through a blood vessel.

5. Sample answer: Cells around or past the blockage will not be able to get nutrients, so they will die. This may lead to the death of the organism.

📋 Differentiated Datasheets
A **BASIC**, B **GENERAL**, C **ADVANCED**

Also editable on the
Holt Lab Generator
CD-ROM

Heart Attacks and Heart Failure

A *heart attack* happens when heart muscle cells do not get enough blood. The heart muscle is damaged. As shown in **Figure 7,** arteries that deliver oxygen to the heart may be blocked. Without oxygen, heart muscle cells may be damaged. If enough heart muscle cells are damaged, the heart may stop.

Heart failure happens when the heart is too weak to pump enough blood to meet the body's needs. Organs, such as the brain, lungs, and kidneys, may be damaged by lack of oxygen and nutrients or by the buildup of fluids or wastes.

Standards Check What is heart failure? 🐾 **7.5.b**

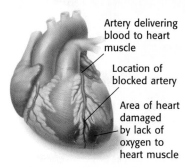

Artery delivering blood to heart muscle

Location of blocked artery

Area of heart damaged by lack of oxygen to heart muscle

Figure 7 *A heart attack happens when an artery to the heart is blocked.*

SECTION Review

 7.5.a, 7.5.b, 7.6.j

Summary

- Parts of the cardiovascular system include the heart, three types of blood vessels, and blood.

- Contractions of the heart pump blood throughout the body. Valves ensure that blood flows in only one direction.

- The three types of blood vessels are arteries, veins, and capillaries.

- Oxygen-poor blood flows from the heart through the lungs, where it picks up oxygen. Oxygen-rich blood flows from the heart to the rest of the body.

- Cardiovascular problems include atherosclerosis, hypertension, strokes, heart attacks, and heart failure.

Understanding Concepts

1 **Modeling** Describe the pathway of blood flow. Begin and end in the left atrium.

2 **Describing** Describe the functions of the five parts of the cardiovascular system.

3 **Comparing** Compare a heart attack and heart failure.

4 **Analyzing** What is the function of valves?

Critical Thinking

5 **Identifying Relationships** How is the structure of capillaries related to their function?

6 **Making Inferences** One of aspirin's effects is that it prevents substances in blood from being too "sticky." Why might doctors prescribe aspirin for patients who have had a heart attack?

7 **Analyzing Ideas** Veins and arteries are everywhere in your body. When a pulse is taken, it is usually taken at an artery in the neck or wrist. Explain why.

8 **Identifying Relationships** How are heart contractions and blood pressure related?

Math Skills

9 **Making Conversions** An adult male's heart pumps about 2.8 million liters of blood per year. If his heart beats 70 times per minute, how much blood does his heart pump with each beat?

Challenge

10 **Predicting Consequences** Cardiac bypass surgery allows surgeons to remove unhealthy blood vessels near the heart. They are replaced with healthy blood vessels from other places in the patient's body. Why might a patient need this type of surgery?

Internet Resources

For a variety of links related to this chapter, go to www.scilinks.org

Topic: The Cardiovascular System; Cardiovascular Problems

SciLinks code: HY70221; HY70220

Answers to Section Review

1. left atrium→left ventricle→arteries→capillaries in body→veins→right atrium→right ventricle→ arteries→capillaries in lungs→veins→left atrium **7.5.a** (supporting)

2. Sample answer: The heart pumps blood to all parts of the body. Blood carries gases and nutrients to cells and carries wastes away from cells. Arteries carry blood away from the heart. Capillaries allow the exchange of materials

between cells and blood. Veins carry blood back to the heart. **7.5.a** (mastering)

3. Sample answer: A heart attack happens when heart muscle cells get insufficient oxygen, and the heart muscle is damaged. The heart may stop. Heart failure happens when the heart cannot pump enough blood to meet the body's needs. **7.5.b** (mastering)

4. Sample answer: Valves keep blood from flowing backward. **7.6.j** (mastering)

5. Sample answer: Capillaries are small and have thin walls, so they are near every cell in the body and allow the exchange of materials between cells and blood. **7.5.a** (mastering)

6. Sample answer: A doctor might prescribe aspirin because it keeps substances in blood from sticking together and blocking vessels, which can cause another heart attack. **7.5.b** (exceeding)

7. The wrist and the neck are places where arteries are close to the surface of the skin, so the pulse can be felt there. **7.6.j** (exceeding)

8. Sample answer: Each heart contraction pumps blood into arteries, which increases pressure in the arteries. This pressure is the systolic blood pressure. **7.6.j** (mastering)

9. 2,800,000 L/y ÷ (70 beats/min × 60 min/h × 24 h/d × 365 d/y) = 0.076 L/beat = 76 mL/beat

10. Sample answer: A patient may need cardiac bypass surgery if blood vessels near the heart were blocked from atherosclerosis. Such a blockage increases the risk of heart attack. **7.5.b** (exceeding)

Section Review Standards Guide

	Supporting	Mastering	Exceeding
7.5.a	1	2, 5	
7.5.b		3	6, 10
7.6.j		4, 8	7

Section Resources

- Directed Reading A **BASIC** (Also in Spanish), B **GENERAL**

- Interactive Reader and Study Guide

- Section Quiz **GENERAL** (Also in Spanish)

- Section Review **GENERAL** (Also in Spanish)

- Vocabulary and Section Summary A **BASIC** (Also in Spanish), B **GENERAL**

Universal Access · Differentiated Instruction

Advanced Learners/GATE

Mapping Cardiovascular Diseases Ask students to create concept maps showing the relationship between atherosclerosis, high cholesterol, hypertension, stroke, heart attack, and heart failure. Have students share their final concept maps with the class. **LS** Visual/Logical

Answer to Standards Check

Heart failure is when the heart cannot pump enough blood to meet the body's needs. **7.5.b** (mastering)

Reviewing Prior Knowledge

Review standard 7.5.a with your students. Ask students to summarize the standard in their own words. Then, ask students to predict how that standard may apply to this section.

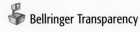 **Bellringer**

Remind students that the levels of organization in the human body are as follows: cells→tissues→ organs→organ systems→organism. Have students focus on standard 7.5.a by asking them to which level of organization blood belongs. (Sample answer: Blood is a tissue because it is composed of similar cells that work together for a specific function.)

Bellringer Transparency

Motivate

Discussion

Blood Ask student volunteers to describe a time when they cut or scraped their skin. Based on the students' experiences, lead a class discussion about the structure and function of blood. Ask students, "Can you see individual blood cells when you bleed? Why or why not?" (no; Blood cells are too small to be seen without aid.) "How are red blood cells important to other cells in the body?" (Red blood cells contain hemoglobin, an oxygen-carrying protein. Red blood cells use hemoglobin to carry oxygen to other cells in the body.) **LS Auditory**

Answer to Standards Check

Red blood cells contain hemoglobin, which gives them their red color and helps them carry oxygen. **7.5.a** (supporting)

SECTION
2

Blood

Key Concept Blood transports many things through the body, including oxygen, nutrients, wastes, heat, immune system cells, and hormones.

What You Will Learn

- Blood is a tissue that is made up of red blood cells, white blood cells, platelets, and plasma.
- Blood pressure is the force exerted by blood on the inside walls of arteries.
- The loss of blood, mixing blood types, or blood disorders can be fatal.

Why It Matters

All the cells in your body depend on blood to stay alive.

Vocabulary

- blood
- blood pressure

READING STRATEGY

Summarizing Read this section silently. In pairs, take turns summarizing the material. Stop to discuss ideas and words that seem confusing.

7.5.a Students know plants and animals have levels of organization for structure and function, including cells, tissues, organs, organ systems, and the whole organism.

7.5.b Students know organ systems function because of the contributions of individual organs, tissues, and cells. The failure of any part can affect the entire system.

7.6.j Students know that contractions of the heart generate blood pressure and that heart valves prevent backflow of blood in the circulatory system.

Blood is the carrier for the cardiovascular system. It moves through miles of blood vessels to reach the cells in your body. So, you must have a lot of blood, right? Not really. An adult human body has about 5 L of blood. Your body most likely has a little less than that. All the blood in your body would not fill two 3 L soda bottles.

Components of Blood

Your cardiovascular system is made up of your heart, your blood vessels, and blood. **Blood** is a connective tissue made up of plasma, red blood cells, platelets, and white blood cells. Blood carries important materials to all parts of your body.

Plasma

The fluid part of the blood is called plasma (PLAZ muh). *Plasma* is a mixture of water, minerals, nutrients, sugars, proteins, and other substances. Red blood cells, white blood cells, and platelets are found in plasma.

Red Blood Cells

Most blood cells are *red blood cells,* or RBCs. RBCs, such as the ones shown in **Figure 1,** supply oxygen for every living cell in your body. Cells need this gas to carry out their functions. Each RBC has hemoglobin (HEE moh GLOH bin). *Hemoglobin* is an oxygen-carrying protein. Hemoglobin attaches to the oxygen you inhale. RBCs can then move oxygen throughout the body. Hemoglobin also gives RBCs their red color.

Standards Check **Describe the function of red blood cells.** 7.5.a

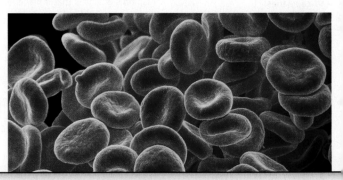

Figure 1 *Red blood cells are made in the bone marrow of certain bones. As red blood cells mature, they lose their nucleus and their DNA.*

Universal Access · Differentiated Instruction

Special Education Students

Functions of Blood Cells Some students may have difficulty remembering a variety of details, such as the functions of different types of blood cells. Help students develop mnemonic or visual clues that will help them remember the main functions of red and white blood cells. (For example: REd = REspiration, and White = Wipe out infections) **LS Verbal**

Advanced Learners/GATE

White Blood Cells Ask students to research the different types of white blood cells (WBCs). Students should identify each type of WBC, describe how each type reacts to a pathogen, and specify which pathogens each type of WBC attacks. Have students present their findings in the form of a comic book. **LS Visual/Verbal**

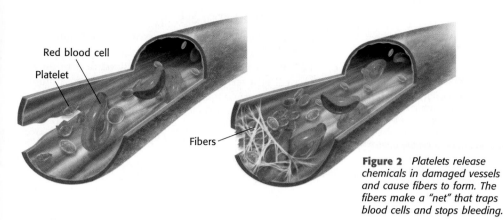

Red blood cell

Platelet

Fibers

Figure 2 *Platelets release chemicals in damaged vessels and cause fibers to form. The fibers make a "net" that traps blood cells and stops bleeding.*

READING STRATEGY

Asking Questions Before students read these two pages, have them read the headings aloud. Then, ask students to formulate and write one question that they expect the text to answer.
LS Intrapersonal

Platelets

Drifting among the blood cells are tiny particles called platelets. *Platelets* are pieces of larger cells found in bone marrow. These larger cells remain in the bone marrow, but pieces are pinched off. Then, these pieces enter the bloodstream as platelets. Platelets last for only 5 to 10 days, but they are an important part of blood. When you cut or scrape your skin, you bleed because blood vessels have been opened. As soon as bleeding starts, platelets begin to clump together in the damaged area. They form a plug that helps reduce blood loss, as shown in **Figure 2.** Platelets also release chemicals that react with proteins in plasma. The reaction causes tiny fibers to form. The fibers help make a blood clot.

White Blood Cells

Sometimes *pathogens* (PATH uh juhnz)—bacteria, viruses, and other microscopic particles that can make you sick—enter your body. When they do, they often meet *white blood cells,* or WBCs. WBCs, shown in **Figure 3,** help keep you healthy by destroying pathogens. WBCs also help clean wounds.

WBCs fight pathogens in several ways. Some WBCs squeeze out of blood vessels and move around in tissues, searching for pathogens. When they find a pathogen, they destroy it. Other WBCs release antibodies. *Antibodies* are chemicals that identify or destroy pathogens. WBCs also keep you healthy by destroying body cells that have died or been damaged. Most WBCs are made in bone marrow. Some WBCs mature in the lymphatic system.

Standards Check What functions do WBCs perform? 📖 **7.5.a**

blood (BLUHD) the fluid that carries gases, nutrients, and wastes through the body and that is made up of platelets, white blood cells, red blood cells, and plasma

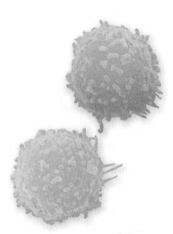

Figure 3 *White blood cells defend the body against pathogens. These white blood cells have been colored yellow to make their shape easier to see.*

ACTIVITY

PSA Have students research carbon monoxide poisoning. Then, have students write and present a public service announcement (PSA) based on their findings. In their PSA, students should describe how carbon monoxide affects the body and how people might become exposed to it. (Students' PSAs should explain that carbon monoxide binds preferentially to red blood cells, preventing oxygen from binding to red blood cells. As a result, body cells are starved of oxygen. PSAs should also include information on both natural sources of carbon monoxide and human-made sources, such as automobile exhaust and cigarettes.) **LS** Verbal

Cultural Awareness

Writing **Blood Disease and Cultures** Ask students to identify a blood disease and the racial, ethnic, or cultural group that the disease predominantly affects. Students should identify the symptoms and causes of the disease. Finally, students should identify how the disease is treated. Have students write an informative pamphlet about their findings. (Diseases may include sickle cell disease and hemophilia.) **LS** Verbal

Universal Access · Differentiated Instruction

Basic Learners

Blood Model Students often benefit from making models of new concepts. Supply students with various materials that they can use to model a blood vessel, including blood cells and platelets. Materials might include paper towel rolls and various candies to represent blood cells. Students can also use a computer to create a graphic model of blood vessels.
LS Kinesthetic

Answer to Standards Check

WBCs fight pathogens, release antibodies, and destroy body cells that have been damaged or have died. **7.5.a** (supporting)

 🕐 10 min

Teacher Notes

In this activity, students will demonstrate systolic and diastolic blood pressure in an artificial apparatus (covers standards 7.6.j and 7.7.d). You can use laboratory film, such as the film used to seal petri dishes, in place of tape to attach the balloon to the pipet bulb.

Materials for Each Group

- balloon, long
- pipet bulb
- tape
- water

Safety Caution

Caution students to pay close attention while attaching the balloon to the pipet bulb, so that the balloon does not snap away and hit someone.

Answers

2. The pressure in the balloon increased.

3. The pressure in the balloon decreased.

4. The balloon represents an artery.

5. Sample answer: The squeezed bulb represents systolic pressure because pressure in the balloon increased, just as a contracted ventricle increases pressure in an artery.

6. 95/60 mm Hg

📋 **Differentiated Datasheets**
A **BASIC**, B **GENERAL**, C **ADVANCED**

Also editable on the Holt Lab Generator CD-ROM

Wordwise

Press- Ask students to identify other words that contain the root *press-*. Then, ask them to define each term in their own words. (Sample answers: compression, impression, and oppress) **LS Verbal**

Healthy Pressure

Maintaining healthy blood pressure is important for good health. Ask an adult to help you research blood pressure in books or on the Internet. Find three strategies you can use to maintain healthy blood pressure. Discuss how you can make these strategies part of your daily life.

blood pressure (BLUDH PRESH uhr) the force that blood exerts on the walls of the arteries

Wordwise The root *press-* means "to press."

Body Temperature Regulation

Your blood does more than carry oxygen and nutrients to your cells. It also helps regulate your body temperature. When you are hot, your blood vessels enlarge. Blood flow to the skin is increased. Heat can then be released into the environment to cool your body. When you are cold, the blood vessels to the skin narrow. Blood flow to the skin is decreased. So, less heat is lost to the environment through your skin.

Blood Pressure

Every time your heart contracts, blood is pushed out of the heart and into your arteries. The force of the blood on the inside walls of arteries is called **blood pressure.**

Blood pressure is expressed in millimeters of mercury (mm Hg). For example, a blood pressure of 110 mm Hg means that the pressure on the artery walls can push a column of mercury to a height of 110 mm.

Blood pressure is usually given as two numbers, such as 110/70 mm Hg. Systolic (sis TAHL ik) pressure is the first number. *Systolic pressure* is the pressure inside large arteries when the ventricles contract. The surge of blood causes the arteries to bulge and produce a pulse. The second number, *diastolic* (DIE uh STAHL ik) *pressure,* is the pressure inside arteries when the ventricles relax. For adults, a blood pressure of 120/80 mm Hg or below is considered healthy. High blood pressure can cause heart or kidney damage.

Standards Check In what unit is blood pressure normally expressed?
🐻 **7.6.j**

Quick Lab

Modeling Blood Pressure

In this activity, you will demonstrate systolic and diastolic blood pressure. You will use a pipet bulb to represent the heart.

1. Fill a **pipet bulb** with **water.** Stretch the mouth of a **long balloon** around the end of the pipet bulb. Secure with **tape.**

2. Carefully squeeze the pipet bulb in one hand. Describe the pressure in the balloon.

3. Release your squeeze on the pipet bulb. Describe the pressure in the balloon now.

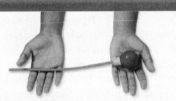

🐻 **7.6.j 7.7.d**

4. If the pipet bulb represents the heart, what does the balloon represent?

5. Which state, bulb squeezed or not squeezed, is similar to systolic pressure? Explain.

6. What is your blood pressure if your diastolic pressure is 60 mm Hg and your systolic pressure is 95 mm Hg?

🕐 10 min

Answer to School-to-Home Activity

Sample answer: Healthy blood pressure can be maintained by eating lots of fresh fruits, vegetables, and whole grains; getting plenty of exercise; and avoiding fried and fatty foods.

Answer to Standards Check

Blood pressure is usually expressed as millimeters of mercury, or mm Hg. **7.6.j** (supporting)

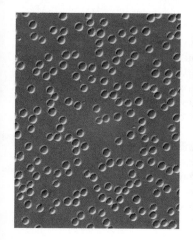
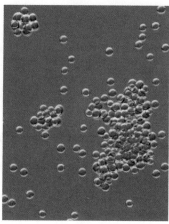

Figure 4 *The slide on the left shows a mixture of blood from two people with the same blood type. The slide on the right shows a mixture of blood from two people with different blood types.* **What is happening in the slides?**

Blood Types

Your blood type refers to the kinds of molecules you have on the surface of your RBCs. These surface molecules are called *antigens* (AN tuh juhnz). Different blood types have different antigens on their RBCs. Different blood types may also have different antibodies in the plasma. As shown in **Figure 4,** these antibodies react to antigens of other blood types as if the antigens were pathogens.

ABO System

The ABO system is one way of classifying blood based on the kinds of antigens on the surface. Every person has one of four blood types: A, B, AB, or O. Type A blood has A antigens; type B has B antigens; and type AB has both A and B antigens. Type O blood has neither A nor B antigens.

Each blood type may also have different antibodies, as shown in **Figure 5.** For example, type A blood has antibodies that react to type B blood. If a person with type A blood is injected with type B blood, the type B antibodies attach themselves to the type B RBCs. These RBCs begin to clump together, and the clumps may block blood vessels. A reaction to the wrong blood type may be fatal.

Rh System

Another antigen that may be on the surface of RBCs is the Rh antigen. A person with the Rh antigen is considered Rh-positive (Rh+). A person without the Rh antigen is Rh-negative (Rh−). If an Rh− person receives a blood transfusion of Rh+ blood, antibodies may react and cause the blood to clump.

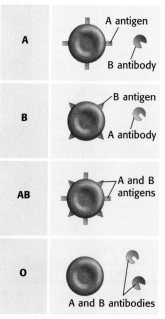

Figure 5 *This figure shows which antigens and antibodies may be present in each blood type.*

Using the Figure

Blood Typing Draw students' attention to **Figure 4,** and lead a class discussion on blood types and blood donation. Ask students to identify which blood type can donate to all other blood types. (O−) Tell students that people with O− blood are known as universal donors. Then, ask students to identify which blood type can receive all other blood types. (AB+) Tell students that people with AB+ blood are known as universal recipients. Answer to caption question: In the slide on the left, which shows a mixture of blood from two people with the same blood type, the blood is mixing without reacting. In the slide on the right, which shows a mixture of blood from two people with different blood types, the blood is clumping together. This reaction occurs when antibodies from one type of blood react with antigens from the other type of blood.
LS Visual/Logical

Teaching Transparency:
L78 Mixing Blood

MISCONCEPTION ALERT

Parts of Blood Cells
Students may not recognize that some parts of blood are not cells. Some of these students may think that platelets are cells. Have students work in small groups to create a memory game that helps them remember the characteristics of each component of blood: plasma, red blood cells, platelets, and white blood cells. Have students illustrate each component on a separate card and write a description of each component on another separate card. Then, ask groups to match each illustration to its description. Have them play the game until they have successfully matched all the pairs.
LS Interpersonal

Universal Access · Differentiated Instruction

Struggling Readers

Sticky Words Some students may struggle with science terms, even if they have learned them in previous classes or chapters. Privately give such students a pad of sticky notes, and tell them to write definitions of key terms and italicized terms on the notes. Direct students to paste their completed sticky notes in the margins of the page. Before students start reading p. 505, ask volunteers to review the definitions of the following words aloud: *plasma* (the fluid part of the blood), *antibodies* (proteins bind to specific antigens in order to identify or destroy them), *pathogens* (bacteria, viruses, and other microorganisms that cause disease), and *RBCs* (red blood cells). **LS** Verbal

Standards Focus

This **Standards Focus** provides you with a quick way to **assess, reteach,** and **re-assess** one or more concepts in the section.

Assess

1. Which blood cells break down dead or damaged cells? (white blood cells) **7.5.a**

2. Which disease results from a lack of an important clotting protein? (hemophilia) **7.5.b**

3. Which type of pressure results from contraction of the ventricles? (systolic pressure) **7.6.j**

 Reteach

Making Tables Have students make tables that describe each part of blood and the function of each part. [LS] Logical **7.5.a**

Re-Assess

Help Wanted Have students write a help wanted advertisement for each of the four main parts of blood. In their ads, students should describe the job responsibilities and the qualifications of the ideal candidate for the job. [LS] Verbal **7.5.a**

Answer to Math Practice

1. 70 beats/min × 60 min/h × 24 h/d = 100,800 beats/d

2. 100,800 beats/d × 365 d/y × 75 y = about 2.76 billion beats

3. Athlete's heart: 50 beats/min × 60 min/h × 24 h/d × 30 d = 2,160,000 beats; average heart: 100,800 beats/d × 30 d = 3,024,000 beats; 3,024,000 − 2,160,000 = 864,000 fewer beats. Explain to students that an athlete's heart is more efficient than a non-athlete's heart, so it can pump the same volume of blood in fewer beats.

Calculating Heartbeats

A person's heart averages about 70 beats per minute.

1. Calculate how many times a heart beats in one day.

2. If a person lives for 75 years, how many times will his or her heart beat?

3. If an athlete's heart beats 50 times per minute, how many fewer times than an average heart will his or her heart beat in 30 days?

Transfusions and Blood Types

Sometimes, a person must be given a blood transfusion. A *transfusion* is the injection of blood or blood components into a person to replace blood that has been lost because of surgery or an injury. Blood loss may lead to shock. *Shock* happens when a person's cells do not get enough blood. Without blood, cells do not get the oxygen and nutrients that they need, and wastes build up. Cell death may occur. Significant cell death may be fatal to the person.

Blood used in transfusions must be carefully handled. **Figure 6** shows bags of blood that may be given in a transfusion. The blood type is clearly marked. Because the ABO blood types have different antigen-antibody reactions, a person receiving blood cannot receive blood from just anyone. **Table 1** shows blood-transfusion possibilities.

Standards Check Why is shock dangerous to a person? **7.5.b**

Figure 6 *These bags of blood clearly show the blood type. Giving the wrong type of blood during a transfusion could be fatal for the transfusion patient.*

Table 1	Blood Transfusion Possibilities	
Type	**Can receive**	**Can donate to**
A	A, O	A, AB
B	B, O	B, AB
AB	A, B, AB, O	AB
O	O	A, B, AB, O

Universal Access • Differentiated Instruction

Advanced Learners/GATE

Blood Types Ask students to find out the approximate percentages of the different blood types in the U.S. population. (Type A: 40%, type B: 11%, type AB: 4%, and type O: 45%) Ask students to apply these percentages to 100 people and, for each blood type, determine how many possible donors and recipients are available within the 100 people. (Type A can receive blood from 85 people and donate to 44 people; type B can receive blood from 56 people and donate to 15 people; type AB can receive blood from 100 people and donate to 4 people; and type O can receive blood from 45 people and donate to 100 people.) Have students present the information to the class. Discuss with the class that Rh factors, not taken into account in this activity, would alter the results. [LS] Logical

Blood Disorders

Two of the most common blood disorders are hemophilia and leukemia. A person with *hemophilia* (HEE moh FIL ee uh) is missing a protein that helps blood clot. Blood clots form in a healthy person when blood vessels have been damaged or opened. A person with hemophilia does not form blood clots normally. Even a small cut may lead to significant blood loss. *Leukemia* is a type of cancer that affects blood cells. A person with leukemia may not be able to make enough healthy WBCs and RBCs. Doctors may treat leukemia with bone-marrow transfusions. Bone marrow is often taken from the hip bones of donors, as indicated by the purple dots in **Figure 7.**

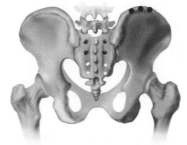

Figure 7 *Bone marrow must be collected from a donor before it can be given to a patient through a bone-marrow transfusion.*

SECTION Review

7.5.a, 7.5.b, 7.6.j

Summary

- The four main components of blood are plasma, red blood cells, platelets, and white blood cells.

- Blood carries oxygen and nutrients to cells, helps protect against disease, and helps regulate body temperature.

- Blood pressure is the force that blood exerts on the inside walls of arteries. It is often expressed in the unit of millimeters of mercury.

- Every person has one of four ABO blood types.

- Losing blood, mixing blood types, and blood disorders can be fatal.

Using Vocabulary

① Write an original definition for *blood* and *blood pressure*.

Understanding Concepts

② **Applying** A person with type B blood can donate blood to people with which type(s) of blood?

③ **Describing** Describe the functions of the four main components of blood.

④ **Concluding** Why is it important for a doctor to know a patient's blood type?

⑤ **Identifying** What causes blood pressure?

Critical Thinking

⑥ **Identifying Relationships** How does the body use blood and blood vessels to help maintain proper body temperature?

⑦ **Predicting Consequences** Some blood diseases affect the ability of red blood cells to deliver oxygen to cells of the body. What might happen to a person with such a disease?

INTERPRETING GRAPHICS The photomicrograph shows a WBC attacking pathogens. Use the image below to answer the next question.

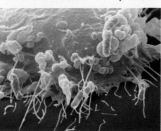

⑧ **Analyzing Relationships** Explain the function of blood that is being demonstrated in the image.

Math Skills

⑨ **Making Calculations** What percentage of normal (120 mm Hg) is a systolic pressure of 174 mm Hg?

Internet Resources

For a variety of links related to this chapter, go to www.scilinks.org
Topic: Blood; Blood Donations
SciLinks code: HY70175; HY70178

SCIENCE HUMOR

Q: What blood type does an optimist have?

A: B⁺ (be positive)!

Answer to Standards Check

Shock is dangerous because cells may not receive blood, so they may not be able to get oxygen. When cells do not get oxygen, they die. Eventually, this cell death may be fatal to a person. **7.5.b** (mastering)

Answers to Section Review

1. Sample answer: Blood carries oxygen to all cells. Blood pressure is the pressure of blood on arterial walls. **7.6.j** (mastering)

2. B and AB

3. Sample answer: Plasma contains water, minerals, nutrients, sugars, proteins, and other substances that are needed by the cells. Red blood cells

carry oxygen to cells in the body. Platelets are cell fragments that clump together to form clots. White blood cells destroy pathogens and dead or damaged cells. **7.5.a** (mastering)

4. Sample answer: A doctor must know a patient's blood type so that the doctor can order the right type of blood if the patient needs a transfusion. **7.5.b** (supporting)

5. Sample answer: When the heart contracts, it squeezes blood out of the heart. Blood pressure is the pressure of blood on arterial walls when the heart is contracted (systolic blood pressure) and relaxed (diastolic blood pressure) **7.6.j** (mastering)

6. Sample answer: As blood circulates in the body, it picks up heat from the cells and carries it through blood vessels that are close to the surface of the skin. Close to the skin's surface, the heat leaves the blood and is released into one's surroundings. Blood vessels dilate when the body is hot, which brings blood closer to skin's surface, and constrict when the body is cold, which keeps blood from the surface. **7.5.a** (exceeding)

7. Sample answer: A person whose red blood cells cannot deliver oxygen to the body's cells may often feel tired or weak. In addition, the lack of oxygen may damage some of the person's cells, tissues, or organs. **7.5.b** (mastering)

8. Sample answer: The function of blood shown in the image is defense against disease. White blood cells attack and destroy disease-causing pathogens. **7.5.a** (mastering)

9. $174 \div 120 \times 100 = 145\%$ of normal

Section Review Standards Guide

	Supporting	Mastering	Exceeding
7.5.a		3, 8	6
7.5.b	4	7	
7.6.j		1, 5	

Section Resources

- Directed Reading
  A **BASIC** (Also in Spanish), B **GENERAL**

- Interactive Reader and Study Guide

- Section Quiz **GENERAL** (Also in Spanish)

- Section Review **GENERAL** (Also in Spanish)

- Vocabulary and Section Summary
  A **BASIC** (Also in Spanish), B **GENERAL**

Preteach

Reviewing Prior Knowledge

Ask student volunteers to read the red and blue heads in the section aloud. Then, ask students to describe what they think the section is about. Finally, ask students to relate what they already know about the respiratory system.

Bellringer

Have students focus on standard 7.5.b by asking them what would happen if a person's lungs stopped working. (Sample answer: If a person's lungs stopped working, he or she could not get oxygen and would die.)

Bellringer Transparency

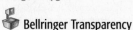

Motivate

ACTIVITY

Deep Breathing Have students place their hands on either side of their ribcage and take a few deep breaths. Then, ask students to describe what they felt while they breathed in and out.

Safety Caution: Warn students not to breathe deeply too quickly or for too long.
LS Kinesthetic

The Respiratory System

Key Concept The respiratory system is responsible for taking in oxygen and releasing carbon dioxide.

What You Will Learn

- The respiratory system includes the diaphragm, lungs, bronchi, trachea, larynx, pharynx, and nose.
- The respiratory system and the cardiovascular system work together to supply oxygen and remove carbon dioxide.
- Respiratory disorders include asthma, emphysema, and SARS.

Why It Matters

Learning about the respiratory system will help you understand how your organ systems work together.

Vocabulary

- respiration
- respiratory system
- pharynx
- larynx
- trachea
- bronchus
- alveolus

READING STRATEGY

Clarifying Concepts Take turns reading this section out loud with a partner. Stop to discuss ideas that seem confusing.

respiration (RES puh RAY shuhn) in biology, the exchange of oxygen and carbon dioxide between living cells and their environment; includes breathing and cellular respiration

respiratory system (RES puhr uh TAWR ee SIS tuhm) a collection of organs whose primary function is to take in oxygen and expel carbon dioxide

> Breathing—you do it all the time. You're doing it right now. But you hardly ever think about it, unless you suddenly can't breathe.

Then, it becomes very clear that you have to breathe in order to live. But why is breathing important? Your body needs oxygen in order to get energy from the foods you eat. Breathing makes this process possible.

Respiration and the Respiratory System

The words *breathing* and *respiration* are often used to mean the same thing. However, breathing is only one part of respiration. **Respiration** is the process by which a body gains and uses oxygen and gets rid of carbon dioxide and water. Respiration is divided into two parts. The first part is breathing, which involves inhaling and exhaling. The second part is cellular respiration, which involves chemical reactions that release energy from food.

Breathing is made possible by your respiratory system. The **respiratory system** is the group of organs that take in oxygen and get rid of carbon dioxide. The nose, throat, lungs, and passageways that lead to the lungs make up the respiratory system. **Figure 1** shows the parts of the respiratory system.

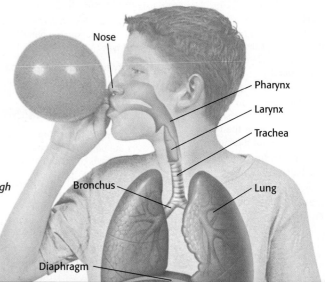

Figure 1 Air moves into and out of the body through the respiratory system.

Nose
Pharynx
Larynx
Trachea
Bronchus
Lung
Diaphragm

Universal Access · Differentiated Instruction

Struggling Readers

Silent Letters Remind students that many words have letters that are not pronounced. Suggest these steps to make a 3-column list for learning to pronounce and spell silent-letter words correctly:

1. In the first column, make a list of the words from the text with their pronunciations, and highlight the silent letters.

2. Add a definition in the second column.

3. Add some other words with the same silent letter patterns in the third column.

Write these three words from the text on the board: *muscles, diaphragm, asthma*. Next to the matching words, add these words with the same silent letter patterns: *scene, descent, phlegm, paradigm, clothes, isthmus*. Tell them to practice pronouncing the word, and to look up the meaning of the word. Tell students to add the information to their silent-letter word lists.
LS Verbal/Auditory

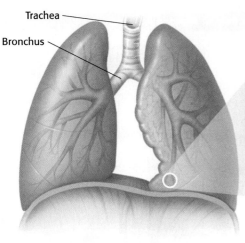

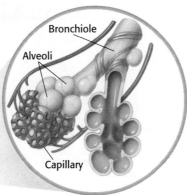

Figure 2 *Inside your lungs, the bronchi branch into bronchioles. The bronchioles lead to tiny sacs called* alveoli.

Nose, Pharynx, and Larynx

Your *nose* is the main passageway into and out of the respiratory system. Air can be breathed in through and out of the nose. Air can also enter and leave through the mouth.

From the nose, air flows through the **pharynx,** or throat. Food and drink also move through the pharynx on the way to the stomach. The pharynx branches into two tubes. One tube, the *esophagus,* leads to the stomach. The other tube leads to the lungs. The larynx sits at the beginning of this tube.

The **larynx** is the part of the throat that contains the vocal cords. The *vocal cords* are a pair of elastic bands that stretch across the larynx. Muscles connected to the larynx control how much the vocal cords are stretched. When air flows between the vocal cords, the cords vibrate. These vibrations make sound.

Trachea

The larynx guards the entrance to a large tube called the **trachea,** or windpipe. Your body has two large, spongelike lungs. The trachea, shown in **Figure 2,** is the passageway for air traveling from the larynx toward the lungs.

Bronchi and Alveoli

The trachea splits into two branches called **bronchi** (singular, *bronchus*). One bronchus connects to each lung. Each bronchus branches into smaller and smaller tubes. They eventually form a smaller series of airways called *bronchioles* (BRAHNG kee OHLZ). In the lungs, each bronchiole branches to form tiny sacs that are called **alveoli** (singular, *alveolus*).

Standards Check Describe the structure and function of the pharynx and larynx. 🐻 **7.5.a**

pharynx (FAR ingks) the passage from the mouth to the larynx and esophagus

larynx (LAR ingks) the area of the throat that contains the vocal cords and produces vocal sounds

trachea (TRAY kee uh) the tube that connects the larynx to the lungs

bronchus (BRAHNG kuhs) one of the two tubes that connect the lungs with the trachea

alveolus (al VEE uh luhs) any of the tiny air sacs of the lungs where oxygen and carbon dioxide are exchanged

7.5.a Students know plants and animals have levels of organization for structure and function, including cells, tissues, organs, organ systems, and the whole organism.
7.5.b Students know organ systems function because of the contributions of individual organs, tissues, and cells. The failure of any part can affect the entire system.

Close

Standards Focus

This **Standards Focus** provides you with a quick way to **assess, reteach,** and **re-assess** one or more concepts in the section.

 Assess

1. Which respiratory disorder is caused by a virus? (SARS) **7.5.b**

2. Through which organ do both food and air travel? (pharynx) **7.5.a**

 **Reteach**

Section Outline Have students use the heads and terms in this section to create an outline that describes the structures and functions of the respiratory system. Encourage students to use their outlines as study tools.
LS Logical **7.5.a**

 Re-Assess

Lung Models Have students make models of healthy lungs and lungs damaged by smoking. Photographs of healthy lungs and damaged lungs can be found in literature from the American Lung Association and the American Cancer Society, as well as in various science and health textbooks. **LS** Visual **7.5.a, 7.5.b**

 Teaching Transparency:
L81 The Role of Blood in Respiration

Teaching Transparency: *LINK TO EARTH SCIENCE* E74 Sources of Indoor Air Pollution

---

Answer to Standards Check

Asthma causes the bronchioles to narrow. **7.5.b** (supporting)

Figure 3 **The Role of Blood in Respiration**

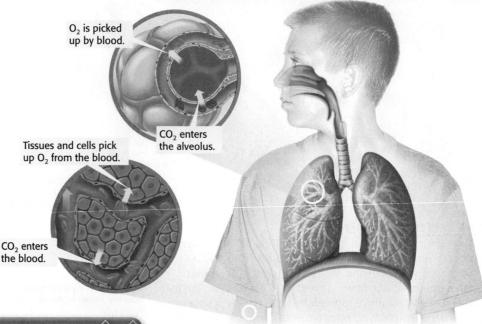

O_2 is picked up by blood.

CO_2 enters the alveolus.

Tissues and cells pick up O_2 from the blood.

CO_2 enters the blood.

Quick Lab

Replicate Respiration

7.5.a

1. Use **scissors** to cut the bottom off an empty **1 liter soda bottle.**

2. Stretch a **latex glove** over the open bottom of the bottle. Secure with **tape.**

3. Insert a **balloon** into the top of the bottle. Pull the lip of the balloon to fit over the mouth of the bottle. Secure with tape.

4. Pull on the fingers of the glove. What happens to the balloon?

5. How does this activity relate to respiration and the diaphragm?

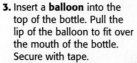

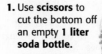

⏱ **15 min**

Breathing

When you breathe, air is sucked into or pushed out of your lungs. However, your lungs have no muscles of their own. Instead, breathing is done by the diaphragm (DIE uh FRAM) and rib muscles. The *diaphragm* is a dome-shaped muscle beneath the lungs. When the diaphragm contracts and moves down, you inhale. The chest cavity's volume gets larger. At the same time, some of your rib muscles contract and lift your rib cage. As a result, your chest cavity gets bigger and a vacuum is created. Air is sucked in. Exhaling is this process in reverse.

Breathing and Cellular Respiration

In *cellular respiration,* oxygen is used by cells to release energy stored in molecules of the sugar glucose. Where does the oxygen come from? When you inhale, you take in oxygen gas. This gas moves into red blood cells and is carried to tissue cells. The oxygen then moves out of the red blood cells and into each cell. Cells use the oxygen to release energy. During this process, carbon dioxide (CO_2) and water are made. Carbon dioxide is exhaled from the lungs. **Figure 3** shows how breathing and blood circulation are related.

Quick Lab

⏱ **15 min**

Teacher Notes

This activity will help students understand the complex interactions of organs that cause inhalation (covers standard 7.5.a).

Materials for Each Group
• balloon
• glove, latex
• scissors
• soda bottle, 1 L, empty
• tape

Safety Caution

Remind students to review all safety cautions and icons before beginning this activity.

Answers

4. The balloon expanded and drew in air.

5. Sample answer: When the glove at the bottom moves down, a vacuum is created. This is the same thing that happens when the diaphragm moves down. The vacuum causes air to be drawn into the lungs during respiration just as the balloon drew in air.

 Differentiated Datasheets
A **BASIC**, B **GENERAL**, C **ADVANCED**

Also editable on the Holt Lab Generator CD-ROM

Respiratory Disorders

Millions of people suffer from respiratory disorders. These disorders include asthma, emphysema, and severe acute respiratory syndrome (SARS). Asthma causes the bronchioles to narrow. A person who has asthma has trouble breathing. An asthma attack may be triggered by irritants such as dust or pollen. Emphysema happens when the alveoli have been damaged. **Figure 4** shows a lung damaged by emphysema. SARS is caused by a virus. A person who has SARS may have a fever and difficulty breathing.

People who have respiratory disorders have trouble getting the oxygen they need. Cells need oxygen for cellular respiration. They can't efficiently free energy stored in glucose without oxygen. If a person's cells are not able to free this energy, the person may feel tired all the time. People with respiratory disorders may also have problems getting rid of carbon dioxide. It may build up inside the body to a toxic level.

Standards Check How does asthma affect bronchioles? 🐻 **7.5.b**

Figure 4 *The photo at the top shows a healthy lung. The photo at the bottom shows the lung of a person who had emphysema.*

Understanding Concepts

1. **Describing** Describe the causes of SARS, emphysema, and some asthma attacks.

2. **Summarizing** How does breathing happen?

3. **Applying** Describe how your cardiovascular and respiratory systems work together.

Critical Thinking

4. **Predicting Consequences** If a respiratory disorder causes lungs to fill with fluid, how could this affect a person's health?

5. **Interpreting Statistics** About 6.3 million children in the United States have asthma. About 4 million of them had an asthma attack last year. What do these statistics tell you about the relationship between asthma and asthma attacks?

Math Skills

6. **Making Calculations** Usable lung capacity is about 6 L. A person can exhale about 3.6 L. What percentage of the lung capacity cannot be exhaled?

Challenge

7. **Identifying Relationships** Emphysema often occurs in people who smoke cigarettes. How could smoking damage alveoli? How could emphysema affect the rest of the body?

Internet Resources

For a variety of links related to this chapter, go to www.scilinks.org
Topic: The Respiratory System; Respiratory Disorders
SciLinks code: HY71307; HY71306

Skills Practice Lab

Teacher Notes

In this lab, students will detect the presence of carbon dioxide in their breath, record the resulting data, and compare this data with that of their classmates (covers standard 7.7.c). Students will then describe how various parts of the body share the task of removing gaseous wastes (covers standards 7.5.a and 7.5.b).

Time Required

One 45-minute class period

Lab Ratings

Teacher Prep 🧪🧪
Student Set-Up 🧪🧪
Concept Level 🧪🧪
Clean Up 🧪🧪

Materials

The materials listed on the student page are enough for two students. You may wish to substitute bromothymol blue indicator solution for the phenol red indicator solution. The bromothymol blue solution will turn green in the presence of carbon dioxide. Use eight drops of bromothymol blue indicator to make the solution. Clear plastic cups (6 oz or 8 oz) may be used instead of 250 mL flasks if glassware is in short supply or if you have concerns about breakage.

Safety Caution

Remind students to review all safety cautions and icons before beginning this lab activity. Tell students to inform you if any glassware is broken. Remind students that they should only exhale through the straw.

Preparation Notes

Tell students that carbon dioxide is in the air in the classroom. Tell them to make sure that they do not expose their indicator solution to air for several minutes before they use it in the experiment.

Skills Practice Lab

Carbon Dioxide in Respiration

Carbon dioxide is important to both plants and animals. Plants take in carbon dioxide during photosynthesis and give off oxygen as a byproduct of the process. Animals—including you—take in oxygen during cellular respiration and give off carbon dioxide as a byproduct of the process.

Procedure

1. Find a partner. Put on your gloves, safety goggles, and apron.

2. Use the graduated cylinder to pour 100 mL of water into a 250 mL flask.

3. Repeat step 2 so that you have two flasks, each containing 100 mL of water.

4. Using an eyedropper, carefully place four drops of phenol red indicator solution into the water of the first flask. The water should turn orange.

5. Place a plastic drinking straw into the solution of phenol red and water. Drape a paper towel over the flask to prevent splashing.

6. Make sure your lab partner has the stopwatch ready. You will soon exhale into the straw. Your lab partner should begin keeping time as soon as you start to exhale through the straw.

OBJECTIVES

Detect the presence of carbon dioxide in your breath before and after exercise.

Compare the data for carbon dioxide in your breath with the data from your classmates.

MATERIALS

- eyedropper
- flask, Erlenmeyer, 250 mL (2)
- gloves, protective
- graduated cylinder, 100 mL
- paper towels
- phenol red indicator solution
- stopwatch, or clock with a second hand
- straw, plastic drinking (2)
- water, 200 mL

SAFETY

7.5.a Students know plants and animals have levels of organization for structure and function, including cells, tissues, organs, organ systems, and the whole organism.
7.5.b Students know organ systems function because of the contributions of individual organs, tissues, and cells. The failure of any part can affect the entire system.

Investigation and Experimentation
7.7.c Communicate the logical connection among hypotheses, science concepts, tests conducted, data collected, and conclusions drawn from the scientific evidence.

Lab Resources

📋 Differentiated Datasheets
A BASIC, B GENERAL, C ADVANCED
💿 Classroom Lab Video/DVD

⊙ **Holt Lab Generator CD-ROM**

Search for any lab by topic, standard, difficulty level, or time. Edit any lab to fit your needs, or create your own labs. Use the Lab Materials QuickList software to customize your lab materials list.

7 Breathe normally, but exhale into the straw in the solution. **Caution:** Do not inhale through the straw. Do not drink the solution, and do not share a straw with anyone. Have your lab partner time how long the solution takes to change color. Record the time.

8 Do jumping jacks or sit-ups for 3 min, and repeat steps 4–7 using the second flask.

Analyze the Results

9 **Describing Events** Describe what happened to the indicator solution.

10 **Organizing Data** Make a table with three columns. Title the columns "Student name," "Time without exercise," and "Time with exercise." Write your data in the appropriate columns. Collect data from your classmates, and add the data to your table.

11 **Examining Data** Look at the data in the first column. What was the longest length of time it took to see a color change? What was the shortest? How do you account for the difference? Repeat for the second column.

12 **Examining Data** Did exercising make a difference in the time it took for the solution to change color? Why or why not?

13 **Constructing Graphs** Make a bar graph that compares your data from the first column with the data of your classmates.

Draw Conclusions

14 **Interpreting Information** Do you think that there is a relationship between the length of time the solution takes to change color and the person's physical characteristics, such as which gender the tester is or whether the tester has an athletic build? Explain.

Big Idea Question

15 **Making Predictions** Which individual organs in the body contribute to getting rid of waste products, such as carbon dioxide? What would happen if these organs failed and excess carbon dioxide could not be removed from the body?

Analyze the Results

9. The phenol red solution turns yellowish. Bromothymol blue turns green.

10. Specific data will depend on student observations; accept all reasonable responses. Students' tables should be set up according to the directions given in the question.

11. Accept all reasonable answers. It is typical for the solution to change color faster when the student is breathing faster after exercise, so the times listed for step 8 should be shorter than those listed for step 7.

12. Sample answer: Exercise decreased the amount of time it took for the solution to change color because the body produces more carbon dioxide during and after exercise.

13. Bar graphs may vary according to the students' observations and the data collected.

Draw Conclusions

14. In general, there should be little difference between genders. An athlete at rest will usually take the longest time to generate a color change in the indicator solution. There are exceptions, and all answers will depend on students' observations.

Big Idea Question

15. Sample answer: The heart, blood vessels, and lungs all play a role in getting rid of carbon dioxide wastes. If the body could not get rid of carbon dioxide, the respiratory system would fail, which may result in death.

Sushma Kashyap, MSc
Alvarado Intermediate School
Rowland Heights, CA

Teacher Notes

In this activity, students will gain hands-on experience finding and selecting research materials from print and electronic sources (covers standard 7.7.b). After completing this activity, students should be able to select reliable and current source material for future research projects.

Answers to You Try It!

1. Students' research maps should contain the term emphysema as the keyword, as well as suitable broader topics.

2. Accept all reasonable sources of information.

3. Sample answer: Recent scientific sources, such as up-to-date science textbooks and journals, are the most relevant to my search.

4. Sample answer: To determine which sources are legitimate and which are not, I will assess if a source is out of date (e.g. includes information that has since been disproven). I will also note whether my sources include personal Web sites and research funded by an organization that benefits from the results. These sources are not reliable and should be dismissed.

5. Sample answer: Specific topics may yield results that are too specialized to be applied to broader ideas. Researching broad topics may yield results that are not specific enough.

📄 Datasheet **GENERAL**

Also editable on the Holt Lab Generator CD-ROM

Science Skills Activity

| Scientific Methods | Research | Data Analysis | Models, Maps & Diagrams |

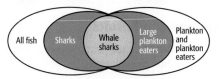

Investigation and Experimentation
7.7.b Use a variety of print and electronic resources (including the World Wide Web) to collect information and evidence as part of a research project.

Evaluating Resources for Research

▶ Tutorial

Before writing a paper, you must gather information. This process can leave you with stacks of books and thousands of Internet sites. Reading all of these sources would take a very long time. How do you know which sources will have the most relevant information? The procedure below can help you determine the best sources for your research.

Procedure

1. Select the keywords of your topic. Keywords should be specific.

2. Create a research map similar to the one below.

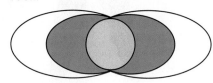

3. Put your keywords in the center circle. Think of broader topics, and place those in the areas outside the center circle. The example below shows a research map on the topic of whale sharks.

All fish | Sharks | Whale sharks | Large plankton eaters | Plankton and plankton eaters

4. List the sources where you may find information about each of your topics including books, CD-ROMs, science magazines, and Web sites.

5. List places where you may find these sources, including computers and libraries.

6. Begin your search with the sources that seem most relevant or have the most information.

7. Scan the books or online articles. Check or print out sources that have good information. Read what you have gathered.

▶ You Try It!

Collect information for a research project on the topic of emphysema. Emphysema is a respiratory disorder that happens when alveoli in the lungs have been damaged. Emphysema is often associated with smoking cigarettes.

Procedure

1. **Constructing Maps** Create a research map to identify your keywords and the broader topics that may be helpful when finding sources.

2. **Organizing Data** Use the topics on your research map to find at least eight sources of information. List your sources by type. For example, all of the textbook sources can be listed together.

Analysis

3. **Evaluating Data** Which of your sources have the most relevant information? Choose the three best sources. Explain why these sources are the most relevant to your research.

4. **Identifying Patterns** You may find sources with information that is out of date or unscientific. These sources should be dismissed. How will you determine which sources are legitimate and which are not?

5. **Evaluating Methods** Why do you think it is important to map specific keywords and broader topics? What might happen if you researched only specific topics? What might happen if you researched only broad topics?

Universal Access · Differentiated Instruction

Basic Learners

Check Along the Way Some students may be more successful if you check their progress along the way to make sure that they are building on an accurate base. Check students' research maps to make sure that their keywords and topics are well chosen before they use the map to find and organize data. Then, check students' sources of information to make sure that the sources are all relevant before students choose the three best ones. **LS** Verbal

Special Education Students

Alternate Research Topics Some students may not be familiar with the concept of emphysema. Allow such students to research a topic that they are more likely to be familiar with, such as kinds of exercise or healthy foods that people should eat. **LS** Verbal/Logical

Chapter Summary

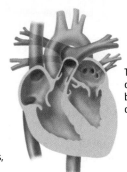

The Big Idea
The human body has organ systems that transport gases, nutrients, and wastes.

Section

Vocabulary

❶ The Cardiovascular System

Key Concept The cardiovascular system circulates blood, gases, and nutrients throughout your body.

- The cardiovascular system is made up of the heart, three types of blood vessels, and blood.
- Contractions of the heart pump blood throughout the entire body.
- Cardiovascular problems include atherosclerosis, high blood pressure, strokes, heart attacks, and heart failure.

The heart is an organ that pumps blood to all parts of the body.

cardiovascular system p. 496
artery p. 498
capillary p. 498
vein p. 498
pulmonary circulation p. 499
systemic circulation p. 499

❷ Blood

Key Concept Blood transports many things through the body, including oxygen, nutrients, wastes, heat, immune system cells, and hormones.

- Blood is a tissue that is made up of red blood cells, white blood cells, platelets, and plasma.
- Blood pressure is the force exerted by blood on the inside walls of arteries.
- The loss of blood, mixing blood types, or blood disorders can be fatal.

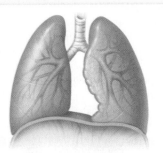

A
B
AB
O

Each blood type has specific antigens and antibodies.

blood p. 502
blood pressure p. 504

❸ The Respiratory System

Key Concept The respiratory system is responsible for taking in oxygen and releasing carbon dioxide.

- The respiratory system includes the diaphragm, lungs, bronchi, trachea, larynx, pharynx, and nose.
- The respiratory system and the cardiovascular system work together to supply oxygen and remove carbon dioxide.
- Respiratory disorders include asthma, emphysema, and SARS.

The bronchi branch into bronchioles inside the lungs.

respiration p. 508
respiratory system p. 508
pharynx p. 509
larynx p. 509
trachea p. 509
bronchus p. 509
alveolus p. 509

Chapter Summary

SUPER SUMMARY

Have students connect the major concepts in this chapter through an interactive Super Summary. Visit go.hrw.com and type in the keyword HY7BD2S to access the Super Summary for this chapter.

Identifying Word Roots
Pulmonary and Cardiovascular

Tell students that the word *pulmonary* includes the root *pulmo-*, which means "lung." Then, tell students that the word *cardiovascular* includes the root *kardia-*, which means "heart." Have students think of as many words as they can that contain these two roots. Then, have them use these words to create a word-search puzzle for their class-mates. Instead of listing the words to find, students should list the definitions of the word parts. **LS** Verbal

Focus on Reading

Making Graphics Have students read The Big Idea, each of the Key Concepts, and the bulleted points for each section. Then, have students create a graphic, such as a concept map or a spider map, that summarizes the information presented.
LS Verbal/Visual

Review Resources

- 🗍 Reinforcement Worksheet **BASIC**
- 🗍 Critical Thinking Worksheet **ADVANCED**
- 🗍 Chapter Review **GENERAL** (Also in Spanish)
- 📖 Standards Review Workbook (Also in Spanish)
- 📖 Study Guide A **BASIC** (Also in Spanish), B **GENERAL**

Assessment Resources

- 🗍 Chapter Tests A **BASIC**, B **GENERAL** (Also in Spanish), C **ADVANCED**
- 🗍 Standards Assessment **GENERAL**

7.5.a, 7.5.b, 7.6.j

Assignment Guide

Section	Questions
1	3, 5–6, 9, 11–14, 21–22
2	2, 4, 10, 16, 18–20, 23, 25
3	7–8, 15, 17

Answers

Using Vocabulary

1. Sample answer: The word *function* means "a use or purpose."

2. Red blood cells **7.5.a** (supporting)

3. Arteries **7.5.b** (supporting)

4. blood pressure **7.6.j** (mastering)

Understanding Concepts

5. a **7.6.j** (mastering)

6. d **7.6.j** (mastering)

7. c **7.5.a** (supporting), **7.5.b** (supporting)

8. a **7.5.b** (supporting)

9. Sample answer: Pulmonary circulation carries blood from the heart to the lungs, and then back to the heart. Systemic circulation carries blood from the heart to the rest of the body, and then back to the heart. **7.6.j** (supporting)

10. Sample answer: The first number represents systolic pressure, which is the pressure in the arteries when the ventricles contract. The second number is diastolic pressure, which is the pressure in the arteries when the ventricles relax. **7.6.j** (supporting)

11. Sample answer: In the cardiovascular system, the heart is an organ, blood is a tissue, and red blood cells and white blood cells are both types of cells. **7.5.a** (mastering)

12. a, right atrium **7.6.j** (supporting)

13. b, left atrium **7.6.j** (supporting)

14. c, right ventricle **7.6.j** (supporting)

Organize

Four-Corner Fold Review the FoldNote that you created at the beginning of the chapter. Add to or correct the FoldNote based on what you have learned.

Using Vocabulary

1 Academic Vocabulary In the sentence "The function of RBCs is to transport oxygen throughout the body," what does the word *function* mean?

Complete each of the following sentences by choosing the correct term from the word bank.

red blood cells	veins
white blood cells	arteries
pulmonary circulation	blood pressure
alveoli	bronchi

2 ___ deliver oxygen to the cells of the body.

3 ___ are blood vessels that carry blood away from the heart.

4 The force that blood exerts on the walls of the arteries is called ___.

Understanding Concepts

Multiple Choice

5 ___ create blood pressure.
- **a.** Heart contractions
- **b.** Arteries
- **c.** Valves
- **d.** Atria

6 The parts of the heart that prevent blood from flowing backward are
- **a.** ventricles.
- **b.** capillaries.
- **c.** atria.
- **d.** valves.

7 Alveoli are surrounded by
- **a.** veins.
- **b.** muscles.
- **c.** capillaries.
- **d.** cholesterol.

8 Air moves into the lungs when the diaphragm muscle
- **a.** contracts and moves down.
- **b.** contracts and moves up.
- **c.** relaxes and moves down.
- **d.** relaxes and moves up.

Short Answer

9 Comparing Compare pulmonary circulation and systemic circulation.

10 Applying Braden's blood pressure is 110/65. What do the two numbers mean?

11 Listing List examples of one organ, one tissue, and two types of cells in the cardiovascular system.

INTERPRETING GRAPHICS The diagram shows how the human heart would look in cross section. Use the diagram below to answer the next three questions.

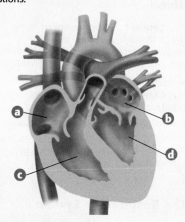

12 Identifying Which letter identifies the chamber that receives blood from systemic circulation? What is this chamber's name?

13 Identifying Which letter identifies the chamber that receives blood from the lungs? What is this chamber's name?

14 Identifying Which letter identifies the chamber that pumps blood to the lungs? What is this chamber's name?

15. Sample answer: Oxygen enters the body through the nose or mouth; travels through the pharynx, larynx, and trachea to the lungs; and enters the alveoli. In the alveoli, oxygen moves through capillary walls into blood. Red blood cells carry the oxygen through the blood vessels of the cardiovascular system to the heart, which pumps the oxygenated blood to all parts of the body. **7.5.b** (mastering)

Writing Skills

16. Answers may vary, but should demonstrate an understanding of why people need transfusions. **7.5.b** (mastering)

Critical Thinking

17. 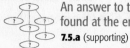 An answer to this exercise can be found at the end of this book. **7.5.a** (supporting)

15 Summarizing Briefly describe the path that oxygen follows in your respiratory system and your cardiovascular system.

Writing Skills

16 Writing Persuasively The blood used for blood transfusions comes from donations to blood banks. Write a paragraph persuading your friends and family members to donate blood. Use your understanding of the importance of blood transfusions in your answer.

Critical Thinking

17 Concept Mapping Use the following terms to create a concept map: *blood, oxygen, alveoli, capillaries,* and *carbon dioxide.*

18 Identifying Relationships How are the functions of red blood cells and white blood cells different?

19 Predicting Consequences What would happen if all of the red blood cells in your blood disappeared?

20 Applying Concepts When a person is not feeling well, a doctor may examine samples of the person's blood to see how many white blood cells are present. Why would this information be useful?

INTERPRETING GRAPHICS Use the image below to answer the next question.

21 Making Comparisons How is the heart similar to the revolving doors in the image?

22 Making Comparisons What organs are affected by heart attacks and strokes? How could this affect the organism?

INTERPRETING GRAPHICS Use the image below to answer the next question.

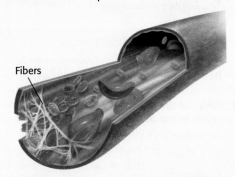

Fibers

23 Making Inferences The image shows platelets and fibers forming a blood clot to seal a broken blood vessel. A person with hemophilia cannot form blood clots normally. What do you think happens when a person with hemophilia gets a cut?

Math Skills

24 Making Conversions After a person donates blood, the blood is stored in 1 pt bags until it is needed for a transfusion. A healthy person has about 5 million RBCs in each cubic millimeter (1 mm^3) of blood.
  a. How many RBCs are in 1 mL of blood? (One milliliter is equal to 1 cm^3 and to 1,000 mm^3.)
  b. How many RBCs are there in 1 pt? (One pint is equal to 473 mL.)

Challenge

25 Applying Concepts Blood types are most often reported using both the ABO system and the Rh system. For example, a person with type A blood that is Rh$^+$ will have A$^+$ blood. What blood type does a person with B antigens, A antibodies, and Rh antigens have?

22. Sample answer: Heart attacks affect the heart, and strokes affect the brain. Damage to the heart or the brain can result in the death of an organism. **7.5.b** (mastering)

23. Sample answer: A person who has hemophilia bleeds for a much longer period of time than a person who does not have hemophilia. A person who has hemophilia may bleed so much that he or she dies. **7.5.b** (mastering)

Math Skills

24. a. 5,000,000 RBCs/mm^3 × 1,000 mm^3/mL = 5 billion RBCs/mL blood

  b. 5,000,000,000 RBCs/mL × 473 mL/pt = 2.365 trillion RBCs/pt blood

Challenge

25. B+

Chapter Review Standards Guide			
	Supporting	Mastering	Exceeding
7.5.a	2, 7, 17–18, 21	11	
7.5.b	3, 7–8	15–16, 19, 22–23	20
7.6.j	9–10, 12–14	4–6, 21	

18. Sample answer: Red blood cells transport oxygen throughout the body. White blood cells fight pathogens, release antibodies, and destroy cells that have died or been damaged. **7.5.a** (supporting)

19. Sample answer: In a very short time, I would probably die because my cells could not get the oxygen that they need to survive. **7.5.b** (mastering)

20. Sample answer: The immune system produces white blood cells to fight disease-causing pathogens. A high white blood cell count may indicate that a person has an infection. **7.5.b** (exceeding)

21. Sample answer: The people who walk through a revolving door are like blood cells. Like the heart, the revolving door works only in one direction; blood cells—or people, in the case of the revolving door—cannot go backwards. **7.6.j** (mastering)

Standards Assessment

Standards Assessment

 7.1.b, 7.1.d, 7.2.e, 7.5, 7.5.a, 7.5.b, 7.6.j

Teacher Notes

To provide practice under more realistic testing conditions, give students 20 min to answer all of the questions in this assessment.

Answer Key	
Question Number	Correct Answer
1	B
2	D
3	A
4	B
5	C
6	A
7	B
8	D
9	A
10	D
11	A
12	C
13	B
14	D
15	B

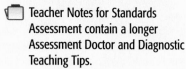

Standards Guide			
	Supporting	Mastering	Exceeding
7.1.b		14	
7.1.d	12–13		
7.2.e		15	
7.5	1		
7.5.a	2, 8, 11	6	
7.5.b	4, 9	7	
7.6.j	3	5, 10	

📋 Standards Assessment **GENERAL**

📋 Teacher Notes for Standards Assessment contain a longer Assessment Doctor and Diagnostic Teaching Tips.

REVIEWING ACADEMIC VOCABULARY

1 Choose the appropriate form of the word *illustrate* for the following sentence: The complementary nature of structure and function is ___ by the anatomy of plants and animals.

A illustrate

B illustrated

C illustration

D illustrating

2 Which of the following words means "the arrangement of the parts of the whole"?

A process

B system

C function

D structure

3 Which of the following words is the closest in meaning to the word *generate*?

A produce

B find

C filter

D destroy

4 Which of the following words means "a part given to the whole"?

A distribution

B contribution

C execution

D retribution

REVIEWING CONCEPTS

5 Which of the following actions pumps blood through the body?

A the expansion of the heart

B the expansion of blood vessels

C the contractions of the heart

D the contractions of the blood vessels

6 Which type of blood vessel allows for the exchange of gases between the blood and body cells?

A capillaries   C ventricles

B arteries   D veins

7 Which of the following is a direct cause of a stroke?

A Cholesterol builds up in an artery and blocks blood flow through it.

B A blood vessel ruptures in the brain, so oxygen flow is cut off.

C The heart cannot pump enough blood to meet the body's needs.

D A blood vessel collapses, so the flow of oxygen to the heart is cut off.

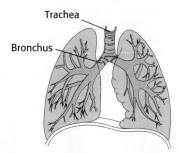
Trachea
Bronchus

8 The diagram above shows parts of the respiratory system. What label could be added to the diagram?

A Capillaries   C Pharynx

B Larynx   D Bronchioles

➕ ASSESSMENT DOCTOR

Question 1: The correct answer is B. The past participle of *illustrate* is *illustrated*. To *illustrate* something is to make clear or to show the subject.

Question 2: The correct answer is D. The *structure* of something is the way it is built or constructed. The structure of an object is closely related to the function that object performs.

Question 3: The correct answer is A. *Produce* is closest in meaning to the word *generate*. To *generate* in a scientific context is to produce through a chemical or physical process.

Question 4: The correct answer is B. A *contribution* is something that is given. Body systems work through the contribution of cells, tissues, and organs.

Question 5: The correct answer is C. Blood flow in the cardiovascular system results from the contraction of the heart muscle.

9 Which of the following occurs when the body becomes too warm and tries to cool itself?

A Blood vessels in the skin enlarge.

B Blood vessels in the skin contract.

C The heart pumps blood more slowly.

D The heart pumps blood more quickly.

10 What is systolic blood pressure?

A The pressure inside capillaries when the heart contracts.

B The pressure inside arteries when the heart relaxes.

C The pressure inside veins when the heart contracts.

D The pressure inside arteries when the heart contracts.

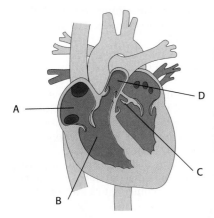

11 Which part of the diagram above shows an atrium?

A part A   C part C

B part B   D part D

12 Why do cells need oxygen?

A Oxygen is used during the process of fermentation.

B Oxygen is used during the process of cell division.

C Oxygen is used during the process of cellular respiration.

D Oxygen is used during the process of meiosis.

13 What is the result of cellular respiration?

A Energy is produced from radiant sunlight and carbon dioxide.

B Energy is produced from sugar molecules and oxygen.

C Sunlight is converted into sugar molecules and oxygen.

D Sunlight is converted into water molecules.

14 A white blood cell is not likely to have a

A mitochondrion.

B cell membrane.

C nucleus.

D chloroplast.

15 Which of the following is the genetic material for a cell?

A ribosome

B DNA

C endoplasmic reticulum

D nucleolus

Standards Assessment

Question 10: The correct answer is D. Systolic pressure is the pressure that blood exerts on arterial walls when the heart contracts. The other type of blood pressure, diastolic pressure, is the pressure blood exerted on the walls of arteries when the heart is relaxed.

Question 11: The correct answer is A. Part A in the diagram is the right atrium, the first stop for deoxygenated blood as it enters the heart from the body.

Question 12: The correct answer is C. During cellular respiration, cells use oxygen to release chemical energy, and in the process they produce carbon dioxide and water.

Question 13: The correct answer is B. Sugar molecules are converted to energy in plants and animals by the process of cellular respiration. Oxygen is required for cellular respiration. If no oxygen is available, organisms may use fermentation to get energy from food.

Question 14: The correct answer is D. Blood cells are animal cells. Like other animal cells, blood cells do not have plant cell parts, such as chloroplasts or cell walls.

Question 15: The correct answer is B. The DNA is the genetic material found in all living things. In eukaryotic cells, such as those of plants and animals, DNA is found arranged in chromosomes in the nucleus. DNA in prokaryotic cells is arranged into one circular chromosome.

Question 6: The correct answer is A. Capillaries are the smallest blood vessels. They are rarely more than 3 cells away from any cell. The thin walls of capillaries allow for the exchange of gases, nutrients, and wastes.

Question 7: The correct answer is B. A stroke occurs when brain cells are injured due to lack of oxygen. A ruptured blood vessel in the brain would cut off oxygen flow to the brain cells around and past the damaged vessel.

Question 8: The correct answer is D. The bronchioles, which branch out from the bronchi, are the items pictured.

Question 9: The correct answer is A. A rise in body temperature leads the brain to tell blood vessels near the surface of the skin to enlarge, allowing heat to be released into the environment.

Science, Technology, and Society

ACTIVITY

Race Menu Anyone who runs a marathon or undertakes another type of long-distance race needs to make sure that they provide their body with adequate glucose from food and drink during the race so that they have the energy to finish. Ask students to explain why runners need to eat and drink during a long-distance race. Then, ask students to write up a "race menu" for a typical marathon runner. **LS Verbal**

Weird Science

Background

Drawings of men playing an instrument that appears to be a didgeridoo appear in caves in Australia. Evidence indicates that the didgeridoo has been used in Australia for about 1,000 years. Aborigines, however, trace the history of the instrument back to the Dreamtime, a time period that the Aborigines refer to as the very beginning of their people. The first reference to the didgeridoo made by a Westerner came from a man named T. B. Wilson in 1835. Wilson described an Aboriginal man playing an instrument that was made of bamboo and was about 1 m long.

Science in Action

Science, Technology, and Society

California Marathons

Some of the world's most popular marathons are held every year in California cities, such as San Diego and San Francisco. A marathon is a 26.2 mi race. The majority of runners take more than four hours to complete a marathon. To compete in a marathon, a runner must have respiratory and circulatory systems that are in top form. Long-distance running requires a lot of oxygen and glucose. Oxygen is taken into the lungs through breathing. Glucose is acquired through the foods we eat. Oxygen and glucose are both carried by blood to muscles. Muscle cells use oxygen to convert glucose into usable energy.

Language Arts ACTIVITY

Think of all the activities you perform that require your respiratory and circulatory systems to function well. In your **Science Journal**, write a list of some ways you can keep these organ systems healthy.

Weird Science

Circular Breathing and the Didgeridoo

Do you play a musical instrument such as a clarinet, flute, or tuba? How long can you blow into it before you have to take a breath? Can you blow into it for one minute? Two minutes? What happens when you stop to breathe? The Aboriginal people of Australia have a musical instrument called the *didgeridoo* (DIJ uh ree DOO). Didgeridoo players can play for hours without stopping to take a breath. They use a technique called *circular breathing* that lets them inhale through the nose and exhale air stored in their mouths at the same time. With a little practice, maybe you can do it, too.

Social Studies ACTIVITY

Select a country that is in Africa or Asia. Research that country's traditional musical instruments or singing style. Write a description in your **Science Journal** that describes the instruments or singing style of that country. How do they differ from those of the United States? Illustrate your report.

Answer to Language Arts Activity
Answers may vary, but may include exercise, a healthy diet, and not smoking.

Answer to Social Studies Activity
Students' descriptions may vary depending on the country or region, the instrument, and the musical or singing style that the students have selected. Descriptions should be clear, interesting, and informative. Students should provide sources and references and should include illustrations that enhance the description.

People in Science

Anthony Roberts, Jr.

Leader in Training Anthony Roberts, Jr., has asthma. When he was in the fifth grade, his school counselor told him about a summer camp—The Boggy Creek Gang Camp—that was just being built. His counselor said that the camp was designed to serve kids who have asthma or other disabilities and diseases, such as AIDS, cancer, diabetes, epilepsy, hemophilia, heart disease, kidney disease, rheumatic diseases, and sickle cell anemia. These kids might have difficulties at a traditional summer camp. Anthony jumped at the chance to go. Anthony grew too old to be a camper, but he was too young to be a regular counselor. Instead he became a *Leader in Training* (LIT). Some camps have LIT programs that help young people make the transition from camper to counselor.

For Anthony, the chance to be an LIT fit perfectly with his love of camping and with his desire to work with kids with disabilities. Anthony remembers the fun he had and wants to help other kids have the same summer fun he did.

Math ACTIVITY

Research how many children under 17 years of age in the United States have asthma. In your **Science Journal,** make a bar graph that shows how the number of children who have asthma has changed since 1981. What does this graph tell you about rates of asthma among children in the United States?

Internet Resources

- To learn more about careers in science, visit www.scilinks.org and enter the SciLinks code HY70225.

- To learn more about these Science in Action topics, visit go.hrw.com and type in the keyword HY7BD2F.

- Check out articles related to this chapter by visiting go.hrw.com. Just type in the keyword HY7BD2C.

Answer to Math Activity

Students should find that asthma rates for children under the age of 17 have increased from 3.2% in 1981 to 5.7% in 2001. Bar graphs should reflect the growth in the asthma rate from the 1980s to the present. As an extension, students can research the costs associated with asthma in children or the ways in which asthma rates differ between races and genders.

People in Science

Teaching Strategy

If appropriate for your class, begin by talking in a general way about summer vacation. Ask students what they like to do during summer vacation, how they spend their time, whether they go to summer camp (day camp or residence camp), and whether they know of anyone who has asthma or another disability that might make summer camp activities difficult. (Ask students not to reveal the names of these individuals.) Then, discuss the Boggy Creek Gang Camp; Anthony Roberts, Jr.; and his role as a leader in training. Your class may be interested to know that the Boggy Creek Gang Camp is one of the Hole in the Wall camps started by actor Paul Newman. The Hole in the Wall Gang was the outlaw gang of which Butch Cassidy was a member. Newman portrayed Cassidy in the 1969 film *Butch Cassidy and the Sundance Kid.* **LS Auditory**

The elements listed in the Standards Course of Study provide a base for presenting, supporting, and assessing the California Grade 7 Science Standards. Use this Standards Course of Study as a base for planning your lessons.

Why Teach

Communication and Control

This chapter was designed to cover the California Grade 7 Science Standards about the human nervous system (7.5.a, 7.5.b, 7.5.g, and 7.6.b). It is one of four chapters describing the human body systems. This chapter further describes the relationship between human body structures and their functions. It introduces students to the complexity of the human nervous system with a special focus on the eye and ear.

After they complete this chapter, students will begin a chapter about human reproduction and development.

 ## California Standards

Focus on Life Sciences

7.5.a Students know plants and animals have levels of organization for structure and function, including cells, tissues, organs, organ systems, and the whole organism.

7.5.b Students know organ systems function because of the contributions of individual organs, tissues, and cells. The failure of any part can affect the entire system.

7.5.g Students know how to relate the structures of the eye and ear to their functions.

7.6.b Students know that for an object to be seen, light emitted by or scattered from it must be detected by the eye.

Investigation and Experimentation

7.7.a Select and use appropriate tools and technology (including calculators, computers, balances, spring scales, microscopes, and binoculars) to perform tests, collect data, and display data.

Chapter Pacing

Getting Started **45 min** pp. 524–525

The Big Idea The human body has organ systems that respond to its internal and external environments. **7.5.b**

Section ① The Nervous System **90 min** pp. 526–533

Key Concept Your nervous system is an organ system that gathers, interprets, and responds to sensory information.

 7.5.a, 7.5.b, 7.7.d

Section ② Sensing the Environment **90 min** pp. 534–541

Key Concept Your organ systems have specialized structures and functions to sense and gather information.

 7.5.a, 7.5.b, 7.5.g, 7.6.b, 7.7.d

Wrapping Up **180 min** pp. 542–551

7.5.g, 7.7.a

Basic Learners	**Advanced Learners/GATE**
TE Responding to Stimuli, p. 527	TE System Failure, p. 530
TE Science Vocabulary, p. 529	TE Natural Tastes, p. 540
📄 Reinforcement Worksheet	TE Generating Questions, p. 544
📄 Chapter Test A	📄 Critical Thinking Worksheet
📄 Differentiated Datasheets A for Labs and Activities ■	📄 Chapter Test C
📖 Study Guide A ■	📄 Differentiated Datasheets C for Labs and Activities ■

Teach

SE **Explore Activity** Measuring Reaction Time, p. 525*

Bellringer
PowerPoint® Resources
L82 A Typical Neuron
L83 What Is a Nerve?
L84 Areas of the Brain at Work
L85 The Spinal Cord
SE **Quick Lab** Building a Neuron, p. 532*

Bellringer
PowerPoint® Resources
L86 Structure of the Eye
L87 Structure of the Ear
SE **Quick Lab** What Does the Ear Drum Do?, p. 539*

SE **Skills Practice Lab** Dissecting a Cow's Eye, pp. 542–543*

Practice

SE **Organize Activity** Double Door, p. 524

SE **Section Review**, p. 533*

SE **Section Review**, p. 541*

SE **Science Skills Activity** Selecting Tools
to Perform Tests, p. 544*
Concept Mapping*
SE **Chapter Review**, pp. 546–547*

Assess

Chapter Pretest

SE **Standards Checks,** pp. 526, 527, 528,
530, 531, 532
TE **Standards Focus,** p. 532
Section Quiz

SE **Standards Checks,** pp. 534, 535, 536,
537, 539, 540
TE **Standards Focus,** p. 540
Section Quiz

SE **Standards Assessment,** pp. 548–549*
Chapter Tests A, B , C
Standards Review Workbook

Resources for Universal Access • Differentiated Instruction

English Learners
TE Using the Figure, pp. 526, 528
TE Group Activity, pp. 528, 529,
531, 534, 537, 538
TE Connection to Real
World, p. 530
TE Pronunciation, p. 534
TE Multiple Meanings, p. 538
Vocabulary and Section
Summary A , B

Section Quizzes
Chapter Tests A, B
Differentiated Datasheets A, B,
and C for Labs and Activities
Study Guide A
Multilingual Glossary

Struggling Readers
TE Reading Strategy, pp. 527, 530
TE Visual Clues, p. 531
TE Deciphering Questions, p. 544

Special Education Students
TE Tracking the Nervous
System, p. 526
TE Related to You, p. 536

To help plan your lessons,
refer to the On Course
Mapping Instruction booklet.

Visual Resources

CHAPTER STARTER TRANSPARENCY

This Really Happened!

BELLRINGER TRANSPARENCIES

Section: The Nervous System
Write a brief paragraph about what happens to a person when a physician tests the person's reflexes by tapping his or her knee with a rubber mallet.

Write your response in your **science journal.**

Section: Sensing the Environment
Write a few sentences that describe how you think the human eye works.

Write your answers in your **science journal.**

TEACHING TRANSPARENCIES

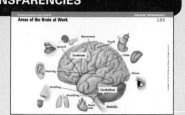

A Typical Neuron — L82

Areas of the Brain at Work — L84

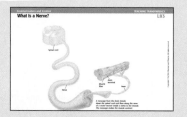 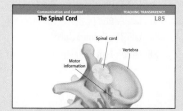

What Is a Nerve? — L83

The Spinal Cord — L85

TEACHING TRANSPARENCIES

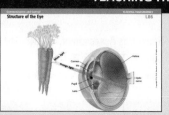 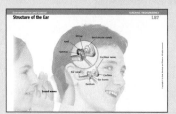

Structure of the Eye — L86

Structure of the Ear — L87

Radiation from the Sun and the Electromagnetic Spectrum

LINK TO EARTH SCIENCE

STANDARDS REVIEW TRANSPARENCIES

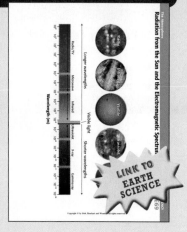

California Science Standard 6.4.e A — Grade 6

6.4.e. Students know differences in pressure, heat, air movement, and humidity result in changes of weather. **SAMPLE**

STANDARD REVIEW

STANDARD PRACTICE

Directions Read each question and circle the letter of the best response.

1. The lines connecting points of equal air pressure on a called

   A contour lines
   B highs
   C isobars
   D lows

ALSO IN SPANISH

CONCEPT MAPPING TRANSPARENCY

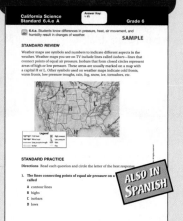

Use the following terms to complete the concept map below:
brain, neurons, medulla, cerebellum, cerebrum, peripheral nerves, dendrites, spinal cord

Planning Resources

PARENT LETTER

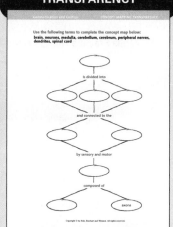

SAMPLE

Dear Parent,

ALSO IN SPANISH

TEST ITEM LISTING

SAMPLE

Holt California Physical Science
Chapter 6 Introduction to Atoms
Test Item Listing
Multiple choice

ALSO IN SPANISH

One-Stop Planner® CD-ROM

This CD-ROM package includes all of the resources shown here and the following time-saving tools:

- **Lab Materials QuickList Software**
- **Customizable Lesson Plans** Correlated to the California Science Standards
- **Holt Calendar Planner**
- **PowerPoint® Resources**

- **Printable Worksheets**
- **ExamView® Test Generator** Correlated to the California Science Standards
- **Holt PuzzlePro®**
- **Interactive Teacher's Edition**

Meeting Individual Needs

DIRECTED READING A

BASIC

ALSO IN SPANISH

DIRECTED READING B

GENERAL

VOCABULARY AND SECTION SUMMARY A

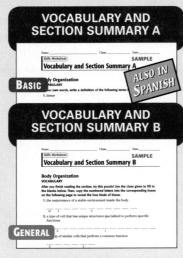

BASIC

ALSO IN SPANISH

VOCABULARY AND SECTION SUMMARY B

GENERAL

REINFORCEMENT

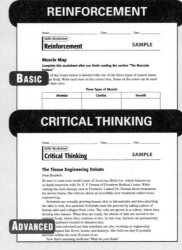

BASIC

CRITICAL THINKING

ADVANCED

INTERACTIVE READER AND STUDY GUIDE

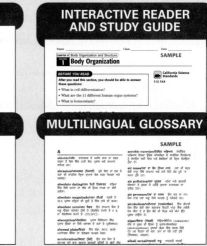

MULTILINGUAL GLOSSARY

Labs and Activities

DIFFERENTIATED DATASHEETS FOR EXPLORE ACTIVITY, QUICK LABS, AND CHAPTER LAB

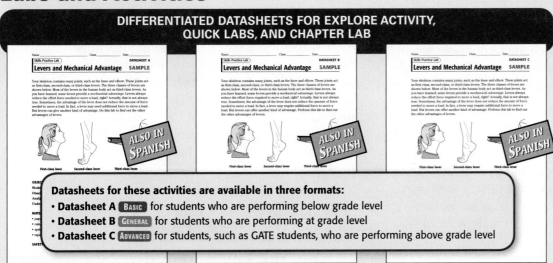

Datasheets for these activities are available in three formats:
- **Datasheet A** **BASIC** for students who are performing below grade level
- **Datasheet B** **GENERAL** for students who are performing at grade level
- **Datasheet C** **ADVANCED** for students, such as GATE students, who are performing above grade level

DATASHEET FOR SCIENCE SKILLS ACTIVITY

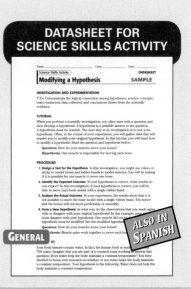

GENERAL

ALSO IN SPANISH

Reviews and Assessments

SECTION REVIEWS

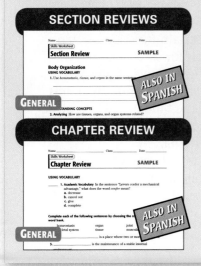

GENERAL

ALSO IN SPANISH

CHAPTER REVIEW

GENERAL

ALSO IN SPANISH

CHAPTER PRETEST

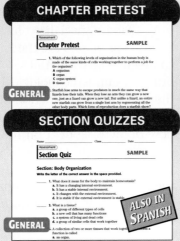

GENERAL

SECTION QUIZZES

GENERAL

ALSO IN SPANISH

CHAPTER TEST A

BASIC

CHAPTER TEST B

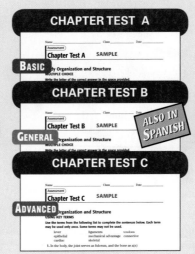

GENERAL

ALSO IN SPANISH

CHAPTER TEST C

ADVANCED

STANDARDS ASSESSMENT

GENERAL

STANDARDS REVIEW WORKBOOK

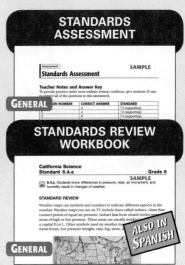

GENERAL

ALSO IN SPANISH

This Teacher Background explains science concepts, principles, and theories that appear in the chapter. Use the information on these pages to refresh or enhance your understanding of the topics covered.

Section 1

The Nervous System

The Brain

An adult human brain, shown in **Figure A,** weighs between 1 and 1.5 kg (about three pounds). The surface area of the brain is about 1,500 cm^2 to 2,000 cm^2, or about the surface area of one to two pages of a newspaper. To fit within the skull, the cortex is folded, forming gyri (folds) and sulci (grooves).

The brain can be divided into several areas, each of which is responsible for a variety of specific functions. Most scientists divide the brain into three areas: forebrain, midbrain, and hindbrain. These three areas are divided into smaller parts, which are responsible for different functions. Although there are several smaller subdivisions of the brain, this discussion focuses mainly on four parts: the cerebrum, diencephalon, cerebellum, and brain stem.

The forebrain houses the largest part of the brain, the cerebrum. The cerebrum rests on the top of the brain. The cerebrum is heavily grooved and folded, and the pattern of the gyri and sulci varies from person to person. The cerebral cortex is the outermost layer of the cerebrum and is loosely divided into four regions or lobes.

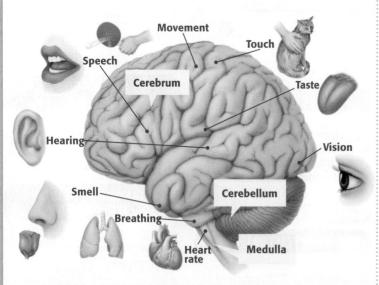

Figure A *The different areas of the brain are responsible for performing different functions.*

The front section of the cerebrum is known as the frontal lobe and is responsible for skilled movements, emotion, thought, and speech. The parietal lobe is located just behind the frontal lobe and is the part of the brain that interprets signals for touch, pain, and temperature. The occipital lobe is located at the back of the brain and is responsible for most visual processing. The temporal lobe is located below the parietal lobe and is responsible for memory storage, hearing, and object-level vision.

The diencephalon is part of the midbrain and is located beneath the middle of the cerebrum and on top of the brain stem. The diencephalon houses two important structures known as the thalamus and the hypothalamus. The thalamus receives incoming sensory signals (except smell, which bypass the thalamus) in sense-specific regions and relays them to the cerebrum for processing. The hypothalamus plays a role in homeostasis; it is responsible for regulating body temperature, sensing hunger and thirst, and controlling the release of hormones from the pituitary gland.

The hindbrain houses the second largest part of the brain, the cerebellum. The cerebellum lies underneath the back of the cerebrum and is responsible for muscle coordination, posture, and balance. Also located in the hindbrain is the brain stem. The brain stem includes the medulla, and it is the part of the brain which controls several life-supporting systems, including blood pressure, heart rate, respiration, and digestion. The brain stem also regulates the sleep cycle.

Section 2

Sensing the Environment

Structure and Function of the Eye

The complementary nature of structure and function is widely evident in the biological sciences. By way of evolutionary processes, organisms have developed structures that are specialized for certain functions. Often, physical principles are the basis for structures and their complementary functions. One example of how physical principles underlie biological structure and function is the structure and function of the human eye. The structure of the human eye is well-suited to the primary purpose of focusing light on the retina.

Before reaching the retina, light passes through a number of transparent components of the eye, including the cornea, the aqueous humor, the pupil of the iris, the lens, and the vitreous humor.

For background information about teaching strategies and issues, refer to the
Professional Reference for Teachers.

The cornea is a clear membrane that both protects the eye and allows light to enter. The cornea has a fixed curvature that allows for light refraction. The aqueous humor, a clear fluid, fills the space between the cornea and the lens. It also helps maintain the convex shape of the cornea, which in turn allows for the convergence of light rays at the lens. The iris is a colored ring of muscles found between the aqueous humor and the lens. The pupil is the round opening in the center of the iris; light must travel through the pupil in order to reach the lens. The lens is a convex disk which focuses light through the vitreous humor (a gel-like substance allowing light to pass without refraction) onto the retina.

The cornea and lens refract light in the same manner as a convex glass lens, causing parellel light rays to converge. Convex glass lens are often used in cameras, telescopes, magnifying glasses, and physics labs. The majority of the refraction in the eye is performed by the cornea. The lens can change shape (which changes the amount of refraction) in order to focus near or far objects. The image formed on the retina is a result of the constant refraction of the cornea and the variable refraction of the lens.

Sense of Hearing

Another example of the complementary nature of structure and function in biology is the anatomical structure and function of the human ear. The structure of the human ear, as shown in **Figure B,** is directly related to its function, which is to detect and interpret sound waves. The human ear can be separated into three parts: the outer ear, the middle ear, and the inner ear.

The external portion of the ear is the outer ear. The visible part of the ear is known as the pinna, and it is shaped to detect and focus sound waves. Sound waves move from the pinna into the ear canal, the tube that runs from the pinna to the middle ear.

The middle ear contains the eardrum, or tympanum, and three tiny bones: the malleus, incus, and stapes. These bones, or ossicles, are more commonly known as the hammer, anvil, and stirrup. The eardrum transfers vibrations of air detected by the outer ear into vibrations of the ossicles. The ossicles then transmit these vibrations into the inner ear.

The inner ear is composed of the cochlea (responsible for hearing) and the vestibular apparatus (responsible for balance). The cochlea is a hollow, spiral and cone-shaped bone filled with fluid which receives the sound vibrations from the middle ear. Auditory information from the inner ear is transmitted to the brain via the auditory nerves.

Information is transmitted along sensory nerves (and most other neurons) by nerve impulses known as action potentials. The action potential is an electrochemical impulse that travels down the axon of a nerve cell. This impulse does not travel as fast as standard electrical current, but instead moves between about 0.2 to 150 m/s, depending on the properties of the axon. Between sensory organs and the brain, sensory information is passed through a series of neurons. Information carried by action potentials is transmitted between neurons by means of a structure called the synapse. In a typical synapse, an ending of the axon (an "axon terminal") of one neuron lies next to the dendrite of a second neuron. The arrival of an action potential at the axon terminal of the first neuron leads to the release of a chemical transmitter into the gap between the cells. The chemical transmitter is detected by the dendrite, and may result in the generation of an action potential in the second neuron.

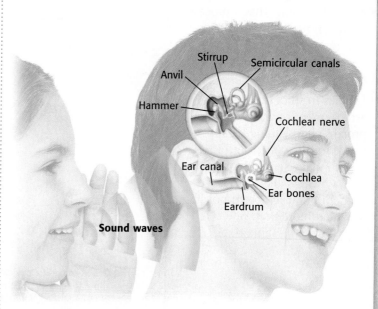

Figure B *The structures of the ear are each responsible for performing specific functions.*

Internet Resources

SciLinks is maintained by the National Science Teachers Association to provide you and your students with interesting, up-to-date links that will enrich your classroom presentation of the chapter.

Visit **www.scilinks.org** and enter the SciLinks code for more information about the topic listed.

Topic: Nervous System
SciLinks code: HY71023

Topic: The Senses
SciLinks code: HY71378

Topic: The Eye
SciLinks code: HY70560

17 Chapter Preview

Improving Comprehension

Use the Graphic Organizer on this page of the Student Edition to introduce the topics that are covered in this chapter, to summarize the chapter material, or to show students how to make a process chart.

Teaching Tips

- Remind students that a process chart can represent anything that is a process, such as a timeline, a list of steps, a chain of events, or a cycle.

- Explain to students that the arrangement of the boxes in a process chart should be appropriate for the content and should make sense. Explain that a process chart can have branches that represent points at which more than one event happens at the same time.

LS Logical

Improving Comprehension

Graphic Organizers are important visual tools that can help you organize information and improve your reading comprehension. The Graphic Organizer below is called a *process chart*. Instructions for creating other types of Graphic Organizers are located in the **Study Skills** section of the Appendix.

How to Make a Process Chart

① Draw a box. In the box, write the first step of a process, chain of events, or cycle.

② Under the box, draw another box, and draw an arrow to connect the two boxes. In the second box, write the next step of the process or the next event in the timeline.

③ Continue adding boxes until each step of the process, chain of events, or cycle is written in a box. For cycles only, draw an arrow to connect the last box and the first box.

When to Use a Process Chart

Science is full of processes. A process chart shows the steps that a process takes to get from one point to another point. Timelines, chains of events, and cycles are examples of the kinds of information that can be organized well in a process chart. As you read, look for information that is described in steps or in a sequence, and draw a process chart that shows the progression of the steps or sequence.

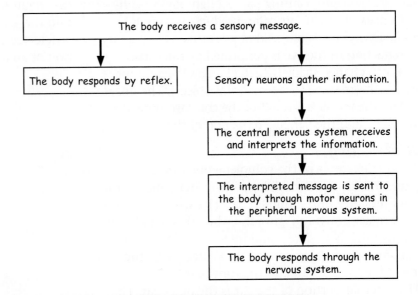

You Try It!

This Reading Strategy can also be used within the chapter that you are about to read. Practice making your own *process chart* as directed in the Reading Strategy for Section ②. Record your work in your **Science Journal.**

Using Other Graphic Organizers

Students can practice using a variety of Graphic Organizers while reading this chapter. The following Graphic Organizers may also be useful in this chapter.

A **concept map** can be used to show how concepts and terms related to neurons are connected, discussed in Section 1. A **concept map** also can be used to show how concepts and terms related to the peripheral nervous system are connected, described in Section 1.

An **idea wheel** can be used to organize details about the parts of the brain, discussed in Section 1.

Instructions for creating these Graphic Organizers are located on pp. 583–591 of the Appendix.

Unpacking the Standards

The information below "unpacks" the standards by breaking them down into basic parts. The higher-level, academic vocabulary is highlighted and defined to help you understand the language of the standards. "What It Means" restates the standards as simply as possible.

Unpacking the Standards

Use the following information with the *What It Means* in the Student Edition to help students understand why studying each standard is important.

California Standard	Academic Vocabulary	What It Means	Why It Matters
7.5.a Students know plants and animals have levels of organization for **structure** and **function,** including cells, tissues, organs, organ systems, and the whole organism.	**structure** (STRUHK chuhr) the arrangement of the parts of a whole **function** (FUHNGK shuhn) use or purpose	Plants and animals are made of smaller parts which are organized by shape and purpose. These layers of organization include cells, tissues, organs, organ systems, and the whole organism.	Multicellular organisms, including humans, function because their cells are organized at many levels. Each subsequent level of organization has unique properties that the prior level of organization does not have.
7.5.b Students know organ systems **function** because of the **contributions** of **individual** organs, tissues, and cells. The failure of any part can **affect** the entire system.	**function** (FUHNGK shuhn) to work **contribution** (KAHN truh BYOO shuhn) a part given toward a whole **individual** (IN duh VIJ oo uhl) being a single, separate entity; particular **affect** (uh FEKT) to change; to have an effect on; to influence	An organ system is able to work because of the work that each of its smaller parts (organs, tissues, and cells) does. If any part of an organ system fails to work well, the entire system is changed.	Organ systems within an organism are interrelated. When one part of a multicellular organism fails to perform its function, the entire organism is affected.
7.5.g Students know how to relate the **structures** of the eye and ear to their **functions.**		You must know how the shapes of the eye and the ear are related to the roles of these parts in the body.	Understanding the relationship between structure and function in human eyes and ears helps scientists heal damaged eyes and ears.
7.6.b Students know that for an object to be seen, light emitted by or scattered from it must be **detected** by the eye.	**detect** (dee TEKT) to notice	For you to see an object, the light that is given off by an object or that bounces off an object must enter your eye.	Before one receives visual stimuli from an object, light must be emitted or scattered by the object.

Words with Multiple Meanings

Words that have both common and scientific meanings can be confusing to students. The following table identifies some of those words that are used in this chapter.

Term	Common meaning	Scientific meaning
nervous	feeling worried or frightened	relating to the nerves, the collection of nerve fibers through which impulses travel
sympathetic	feeling sorry for; feeling pity or compassion	describing a part of the autonomic nervous system, which controls involuntary functions

Practice Have students define the following words: *nervous* and *sympathetic*. Then, give students the definitions for the scientific meanings of these terms. (These definitions can be found in the glossary of this book.) Have students write sentences that use the common meanings of these words. Then, have students write sentences that use the scientific meanings of the words.

Chapter Overview

In this chapter, students will learn about the nervous system and how the body responds to its environment. Students will learn about the relationship of structure and function in the human eye and ear. They will also learn how the human body uses specialized organs for sight, hearing, taste, and smell.

MISCONCEPTION ALERT

Nervous System Function

Identify It! Because students are most often reacting to a stimulus to the skin, they may think the nervous system functions only at the level of the skin. Ask students to identify what they think the nervous system does for them. (Students may answer that the nervous system is responsible for the sense of touch or of "feeling" things.)

Correct It! Help students understand in a general way that the nervous system function has several levels: the skin, which works together with other body systems, such as the muscles, to help the body respond to its environment. Ask students to explain how they know that they are hungry or what the role of the nervous system is with aches and pains, such as toothaches, headaches, and fevers.

Assess It! Ask groups of students to brainstorm and create a list of what might happen if the skin could not "sense" what it touched. (Sample answer: not being able to distinguish between hot and cold and, as a result, getting burned; not knowing when to move away from something harmful)

Communication and Control

The Big Idea The human body has organ systems that respond to its internal and external environments.

 California Standards

Focus on Life Sciences
7.5 The anatomy and physiology of plants and animals illustrate the complementary nature of structure and function. (Sections 1 and 2)
7.6 Physical principles underlie biological structures and functions. (Section 2)

Investigation and Experimentation
7.7 Scientific progress is made by asking meaningful questions and conducting careful investigations. (Science Skills Activity)

Math
7.1.1 Algebra and Functions
7.2.1, 7.2.8 Mathematical Reasoning

English–Language Arts
7.1.3 Reading
7.2.5 Writing

About the Photo

This picture may look like it shows a flower garden or a coral reef. But it really shows something much closer to home. It shows the human tongue (magnified thousands of times, of course). Both the large red bumps and the smaller pink bumps are papillae (puh PIL ee), which contain the taste buds. You use taste and other senses to gather information about your surroundings.

Organize

Double Door
Before you read this chapter, create the FoldNote entitled "Double Door." Write "The nervous system" on one flap of the double door and "Sensing the environment" on the other flap. As you read the chapter, compare the two topics, and write characteristics of each topic on the inside of the appropriate flap.

Instructions for creating FoldNotes are located in the Study Skills section on p. 579 of the Appendix.

 California Standards Alignment

Focus on Life Sciences

7.5.a Students know plants and animals have levels of organization for structure and function, including cells, tissues, organs, organ systems, and the whole organism. **pp. 526–527, 530, 532–536, 540–541, 546–548**

7.5.b Students know organ systems function because of the contributions of individual organs, tissues, and cells. The failure of any part can affect the entire system. **pp. 525–535, 540–541, 546–548**

7.5.g Students know how to relate the structures of the eye and ear to their functions. **pp. 536–539, 541–543, 546–549**

7.6.b Students know that for an object to be seen, light emitted by or scattered from it must be detected by the eye. **pp. 536–537, 541, 547–549**

Investigation and Experimentation

7.7.a Select and use appropriate tools and technology (including calculators, computers, balances, spring scales, microscopes, and binoculars) to perform tests, collect data, and display data. **pp. 542–543, 544**

Math Standards

Algebra and Functions 7.1.1 Use variables and appropriate operations to write an expression, an equation, an inequality, or a system of equations or inequalities that represents a verbal description (e.g., three less than a number, half as large as area A). **p. 541**

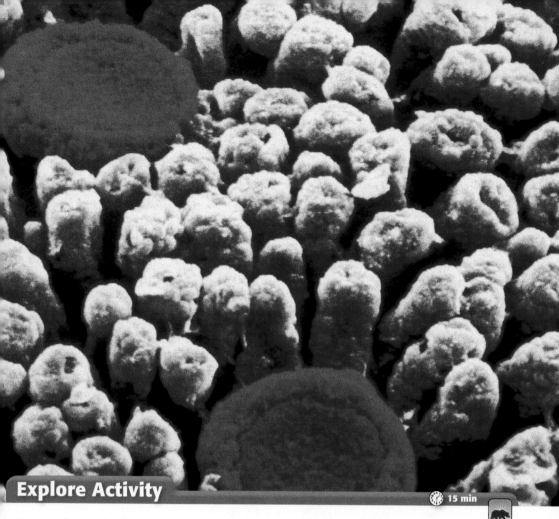

Explore Activity

Measuring Reaction Time

If you want to catch an object, your brain sends a message to the muscles in your arm. In this exercise, you will see how long sending that message takes.

Procedure

1. Sit in a **chair** with one of your arms in a "handshake" position. A partner should stand facing you and should hold a **meterstick** vertically. Position the stick to fall between your thumb and fingers.

2. Tell your partner to let go of the meterstick without warning you. Catch the stick between your thumb and fingers. Your partner should catch the meterstick if it tips over.

3. Record the number of centimeters that the stick dropped before you caught it. That distance represents your reaction time.

4. Repeat steps 1–3 three times. Calculate the average distance.

5. Repeat steps 1–4 with your other hand.

6. Trade places with your partner, and repeat steps 1–5.

⏱ 15 min

7.5.b

Analysis

7. Compare your results with your partner's. Why may one person react more quickly than another?

8. In this activity, how are your muscles and your brain working together? Be specific.

Mathematical Reasoning 7.2.1 Use estimation to verify the reasonableness of calculated results. **p. 547**

Mathematical Reasoning 7.2.8 Make precise calculations and check the validity of the results from the context of the problem. **p. 529**

English–Language Arts Standards

Reading 7.1.3. Clarify word meaning through the use of definition, example, restatement, or contrast. **p. 526**

Writing 7.2.5 Write summaries of reading materials: Include the main ideas and most significant details. Use the student's own words, except for quotations. Reflect underlying meaning, not just the superficial details. **p. 547**

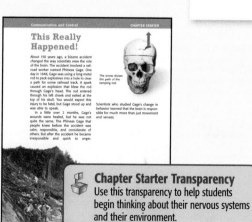

Chapter Starter Transparency
Use this transparency to help students begin thinking about their nervous systems and their environment.

Explore Activity

⏱ 15 min

Teacher Notes

This activity allows students to investigate reaction time (covers standard 7.5.b). Allow students a practice trial. Instruct students to look only at the ruler and not at their partner. Point out that looking at their partner could distort the results of the investigation, because the partner might give a clue about when he or she will drop the meterstick.

Materials for Each Group
- chair
- meterstick

Safety Caution

Remind students to handle the meterstick carefully and to keep it away from their face and far away from the faces and eyes of their classmates.

Answers

7. Accept all reasonable answers. One person might respond faster than another depending on how rested that person is, how well the person uses his or her right and left hands, and how well the person can concentrate on an activity.

8. Sample answer: My brain is telling my muscles when to contract and grab the stick. My brain is using information that I gather with my eyes to decide when to grab the stick.

📋 Differentiated Datasheets
A **BASIC**, B **GENERAL**, C **ADVANCED**

Also editable on the Holt Lab Generator CD-ROM

Preteach

Reviewing Prior Knowledge

Ask student volunteers to read and review the red heads in the section aloud. Then, ask students what they think the section is about. Finally, ask students what they already know about the nervous system.

 Bellringer

Have students focus on standard 7.5.b by asking them to write a brief paragraph about what happens when a physician tests a person's reflexes by tapping his or her knee with a rubber mallet.

Bellringer Transparency

Motivate

Discussion

Reacting to Stimuli   Ask students to describe a time when they reacted quickly to something. Have them describe what happened, how quickly they reacted, and what they thought as they reacted. (Sample answers: jerking a hand away from a hot object, quickly catching a falling object.) 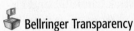 **Intrapersonal**

Using the Figure

Teamwork   Have students examine **Figure 1.** Then, use the question in the caption as the starting point for a discussion about how the nervous system functions. (Answer to caption question: The PNS connects all parts of the body to the CNS.) **Verbal**

Answer to Standards Check

The CNS processes and responds to messages from the PNS. The PNS transmits information to the CNS.

7.5.a (supporting)

What You Will Learn

- The central nervous system processes and responds to all messages coming from the peripheral nervous system.
- The somatic nervous system controls voluntary movements. The autonomic nervous system controls functions that are involuntary.
- The brain is made of many parts that function together as the control center of the nervous system.

Why It Matters

Without a nervous system, you would not be able to sense or respond to your environment.

Vocabulary

- central nervous system
- peripheral nervous system
- neuron
- nerve
- brain

READING STRATEGY

Clarifying Concepts   Take turns reading this section out loud with a partner. Stop to discuss ideas that seem confusing.

7.5.a Students know plants and animals have levels of organization for structure and function, including cells, tissues, organs, organ systems, and the whole organism.
7.5.b Students know organ systems function because of the contributions of individual organs, tissues, and cells. The failure of any part can affect the entire system.

The Nervous System

Key Concept   Your nervous system is an organ system that gathers, interprets, and responds to sensory information.

▶ What is one thing that you have done today that did NOT involve your nervous system? This is a trick question! In fact, your nervous system controls almost everything that you do.

Two Systems Within a System

The nervous system acts as the body's central command post. It has two basic functions. First, it gathers and interprets information. This information comes from inside your body and from the world outside your body. Then, the nervous system responds to that information as needed.

The nervous system has two parts: the central nervous system and the peripheral nervous system. The **central nervous system** (CNS) is the brain and spinal cord. The CNS processes and responds to all messages coming from the peripheral nervous system. The **peripheral nervous system** (PNS) includes all of the parts of the nervous system except for the brain and the spinal cord. The PNS connects all parts of the body to the CNS. The PNS uses specialized structures called *nerves* to carry information between your body and your CNS. **Figure 1** shows the major divisions of the nervous system.

Standards Check   Describe the difference between the function of the CNS and the function of the PNS.   **7.5.a**

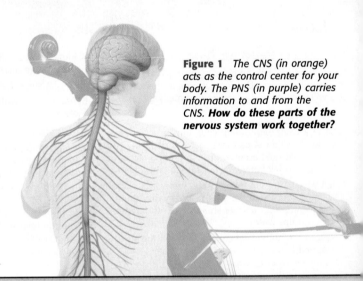

Figure 1   The CNS (in orange) acts as the control center for your body. The PNS (in purple) carries information to and from the CNS. **How do these parts of the nervous system work together?**

Universal Access · Differentiated Instruction

Special Education Students

Tracking the Nervous System   Pair students who have visual impairments with full-sighted students. Have full-sighted students look at **Figure 1** and use rulers to gently track the path of the CNS on their partners' backs. Ask students to trace both the spinal cord and the PNS radiating out from the spinal cord. Ask partners to reverse positions and repeat the process. **Kinesthetic**

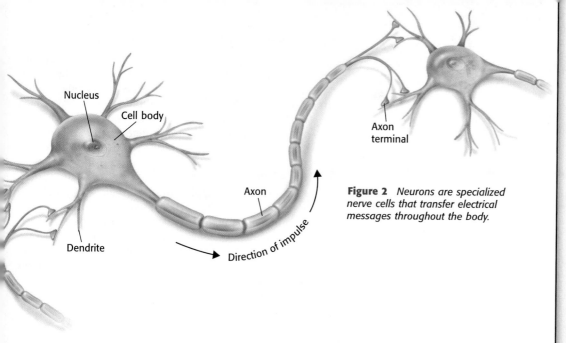

Nucleus

Cell body

Axon terminal

Axon

Dendrite

Direction of impulse

Figure 2 *Neurons are specialized nerve cells that transfer electrical messages throughout the body.*

The Peripheral Nervous System

Messages about your environment travel through the nervous system along neurons. A **neuron** is a nerve cell that is specialized to transfer messages in the form of fast-moving electrical energy. These electrical messages are called *impulses*. Impulses may travel as fast as 150 m/s or as slow as 0.2 m/s. **Figure 2** shows a typical neuron transferring an impulse.

Neuron Structure

In many ways, a neuron is similar to other cells. A neuron has a large region called the *cell body*. The cell body has a nucleus and cell organelles. But neurons also have special structures called *dendrites* and *axons*. Dendrites are usually short, branched extensions of the cell. A neuron receives information from other cells through its dendrites. A neuron may have many dendrites, which allows it to receive impulses from thousands of other cells.

Impulses are carried away from the cell body by axons. Axons are elongated extensions of a neuron. They can be very short or quite long. Some long axons extend almost 1 m from your lower back to your toes. The end of an axon often has branches that allow information to pass to other cells. The tip of each branch is called an *axon terminal*.

Standards Check In your own words, describe the structure of a neuron. 📖 **7.5.a**

central nervous system
(SEN trahl NUHR vuhs SIS tuhm) the brain and the spinal cord

peripheral nervous system
(puh RIF uhr uhl NUHR vuhs SIS tuhm) all of the parts of the nervous system except for the brain and the spinal cord
Wordwise The root *peri-* means "around" or "near." The root *pher-* means "to bear" or "to go."

neuron (NOO RAHN) a nerve cell that is specialized to receive and conduct electrical impulses

Simulating Neuron Impulses
Form a circle and hold hands. Explain that each person in the circle represents a neuron. Every left hand represents a dendrite, every body represents a cell body, and every right hand represents an axon. Join the circle, and initiate a nerve impulse by gently squeezing the hand of the student to your right. Instruct students to pass the nerve impulse to the person on their right by gently squeezing his or her hand. Once students understand the mechanics of the activity, have them call out *dendrite, cell body,* and *axon* as the impulse is passed along. **LS** Kinesthetic/Interpersonal Co-op Learning

Using the Figure

Following an Impulse Ask students to imagine that an electrical impulse is sent from the brain along neurons, similar to the one shown in **Figure 2** on the previous page, and along a nerve as shown in **Figure 3**. Discuss with students the path of the impulse from the brain, along the neuron to the spinal cord, and then along the nerve to the muscle. Draw a diagram on the board or have students trace the path using **Figures 2** and **3**. Then, ask students to predict what will happen in the muscle next. (The muscle will move and special receptors called proprioceptors will send a message back to the brain to identify the muscle's new location.) **LS** Logical

Teaching Transparency:
L83 What Is a Nerve?

Sensory Neurons: Collecting Information

Remember that neurons are a type of nerve cell that carries impulses. Some neurons are *sensory neurons*. These neurons gather information about what is happening in and around your body. They have specialized nerve endings called *receptors*. Receptors detect changes inside and outside the body. For example, receptors in your eyes detect light. Sensory neurons then send this information to the CNS for processing.

Motor Neurons: Delivering Orders

Neurons that send impulses from the brain and spinal cord to other systems are called *motor neurons*. When muscles get impulses from motor neurons, the muscles respond by contracting. For example, motor neurons cause muscles around your eyes to contract when you are in bright light. These muscles make you squint so that less light enters your eyes. Motor neurons also send messages to glands, such as sweat glands. These messages tell sweat glands when to make sweat.

Nerves

The central nervous system is connected to the rest of your body by nerves. A **nerve** is a collection of axons bundled together with blood vessels and connective tissue. Nerves are found everywhere in your PNS. Most nerves have axons of both sensory neurons and motor neurons. Axons are parts of nerves, but nerves are more than simply axons. **Figure 3** shows the structure of a nerve. The axon in this nerve transmits information from the spinal cord to muscle fibers.

Standards Check What would happen if your nerves stopped working? **7.5.b**

nerve (NUHRV) a collection of nerve fibers through which impulses travel between the central nervous system and other parts of the body

Spinal cord

Nerve

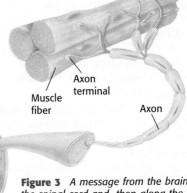

Muscle fiber

Axon terminal

Axon

Figure 3 *A message from the brain travels down the spinal cord and then along the axon of a motor neuron inside a nerve to the muscle. The message makes the muscle contract.*

Answer to Standards Check

If your nerves stopped working, information gathered by your senses would not be sent to your brain. **7.5.b** (mastering)

Somatic and Autonomic Nervous Systems

Remember, the peripheral nervous system (PNS) connects the central nervous system (CNS) to the rest of the body. And the PNS includes two main kinds of neurons: sensory neurons and motor neurons. You know that sensory neurons collect information from your senses and send that information to the CNS. You also know that motor neurons carry out the CNS's responses to that sensory information. The PNS has two types of motor neurons to carry out these responses: somatic neurons and autonomic neurons.

Somatic Nervous System

Most of the neurons that are part of the *somatic nervous system* are under your conscious control. These neurons stimulate skeletal muscles. So, the neurons control voluntary movements, such as writing, talking, smiling, or jumping.

Autonomic Nervous System

Autonomic neurons do not need your conscious control. These neurons are part of the autonomic nervous system. The *autonomic nervous system* controls body functions that you do not think about, such as digestion and heart rate (the number of times that your heart beats per minute).

The main job of the autonomic nervous system is to keep all of the body's functions in balance. Depending on the situation, the autonomic nervous system can speed up or slow down these functions. The autonomic nervous system has two divisions: the *sympathetic nervous system* and the *parasympathetic nervous system*. These two divisions work together to maintain a stable internal state, called *homeostasis*. **Table 1** shows some effects of these divisions.

Table 1	Effects of the Autonomic Nervous System on the Body	
Organ	**Effect of sympathetic division**	**Effect of parasympathetic division**
Eyes	dilates (enlarges) pupils; making seeing objects easier	constricts pupils; makes vision normal
Heart	increases heart rate; increases blood flow	slows heart rate; slows blood flow
Lungs	dilates (enlarges) bronchioles; increases oxygen in blood	constricts bronchioles
Blood vessels	constricts blood vessels; increases blood pressure	has little or no effect
Intestines	slows digestion; reduces blood flow to stomach and intestines	returns digestion to normal

MATH PRACTICE

Time to Travel

To calculate how long an impulse takes to travel a certain distance, you can use the following equation:

$$time = \frac{distance}{speed}$$

If an impulse travels 100 m/s, about how long will it take the impulse to travel 10 m? Record your work in your **Science Journal.**

Teach, *continued*

Anticipation Guide Before students read about the central nervous system, ask them whether the following statements are true or false.

1. The brain is the body's largest organ. (false)

2. The largest part of the brain is the cerebrum. (true)

3. The medulla is responsible for speech and balance. (false)

4. The spinal cord is about as big around as your thumb. (true)

Have students evaluate their answers after they have read this section. **LS** Verbal

Connection To *Real World*

Nerve Block Sometimes it isn't possible to inject anesthetic into a part of the body that needs to be anesthetized. In these cases, a nerve block is performed. In this procedure, anesthetic is injected into or around a nerve that serves the body part that needs to be anesthetized. Have students research nerve block anesthesia to create a pamphlet or brochure that explains the procedure to a patient who may need it. Students may also do this activity in groups. Part of the group can perform the research about nerve block, while the other part of the group can create the brochure. **LS** Verbal **Co-op Learning**

Answer to Standards Check

The brain is the main control center of the nervous system. It is responsible for controlling both voluntary and involuntary actions. **7.5.a** (mastering)

The Central Nervous System

The central nervous system receives information from the sensory neurons. Then, the CNS responds by sending messages to the body through motor neurons in the PNS.

The Brain

The largest organ in the nervous system is the brain. The **brain** is the main control center of the nervous system. Many processes that the brain controls happen automatically. These processes are *involuntary*. For example, you could not stop digesting food even if you tried. On the other hand, some actions controlled by your brain are *voluntary*. When you want to move your arm, your brain sends signals along motor neurons to muscles in your arm. Then, the muscles contract, and your arm moves. The brain has three main parts: the cerebrum (suh REE bruhm), the cerebellum (SER uh BEL uhm), and the medulla (mi DUHL uh). Each part has its own job.

Standards Check What is the brain's function in the nervous system? Describe what the brain controls. 🔊 **7.5.a**

The Cerebrum

The largest part of your brain is called the *cerebrum*. It looks like a mushroom cap. This dome-shaped area is where you think and where most memories are stored. The cerebrum controls voluntary movements. It also allows you to sense touch, light, sound, odors, taste, pain, heat, and cold.

The cerebrum is made up of two halves, called *hemispheres*. The left hemisphere directs the right side of the body, and the right hemisphere directs the left side of the body. **Figure 4** shows some of the activities that each hemisphere controls. However, most brain activities use both hemispheres.

brain (BRAYN) the organ that is the main control center of the nervous system

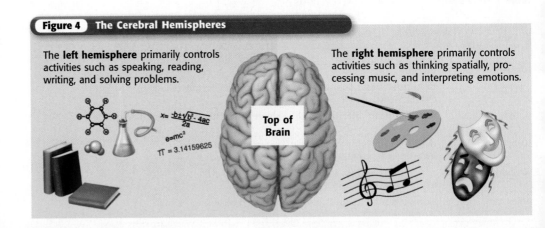

Figure 4 **The Cerebral Hemispheres**

The **left hemisphere** primarily controls activities such as speaking, reading, writing, and solving problems.

$$x = \frac{-b \pm \sqrt{b^2 - 4ac}}{2a}$$

$$e = mc^2$$

$$\pi = 3.14159625$$

Top of Brain

The **right hemisphere** primarily controls activities such as thinking spatially, processing music, and interpreting emotions.

Universal Access • Differentiated Instruction

Advanced Learners/GATE

System Failure Challenge students by asking them to explain how a failure of a system can illustrate how the system works. For example, have students select a disorder or disease of the nervous system (such as meningitis or cerebral palsy). Then have them answer the following questions:

1. What causes the disorder or disease?

2. What symptoms does a person with the disorder or disease have?

3. Are there any treatments for the disorder or disease, and if so, what are they?

Finally, have students try to answer the following question: "How does the disorder or disease illustrate how the nervous system works?" **LS** Verbal

The Cerebellum

The second-largest part of your brain is the *cerebellum*. It lies beneath the back of the cerebrum. The cerebellum processes sensory information from your body, such as from skeletal muscles and joints. This information allows the brain to keep track of the body's position. Look at the girl in **Figure 5.** If she begins to lose her balance, her cerebellum sends impulses telling skeletal muscles to contract. Those muscles shift her weight and keep her from losing her balance.

The Medulla

The *medulla* is the part of your brain that connects to your spinal cord. The medulla is about 3 cm long, and you can not live without it. The medulla controls involuntary processes, such as involuntary breathing and the regulation of blood pressure and heart rate.

Your medulla constantly receives sensory impulses from receptors in your blood vessels. It uses this information to regulate your blood pressure. If your blood pressure gets too low, the medulla sends out impulses that tell blood vessels to tighten up. As a result, blood pressure rises. The medulla also sends impulses to the heart to make the heart beat faster or slower. **Figure 6** shows the locations of the three main parts of the brain and some of the functions of each part.

Standards Check Explain why the medulla is important. 7.5.b

Figure 5 *Your cerebellum causes skeletal muscles to make adjustments so that you will stay upright.*

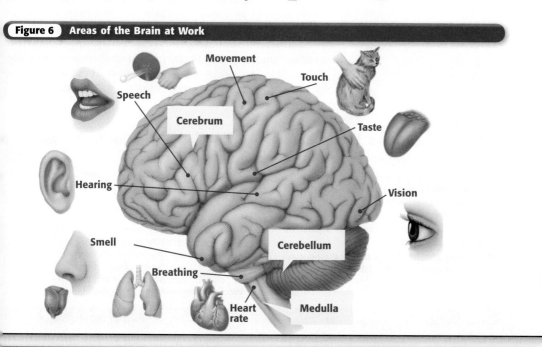

Figure 6 Areas of the Brain at Work

Movement · Touch · Speech · Cerebrum · Taste · Hearing · Smell · Breathing · Heart rate · Cerebellum · Medulla · Vision

Standards Focus

This **Standards Focus** provides you with a quick way to **assess, reteach,** and **re-assess** one or more concepts in the section.

Assess

1. What are the three parts of the human brain, and which is the largest? (Sample answer: The cerebrum is the largest part. The other two parts are the cerebellum and the brainstem.) **7.5.a**

2. What are the components of the central nervous system? (brain and spinal cord) **7.5.a**

3. What does the peripheral nervous system do? (Sample answer: The PNS is the connector and messenger between the CNS and all parts of the body.) **7.5.b**

Reteach

Spinal Injury Have students discuss in groups the dangers of spinal injury. Have the groups make presentations showing steps to prevent the body from sports-related spinal injury.
LS Verbal/Visual **7.5.b**

Re-Assess

Owner's Guide Have students develop a CNS owner's guide including information about the various parts of the CNS and a diagram showing their location. Encourage students to share their guide with the class by giving a presentation. **LS** Verbal **7.5.b**

📁 Teaching Transparency:
L85 The Spinal Cord

Answer to Standards Check

Sensory neurons in skin send impulses along their axons to the spinal cord. The spinal cord relays these messages to the brain. The brain sends impulses along the spinal cord to the motor neurons and muscles. **7.5.a** (supporting)

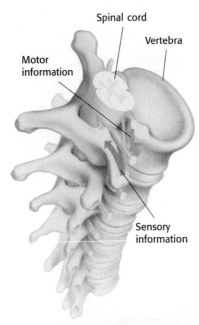

Figure 7 *The spinal cord carries information to and from the brain. Vertebrae protect the spinal cord.*

The Spinal Cord

Your spinal cord, which is part of your central nervous system, is about as big around as your thumb. The spinal cord is made of neurons and bundles of axons that pass impulses to and from the brain. As shown in **Figure 7,** the spinal cord is surrounded by protective bones called *vertebrae* (VUHR tuh BRAY).

The axons in your spinal cord allow your brain to communicate with your PNS. The axons of sensory neurons in your skin and muscles carry impulses to your spinal cord. The spinal cord relays these impulses to your brain. The brain interprets these impulses as pain, temperature, or other sensations. Then, the brain responds to the situation. Impulses moving from the brain down the spinal cord are relayed to motor neurons. The axons of motor neurons carry the impulses to muscles and glands all over your body.

Standards Check Describe the path of an impulse from the skin to the brain and the path of the response. **7.5.a**

Spinal Cord Injury

A spinal cord injury may block all information to and from the brain. Sensory information coming from below the injury may not get to the brain. For example, a spinal cord injury may block all sensory impulses from the feet and legs. People who have such an injury can not sense pain, touch, or temperature with their feet. And motor commands from the brain to the injured area may not reach the peripheral nerves. So, the person may not be able to move his or her legs.

Each year, thousands of people are paralyzed by spinal cord injuries. Among young people, spinal cord injuries are sometimes related to sports or other activities. These injuries may be prevented by wearing proper safety equipment.

Quick Lab

Building a Neuron

1. Your teacher will provide **at least four colors of modeling clay.** Build a model of a neuron by using various colors of clay for the various parts of the neuron.

2. Use **tape** to attach your model to a **piece of plain white paper.**

3. On the paper, label each part of the neuron. Draw an arrow from the label to the part.

4. Use a **colored pencil, marker,** or **crayon** to draw arrows showing the path of an impulse traveling in your neuron. Tell whether the impulse is a sensory impulse or a motor impulse. Then, describe what will happen when the impulse reaches its destination.

7.5.a
7.7.d

🕐 20 min

Quick Lab

🕐 **20 min**

Teacher Notes

This model helps students understand neuron function (covers standards 7.5.a and 7.7.d). You may also use white glue to place the neuron model to a piece of paper. In the absence of modeling clay, other art supplies may be used.

Materials For Each Group

• clay, modeling
• colored pencil, marker, or crayon
• paper, white, 1 piece
• tape

Safety Caution

Remind students to review all safety cautions and icons before beginning this lab activity.

Answer

4. Drawings should include identification of the neuron as sensory or motor and a description of what happens when the impulse reaches its destination.

📁 Differentiated Datasheets
A **BASIC**, B **GENERAL**, C **ADVANCED**

Also editable on the Holt Lab Generator CD-ROM

Summary

- The central nervous system (CNS) is the brain and the spinal cord.
- The peripheral nervous system (PNS) is all of the parts of the nervous system except for the brain and spinal cord.
- Nerves in the peripheral nervous system are bundles of axons, blood vessels, and connective tissue.
- Sensory neurons have receptors that detect information about the body and its environment. Motor neurons carry messages from the brain and spinal cord to other parts of the body.
- The PNS has two types of motor neurons: somatic neurons and autonomic neurons.
- The cerebrum is the largest part of the brain and controls thinking, sensing, and voluntary movement.
- The cerebellum is the part of the brain that keeps track of the body's position and that helps maintain balance.
- The medulla controls involuntary processes, such as breathing and the regulation of heart rate, blood pressure, and body temperature.

Using Vocabulary

1 Write an original definition for *neuron* and *nerve*.

2 Use *brain* and *peripheral nervous system* in the same sentence.

Understanding Concepts

3 **Describing** What is one function of each of the three main parts of the brain?

4 **Comparing** How are the somatic nervous system and the autonomic nervous system related?

5 **Analyzing** What is the relationship between the peripheral nervous system and the central nervous system?

6 **Evaluating** Explain how a severe injury to the spinal cord can affect other parts of the body.

Critical Thinking

7 **Applying Concepts** Some medications slow a person's nervous system. These drugs are often labeled "May cause drowsiness." Explain why a person needs to know about this side effect.

8 **Predicting Consequences** Explain how your life would change if your autonomic nervous system suddenly stopped working.

9 **Making Inferences** Briefly explain why the nervous system is made up of many smaller parts that have specialized functions.

INTERPRETING GRAPHICS Use the figure below to answer the next two questions.

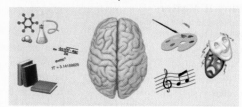

10 **Identifying Relationships** Which hemisphere of the brain recognizes and processes words, numbers, and letters? faces, places, and objects?

11 **Analyzing Processes** For a person whose left hemisphere is primarily in control, would it be easier to learn to play a new computer game by reading the rules and following instructions or by watching a friend play and imitating his actions?

Challenge

12 **Analyzing Relationships** The nervous system is one of eleven systems of the human body. Describe how the other body systems depend on the nervous system to function. How does the nervous system depend on the other body systems?

Internet Resources

For a variety of links related to this chapter, go to www.scilinks.org
Topic: Nervous System
SciLinks code: HY71023

Answers to Section Review

1. Sample answer: A neuron is a special cell that can receive and send electrical impulses. A nerve is a bundle of axons and other tissues.

2. Sample answer: The PNS consists of nerves that connect all parts of the body to the brain and spinal cord. **7.5.a** (supporting)

3. Sample answer: The cerebrum controls speech and touch. The cerebellum receives sensory input and aids balance. The medulla controls some involuntary processes, like heart rate and blood pressure. **7.5.a** (supporting), **7.5.b** (supporting)

4. Sample answer: The somatic nervous system controls voluntary actions like singing. The autonomic nervous system controls involuntary actions like digestion. Both control actions. **7.5.a** (supporting), **7.5.b** (mastering)

5. Sample answer: The PNS gathers information and sends it to the CNS, which translates the information. **7.5.a** (supporting), **7.5.b** (mastering)

6. Sample answer: A spinal injury may damage nerves in the spinal cord that send or receive messages between the brain and the body. Damage to these nerves may stop the brain from receiving sensory input or making from any movements in the parts of the body controlled by the damaged nerves. **7.5.b** (mastering)

7. Sample answer: A drug that causes drowsiness may affect the way that impulses travel in neurons, increasing the time it takes a message to get to and from the brain. It is important to be aware of these side effects so that activities that require a fast reaction time can be avoided.

8. Sample answer: If my autonomic nervous system suddenly stopped working, I would not be able to digest my food, my eyes would not adjust to light or darkness, and my lungs wouldn't work properly. **7.5.b** (mastering)

9. Each part of the nervous system performs functions that are important to the system. For example, neurons send and receive impulses. **7.5.a** (mastering)

10. left; right

11. Sample answer: It would be easier to learn the new game by reading the rules and following the instructions.

12. Sample answer: The nervous system gathers information that is important to other organ systems. For example, muscles move because they receive signals from the nervous system. Cells within the nervous system depend on the respiratory and circulatory system for oxygen. These cells also depend on the digestive and circulatory system for nutrients. **7.5.b** (mastering)

Section Review Standards Guide

	Supporting	Mastering	Exceeding
7.5.a	2, 3, 4, 5	9	
7.5.b	3	4, 5, 6, 8, 12	

Section Resources

- Directed Reading A **BASIC** (Also in Spanish), B **GENERAL**
- Interactive Reader and Study Guide
- Section Quiz **GENERAL** (Also in Spanish)
- Section Review **GENERAL** (Also in Spanish)
- Vocabulary and Section Summary A **BASIC** (Also in Spanish), B **GENERAL**

Preteach

Reviewing Prior Knowledge

Tell students that a key idea of this chapter is how organ systems can sense and gather information. Ask students to describe what they already know about how the nervous system gathers information. (Students should recall that neurons, particularly sensory neurons, gather information about what is happening in and around their body.)

Bellringer

Have students focus on standard 7.5.g by writing a few sentences that describe how they think the human eye works. Students can write their ideas in their **Science Journal.**

Bellringer Transparency

Motivate

Sense Skit Organize the class into groups and assign each group one of the senses. Each group should imagine what it would be like to live without that sense. Allow students 10 to 15 minutes to develop a skit about living without the sense.

LS Intrapersonal/Kinesthetic

Co-op Learning

Answer to Standards Check

Skin can detect pressure, temperature, pain, and vibration. **7.5.a** (supporting)

What You Will Learn

- Pressure, temperature, pain, and vibration are four sensations detected by receptors in the skin.
- A feedback mechanism is a cycle of events in which information from one step controls or affects another step.
- You see an object when it reflects visible light toward your eyes.
- Hearing is the sense that allows you to experience sound energy.

Why It Matters

You respond to the information gathered by your senses.

Vocabulary

- integumentary system
- reflex
- feedback mechanism
- pupil
- retina
- iris
- cochlea

READING STRATEGY

Graphic Organizer In your **Science Journal**, create a Process Chart that shows how your body regulates your temperature.

Figure 1 *Each type of receptor in your skin has its own structure and function.*

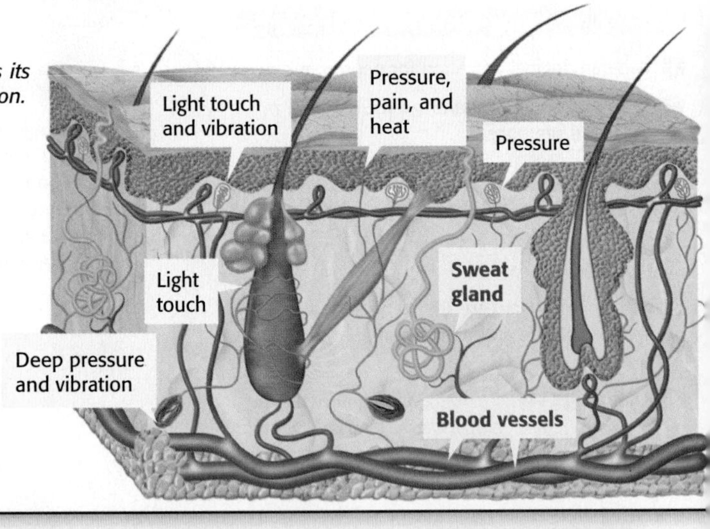

7.5.a Students know plants and animals have levels of organization for structure and function, including cells, tissues, organs, organ systems, and the whole organism.

7.5.b Students know organ systems function because of the contributions of individual organs, tissues, and cells. The failure of any part can affect the entire system.

7.5.g Students know how to relate the structures of the eye and ear to their functions.

7.6.b Students know that for an object to be seen, light emitted by or scattered from it must be detected by the eye.

Sensing the Environment

Key Concept Your organ systems have specialized structures and functions to sense and gather information.

▶ You feel a tap on your shoulder. Who tapped you? You turn to look, hoping to see a friend. Your senses are on the job! The tap produces impulses in sensory receptors on your shoulder. These impulses travel to your brain.

Once the impulses reach your brain, they create an awareness called a *sensation*. In this case, the sensation is that of being touched on your shoulder. But you still do not know who tapped you. So, you turn around. The sensory receptors in your eyes send impulses to your brain. Now, your brain recognizes your best friend.

Sense of Touch

When you shake hands or feel a breeze, the sensation that you experience is touch. Touch arises from the stimulation of sensory receptors in the skin. Skin is part of the integumentary system. The **integumentary system** is an organ system that protects the body from damage. This system includes hair, skin, and nails. As **Figure 1** shows, skin is not only protective. It also has many kinds of sensory receptors. Each kind of receptor responds mainly to one kind of stimulus. For example, *thermoreceptors* respond to temperature change. Each kind of receptor produces a specific sensation of touch, such as pressure, temperature, pain, or vibration.

Standards Check What sensations can your skin detect? **7.5.a**

Light touch and vibration

Pressure, pain, and heat

Pressure

Light touch

Sweat gland

Deep pressure and vibration

Blood vessels

Universal Access · Differentiated Instruction

English Learners

Pronunciation Direct students' attention to the word *integumentary* in the third paragraph. Remind them that bold words are defined in the margins with the correct pronunciation. Point out that this book uses its own phonetic spelling that may be easier than what they find in a dictionary. Make sure they realize that the capitalized letters represent the stressed syllable and that stress in English can be on any syllable. Have students practice pronouncing this word; tell them to move their body taller on the stressed syllable and to make it louder and higher in pitch. For additional practice, have them look at the key words defined on 532 (*vertebrae*), up to page 538 (*cochlea*). Remind them that the glossary also provides the pronunciation and definitions of key words. **LS** Visual/Verbal

---

Responding to Sensory Messages

When you step on something sharp, as the man in **Figure 2** did, pain receptors in your foot or toe send impulses to your spinal cord. Almost immediately, a message to move your foot travels back to the muscles in your leg and foot. Without thinking, you quickly lift your foot. This immediate, involuntary action is called a **reflex.** Your brain is not telling your leg to move. In fact, by the time that the message reaches your brain, your leg and foot have already moved. If you had to wait for your brain to act, your toes could get seriously hurt!

Standards Check Why are reflexes important? **7.5.b**

Feedback Mechanisms

Most of the time, the brain processes information from skin receptors. For example, on a hot day, heat receptors in your skin detect an increase in your temperature. The receptors send impulses to the brain. Your brain responds by sending messages that cause your sweat glands to make sweat. As sweat evaporates, it cools your body. Your brain also tells the blood vessels in your skin to dilate (open wider). Blood flow increases. Thermal energy from the blood in your skin moves to your surroundings. This process also cools your body. As your body cools, it sends messages to your brain. The brain responds by sending messages that cause sweat glands to reduce their activity and blood vessels to constrict.

This cooling process is one of your body's feedback mechanisms. A **feedback mechanism** is a cycle of events in which information from one step controls or affects a previous step. The temperature-regulating feedback mechanism helps keep your body temperature within safe limits. This cooling mechanism works like a thermostat on an air conditioner. Once a room reaches a certain temperature, the thermostat sends a message that causes the air conditioner to stop blowing cold air.

integumentary system (in TEG yoo MEN tuhr ee SIS tuhm) the organ system that forms a protective covering on the outside of the body

reflex (REE FLEKS) an involuntary and almost immediate movement in response to a stimulus

feedback mechanism (FEED BAK MEK uh NIZ uhm) a cycle of events in which information from one step controls or affects a previous step

Figure 2 A reflex, such as lifting your foot when you step on something sharp, is one way in which your nervous system responds to your environment.

SCIENCE HUMOR

Q: How do nerves shop?

A: They buy only on impulse.

Discussion

Pupil Action Ask students to describe what happens to their eyes and vision when they leave a dark movie theater on a sunny day. **LS** Verbal

Discussion

Eye Strain To see objects within a distance of 6 m, the muscles in the eye must work constantly to focus. Long periods of focusing on very near objects, such as a book or computer screen, can tire the eye muscles and cause eyestrain. Ask students to suggest ways to avoid straining eye muscles during these activities. (Answers may include taking breaks from the activity once an hour, looking up, and allowing the eyes to relax occasionally.) **LS** Logical

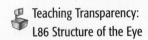
Teaching Transparency:
L86 Structure of the Eye

Teaching Transparency: **LINK TO EARTH SCIENCE** E69 Radiation from the Sun and the Electromagnetic Spectrum

Answer to Standards Check

When light enters the eye through the pupil, the light travels through the lens to the retina. The retina sends electrical impulses through the optic nerve to the brain. **7.6.b** (mastering)

Sense of Sight

Cameras capture images of objects that reflect visible light. Sight is the sense that allows you to see the size, shape, motion, and color of objects around you. You see an object when your eyes, like a camera, receive visible light that is scattered, reflected, or emitted by the object. Once your eyes detect the light, your brain can form visual images. Your eyes are complex sensory organs, as **Figure 3** shows. A clear membrane called the *cornea* covers the front of the eye. The cornea protects the eye but allows light to enter. Light from an object enters the front of your eye through an opening called the **pupil.** Then, the light travels through the lens to the back of the eye. There, the light strikes the **retina,** a layer of light-sensitive cells.

The retina is packed with retinal cells called *photoreceptors*. A photoreceptor is a special neuron that responds to light energy by causing other cells in the retina to create electric impulses. The brain perceives these impulses as light. The retina has two kinds of photoreceptors: rods and cones. Rods are very sensitive to dim light. They are important for night vision. Impulses from rods are interpreted as black-and-white images. Cones are very sensitive to bright light. Impulses from cones allow you to see fine details and colors. Impulses from the rods and cones travel along axons. The impulses leave the back of each eye through an optic nerve. The optic nerve carries the impulses to your brain, where the impulses are interpreted.

Standards Check Explain what happens when light enters the eye. 🐻 **7.6.b**

pupil (PYOO puhl) the opening that is located in the center of the iris of the eye and that controls the amount of light that enters the eye

retina (RET 'n uh) the light-sensitive inner layer of the eye, which it receives images formed by the lens and transmits them through the optic nerve to the brain

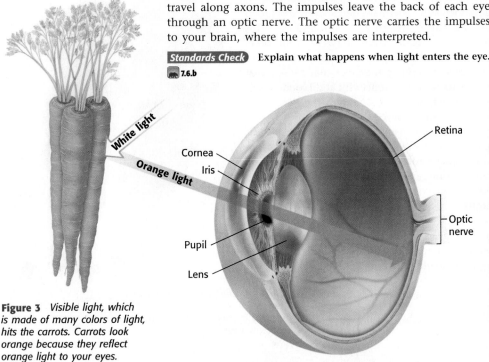

Figure 3 *Visible light, which is made of many colors of light, hits the carrots. Carrots look orange because they reflect orange light to your eyes.*

Universal Access · Differentiated Instruction

Special Education Students

Related to You Some students learn best when they can directly relate information to themselves. Have such students look in a mirror. Ask these questions:

1. What color are your pupils? (they look black)

2. What are your pupils made of? (my pupils are holes)

3. What color are your irises? (Answers may vary.)

4. What are your irises made of? (muscle)

5. What do your irises do? (control the light that enters the eye and give color to the eye)

6. What color are your corneas? (clear)

7. What do corneas do? (protect the eye)

LS Visual/Intrapersonal

Reacting to Light

Your pupil looks like a black dot in the center of your eye. In fact, it is an opening that lets light enter the eye. The pupil is surrounded by the **iris,** a ring of muscle. The iris controls the amount of light entering the eye and gives the eye its color. In bright light, the iris contracts, which makes the pupil smaller in diameter. A smaller pupil reduces the amount of light entering the eye and passing onto the retina. In dim light, the iris relaxes, which dilates the pupil to let in more light.

Standards Check How does your iris react to bright light? 7.5.g

Focusing the Light

Light travels in straight lines until it passes through the cornea and the lens. The *lens* is an oval-shaped piece of clear, curved material behind the iris. The lens refracts, or bends light. Muscles in the eye change the shape of the lens in order to focus light onto the retina. When you look at objects that are close to the eye, the lens becomes more curved. When you look at objects that are far away, the lens gets flatter.

Figure 4 shows some common vision problems. In some eyes, the lens focuses the light in front of the retina, which results in nearsightedness. If the lens focuses the light just behind the retina, the result is farsightedness. Glasses, contact lenses, or surgery can usually correct these vision problems.

Brain Brochure

How does the brain keep track of various activities? Develop a brochure that discusses the structure and function of the human brain. Go to **go.hrw.com,** and type in the keyword HY7BD4W.

 iris (IE ris) the colored, circular part of the eye

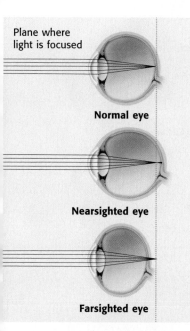

Plane where light is focused

Normal eye

Nearsighted eye

Farsighted eye

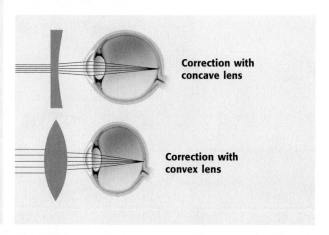

Figure 4 *A concave lens bends light rays outward to correct nearsightedness. A convex lens bends light rays inward to correct farsightedness.*

Correction with concave lens

Correction with convex lens

MISCONCEPTION ALERT

Writing **Colorblindness** Students may think that people who are colorblind see in black and white. People who are colorblind can usually perceive colors, but certain colors may appear very similar to one another. This similarity is caused by a lack of at least one of the three cones in the eye. Many people do not know that they are colorblind because they have learned to distinguish other differences in their perception of colors. Have students research one kind of colorblindness, (such as red-green) and present their findings to the class. Students might decide to prepare a visual that shows what a person with a particular kind of colorblindness actually sees. **LS Logical**

Teach, *continued*

Homework

Bats and Echolocation

PORTFOLIO

Some students may know that bats do not see well. However, they may not know how bats are able to fly or catch prey without the benefit of sight. Have students research *echolocation*, which is the process by which bats can detect the location and size of objects by using sound waves. Interested students could make a poster or oral presentation that illustrates how echolocation works. **LS Verbal**

Group ACTiViTY

Protect Your Ears Have students create a campaign for hearing safety. Students should research forms of hearing damage and what they can do to protect themselves from hearing impairment or hearing loss. Students should create posters and brochures that warn students of potential dangers to the health of their ears, including a list of ways in which people can protect their hearing. Students should display their posters in the school and hand out brochures to other students. **LS Verbal** **Co-op Learning**

Teaching Transparency: L87 Structure of the Ear

Sense of Hearing

Sound is produced when something, such as a drum, vibrates. Vibrations push on nearby air particles, which push on other air particles. The vibrations create waves of sound energy. Hearing is the sense that allows you to experience sound energy.

Ears are organs that are specialized for hearing. Each ear has an outer, middle, and inner portion, as shown in **Figure 5.** The outer ear consists of the ear canal. The middle ear includes the *tympanic membrane,* or eardrum. The middle ear also includes the three ear bones: the hammer, anvil, and stirrup. The inner ear includes the cochlea and the auditory nerve.

Sound waves reaching the outer ear are funneled into the middle ear. There, the waves make the eardrum vibrate. The eardrum is a thin membrane separating the outer ear from the middle ear. The vibrating eardrum makes three small bones in the middle ear vibrate. One of these bones, the stirrup, vibrates against the **cochlea,** a fluid-filled organ of the inner ear. Inside the cochlea, vibrations make waves that are just like the waves you make by tapping on a glass of water. Neurons in the cochlea respond to the waves by creating electric impulses. These impulses travel along the *cochlear nerve,* or auditory nerve, to the area of the brain where sound is interpreted.

cochlea (KAHK lee uh) a coiled tube that is found in the inner ear and that is essential to hearing

Figure 5 *A sound wave travels into the outer ear. The wave becomes bone vibrations in the middle ear, liquid vibrations in the inner ear, and finally, nerve impulses that travel to the brain.*

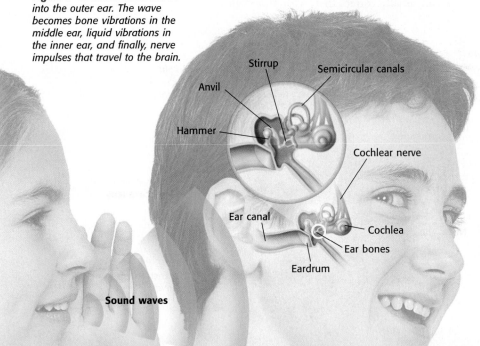

Stirrup
Anvil
Semicircular canals
Hammer
Cochlear nerve
Ear canal
Cochlea
Ear bones
Eardrum
Sound waves

Universal Access · Differentiated Instruction

English Learners

Multiple Meanings Words with multiple meanings can be quite confusing for some students. Discuss the meanings of the following words. Make sure students understand which meaning is used in the text.

Word list: drum, waves, canal, hammer, anvil, stirrup, electrical, faint

(Sample answers: drum—musical instrument, informal name for tympanic membrane; waves—ocean

bulges, motion of hand(s), method by which sound travels; canal—artificial waterway, tube or duct; hammer—pounding tool, a vibrating bone in the inner ear; anvil—metal pounding block, a vibrating bone in the inner ear; stirrup—part of a saddle to hold a human foot, a vibrating bone in the inner ear; electrical—things that plug into a wall socket, having to do with a chemical reaction in the body; faint—to pass out, barely detectable)

LS Verbal/Logical

Quick Lab

What Does the Ear Drum Do?

In this activity, you will use simple materials to model the human ear. This model will help you understand how the ear functions.

▶ Try It!

1. Stretch a **piece of plastic wrap** over one end of a **cardboard tube.** Secure the edges of the plastic with a **rubber band.**

2. Use a **piece of paper** to make a cone. Tape the cone together so that it does not unroll.

3. Place the small end of the cone into the open end of the cardboard tube.

4. Use **modeling clay** to place an **index card** vertically on the table.

5. Point a **flashlight** at the plastic wrap–covered end of the tube so that the light reflects onto the index card.

▶ Think About It!

6. Shout, sing, and talk into the open end of the cone. Record your observations.

7. Draw the model that you created. Label the part of the human ear that the model represents and describe the function of that part.

8. Why did the light vibrate?

9. How are the parts of the ear specialized to perform their jobs?

🕑 30 min

The External Ear and Sound

You have just read that the human ear is structured to efficiently transfer sound waves into electric impulses. But how is sound gathered and delivered to the ear? The external ear, the part of the ear that you can see, gathers sound waves. It also directs those sound waves into your ear canal. The external ear of a human is fixed in place, but many animals can adjust the position of their external ears to listen to faint sounds. Being able to change the position of the external ear also helps some animals, such as rabbits, determine the direction from which a sound is coming.

Standards Check Describe the role that the external ear plays in hearing. 🐻 **7.5.g**

Keeping Your Balance

Your ears enable you not only to hear but also to maintain your balance. The *semicircular canals,* special fluid-filled canals in your inner ear, are filled with hair cells. These hair cells respond to changes in the position of your head with respect to gravity. The hair cells help your brain determine the orientation and position of your head.

Homework

✏️ *Writing*   **Elephant Talk**   Sound is produced by vibrating objects. Some sounds, called *infrasonic sounds*, are too low for human ears to detect. Have students research how elephants use infrasonic sounds to communicate with each other, and then have them write a report about what they learn.

LS Verbal

Answer to Standards Check

The role of the external ear is to gather sound and direct it into the ear canal.
7.5.g (mastering)

Quick Lab

🕑 30 min

Teacher Notes

This model demonstrates the relationship between the structure of the ear and its function (covers standards 7.5.g and 7.7.d). Students may draw a faint grid on the index card to help them see the vibrations of the light.

Materials For Each Student
- card, index
- clay, modeling
- flashlight
- paper, 1 piece
- plastic wrap
- rubber band
- tube, cardboard

Answers

8. Sample answer: The light vibrated because the sound made the plastic wrap vibrate.

9. Sample answer: The eardrum, or tympanic membrane, is able to vibrate as sound strikes the eardrum's surface.

📋 Differentiated Datasheets
A **BASIC**, B **GENERAL**, C **ADVANCED**

Also editable on the
Holt Lab Generator
CD-ROM

Standards Focus

This **Standards Focus** provides you with a quick way to **assess, reteach,** and **re-assess** one or more concepts in the section.

Assess

Ask students whether each of the statements below is true or false. Have students correct false statements.

1. Rods help you see color and detail in bright light. (false)
7.5.g, 7.6.b

2. Cones provide a colorful view of the world. (true) **7.5.g, 7.6.b**

3. Your brain combines signals from the senses of smell and hearing to give the sensation of flavor. (false) **7.5.b**

Reteach

Ear Review Have students review standard 7.5.g by drawing a diagram of the ear and then writing a brief paragraph describing how the structure of the ear relates to how it works. **LS Visual/ Verbal 7.5.g**

Re-Assess

Making Sense of It Have students write and illustrate a pamphlet or brochure that explains each of the senses. The pamphlet or brochure should be written for someone who does not know much about science. **LS Verbal/ Visual 7.5.g**

Answer to Standards Check

Taste and olfactory cells gather important information from the environment. For example, olfactory cells gather information about what is in the air.
7.5.a (mastering)

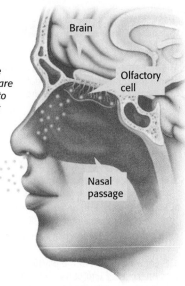

Figure 6 *Olfactory cells line the nasal cavity. These cells are sensory receptors that react to chemicals in the air and that allow you to smell.*

Brain

Olfactory cell

Nasal passage

SCHOOL to HOME

Disorders of the Senses
With a parent or guardian, research a disorder of one of the five senses discussed in this section. What causes this disorder? What technology is used to help people who are affected by this disorder? Create a poster that illustrates your research.

ACTIVITY

Sense of Taste

Taste is the sense that allows you to detect chemicals and to distinguish flavors. Your tongue is covered with tiny bumps called *papillae* (puh PIL ee). Most papillae contain taste buds. Taste buds contain clusters of *taste cells,* the receptors for taste. Taste cells respond to dissolved-food molecules. Taste cells react to five basic tastes: sweetness (sugar), sourness (lemon), saltiness (salt), savoriness (meats and cheeses), and bitterness (some medicines). When the brain combines information from all of the taste buds, you taste a "combination" flavor.

Sense of Smell

As you can see in **Figure 6,** receptors for smell are located on *olfactory cells* in the upper part of your nasal cavity. An olfactory cell is a nerve cell that responds to chemical molecules in the air. You smell something when the receptors react to molecules that have been inhaled. The molecules dissolve in the moist lining of the nasal cavity and trigger an impulse. Olfactory cells send those impulses to the brain, which interprets the impulses as odors.

Taste buds and olfactory cells both detect dissolved molecules. Your brain combines information from both senses to give you sensations of flavor.

Standards Check How do your taste cells and olfactory cells communicate with your nervous system? **7.5.a**

Universal Access · Differentiated Instruction

Advanced Learners/GATE

Natural Tastes Ask students to work together to create a poster showing natural foods that fall into each of the five taste areas: sweet, sour, salty, bitter, and savoriness (umami). Encourage them to use both pictures and word labels. (Sample answers: sweet–peach, baby carrot, watermelon; sour– rhubarb, lemons, vinegar; salty–fish, green olives, some cheese; bitter–horseradish, turnips, brussels sprouts; savoriness–cheeses, meats) **LS Visual/ Interpersonal**

Cultural Awareness

Spicy Tastes Chili peppers contain a chemical compound called capsaicin. Capsaicin triggers the pain receptors in the mouth. These receptors react to capsaicin as they would to heat. This is why spicy foods containing chili peppers feel like they are burning your mouth. Chili peppers are an important component in many different types of cuisines. Have students research the ways different cultures use chili peppers.

Summary

- Touch allows you to respond to temperature, pressure, pain, and vibration on the skin.
- Reflexes and feedback mechanisms help you respond to your environment.
- Sight allows you to respond to light energy. The eye has specialized structures to respond to light.
- Hearing allows you to respond to sound energy. The ear has specialized structures to respond to the information in sound waves.
- Taste allows you to distinguish flavors.
- Smell allows you to perceive various odors.

Using Vocabulary

1 Write an original definition for *reflex* and *feedback mechanism*.

2 Use *retina* and *cochlea* in separate sentences.

Understanding Concepts

3 **Listing** What are three sensations that receptors in the skin detect?

4 **Comparing** Explain how light and sight are related.

5 **Describing** How do your senses of hearing, taste, and smell work?

6 **Concluding** Why are bright colors difficult to see in a room lit by candles?

7 **Comparing** How is your sense of taste similar to your sense of smell, and how do these senses work together?

8 **Describing** How does the feedback mechanism that regulates body temperature work?

Critical Thinking

9 **Making Inferences** Why is it important for the human body to have reflexes?

---

10 **Applying Concepts** Rods help you detect objects and shapes in dim light. Explain why it is important for human eyes to have both rods and cones.

11 **Analyzing Relationships** How do the parts of the ear work together to convert sound waves into nerve impulses?

INTERPRETING GRAPHICS Use the images below to answer the next question.

12 **Analyzing Relationships** Describe the similarities between an eye and a camera lens.

Math Skills

13 **Solving Problems** Suppose a nerve impulse must travel 0.90 m from your toe to your central nervous system. If the impulse travels at 150 m/s, calculate how long it will take the impulse to arrive. If the impulse travels at 0.2 m/s, how long will it take the impulse to arrive?

Challenge

14 **Analyzing Relationships** How do your eyes and ears work together to help you move around a room? (Hint: What functions, other than hearing, do the ears have?)

Internet Resources

For a variety of links related to this chapter, go to www.scilinks.org
Topic: The Senses; The Eye
SciLinks code: HY71378; HY70560

---

9. Sample answer: Reflexes protect by acting faster than the body would act if the brain had to process information and send a message. **7.5.a** (supporting), **7.5.b** (supporting)

10. In bright light, cones trigger impulses that provide information about color, shape, and motion. At night, rods allow you to detect something in the dark, even if you can't tell much about its color or shape. **7.5.g** (exceeding), **7.6.b** (exceeding)

11. The external ear directs sound into the ear canal. At the end of the ear canal, the eardrum vibrates and causes the middle ear bones to vibrate. They translate the movement to the cochlea. Neurons in the cochlea send impulses along the auditory nerve to the area of the brain that interprets sound. **7.5.g** (mastering)

12. The iris is a muscle in the eye that controls how much light enters the eye. The camera lens can be adjusted to control the amount of light that enters the camera. **7.5.g** (mastering), **7.6.b** (mastering)

13. 0.90 m ÷ 150 m/s = 0.006 s; 0.90 m ÷ 0.2 m/s = 4.5 s

14. Your eyes communicate information about the room that you are in and your position relative to the room. Your ears also function to help your brain determine the orientation of your head as well as its position. **7.5.b** (exceeding), **7.5.g** (mastering)

Section Review Standards Guide

	Supporting	Mastering	Exceeding
7.5.a	3, 7, 9	8	
7.5.b	9		14
7.5.g		2, 4, 5, 11, 12, 14	10
7.6.b		4, 12	6, 10

Answers to Section Review

1. Sample answer: A reflex is an unconscious, immediate response to a stimulus. A feedback mechanism is a series of steps in which one step affects a previous step.

2. Sample answer: The retina converts light to electrical impulses. The cochlea converts sound to electrical impulses. **7.5.g** (mastering)

3. temperature, pressure, and pain **7.5.a** (supporting)

4. Sample answer: Light enters the eye striking the retina. Retinal cells produce electrical impulses that are sent to the brain where they are interpreted as images. **7.5.g** (mastering), **7.6.b** (mastering)

5. Answers may vary. Accept all reasonable answers that describe how the senses function. **7.5.g** (mastering)

6. Sample answer: Cones in the retina do not work as well in dim light. **7.6.b** (exceeding)

7. Sample answer: Receptors for smell detect chemicals in air. Receptors for taste detect chemicals in your mouth. The brain combines information from both to give a sensation of flavor. **7.5.a** (supporting)

8. Sample answer: If the temperature is too high or too low, the brain tells the body to take steps to correct it. Once the temperature is correct, the brain tells the body to stop what it was doing to raise or lower the temperature. **7.5.a** (mastering)

Section Resources

- Directed Reading A **BASIC** (Also in Spanish), B **GENERAL**
- Interactive Reader and Study Guide
- Section Quiz **GENERAL** (Also in Spanish)
- Section Review **GENERAL** (Also in Spanish)
- Vocabulary and Section Summary A **BASIC** (Also in Spanish), B **GENERAL**

Teacher Notes

If cow eyes are not available, this lab may also be used for the dissection of any large mammal's eye (covers standard 7.5.g and 7.7.a).

Time Required

One 45-minute class period

Lab Ratings

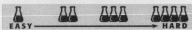

EASY ――――――――→ HARD

Teacher Prep 🧪🧪🧪
Student Set-Up 🧪🧪
Concept Level 🧪🧪🧪
Clean Up 🧪🧪

Materials

The materials listed on the student page are enough for a group of three to four students.

Safety Caution

Remind students to review all safety cautions and icons before beginning this lab activity. Students should wear protective aprons over their clothing and goggles over their eyes. Students should also wear gloves. Students should use caution with scalpels, scissors, probes, and should not eat any of the materials used. Students should not allow the preservative chemicals to contact their skin.

Skills Practice Lab

OBJECTIVES

Dissect a cow's eye.

Identify the parts of a mammal's eye.

Describe the function of each part of a mammal's eye.

MATERIALS

- cow's eye, preserved
- dissection tray
- gloves, disposable
- newspaper
- paper towels
- probe, blunt
- scalpel
- scissors
- scissors, fine point
- tweezers

SAFETY

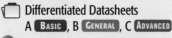

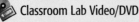
7.5.g Students know how to relate the structures of the eye and ear to their functions.

Investigation and Experimentation
7.7.a Select and use appropriate tools and technology (including calculators, computers, balances, spring scales, microscopes, and binoculars) to perform tests, collect data, and display data.

Dissecting a Cow's Eye

Eyes are sensory organs that detect light. Like a camera, eyes are composed of various parts that each have a specific function. By examining the shape, appearance, and arrangement of the parts of an eye, you can learn more about how the eye works.

Procedure

① Put on safety goggles, gloves, and a lab apron. **Caution:** Be extremely careful when using sharp and pointed instruments, such as scalpels.

② Place your cow's eye into a dissecting tray. Observe the outer structure of the eye. Make a sketch of what you see. Use the image below to label the following parts on your sketch: optic nerve, cornea, pupil, iris, and muscles.

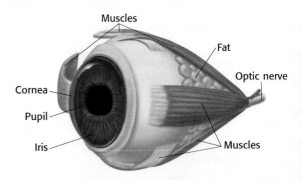

③ Make a small slit in the cornea to drain the clear liquid stored under this thick covering. This liquid is called *vitreous humor*. The vitreous humor helps the eye maintain its shape and hold the retina in place.

④ Use your scalpel and scissors to divide the eye in half so that the front half includes the cornea, pupil, and iris. Although a sharp scalpel can slice into the eye, dissecting scissors will help you cut through this tough tissue in a straight line. As you cut through the eye, more vitreous humor may come out of the eye.

Lab Resources

📋 **Differentiated Datasheets**
A **BASIC**, B **GENERAL**, C **ADVANCED**

💾 Classroom Lab Video/DVD

⊙ Holt Lab Generator CD-ROM

Search for any lab by topic, standard, difficulty level, or time. Edit any lab to fit your needs, or create your own labs. Use the Lab Materials QuickList software to customize your lab materials list.

⏱ **45 min**

5. Sketch the eye again. Use the image on the previous page to label the following parts: lens, retina, pupil, cornea, and optic nerve.

6. Examine the front half of the eye. Use your scalpel or scissors to cut out the cornea along its rim. Note the thickness of the cow's cornea.

7. The removal of the cornea reveals the muscular iris and the pupil opening. You should be able to pull out the iris in one piece. Describe the appearance of the cornea and pupil.

8. Remove the lens. Use a paper towel to gently dry this part of the eye. Use the lens to read a portion of a newspaper. How does the lens change the appearance of the newspaper?

9. Examine the other half of the eye. Note the thin sheet of tissue. This is the retina. Find where the nerve fibers of the retina join together. Identify where these fibers exit the eye.

Analyze the Results

10. **Analyzing Data** Why is the eye filled with vitreous humor?

11. **Classifying** Is the pupil a physical structure of the eye? Explain your answer. How does the actual structure of the pupil complement its function?

12. **Explaining Events** An eye lens focuses light as the light enters the eye. Does the lens of an eye work only when an animal is alive? How can you tell?

Draw Conclusions

13. **Applying Conclusions** Describe the path of light as light travels into and through the eye.

14. **Drawing Conclusions** How is an eye similar to a camera? What structures of an eye are similar to the shutter and film in a camera?

Big Idea Question

15. **Interpreting Information** How do the parts of the eye that you have labeled in your two sketches work together to sense and communicate the surroundings?

Analyze the Results

10. The eye is filled with vitreous humor because the vitreous humor helps the eye keep its shape.

11. The pupil is an opening into the eye. It is not a physical structure. The function of the pupil is to allow light into the eye. The fact that it is an opening into the eye means that the structure of the pupil fits its function.

12. The lens is a physical structure that works whether or not the animal is alive. You can see that this is the case because the lens was able to magnify the newsprint.

Draw Conclusions

13. Light passes through the cornea and enters the eye through the pupil. Light then passes through the lens and vitreous humor. Finally, light strikes the retina.

14. Both an eye and a camera are able to form images with small amounts of light. The shutter of a camera is like the eyelid, while the film of a camera is like the retina of the eye.

Big Idea Question

15. Answers may vary. Accept all reasonable answers that discuss the cooperation of eye structures, such as the pupil, lens, and retina.

Sushma Kashyap
Alvarado Intermediate School
Rowland Heights, California

Teacher Notes

This activity has students plan an experiment to test how external temperature affects the sensitivity of skin (covers standard 7.7.a).

Answers to You Try It!

2. Sample answer: My hypothesis gives a possible answer to the question that I am testing. It is based on information that I already have.

3. Sample answers: temperature of skin, area of skin, and age of person being tested. I selected temperature of the skin.

4. Sample answer: room temperature water, warm water, cold water, thermometers, large beakers or bowls, and eyedroppers.

5. Sample answer: If I select inappropriate tools, I may not be able to gather data that will help me test my hypothesis.

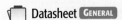 Datasheet GENERAL

Also editable on the Holt Lab Generator CD-ROM

Science Skills Activity

| Scientific Methods | Research | Data Analysis | Models, Maps & Diagrams |

Investigation and Experimentation

7.7.a Select and use appropriate tools and technology (including calculators, computers, balances, spring scales, microscopes, and binoculars) to perform tests, collect data, and display data.

Selecting Tools to Perform Tests

▶ Tutorial

Scientists ask many questions about the natural world. They conduct experiments to find answers to these questions. A scientist must choose the correct equipment and tools in order to perform the experiment and communicate the results. It is very important to select the appropriate tools before beginning the experiment so that data is not lost.

Procedure

1 Write a hypothesis. The hypothesis should offer an explanation for the question that you are asking. The hypothesis must also be testable. If it is not testable, rewrite the hypothesis.

> *Question:* How do eyes respond when the intensity of light changes?
> *Hypothesis:* The iris of an eye will open in dim light and close in bright light.

2 List the possible variables in your experiment. Select only one variable to test in your experiment.

> *Variables:*
> – intensity of light
> – ~~time~~
> – ~~amount of sleep of test subjects~~

3 List the materials that you will need to perform the experiment. This list should also include equipment that you need for safety.

> *Materials:*
> – flashlight
> – black paper
> – test subjects

4 Determine the scientific equipment and tools that you will need to perform the tests involved in your experiment. For example, metric rulers are used to measure the dimensions of objects. Scales are used to measure the mass of objects. Cameras capture many important details of an experimental setup.

> *Scientific Equipment and Tools:*
> – digital camera
> – metric ruler

▶ You Try It!

You are a member of a research team that is trying to determine how external temperature affects the sensitivity of skin. Therefore, you need to find an answer to the following question: Does the temperature of the environment change the way that skin perceives sensation?

Procedure

1 Use the steps above to plan an experiment and to select the appropriate tools and equipment to perform your tests.

Analysis

2 **Forming a Hypothesis** How does your hypothesis explain or answer your question?

3 **Analyzing Ideas** List the possible variables in this experiment. Choose one variable.

4 **Analyzing Methods** What equipment and tools will you need to test this variable?

5 **Predicting Consequences** What might happen if you select inappropriate tools?

Universal Access · Differentiated Instruction

Struggling Readers

Deciphering Questions Students may need help understanding the meaning of the question "Does the temperature of the environment change the way that skin perceives sensation?" Work through the sentence as follows: Ask students what the "temperature of the environment" means. (how hot or cold the air around us is) Ask students what "the way the skin perceives sensation" means. (how the skin reacts to things it can sense or feel) **LS Verbal**

Advanced Learners/GATE

Generating Questions Point out that ideas such as "trying to determine how external temperature affects the sensitivity of skin" can generate multiple study questions. Ask students to think of a second question, and then complete the four analysis steps with that question. (Sample alternative question: Is skin more sensitive in low temperatures than in high temperatures?) **LS Verbal/Logical**

Chapter Summary

The Big Idea The human body has organ systems that respond to its internal and external environments.

Section

1 The Nervous System

Key Concept Your nervous system is an organ system that gathers, interprets, and responds to sensory information.

- The central nervous system processes and responds to all messages coming from the peripheral nervous system.
- The somatic nervous system controls voluntary movements. The autonomic nervous system controls functions that are involuntary.
- The brain is made up of many parts that function together as the control center of the nervous system.

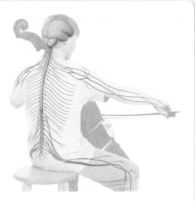

The nervous system is an important human organ system.

2 Sensing the Environment

Key Concept Your organ systems have specialized structures and functions to sense and gather information.

- Pressure, temperature, pain, and vibration are four sensations detected by receptors in the skin.
- A feedback mechanism is a cycle of events in which information from one step controls or affects another step.
- You see an object when it reflects visible light toward your eyes.
- Hearing is the sense that allows you to experience sound energy.

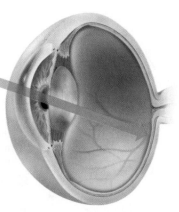

The eye gathers information about the body's external environment.

Vocabulary

central nervous system p. 526
peripheral nervous system p. 526
neuron p. 527
nerve p. 528
brain p. 530

integumentary system p. 534
reflex p. 535
feedback mechanism p. 535
pupil p. 536
retina p. 536
iris p. 537
cochlea p. 538

Chapter Summary

SUPER SUMMARY

Have students connect the major concepts in this chapter through an interactive Super Summary. Visit go.hrw.com and type in the keyword HY7BD4S to access the Super Summary for this chapter.

Identifying Word Parts

Compound Words Ask students to look over the vocabulary words from this chapter and to identify the word that is a compound word, a word that is made up of two words put together. (the word *feedback* in *feedback mechanism* is a compound word) Then, have students work in small groups to find additional compound words in this chapter. **LS Logical**

Focus on Speaking

Scientific Presentation Have students create an oral presentation on either the eye or the ear. The objective of the presentation is to show their audience how the structure of the eye or the ear is related to its function. Students should use overheads or a computer slideshow to accompany their presentation. **LS Visual/Interpersonal**

Review Resources

- 📄 Reinforcement Worksheet **BASIC**
- 📄 Critical Thinking Worksheet **ADVANCED**
- 📄 Chapter Review **GENERAL** (Also in Spanish)
- 📘 Standards Review Workbook (Also in Spanish)
- 📖 Study Guide A **BASIC** (Also in Spanish), B **GENERAL**

Assessment Resources

- 📄 Chapter Tests A **BASIC**, B **GENERAL** (Also in Spanish), C **ADVANCED**
- 📄 Standards Assessment **GENERAL**

Chapter Review

Assignment Guide

Section	Questions
1	1, 2, 4, 6, 10–11, 31–14, 17–18, 20–22, 30
2	3, 5, 7–9, 12, 15–16, 19, 23–29

Answers

Using Vocabulary

1. Sample answer: Structure refers to the shape and/ or composition of an object. Function refers to the job or capabilities of an object.

2. central nervous system
   7.5.a (supporting), **7.5.b** (supporting)

3. retina **7.5.g** (mastering)

4. reflex

5. cochlea **7.5.g** (mastering)

6. neuron **7.5.a** (supporting)

Understanding Concepts

7. c **7.5.a** (supporting), **7.5.b** (supporting)

8. a **7.5.g** (mastering)

9. a **7.6.b** (mastering)

10. a **7.5.a** (supporting)

11. d **7.5.a** (supporting), **7.5.b** (supporting)

12. b **7.5.g** (mastering)

13. Sample answer: The main difference is that the somatic nervous system controls voluntary movements and activities while the autonomic nervous system controls body functions that are automatic. Both systems are important because together they keep your body active and alive. You are able to do all of your voluntary activities while most of your remaining body functions are controlled by the autonomic nervous system.
    7.5.a (mastering), **7.5.b** (mastering)

14. Sample answer: The PNS receives stimuli from inside and outside the body and sends messages to the CNS. The CNS processes the messages and sends responses. The PNS carries the responses to the part of the body that will respond to a stimulus. **7.5.a** (mastering), **7.5.b** (mastering)

Organize

Double Door Review the FoldNote that you created at the beginning of the chapter. Add to or correct the FoldNote based on what you have learned.

Using Vocabulary

❶ **Academic Vocabulary** Explain how the terms *structure* and *function* differ.

Complete each of the following sentences by choosing the correct term from the word bank.

cochlea	axon
reflex	nerve
retina	central nervous
neuron	system

❷ The two parts of your ___ are your brain and spinal cord.

❸ Sensory receptors in the ___ detect light.

❹ A(n) ___ is an involuntary and almost immediate movement in response to a stimulus.

❺ The ___ is a part of the ear that responds to vibrations by creating electric impulses.

❻ A(n) ___ is a specialized cell that receives and conducts electric impulses.

Understanding Concepts

Multiple Choice

❼ Which of the following has receptors for smelling?
a. cochlea cell
b. thermoreceptors
c. olfactory cell
d. optic nerve

❽ Which of the following allows you to see the world in color?
a. cones
b. rods
c. lenses
d. retinas

❾ What must first happen in order for you to see?
a. An object must reflect light.
b. Light must strike the cochlea.
c. The tympanic membrane must be open.
d. Motor neurons must send impulses.

❿ The peripheral nervous system does NOT include
a. the spinal cord.
b. axons.
c. sensory receptors.
d. motor neurons.

⓫ Which part of the brain regulates blood pressure?
a. right cerebral hemisphere
b. left cerebral hemisphere
c. cerebellum
d. medulla

⓬ Which part of the ear gathers and directs sound waves into the ear canal?
a. stirrup
b. external ear
c. inner ear
d. eardrum

Short Answer

⓭ **Concluding** What is the difference between the somatic nervous system and the autonomic nervous system? Why are both systems important to the body?

⓮ **Comparing** What is the relationship between the CNS and the PNS?

⓯ **Describing** What is the function of the bones in the middle ear?

15. Sample answer: The bones of the middle ear transmit vibrations from the eardrum to the cochlea, which converts the vibrations into electrical impulses that are interpreted by the brain as sound. **7.5.g** (mastering)

Writing Skills

16. Students should identify why the shape and structure of the eye or ear helps the organs function. **7.5.a** (mastering), **7.5.g** (mastering)

Critical Thinking

17. An answer to this exercise can be found at the end of this book.

18. Sample answer: A feedback mechanism is a series of events in which one step affects an earlier step in the process. Usually, a feedback mechanism operates over a period of time. A reflex is an immediate and unconscious response to a stimulus. It is not a process.

19. Sample answer: The lens of your eye changes shape so that light rays are focused on the retina and so that you are able to see images from a wide range of distances. **7.5.g** (mastering)

20. Sample answer: The speed of a reflex response can prevent serious harm to the body. Thinking about taking an action might take too long, and an injury could happen while you were thinking about what to do.

Writing Skills

16 **Communicating Concepts** Sensory organs, such as your eyes and ears, have special structures. Write a brief essay describing the relationship between the structures and functions of your eyes or ears.

Critical Thinking

17 **Concept Mapping** Use the following terms to create a concept map: *nervous system, spinal cord, medulla, peripheral nervous system, brain, cerebrum, central nervous system,* and *cerebellum.*

18 **Making Comparisons** Compare a feedback mechanism with a reflex.

19 **Analyzing Ideas** Why is it important for the eye to have a lens that can change shape?

20 **Applying Concepts** Why must your reflexes happen without thinking you about them?

21 **Predicting Consequences** What would happen if your autonomic nervous system stopped working?

22 **Making Comparisons** How are the peripheral nervous system and the central nervous system similar? How are they different?

23 **Making Inferences** Sensory organs are concentrated in the human head. You cannot see, hear, taste, or smell with any other part of your body. Why are the eyes, ears, tongue, and nose located so close to one another?

24 **Expressing Opinions** Most mammals, such as cats and dogs, walk on four legs. When they walk into a room, their head is the first part of their body to enter. Why is it important for their head to enter first?

25 **Applying Concepts** Draw an eye. Label all of the parts that you have learned about, and describe the function of each part.

26 **Analyzing Processes** Describe the steps involved in converting a sound wave into a nerve impulse in the human ear. Be sure to include the name of each structure involved in each step.

27 **Making Comparisons** How do the structure and function of the external ear of a human relate to the structure and function of the external ear of a rabbit?

INTERPRETING GRAPHICS Use the diagram below to answer the next question.

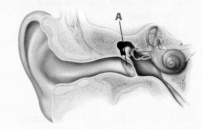

28 **Making Inferences** In the diagram above, how would the function of the ear be affected if A were not present?

Math Skills

29 **Solving Problems** Sound travels about 347 m/s. If your ear canal is 15 mm long, how long does a sound take to travel from the entrance of your ear canal to your eardrum?

Challenge

30 **Analyzing Relationships** Describe how your nervous system responds to and regulates its internal environment.

21. Sample answer: You would eventually die if your autonomic nervous system shut down. Your body could not maintain homeostasis, and functions such as digestion, breathing, and heart rate would soon all stop working properly. **7.5.b** (mastering)

22. Sample answer: The PNS and the CNS are both part of the nervous system. The PNS includes all parts of your nervous system except the brain and spinal cord, which are part of the CNS. The PNS gathers information about the body's internal and external environment, and the CNS interprets this information.
7.5.a (mastering), **7.5.b** (mastering)

23. Sample answer: One reason these sensory organs might be close to one another is that they are all close to the brain reducing the time it takes for information to travel between these organs and the brain. **7.5.a** (exceeding), **7.5.b** (exceeding)

24. Sample answer: When a dog enters a room, the first part of its body to enter is its head. This allows the dog to use its eyes, ears, nose, and whiskers to gather information about the room it is entering. **7.5.a** (exceeding), **7.5.b** (exceeding)

25. Answers should include these parts: retina, optic nerve, cornea, iris, pupil, and lens.
7.5.g (mastering), **7.6.b** (mastering)

26. Sample answer: Sound waves enter the external ear, which directs the sound waves into the ear canal. The ear canal ends in the eardrum, which vibrates with the sound waves. Small bones in the middle ear connect to the fluid-filled cochlea. They vibrate as well. The cochlea translates these vibrations into impulses, which the auditory nerve transmits to the brain.
7.5.g (mastering)

27. Sample answer: Human outer ears cannot move or bend in the direction of the sound. A rabbit's outer ear can bend or swivel toward a sound to help the rabbit determine the direction from which a sound is coming. **7.5.g** (mastering)

28. Sample answer: Without an eardrum, the small bones of the middle ear would not vibrate with sound and the person would not be able to hear. **7.5.b** (mastering), **7.5.g** (exceeding)

Math Skills

29. 15 mm $\times$ (1 m $\div$ 1000 mm/m) = 0.015 m; 0.015m $\div$ 347 m/s = 0.00004 s

Challenge

30. Sample answer: The nervous system is able to detect when the body is hot, cold, hungry, or uncomfortable. The nervous system is then responsible for responding to these needs and coordinating the actions that need to be accomplished to take care of the need.
7.5.a (exceeding), **7.5.b** (exceeding)

Chapter Review Standards Guide			
	Supporting	Mastering	Exceeding
7.5.a	2, 6, 7, 10, 11	13, 14, 16, 22	23, 24, 30
7.5.b	2, 7, 11	13, 14, 21, 22, 28	23, 24, 30
7.5.g		3, 5, 8, 12, 15, 16, 19, 25–28	
7.6.b		9, 25	

Teacher Notes

To provide practice under more realistic testing conditions, give students 20 min to answer all of the questions in this assessment.

Answer Key

Question Number	Correct Answer
1	D
2	A
3	B
4	B
5	C
6	B
7	A
8	A
9	C
10	C
11	D
12	C
13	B
14	C
15	D
16	B

Standards Guide

	Supporting	Mastering	Exceeding
7.1.e			16
7.3.d			15
7.5.a	1	6, 9, 10	
7.5.b	2	7, 8, 11	
7.5.g	3	10, 11	
7.6.b	4	12	
7.6.e		14	
7.7.a	5	13	

🗂 Standards Assessment GENERAL

🗂 Teacher Notes for Standards Assessment contain a longer Assessment Doctor and Diagnostic Teaching Tips.

Standards Assessment

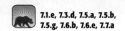 7.1.e, 7.3.d, 7.5.a, 7.5.b, 7.5.g, 7.6.b, 7.6.e, 7.7.a

REVIEWING ACADEMIC VOCABULARY

1 Which of the following words means "the way in which something is put together"?

A built

B gathered

C symbolize

D structure

2 In the sentence "Cells, tissues, and organs contribute to the health of the human body," what does the word *contribute* mean?

A to help bring about a result

B to give money with others

C to submit writing for publication

D to pay a fee or tax

3 In the following sentence "A neuron's function is to pass along electric impulses," what does the word *function* mean?

A variable

B role

C relationship

D action

4 Which of the following words is closest in meaning to the word *detected*?

A retracted

B discovered

C interrupted

D investigated

5 Which of the following is the noun form of the word select?

A selective

B selected

C selection

D selectable

REVIEWING CONCEPTS

6 What two organs make up the central nervous system?

A the neurons and the receptors

B the brain and the spinal cord

C the cerebrum and the eyes

D the skin and the vertebrae

7 What role does the peripheral nervous system play in the body?

A It connects all parts of the body to the central nervous system.

B It sends messages along the spinal cord to muscles and glands.

C It controls activities such as speaking, reading, and writing.

D It interprets electric impulses from the nerves as sensations.

8 When you are startled, your heart rate increases, your pupils dilate, and your digestion slows. Which part of the nervous system controls this response?

A the sympathetic nervous system

B the parasympathetic nervous system

C the somatic nervous system

D the central nervous system

9 What part of the neuron is found at point E in the diagram above?

A dendrite

B axon

C axon terminal

D motor neuron

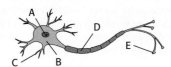 **ASSESSMENT DOCTOR**

Question 1: The correct answer is D. *Structure* means "the way in which something is put together."

Question 2: The correct answer is A. *Contribute* in this context means "to help bring about a result." The functioning of cells, tissues, and organs helps keep the body healthy.

Question 3: The correct answer is B. A neuron's role or function is to pass along electrical impulses.

Question 4: The correct answer is B. *Detected* means "discovered the existence or presence of." The word *detective* has the same root, which means "to uncover."

Question 5: The correct answer is C. *Selection* is the noun form of the word *select*.

Question 6: The correct answer is B. The brain and the spinal cord make up the central nervous system. The spinal cord passes messages to and from the brain, which responds through motor neurons to move muscles or stimulate glands throughout the body.

Question 7: The correct answer is A. The peripheral nervous system connects all parts of the body to the central nervous system through a network of nerves.

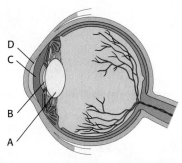

D
C
B
A

10 At which point in the diagram above do you find the muscle that controls how much light enters the eye?

A point A

B point B

C point C

D point D

11 What role does the cochlea play in hearing?

A It catches and funnels sound into the middle ear.

B It causes the stirrup, a bone in the ear, to vibrate.

C It makes the tympanic membrane, or eardrum, vibrate.

D It changes sound waves into electric impulses.

12 Why do your eyes see a banana as yellow?

A because the banana absorbs yellow light

B because the banana reflects white light

C because the banana reflects yellow light

D because the banana contains cone cells

REVIEWING PRIOR LEARNING

13 Which of the following would you most likely need to conduct an experiment testing the function of rods and cones?

A slides of eye cells

B a light with a dimmer switch

C hot and cold packs

D a diagram of the middle ear

14 Which of the following explains why humans see various colors?

A Different wavelengths produce different temperatures.

B Ultraviolet markings on objects determine what colors we see.

C Cone cells respond differently to light of various wavelengths.

D Chemical reactions convert visible light into various colors.

15 What characteristic do all animals in the phylum Chordata have in common?

A They have retractable claws.

B They nurse their young.

C They have a backbone.

D They have a hollow nerve cord.

16 Through what process do neurons increase their numbers?

A interphase

B mitosis

C respiration

D meiosis

Standards Assessment

ASSESSMENT DOCTOR

Question 8: The correct answer is A. The sympathetic nervous system is a subdivision of the autonomic nervous system, which controls involuntary functions. When you are startled, your body prepares to fight or run by increasing heart rate and blood flow, dilating your pupils, and slowing your digestion.

Question 9: The correct answer is C. The axon terminal is shown at point E in the diagram. The end of the axon has branches, and the tips of these branches are axon terminals. An axon terminal allows impulses to pass from the axon to another cell.

Question 10: The correct answer is C. The iris, found at point C in the diagram, is the muscle that controls how much light enters the eye. When the iris contracts, the pupil shrinks and lets in less light. When the iris relaxes, the pupil dilates and lets in more light.

Question 11: The correct answer is D. Neurons in the cochlea, a fluid-filled organ of the inner ear, change sound waves into electrical impulses.

Question 12: The correct answer is C. We see a banana as yellow because the banana reflects yellow light to our eyes.

Question 13: The correct answer is B. A light with a dimmer switch would be an important tool when testing the function of rods and cones, since their functions depend on the level of light available.

Question 14: The correct answer is C. The cone cells in the retina of the eye respond differently to light of different wavelengths.

Question 15: The correct answer is D. Members of the phylum Chordata all have a hollow nerve cord.

Question 16: The correct answer is B. Mitosis is the four-stage process during which a parent cell becomes two identical daughter cells.

Science in Action

Scientific Discoveries

Discussion

Encourage a class discussion on the placebo effect by asking students the following questions:

1. Do you think other therapies, such as acupuncture, homeopathy, or chiropractic care can act as placebos? (Answers may vary.)

2. Do you think it would ever be ethical for a doctor to give a patient a placebo? (Answers may vary.)

3. Do you think a person could become addicted to a placebo? (Answers may vary.)

Science, Technology, and Society

Discussion

Discuss the possibilities of having computers do specialized functions for people with disabilities. Ask students the following questions: What are some things computers can do that humans can't do? (Answers may vary.) What are some of the possibilities for memory, movement, and sensation? (Answers may vary.) What can humans do that computers can't do? (Answers may vary.)

Scientific Discoveries

The Placebo Effect

A placebo (pluh SEE boh) is an inactive substance, such as a sugar pill, used in experimental drug trials. Some of the people who are test subjects are given a placebo as if it were the drug being tested. Usually, neither the doctor conducting the trial nor the test subjects know whether a person is taking a placebo or the test drug. In theory, any change in a subject's condition should be the result of the test drug. But for many years, scientists have known about the *placebo effect,* the effect of feeling better after taking the placebo pill. What makes someone who takes the placebo feel better? By studying brain activity, scientists are beginning to understand the placebo effect.

Social Studies ACTIVITY

Research the differences and similarities between ancient Chinese medical practices and traditional Western medical treatment. Both types of treatment depend in part on a patient's mental and emotional response to treatment. How might the placebo effect be part of both medical traditions? Create a poster showing the results of your research.

Science, Technology, and Society

Making Technology Accessible

When you think of a computer, you may think of a keyboard, a monitor, and a mouse. But computers can take many forms. Thanks to the Archimedes Project founded at Stanford University, now computers are accessible to people who have limited physical abilities. The goal of the Archimedes Project is to create technology that enables people who have a condition such as cerebral palsy or who are quadriplegic to use computers for many tasks.

Language Arts ACTIVITY

At the library or on the Internet, find examples of accessible technology. Research how the technology has been modified for people with disabilities. Write a report in your **Science Journal** about this technology. How does the life of a person with disabilities change when he or she has access to technology?

Answer to Social Studies Activity

Students' posters may include a variety of ancient Chinese medical practices, including acupuncture, acupressure, and herbal medicines. The student should indicate that, in addition to the physical effect of the treatment, any medical treatment might include a mental or emotional component that can be strengthened or weakened by the treatment being employed.

Answer to Language Arts Activity

Students' reports should include examples of how computer technology has been modified for people with disabilities. Students should include stories of how people's lives have been changed through improved access to specialized computer technology.

People in Science

Bertha Madras

Studying Brain Activity The brain is an amazing organ. Sometimes, though, drugs or disease keep the brain from working properly. Bertha Madras is a biochemist who studies drug addiction. Dr. Madras studies brain activity to see how substances, such as cocaine, target cells or areas of the brain. Using a variety of brain-scanning techniques, Dr. Madras can observe a brain on drugs. She can see how a drug affects the normal activity of the brain. During her research, Dr. Madras realized that some of her results could be applied to Parkinson's disease and to attention deficit hyperactivity disorder (ADHD) in adults. Her research has led to new treatments for both problems.

Math Activity

Using a search engine on a computer connected to the Internet, search the Internet for "reaction time experiment." Go to one of the Web sites and take the response-time experiment. Record the time that it took you to respond. Repeat the test nine more times, and record your response time for each trial. Then, make a line graph or a bar graph of your response times. Did your response times change? In what way did they change?

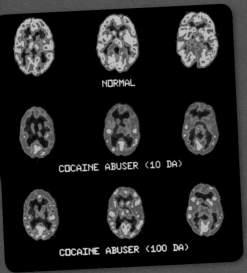

NORMAL

COCAINE ABUSER (10 DA)

COCAINE ABUSER (100 DA)

Internet Resources

- To learn more about careers in science, visit www.scilinks.org and enter the SciLinks code HY70225.

- To learn more about these Science in Action topics, visit go.hrw.com and type in the keyword HY7BD4F.

- Check out articles related to this chapter by visiting go.hrw.com. Just type in the keyword HY7BD4C.

People in Science

Background

Bertha Madras, Ph.D., is a professor of Psychiatry at Harvard Medical School. She also serves as chair of the Division of Neurochemistry at the New England Regional Primate Research Center (part of Harvard Medical School).

Madras has published more than 100 articles and served on a number of committees dedicated to brain and drug research. Madras also volunteers her time as a science teacher and regularly speaks to groups about the impact of drugs on the brain. To help people understand how drugs affect the brain, Madras has developed an exhibit and a CD-ROM called "Changing Your Mind: Drugs and the Brain."

Answer to Math Activity

Students will find several response-time experiments on the Internet. Students may find that their response times improved as they repeated the experiment, perhaps indicating that they were improving their ability to anticipate the cue and to respond to it. Other students may find that their response times declined as they played, indicating that their brains and muscles had become fatigued. Students' graphs should indicate what kind of experiment they took and should reflect their response times.

The elements listed in the Standards Course of Study provide a base for presenting, supporting, and assessing the California Grade 7 Science Standards. Use this Standards Course of Study as a base for planning your lessons.

Why Teach
Reproduction and Development

This chapter was designed to cover the California Grade 7 Science Standards about the human reproductive system (7.1.f, 7.2.b, 7.5.a, 7.5.d, and 7.5.e). It is the last in a series of chapters about the human body systems. This chapter introduces students to the structures of the male and female reproductive systems. This chapter also describes important events in the development of a fertilized egg into an embryo.

Chapter Pacing

Getting Started — 45 min, pp. 554–555
The Big Idea The human body has organ systems that function in reproduction and growth.
7.2.b

Section 1 Human Reproduction — 90 min, pp. 556–561
Key Concept Humans reproduce sexually. They have specialized organs that are responsible for reproduction.
7.2.b, 7.5.a, 7.5.d

Section 2 Growth and Development — 90 min, pp. 562–567
Key Concept Between fertilization and birth, many changes occur. Humans continue to grow and develop until death.
7.1.f, 7.5.d, 7.5.e, 7.7.d

Wrapping Up — 225 min, pp. 568–577
7.5.e, 7.7.b, 7.7.c, 7.7.d

California Standards

Focus on Life Sciences
7.1.f Students know that as multicellular organisms develop, their cells differentiate.

7.2.b Students know sexual reproduction produces offspring that inherit half their genes from each parent.

7.5.a Students know plants and animals have levels of organization for structure and function, including cells, tissues, organs, organ systems, and the whole organism.

7.5.d Students know how the reproductive organs of the human female and male generate eggs and sperm and how sexual activity may lead to fertilization and pregnancy.

7.5.e Students know the function of the umbilicus and placenta during pregnancy.

Investigation and Experimentation
7.7.b Use a variety of print and electronic resources (including the World Wide Web) to collect information and evidence as part of a research project.

7.7.c Communicate the logical connection among hypotheses, science concepts, tests conducted, data collected, and conclusions drawn from the scientific evidence.

7.7.d Construct scale models, maps, and appropriately labeled diagrams to communicate scientific knowledge (e.g., motion of Earth's plates and cell structure).

Basic Learners
- TE Reproductive System Charts, p. 556
- TE Charting Pregnancy, p. 565
- TE Brainstorming, p. 570
- Reinforcement Worksheet
- Chapter Test A
- Differentiated Datasheets A for Labs and Activities ■
- Study Guide A ■

Advanced Learners/GATE
- TE Traits, p. 558
- TE Reproductive Organ Size, p. 562
- TE Animal Reproduction, p. 570
- Critical Thinking Worksheet
- Chapter Test C
- Differentiated Datasheets C for Labs and Activities ■

Key

SE Student Edition
TE Teacher's Edition

📁 Chapter Resource File
📖 Workbook
📊 Transparency

💿 CD or CD-ROM
*   Datasheet or blackline master available

■ Also available in Spanish

All resources listed below are also available on the One-Stop Planner.

Teach

SE **Explore Activity** Dance of the Chromosomes, p. 555* ■

📊 **Bellringer**
💿 **PowerPoint® Resources**
📊 L88 The Male Reproductive System
📊 L89 The Female Reproductive System
📊 L90 Genetic Inheritance and Sexual Reproduction
SE **Quick Lab** Modeling Inheritance, p. 559* ■

📊 **Bellringer**
💿 **PowerPoint® Resources**
📊 L91 Fertilization and Implantation
📊 L92 Human Fetus and Its Life Support
SE **Quick Lab** Development Timeline, p. 564* ■

SE **Skills Practice Lab** It's a Comfy, Safe World, pp. 568–569* ■

Practice

SE **Organize Activity** Pyramid, p. 554

SE **Section Review**, p. 561* ■

SE **Section Review**, p. 567* ■

SE **Science Skills Activity** Using Print Resources for Research, p. 570* ■
📊 **Concept Mapping***
SE **Chapter Review**, pp. 572–573* ■

Assess

📁 **Chapter Pretest**

SE **Standards Checks**, pp. 556, 557, 558
TE **Standards Focus**, p. 560
📁 **Section Quiz** ■

SE **Standards Checks**, pp. 562, 563, 564, 566
TE **Standards Focus**, p. 566
📁 **Section Quiz** ■

SE **Standards Assessment**, pp. 574–575*
📁 **Chapter Tests A, B** ■**, C**
📖 **Standards Review Workbook** ■

Resources for Universal Access • Differentiated Instruction

English Learners
TE Causes of STDs, p. 560
TE Using the Figure, pp. 563, 565
TE Paired Summarizing, p. 565
📁 Vocabulary and Section Summary A ■, B
📁 Section Quizzes ■
📁 Chapter Tests A, B ■
📁 Differentiated Datasheets A, B, and C for Labs and Activities ■
📖 Study Guide A ■
📖 Multilingual Glossary

Struggling Readers
TE Reading Strategy, p. 557
TE Developmental Stages, p. 566

Special Education Students
TE Appropriate Behavior, p. 557
TE Baby Size, p. 563
TE Use the Timeline, p. 564

To help plan your lessons, refer to the On Course Mapping Instruction booklet.

Visual Resources

CHAPTER STARTER TRANSPARENCY

Strange but True!

BELLRINGER TRANSPARENCIES

Section: Human Reproduction
Use the words below to answer the questions that follow.

together
alone
sperm
eggs

1. What is one difference between the male and female reproductive systems?

2. What is one thing the male and female reproductive systems have in common?

Write your answers in your **science journal**.

Section: Growth and Development
Name the stages of physical development you have passed through in your life thus far.

Write your answers in your **science journal**.

TEACHING TRANSPARENCIES

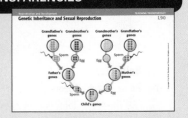

The Male Reproductive System · L88

Genetic Inheritance and Sexual Reproduction · L90

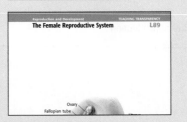

The Female Reproductive System · L89

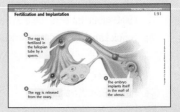

Fertilization and Implantation · L91

TEACHING TRANSPARENCIES

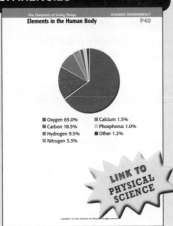

The Human Fetus and Its Life Support · L92

- Placenta
- Umbilical cord
- Umbilicus
- Amnion
- Uterus
- Cervix

Elements in the Human Body · P40

- Oxygen 65.0%
- Carbon 18.5%
- Hydrogen 9.5%
- Nitrogen 3.3%
- Calcium 1.5%
- Phosphorus 1.0%
- Other 1.2%

LINK TO PHYSICAL SCIENCE

STANDARDS REVIEW TRANSPARENCIES

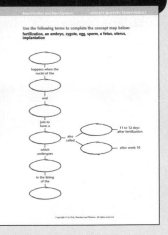

California Science Standard 6.4.e A · Grade 6

ALSO IN SPANISH

CONCEPT MAPPING TRANSPARENCY

Use the following terms to complete the concept map below: fertilization, an embryo, zygote, egg, sperm, a fetus, uterus, implantation

Planning Resources

PARENT LETTER

SAMPLE

Dear Parent,

ALSO IN SPANISH

TEST ITEM LISTING

SAMPLE

ALSO IN SPANISH

One-Stop Planner® CD-ROM

This CD-ROM package includes all of the resources shown here and the following time-saving tools:

- **Lab Materials QuickList Software**

- **Customizable Lesson Plans** Correlated to the California Science Standards

- **Holt Calendar Planner**

- **PowerPoint® Resources**

- **Printable Worksheets**

- **ExamView® Test Generator** Correlated to the California Science Standards

- **Holt PuzzlePro®**

- **Interactive Teacher's Edition**

Meeting Individual Needs

DIRECTED READING A
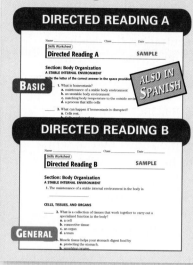
Skills Worksheet
Directed Reading A SAMPLE

Section: Body Organization
A STABLE INTERNAL ENVIRONMENT
Write the letter of the correct answer in the space provided.

BASIC

_____ 1. What is homeostasis?
 a. maintenance of a stable body environment
 b. an unstable body environment
 c. matching body temperature to the outside environment
 d. a process that kills cells

_____ 2. What can happen if homeostasis is disrupted?
 a. Cells rest.

ALSO IN SPANISH

DIRECTED READING B
Skills Worksheet
Directed Reading B SAMPLE

Section: Body Organization
A STABLE INTERNAL ENVIRONMENT
1. The maintenance of a stable internal environment in the body is

CELLS, TISSUES, AND ORGANS

_____ 2. What is a collection of tissues that work together to carry out a specialized function in the body?
 a. a cell
 b. connective tissue
 c. an organ
 d. a team

_____ 3. Muscle tissue helps your stomach digest food by
 a. protecting the stomach.
 b. supplying oxygen.

GENERAL

VOCABULARY AND SECTION SUMMARY A

Skills Worksheet
Vocabulary and Section Summary A SAMPLE

Body Organization
VOCABULARY
In your own words, write a definition of the following terms

1. tissue

ALSO IN SPANISH

BASIC

VOCABULARY AND SECTION SUMMARY B
Skills Worksheet
Vocabulary and Section Summary B SAMPLE

Body Organization
VOCABULARY
After you finish reading the section, try this puzzle! Use the clues given to fill in the blanks below. Then, copy the numbered letters into the corresponding boxes on the following page to reveal the four kinds of tissue.

1. the maintenance of a stable environment inside the body

2. _____ up of similar cells that perform a common function

GENERAL

REINFORCEMENT

Skills Worksheet
Reinforcement SAMPLE

Muscle Map
Complete this worksheet after you finish reading the section "The Muscular System."

Each of the boxes below is labeled with one of the three types of muscle tissue in your body. Write each note in the correct box. Some of the notes can be used more than once.

BASIC

Three Types of Muscle

Skeletal	Cardiac	Smooth

CRITICAL THINKING
Skills Worksheet
Critical Thinking SAMPLE

The Tissue Engineering Debate
Dear Readers:
Be sure to read next week's issue of *Amazing Medicine*, which features an in-depth interview with Dr. E. P. Dermis of Frontiers Medical Center. While visiting the burn therapy unit at Frontiers, I asked Dr. Dermis about treatments for severe burns. She told me about an incredible new treatment called *tissue engineering*.

Scientists are actually growing human skin in laboratories and then attaching the skin to real, live patients! Scientists start the process by taking a piece of human skin and collagen from cows. The cells are grown in a culture, where they develop into tissues. When they are ready, the sheets of skin are moved to the patient's body, where they continue to live. In this way, doctors can permanently _____ patient's burned or diseased skin.

_____ is informed me that scientists are also working on engineering _____ organs like livers, hearts, and kidneys. She believes they'll probably succeed within the next 20 years or so.

Now that's amazing medicine! What do you think?

ADVANCED

INTERACTIVE READER AND STUDY GUIDE
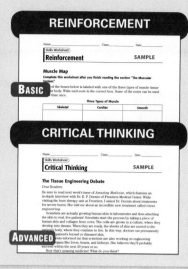
CHAPTER 18 Body Organization and Structure SAMPLE
Body Organization

BEFORE YOU READ
After you read this section, you should be able to answer these questions:
• What is cell differentiation?
• What are the 11 different human organ systems?
• What is homeostasis?

California Science Standards
7.1.7, 2.6.b

MULTILINGUAL GLOSSARY
SAMPLE

A

abiotic/ਅਜੀਵ ...

abrasion/ਖਰਾਸ਼ ...

absolute dating/ਬਿਲਕੁਲ ...

absolute magnitude/ਬਿਲਕੁਲ ...

absolute zero/ਬਿਲਕੁਲ ਸਿਫ਼ਰ ...

absorption/ਸੋਖਣਾ ...

abyssal plain/ਅਥਾਹ ...

acceleration/ਤੇਜ਼ੀ ...

aerobic exercise/ਹਵਾਈ ...

air mass/ਹਵਾ ਦਾ ...

air pollution/ਹਵਾ ...

air pressure/ਹਵਾ ਦਾ ...

alcoholism/ਸ਼ਰਾਬ ...

algae/ਕਾਈ ...

alkali metal/ਖਾਰੀ ...

Labs and Activities

DIFFERENTIATED DATASHEETS FOR EXPLORE ACTIVITY, QUICK LABS, AND CHAPTER LAB

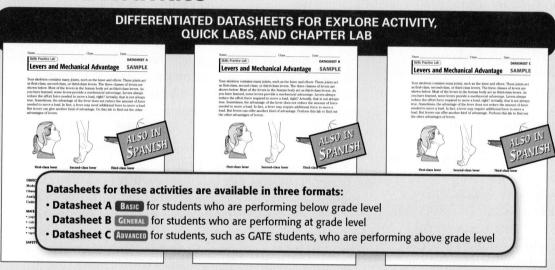

Skills Practice Lab DATASHEET A
Levers and Mechanical Advantage SAMPLE

Your skeleton contains many joints, such as the knee and elbow. These joints act as first-class, second-class, or third-class levers. The three classes of levers are shown below. Most of the levers in the human body act as third-class levers. As you have learned, some levers provide a *mechanical advantage*. Levers always reduce the effort force needed to move a load. Sometimes, the advantage of the lever does not reduce the amount of force needed to move a load. In fact, a lever may need additional force to move a load. But levers can give another kind of advantage. Do this lab to find out the other advantages of levers.

First-class lever   Second-class lever   Third-class lever

Skills Practice Lab DATASHEET B
Levers and Mechanical Advantage SAMPLE

Your skeleton contains many joints, such as the knee and elbow. These joints act as first-class, second-class, or third-class levers. The three classes of levers are shown below. Most of the levers in the human body act as third-class levers. As you have learned, some levers provide a *mechanical advantage*. Levers always reduce the effort force required to move a load, right? Actually, that is not always true. Sometimes, the advantage of the lever does not reduce the amount of force needed to move a load. In fact, a lever may require additional force to move a load. But levers can offer another kind of advantage. Perform this lab to find out the other advantages of levers.

First-class lever   Second-class lever   Third-class lever

Skills Practice Lab DATASHEET C
Levers and Mechanical Advantage SAMPLE

Your skeleton contains many joints, such as the knee and elbow. These joints act as first-class, second-class, or third-class levers. The three classes of levers are shown below. Most of the levers in the human body act as third-class levers. As you have learned, some levers provide a *mechanical advantage*. Levers always reduce the effort force required to move a load, right? Actually, that is not always true. Sometimes, the advantage of the lever does not reduce the amount of force needed to move a load. In fact, a lever may require additional force to move a load. But levers can offer another kind of advantage. Perform this lab to find out the other advantages of levers.

First-class lever   Second-class lever   Third-class lever

ALSO IN SPANISH

Datasheets for these activities are available in three formats:
• **Datasheet A** BASIC for students who are performing below grade level
• **Datasheet B** GENERAL for students who are performing at grade level
• **Datasheet C** ADVANCED for students, such as GATE students, who are performing above grade level

DATASHEET FOR SCIENCE SKILLS ACTIVITY
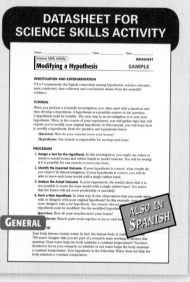
Science Skills Activity DATASHEET
Modifying a Hypothesis SAMPLE

INVESTIGATION AND EXPERIMENTATION
7.7.e Communicate the logical connection among hypotheses, science concepts, tests conducted, data collected, and conclusions drawn from the scientific evidence.

TUTORIAL
When you perform a scientific investigation, you often start with a question and then develop a hypothesis. A hypothesis is a possible answer to the question. A hypothesis must be testable. The next step in an investigation is to test your hypothesis. Often, in the course of your experiment, you will gather data that will require you to modify your original hypothesis. In this tutorial, you will learn how to modify a hypothesis. Read the question and hypothesis below.

Question: How do your bones move?
Hypothesis: One muscle is responsible for moving each bone.

PROCEDURE
1. **Design a Test for the Hypothesis** In this investigation, you might use rulers or sticks to model bones and rubber bands to model muscles. You will be testing if it is possible for one muscle to move a bone.
2. **Identify the Expected Outcome** If your hypothesis is correct, what results do you expect? In this investigation, if your hypothesis is correct, you will be able to move each bone model with a single rubber band.
3. **Analyze the Actual Outcome** In your experiment, the results show that it is not possible to move the bone model with a single rubber band. You notice that the bones will not move predictably or smoothly.
4. **Form a New Hypothesis** In what way do the observations that you made agree with or disagree with your original hypothesis? In this example, your observations disagree with your hypothesis. One muscle did not move each bone. Your hypothesis must be modified. See the modified hypothesis below.

Question: How do your muscles move your bones?
Hypothesis: Muscle pairs work together to move each bone.

GENERAL

ALSO IN SPANISH

Your body tissues contain water. In fact, the human body is made of about 70% water. Imagine that you are part of a research team working to answer this question: Does water help the body maintain a constant temperature? You have decided to focus your research on whether or not water helps the body maintain a constant temperature. Your hypothesis is the following: Water does not help the body maintain a constant temperature.

Reviews and Assessments

SECTION REVIEWS
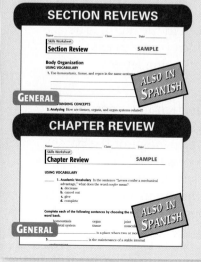
Skills Worksheet
Section Review SAMPLE

Body Organization
USING VOCABULARY
1. Use *homeostasis*, *tissue*, and *organ* in the same sentence.

ALSO IN SPANISH

UNDERSTANDING CONCEPTS
2. **Analyzing** How are tissues, organs, and organ systems related?

GENERAL

CHAPTER REVIEW
Skills Worksheet
Chapter Review SAMPLE

USING VOCABULARY
1. **Academic Vocabulary** In the sentence "Levers confer a mechanical advantage," what does the word *confer* mean?
 a. decrease
 b. cancel out
 c. give
 d. complete

Complete each of the following sentences by choosing the correct ____ from the word bank.

homeostasis   organ   tissue
_____ letal system   joint   muscular ____

2. _____ is a place where two or ____

3. _____ is the maintenance of a stable internal ____

GENERAL

CHAPTER PRETEST
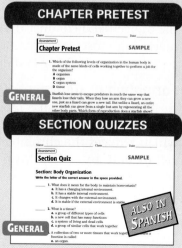
Assessment
Chapter Pretest SAMPLE

_____ 1. Which of the following levels of organization in the human body is made of the same kinds of cells working together to perform a job for the organism?
 A organism
 B organ
 C organ systems
 D tissue

_____ 2. Starfish lose arms to escape predators in much the same way that lizards lose their tails. When they lose an arm they can grow a new one, just as a lizard can grow a new tail. But unlike a lizard, an entire new starfish can grow from a single lost arm by regenerating all the other body parts. Which form of reproduction does a starfish show?

GENERAL

SECTION QUIZZES
Assessment
Section Quiz SAMPLE

Section: Body Organization
Write the letter of the correct answer in the space provided.

_____ 1. What does it mean for the body to maintain homeostasis?
 a. It has a changing internal environment.
 b. It has a stable internal environment.
 c. It changes with the external environment.
 d. It is stable if the external environment is stable.

_____ 2. What is a tissue?
 a. a group of different types of cells
 b. a new cell that has many functions
 c. a system of living and dead cells
 d. a group of similar cells that work together

_____ 3. A collection of two or more tissues that work together to ____ a function is called
 a. an organ.

ALSO IN SPANISH

GENERAL

CHAPTER TEST A
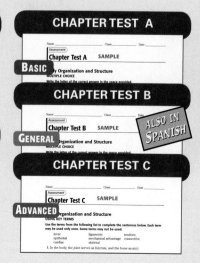
Assessment
Chapter Test A SAMPLE

Body Organization and Structure
MULTIPLE CHOICE
Write the letter of the correct answer in the space provided.

BASIC

CHAPTER TEST B
Assessment
Chapter Test B SAMPLE

Body Organization and Structure
MULTIPLE CHOICE
Write the letter of the correct answer in the space provided.

GENERAL

ALSO IN SPANISH

CHAPTER TEST C
Assessment
Chapter Test C SAMPLE

Body Organization and Structure
USING KEY TERMS
Use the terms from the following list to complete the sentences below. Each term may be used only once. Some terms may not be used.

lever	ligaments	tendons
epithelial	mechanical advantage	connective
cardiac	skeletal	

1. In the body, the joint serves as fulcrum, and the bone as a(n) ____

ADVANCED

STANDARDS ASSESSMENT
Assessment
Standards Assessment SAMPLE

Teacher Notes and Answer Key
To provide practice under more realistic testing conditions, give students 20 min to answer all of the questions in this assessment.

QUESTION NUMBER	CORRECT ANSWER	STANDARD
1	A	7.0 (supporting)
2	B	7.0 (supporting)
3	A	7.0 (supporting)

GENERAL

STANDARDS REVIEW WORKBOOK
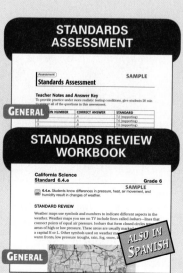
California Science
Standard 6.4.e Grade 6
SAMPLE
6.4.e. Students know differences in pressure, heat, air movement, and humidity result in changes of weather.

STANDARD REVIEW
Weather maps use symbols and numbers to indicate different aspects of the weather. Weather maps you see on TV include lines called *isobars*—lines that connect points of equal air pressure. Isobars that form closed circles show areas of high or low pressure. These areas are usually marked with a capital H or L. Other symbols used on weather maps ____ warm fronts, low pressure troughs, rain, fog, snow, ____

GENERAL

ALSO IN SPANISH

This Teacher Background explains science concepts, principles, and theories that appear in the chapter. Use the information on these pages to refresh or enhance your understanding of the topics covered.

Section 1

Human Reproduction

The Male Reproductive System

As **Figure A** shows, the external organs of the male reproductive system are the scrotum and the penis. Testes, which produce sperm (the male gamete), are located in the scrotum where the temperature, on average, is 2°C cooler than the internal abdominal temperature. This slight drop in temperature makes normal sperm production possible. Testosterone, the most commonly known male hormone, is produced in the Leydig cells which are interspersed between the seminiferous tubules of the testes. The penis is composed of three cylinders of spongy erectile tissue which become filled with blood during sexual arousal. As the blood fills the tissue and the pressure increases in the penis, veins draining the penis are sealed.

In addition to the internal reproductive organs referred to in this chapter, there are three types of accessory glands associated with the male reproductive system. Each accessory gland has an important function in reproduction. Seminal vesicles are responsible for adding roughly 60% of the volume to semen. The substances added by the seminal vesicles are ascorbic acid, a coagulating enzyme, fructose (a energy source for sperm), mucus, and prostaglandins. Another acccessory gland, the prostate gland, contributes anticoagulating enzymes and citrate (a sperm nutrient) to semen. The third type of accessory glands, bulbourethral glands, are responsible for secreting a clear mucus into the urethra before ejaculation. This mucus neutralizes the acidity of any urine left in the urethra and may contain sperm released before ejaculation. These sperm may cause fertilization and pregnancy.

Once it has entered the vagina, sperm undergoes many changes that enhance the likelihood of fertilization. First, the coagulating enzyme added by the seminal vesicles causes the semen to be viscous. When the prostaglandins in semen cause the uterine muscles to contract, the viscous semen is moved further into the uterus. At this point, anticoagulating enzymes cause the semen to be less viscous, allowing the sperm to move freely in the uterus.

The Female Reproductive System

The external organs of the female reproductive system are the clitoris and two sets of labia which surround the vaginal opening and the clitoris. The internal organs of the female reproductive system are shown in **Figure B.** Two ovaries, the female gonads, rest in the abdominal cavity and each contain many thousands of follicles. Each follicle, formed before the birth of the woman, consists of one egg cell (the female gamete) and up to two layers of follicle cells which nourish and protect the egg cell. The follicle cells also produce the primary female sex hormones, the estrogens.

Generally, one egg cell is released at ovulation. The remaining follicle cells, once associated with that particular egg cell, harden and produce additional estrogens and progesterone. The progesterone maintains the uterine lining until, in the absence of fertilization, the egg cell dies. The female reproductive system is not a closed system. During ovulation, egg cells are released into the abdominal cavity and drawn into the oviduct, or fallopian tube, associated with the ovary from which the egg cell erupted. The oviduct is lined with cilia which draw in the egg cell and conduct the cell to the uterus. The uterus is a muscular organ, which is able to expand to accomodate a growing and developing fetus.

Formation of Gametes

In order for sexual reproduction to be possible, somatic cells in human beings must undergo meiosis which reduces the chromosome content of the parent cell by half. In males, this process is called *spermatogenesis* and in females this process is called *oogenesis*. The end result of each process is the production of gametes, or sex cells, that have one copy of each chromosome.

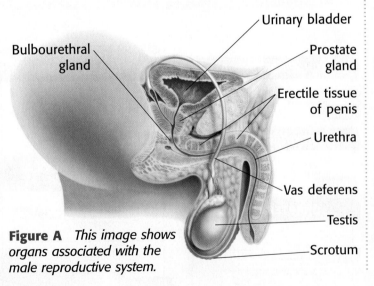

Figure A *This image shows organs associated with the male reproductive system.*

Labels: Urinary bladder · Bulbourethral gland · Prostate gland · Erectile tissue of penis · Urethra · Vas deferens · Testis · Scrotum

Figure B *This image shows organs associated with the female reproductive system.*

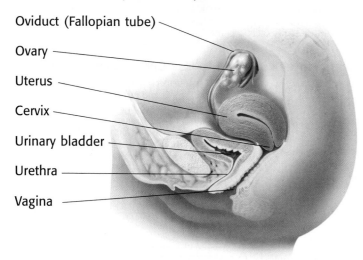

Oviduct (Fallopian tube)

Ovary

Uterus

Cervix

Urinary bladder

Urethra

Vagina

While these processes are superficially similar, there are several significant differences. One significant difference is the fact that spermotogenesis is an ongoing process that occurs throughout much of the adult life of a male. In females, oogenesis occurs before birth and is not known to repeat at any other time.

Section 2

Growth and Development

From Fertilization to Embryo

Even though humans possess 23 different chromosomes, one pair of chromosomes determines the gender of a baby. The chromosomes that determine gender are referred to as X and Y. A female has two X chromosomes and a male has one X chromosome and one Y chromosome. Because the egg contains only the X chromosome, the sex of the baby is determined by the sperm, which may contain either an X or a Y chromosome.

During the development of an embryo, some cells become fixed in their developmental program and are said to be *differentiated*. For example, cells that will eventually divide to give rise to the stomach and intestines are distinguished at a very early stage from cells that will divide to give rise to the central nervous system and parts of the eyes. At later stages of development, a more fine-grained differentiation takes place. For example, some cells in the retina of the eye become rod cells (for vision in dim light) and others become cone cells (for color vision). After differentiation, most cells in humans lose the ability to become other types of cells.

From Embryo to Fetus

The placenta is responsible for providing oxygen to the developing fetus and removing wastes produced by the fetus. The umbilical cord (which attaches to the body of the fetus at the umbilicus) contains arteries and veins that connect the fetus to the placenta. Although the blood of the mother and of her fetus typically do not mix, oxygen and nutrients pass from the mother's blood to the fetus. Wastes, such as carbon dioxide from the fetus, are removed. The placenta helps to nourish and protect the fetus. However, alcohol and many other drugs can easily pass from the mother's blood into the blood of the fetus, as can many infectious viruses, such as the human immunodeficiency virus (HIV). Many kinds of drugs—prescription, non-prescription, and illegal—can pass through the placenta by passive diffusion, and may result in problems such as low birth weight, deformities, and premature birth. The chemicals associated with smoking tobacco are also known to have a negative effect on the placenta's ability to transport materials. In addition, tobacco can cause developmental problems in a baby's lungs and brain resulting in low-birth weight.

The development of a baby from a single cell progresses at an astounding rate. Pregnancy progress is measured by trimesters. During the first trimester, the mother commonly experiences morning sickness, and little if any, weight gain or outward signs of pregnancy. During the second trimester, the fetus grows in size and the bony skeleton develops. Due to the increased size of the fetus, the mother begins to look pregnant and to feel the baby's movements. During the final trimester, the fetus continues to grow in size, and the circulatory and respiratory systems mature. The mother grows to what is often an awkward, uncomfortable size and often walks with a waddle. The mother also often experiences increased body temperature, swelling of the extremities, hair growth on extremities and face, leg cramps, Braxton-Hicks contractions, stretch marks, colostrum, decreased libido, and increased discharge.

Internet Resources

SciLinks is maintained by the National Science Teachers Association to provide you and your students with interesting, up-to-date links that will enrich your classroom presentation of the chapter.

Visit **www.scilinks.org** and enter the SciLinks code for more information about the topic listed.

Topic: Reproduction System Irregularities or Disorders
SciLinks code: HY71298

Topic: Medicine in California
SciLinks code: HY7C09

Topic: Before Birth
SciLinks code: HY70140

Topic: Growth and Development
SciLinks code: HY70700

18 Chapter Preview

Chapter Pretest
Use the Chapter Pretest in the Chapter Resource File to determine the prior knowledge of your students. The Test Doctors and diagnostic teaching tips in the Teacher Notes pages will help you tailor your instruction to your students' specific needs.

Improving Comprehension

Use the Graphic Organizer on this page of the Student Edition to introduce the topics that are covered in this chapter, to summarize the chapter material, or to show how to make combination notes.

Teaching Tips
- Remind students that combination notes provide a way to express information in both words and pictures.
- Remind students that the pictures on the right side of the chart are graphic representations of the information on the left.

LS Logical

Improving Comprehension

Graphic Organizers are important visual tools that can help you organize information and improve your reading comprehension. The Graphic Organizer below is called *combination notes*. Instructions for creating other types of Graphic Organizers are located in the **Study Skills** section of the Appendix.

How to Make Combination Notes
1. Draw a table like the one shown below. Draw the columns to be as long as you want them to be.
2. Write the topic of your notes in the section at the top of the table.
3. In the left column, write important phrases or sentences about the topic. In the right column, draw diagrams or pictures that illustrate the information in the left column.

When to Use Combination Notes
Combination notes let you express scientific information in words and pictures at the same time. Use combination notes to express information that a picture could help explain. The picture could be a diagram, a sketch, or another useful visual representation of the written information in your notes.

Human Development	
• The process of human development usually begins when a man deposits millions of sperm into a woman's vagina and one sperm fertilizes an egg. • Eleven to twelve days after fertilization, the fertilized egg is called an *embryo*. • A normal pregnancy lasts about 40 weeks from the first day of a woman's last menstrual period.	**Human Development Timeline** <table><tr><td>Week #</td><td>What happens?</td></tr><tr><td>2</td><td>Fertilization takes place.</td></tr><tr><td>5</td><td>The spinal cord and brain begin to form.</td></tr><tr><td>11</td><td>The embryo is now called a fetus.</td></tr><tr><td>17</td><td>A layer of fat forms under the skin.</td></tr><tr><td>25</td><td>The lungs are almost ready to breathe air.</td></tr><tr><td>29</td><td>The eyes are open.</td></tr><tr><td>36</td><td>The skull has hardened.</td></tr><tr><td>40</td><td>The baby is born.</td></tr></table>

You Try It!

This Reading Strategy can also be used within the chapter that you are about to read. Practice making your own *combination notes* as directed in the Reading Strategy for Section 1. Record your work in your **Science Journal**.

Using Other Graphic Organizers

Students can practice using a variety of Graphic Organizers while reading this chapter. The following Graphic Organizers may also be useful in this chapter.

A **process chart** can be used to describe the egg's journey, discussed in Section 1.

A **process chart** also can be used to show the stages of human development from birth to death, discussed in Section 2.

A **comparison table** can be used to compare fraternal and identical twins, described in Section 1.

Instructions for creating these Graphic Organizers are located on pp. 583–591 of the Appendix.

Unpacking the Standards

The information below "unpacks" the standards by breaking them down into basic parts. The higher-level, academic vocabulary is highlighted and defined to help you understand the language of the standards. "What It Means" restates the standards as simply as possible.

Unpacking the Standards

Use the following information with the *What It Means* in the Student Edition to help students understand why studying each standard is important.

California Standard	Academic Vocabulary	What It Means	Why It Matters
7.1.f Students know that as multicellular organisms develop, their cells **differentiate.**	**differentiate** (DIF uhr EN shee AYT) to become specialized in structure and function	As a living thing that is made of more than one cell grows, the structure of its cells change so that the cells perform specific jobs.	Differentiation allows multicellular organisms to accomplish the tasks of living efficiently. It also explains the presence of many types of cells.
7.2.b Students know **sexual** reproduction produces offspring that inherit half their genes from each parent.	**sexual** (SEK shoo uhl) having to do with sex	Offspring that are produced through sexual reproduction get half of their genetic material from one parent and half of their genetic material from the other parent.	Sexual reproduction is responsible for the variety that exists between individuals in a single species.
7.5.a Students know plants and animals have levels of organization for **structure** and **function,** including cells, tissues, organs, organ systems, and the whole organism.	**structure** (STRUHK chuhr) the arrangement of the parts of a whole **function** (FUHNGK shuhn) use or purpose	Plants and animals are made of smaller parts which are organized by shape and purpose. These layers of organization include cells, tissues, organs, organ systems, and the whole organism.	Multicellular organisms, including humans, function because their cells are organized at many levels. Each subsequent level of organization has unique properties that the prior level of organization does not have.
7.5.d Students know how the reproductive organs of the human female and male **generate** eggs and sperm and how **sexual** activity may lead to fertilization and pregnancy.	**generate** (JEN uhr AYT) to bring about, to produce	The reproductive organs of women make eggs, and the reproductive organs of men make sperm. When human sperm is present in the woman during ovulation, fertilization and pregnancy may happen.	Knowledge about fertility cycles, pregnancy, and methods for avoiding pregnancy can help one make responsible choices about sexual behavior.
7.5.e Students know the **function** of the umbilicus and placenta during pregnancy.		You must know the purpose of the umbilical cord and the placenta during pregnancy.	Students should understand that the placenta is the structure through which nutrients and gases pass between a mother and a fetus. The placenta does not protect the fetus from harmful substances.

Words with Multiple Meanings

Words that have both common and scientific meanings can be confusing to students. The following table identifies some of those words that are used in this chapter.

Term	Common meaning	Scientific meaning
egg	a thin-shelled product from a bird used in cooking	a sex cell produced by a female
labor	to work	the process by which the fetus and the placenta come out of the uterus

Practice Have students complete the sentences below to help them understand how the scientific and common meanings of the word *labor* can differ.

a. The farmers had to ___ to clear the brush from the field. (labor)

b. My mom was in ___ for 12 hours before my baby brother was born. (labor)

Have students write one definition for the common meaning of the word and one definition for the scientific meaning.

Chapter Overview

This chapter describes the male and female human reproduction systems. It also describes the processes of human reproduction and development.

MISCONCEPTION ALERT

Locating the Fetus

Identify It!   Some students may think that babies develop in the stomach. Other students may be confused about the location of the uterus. Ask students to draw a diagram to illustrate where in a pregnant woman they think a fetus is located. Encourage students to label their drawings. (Answers may vary.)

Correct It!   Use diagrams in this chapter to explain that babies develop in a woman's uterus. Tell students that the uterus sits above the bladder but under the intestine. As the fetus grows, compression of the abdominal and thoracic organs can be a problem late in pregnancy. The compression of organs can cause an expectant mother to experience fatigue, backache, indigestion, circulatory problems, and reduced lung capacity. Use a diagram of internal human anatomy to discuss what organs may be affected by the enlargement of the uterus. (Answers may include the heart, lungs, bladder, intestines, and stomach.)

Assess It!   Ask students to identify mistakes in their original drawings. Ask students to draw another diagram to illustrate where in a pregnant woman they now think a fetus is located.

Reproduction and Development

The Big Idea   The human body has organ systems that function in reproduction and growth.

 California Standards

Focus on Life Sciences

7.1   All living organisms are composed of cells, from just one to many trillions, whose details usually are visible only through a microscope. (Section 2)

7.2   A typical cell of any organism contains genetic instructions that specify its traits. Those traits may be modified by environmental influences. (Section 1)

7.5   The anatomy and physiology of plants and animals illustrate the complementary nature of structure and function. (Sections 1 and 2)

Investigation and Experimentation

7.7   Scientific progress is made by asking meaningful questions and conducting careful investigations. (Science Skills Activity)

Math

7.1.2, 7.1.3   Number Sense

English–Language Arts

7.1.3   Reading
7.2.5   Writing

About the Photo

When your mother was about 13 weeks pregnant with you, you probably looked much like this person. You started out as a single cell, and you became a complete person. And you are still growing and changing!

Organize

Pyramid

Before you read this chapter, create the FoldNote entitled "Pyramid." Label the sides of the pyramid with "The male reproductive system," "The female reproductive system," and "Growth and development." As you read the chapter, define each topic, and write characteristics of each topic on the appropriate side of the pyramid.

Instructions for creating FoldNotes are located in the Study Skills section on p. 579 of the Appendix.

 California Standards Alignment

Focus on Life Sciences

7.1.f   Students know that as multicellular organisms develop, their cells differentiate. pp. 563–565, 567, 572

7.2.b   Students know sexual reproduction produces offspring that inherit half their genes from each parent. pp. 555, 558–559, 561, 573

7.5.a   Students know plants and animals have levels of organization for structure and function, including cells, tissues, organs, organ systems, and the whole organism. pp. 556–557, 561, 572

7.5.d   Students know how the reproductive organs of the human female and male generate eggs and sperm and how sexual activity may lead to fertilization and pregnancy. pp. 556–559, 561–562, 566–567, 572–573

7.5.e   Students know the function of the umbilicus and placenta during pregnancy. pp. 563–564, 567–569, 572–573

Investigation and Experimentation

7.7.b   Use a variety of print and electronic resources (including the World Wide Web) to collect information and evidence as part of a research project. p. 570

7.7.c   Communicate the logical connection among hypotheses, science concepts, tests conducted, data collected, and conclusions drawn from the scientific evidence. pp. 568–569

7.7.d   Construct scale models, maps, and appropriately labeled diagrams to communicate scientific knowledge (e.g., motion of Earth's plates and cell structure). pp. 564, 568–569

Teacher Notes

Students will be modeling what happens in a cell that has one pair of chromosomes as it undergoes meiosis (covers standard 7.2.b). This activity will review meiosis as it prepares students for the discussion of gamete formation in this chapter. Encourage students to bring any instrumental dance music that they enjoy so that the music can help them feel comfortable. Work with groups during the dance creation process to ensure that all groups are depicting the division of diploid cells to create haploid cells.

Materials for Each Group

No materials are needed, but an open area is needed for groups to practice and then demonstrate their dances.

Answers

6. When fertilization occurs, the sperm and egg each contribute one copy of each chromosome to the newly fertilized egg cell.

7. The new cell has two copies of each chromosome.

📋 Differentiated Datasheets
A **BASIC**, B **GENERAL**, C **ADVANCED**

> **Also editable on the Holt Lab Generator CD-ROM**

Explore Activity

🕐 20 min

Dance of the Chromosomes

During meiosis, cells that have two copies of each chromosome divide to form sex cells that have one copy of each chromosome. This is an important process in human reproduction. Females produce sex cells called eggs. Males produce sex cells called sperm. Create a dance that illustrates the steps involved in the formation of egg and sperm cells.

Procedure

1. Review the process of meiosis as presented in Chapter 6, Heredity.

2. Work in a group with three other students.

3. Begin with a diploid cell that contains one pair of chromosomes. A diploid cell has two copies of each chromosome. To each group member assign the role of one chromosome or other cell part.

4. Create a dance that illustrates the behavior of these chromosomes during the formation of haploid sex cells. Haploid cells have one copy of each chromosome. **7.2.b**

5. Perform your dance for your classmates.

Analysis

6. Why is it important that sperm and eggs have only one copy of each chromosome?

7. When a sperm fertilizes an egg, how many copies of each chromosome does the new cell have?

Math Standards

Number Sense 7.1.2 Add, subtract, multiply, and divide rational numbers (integers, fractions, and terminating decimals) and take positive rational numbers to whole-number powers. **pp. 569, 573**

Number Sense 7.1.3 Convert fractions to decimals and percentages and use these representations in estimations, computations, and applications. **p. 561**

English–Language Arts Standards

Reading 7.1.3 Clarify word meaning through the use of definition, examples, restatement, or contrast. **p. 562**

Writing 7.2.5 Write summaries of reading materials (a) Include the main ideas and most significant details; (b) Use the student's own words, except for quotations; (c) Reflect underlying meaning, not just the superficial details. **p. 572**

Strange but True!

> 📦 **Chapter Starter Transparency**
> Use this transparency to help students begin thinking about reproduction and development.

Preteach

Reviewing Prior Knowledge

Ask students what they know about inheritance and genetics. Tell them to think about their own appearance and characteristics to help them remember the outcome of the reproductive process.

Bellringer

Have students focus on standard 7.5.d by asking them to use the words below to answer the questions that follow:

together, alone, sperm, eggs

1. What is one difference between the male and female reproductive systems? (Sample answer: The male system produces sperm, and the female system produces eggs.)

2. What is one thing the male and female reproductive systems have in common? (Sample answer: Neither system can reproduce alone. But together, they can produce a new human being.)

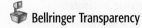 Bellringer Transparency

Motivate

Discussion

Reproduction Lead a discussion about the similarities and differences between the ways different animals reproduce sexually. Help them understand that the end result of reproduction is the same for all animal species, but the means differ widely. **LS Verbal**

Answer to Standards Check

Sperm are produced in the testes.
7.5.d (mastering)

Teaching Transparency:
L88 The Male Reproductive System

What You Will Learn

- The testes and penis are two structures of the male reproductive system.
- The ovaries, uterus, and vagina are three structures of the female reproductive system.
- Sperm are produced in the testes. Eggs are produced in the ovaries.
- During fertilization, each parent contributes one chromosome from each of his or her chromosome pairs to an offspring.

Why It Matters

Sexual reproduction results in offspring that resemble their parents but that are unique individuals.

Vocabulary

- testes
- penis
- ovary
- uterus
- vagina

READING STRATEGY

Graphic Organizer In your **Science Journal,** create Combination Notes that express how a child inherits genes from his or her grandparents. Use words and pictures or diagrams.

7.2.b Students know sexual reproduction produces offspring that inherit half their genes from each parent.
7.5.a Students know plants and animals have levels of organization for structure and function, including cells, tissues, organs, organ systems, and the whole organism.
7.5.d Students know how the reproductive organs of the human female and male generate eggs and sperm and how sexual activity may lead to fertilization and pregnancy.

Human Reproduction

Key Concept Humans reproduce sexually. They have specialized organs that are responsible for reproduction.

▶ About nine months after a human sperm and egg combine and start to grow inside a woman's uterus, she gives birth to her baby. How do humans produce sperm and eggs?

The Male Reproductive System

The function of the male reproductive system is to make and deliver sperm to the female reproductive system. To perform this function, organs of the male reproductive system, shown in **Figure 1,** make sperm, hormones, and fluids. The **testes** (singular, *testis*) are a pair of organs that hang outside the body in the *scrotum,* a skin sac. Testes make sperm and testosterone (tes TAHS tuhr OHN), the main male sex hormone. Testosterone regulates sperm production and the development of male characteristics.

As sperm leave a testis, they are stored in the *epididymis* (EP uh DID i mis), a tube in which sperm mature. Another tube, a *vas deferens* (VAS DEF uh RENZ), passes from the epididymis into the body and through the *prostate gland*. As sperm move through the vas deferens, they mix with fluids from several glands, including the prostate gland. This mixture is *semen.*

Semen passes through the vas deferens into the *urethra* (yoo REE thruh), the tube that runs from the bladder through the penis. The **penis** is the external organ through which semen exits a male's body and can enter a female's body.

Standards Check Where are sperm produced? **7.5.d**

Figure 1 The Male Reproductive System

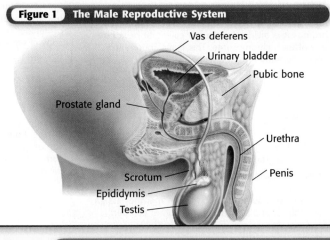

- Vas deferens
- Urinary bladder
- Pubic bone
- Prostate gland
- Urethra
- Penis
- Scrotum
- Epididymis
- Testis

Universal Access · Differentiated Instruction

Basic Learners

Reproductive System Charts Some students will have difficulty remembering how the reproductive system works. Help clarify the process by giving each student a copy of the two reproductive system diagrams in this section. Ask students to use colored markers to draw arrows that identify the path of sperm and eggs. **LS Kinesthetic**

Delivery of Sperm

Of the sperm that leave the body, most sperm exit the penis during *ejaculation*. But, some sperm may exit the penis before ejaculation without the male's knowledge. Sexual activity that includes the release of any sperm—even a few—may lead to *fertilization* and pregnancy. Fertilization occurs when a sperm penetrates, or enters, an egg.

The Female Reproductive System

The female reproductive system, shown in **Figure 2,** produces eggs, nurtures fertilized eggs (zygotes), and gives birth. The two **ovaries** are the organs that make eggs. Ovaries also release estrogen (ES truh juhn) and progesterone (proh JES tuhr OHN), the main female sex hormones. These hormones regulate the release of eggs and development of female characteristics.

Standards Check Where are eggs produced in the female reproductive system? 🐻 **7.5.d**

The Egg's Journey

During *ovulation* (AHV yoo LAY shuhn), an egg is released from an ovary and passes into a *fallopian tube* (fuh LOH pee uhn TOOB). From each ovary, one of two fallopian tubes, also called *oviducts*, leads to the uterus. The egg passes through the fallopian tube into the uterus. Fertilization usually happens in the fallopian tube. If the egg is fertilized, the resulting zygote enters the uterus. The zygote may become embedded in the thickened lining of the uterus. The **uterus** is the organ in which a zygote develops into a baby.

When a baby is born, he or she passes from the uterus through the vagina and emerges outside the body. The **vagina** is the canal between the outside of the body and the uterus.

Figure 2 The Female Reproductive System

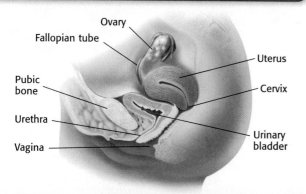

Ovary
Fallopian tube
Uterus
Pubic bone
Cervix
Urethra
Vagina
Urinary bladder

---

testes (TES TEEZ) the primary male reproductive organs, which produce sperm and testosterone (singular, *testis*)

penis (PEE nis) the male organ that transfers sperm to a female and that carries urine out of the body

ovary (OH vuh ree) in the female reproductive system of animals, an organ that produces eggs

uterus (YOO tuhr uhs) in female placental mammals, the hollow, muscular organ in which an embryo embeds itself and develops into a fetus

vagina (vuh JIEN uh) the female reproductive organ that connects the outside of the body to the uterus

Universal Access · Differentiated Instruction

Special Education Students

Appropriate Behavior Students with behavior issues often act out inappropriately during lessons involving the reproductive system. Be proactive and set the stage for the success of all students. Tell them that sometimes people get giggly or want to clown around when discussing the reproductive system. Ask the students to use the textbook to define reproductive system components and explain to them that they will be using these definitions (instead of any slang). Read each page of the section aloud with the students and together create a graphic organizer with the information. **LS** Intrapersonal

Teach, continued

CONNECTION ACTIVITY
Math

Charting Ovulation Pair students and give each pair a sheet of paper with calendars for six months, beginning with the current month. Ask students to assume that today is the 7th day of a menstrual cycle, and have them circle the first day of ovulation on each of the six months. (Students should circle the day that is 7 days away, and then for each successive month, they should count 28 days and circle that date.) **LS Visual**

 Teaching Transparency: L90 Genetic Inheritance and Sexual Reproduction

Cultural Awareness

Dominant and Recessive Traits Explain to students that some nationalities have more dominant visual traits than others. Share the following dominant and recessive information with students and have them identify the dominant traits associated with their own ancestral nationality.

Dominant	Recessive
Brown eyes	Green, hazel, blue, gray eyes
Far sightedness	Normal vision
Normal vision	Near sightedness
Dark hair	Blond, light, red hair
Curly hair	Straight hair
Freckles	No freckles
Full head of hair	Baldness (males)
Broad lips	Thin lips
Dimples	No dimples

Answer to Standards Check

The menstrual cycle is a series of changes that prepares a woman's body for pregnancy. It is an important cycle in the female reproductive system.
7.5.a (supporting), **7.5.d** (mastering)

SCHOOL to HOME

Twins and More

With an adult family member or guardian, discuss some challenges that are created by the birth of twins, triplets, quadruplets, or other multiples. Include financial, mental, emotional, and physical challenges.

Create a poster that shows these challenges. Include ways to meet each challenge.

If twins or other multiples are in your family, discuss how the individuals differ and how they are alike.

ACTIVITY

Universal Access · Differentiated Instruction

Advanced Learners/GATE

Traits Ask students who can benefit from extra in-depth learning to create posters showing at least 50 sets of dominant and recessive traits. Have students work together, so the posters do not include any duplicates. **LS Visual**

Menstrual Cycle

From puberty through her late 40s or early 50s, a woman's reproductive system goes through the *menstrual cycle* (MEN struhl SIE kuhl), a monthly cycle of changes. This cycle of about 28 days prepares the body for pregnancy. The first day of *menstruation* (MEN STRAY shuhn), the monthly discharge of blood and tissue from the uterus, is counted as the first day of the cycle. Menstruation lasts about 5 days. When menstruation ends, the lining of the uterus thickens.

Ovulation occurs on about the 14th day of the cycle. Before ovulation, an egg develops within a *follicle*. Follicles are structures in the ovaries. Ovulation occurs when the egg is released from the ovary into one of the fallopian tubes. The fallopian tubes lead from the ovaries into the uterus. If the egg is not fertilized, menstruation begins and flushes the egg away.

Standards Check What is the purpose of the menstrual cycle?
7.5.a, 7.5.d

Fertilization

If sperm are present in the female reproductive system within a few days of ovulation, fertilization may occur. During fertilization, a single sperm penetrates an egg. Mature egg or sperm has only one copy of each chromosome. After fertilization, the fertilized egg has two copies of each chromosome. Remember, chromosomes and the genes that they contain are the genetic information in each of your cells. As **Figure 3** shows, the sperm and egg each contribute one chromosome to each chromosome pair in the fertilized egg, which is called a *zygote*.

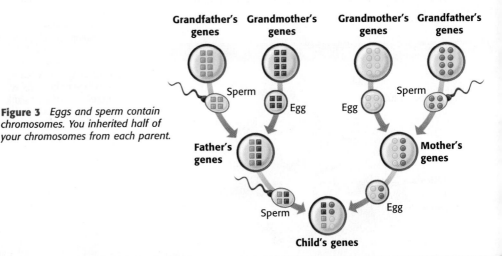

Figure 3 *Eggs and sperm contain chromosomes. You inherited half of your chromosomes from each parent.*

SCIENCE HUMOR

Q: How did the twins' full-length mirror get broken?

A: They got confused while playing catch.

Modeling Inheritance

During sexual reproduction, parents contribute genetic information to offspring. In this activity, you will model inheritance, the passing on of genetic information from parent to offspring.

1. Copy the table shown to the right. A trait is a form of a genetic characteristic. For example, blue fur is a form of fur color. For most characteristics, there is more than one trait that a parent may pass along to its offspring during sexual reproduction. The gene for each trait is called an *allele*. Alleles are represented by letters: capital letters for dominant alleles and lowercase letters for recessive alleles. For each characteristic, each parent gives one allele to each offspring. By knowing an offspring's two alleles for a characteristic, you can determine what the offspring looks like for that characteristic.

2. For each characteristic, flip a **coin** to pick which allele each parent will pass to the offspring. Heads represents a dominant allele (capital letter). Tails represents a recessive allele (lower case letter).

Parent Alleles				
Characteristic	**Mother**		**Father**	
Fur color	F	f	F	f
Number of eyes	E	e	E	e
Number of antennae	A	a	A	a

3. Record your results in your data table by circling the allele that each parent contributed.

4. Below your table, write the alleles that the offspring receives, such as FF, Ee, and aa.

5. Use the chart that your teacher drew to decide what the offspring in your model looks like. Sketch the offspring.

6. What did each parent contribute to the offspring?

7. Each parent has blue fur, five eyes, and four antennae. Does the offspring look like the parent? Why or why not?

⏱ 20 min

Multiple Births

In a multiple birth, a mother gives birth to two or more babies at a time. The birth of twins is the most common multiple birth. Identical twins develop from a single egg that splits into two. Identical twins can be so similar that their parents cannot tell them apart. The boys in **Figure 4** are identical twins. Fraternal twins develop from two eggs and are more common than identical twins are. Fraternal twins can look very different from each other and can be of opposite sexes.

In every 1,000 births, about 30 sets of twins are born. About one-third of twin births are of identical twins. Some multiple births are of triplets (three babies). In the United States, there are about two sets of triplets in every 1,000 births. Rarer types of multiple births are births of quadruplets (four babies) and quintuplets (five babies). Births of five or more babies happen only once in about 53,000 births.

Figure 4 *Identical twins have genes that are exactly the same. Many identical twins who are raised apart have similar personalities and interests.*

Discussion

Multiple Births Tell students that a Russian woman in the 18th century gave birth to 69 children, of which 67 lived to reach adulthood. Ask students: "If this woman began ovulation at age 12 and stopped ovulating at age 50 and pregnancy lasts 9 months, how could she have had so many children?" (Write the following answer on the board to demonstrate how it is possible that she had 69 children: She had 27 pregnancies, all of them producing 2 or more children. She had 16 pairs of twins, 7 sets of triplets, and 4 sets of quadruplets.

$$(16 \times 2) + (7 \times 3) + (4 \times 4) = 69$$

LS Logical

ACTIVITY

Reproductive System Cancer
Have students work in small groups to research breast, testicular, ovarian, prostate, or cervical cancer. Ask students to focus on the incidence of the disease, its risk factors, and the importance of early detection. Have students use the information they gather to design and create a public service brochure—complete with artwork—designed to educate the public about the disease. Allow students time to present and discuss their brochures in class.
LS Visual

⏱ 20 min

Teacher Notes

Before completing this lab, review the inheritance of genetic material in humans using **Figure 3** in this section. Put the following chart on the board. This lab helps students understand genetic inheritance (covers standard 7.2.b).

	Homozygous Dominant	**Heterozygous Dominant**	**Homozygous Recessive**
Fur color	FF- blue fur	Ff- blue fur	ff- red fur
Number of eyes	EE- 5 eyes	Ee- 5 eyes	ee- 3 eyes
Number of antennae	AA- 4 antennae	Aa- 4 antennae	aa- 6 antennae

Materials for Each Student
• coin (1)

Answers

6. Each parent contributed half of the offspring's genetic material.

7. Answers may vary. Students should describe what the offspring looks like and compare the offspring to the parents.

📄 Differentiated Datasheets
A **BASIC**, B **GENERAL**, C **ADVANCED**

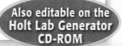
Also editable on the **Holt Lab Generator CD-ROM**

Standards Focus

This **Standards Focus** provides you with a quick way to **assess, reteach,** and **re-assess** one or more concepts in the section.

Assess

1. What purpose does the epididymis serve? (It's the site where sperm mature and are stored before they leave the testes.) **7.5.d**

1. From where does the fertilized egg get its chromosomes? (Half of the chromosomes in a fertilized egg come from the sperm and half come from the egg.) **7.2.b**

Reteach

Making Puzzles Organize the class into small groups. Challenge each group to create a crossword puzzle using the vocabulary words and italicized terms from each section. Have each group write appropriate clues and construct a puzzle. Then, have groups exchange puzzles. Allow time for students to solve puzzles.

LS Logical/Interpersonal

Re-Assess

Tracing the Path If appropriate for your class, ask students to make diagrams that illustrate the path an egg or sperm must travel before fertilization. Have them label anatomical structures and indicate, with arrows, the direction in which the sex cell travels.

LS Visual **7.5.d**

Choose Your Parents

Introduce the animal contestants of a new game show called "Choose Your Parents!" Go to **go.hrw.com,** and type in the keyword HY7BD5W.

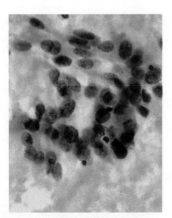

Figure 5 *Cancer of the cervix is one of the most common forms of reproductive system cancers in women.*

Table 1	The Spread of STDs in the United States
STD	**Approximate number of new cases each year**
Chlamydia	3 to 10 million
Genital HPV (human papillomavirus)	5.5 million
Genital herpes	1 million
Gonorrhea	650,000
Syphilis	70,000
HIV/AIDS	40,000 to 50,000

Reproductive System Problems

Most of the time, the reproductive system functions well. But problems such as disease and infertility can cause it to fail.

Sexually Transmitted Diseases (STDs)

Chlamydia and herpes are common sexually transmitted diseases. A *sexually transmitted disease* (STD) is a disease that can pass from one person to another person during sexual contact. STDs are also called *sexually transmitted infections* (STIs). These diseases affect many people each year, as shown in **Table 1.** The STD *acquired immune deficiency syndrome* (AIDS) is caused by the *human immunodeficiency virus* (HIV). AIDS is a fatal disease. HIV destroys the immune system by attacking white blood cells. Because of their weakened immune system, people who have AIDS generally die from infections other than HIV infection. These people are said to have died of AIDS-related causes.

The *hepatitis B virus* (HBV) causes an STD that is a liver disease. HBV can be spread by sexual contact. In the United States, about 140,000 new hepatitis B cases occur each year.

Cancer

Sometimes, cancer happens in reproductive organs. *Cancer* is a disease in which cells grow at an uncontrolled rate. Cancer cells start out as normal cells. Then, something triggers, or causes, uncontrolled cell growth. These triggers vary for different types of cancer.

In men, the two most common reproductive system cancers are cancer of the testes and cancer of the prostate gland. In women, the two most common reproductive system cancers are breast cancer and cancer of the cervix. The *cervix* is the lower part, or neck, of the uterus. The cervix opens to the vagina. **Figure 5** shows cancerous cells from the cervix.

Infertility

In the United States, about 15% of married couples have difficulty producing offspring. Many of these couples are *infertile,* or unable to have children. Men who do not produce enough healthy sperm may be infertile. Women who do not ovulate normally may be infertile. Assisted reproductive technology (ART), one type of which is shown in **Figure 6,** helps some infertile couples conceive. Sexually transmitted diseases, such as gonorrhea and chlamydia, can cause infertility in women. STD-related infertility occurs in men, but not as commonly as in women.

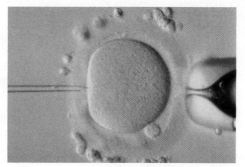

Figure 6 *In one type of assisted reproductive technology (ART), a single sperm is injected into a single egg.*

SECTION Review

7.2.b, 7.5.a, 7.5.d

Summary

The male reproductive system produces sperm and can deliver sperm to the female reproductive system.

The female reproductive system produces eggs, nurtures zygotes, and gives birth.

If sperm are present in the female reproductive system within a few days of ovulation, fertilization may occur.

A fertilized egg has one chromosome from each chromosome pair of the parents.

Humans usually have one child per birth, but some people have multiple births.

Human reproduction can be affected by infertility and by diseases such as cancer.

Using Vocabulary

1 Use *uterus* and *vagina* in the same sentence.

Understanding Concepts

2 Identifying What are the structures and functions of the male and female reproductive systems?

3 Comparing How is the production of sperm in the male reproductive system similar to the production of eggs in the female reproductive system?

4 Describing What are two reproductive system problems?

Critical Thinking

5 Predicting Consequences In females, an egg travels to the uterus through a fallopian tube approximately once a month. However, untreated STDs in women can block the fallopian tubes. How is fertilization affected in this situation?

6 Applying Concepts Twins can happen when a zygote splits in two or when two eggs are fertilized at the same time. Describe the difference between these situations in terms of how the offspring inherit genetic material from their father.

Math Skills

7 Making Calculations In one country, 7 out of 1,000 infants die before their first birthday. Convert this statistic into a percentage.

Challenge

8 Identifying Relationships How do the male and female reproductive systems rely on other organ systems?

Internet Resources

For a variety of links related to this chapter, go to www.scilinks.org

Topic: Reproduction System Irregularities or Disorders; Medicine in California

SciLinks code: HY71298; HY7C09

---

6. Answers may vary. When a single fertilized egg splits in two, each cell contains identical genes. If each cell develops into a separate baby, they will be identical twins. When two separate eggs are fertilized, their genes are different. This results in fraternal twins. **7.2.b** (exceeding)

7. $7 \div 1,000 = 0.007$; $0.007 \times 100\% = 0.7\%$; This is less than 1%.

8. Sample answer: The male and female reproductive systems are nourished by nutrients that are carried to them by the circulatory system. The nervous system also gathers information about and coordinates the activities of the reproductive systems. There are many ways that the reproductive system relies on other body systems.
7.5.a (mastering), **7.5.d** (exceeding)

Section Review Standards Guide			
	Supporting	**Mastering**	**Exceeding**
7.2.b			6
7.5.a		8	
7.5.d	1, 4	2–3	5, 8

Answers to Section Review

1. Sample answer: A woman's vagina is the canal that connects the uterus to the outside world. **7.5.d** (supporting)

2. Answers may vary. In males, testes make sperm and produce testosterone, which help regulate sperm production and the development of male characteristics. The penis is the external male organ that transfers semen into the female's body. In females, ovaries are the organs that make eggs and release estrogen and progesterone, which regulate the release of eggs and the development of female characteristics. The uterus is the organ in which the fertilized egg develops. The vagina is the canal that connects the uterus to the outside world, through which a baby passes when it is born. **7.5.d** (mastering)

3. Sperm and eggs are both sex cells. This means that they each have one copy of each chromosome. Sex cells are made in reproductive organs. **7.5.d** (mastering)

4. One reproductive system problem is infertility. Infertility is the inability to have children. Sexually transmitted diseases (STDs) are a second reproductive system problem. STDs can infect the reproductive system and may cause infertility. **7.5.d** (supporting)

5. An egg cannot be fertilized. **7.5.d** (exceeding)

Section Resources

- Directed Reading A **BASIC** (Also in Spanish), B **GENERAL**
- Interactive Reader and Study Guide
- Section Quiz **GENERAL** (Also in Spanish)
- Section Review **GENERAL** (Also in Spanish)
- Vocabulary and Section Summary A **BASIC** (Also in Spanish), B **GENERAL**

Reviewing Prior Knowledge

Ask students to name two specialized organs that human males use for reproduction and two specialized organs that human females use for reproduction. (Sample answer: male–testes, penis; female–ovary, uterus)

Bellringer

Have students focus on standard 7.5.d by writing the following statement on the board:

Name the stages of physical development you have passed through thus far in your life.

Have students list the stages in their **Science Journal.** Remind students that their growth and development began while they were still in the uterus. (Accept all reasonable answers. Make sure students realize that the stages are 1–Fertilization to Embryo, 2–Embryo to Fetus, 3–Birth, 4–Infancy and Childhood, 5–Adolescence, 6–Adulthood)

Bellringer Transparency

Motivate

Discussion

Life Stages Ask students to name as many characteristics of each of the following as they can: infancy, childhood, adolescence, and adulthood. Tell students that while there are individual differences, all people go through these stages. **LS** Logical

Answer to Standards Check

Fertilization occurs in the female reproductive system, generally in the fallopian tube or oviduct. Implantation occurs in the uterus. **7.5.d** (mastering)

Teaching Transparency:
L91 Fertilization and Implantation

What You Will Learn
- Fertilization is the beginning of an embryo's development during pregnancy.
- Organs and tissues develop as an embryo becomes a fetus.
- A developing human relies on the placenta and umbilical cord.
- There are many stages of human development from birth to death.

Why It Matters
The processes of growth and development shape human lives.

Vocabulary
- embryo
- placenta
- pregnancy
- umbilical cord
- fetus

READING STRATEGY

Outlining In your **Science Journal,** create an outline of the section. Use the headings from the section in your outline.

embryo (EM bree OH) in humans, a developing individual, from fertilization through the 10th week of pregnancy

7.1.f Students know that as multicellular organisms develop, their cells differentiate.
7.5.d Students know how the reproductive organs of the human female and male generate eggs and sperm and how sexual activity may lead to fertilization and pregnancy.
7.5.e Students know the function of the umbilicus and placenta during pregnancy.

Growth and Development

Key Concept Between fertilization and birth, many changes occur. Humans continue to grow and develop until death.

To develop into a baby, a single cell must divide many times. But the development of a baby from a single cell is only the first stage of human development.

From Fertilization to Embryo

Ordinarily, the process of human development starts as a result of sexual activity in which a man ejaculates millions of sperm into a woman's vagina. A few hundred sperm move from the vagina, through the uterus, and into a fallopian tube, or oviduct. If an egg is there, these sperm cover the egg's protective outer coating. Usually, only one sperm pierces, or *penetrates,* the coating. Penetration by a sperm causes a change in the coating that prevents penetration by other sperm. The sperm's nucleus and the egg's nucleus join, and the egg is fertilized.

Over five or six days, the fertilized egg, or zygote, travels down the fallopian tube to the uterus. The fertilized egg is also known as an **embryo.** During the trip, the embryo undergoes many cell divisions. By seven to eight days after fertilization, the embryo has become a tiny ball of cells. Then, implantation occurs. *Implantation* is the embedding of the embryo in the thick, nutrient-rich lining of the uterus. **Figure 1** shows fertilization and implantation.

Standards Check Where do the processes of fertilization and implantation occur? **7.5.d**

Figure 1 Fertilization and Implantation

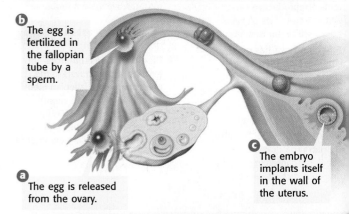

b The egg is fertilized in the fallopian tube by a sperm.

a The egg is released from the ovary.

c The embryo implants itself in the wall of the uterus.

Universal Access • Differentiated Instruction

Advanced Learners/GATE

Reproductive Organ Size Some students may benefit from a chance to explore a topic beyond the details given in the textbook. Ask these students to conduct research on the Internet to find out the general size of fallopian tubes and ovaries. Then, have students draw or create models of life-size ovaries and fallopian tubes.
LS Kinesthetic

From Embryo to Fetus

After implantation, the placenta forms. The **placenta** is a special two-way exchange organ. The placenta's network of blood vessels provides the embryo with oxygen and nutrients from the mother's blood. The embryo's wastes move into the mother's blood through the placenta. The mother's body then excretes the wastes. In the placenta, the embryo's blood and the mother's blood flow near each other but usually do not mix.

Weeks 1 and 2

Doctors commonly measure a woman's **pregnancy** as starting from the first day of her last menstrual period. On that day, fertilization has not yet taken place, but that day is an easy-to-recognize date from which to count. A normal pregnancy lasts about 40 weeks from that day.

Weeks 3 and 4

Fertilization occurs at about the end of week 2. In week 3, the zygote moves to the uterus. The zygote is an early stage of embryo. The embryo is called a *zygote* only from the time that the sperm and egg nuclei join until the time of the first cell division. As it moves, the embryo divides many times. It becomes a ball of cells that implants itself in the wall of the uterus. In this stage, some cells begin to specialize, or become *differentiated*. For example, some cells become blood cells.

Weeks 5 to 8

Weeks 5 to 8 of pregnancy are weeks 3 to 6 of embryonic development. From this stage until birth, the embryo is surrounded by a thin membrane called the *amnion* (AM nee AHN). Amniotic fluid fills the amnion, which cushions and protects the growing embryo. In week 5, the umbilical cord forms. The **umbilical cord** connects the embryo to the placenta. **Figure 2** shows the umbilical cord, amnion, and placenta. The umbilical cord is attached to the fetus at the *umbilicus,* or navel.

In this stage, the heart, brain, other organs, and blood vessels start to form and grow quickly. In weeks 5 and 6, eyes and ears form and the spinal cord begins to develop. In week 6, tiny limb buds that will become arms and legs appear. In week 8, muscles start to develop. Nerves in the shoulders and upper arms grow. Fingers and toes start to form. The embryo, now about 16 mm long, can swallow and blink.

Standards Check Why is the umbilical cord important? **7.5.e**

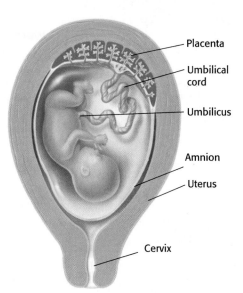

Placenta
Umbilical cord
Umbilicus
Amnion
Uterus
Cervix

Figure 2 *The placenta, amnion, and umbilical cord are the life support system for the fetus. This fetus is about 20 to 22 weeks old.* **What is the function of the placenta?**

placenta (pluh SEN tuh) the partly fetal and partly maternal organ by which materials are exchanged between a fetus and the mother

pregnancy (PREG nuhn see) in medical practice, the period of time between the first day of a woman's last menstrual period and the delivery of her baby (about 280 days, or 40 weeks)

Wordwise differentiated
The prefix *dif-* means "apart" or "in different directions." The root *fer-* means "to bring" or "to bear."

umbilical cord (uhm BIL i kuhl KAWRD) the ropelike structure through which blood vessels pass and by which a developing mammal is connected to the placenta

Quick Lab ⏱ 15 min

Teacher Notes

This lab helps students understand a fetus's development during pregnancy (covers standards 7.1.f, 7.5.e, and 7.7.d). Make sure students tape the two pieces of paper side-to-side in the vertical position so that they have enough length to list all of the weeks on their timeline and have enough width to draw the lines as long as necessary. You may want to prepare the paper for the students before they begin the lab.

Materials for Each Student
• paper, 2 pieces
• tape

Answers

4. week 5

5. The placenta supplies oxygen and nutrients from the mother's blood and passes wastes from the embryo to the mother's blood so she can excrete them.

6. weeks 3 and 4

7. weeks 17 to 24

📋 **Differentiated Datasheets**
A **BASIC**, B **GENERAL**, C **ADVANCED**

Also editable on the Holt Lab Generator CD-ROM

Answer to Standards Check

The fetus is able to make a fist and move. **7.1.f** (mastering)

---

fetus (FEET uhs) a developing human from the end of the 10th week of pregnancy until birth

Quick Lab

Development   **7.1.f**
Timeline   **7.5.e**
   7.7.d

Use the timeline in **Figure 3** and the text in this section to show the developing human's size increase during pregnancy.

1. Take **two pieces of paper** and **tape** them together.

2. Along the long edge of the paper, write the week numbers as shown in **Figure 3**.

3. Above each appropriate week number, draw a line that represents the size of the embryo or fetus at that week. List the major developments that occur at each stage.

4. When does the umbilical cord form?

5. What is the placenta's role in fetal development?

6. When do the fetus's blood cells begin to differentiate, or become specialized?

7. Between what weeks does the largest growth spurt occur?

⏱ **15 min**

Weeks 9 to 16

In this stage, the embryo changes as cells continue to form tissues and organs. At week 9, the embryo may make tiny movements. After week 10, the embryo is called a **fetus** (FEET uhs). At week 13, the fetus's face begins to look more human. Fetal muscle tissue grows stronger. As a result, the fetus can make a fist, and move. The fetus grows rapidly during this stage. Within a month, the size of the fetus doubles and then triples. For example, in week 10, the fetus is about 36 mm long. At week 16, the fetus is about 108 to 116 mm long. **Figure 3** shows changes that occur in the fetus as the fetus develops.

Standards Check   Describe two things that a fetus can do in weeks 9 to 16 as a result of stronger fetal muscle tissue. 🐾 **7.1.f**

Weeks 17 to 24

By week 17, the fetus can make faces. Usually, in week 18, the fetus starts to make movements that the mother can feel. By week 18, the fetus can hear sounds through the mother's body and may even jump at loud noises. By week 23, fetal movements may be vigorous. A fetus that is born at week 24 might survive if given intensive medical care. In weeks 17 to 24, the fetus grows to a length of 25 to 30 cm.

Weeks 25 to 36

At about 25 or 26 weeks, the fetus's lungs are well developed but not fully mature. The fetus still gets oxygen from its mother through the placenta. The fetus will not take its first breath of air until it is born. By the 32nd week, the fetus's eyes can open and close. Studies of fetal heart rate and brain activity show that fetuses respond to light. Some scientists have observed brain activity and eye movements in sleeping fetuses that resemble the brain activity and eye movements of sleeping children or adults. These scientists think that a sleeping fetus may dream. After 36 weeks, the fetus is almost ready to be born.

Birth

At 37 to 38 weeks, the fetus is fully developed. A full-term pregnancy usually lasts about 40 weeks. Typically, as birth begins, the mother's uterus begins a series of muscular contractions called *labor*. Usually, these contractions push the fetus through the mother's vagina, and the baby is born. The newborn is still connected to the placenta by its umbilical cord, which is tied and cut. All that will remain of the point where the umbilical cord was attached is the baby's navel. Soon, the mother expels the placenta, and labor is complete.

MISCONCEPTION ⚠ **ALERT**

Pregnancy   Most students probably think that a woman is actually pregnant during what is called "Week 1" of a pregnancy. Ask students to carefully read the second paragraph on p. 563. Tell students that fertilization has not taken place on the last day of a woman's period, so she is not pregnant yet. Ask students to explain why pregnancy weeks are counted from before the pregnancy began. (Sample answer: Pregnancies are counted from the last day of the last menstrual cycle because it is an easily recognizable date.)

Universal Access • Differentiated Instruction

Special Education Students

Use the Timeline   Make sure all students understand the timeline on the opposite page. Ask students to work with a partner and to write the week numbers from the timeline on the left side of two pieces of paper (2 through 20 on the first piece and 22 through 40 on the second piece) so they have plenty of space to write. Have them recreate the timeline using their own words. **LS Visual/Interpersonal**

Figure 3 Pregnancy Timeline

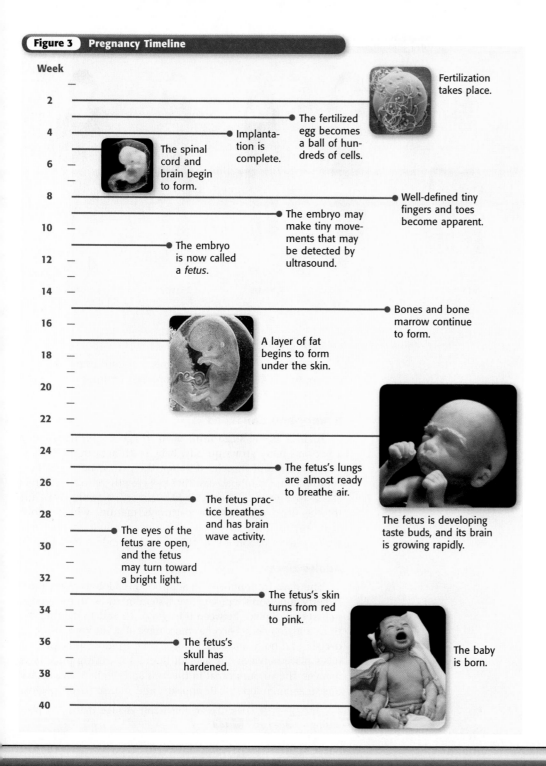

Week

2 — Fertilization takes place.

4 — The fertilized egg becomes a ball of hundreds of cells.

Implantation is complete.

6 — The spinal cord and brain begin to form.

8 — Well-defined tiny fingers and toes become apparent.

10 — The embryo may make tiny movements that may be detected by ultrasound.

12 — The embryo is now called a *fetus*.

14 —

16 — Bones and bone marrow continue to form.

18 — A layer of fat begins to form under the skin.

20 —

22 —

24 —

26 — The fetus's lungs are almost ready to breathe air.

28 — The fetus practice breathes and has brain wave activity.

30 — The eyes of the fetus are open, and the fetus may turn toward a bright light.

The fetus is developing taste buds, and its brain is growing rapidly.

32 —

34 — The fetus's skin turns from red to pink.

36 — The fetus's skull has hardened.

38 —

The baby is born.

40 —

Using the Figure

Pregnancy Timeline Direct students' attention to **Figure 3.** Ask them to identify the weeks during which the major organs and body structures form. (weeks 5–12) Ask them to describe the events that occur during the remainder of the pregnancy. (All of the organs and body structures formed earlier in the pregnancy grow and mature during weeks 13–40. As all of the structures grow and develop, the fetus becomes more prepared for birth and to survive outside the uterus.) **LS** Visual

CONNECTION ACTIVITY
Earth Science

Sonograms Sound waves can be used to make images. Sonograms are images obtained by bouncing high-frequency sound waves off of an object. Sonar uses sound waves to take pictures of things underwater. Have students research how sonar is used to navigate ships and locate objects underwater. **LS** Visual/Verbal

Homework

Writing **Fetal Alcohol Syndrome** Point out to students that drinking alcohol during the first few weeks of a pregnancy can lead to birth defects and miscarriages. Have students research the causes and consequences of Fetal Alcohol Syndrome (FAS) and present their findings in a short report. **LS** Verbal

---

Universal Access · Differentiated Instruction

Basic Learners

Charting Pregnancy Many students learn best when they have hands-on examples. Divide students into small groups. Give each group a calendar (or calendars) that covers at least nine months from the current date. Ask groups to determine the due date of a woman who is pregnant and finished her last menstrual cycle six weeks ago today. (Students should select a date that is 34 weeks from the current date.) **LS** Logical/Kinesthetic

English Learners

Paired Summarizing Have students work in pairs to write a short summary of the text under each subhead under "Embryo to Fetus." To accomplish this, ask them to take turns reading one paragraph at a time, and summarizing what they have read. Then, tell them to write down one sentence summaries of each section and then to compare their sentences to the key details in **Figure 3.** **LS** Verbal/Auditory

Standards Focus

This **Standards Focus** provides you with a quick way to **assess**, **reteach**, and **re-assess** one or more concepts in the section.

Assess

1. What is implantation? (It is the process by which an embryo embeds itself in the uterus.) **7.5.d**

2. What function does the placenta serve in the reproductive process? (It is a two-way exchange organ that allows oxygen and nutrients to travel to the fetus from the mother and allows wastes to travel from the fetus to the mother for her to excrete.) **7.5.e**

Reteach

From Birth to Adulthood Have students work in pairs to design, create, and illustrate a pamphlet or brochure that briefly describes human growth and development from birth to old age.

LS Interpersonal

Re-Assess

Life as a Fetus Ask students to imagine that they have not yet been born. Have them write first-person stories describing their time *in utero*. Encourage creativity, but direct students to include the actual stages of development that fetuses go through. Allow time for students to share their stories with the class. **LS** Verbal

7.1.f, 7.5.e

Answer to Standards Check

A person's reproductive system becomes mature. **7.5.d** (exceeding)

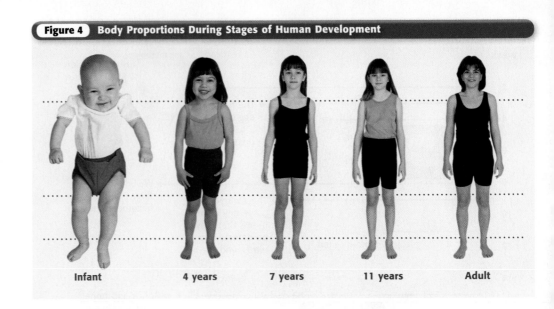

Figure 4 Body Proportions During Stages of Human Development

| Infant | 4 years | 7 years | 11 years | Adult |

From Birth to Death

After birth, the human body goes through several stages of development. A human's body proportions during those stages are shown in **Figure 4.**

Infancy and Childhood

Infancy is the stage from birth to age 2. During infancy, a person's body grows quickly. Baby teeth appear. As the nervous system and muscles develop, the person becomes more coordinated. Childhood, another fast-growth period, lasts from age 2 to puberty. In childhood, permanent teeth grow and replace baby teeth. Nerve pathways mature, which allows a person to learn new skills. Muscle coordination increases, which allows people to do things such as ride a bicycle.

Adolescence

The stage from puberty to adulthood is adolescence. During puberty, a person's reproductive system matures. In most boys, puberty takes place between the ages of 11 and 16. During this time, a male's body becomes more muscular, his voice becomes deeper, and body and facial hair appear. In most girls, puberty takes place between the ages of 9 and 14. During puberty in females, the amount of fat in the hips and thighs increases, the breasts enlarge, body hair appears, and menstruation begins.

Standards Check Describe an important change that takes place during adolescence. **7.5.d**

Adulthood

From about age 20 to age 40 is the stage of young adulthood. Physical development is at its peak. Beginning around age 30, changes associated with aging begin. These changes are gradual and vary from person to person. Some early signs of aging include loss of muscle flexibility, deterioration of eyesight, increase in body fat, and some loss of hair.

The aging process continues in middle age, which occurs from age 40 to age 65. During this time, hair may turn gray, athletic abilities usually decline, and skin may wrinkle. A person who is more than 65 years old is considered an older adult. Although the aging process continues through the end of life, many older adults lead very active lives, as **Figure 5** shows.

Figure 5 *Many older adults can still enjoy activities that they enjoyed when they were younger.*

SECTION Review

7.1.f, 7.5.d, 7.5.e

Summary

- Fertilization occurs when a sperm from the male joins with an egg from the female.

- First as an embryo and then as a fetus, a developing human undergoes many changes between implantation and birth.

- During the development of a human, cells differentiate.

- The umbilical cord and placenta support the developing human during pregnancy by providing oxygen and nutrients and by removing waste materials.

- The first stage of human development lasts from fertilization to birth.

- After birth, a human goes through four more stages of growth and development.

Using Vocabulary

❶ Write an original definition for *umbilical cord*.

❷ Use *embryo* and *fetus* in the same sentence.

Understanding Concepts

❸ **Describing** Outline the order of the development of tissues and organs in an embryo and fetus.

❹ **Summarizing** Describe the processes of fertilization and implantation.

❺ **Listing** What are five stages of human development?

INTERPRETING GRAPHICS Use the image below to answer the next question.

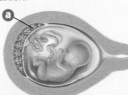

❻ **Evaluating** What is the role of the structure indicated by **a**?

Critical Thinking

❼ **Applying Concepts** Why does the egg's covering change after a sperm has entered the egg?

❽ **Analyzing Ideas** Do you think that one stage of a human's life is more important than other stages are? Explain your answer.

Math Skills

❾ **Making Calculations** Alice is 80 years old, and she entered puberty when she was 12 years old. Calculate the percentage of her life that she has spent in each of the four stages of development after birth.

Internet Resources

For a variety of links related to this chapter, go to www.scilinks.org
Topic: Before Birth; Growth and Development
SciLinks code: HY70140; HY70700

---

7. The covering keeps other sperm from entering the egg and uniting with the nucleus. This is important because it helps maintain the correct chromosome number. **7.5.d** (exceeding)

8. Sample answer: Adolescence is the most important stage because that is when humans reach sexual maturity. Without sexual maturity, the species could not survive.

9. • infancy: 2 y ÷ 80 y = 0.025 = 2.55%

   • childhood (age 2 to age 12): 10 y ÷ 80 y = 0.125 = 12.5%

   • adolescence (age 12 to age 20): 8 y ÷ 80 y = 0.1 = 10%

   • adulthood (age 20 to age 80): 60y ÷ 80y = 0.75 = 75%

Section Review Standards Guide

	Supporting	Mastering	Exceeding
7.1.f		3	
7.5.d		4	7
7.5.e	1–2	6	

Answers to Section Review

1. The umbilical cord is a cord that forms during the 5th week of pregnancy and connects the embryo or fetus to the placenta. **7.5.e** (supporting)

2. Sample answer: An embryo is less developed than a fetus is. **7.5.e** (supporting)

3. Sample answer: An embryo begins as a single fertilized egg cell, then develops into a ball of cells that embeds itself in the wall of the uterus. Soon, the amnion, placenta, and umbilical cord form to protect and nourish the embryo. The embryo develops and, after week 10, it is called a fetus. By week 12, all of the major organ systems have begun to form and grow. By week 16, the fetus is moving strongly enough for the mother to feel the movements. From week 12 to week 40, all body systems continue to grow and strengthen. At about week 40, the fetus is ready to be born. **7.1.f** (mastering)

4. Fertilization happens when a sperm's nucleus unites with an egg's nucleus to form a zygote. Implantation takes place when an embryo embeds itself in the wall of the uterus. **7.5.d** (mastering)

5. fertilization to birth, infancy, childhood, adolescence, and adulthood

6. The role of structure *a*, which is the placenta, is to provide nutrients and oxygen to the fetus or embryo and remove wastes. **7.5.e** (mastering)

Section Resources

📁 Directed Reading
   A **BASIC** (Also in Spanish), B **GENERAL**

📁 Interactive Reader and Study Guide

📁 Section Quiz **GENERAL** (Also in Spanish)

📁 Section Review **GENERAL** (Also in Spanish)

📁 Vocabulary and Section Summary
   A **BASIC** (Also in Spanish), B **GENERAL**

Skills Practice Lab

Teacher Notes

This lab demonstrates the relationship between the structure and function of reproductive organs. Using models, this lab also illustrates the role and importance of the umbilicus and umbilical cord during pregnancy (covers standards 7.5.e, 7.7.c, and 7.7.d).

Time Required

Two 45-minute class periods

Lab Ratings

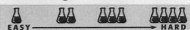

Teacher Prep 🔥🔥
Student Set-Up 🔥
Concept Level 🔥
Clean Up 🔥🔥🔥

Materials

This lab may require some large plastic bags, a meterstick, and various other materials depending on the students' designs. Soft-boiled eggs will simplify the cleanup. Students may want to wear gloves.

Safety Caution

Remind students to review all safety cautions and icons before beginning this lab activity. Students should wash their hands after handling the eggs.

Preparation Notes

Students will be dropping their models, so this lab should be done over a large plastic sheet. You may want to do this lab outside, because it may be quite messy. Students can modify their models in any way they feel will improve the protection.

Using Scientific Methods

Skills Practice Lab

OBJECTIVES

Construct a model of a human uterus protecting a fetus.

Compare the protection that a bird's egg gives a developing baby bird with the protection that a human uterus gives a fetus.

MATERIALS

- computer (optional)
- cotton, soft fabric, or other soft materials
- eggs, soft-boiled and in the shell (2 to 4)
- eggs, soft-boiled and peeled (3 or 4)
- gloves, protective
- mineral oil, cooking oil, syrup, or other thick liquid
- plastic bags, sealable
- water

SAFETY

7.5.e Students know the function of the umbilicus and placenta during pregnancy.

Investigation and Experimentation

7.7.c Communicate the logical connection among hypotheses, science concepts, tests conducted, data collected, and conclusions drawn from the scientific evidence.

7.7.d Construct scale models, maps, and appropriately labeled diagrams to communicate scientific knowledge (e.g., motion of Earth's plates and cell structure).

It's a Comfy, Safe World!

Before hatching, baby birds live inside a hard, protective shell until the baby has used up all of the food supply. Before birth, most mammal babies develop within their mother's uterus, in which they are surrounded by fluid and connected to a placenta. Before human babies are born, they lead a comfy life. By the seventh month of development, they suck their thumb, blink their eyes, and perhaps even dream.

Ask a Question

1 Inside which structure is a developing organism better protected from bumps and blows: the uterus of a placental mammal or the egg of a bird?

Form a Hypothesis

2 A placental mammal's uterus protects a developing organism from bumps and blows better than a bird's egg does.

Test the Hypothesis

3 Brainstorm ways to construct and test your model of a mammalian uterus. Then, use the materials provided by your teacher to build your model. A peeled, soft-boiled egg will represent the fetus inside your model uterus.

4 Make a data table similar to **Table 1** below. Test your model, examine the egg for damage, and record your results.

Table 1 First Test of Model Uterus	
Original model	**Modified model**
DO NOT WRITE IN BOOK	

5 Modify your model as necessary; test this modified model by using another peeled, soft-boiled egg; and record your results.

6 When you have completed the model's design, obtain another peeled, soft-boiled egg and a soft-boiled egg in the shell. The egg in the shell represents the baby bird inside the egg.

Lab Resources

📋 Differentiated Datasheets
A BASIC, B GENERAL, C ADVANCED

📼 Classroom Lab Video/DVD

Holt Lab Generator CD-ROM

Search for any lab by topic, standard, difficulty level, or time. Edit any lab to fit your needs, or create your own labs. Use the Lab Materials QuickList software to customize your lab materials list.

7 Make a data table similar to **Table 2** below. Test only the peeled egg inside the model. Then, test the egg in the shell as is. Examine the eggs for damage. Record the results in your data table.

Table 2	Final Test of Model Uterus
	Test results
Model	DO NOT WRITE IN BOOK
Egg in shell	

Analyze the Results

8 **Explaining Events** Explain how the test results for the model differ from the test results for the egg in a shell.

9 **Analyzing Results** What modification to your model protected the "fetus" most effectively?

Draw Conclusions

10 **Evaluating Data** Review your hypothesis. Did your data support your hypothesis? Why or why not?

11 **Evaluating Models** What modifications to your model might make it more like a uterus?

Big Idea Question

12 **Analyzing Relationships** How is a human placenta and umbilical cord specialized to protect and provide for a developing human before he or she is born?

Applying Your Data

Use the Internet or the library to find information about the development of monotremes, such as the echidna or the platypus, and the development of marsupials, such as the koala or the kangaroo. Then, using what you have learned in this lab, compare the development of placental mammals with the development of marsupials and monotremes.

Analyze the Results

8. Answers may vary. An egg floating in a viscous liquid in a plastic bag, wrapped in soft cotton and placed inside another bag should not be damaged when dropped from a height of 1 m. An egg protected only by a shell should break. In general, the more protected the fetus or egg, the more resistant to damage it is and the less damage it will suffer when dropped from a height of 1 m.

9. Answers may vary according to students' modifications. Most students will observe that the more soft wrapping and/or viscous fluid protecting the egg, the better the egg survived the drop from 1 m.

Draw Conclusions

10. Accept all reasonable answers. Students' answers may vary depending on the data collected.

11. Accept all reasonable answers. Students' answers may vary depending on their model and the data collected.

Big Idea Question

12. Accept all reasonable answers that describe the function of the placenta and uterus.

Applying Your Data

Students should recognize that all mammals have internal fertilization. Students should include the ideas that monotreme mammals lay eggs with leathery shells and, after the eggs hatch, nurture their young with milk that oozes from pores in the mother's skin. Marsupial mammals give birth to live young that are very underdeveloped; the young move to a pouch and continue their development in the pouch. Placental mammals also give birth to live young, but their young are more developed than those of marsupial mammals. Even so, placental mammals may have to care for their young for several years.

TEACHER TESTED & APPROVED

Christine Erskine
Brier Elementary School
Fremont, California

Teacher Notes

After students have made a list of key words, tell them that most research is completed for the betterment of people. Explain that, to this end, most researchers share their ideas with other researchers. Encourage students to share their key word lists with each other.

Answers to You Try It!

3. Key words help you find what is most important to you when you are reading print resources.

4. Answers may vary. Accept all reasonable answers that describe the student's experience.

5. Answers may vary. Students should list specific print resources.

6. Answers may vary. Students will need to describe where they need to go to find information regarding their research.

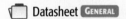 Datasheet GENERAL

Also editable on the Holt Lab Generator CD-ROM

Science Skills Activity

| Scientific Methods | Research | Data Analysis | Models, Maps & Diagrams |

Investigation and Experimentation

7.7.b Use a variety of print and electronic resources (including the World Wide Web) to collect information and evidence as part of a research project.

Using Print Resources for Research

▶ Tutorial

Print resources that you might use in a research project include newspapers, magazines, journals, encyclopedias, and other books. Reading is one way to get information from a print resource. But there are several other ways to quickly get information from a print resource. The following tips are ways to help you quickly find what you are looking for.

Procedure

1 **List Your Keywords** After you have gathered your print resources, make a list of keywords that are important to your research project.

2 **Find the Main Idea** Often, the main idea of the paragraph is stated in the first sentence. And the last sentence restates that idea.

3 **Important Headings and Illustrations** When you find a page that appears to have useful information, read the headings on that page to see if they relate to your topic. Then, look at any pictures, diagrams, charts, or maps on the page to see if they relate to your topic. Be sure to read the captions.

4 **Scan the Resource** Read only a few words here and there. Scan a passage in order to find keywords. By scanning, you can decide which parts of the text you should concentrate on.

5 **Skim the Resource** Read only a sentence or two. Look for sentences that look especially important. Skim a passage to get a general idea of what it is about or to determine if you want to read some parts more carefully.

▶ You Try It!

Some scientists study the reproduction and development of animals to understand human reproduction and development. Use chapter 14 in this textbook and the procedure above to research how and why animals reproduce.

Procedure

1 Before you begin, what keywords will be helpful to search for?

2 Follow each of the steps outlined above and make notes in a chart similar to the one below.

> Research Topic:
> Key Words:
> Print Source:
> Important Information:

Analysis

3 **Describing** Why is choosing your key words before you begin your research important?

4 **Evaluating** Did this print resource include useful information for your research topic?

5 **Designing** What other print resources would be useful for researching this topic? Newspapers, journals, and magazines often have information about new discoveries. Books usually have explanations of processes and facts that have been accepted by many scientists.

6 **Concluding** Describe the additional steps that you would need to follow to continue your research on this topic. Where might you find print resources that are useful for your research?

Universal Access · Differentiated Instruction

Basic Learners

Brainstorming Some students struggle with brainstorming on their own. Allow students to brainstorm key words in pairs. Make sure to pair students so that the students complement each other's skills. **LS Interpersonal**

Advanced Learners/GATE

Animal Reproduction Some students can benefit from more in-depth activities. Ask these students to actually locate a couple of the research sources and write a short report explaining how and why animals reproduce. Ask them to orally share the information they find with the rest of the class. **LS Interpersonal**

Chapter Summary

The Big Idea The human body has organ systems that function in reproduction and growth.

Section		Vocabulary

1 Human Reproduction

Key Concept Human beings reproduce sexually. They have specialized organs that are responsible for reproduction.

- The testes and penis are two structures of the male reproductive system.
- The ovaries, uterus, and vagina are three structures of the female reproductive system.
- Sperm and eggs are produced in specialized reproductive organs.
- During fertilization, each parent contributes one chromosome from each of his or her chromosome pairs to an offspring.

Male reproductive system

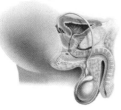

Female reproductive system

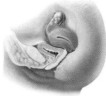

Male and female reproductive systems have specialized organs for reproduction.

testes p.556
penis p. 556
ovary p. 557
uterus p. 557
vagina p. 557

2 Growth and Development

Key Concept Between fertilization and birth, many changes occur. Humans continue to grow and develop until death.

- Fertilization is the beginning of an embryo's development during pregnancy.
- Organs and tissues develop as an embryo becomes a fetus.
- The embryo relies on the placenta and umbilical cord.
- There are many stages of human development from birth to death.

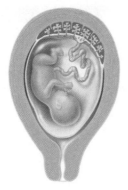

A developing fetus relies on the umbilical cord and placenta.

embryo p. 562
placenta p. 563
pregnancy p. 563
umbilical cord p. 563
fetus p. 564

Review Resources

- 📁 Reinforcement Worksheet **BASIC**
- 📁 Critical Thinking Worksheet **ADVANCED**
- 📁 Chapter Review **GENERAL** (Also in Spanish)
- 📘 Standards Review Workbook (Also in Spanish)
- 📘 Study Guide A **BASIC** (Also in Spanish), B **GENERAL**

Assessment Resources

- 📁 Chapter Tests A **BASIC**, B **GENERAL** (Also in Spanish), C **ADVANCED**
- 📁 Standards Assessment **GENERAL**

Chapter Summary

SUPER SUMMARY

Have students connect the major concepts in this chapter through an interactive Super Summary. Visit go.hrw.com and type in the keyword HY7BD5S to access the Super Summary for this chapter.

Identifying Word Parts

Singular and Plurals Discuss that some words form plurals in unusual ways. Ask students to make two columns on a piece of paper. Tell them to write the singular form of each vocabulary word in the left column and the plural form in the right column. Point out that they can use a dictionary if they need help. (Answer: *testis, testes; penis, penises* or *penes; ovary, ovaries; uterus, uteri* or *uteruses; vagina, vaginas* or *vaginae; embryo, embryos; placenta, placentas* or *placentae; pregnancy, pregnancies; umbilical cord, umbilical cords; fetus, fetuses*)
LS Visual

Focus on Speaking

Explaining the Standards Organize the class into small groups, and assign each group a standard covered in the chapter. Ask each group to give an oral presentation that explains their standard and how the standard relates to the material in the chapter. Every student in the group should have a chance to speak. After each presentation, invite the class to ask the presenting group questions.
LS Verbal/Interpersonal

Chapter Review

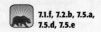
Assignment Guide

Section	Questions
1	1, 3, 5–9, 11, 14, 15, 18–20, 27–28
2	2, 12, 13, 16, 17, 22

Answers

Using Vocabulary

1. a

2. An embryo is a developing human, from when the zygote becomes a ball of cells by the third week, through the 10th week of pregnancy. A fetus is a developing human from the 10th week of pregnancy until birth. **7.5.d** (mastering)

3. Testes are male organs that produce sperm. Ovaries are female organs that produce eggs. **7.5.d** (mastering)

4. The uterus is the female organ in which a fertilized egg is embedded and the fetus develops. The vagina is the female organ that connects the uterus to the outside of the body. **7.5.d** (mastering)

5. Fertilization happens when the nucleus of a sperm unites with the nucleus of an egg. Implantation is when the embryo embeds itself in the wall of the uterus. **7.5.d** (mastering)

6. The umbilical cord links the fetus with the placenta. The placenta is the organ that helps the fetus get oxygen and nutrients and helps the fetus get rid of wastes. **7.5.e** (mastering)

Understanding Concepts

7. a **7.1.f** (supporting), **7.5.a** (supporting)

8. c **7.5.d** (supporting)

9. a **7.5.d** (supporting)

10. d **7.5.a** (mastering), **7.5.d** (mastering)

11. The testes produce sperm, and the ovaries produce eggs. **7.5.d** (mastering)

12. The placenta is a specialized organ that allows the fetus to get oxygen and get rid of wastes. **7.5.e** (mastering)

Organize

Pyramid Review the FoldNote that you created at the beginning of the chapter. Add to or correct the FoldNote based on what you have learned.

Using Vocabulary

1 **Academic Vocabulary** In the sentence "Human reproductive organs in the female and male generate eggs and sperm," what does the word *generate* mean?
a. make
b. cause
c. touch off
d. spawn

For each pair of terms, explain how the meanings of the terms differ.

2 *embryo* and *fetus*

3 *testes* and *ovaries*

4 *uterus* and *vagina*

5 *fertilization* and *implantation*

6 *umbilical* cord and *placenta*

Understanding Concepts

Multiple Choice

7 Tissues and organs develop as an embryo becomes a fetus. Humans grow in size as they become adults. How are cells responsible for the growth that humans experience as they become adults?
a. through cell division
b. through cell expansion
c. through cell death
d. through cell contraction

8 All of the following are sexually transmitted diseases EXCEPT
a. chlamydia.
b. AIDS.
c. infertility.
d. genital herpes.

9 The formation of identical twins occurs when
a. a fertilized egg splits in two.
b. two separate eggs are fertilized.
c. implantation occurs.
d. menstruation occurs.

10 Which of the following is a function of the reproductive system?
a. to produce all of the body's hormones
b. to regulate body temperature
c. to make hormones that fight disease
d. to regulate the development of male and female characteristics

Short Answer

11 **Identifying** Which human reproductive organs produce sperm? Which produce eggs?

12 **Describing** Explain how the fetus gets oxygen and nutrients and how the fetus gets rid of wastes.

13 **Summarizing** What are four stages of human life after birth? Describe each stage.

14 **Listing** Name and describe three problems that can affect the human reproductive system.

15 **Modeling** Draw a diagram showing the structures of the male and female reproductive systems. Label each structure, and explain how each structure contributes to fertilization and implantation.

16 **Describing** When do cells begin to differentiate in a developing human?

Writing Skills

17 **Writing from Research** You have been asked to research the effects of vitamins on the growth and development of a human fetus. Develop a thesis for your research project. Then, briefly describe your project.

13. infancy, childhood, adolescence, and adulthood; Infancy is the stage from birth to age 2. Childhood lasts from age 2 to puberty. Adolescence is the stage from puberty to adulthood. Adulthood begins at about age 20.

14. Sample answer: Infertility is a problem because it may prevent people from having babies. STDs are a problem because they can damage a person's reproductive system, and they may also cause infertility. Cancer is a problem because it can damage a person's reproductive system and may result in infertility or death. **7.5.d** (supporting)

15. Drawings should resemble the images in Section 1, Figure 1, The Male Reproductive System, and Section 1, Figure 2, The Female Reproductive System. **7.5.a** (mastering), **7.5.d** (mastering)

16. Cells begin to differentiate in weeks 3 and 4 of an embryo's life. **7.1.f** (mastering)

Writing Skills

17. Answers may vary. Students should write a main idea or hypothesis about the effect of vitamins on a human fetus. They may describe gathering research or interviewing doctors and mothers about vitamin use during pregnancy.

Critical Thinking

18 **Concept Mapping** Use the following terms to create a concept map: *testes, penis, ovary, uterus, vagina, embryo, placenta, reproductive organs,* and *umbilical cord.*

19 **Applying Concepts** How do parents contribute genetic material to their offspring?

20 **Making Inferences** The birth of twins is the most common type of multiple birth—30 sets of twins are born for every 1,000 births. But the birth of quintuplets is very rare—1 set of quintuplets is born in about 53,000 births. Why might multiple births in which a large number of babies are born be less common than multiple births in which a small number of babies are born?

21 **Drawing Conclusions** Menstruation is affected by a hormone called *estrogen.* A woman who produces little estrogen may not have a menstrual cycle. In turn, the production of estrogen is affected by body fat. A woman who has little body fat usually produces less estrogen. What might happen to the menstrual cycle of a female athlete who exercises a lot?

INTERPRETING GRAPHICS Use the image below to answer the next question.

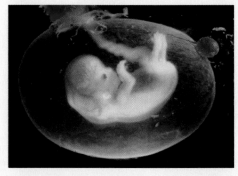

22 **Identifying Relationships** What is the name and function of the cord that connects the fetus to its mother?

INTERPRETING GRAPHICS The following graph shows the cycles of the female hormone estrogen and the male hormone testosterone. The blue line shows the estrogen level in a female over the 28 days of her menstrual cycle. The red line shows the testosterone level in a male over the same time period. Use the graph below to answer the next four questions.

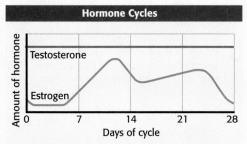

Hormone Cycles

23 **Evaluating Data** Over the 28 days, how do the day-to-day levels of testosterone differ from the day-to-day levels of estrogen?

24 **Applying Concepts** Compare the estrogen cycle to a woman's menstrual cycle. How are they related?

25 **Making Inferences** Why might the level of testosterone stay the same?

26 **Making Inferences** Do you think that the above estrogen cycle would change in a pregnant woman? Explain your answer.

Math Skills

27 **Making Calculations** Identical twin births happen once in 100 births. How many sets of identical twins might you expect at a school that has 2,700 students?

Challenge

28 **Identifying Relationships** How is the placenta specialized for its function?

---

24. Estrogen affects the menstrual cycle. **7.5.d** (exceeding)

25. Testosterone levels stay the same because the male reproductive system does not have a cycle like the female reproductive does.
7.5.d (exceeding)

26. Sample answer: yes; I think it might change because estrogen affects the menstrual cycle. During pregnancy, the menstrual cycle stops, so the level of estrogen will level off until the pregnancy is over.
7.5.d (exceeding)

Math Skills

27. About 27 pairs of identical twins; $(2700 \div 100 = 27)$

Challenge

28. Answers may vary. Sample answer: The placenta is specialized for its function because it allows the blood of the fetus and the blood of the mother to exchange nutrients, waste products, and oxygen without the blood mixing. **7.5.e** (mastering)

Chapter Review Standards Guide			
	Supporting	**Mastering**	**Exceeding**
7.1.f	7	16	
7.2.b		19	
7.5.a	7	10, 15	
7.5.d	8–9, 14, 23	2–5, 10–11, 15, 18, 21	24–26
7.5.e		6, 12, 18, 22, 28	

Critical Thinking

18. An answer to this exercise can be found at the end of this book.
7.5.d (mastering), **7.5.e** (mastering)

19. Parents contribute one copy of each gene to their offspring. The sperm carries the chromosomes of the father. The egg contains the chromosomes of the mother. **7.2.b** (mastering)

20. Sample answer: Multiple births happen when a fertilized egg splits or when two or more eggs are fertilized at the same time. It is rare for a fertilized egg to split more than once or for more than two eggs to be fertilized at the same time. So, there are fewer multiple births of higher numbers of babies.

21. Sample answer: A female athlete that exercises a great deal will likely have very little body fat. As a result, she may produce less estrogen and stop menstruating. **7.5.d** (mastering)

22. The name of the cord that connects the fetus to its mother is called the umbilical cord. Its purpose is to connect the fetus to the placenta, which provides nutrients and oxygen to the fetus. **7.5.e** (mastering)

23. Estrogen levels fluctuate, but testosterone levels stay the same throughout the month.
7.5.d (supporting)

Standards Assessment

7.1.c, 7.1.f, 7.2.a, 7.2.b,
7.2.c, 7.2.d, 7.2.e, 7.5.a,
7.5.d, 7.5.e

Teacher Notes

To provide practice under more realistic testing conditions, give students 20 min to answer all of the questions in this assessment.

Answer Key	
Question Number	Correct Answer
1	C
2	A
3	B
4	D
5	D
6	A
7	A
8	B
9	D
10	A
11	A
12	A
13	A
14	C
15	B

Standards Guide			
	Supporting	Mastering	Exceeding
7.1.c		12	
7.2.a		15	
7.2.c		14	
7.2.e		13	
7.1.f	5		
7.2.b	4	10	
7.5.a	2	11	
7.5.d	3	7–8	9
7.5.e	1	6	

☐ Standards Assessment **GENERAL**

☐ Teacher Notes for Standards Assessment contain a longer Assessment Doctor and Diagnostic Teaching Tips.

REVIEWING ACADEMIC VOCABULARY

1 In the sentence "The placenta performs an important function for the fetus," what does the word *function* mean?

- A position
- B organ
- C purpose
- D result

2 Which of the following words best completes the sentence: The uterus is a special ___ in which a baby develops.

- A structure
- B system
- C organism
- D method

3 Which of the following words is the closest in meaning to the word *generate*?

- A explain
- B produce
- C identify
- D accomplish

4 Which of the following sets of words best completes the following sentence:
In ___ , offspring receive traits from both of their parents.

- A asexual reproduction
- B sexual function
- C sexual selection
- D sexual reproduction

5 What is the noun used to describe "the process in which cells change to carry out specialized functions"?

- A production
- B fabrication
- C distinction
- D differentiation

REVIEWING CONCEPTS

6 Which of the following best describes the function of the placenta?

- A The placenta provides oxygen and nutrients to the fetus.
- B The placenta is the organ that holds the fetus as it grows and develops.
- C The placenta is a thin membrane that fills with fluid to protect the fetus.
- D The placenta sends nutrients to the mother's body.

7 Which of the following can cause a woman to become pregnant?

- A A man ejaculates sperm in or near the women's vagina.
- B The woman experiences a menstrual cycle.
- C A man ejaculates his sperm during puberty.
- D The woman ovulates until middle age.

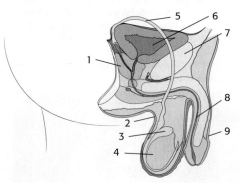

8 In the diagram above, which number labels the structure that produces sperm?

- A 2
- B 4
- C 5
- D 9

+ ASSESSMENT DOCTOR

Question 1: The correct answer is C. The placenta has a specific function, or purpose, it is used for.

Question 2: The correct answer is A. The uterus is the special organ or structure in which a baby develops.

Question 3: The correct answer is B. Males and females *generate* or produce sperm and eggs.

Question 4: The correct answer is D. Offspring inherit characteristics of each parent through the process of sexual reproduction.

Question 5: The correct answer is D. Cells experience differentiation, or change to perform certain functions, as an organism develops.

Question 6: The correct answer is A. The placenta provides oxygen and nutrients and removes the fetus's waste.

Question 7: The correct answer is A. Fertilization cannot occur unless sperm are present during or shortly after ovulation.

Question 8: The correct answer is B. The testes are where sperm are produced.

9 In humans, what has to occur for an egg to be considered fertilized?

  A A sperm has to penetrate the outer coating of the egg.

  B An egg has to be present when sperm enter the woman.

  C A few hundred sperm have to cover the outer coating of the egg.

  D The sperm nucleus and the egg nucleus must join.

10 Why does a child usually have physical characteristics from both parents?

  A The child inherited genes from each parent.

  B The child's genes are mixed while the child is in the uterus.

  C The child's cells differentiate during development.

  D The environment of the child is the same as that of the parents.

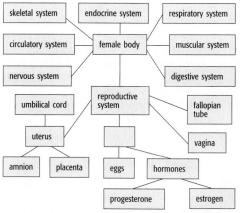

11 Which of the following best fits into the blank space in the concept map above?

  A ovary

  B scrotum

  C zygote

  D menstruation

REVIEWING PRIOR LEARNING

12 In a human cell, where are chromosomes located?

  A nucleus

  B vacuole

  C chloroplasts

  D mitochondria

13 Which of the following is the genetic material of all organisms?

  A deoxyribonucleic acid

  B endoplasmic reticulum

  C adenosine triphosphate

  D restriction endonuclease

14 What determines an inherited trait?

  A Traits are inherited as a child grows older.

  B Cell differentiation determines inherited traits.

  C Inherited traits are determined by one or more genes.

  D A child's parents decide what traits will be inherited.

15 Which of these describes a reproduction method of a sexual organism?

  A forming a tuber

  B fusing of sex cells from two parents

  C producing runners

  D division through binary fission

Standards Assessment

Question 9: The correct answer is D. When the nucleus of the egg joins with the nucleus of the sperm, the egg is considered fertilized.

Question 10: The correct answer is A. When an egg is fertilized, the egg's DNA and the sperm's DNA are both present in the fertilized egg's nucleus.

Question 11: The correct answer is A. Egg cells are stored in ovaries. Also, hormones are produced in the ovaries.

Question 12: The correct answer is A. Genetic information is stored in the nucleus of a cell.

Question 13: The correct answer is A. DNA, the genetic material of living organisms, is short for deoxyribonucleic acid.

Question 14: The correct answer is C. Inherited traits are traits determined by one or more genes.

Question 15: The correct answer is B. A sexual organism reproduces when two parents each provide a sex cell and the cells fuse together.

Scientific Discoveries

Background

A stem cell is an undifferentiated cell that can give rise to specialized or differentiated cells. There are three categories of stem cells: totipotent, pluripotent, and multipotent. Totipotent stem cells give rise to any cell in an organism. An entire organism can arise from a single totipotent stem cell. No totipotent stem cell lines have been isolated for research. Pluripotent stem cells, like embryonic stem cells, can give rise to most cell types in an organism. Human embryonic stem cells are collected from a human blastocyst produced through in vitro fertilization. There are several lines of human embryonic stem cells being used for research. Multipotent stem cells are found in mature tissues. These stem cells, also known as adult stem cells, do not give rise to a variety of cell types. Adult stem cells give rise to a small range of cells important to the viability and health of the tissue from which they were isolated.

Science, Technology, and Society

Discussion

Lead students in a discussion about the implications of fetal surgery technology for treating fetal disorders. What sorts of disorders might be successfully treated? (anatomical disorders and discrete tumors) What type of disorders would be more difficult to treat? (genetic disorders and disorders affecting the entire fetus)

Science in Action

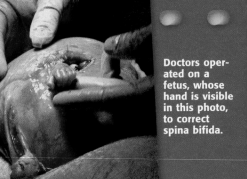

Doctors operated on a fetus, whose hand is visible in this photo, to correct spina bifida.

Science Discoveries

Embryonic Stem Cell Research

In the future, you may be able to buy new tissue for diseased or injured organs. Embryonic stem cells are undifferentiated cells from human embryos. In the right conditions, these cells are able to differentiate into any kind of human cell. Researchers at the University of California in San Francisco are working to develop regenerative medicine using embryonic stem cells. Regenerative medicine involves getting undifferentiated stem cells to differentiate into the type of cells that make the diseased tissues or organs in a patient. If USC researchers succeed, doctors will in the future be able to treat patients who have conditions such as Parkinson's disease and heart disease.

Language Arts ACTIVITY

Embryonic stem cell research is controversial. Research the advantages and disadvantages of this kind of research. On a poster, compare the benefits and drawbacks of embryonic stem cell research.

Science, Technology, and Society

Fetal Surgery

Sometimes, a developing fetus has a serious medical problem. In many such cases, surgery after birth can correct the problem. But some problems can be treated while the fetus is still in the uterus. For example, fetal surgery may be used to correct spina bifida (a disease in which part of the spinal cord is exposed because the backbone doesn't form properly). Doctors now can fix several types of problems before a baby is born.

Social Studies ACTIVITY

Research the causes of spina bifida. Write a brochure that tells expectant mothers what precautions they can take to prevent spina bifida.

Answer to Language Arts Activity

Answers may vary. Accept all reasonable answers.

Answer to Social Studies Activity

Spina bifida (a Latin term meaning *split spine*) is a group of congenital birth defects that affect the development of the central nervous system—the brain and the spinal cord—and nerve tissues. Spina bifida occurs about 10 to 20 times per 1,000 births. With severe spina bifida, a person's legs and feet are paralyzed. There are often problems with bowel and bladder control. The long-term effects of spina bifida depend on the type and severity of the defect. Up to 75% of the cases of spina bifida could be prevented if the mother takes folic acid daily before pregnancy and during the first trimester.

Careers

Reva Curry

Diagnostic Medical Sonographer Sounds are everywhere in our world. But only some of those sounds—such as your favorite music playing on the stereo or the dog barking next door—are sounds that we can hear. There are sound waves whose frequency is too high for us to hear. These high-pitched sounds are called *ultrasound*. Some animals, such as bats, use ultrasound to hunt and to avoid midair collisions.

Humans use ultrasound, too. Ultrasound machines can peer inside the human body to look at hearts, blood vessels, and fetuses. Diagnostic medical sonographers are people who use sonography equipment to diagnose medical problems. Diagnostic medical sonographers also use sonography to follow the growth and development of a fetus while the fetus is still in the uterus. One of the leading professionals in the field of diagnostic medical sonography is Dr. Reva Curry. Dr. Curry spent many years as a sonographer. Her primary job was to use high-tech ultrasound instruments to create images of parts of the body and interpret the images for other professionals. Today, Dr. Curry works with students as the dean of a community college.

Math ACTIVITY

At 20°C, the speed of sound in water is 1,482 m/s, and the speed of sound in steel is 5,200 m/s. How long would it take a sound to travel 815.1 m in water? In the same amount of time, how far would a sound travel in a steel beam? Record your work in your **Science Journal**.

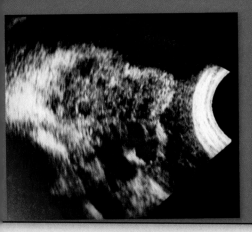

Internet Resources

- To learn more about careers in science, visit www.scilinks.org and enter the SciLinks code HY70225.

- To learn more about these Science in Action topics, visit go.hrw.com and type in the keyword HY7BD5F.

- Check out articles related to this chapter by visiting go.hrw.com. Just type in the keyword HY7BD5C.

Answer to Math Activity
0.55 s; 2,860 m

Appendix

Contents

$$density = \frac{mass}{volume}$$

Appendix

Study Skills: Making and Using FoldNotes

Have you ever tried to study for a test or quiz but didn't know where to start? Or have you read a chapter and found that you can remember only a few ideas? Well, FoldNotes are a fun and exciting way to help you learn and remember the ideas you encounter as you learn science!

FoldNotes are tools that you can use to organize concepts. One FoldNote focuses on a few main concepts. FoldNotes help you learn and remember how the concepts fit together. FoldNotes can help you see the "big picture." Below, you will find instructions for building 10 different FoldNotes.

Pyramid

A pyramid provides a unique way for taking notes. The three sides of the pyramid can summarize information into three categories. Use the pyramid as a tool for studying information in a chapter.

1. Place a **sheet of paper** in front of you. Fold the lower left-hand corner of the paper diagonally to the opposite edge of the paper.

2. Cut off the tab of paper created by the fold (at the top).

3. Open the paper so that it is a square. Fold the lower right-hand corner of the paper diagonally to the opposite corner to form a triangle.

4. Open the paper. The creases of the two folds will have created an X.

5. Using **scissors,** cut along one of the creases. Start from any corner, and stop at the center point to create two flaps. Use **tape** or **glue** to attach one of the flaps on top of the other flap.

Double-Door Fold

A double-door fold is useful when you want to compare the characteristics of two topics. The double-door fold can organize characteristics of the two topics side by side under the flaps. Similarities and differences between the two topics can then be easily identified.

1. Fold a **sheet of paper** in half from the top to the bottom. Then, unfold the paper.

2. Fold the top and bottom edges of the paper to the center crease.

Booklet

A booklet is a useful tool for taking notes as you read a chapter. Each page of the booklet can contain a main topic from the chapter. Write details of each main topic on the appropriate page to create an outline of the chapter.

1. Fold a **sheet of paper** in half from left to right. Then, unfold the paper.

2. Fold the sheet of paper in half again from the top to the bottom. Then, unfold the paper.

3. Refold the sheet of paper in half from left to right.

4. Fold the top and bottom edges to the center crease.

5. Completely unfold the paper.

6. Refold the paper from top to bottom.

7. Using **scissors,** cut a slit along the center crease of the sheet from the folded edge to the creases made in step 4. Do not cut the entire sheet in half.

8. Fold the sheet of paper in half from left to right. While holding the bottom and top edges of the paper, push the bottom and top edges together so that the center collapses at the center slit. Fold the four flaps to form a four-page book.

Layered Book

A layered book is a useful tool for taking notes as you read a chapter. The four flaps of the layered book can summarize information into four categories. Write details of each category on the appropriate flap to create a summary of the chapter.

1. Lay one **sheet of paper** on top of **another sheet.** Slide the top sheet up so that 2 cm of the bottom sheet is showing.

2. Holding the two sheets together, fold down the top of the two sheets so that you see four 2 cm tabs along the bottom.

3. Using a stapler, staple the top of the FoldNote.

Key-Term Fold

A key-term fold is a useful for studying definitions of key terms in a chapter. Each tab can contain a key term on one side and its definition on the other. Use the key-term fold to quiz yourself on the definitions of the key terms in a chapter.

1. Fold a **sheet of lined notebook paper** in half from left to right.

2. Using **scissors,** cut along every third line from the right edge of the paper to the center fold to make tabs.

Four-Corner Fold

A four-corner fold is useful when you want to compare the characteristics of four topics. The four-corner fold can organize the characteristics of the four topics side by side under the flaps. Similarities and differences between the four topics can then be easily identified.

1. Fold a **sheet of paper** in half from left to right. Then, unfold the paper.

2. Fold each side of the paper to the crease in the center of the paper.

3. Fold the paper in half from the top to the bottom. Then, unfold the paper.

4. Using **scissors,** cut the top flap creases made in step 3 to form four flaps.

Three-Panel Flip Chart

A three-panel flip chart is useful when you want to compare the characteristics of three topics. The three-panel flip chart can organize the characteristics of the three topics side by side under the flaps. Similarities and differences between the three topics can then be easily identified.

1. Fold a **piece of paper** in half from the top to the bottom.

2. Fold the paper in thirds from side to side. Then, unfold the paper so that you can see the three sections.

3. From the top of the paper, cut along each of the vertical fold lines to the fold in the middle of the paper. You will now have three flaps.

Table Fold

A table fold is a useful tool for comparing the characteristics of two or three topics. In a table fold, all topics are described in terms of the same characteristics so that you can easily make a thorough comparison.

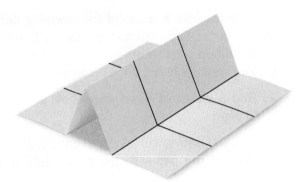

1. Fold a **piece of paper** in half from the top to the bottom. Then, fold the paper in half again.

2. Fold the paper in thirds from side to side.

3. Unfold the paper completely. Carefully trace the fold lines by using a pen or pencil.

Two-Panel Flip Chart

A two-panel flip chart is useful when you want to compare the characteristics of two topics. The two-panel flip chart can organize the characteristics of the two topics side by side under the flaps. Similarities and differences between the two topics can then be easily identified.

1. Fold a **piece of paper** in half from the top to the bottom.

2. Fold the paper in half from side to side. Then, unfold the paper so that you can see the two sections.

3. From the top of the paper, cut along the vertical fold line to the fold in the middle of the paper. You will now have two flaps.

Tri-Fold

A tri-fold is a useful tool that helps you track your progress. By organizing the chapter topic into what you know, what you want to know, and what you learn, you can see how much you have learned after reading a chapter.

1. Fold a piece a paper in thirds from the top to the bottom.

2. Unfold the paper so that you can see the three sections. Then, turn the paper sideways so that the three sections form vertical columns.

3. Trace the fold lines by using a **pen** or **pencil.** Label the columns "Know," "Want," and "Learn."

Study Skills: Making and Using Graphic Organizers

Have you ever wished that you could "draw out" the many concepts you learn in your science class? Sometimes, being able to see how concepts are related really helps you remember what you've learned. Graphic Organizers do just that! They give you a way to draw or map out concepts.

All you need to make a Graphic Organizer is a piece of paper and a pencil. Below you will find instructions for nine different Graphic Organizers designed to help you organize the concepts you'll learn in this book.

Concept Map

How to Make a Concept Map

1. Identify main ideas from the text, and write the ideas as short phrases or single words.

2. Select a main concept. Place this concept at the top or center of a piece of paper.

3. Place other ideas under or around the main concept based on their relationship to the main concept. Draw a circle around each idea.

4. Draw lines between the concepts, and add linking words to connect the ideas.

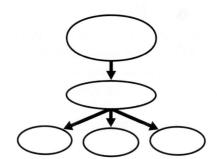

When to Use a Concept Map

Concept maps are useful when you are trying to identify how several ideas are connected to a main concept. Concept maps may be based on vocabulary terms or on main topics from the text. As you read about science, look for terms that can be organized in a concept map.

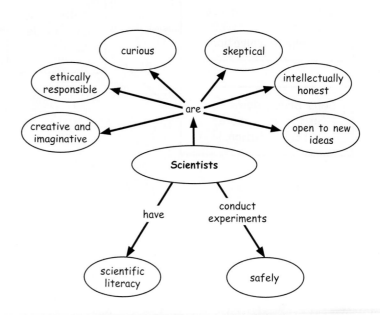

Cause-and-Effect Map

How to Make a Cause-and-Effect Map

1. Draw a box, and write a cause in the box. You can have as many cause boxes as you want. The diagram shown here is one example of a cause-and-effect map.

2. Draw another box to the right of the cause box to represent an effect. You can have as many effect boxes as you want. Draw arrows from each cause box to the appropriate effect boxes.

3. In the cause boxes, explain the process that makes up the cause. In the effect boxes, write a description of the effect or details about the effect.

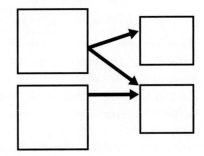

When to Use a Cause-and-Effect Map

A cause-and-effect map is a useful tool for illustrating a specific type of scientific process. Use a cause-and-effect map when you want to describe how, when, or why one event causes another event. As you read, look for events that are either causes or results of other events, and draw a cause-and-effect map that shows the relationships between the events.

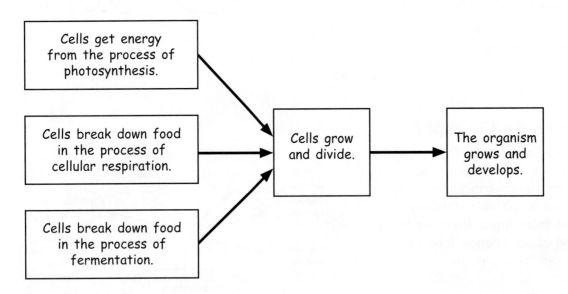

Spider Map

How to Make a Spider Map

1. Draw a diagram like the one shown here. In the circle, write the main topic.

2. From the circle, draw legs to represent the main ideas or characteristics of the topic. Draw as many legs as you want to draw. Write an idea or characteristic along each leg.

3. From each leg, draw horizontal lines. As you read the chapter, write details about each idea on the idea's horizontal lines. To add more details, make the legs longer and add more horizontal lines.

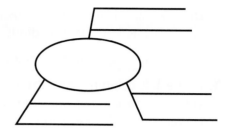

When to Use a Spider Map

A spider map is an effective tool for classifying the details of a specific topic in science. A spider map divides a topic into ideas and details. As you read about a topic, look for the main ideas or characteristics of the topic. Within each idea, look for details. Use a spider map to organize the ideas and details of each topic.

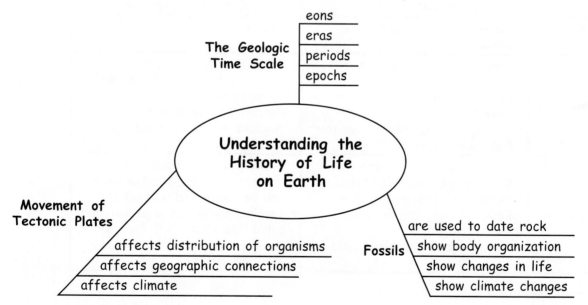

Comparison Table

How to Make a Comparison Table

1. Draw a table like the one shown here. Draw as many columns and rows as you want to draw.

2. In the top row, write the topics that you want to compare.

3. In the left column, write the general characteristics that you want to compare. As you read the chapter, fill in the characteristics for each topic in the appropriate boxes.

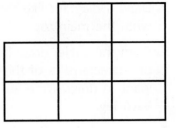

When to Use a Comparison Table

A comparison table is useful when you want to compare the characteristics of two or more topics in science. Organizing information in a table helps you compare several topics at one time. In a table, all topics are described in terms of the same list of characteristics, which helps you make a thorough comparison. As you read, look for topics whose characteristics you may want to compare in a table.

	Skeletal System	Muscular System
Parts	• bones, cartilage, connective tissue	• muscles
Structure	• Bone is made of connective tissue and minerals. • Compact bone is rigid and dense bone tissue. • Spongy bone is bone tissue that has open spaces.	• Smooth muscle is in the digestive tract and in the walls of blood vessels. • Cardiac muscle is in the heart. • Skeletal muscle is attached to bones.
Function	• Some bones protect organs. • Bones store minerals that help nerves and muscles function. • Bones provide the body with structure. • Some bones make blood cells.	• Muscles let a person move. • Voluntary action is action that can be controlled. (skeletal) • Involuntary action is action that cannot be controlled. (smooth, cardiac, or skeletal) • Muscles often work in pairs.

Venn Diagram

How to Make a Venn Diagram

1. Draw a diagram like the one shown here. Draw one circle for each topic. Make sure that each circle partially overlaps the other circles.

2. In each circle, write a topic that you want to compare with the topics in the other circles.

3. In the areas of the diagram where circles overlap, write the characteristics that the topics in the overlapping circles share.

4. In the areas of the diagram where circles do not overlap, write the characteristics that are unique to the topic of the particular circle.

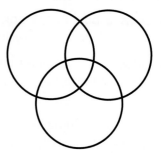

When to Use a Venn Diagram

A Venn diagram is a useful tool for comparing two or three topics in science. A Venn diagram shows which characteristics the topics share and which characteristics are unique to each topic. Venn diagrams are ideal when you want to illustrate relationships in a pair or small group of topics. As you read, look for topics that have both shared and unique characteristics, and draw a Venn diagram that shows how the topics are related.

Seed Plants
- produce seeds
- gametophytes are dependent on sporophyte
- do not need water to reproduce sexually
- grouped into gymnosperms and angiosperms

- carry out photosynthesis
- reproduce sexually and asexually
- have a two-stage lifecycle
- have qualities that are useful for humans

Seedless Plants
- need water to reproduce sexually
- gametophytes live independently of sporophyte
- divided into two groups: vascular and nonvascular

Appendix

Process Chart

How to Make a Process Chart

1. Draw a box. In the box, write the first step of a process, chain of events, or cycle.

2. Under the box, draw another box, and draw an arrow to connect the two boxes. In the second box, write the next step of the process or the next event in the timeline.

3. Continue adding boxes until each step of the process, chain of events, or cycle is written in a box. For cycles only, draw an arrow to connect the last box and the first box.

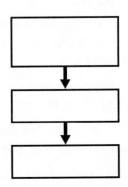

When to Use a Process Chart

Science is full of processes. A process chart shows the steps that a process takes to get from one point to another point. Timelines, chains of events, and cycles are examples of the kinds of information that can be organized well in a process chart. As you read, look for information that is described in steps or in a sequence, and draw a process chart that shows the progression of the steps or sequence.

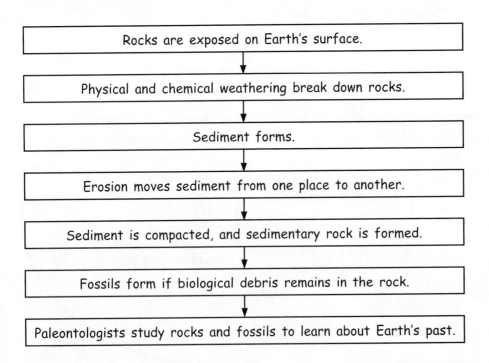

Idea Wheel

How to Make an Idea Wheel

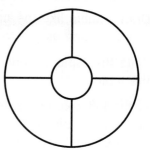

1. Draw a circle. Draw a larger circle around the first circle. Divide the ring between the circles into sections by drawing lines from one circle to the other across the ring. Divide the ring into as many sections as you want.

2. Write a main idea or topic in the smaller circle. Label each section in the ring with a category or characteristic of the main idea.

3. In each section of the ring, include details that are unique to the topic.

When to Use an Idea Wheel

An idea wheel is an effective type of visual organization in which ideas in science can be divided into categories or parts. It is also a useful way to illustrate characteristics of a main idea or topic. As you read, look for topics that are divided into ideas or categories that can be organized around an idea wheel.

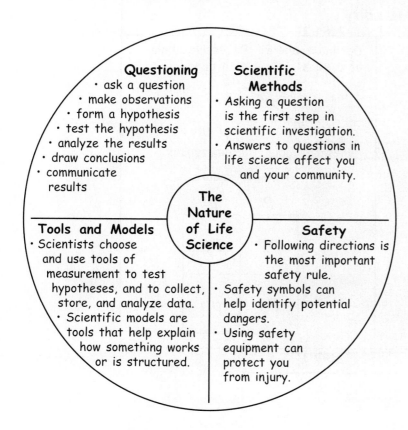

Combination Notes

How to Make Combination Notes

1. Draw a table like the one shown here. Draw the columns to be as long as you want them to be.

2. Write the topic of your notes in the section at the top of the table.

3. In the left column, write important phrases or sentences about the topic. In the right column, draw diagrams or pictures that illustrate the information in the left column.

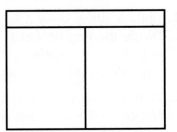

When to Use Combination Notes

Combination notes let you express scientific information in words and pictures at the same time. Use combination notes to express information that a picture could help explain. The picture could be a diagram, a sketch, or another useful visual representation of the written information in your notes.

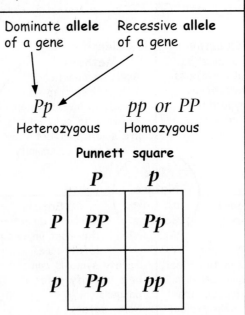

Heredity	
• Gregor Mendel helped establish the basics of modern genetics. • Mendel discovered that an offspring inherits two **alleles** for each gene, one allele from each parent. • Through **meiosis** and sexual reproduction, genetic material combines. • **Punnett squares** are used to predict the possible **genotypes** for a particular combination of genes.	Dominate **allele** of a gene Recessive **allele** of a gene *Pp* *pp or PP* Heterozygous Homozygous **Punnett square** 	*P*	*p* *P*	*PP*	*Pp* *p*	*Pp*	*pp*

Pyramid Chart

How to Make a Pyramid Chart

1. Draw a triangle that is divided into sections like the one shown here. Draw as many sections as you need to draw.

2. Draw a box to the left of the triangle, as shown in the example. Write the topic of your pyramid chart in the box.

3. In each section of your triangle, write information about the topic in the appropriate level of the pyramid.

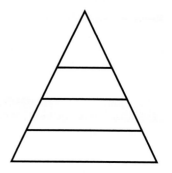

When to Use a Pyramid Chart

A pyramid chart is used to organize information in a hierarchy of importance, detail, or magnitude. As the shape of the pyramid suggests, the pyramid's bottom level contains information that is largest in terms of magnitude and broadest, or least specific, in terms of detail. As you read about science, look for information that you can organize into a hierarchy.

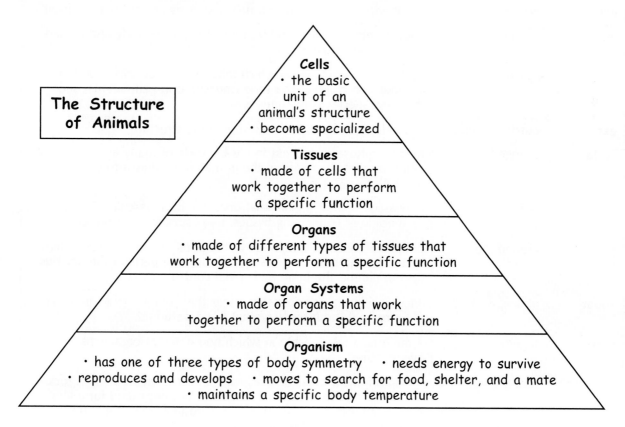

The Structure of Animals

Cells
- the basic unit of an animal's structure
- become specialized

Tissues
- made of cells that work together to perform a specific function

Organs
- made of different types of tissues that work together to perform a specific function

Organ Systems
- made of organs that work together to perform a specific function

Organism
- has one of three types of body symmetry   • needs energy to survive
- reproduces and develops   • moves to search for food, shelter, and a mate
- maintains a specific body temperature

Appendix

Understanding Word Parts

Many scientific words are made up of parts based on Greek and Latin languages. Understanding the meaning of the parts will help you understand the meaning of the scientific words. The table below provides a definition and an example of prefixes, roots, and suffixes that you will see in this textbook.

Prefix	Definition	Example
a-	not	asexual reproduction: reproduction that does not involve the union of sex cells
aero-	air	aerobic: describes a process that requires oxygen, usually from air
amphi-	both	amphibian: an animal that lives both in water and on land
bio-	life	biology: the science of life
di-	apart	divergent boundary: the type of tectonic plate boundary in which tectonic plates move apart
dif-	apart; in different directions	differentiation: the process in which the structure and function of the parts of an organism change, or develop in different directions, or pathways, to enable specialization of those parts
ecto-	outside	ectotherm: an organism that needs sources of heat outside itself
endo-	within	endoskeleton: a skeleton that forms within the body and is made of bone and cartilage
ev-	space of time	evolution: the process in which inherited characteristics within a population change over time (measured in generations) such that new species sometimes arise
exo-	outside; external	exoskeleton: a hard, external, supporting structure
meta-	changed	metamorphosis: a process in the life cycle of many animals during which a rapid change from the immature organism to the adult takes place
non-	not	nonvascular plant: a plant that does not have vascular tissue, or specialized conducting tissues, true roots, stems, and leaves
peri-	around; near	peripheral nervous system: all of the parts of the nervous system except for the brain and the spinal cord; the parts of the nervous system around the brain and spinal cord
super-	above; over	superposition: a principle that states that younger rocks lie above older rocks if the layers have not been disturbed
sym-	together	symbiosis: a relationship in which two different organisms live together
un-	not; the lack of	unconformity: a break in the geologic record created when rock layers are eroded or when sediment is not deposited for a long period of time; a gap in the rock record that does not show a continuous record of geologic time
trans-	across; through	transmission: the passing of light or another form of energy through matter

Appendix

Word root	Definition	Example
chlor	green	chloroplast: an organelle found in plant and algae cells where photosynthesis occurs; contains green pigment
dipl	twice, double	diploid: a cell that contains two haploid sets of chromosomes
funct	to perform	function: the special, normal, or proper performance of an organ
gymn	naked	gymnosperm: a woody, vascular seed plant whose seeds are "naked," or not enclosed by an ovary or fruit
lip	fat	lipid: a fat molecule or a molecule that has similar properties; examples include oils, waxes, and steroids
micro	small	microscope: an instrument that produces an enlarged image of a small object
mut	to change	mutation: a change in the nucleotide-base sequence of a gene or DNA molecule
paleo	old	paleontology: the scientific study of fossils
phot	light	photosynthesis: the process by which plants, algae, and some bacteria use sunlight, carbon dioxide, and water to make food
press	to press	blood pressure: the force of blood pressing on the walls of arteries
sed	to sit; to settle	sediment: fragments of organic or inorganic material that are transported and deposited by wind, water, or ice and that settle, or accumulate, in layers on Earth's surface
sperm	seed	angiosperm: a flowering plant that produces seeds within a fruit
struct	to build; to arrange	structure: the arrangement of parts in an organism
tax	to arrange	taxonomy: the science of describing, naming, and classifying organisms; a logical arrangement of different kinds of organisms
thesis	proposition	hypothesis: a testable idea or explanation that leads to scientific investigation
zo	pertaining to animals	Cenozoic: the current geologic era; also called the *Age of Mammals*

Suffix	Definition	Example
-emia	condition of the blood	leukemia: a progressive cancer of the blood-forming organs
-ism	a belief in	catastrophism: a principle that states that geologic change occurs suddenly; the belief that geologic change happens suddenly
-logy	the science of	biology: the scientific study of life
-nomy	the science of	taxonomy: the science of describing, naming, and classifying organisms
-ole	little	bronchiole: one of the small branches of the bronchi
-scope	an instrument for seeing or observing	microscope: an instrument that produces an enlarged image of a small object

Common Words with Multiple Meanings

Scientific words may have common meanings that you already know. Understanding the difference between common meanings and scientific meanings will help you develop a scientific vocabulary. The table below provides common and scientific meanings for words that you will see in this textbook.

Word	Common meaning	Scientific meaning
area	a region (for example, a rural area)	a measure of the size of a surface or a region
cell	a small, confining room	the smallest structural and functional unit of all living organisms
class	a group of students who are taught together at regular meetings	a taxonomic category below the phylum and above the order
condensation	the droplets of liquid on the outside of a glass or window	the change of state from a gas to a liquid
consumer	someone who purchases goods or services	an organism that eats other organisms or organic matter
date	an engagement to go out socially	to measure the age of an event or object
daughter	one's female child	the offspring of cell division; not dependent on gender
egg	a thin-shelled product from a bird used in cooking	a sex cell produced by a female
family	all of the members of a household	the taxonomic category below the order and above the genus
fault	responsibility for a mistake	a break in a body of rock along which one block slides relative to another
gas	short for *gasoline*; a liquid fuel used by vehicles, such as cars and buses	a form of matter that does not have a definite volume or shape
host	to serve as the entertainer or receiver of guests	an organism from which a parasite takes food or shelter
instrument	a device used for making music (for example, a trumpet)	a piece of equipment used during experimentation (for example, a scalpel)
kingdom	a region ruled by a king or queen	the taxonomic category below the domain and above the phylum
labor	to work	the process by which the fetus and the placenta come out of the uterus
law	a rule of conduct established by the government	a descriptive statement or equation that reliably predicts events under certain conditions

Word	Common meaning	Scientific meaning
legend	a romanticized story or myth	a list of map symbols and their meanings
mass	a quantity of material that has an unspecified shape	a measure of the amount of matter in an object
matter	a subject of concern or topic of discussion	anything that has mass and takes up space
medium	an intermediate measurement between small and large	a physical environment in which phenomena occur
model	a person who poses (for example, a fashion model)	a pattern, plan, representation, or description designed to show the structure or workings of an object, system, or concept
order	a command	the taxonomic category below the class and above the family
organ	a musical instrument similar to a piano	a collection of tissues that carry out a specialized function of the body
organic	describes an organism or object that is produced without the use of synthetic drugs, fertilizers, or hormones	describes a material that is derived from living organisms and that contains carbon
product	something available for sale (for example, a computer product)	a substance that forms in a chemical reaction
reaction	a response to a stimulus	the process by which one or more substances change to produce one or more different substances
resolution	an expression of intent (for example, a New Year's resolution)	in microscopes, the ability to form images in fine detail
scale	a machine used to measure weight	the relationship between the measurements on a model, map, or diagram and the actual measurement or distance
slide	a piece of playground equipment	a thin piece of glass on which a specimen is placed for viewing with a microscope
stereo	a machine that plays music	three-dimensional
table	a piece of furniture that has a flat, horizontal surface	an orderly arrangement of data
theory	an assumption based on limited knowledge	a system of ideas that explains many related observations and is supported by a large body of evidence acquired through scientific investigation
tissue	a soft, absorbent piece of paper	a group of similar cells that perform a common function
volume	a measure of how loud a sound is	a measure of the size of a body or region in three-dimensional space

Math Refresher

Science requires an understanding of many math concepts. The following pages will help you review some important math skills.

Averages

An **average,** or **mean,** simplifies a set of numbers into a single number that *approximates* the value of the set.

> **Example:** Find the average of the following set of numbers: 5, 4, 7, and 8.

Step 1: Find the sum.

$$5 + 4 + 7 + 8 = 24$$

Step 2: Divide the sum by the number of numbers in your set. Because there are four numbers in this example, divide the sum by 4.

$$\frac{24}{4} = 6$$

The average, or mean, is **6.**

Ratios

A **ratio** is a comparison between numbers, and it is usually written as a fraction.

> **Example:** Find the ratio of thermometers to students if you have 36 thermometers and 48 students in your class.

Step 1: Make the ratio.

$$\frac{36 \text{ thermometers}}{48 \text{ students}}$$

Step 2: Reduce the fraction to its simplest form.

$$\frac{36}{48} = \frac{36 \div 12}{48 \div 12} = \frac{3}{4}$$

The ratio of thermometers to students is **3 to 4,** or $\frac{3}{4}$. The ratio may also be written in the form 3:4.

Proportions

A **proportion** is an equation that states that two ratios are equal.

$$\frac{3}{1} = \frac{12}{4}$$

To solve a proportion, first multiply across the equal sign. This is called *cross-multiplication*. If you know three of the quantities in a proportion, you can use cross-multiplication to find the fourth.

> **Example:** Imagine that you are making a scale model of the solar system for your science project. The diameter of Jupiter is 11.2 times the diameter of Earth. If you are using a plastic-foam ball that has a diameter of 2 cm to represent Earth, what must the diameter of the ball representing Jupiter be? $\frac{11.2}{1} = \frac{x}{2 \text{ cm}}$

Step 1: Cross-multiply.

$$\frac{11.2}{1} \diagup\!\!\!\!\diagdown \frac{x}{2}$$

$$11.2 \times 2 = x \times 1$$

Step 2: Multiply.

$$22.4 = x \times 1$$

Step 3: Isolate the variable by dividing both sides by 1.

$$x = \frac{22.4}{1}$$

$$x = 22.4 \text{ cm}$$

You will need to use a ball that has a diameter of **22.4** cm to represent Jupiter.

Percentages

A **percentage** is a ratio of a given number to 100.

> **Example:** What is 85% of 40?

Step 1: Rewrite the percentage by moving the decimal point two places to the left.

$$0.\underset{\curvearrowleft}{85}$$

Step 2: Multiply the decimal by the number that you are calculating the percentage of.

$$0.85 \times 40 = 34$$

85% of 40 is **34.**

Decimals

To **add** or **subtract decimals,** line up the digits vertically so that the decimal points line up. Then, add or subtract the columns from right to left. Carry or borrow numbers as necessary.

> **Example:** Add the following numbers: 3.1415 and 2.96.

Step 1: Line up the digits vertically so that the decimal points line up.

$$\begin{array}{r} 3.1415 \\ + 2.96 \\ \hline \end{array}$$

Step 2: Add the columns from right to left, and carry when necessary.

$$\begin{array}{r} {\scriptstyle 1\ 1} \\ 3.1415 \\ + 2.96 \\ \hline 6.1015 \end{array}$$

The sum is **6.1015.**

Fractions

Numbers tell you how many; **fractions** tell you *how much of a whole.*

> **Example:** Your class has 24 plants. Your teacher instructs you to put 5 plants in a shady spot. What fraction of the plants in your class will you put in a shady spot?

Step 1: In the denominator, write the total number of parts in the whole.

$$\frac{?}{24}$$

Step 2: In the numerator, write the number of parts of the whole that are being considered.

$$\frac{5}{24}$$

So, $\frac{5}{24}$ of the plants will be in the shade.

Reducing Fractions

It is usually best to express a fraction in its simplest form. Expressing a fraction in its simplest form is called *reducing* a fraction.

> **Example:** Reduce the fraction $\frac{30}{45}$ to its simplest form.

Step 1: Find the largest whole number that will divide evenly into both the numerator and denominator. This number is called the *greatest common factor* (GCF).

Factors of the numerator 30:
1, 2, 3, 5, 6, 10, **15,** 30

Factors of the denominator 45:
1, 3, 5, 9, **15,** 45

Step 2: Divide both the numerator and the denominator by the GCF, which in this case is 15.

$$\frac{30}{45} = \frac{30 \div 15}{45 \div 15} = \frac{2}{3}$$

Thus, $\frac{30}{45}$ reduced to its simplest form is $\frac{2}{3}$.

Appendix

Adding and Subtracting Fractions

To **add** or **subtract fractions** that have the **same denominator,** simply add or subtract the numerators.

Examples:

$$\frac{3}{5} + \frac{1}{5} = ? \quad \text{and} \quad \frac{3}{4} - \frac{1}{4} = ?$$

Step 1: Add or subtract the numerators.

$$\frac{3}{5} + \frac{1}{5} = \frac{4}{} \quad \text{and} \quad \frac{3}{4} - \frac{1}{4} = \frac{2}{}$$

Step 2: Write the sum or difference over the denominator.

$$\frac{3}{5} + \frac{1}{5} = \frac{4}{5} \quad \text{and} \quad \frac{3}{4} - \frac{1}{4} = \frac{2}{4}$$

Step 3: If necessary, reduce the fraction to its simplest form.

$$\frac{4}{5} \text{ cannot be reduced, and } \frac{2}{4} = \frac{1}{2}.$$

To **add** or **subtract fractions** that have **different denominators,** first find the least common denominator (LCD).

Examples:

$$\frac{1}{2} + \frac{1}{6} = ? \quad \text{and} \quad \frac{3}{4} - \frac{2}{3} = ?$$

Step 1: Write the equivalent fractions that have a common denominator.

$$\frac{3}{6} + \frac{1}{6} = ? \quad \text{and} \quad \frac{9}{12} - \frac{8}{12} = ?$$

Step 2: Add or subtract the fractions.

$$\frac{3}{6} + \frac{1}{6} = \frac{4}{6} \quad \text{and} \quad \frac{9}{12} - \frac{8}{12} = \frac{1}{12}$$

Step 3: If necessary, reduce the fraction to its simplest form.

The fraction $\frac{4}{6} = \frac{2}{3}$, and $\frac{1}{12}$ cannot be reduced.

Multiplying Fractions

To **multiply fractions,** multiply the numerators and the denominators together, and then reduce the fraction to its simplest form.

Example:

$$\frac{5}{9} \times \frac{7}{10} = ?$$

Step 1: Multiply the numerators and denominators.

$$\frac{5}{9} \times \frac{7}{10} = \frac{5 \times 7}{9 \times 10} = \frac{35}{90}$$

Step 2: Reduce the fraction.

$$\frac{35}{90} = \frac{35 \div 5}{90 \div 5} = \frac{7}{18}$$

Dividing Fractions

To **divide fractions,** first rewrite the divisor (the number you divide by) upside down. This number is called the *reciprocal* of the divisor. Then multiply and reduce if necessary.

Example:

$$\frac{5}{8} \div \frac{3}{2} = ?$$

Step 1: Rewrite the divisor as its reciprocal.

$$\frac{3}{2} \rightarrow \frac{2}{3}$$

Step 2: Multiply the fractions.

$$\frac{5}{8} \times \frac{2}{3} = \frac{5 \times 2}{8 \times 3} = \frac{10}{24}$$

Step 3: Reduce the fraction.

$$\frac{10}{24} = \frac{10 \div 2}{24 \div 2} = \frac{5}{12}$$

Appendix

Scientific Notation

Scientific notation is a short way of representing very large and very small numbers without writing all of the place-holding zeros.

Example: Write 653,000,000 in scientific notation.

Step 1: Write the number without the place-holding zeros.
653

Step 2: Place the decimal point after the first digit.
6.53

Step 3: Find the exponent by counting the number of places that you moved the decimal point.
6.53000000
The decimal point was moved eight places to the left. Therefore, the exponent of 10 is positive 8. If you had moved the decimal point to the right, the exponent would be negative.

Step 4: Write the number in scientific notation.
6.53×10^8

Finding Area

Area is the number of square units needed to cover the surface of an object.

Formulas:
area of a square = side × side
area of a rectangle = length × width
area of a triangle = $\frac{1}{2}$ × base × height

Examples: Find the areas.

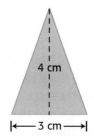

Triangle
area = $\frac{1}{2}$ × base × height
area = $\frac{1}{2}$ × 3 cm × 4 cm
*area = **6 cm²***

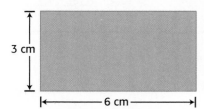

Rectangle
area = length × width
area = 6 cm × 3 cm
*area = **18 cm²***

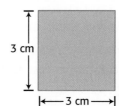

Square
area = side × side
area = 3 cm × 3 cm
*area = **9 cm²***

Finding Volume

Volume is the amount of space that something occupies.

Formulas:
volume of a cube = side × side × side

volume of a prism = area of base × height

Examples: Find the volume of the solids.

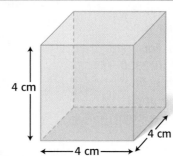

Cube
volume = side × side × side
volume = 4 cm × 4 cm × 4 cm
*volume = **64 cm³***

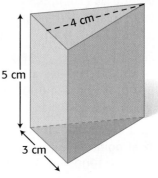

Prism
volume = area of base × height
volume = (area of triangle) × height
volume = ($\frac{1}{2}$ × 3 cm × 4 cm) × 5 cm
volume = 6 cm² × 5 cm
*volume = **30 cm³***

Making Graphs

Line Graphs

Line graphs are most often used to demonstrate continuous change. For example, Mr. Smith's students analyzed the population records for their hometown, Appleton, between 1900 and 2000. Examine the data at right.

Because the year and the population change, they are the *variables*. The population is determined by, or dependent on, the year. Therefore, the population is called the **dependent variable,** and the year is called the **independent variable.** Each set of data is called a **data pair.** To prepare a line graph, you must first organize data pairs into a table like the one at right.

Population of Appleton, 1900–2000	
Year	**Population**
1900	1,800
1920	2,500
1940	3,200
1960	3,900
1980	4,600
2000	5,300

How to Make a Line Graph

1. Place the independent variable along the horizontal (*x*) axis. Place the dependent variable along the vertical (*y*) axis.

2. Label the *x*-axis "Year" and the *y*-axis "Population." Look at your largest and smallest values for the population. For the *y*-axis, determine a scale that will provide enough space to show these values. You must use the same scale for the entire length of the axis. Next, find an appropriate scale for the *x*-axis.

3. Choose reasonable starting points for each axis.

4. Plot the data pairs as accurately as possible.

5. Choose a title that accurately represents the data.

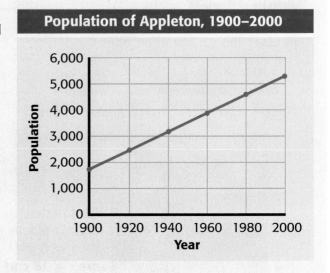

Population of Appleton, 1900–2000

How to Determine Slope

Slope is the ratio of the change in the *y*-value to the change in the *x*-value, or "rise over run."

1. Choose two points on the line graph. For example, the population of Appleton in 2000 was 5,300 people. Therefore, you can define point *a* as (2000, 5,300). In 1900, the population was 1,800 people. You can define point *b* as (1900, 1,800).

2. Find the change in the *y*-value.
(*y* at point *a*) − (*y* at point *b*) =
5,300 people − 1,800 people =
3,500 people

3. Find the change in the *x*-value.
(*x* at point *a*) − (*x* at point *b*) =
2000 − 1900 = 100 years

4. Calculate the slope of the graph by dividing the change in *y* by the change in *x*.

$$slope = \frac{change\ in\ y}{change\ in\ x}$$

$$slope = \frac{3,500\ people}{100\ years}$$

$$slope = 35\ people\ per\ year$$

In this example, the population in Appleton increased by a fixed amount each year. The graph of these data is a straight line. Therefore, the relationship is **linear.** When the graph of a set of data is not a straight line, the relationship is **nonlinear.**

Using Algebra to Determine Slope

The equation in step ❹ may also be arranged to be

$$y = kx$$

where y represents the change in the y-value, k represents the slope, and x represents the change in the x-value.

$$slope = \frac{change\ in\ y}{change\ in\ x}$$

$$k = \frac{y}{x}$$

$$k \times x = \frac{y \times x}{x}$$

$$kx = y$$

Bar Graphs

Bar graphs are useful for comparing data values. For example, if you want to compare the amounts of several types of municipal solid waste, you might use a bar graph. The table at right contains the data used to make the bar graph below.

How to Make a Bar Graph

❶ Use an appropriate scale and a reasonable starting point for each axis.

❷ Label the axes, and plot the data.

❸ Choose a title that accurately represents the data.

United States Municipal Solid Waste	
Material	**Percentage of total waste**
Paper	38.1
Yard waste	12.1
Food waste	10.9
Plastics	10.5
Metals	7.8
Rubber, leather, and textiles	6.6
Glass	5.5
Wood	5.3
Other	3.2

Appendix

Pie Graph

A pie graph shows how each group of data relates to all of the data. Each part of the circle forming the graph represents a category of the data. The entire circle represents all of the data. For example, a biologist studying a hardwood forest found that there were five types of trees. The data table at right summarizes the biologist's findings.

Hardwood Trees	
Type of tree	Number found
Oak	600
Maple	750
Beech	300
Birch	1,200
Hickory	150
Total	3,000

How to Make a Pie Graph

1 To make a pie graph of these data, first find what percentage all of the trees of each type of tree represents. Divide the number of trees of each type by the total number of trees, and multiply by 100.

$$\frac{600 \text{ oak}}{3,000 \text{ trees}} \times 100 = 20\%$$

$$\frac{750 \text{ maple}}{3,000 \text{ trees}} \times 100 = 25\%$$

$$\frac{300 \text{ beech}}{3,000 \text{ trees}} \times 100 = 10\%$$

$$\frac{1,200 \text{ birch}}{3,000 \text{ trees}} \times 100 = 40\%$$

$$\frac{150 \text{ hickory}}{3,000 \text{ trees}} \times 100 = 5\%$$

2 Now, determine the size of the wedges that make up the pie graph. Multiply each percentage by 360°. Remember that a circle contains 360°.

20% × 360° = 72°   25% × 360° = 90°

10% × 360° = 36°   40% × 360° = 144°

5% × 360° = 18°

3 Check that the sum of the percentages is 100 and that the sum of the degrees is 360.

20% + 25% + 10% + 40% + 5% = 100%

72° + 90° + 36° + 144° + 18° = 360°

4 Use a compass to draw a circle and mark the center of the circle.

5 Then, use a protractor to draw angles of 72°, 90°, 36°, 144°, and 18° in the circle.

6 Finally, label each part of the graph, and choose an appropriate title.

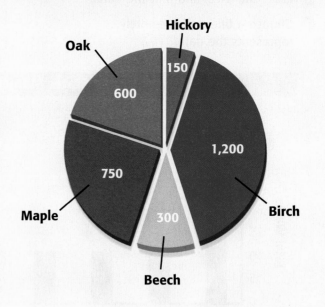

A Community of Hardwood Trees

Physical Science Refresher

Atoms and Elements

Every object in the universe is made up of particles of some kind of matter. **Matter** is anything that takes up space and has mass. All matter is made up of elements. An **element** is a substance that cannot be separated into simpler components by ordinary chemical means. The reason is that each element consists of only one kind of atom. An **atom** is the smallest unit of an element that maintains the properties of that element.

Atomic Structure

Atoms are made up of small particles called **subatomic particles.** The three major types of subatomic particles are **electrons, protons,** and **neutrons.** Electrons have a negative electric charge, protons have a positive electric charge, and neutrons have no electric charge. The protons and neutrons are packed close to one another to form the **nucleus.** The protons give the nucleus a positive charge. Electrons are most likely to be found in regions around the nucleus called **electron clouds.** The negatively charged electrons are attracted to the positively charged nucleus. An atom may have several energy levels in which electrons are located.

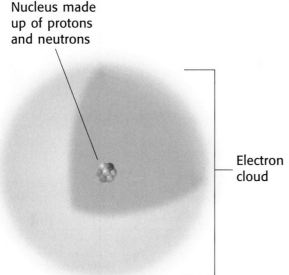

Nucleus made up of protons and neutrons

Electron cloud

Atomic Number

To help in the identification of elements, scientists have assigned an **atomic number** to each kind of atom. The atomic number is the number of protons in the atom. Atoms that have the same number of protons are the same kind of element. In an uncharged, or electrically neutral, atom, the numbers of protons and electrons are equal. Therefore, the atomic number equals the number of electrons in an uncharged atom. The number of neutrons, however, can vary for a given element. Atoms of the same element that have different numbers of neutrons are called **isotopes.**

Periodic Table of the Elements

In the periodic table, the elements are arranged from left to right in order of increasing atomic number. Each element in the table is in a separate box. An uncharged atom of each element has one more electron and one more proton than does an uncharged atom of the element to its left. Each horizontal row of the table is called a **period.** Changes in chemical properties of elements across a period correspond to changes in the electron arrangements of the atoms of the elements. Each vertical column of the table, known as a **group,** lists elements that have similar properties. The elements in a group have similar chemical properties because their atoms have the same number of electrons in their outer energy level. For example, the elements helium, neon, argon, krypton, xenon, and radon have similar properties and are known as the *noble gases.*

Molecules and Compounds

When two or more elements are joined chemically, the resulting substance is called a **compound.** A compound is a new substance whose properties differ from the properties of the elements that compose the compound. For example, water, H_2O, is a compound formed when hydrogen, H, and oxygen, O, combine. The smallest complete unit of a compound that has the properties of that compound is called a **molecule.** A chemical formula indicates the elements in a compound. It also indicates the relative number of atoms of each element present. The chemical formula for water is H_2O, which indicates that each water molecule consists of two atoms of hydrogen and one atom of oxygen. The subscript number after the symbol for an element indicates how many atoms of that element are in a single molecule of the compound.

Acids, Bases, and pH

An **ion** is an atom or group of atoms that has an electric charge because it has lost or gained one or more electrons. When an acid, such as hydrochloric acid, HCl, is mixed with water, it separates into ions. An **acid** is a compound that produces hydrogen ions, H^+, in water. The hydrogen ions then combine with water molecules to form hydronium ions, H_3O^+. A **base,** on the other hand, is a substance that produces hydroxide ions, OH^-, in water.

To determine whether a solution is acidic or basic, scientists use pH. The **pH** is a measure of the hydronium ion concentration in a solution. The pH scale ranges from 0 to 14. The middle point, pH = 7, is neutral—neither acidic nor basic. Acids have a pH less than 7; bases have a pH greater than 7. The lower the number is, the more acidic the solution. The higher the number is, the more basic the solution.

Chemical Equations

A chemical reaction occurs when a chemical change takes place. (In a chemical change, new substances that have new properties form.) A chemical equation is a useful way of describing a chemical reaction by means of chemical formulas. The equation indicates what substances react and what the products are. For example, when carbon and oxygen combine, they can form carbon dioxide. The equation for the reaction is as follows: $C + O_2 \rightarrow CO_2$.

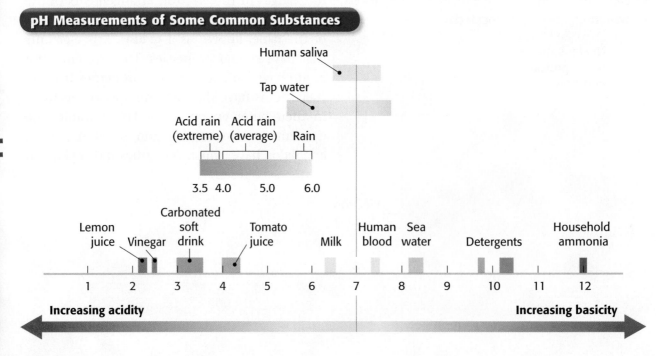

pH Measurements of Some Common Substances

Human saliva

Tap water

Acid rain (extreme) Acid rain (average) Rain

3.5 4.0 5.0 6.0

Lemon juice Vinegar Carbonated soft drink Tomato juice Milk Human blood Sea water Detergents Household ammonia

1 2 3 4 5 6 7 8 9 10 11 12

Increasing acidity **Increasing basicity**

Physical Science Laws and Principles

Newton's Laws of Motion

Newton's first law of motion states that an object at rest remains at rest and an object in motion remains in motion at constant speed and in a straight line unless acted on by an unbalanced force.

The first part of the law explains why a football will remain on a tee until it is kicked off or until a gust of wind blows it off.

The second part of the law explains why a bike rider will continue moving forward after the bike comes to an abrupt stop. Gravity and the friction of the sidewalk will eventually stop the rider.

Newton's second law of motion states that the acceleration of an object depends on the mass of the object and the amount of force applied.

The first part of the law explains why the acceleration of a 4 kg bowling ball will be greater than the acceleration of a 6 kg bowling ball if the same force is applied to both balls.

The second part of the law explains why the acceleration of a bowling ball will be larger if a larger force is applied to the bowling ball.

The relationship of acceleration (a) to mass (m) and force (F) can be expressed mathematically by the following equation:

$$acceleration = \frac{force}{mass}, \text{ or } a = \frac{F}{m}$$

This equation is often rearranged to the form

$$force = mass \times acceleration, \text{ or } F = m \times a$$

Newton's third law of motion states that whenever one object exerts a force on a second object, the second object exerts an equal and opposite force on the first.

This law explains that a runner is able to move forward because of the equal and opposite force that the ground exerts on the runner's foot after each step.

Law of Conservation of Mass

Mass cannot be created or destroyed during ordinary chemical or physical changes.

The total mass in a closed system is always the same no matter how many physical changes or chemical reactions occur.

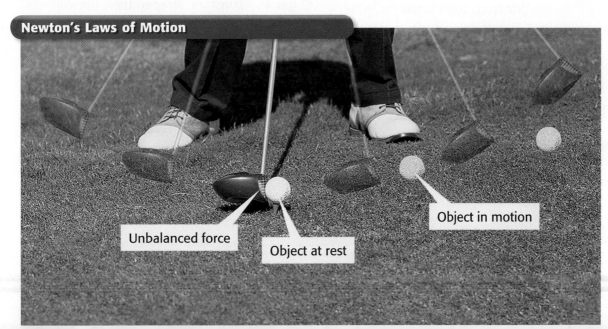

Newton's Laws of Motion

Unbalanced force

Object at rest

Object in motion

Law of Universal Gravitation

All objects in the universe attract each other by a force called *gravity*. The size of the force depends on the masses of the objects and the distance between the objects.

The first part of the law explains why lifting a bowling ball is much harder than lifting a marble. Because the bowling ball has a much larger mass than the marble does, the amount of gravity between Earth and the bowling ball is greater than the amount of gravity between Earth and the marble.

The second part of the law explains why a satellite can remain in orbit around Earth. The satellite is carefully placed at a distance great enough to prevent Earth's gravity from immediately pulling the satellite down but small enough to prevent the satellite from completely escaping Earth's gravity and wandering off into space.

Law of Conservation of Energy

Energy can be neither created nor destroyed.

The total amount of energy in a closed system is always the same. Energy can be changed from one form to another, but all of the different forms of energy in a system always add up to the same total amount of energy no matter how many energy conversions occur.

Charles's Law

Charles's law states that for a fixed amount of gas at a constant pressure, the volume of the gas increases as the temperature of the gas increases. Likewise, the volume of the gas decreases as the temperature of the gas decreases.

If a basketball that was inflated indoors is left outside on a cold winter day, the air particles inside the ball will move more slowly. They will hit the sides of the basketball less often and with less force. The ball will get smaller as the volume of the air decreases.

Boyle's Law

Boyle's law states that for a fixed amount of gas at a constant temperature, the volume of a gas increases as the pressure of the gas decreases. Likewise, the volume of a gas decreases as its pressure increases.

If an inflated balloon is pulled down to the bottom of a swimming pool, the pressure of the water on the balloon increases. The pressure of the air particles inside the balloon must increase to match that of the water outside, so the volume of the air inside the balloon decreases.

Appendix

Pascal's Principle

Pascal's principle states that a change in pressure at any point in an enclosed fluid will be transmitted equally to all parts of that fluid.

When a mechanic uses a hydraulic jack to raise an automobile off the ground, he or she increases the pressure on the fluid in the jack by pushing on the jack handle. The pressure is transmitted equally to all parts of the fluid-filled jacking system. As fluid presses the jack plate against the frame of the car, the car is lifted off the ground.

Archimedes' Principle

Archimedes' principle states that the buoyant force on an object in a fluid is equal to the weight of the volume of fluid that the object displaces.

A person floating in a swimming pool displaces 20 L of water. The weight of that volume of water is about 200 N. Therefore, the buoyant force on the person is 200 N.

Bernoulli's Principle

Bernoulli's principle states that as the speed of a moving fluid increases, the fluid's pressure decreases.

The lift on an airplane wing can be explained in part by using Bernoulli's principle. Because of the shape of the wing, the air moving over the top of the wing is moving faster than the air below the wing. This faster-moving air above the wing exerts less pressure than the slower-moving air below it does. The resulting increased pressure below exerts an upward force and pushes the wing up.

Law of Reflection

The **law of reflection** states that the angle of incidence is equal to the angle of reflection. This law explains why light reflects off a surface at the same angle that the light strikes the surface.

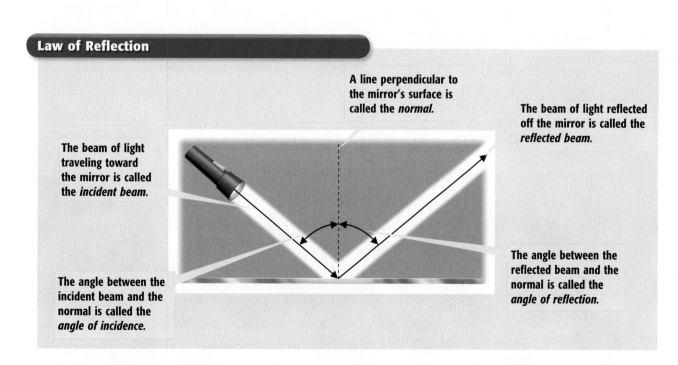

Law of Reflection

A line perpendicular to the mirror's surface is called the *normal*.

The beam of light reflected off the mirror is called the *reflected beam.*

The beam of light traveling toward the mirror is called the *incident beam.*

The angle between the incident beam and the normal is called the *angle of incidence.*

The angle between the reflected beam and the normal is called the *angle of reflection.*

Appendix

Useful Equations

Average Speed

The rate at which an object moves is its *speed*. Speed depends on the distance traveled and the time taken to travel that distance. **Average speed** is calculated using the following equation:

$$\text{average speed} = \frac{\text{total distance}}{\text{total time}}$$

> **Example:** A bicycle messenger traveled a distance of 136 km in 8 h. What was the messenger's average speed?
>
> $$\frac{136 \text{ km}}{8 \text{ h}} = 17 \text{ km/h}$$
>
> The messenger's average speed was **17 km/h.**

Velocity

The speed of an object in a particular direction is **velocity.** Speed and velocity are not the same even though they are calculated by using the same equation. Velocity must include a direction, so velocity is described as speed in a certain direction. For example, the speed of a plane that is traveling south at 600 km/h is 600 km/h. The velocity of a plane that is traveling south at 600 km/h is 600 km/h south.

Velocity can also be thought of as the rate of change of an object's position. An object's velocity remains constant only if its speed and direction don't change. Therefore, constant velocity occurs only along a straight line.

Average Acceleration

The rate at which velocity changes is called *acceleration*. **Average acceleration** can be calculated by using the following equation:

$$\frac{\text{average}}{\text{acceleration}} = \frac{\text{final velocity} - \text{starting velocity}}{\text{time it takes to change velocity}}$$

> **Example:** Calculate the average acceleration of an Olympic sprinter who reached a velocity of 20 m/s south at the finish line of a 100 m dash. The race was in a straight line and lasted 10 s.
>
> $$\frac{20 \text{ m/s} - 0 \text{ m/s}}{10 \text{ s}} = 2 \text{ m/s/s}$$
>
> The sprinter's average acceleration was **2 m/s/s south.**

The winner of this race is the athlete who has the greatest average speed.

Net Force

Forces in the Same Direction

When forces are in the same direction, add the forces together to determine the net force.

Example: Calculate the net force on a stalled car that is being pushed by two people. One person is pushing with a force of 13 N northwest, and the other person is pushing with a force of 8 N in the same direction.

$$13 \text{ N} + 8 \text{ N} = 21 \text{ N}$$

The net force is **21 N northwest.**

Forces in Opposite Directions

When forces are in opposite directions, subtract the smaller force from the larger force to determine the net force. The net force will be in the direction of the larger force.

Example: Calculate the net force on a rope that is being pulled on each end. One person is pulling on one end of the rope with a force of 12 N south. Another person is pulling on the opposite end of the rope with a force of 7 N north.

$$12 \text{ N} - 7 \text{ N} = 5 \text{ N}$$

The net force is **5 N south.**

The forces exerted by the dogs on the rope are in opposite directions. The net force is found by subtracting the smaller force from the larger force.

Pressure

Pressure is the force exerted over a given area. The SI unit for pressure is the pascal (Pa).

$$pressure = \frac{force}{area}$$

Example: Calculate the pressure of the air in a soccer ball if the air exerts a force of 25,000 N over an area of 0.15 m^2.

$$pressure = \frac{25{,}000 \text{ N}}{1 \text{ m}^2} = \frac{167{,}000 \text{ N}}{\text{m}^2} = 167{,}000 \text{ Pa}$$

The pressure of the air inside the soccer ball is **167,000 Pa.**

Density

The mass per unit volume of a substance is **density.** Thus, a material's density is the amount of matter it contains in a given space. To find density, you must measure both mass and volume. Density is calculated by using the following equation:

$$density = \frac{mass}{volume}$$

Example: Calculate the density of a sponge that has a mass of 10 g and a volume of 40 cm^3.

$$\frac{10 \text{ g}}{40 \text{ cm}^3} = \frac{0.25 \text{ g}}{\text{cm}^3}$$

The density of the sponge is $\frac{0.25 \text{ g}}{\text{cm}^3}$.

Concentration

A measure of the amount of one substance that is dissolved in another substance is **concentration.** The substance that is dissolved is the solute. The substance that dissolves another substance is the solvent. Concentration is calculated by using the following equation:

$$concentration = \frac{mass\ of\ solute}{volume\ of\ solvent}$$

Example: Calculate the concentration of a solution in which 10 g of sugar is dissolved in 125 mL of water.

$$\frac{10\ g\ of\ sugar}{125\ mL\ of\ water} = \frac{0.08\ g}{mL}$$

The concentration of this solution is $\frac{0.08\ g}{mL}$.

These solutions were made by using the same volume of water. But less solute was dissolved in the beaker on the left. So, the concentration of the solution on the left is lower than the concentration of the solution on the right.

Work

Work is done by exerting a force through a distance. Work is expressed in joules (J), which are equivalent to newton-meters (N•m).

$$work = force \times distance$$

Example: Calculate the amount of work done by a man who lifts a 100 N toddler 1.5 m off the floor.

$work = 100\ N \times 1.5\ m = 150\ N•m = 150\ J$

The man did **150 J** of work.

Power

Power is the rate at which work is done. Power is expressed in watts (W), which are equivalent to joules per second (J/s).

$$power = \frac{work}{time}$$

Example: Calculate the power of a weight-lifter who raises a 300 N barbell 2.1 m off the floor in 1.25 s.

$work = 300\ N \times 2.1\ m = 630\ N•m = 630\ J$

$$power = \frac{30\ J}{1.25\ s} = \frac{504\ J}{s} = 504$$

The weightlifter's power is **504 W.**

Heat

Heat is the energy transferred between objects that are at different temperatures. Heat is expressed in joules (J). In general, if you know an object's mass, change in temperature, and specific heat, you can calculate heat. Specific heat is the amount of energy needed to change the temperature of 1 kg of a substance by 1°C. Specific heat is expressed in joules per kilogram-degree Celsius (J/kg•°C).

heat = specific heat × mass × change in temperature

Example: Calculate the heat transferred to a mass of 0.2 kg of water to change the temperature of the water from 25°C to 80°C. The specific heat of water is 4,184 J/kg•°C.

$$heat = 4{,}184 \text{ J/kg•°C} \times 0.2 \text{ kg} \times (80°C - 25°C) = 46{,}024 \text{ J}$$

The heat transferred is **46,024 J.**

As the air in this balloon absorbs heat, the temperature of the air rises.

Work and Heat

James Joule, an English scientist, performed experiments to explore the relationship between **work** and **heat.** He found that a given amount of work always generated the same amount of heat. By applying the law of conservation of energy, we know that the amount of heat generated can never be larger than the work done.

Example: What is the maximum amount of heat that can be generated from the work done if a force of 75 N is exerted over a distance of 5 m?

$$work = 75 \text{ N} \times 5 \text{ m} = 375 \text{ N•m} = 375 \text{ J}$$

The maximum amount of heat that can be generated is **375 J.**

Example: A force of 299 N is exerted through a distance of 210 m. The resulting work is converted into heat and absorbed by 2.0 kg of water. What is the maximum change in temperature if the specific heat of water is 4,184 J/kg•°C?

$$work = 299 \text{ N} \times 210 \text{ m} = 62{,}790 \text{ N•m} = 62{,}790 \text{ J}$$

$$\frac{change \ in}{temperature} = \frac{heat}{mass \times specific \ heat}$$

$$\frac{change \ in}{temperature} = \frac{62{,}790 \text{ J}}{2.0 \text{ kg} \times 4{,}184 \text{ J/kg•°C}} = 7.5°C$$

The maximum change in temperature is **7.5°C.**

Scientific Methods

The ways in which scientists answer questions and solve problems are called **scientific methods.** The same steps are often used by scientists as they look for answers. However, there is more than one way to use these steps. Scientists may use all of the steps or just some of the steps during an investigation. They may even repeat some of the steps. The goal of using scientific methods is to come up with reliable answers and solutions.

Six Steps of Scientific Methods

 Good questions come from careful **observations.** You make observations by using your senses to gather information. Sometimes, you may use instruments, such as microscopes and telescopes, to extend the range of your senses. As you observe the natural world, you will discover that you have many more questions than answers. These questions drive investigations.

Questions beginning with *what, why, how,* and *when* are important in focusing an investigation. Here is an example of a question that could lead to an investigation.

> **Question:** How does acid rain affect plant growth?

 After you ask a question, you need to form a **hypothesis.** A hypothesis is a clear statement of what you expect the answer to your question to be. Your hypothesis will represent your best "educated guess" based on what you have observed and what you already know. A good hypothesis is testable. Otherwise, the investigation can go no further. Here is a hypothesis based on the question "How does acid rain affect plant growth?"

> **Hypothesis:** Acid rain slows plant growth.

The hypothesis can lead to predictions. A prediction is what you think the outcome of your experiment or data collection will be. Predictions are usually stated in an if-then format. Here is a sample prediction for the hypothesis that acid rain slows plant growth.

> **Prediction:** If a plant is watered with only acid rain (which has a pH of 4), then the plant will grow at half its normal rate.

3 Test the Hypothesis

After you have formed a hypothesis and made a prediction, your hypothesis should be tested. One way to test a hypothesis is with a controlled experiment. A **controlled experiment** tests only one factor at a time. In an experiment to test the effect of acid rain on plant growth, the **control group** would be watered with normal rainwater. The **experimental group** would be watered with acid rain. All of the plants should receive the same amount of sunlight and water each day. The air temperature should be the same for all groups. However, the acidity of the water will be a variable. In fact, any factor that differs from one group to another is a **variable.** If your hypothesis is correct, then the acidity of the water and plant growth are *dependant variables.* The amount that a plant grows is dependent on the acidity of the water. However, the amount of water and the amount of sunlight received by each plant are *independent variables.* Either of these factors could change without affecting the other factor.

Sometimes, the nature of an investigation makes a controlled experiment impossible. For example, Earth's core is surrounded by thousands of meters of rock. Under such circumstances, a hypothesis may be tested by making detailed observations.

4 **Analyze the Results**

After you have completed your experiments, made your observations, and collected your data, you must analyze all of the information that you have gathered. Tables and graphs are often used in this step to organize the data.

5 **Draw Conclusions**

After analyzing your data, you can determine if your results support your hypothesis. If your hypothesis is supported, you (or others) might want to repeat the observations or experiments to verify your results. If your hypothesis is not supported by the data, you may have to check your procedure for errors. You may even have to reject your hypothesis and make a new one. If you cannot draw a conclusion from your results, you may have to try the investigation again or carry out further observations or experiments.

6 **Communicate Results**

After any scientific investigation, you should report your results. By preparing a written or oral report, you let others know what you have learned. They may repeat your investigation to see if they get the same results. Your report may even lead to another question and then to another investigation.

Appendix

Scientific Methods in Action

Scientific methods contain loops in which several steps may be repeated over and over again. In some cases, certain steps are unnecessary. Thus, there is not a "straight line" of steps. For example, sometimes scientists find that testing one hypothesis raises new questions and new hypotheses to be tested. And sometimes, testing the hypothesis leads directly to a conclusion. Furthermore, the steps in scientific methods are not always used in the same order. Follow the steps in the diagram, and see how many different directions scientific methods can take you.

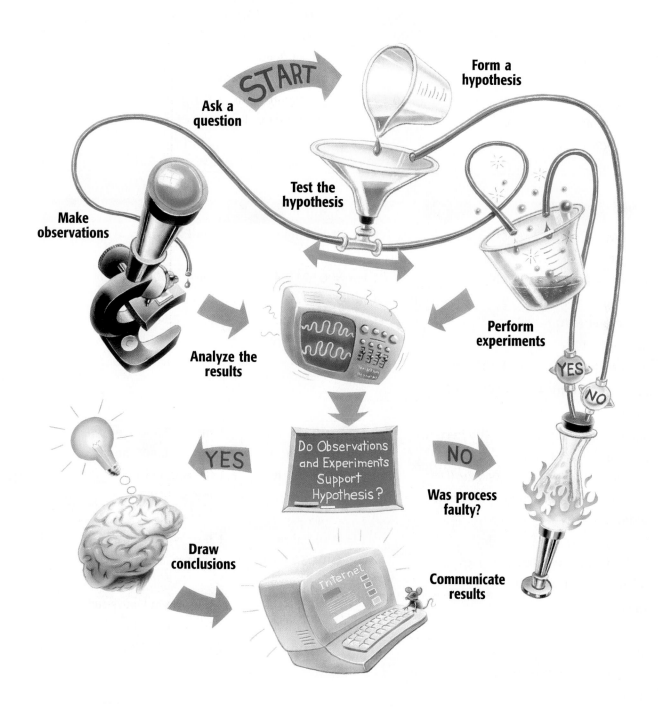

START

Ask a question

Form a hypothesis

Test the hypothesis

Make observations

Analyze the results

Perform experiments

YES   NO

YES   Do Observations and Experiments Support Hypothesis?   NO

Was process faulty?

Draw conclusions

Communicate results

SI Measurement

The International System of Units, or SI, is the standard system of measurement used by many scientists. Using the same standards of measurement makes it easier for scientists to communicate with one another.

SI works by combining prefixes and base units. Each base unit can be used with different prefixes to define smaller and larger quantities. The table below lists common SI prefixes.

SI Prefixes

Prefix	Symbol	Factor	Example
kilo-	k	1,000	kilogram, 1 kg = 1,000 g
hecto-	h	100	hectoliter, 1 hL = 100 L
deka-	da	10	dekameter, 1 dam = 10 m
		1	meter, liter, gram
deci-	d	0.1	decigram, 1 dg = 0.1 g
centi-	c	0.01	centimeter, 1 cm = 0.01 m
milli-	m	0.001	milliliter, 1 mL = 0.001 L
micro-	μ	0.000 001	micrometer, 1 μm = 0.000 001 m

SI Conversion Table

SI units	From SI to English	From English to SI
Length		
kilometer (km) = 1,000 m	1 km = 0.621 mi	1 mi = 1.609 km
meter (m) = 100 cm	1 m = 3.281 ft	1 ft = 0.305 m
centimeter (cm) = 0.01 m	1 cm = 0.394 in.	1 in. = 2.540 cm
millimeter (mm) = 0.001 m	1 mm = 0.039 in.	
micrometer (μm) = 0.000 001 m		
nanometer (nm) = 0.000 000 001 m		
Area		
square kilometer (km^2) = 100 hectares	1 km^2 = 0.386 mi^2	1 mi^2 = 2.590 km^2
hectare (ha) = 10,000 m^2	1 ha = 2.471 acres	1 acre = 0.405 ha
square meter (m^2) = 10,000 cm^2	1 m^2 = 10.764 ft^2	1 ft^2 = 0.093 m^2
square centimeter (cm^2) = 100 mm^2	1 cm^2 = 0.155 in.^{2}	1 in.^{2} = 6.452 cm^2
Volume		
liter (L) = 1,000 mL = 1 dm^3	1 L = 1.057 fl qt	1 fl qt = 0.946 L
milliliter (mL) = 0.001 L = 1 cm^3	1 mL = 0.034 fl oz	1 fl oz = 29.574 mL
microliter (μL) = 0.000 001 L		
Mass	*Equivalent weight at Earth's surface	
kilogram (kg) = 1,000 g	1 kg = 2.205 lb*	1 lb* = 0.454 kg
gram (g) = 1,000 mg	1 g = 0.035 oz*	1 oz* = 28.350 g
milligram (mg) = 0.001 g		
microgram (μg) = 0.000 001 g		

Measuring Skills

Using a Graduated Cylinder

When using a graduated cylinder to measure volume, keep the following procedures in mind:

1. Place the cylinder on a flat, level surface before measuring liquid.

2. Move your head so that your eye is level with the surface of the liquid.

3. Read the mark closest to the liquid level. On glass graduated cylinders, read the mark closest to the center of the curve in the liquid's surface.

Using a Meterstick or Metric Ruler

When using a meterstick or metric ruler to measure length, keep the following procedures in mind:

1. Place the ruler firmly against the object that you are measuring.

2. Align one edge of the object exactly with the 0 end of the ruler.

3. Look at the other edge of the object to see which of the marks on the ruler is closest to that edge. (Note: Each small slash between the centimeters represents a millimeter, which is one-tenth of a centimeter.)

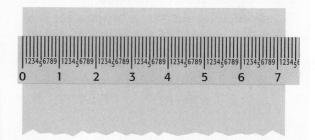

Using a Triple-Beam Balance

When using a triple-beam balance to measure mass, keep the following procedures in mind:

1. Make sure the balance is on a level surface.

2. Place all of the countermasses at 0. Adjust the balancing knob until the pointer rests at 0.

3. Place the object to be measured on the pan. **Caution:** Do not place hot objects or chemicals directly on the balance pan.

4. Move the largest countermass along the beam to the right until it is at the last notch that does not tip the balance. Follow the same procedure with the next-largest countermass. Then, move the smallest countermass until the pointer rests at 0.

5. Add the readings from the three beams together to determine the mass of the object.

6. When determining the mass of crystals or powders, first find the mass of a piece of filter paper. Then, add the crystals or powder to the paper, and remeasure. The actual mass of the crystals or powder is the total mass minus the mass of the paper. When finding the mass of liquids, first find the mass of the empty container. Then, find the combined mass of the liquid and container. The mass of the liquid is the total mass minus the mass of the container.

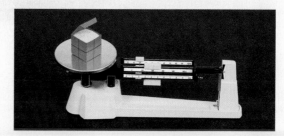

Using the Microscope

Parts of the Compound Light Microscope

- The **ocular lens** magnifies the image 10×.
- The **low-power objective** magnifies the image 10×.
- The **high-power objective** magnifies the image either 40× or 43×.
- The **revolving nosepiece** holds the objectives and can be turned to change from one magnification to the other.
- The **body tube** maintains the correct distance between the ocular lens and objectives.
- The **coarse-adjustment knob** moves the body tube up and down to allow focusing of the image.
- The **fine-adjustment knob** moves the body tube slightly to bring the image into sharper focus. It is usually located in the center of the coarse-adjustment knob.
- The **stage** supports a slide.
- **Stage clips** hold the slide in place for viewing.
- The **diaphragm** controls the amount of light coming through the stage.
- The light source provides a **light** for viewing the slide.
- The **arm** supports the body tube.
- The **base** supports the microscope.

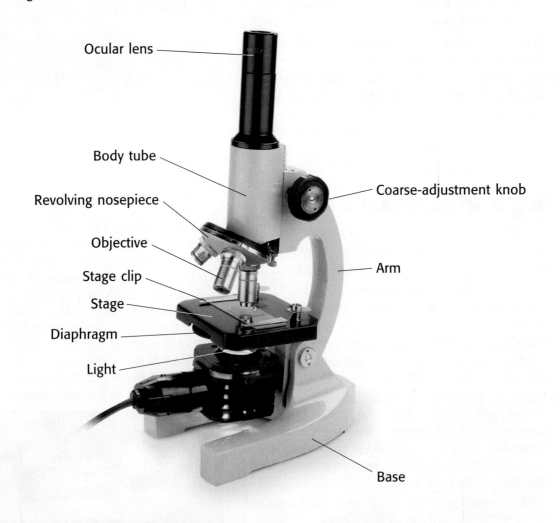

Ocular lens

Body tube

Revolving nosepiece

Objective

Stage clip

Stage

Diaphragm

Light

Coarse-adjustment knob

Arm

Base

Appendix

Proper Use of the Compound Light Microscope

1. Use both hands to carry the microscope to your lab table. Place one hand beneath the base, and use the other hand to hold the arm of the microscope. Hold the microscope close to your body while carrying it to your lab table.

2. Place the microscope on the lab table at least 5 cm from the edge of the table.

3. Check to see what type of light source is used by your microscope. If the microscope has a lamp, plug it in and make sure that the cord is out of the way. If the microscope has a mirror, adjust the mirror to reflect light through the hole in the stage.
   Caution: If your microscope has a mirror, do not use direct sunlight as a light source. Direct sunlight can damage your eyes.

4. Always begin work with the low-power objective in line with the body tube. Adjust the revolving nosepiece.

5. Place a prepared slide over the hole in the stage. Secure the slide with the stage clips.

6. Look through the ocular lens. Move the diaphragm to adjust the amount of light coming through the stage.

7. Look at the stage from eye level. Slowly turn the coarse adjustment to lower the objective until the objective almost touches the slide. Do not allow the objective to touch the slide.

8. Look through the ocular lens. Turn the coarse adjustment to raise the low-power objective until the image is in focus. Always focus by raising the objective away from the slide. Never focus the objective downward. Use the fine adjustment to sharpen the focus. Keep both eyes open while viewing a slide.

9. Make sure that the image is exactly in the center of your field of vision. Then, switch to the high-power objective. Focus the image by using only the fine adjustment. Never use the coarse adjustment at high power.

10. When you are finished using the microscope, remove the slide. Clean the ocular lens and objectives with lens paper. Return the microscope to its storage area. Remember to use both hands when carrying the microscope.

Making a Wet Mount

1. Use lens paper to clean a glass slide and a coverslip.

2. Place the specimen that you wish to observe in the center of the slide.

3. Using a medicine dropper, place one drop of water on the specimen.

4. Hold the coverslip at the edge of the water and at a 45° angle to the slide. Make sure that the water runs along the edge of the coverslip.

5. Lower the coverslip slowly to avoid trapping air bubbles.

6. Water might evaporate from the slide as you work. Add more water to keep the specimen fresh. Place the tip of the medicine dropper next to the edge of the coverslip. Add a drop of water. (You can also use this method to add stain or solutions to a wet mount.) Remove excess water from the slide by using the corner of a paper towel as a blotter. Do not lift the coverslip to add or remove water.

Periodic Table of the Elements

Each square on the table includes an element's name, chemical symbol, atomic number, and atomic mass.

The color of the chemical symbol indicates the physical state at room temperature. Carbon is a solid.

6	— Atomic number
C	— Chemical symbol
Carbon	— Element name
12.0	— Atomic mass

The background color indicates the type of element. Carbon is a nonmetal.

Background
- Metals
- Metalloids
- Nonmetals

Chemical symbol
- Solid
- Liquid
- Gas

Period 1

| 1 |
| **H** |
| Hydrogen |
| 1.0 |

A row of elements is called a *period*.

A column of elements is called a *group* or *family*.

Values in parentheses are the mass numbers of those radioactive elements' most stable or most common isotopes.

These elements are placed below the table to allow the table to be narrower.

	Group 1	Group 2	Group 3	Group 4	Group 5	Group 6	Group 7	Group 8	Group 9
Period 2	3 **Li** Lithium 6.9	4 **Be** Beryllium 9.0							
Period 3	11 **Na** Sodium 23.0	12 **Mg** Magnesium 24.3							
Period 4	19 **K** Potassium 39.1	20 **Ca** Calcium 40.1	21 **Sc** Scandium 45.0	22 **Ti** Titanium 47.9	23 **V** Vanadium 50.9	24 **Cr** Chromium 52.0	25 **Mn** Manganese 54.9	26 **Fe** Iron 55.8	27 **Co** Cobalt 58.9
Period 5	37 **Rb** Rubidium 85.5	38 **Sr** Strontium 87.6	39 **Y** Yttrium 88.9	40 **Zr** Zirconium 91.2	41 **Nb** Niobium 92.9	42 **Mo** Molybdenum 95.9	43 **Tc** Technetium (98)	44 **Ru** Ruthenium 101.1	45 **Rh** Rhodium 102.9
Period 6	55 **Cs** Cesium 132.9	56 **Ba** Barium 137.3	57 **La** Lanthanum 138.9	72 **Hf** Hafnium 178.5	73 **Ta** Tantalum 180.9	74 **W** Tungsten 183.8	75 **Re** Rhenium 186.2	76 **Os** Osmium 190.2	77 **Ir** Iridium 192.2
Period 7	87 **Fr** Francium (223)	88 **Ra** Radium (226)	89 **Ac** Actinium (227)	104 **Rf** Rutherfordium (261)	105 **Db** Dubnium (262)	106 **Sg** Seaborgium (266)	107 **Bh** Bohrium (264)	108 **Hs** Hassium (277)	109 **Mt** Meitnerium (268)

Lanthanides

58 **Ce** Cerium 140.1	59 **Pr** Praseodymium 140.9	60 **Nd** Neodymium 144.2	61 **Pm** Promethium (145)	62 **Sm** Samarium 150.4

Actinides

90 **Th** Thorium 232.0	91 **Pa** Protactinium 231.0	92 **U** Uranium 238.0	93 **Np** Neptunium (237)	94 **Pu** Plutonium (244)

Topic: **Periodic Table**
Go To: **go.hrw.com**
Keyword: **HN0 PERIODIC**
Visit the HRW Web site for
updates on the periodic table.

Group 18

| 2 |
| **He** |
| Helium |
| 4.0 |

This zigzag line
reminds you where
the metals, nonmetals,
and metalloids are.

Group 13	**Group 14**	**Group 15**	**Group 16**	**Group 17**
5 **B** Boron 10.8	6 **C** Carbon 12.0	7 **N** Nitrogen 14.0	8 **O** Oxygen 16.0	9 **F** Fluorine 19.0

| 10 |
| **Ne** |
| Neon |
| 20.2 |

| 13 **Al** Aluminum 27.0 | 14 **Si** Silicon 28.1 | 15 **P** Phosphorus 31.0 | 16 **S** Sulfur 32.1 | 17 **Cl** Chlorine 35.5 | 18 **Ar** Argon 39.9 |

Group 10	**Group 11**	**Group 12**	**Group 13**	**Group 14**	**Group 15**	**Group 16**	**Group 17**	**Group 18**
28 **Ni** Nickel 58.7	29 **Cu** Copper 63.5	30 **Zn** Zinc 65.4	31 **Ga** Gallium 69.7	32 **Ge** Germanium 72.6	33 **As** Arsenic 74.9	34 **Se** Selenium 79.0	35 **Br** Bromine 79.9	36 **Kr** Krypton 83.8
46 **Pd** Palladium 106.4	47 **Ag** Silver 107.9	48 **Cd** Cadmium 112.4	49 **In** Indium 114.8	50 **Sn** Tin 118.7	51 **Sb** Antimony 121.8	52 **Te** Tellurium 127.6	53 **I** Iodine 126.9	54 **Xe** Xenon 131.3
78 **Pt** Platinum 195.1	79 **Au** Gold 197.0	80 **Hg** Mercury 200.6	81 **Tl** Thallium 204.4	82 **Pb** Lead 207.2	83 **Bi** Bismuth 209.0	84 **Po** Polonium (209)	85 **At** Astatine (210)	86 **Rn** Radon (222)
110 **Ds** Darmstadtium (281)	111 **Uuu** Unununium (272)	112 **Uub** Ununbium (285)	113 **Uut** Ununtrium (284)	114 **Uuq** Ununquadium (289)	115 **Uup** Ununpentium (288)			

The discovery of elements
113, 114, and 115 has been
reported but not confirmed.

The names and three-letter symbols of elements are temporary. They
are based on the atomic numbers of the elements. Official names and
symbols will be approved by an international committee of scientists.

63 **Eu** Europium 152.0	64 **Gd** Gadolinium 157.2	65 **Tb** Terbium 158.9	66 **Dy** Dysprosium 162.5	67 **Ho** Holmium 164.9	68 **Er** Erbium 167.3	69 **Tm** Thulium 168.9	70 **Yb** Ytterbium 173.0	71 **Lu** Lutetium 175.0
95 **Am** Americium (243)	96 **Cm** Curium (247)	97 **Bk** Berkelium (247)	98 **Cf** Californium (251)	99 **Es** Einsteinium (252)	100 **Fm** Fermium (257)	101 **Md** Mendelevium (258)	102 **No** Nobelium (259)	103 **Lr** Lawrencium (262)

Appendix

Domains and Kingdoms

All organisms are divided into one of three domains: Domain Archaea, Domain Bacteria, or Domain Eukarya. Some of the groups within these domains are shown below. (Remember that genus names are italicized.)

Domain Archaea

The organisms in this domain are single-celled prokaryotes, many of which live in extreme environments.

Archaea		
Group	**Example**	**Characteristics**
Methanogens	*Methanococcus*	produce methane gas; can't live in oxygen
Thermophiles	*Sulpholobus*	require sulphur; can't live in oxygen
Halophiles	*Halococcus*	live in very salty environments; most can live in oxygen

Domain Bacteria

Organisms in this domain are single-celled prokaryotes and are found in moderate environments.

Bacteria		
Group	**Example**	**Characteristics**
Bacilli	*Escherichia*	rod shaped; some fix nitrogen; some cause disease
Cocci	*Streptococcus*	spherical shaped; cause diseases; can form spores
Spirilla	*Treponema*	spiral shaped; cause diseases, such as syphilis

Domain Eukarya

Organisms in this domain are single-celled or multicellular eukaryotes.

Kingdom Protista

There are single-celled and multicellular organisms in this kingdom.

Protists		
Group	**Example**	**Characteristics**
Sarcodines	*Amoeba*	radiolarians; single-celled consumers
Ciliates	*Paramecium*	single-celled consumers
Flagellates	*Trypanosoma*	single-celled parasites
Sporozoans	*Plasmodium*	single-celled parasites
Euglenas	*Euglena*	single celled; photosynthesize
Diatoms	*Pinnularia*	most are single celled; photosynthesize
Dinoflagellates	*Gymnodinium*	single celled; some photosynthesize
Algae	*Volvox*	single celled or multicellular; photosynthesize
Slime molds	*Physarum*	single celled or multicellular; consumers or decomposers
Water molds	powdery mildew	single celled or multicellular; parasites or decomposers

Kingdom Fungi

There are single-celled and multicellular eukaryotes in this kingdom. There are four major groups of fungi.

Fungi		
Group	**Examples**	**Characteristics**
Threadlike fungi	bread mold	spherical; decomposers
Sac fungi	yeast; morels	saclike; parasites and decomposers
Club fungi	mushrooms; rusts; smuts	club shaped; parasites and decomposers
Lichens	British soldier	symbiotic with algae

Kingdom Plantae

The organisms in this kingdom are multicellular eukaryotes. They have specialized organ systems for different life processes. They are classified in divisions instead of phyla.

Plants		
Group	**Examples**	**Characteristics**
Threadlike fungi	mosses; liverworts	reproduce by spores
Club mosses	*Lycopodium;* ground pine	reproduce by spores
Horsetails	rushes	reproduce by spores
Ferns	spleenworts; sensitive fern	reproduce by spores
Conifers	pines; spruces; firs	reproduce by seeds; cones
Cycads	*Zamia*	reproduce by seeds
Gnetophytes	*Welwitschia*	reproduce by seeds
Ginkgoes	*Ginkgo*	reproduce by seeds
Angiosperms	all flowering plants	reproduce by seeds; flowers

Kingdom Animalia

This kingdom contains multicellular eukaryotes. Most of the organisms in this kingdom have specialized tissues and complex organ systems.

Animals		
Group	**Examples**	**Characteristics**
Sponges	glass sponges	no symmetry or segmentation; aquatic
Cnidarians	jellyfish; coral	radial symmetry; aquatic
Flatworms	planaria; tapeworms; flukes	bilateral symmetry; organ systems
Roundworms	*Trichina;* hookworms	bilateral symmetry; organ systems
Annelids	earthworms; leeches	bilateral symmetry; organ systems
Mollusks	snails; octopuses	bilateral symmetry; organ systems
Echinoderms	sea stars; sand dollars	radial symmetry; organ systems
Arthropods	insects; spiders; lobsters	bilateral symmetry; organ systems
Chordates	fish; amphibians; reptiles; birds; mammals	bilateral symmetry; complex organ systems

Temperature Scales

Temperature can be expressed by using three scales: the Fahrenheit, Celsius, and Kelvin scales. The SI unit for temperature is the kelvin (K). Although 0 K is much colder than 0°C, a change of 1 K is equal to a change of 1°C.

Three Temperature Scales

	Fahrenheit	Celsius	Kelvin
Water boils	212°	100°	373
Body temperature	98.6°	37°	310
Room temperature	68°	20°	293
Water freezes	32°	0°	273

Temperature Conversion Table

Conversion	Equation	Example
degrees Celsius to degrees Fahrenheit $°C \rightarrow °F$	$°F = \left(\dfrac{9}{5} \times °C \right) + 32$	Convert 45°C to °F. $°F = \left(\dfrac{9}{5} \times 45°C \right) + 32 = 113°F$
degrees Fahrenheit to degrees Celsius $°F \rightarrow °C$	$°C = \dfrac{5}{9} \times (°F - 32)$	Convert 68°F to °C. $°C = \dfrac{5}{9} \times (68°F - 32) = 20°C$
degrees Celsius to kelvins $°C \rightarrow K$	$K = °C + 273$	Convert 45°C to K. $K = 45°C + 273 = 318 \ K$
kelvins to degrees Celsius $K \rightarrow °C$	$°C = K - 273$	Convert 32 K to °C. $°C = 32K - 273 = -241°C$

Appendix

English and Spanish Glossary

with Academic Vocabulary

A

absolute dating (AB suh LOOT DAYT ing) any method of measuring the age of an event or object in years (246)

datación absoluta cualquier método que sirve para determinar la edad de un suceso u objeto en años (246)

absorption (ab SAWRP shuhn) in optics, the transfer of light energy to particles of matter (84)

absorción en la óptica, la transferencia de energía luminosa a las partículas de materia (84)

adaptation (AD uhp TAY shuhn) a characteristic that improves an individual's ability to survive and reproduce in a particular environment (298)

adaptación una característica que mejora la capacidad de un individuo para sobrevivir y reproducirse en un determinado ambiente (298)

*adaptive (uh DAP tiv) able to adjust to changes (295)

adaptativo capaz de adecuarse a los cambios (295)

*affect (uh FEKT) to change; to have an effect on; to influence (261, 421, 463, 493, 523)

afectar cambiar algo; tener un efecto; influir (261, 421, 463, 493, 523)

allele (uh LEEL) one of the alternative forms of a gene that governs a characteristic, such as hair color (180)

alelo una de las formas alternativas de un gene que rige un carácter, como por ejemplo, el color del cabello (180)

alveolus (al VEE uh luhs) any of the tiny air sacs of the lungs where oxygen and carbon dioxide are exchanged (509)

alveolo cualquiera de las diminutas bolsas de aire de los pulmones, en donde ocurre el intercambio de oxígeno y dióxido de carbono (509)

angiosperm (AN jee oh SPUHRM) a flowering plant that produces seeds within a fruit (362)

angiosperma una planta que da flores y que produce semillas dentro de la fruta (362)

Animalia (AN i MAY lee uh) a kingdom made up of complex, multicellular organisms that lack cell walls, can usually move around, and quickly respond to their environment (342)

Animalia un reino formado por organismos pluricelulares complejos que no tienen pared celular, normalmente son capaces de moverse y reaccionan rápidamente a su ambiente (342)

*appropriate (uh PROH pree it) correct for the use; proper (5)

apropiado correcto para un determinado uso; adecuado (5)

*appropriately (uh PROH pree it lee) in a correct or proper way (5)

apropiadamente de forma correcta o apropiada (5)

*approximately (uh PRAHK suh mit lee) almost; about (261)

aproximadamente casi; alrededor de (261)

Archaea (ahr KEE uh) in a modern taxonomic system, a domain made up of prokaryotes that differ from other prokaryotes in the makeup of their cell walls and in their genetics; this domain aligns with the traditional kingdom Archaebacteria (339)

Archaea en un sistema taxonómico moderno, un dominio compuesto por procariotes que se diferencian de otros procariotes por la composición de su pared celular y su composición genética; este dominio coincide con el reino tradicional Archaebacteria (339)

* Academic Vocabulary

area (ER ee uh) a measure of the size of a surface or a region (23)

área una medida del tamaño de una superficie o región (23)

artery (ART uhr ee) a blood vessel that carries blood away from the heart to the body's organs (498)

arteria un vaso sanguíneo que transporta sangre del corazón a los órganos del cuerpo (498)

asexual reproduction (ay SEK shoo uhl REE pruh DUHK shuhn) reproduction that does not involve the union of sex cells and in which one parent produces offspring that are genetically identical to the parent (54)

reproducción asexual reproducción que no involucra la unión de células sexuales, en la que un solo progenitor produce descendencia que es genéticamente igual al progenitor (54)

ATP (AY TEE PEE) adenosine triphosphate, a molecule that acts as the main energy source for cell processes (60)

ATP adenosín trifosfato, una molécula orgánica que funciona como la fuente principal de energía para los procesos celulares (60)

B

Bacteria (bak TIR ee uh) in a modern taxonomic system, a domain made up of prokaryotes that differ from other prokaryotes in the makeup of their cell walls and in their genetics; this domain aligns with the traditional kingdom Eubacteria (339)

Bacteria en un sistema taxonómico moderno, un dominio compuesto por procariotes que se diferencian de otros procariotes por la composición de su pared celular y su composición genética; este dominio coincide con el reino tradicional Eubacteria (339)

blood (BLUHD) the fluid that carries gases, nutrients, and wastes through the body and that is made up of platelets, white blood cells, red blood cells, and plasma (502)

sangre el líquido que lleva gases, nutrientes y desechos por el cuerpo y que está formado por plaquetas, glóbulos blancos, glóbulos rojos y plasma (502)

blood pressure (BLUHD PRESH uhr) the force that blood exerts on the walls of the arteries (504)

presión sanguínea la fuerza que la sangre ejerce en las paredes de las arterias (504)

brain (BRAYN) the mass of nerve tissue that is the main control center of the nervous system (530)

encéfalo el órgano que es el centro principal de control del sistema nervioso (530)

bronchus (BRAHNG kuhs) one of the two tubes that connect the lungs with the trachea (509)

bronquio uno de los dos tubos que conectan los pulmones con la tráquea (509)

C

cancer (KAN suhr) a tumor in which the cells begin dividing at an uncontrolled rate and can become invasive (157)

cáncer un tumor en el cual las células comienzan a dividirse a una tasa incontrolable y pueden volverse invasivas (157)

capillary (CAP uh LER ee) a tiny blood vessel that allows an exchange between blood and cells in tissue (498)

capilar diminuto vaso sanguíneo que permite el intercambio entre la sangre y las células de los tejidos (498)

carbohydrate (CAHR boh HIE drayt) a class of molecules that includes sugars, starches, and fiber; contains carbon, hydrogen, and oxygen (59)

carbohidrato una clase de moléculas entre las que se incluyen azúcares, almidones y fibra; contiene carbono, hidrógeno y oxígeno (59)

cardiovascular system (KAHR dee OH VAS kyoo luhr SIS tuhm) a collection of organs that transport blood throughout the body; the organs in this system include the heart, the arteries, and the veins (496)

aparato cardiovascular un conjunto de órganos que transportan la sangre a través del cuerpo; los órganos de este sistema incluyen al corazón, las arterias y las venas (496)

Glossary

cartilage (KAHRT uhl ij) a flexible and strong connective tissue (444)

    cartílago un tejido conectivo flexible y fuerte (444)

catastrophism (kuh TAS truh FIZ uhm) a principle that states that geologic change occurs suddenly (235)

    catastrofismo un principio que establece que los cambios geológicos ocurren súbitamente (235)

cell (SEL) the smallest functional and structural unit of all living organisms; usually consists of a nucleus, cytoplasm, and a membrane (52, 114)

    célula la unidad funcional y estructural más pequeña de todos los seres vivos; generalmente está compuesta por un núcleo, un citoplasma y una membrana (52, 114)

cell cycle (SEL SIE kuhl) the life cycle of a cell (152)

    ciclo celular el ciclo de vida de una célula (152)

cell membrane (SEL MEM BRAYN) a phospholipid layer that covers a cell's surface and acts as a barrier between the inside of a cell and the cell's environment (117)

    membrana celular una capa de fosfolípidos que cubre la superficie de la célula y funciona como una barrera entre el interior de la célula y el ambiente de la célula (117)

cellular respiration (SEL yoo luhr RES puh RAY shuhn) the process by which cells use oxygen to produce energy from food (149, 397)

    respiración celular el proceso por medio del cual las células utilizan oxígeno para producir energía a partir de los alimentos (149, 397)

cell wall (SEL WAWL) a rigid structure that surrounds the cell membrane and provides support to the cell (120)

    pared celular una estructura rígida que rodea la membrana celular y le brinda soporte a la célula (120)

central nervous system (SEN truhl NUHR vuhs SIS tuhm) the brain and the spinal cord; its main function is to control the flow of information in the body (526)

    sistema nervioso central el cerebro y la médula espinal; su principal función es controlar el flujo de información en el cuerpo (526)

chlorophyll (KLAWR uh FIL) a green pigment that captures light energy for photosynthesis (396)

    clorofila un pigmento verde que capta la energía luminosa para la fotosíntesis (396)

chloroplast (KLAWR uh PLAST) an organelle found in plant and algae cells where photosynthesis occurs (124)

    cloroplasto un organelo que se encuentra en las células vegetales y en las células de las algas, en el cual se lleva a cabo la fotosíntesis (124)

chromosome (KROH muh SOHM) in a eukaryotic cell, one of the structures in the nucleus that are made up of DNA and protein; in a prokaryotic cell, the main ring of DNA (152)

    cromosoma en una célula eucariótica, una de las estructuras del núcleo que está hecha de ADN y proteína; en una célula procariótica, el anillo principal de ADN (152)

classification (KLAS uh fi KAY shuhn) the division of organisms into groups, or classes, based on specific characteristics (332)

    clasificación la división de organismos en grupos, o clases, en función de características específicas (332)

closed circulatory system (KLOHZD SUHR kyuh luh TAWR ee SIS tuhm) circulatory system in which the heart circulates blood through a network of vessels that form a closed loop (440)

    aparato circulatorio cerrado un aparato circulatorio en el que el corazón hace que la sangre circule a través de una red de vasos que forman un circuito cerrado; la sangre no sale de los vasos sanguíneos y los materiales pasan a través de las paredes de los vasos por difusión (440)

cochlea (KAHK lee uh) a coiled tube that is found in the inner ear and that is essential to hearing (538)

cóclea un tubo enrollado que se encuentra en el oído interno y es esencial para poder oír (538)

coelum (SEE luhm) a body cavity that contains the internal organs (426)

celoma una cavidad del cuerpo que contiene los órganos internos (426)

*communicate (kuh MYOO ni KAYT) to make known; to tell (5)

comunicar hacer saber; decir (5)

compound light microscope (kahm POWND LIET MIE kruh SKOHP) an instrument that magnifies small objects so that they can be seen easily by using two or more lenses (21)

microcopio óptico compuesto un instrumento que magnifica objetos pequeños de modo que se puedan ver fácilmente usando dos o más lentes (21)

*computer (kuhm PYOOT uhr) an electronic device that stores, retrieves, and calculates data (5)

computadora un dispositivo electrónico que almacena, recupera y calcula datos (5)

concave lens (kahn KAYV LENZ) a lens that is thinner in the middle than at the edges (94)

lente cóncava una lente que es más delgada en la parte media que en los bordes (94)

*concept (KAHN SEPT) an idea or thought (5)

concepto una idea o un pensamiento (5)

*conclusion (kuhn KLOO zhuhn) an idea developed from reasoning and investigating (295)

conclusión una idea que se desarrolla a partir del razonamiento y la investigación (295)

*conduct (kuhn DUHKT) to carry out; to do (5)

realizar llevar a cabo; hacer (5)

*confer (kuhn FUHR) to give (463)

conceder dar (463)

*construct (kuhn STRUHKT) to build; to make from parts (5, 295, 329)

construir armar; hacer con partes (5, 295, 329)

consumer (kuhn SOOM uhr) an organism that eats other organisms or organic matter (57, 426)

consumidor un organismo que se alimenta de otros organismos o de materia orgánica (57, 426)

continental drift (KAHN tuh NENT'l DRIFT) the hypothesis that a single large landmass broke up into smaller landmasses to form the continents, which then drifted to their present locations; the movement of continents (272)

deriva continental la hipótesis de que una sola masa de tierra se dividió en masas de tierra más pequeñas para formar los continentes, los cuales se fueron a la deriva hasta terminar en sus ubicaciones actuales; el movimiento de los continentes (272)

*contribution (KAHN truh BYOO shuhn) a part given toward a whole (421, 463, 493, 523)

contribución parte que se da a un todo (421, 463, 493, 523)

controlled experiment (kuhn TROHLD ek SPER uh muhnt) an experiment that tests only one factor at a time by using a comparison of a control group with an experimental group (16)

experimento controlado un experimento que prueba sólo un factor a la vez, comparando un grupo de control con un grupo experimental (16)

convex lens (kahn VEKS LENZ) a lens that is thicker in the middle than at the edges (93)

lente convexa una lente que es más gruesa en la parte media que en los bordes (93)

*cycle (SIE kuhl) a repeating series of changes (49, 231, 261, 357, 393, 421)

ciclo una serie de cambios que se repiten (49, 231, 261, 357, 393, 421)

cytokinesis (SIET oh ki NEE sis) the division of the cytoplasm of a cell (153)

citoquinesis la división del citoplasma de una célula (153)

cytoskeleton (SIET oh SKEL uh tuhn) the cytoplasmic network of protein filaments that plays an essential role in cell movement, shape, and division (122)

citoesqueleto la red citoplásmica de filamentos de proteínas que juega un papel esencial en el movimiento, forma y división de la célula (122)

D

decomposer (dee kuhm POHZ uhr) an organism that gets energy by breaking down the remains of dead organisms or animal wastes and consuming or absorbing the nutrients (57)

descomponedor un organismo que, para obtener energía, desintegra los restos de organismos muertos o los desechos de animales y consume o absorbe los nutrientes (57)

* **derived** (di RIEVD) gotten from something else (295, 329)

derivado que se obtiene de otra cosa (295, 329)

* **detect** (dee TEKT) to notice (73, 523)

detectar notar (73, 523)

* **device** (di VIES) a piece of equipment made for a specific use (463)

dispositivo un equipo hecho para un uso específico (463)

* **differentiate** (DIF uhr EN shee AYT) to become specialized in structure and function (111, 393, 553)

diferenciarse especializarse en estructura y función (111, 393, 553)

differentiation (DIF uhr EN shee AY shuhn) the process in which the structure and function of the parts of an organism change to enable specialization of those parts (427)

diferenciación el proceso por medio del cual la estructura y función de las partes de un organismo cambian para permitir la especialización de esas partes (427)

diploid (DIP loyd) a cell that contains two haploid sets of chromosomes (189)

diploide una célula que contiene dos juegos de cromosomas haploides (189)

* **display** (di SPLAY) to show (5)

presentar mostrar (5)

* **distribution** (DIS tri BYOO shuhn) the relative arrangement of objects or organisms in time or space (261)

distribución disposición relativa de objetos u organismos en el tiempo o el espacio (261)

* **diversity** (duh VUHR suh tee) variety (295)

diversidad variedad (295)

DNA (DEE EN AY) **d**eoxyribo**n**ucleic **a**cid, a molecule that is present in all living cells and that contains the information that determines the traits that a living thing inherits and needs to live (208)

ADN **á**cido **d**esoxirribo**n**ucleico, una molécula que está presente en todas las células vivas y que contiene la información que determina los caracteres que un ser vivo hereda y necesita para vivir (208)

dominant trait (DAHM uh nuhnt TRAYT) the trait observed in the first generation when parents that have different traits are bred (177)

carácter dominante el carácter que se observa en la primera generación cuando se cruzan progenitores que tienen caracteres diferentes (177)

dormant (DAWR muhnt) describes the inactive state of a seed or other plant part when conditions are unfavorable to growth (402)

aletargado término que describe el estado inactivo de una semilla u otra parte de las plantas cuando las condiciones son desfavorables para el crecimiento (402)

Glossary

E

electromagnetic spectrum (ee LEK troh mag NET ik SPEK truhm) all of the frequencies or wavelengths of electromagnetic radiation (77)

espectro electromagnético todas las frecuencias o longitudes de onda de la radiación electromagnética (77)

electromagnetic wave (ee LEK troh mag NET ik WAYV) a wave that consists of electric and magnetic fields that vibrate at right angles to each other (76)

onda electromagnética una onda que está formada por campos eléctricos y magnéticos que vibran formando un ángulo recto unos con otros (76)

electron microscope (ee LEK TRAHN MIE kruh SKOHP) a microscope that focuses a beam of electrons to magnify objects (21)

microscopio electrónico microscopio que enfoca un haz de electrones para aumentar la imagen de los objetos (21)

embryo (EM bree OH) in humans, a developing individual from fertilization through the 10th week of pregnancy (562)

embrión en los seres humanos, un individuo en desarrollo desde la fecundación hasta el final de la décima semana del embarazo (562)

endoplasmic reticulum (en doh PLAZ mik ri TIK yuh luhm) a system of membranes that is found in a cell's cytoplasm and that assists in the production, processing, and transport of proteins and in the production of lipids (123)

retículo endoplásmico un sistema de membranas que se encuentra en el citoplasma de la célula y que tiene una función en la producción, procesamiento y transporte de proteínas y en la producción de lípidos (123)

endoskeleton (EN doh SKEL uh tuhn) an internal skeleton made of bone and cartilage (434)

endoesqueleto un esqueleto interno hecho de hueso y cartílago (434)

*** energy** (EN uhr jee) the capacity to do work (111, 145, 357, 393)

energía la capacidad de realizar un trabajo (111, 145, 357, 393)

*** environment** (en VIE ruhn muhnt) the surrounding natural conditions that affect an organism (231, 261)

ambiente las condiciones naturales circundantes que afectan a un organismo (231, 261)

Eukarya (yoo KAR ee uh) in a modern taxonomic system, a domain made up of all eukaryotes; this domain aligns with the traditional kingdoms Protista, Fungi, Plantae, and Animalia (340)

Eukarya en un sistema taxonómico moderno, un dominio compuesto por todos los eucariotes; este dominio coincide con los reinos tradicionales Protista, Fungi, Plantae y Animalia (340)

eukaryote (yoo KAR ee OHT) an organism made up of cells that have a nucleus enclosed by a membrane; eukaryotes include protists, animals, plants, and fungi but not archaea or bacteria (119)

eucariote un organismo cuyas células tienen un núcleo contenido en una membrana; entre los eucariotes se encuentran protistas, animales, plantas y hongos, pero no arqueas ni bacterias (119)

*** evidence** (EV uh duhns) information showing whether an idea or belief is true or valid (231, 261, 295)

prueba información que demuestra si una idea o creencia es verdadera o válida (231, 261, 295)

evolution (EV uh LOO shuhn) the process in which inherited characteristics within a population change over generations such that new species sometimes arise (299)

evolución el proceso por medio del cual las características heredadas dentro de una población cambian con el transcurso de las generaciones de manera tal que a veces surgen nuevas especies (299)

Glossary

*Academic Vocabulary

exoskeleton (EKS oh SKEL uh tuhn) a hard, external, supporting structure (433)

exoesqueleto una estructura de soporte, dura y externa (433)

*expand (ek SPAND) to make more detailed; to enlarge (295, 329)

expandir hacer más detallado; agrandar (295, 329)

extinct (ek STINGKT) describes a species that has died out completely (316)

extinto término que describe a una especie que ha desaparecido por completo (316)

extinction (ek STINGK shuhn) the death of every member of a species (278)

extinción la muerte de todos los miembros de una especie (278)

F

*factor (FAK tuhr) a condition or event that brings about or contributes to a result (295)

factor una condición o un suceso que produce un resultado o contribuye a él (295)

feedback mechanism (FEED BAK MEK uh NIZ uhm) a cycle of events in which information from one step controls or affects a previous step (535)

mecanismo de retroalimentación un ciclo de sucesos en el que la información de una etapa controla o afecta a una etapa anterior (535)

fermentation (FUHR muhn TAY shuhn) the breakdown of food without the use of oxygen (149)

fermentación la descomposición de los alimentos sin utilizar oxígeno (149)

fetus (FEET uhs) a developing human from the end of the 10th week of pregnancy until birth (564)

feto un ser humano en desarrollo desde el final de la décima semana del embarazo hasta el nacimiento (564)

first aid (FUHRST AYD) emergency medical care for someone who has been hurt or who is sick (37)

primeros auxilios atención médica de emergencia para una persona que se lastimó o está enferma (37)

fossil (FAHS uhl) the trace or remains of an organism that lived long ago, most commonly preserved in sedimentary rock (264, 300)

fósil los indicios o los restos de un organismo que vivió hace mucho tiempo, comúnmente preservados en las rocas sedimentarias (264, 300)

fossil record (FAHS uhl REK uhrd) the history of life in the geologic past as indicated by the traces or remains of living things (300)

registro fósil la historia de la vida en el pasado geológico según la indican los rastros o restos de seres vivos (300)

*framework (FRAYM WUHRK) a basic structure that supports something (421, 463)

armazón estructura básica que sostiene algo (421, 463)

function (FUHNGK shuhn) the special, normal, or proper activity of an organ or part (130)

función la actividad especial, normal o adecuada de un órgano o parte (130)

*function (FUHNGK shuhn) (n.) use or purpose (111, 357, 393, 421, 463, 493, 523, 553)

función uso o propósito (111, 357, 393, 421, 463, 493, 523, 553)

*function (FUHNGK shuhn) (v.) to work (49, 111, 205, 329, 421, 463, 493, 523)

funcionar trabajar (49, 111, 205, 329, 421, 463, 493, 523)

Fungi (FUHN JIE) a kingdom made up of non-green, eukaryotic organisms that have no means of movement, reproduce by using spores, and get food by breaking down substances in their surroundings and absorbing the nutrients (340)

Fungi un reino formado por organismos eucarióticos no verdes que no tienen capacidad de movimiento, se reproducen por esporas y obtienen alimento al descomponer sustancias de su entorno y absorber los nutrientes (340)

G

gene (JEEN) one set of instructions for an inherited trait (180)

gene un conjunto de instrucciones para un carácter heredado (180)

*generate (JEN uhr AYT) to bring about; to produce (357, 393, 493, 553)

generar provocar; producir (357, 393, 493, 553)

genotype (JEE nuh TIEP) the entire genetic makeup of an organism; also the combination of genes for one or more specific traits (181)

genotipo la constitución genética completa de un organismo; *también,* la combinación de genes para uno o más caracteres específicos (181)

geologic time scale (JEE uh LAHJ ik TIEM SKAYL) the standard method used to divide Earth's long natural history into manageable parts (276)

escala de tiempo geológico el método estándar que se usa para dividir la larga historia natural de la Tierra en partes razonables (276)

Golgi complex (GOHL jee KAHM PLEKS) a cell organelle that helps make and package materials to be transported out of the cell (125)

aparato de Golgi un organelo celular que ayuda a hacer y a empacar los materiales que serán transportados al exterior de la célula (125)

gymnosperm (JIM noh SPUHRM) a woody, vascular seed plant whose seeds are not enclosed by an ovary or fruit (362)

gimnosperma una planta leñosa vascular que produce semillas que no están contenidas en un ovario o fruto (362)

H

half-life (HAF LIEF) the time required for half of a sample of a radioactive isotope to break down by radioactive decay to form a daughter isotope (247)

vida media el tiempo que se requiere para que la mitad de una muestra de un isótopo radiactivo se descomponga por desintegración radiactiva y forme un isótopo hijo (247)

haploid (HAP LOYD) describes a cell, nucleus, or organism that has only one set of unpaired chromosomes (189)

haploide término que describe a una célula, núcleo u organismo que tiene sólo un juego de cromosomas que no están asociados en pares (189)

heredity (hee RED i tee) the passing of genetic traits from parent to offspring (174)

herencia la transmisión de caracteres genéticos de padres a hijos (174)

homeostasis (HOH mee OH STAY sis) the maintenance of a constant internal state in a changing environment (53)

homeostasis la capacidad de mantener un estado interno constante en un ambiente en cambio (53)

homologous chromosomes (hoh MAHL uh guhs KROH muh SOHMZ) chromosomes that have the same sequence of genes and the same structure (189)

cromosomas homólogos cromosomas con la misma secuencia de genes y la misma estructura (189)

hypothesis (hie PAHTH uh sis) a testable idea or explanation that leads to scientific investigation (14)

hipótesis una idea o explicación que conlleva a la investigación científica y que se puede probar (14)

*Academic Vocabulary

Glossary

I

*__identical__ (ie DEN ti kuhl) being exactly the same (145, 171)

__idéntico__ exactamente igual (145, 171)

*__impact__ (IM PAKT) a striking together; collision (231)

__impacto__ choque; colisión (231)

*__incidence__ (IN suh duhns) the point at which a line or something moving in a straight line, such as a ray of light, meets a surface (73)

__incidencia__ el punto en el que una línea o algo que se mueve en línea recta, como un rayo de luz, se encuentra con una superficie (73)

__index fossil__ (IN DEKS FAHS uhl) a fossil that is used to establish the age of a rock layer because the fossil is distinct, abundant, and widespread and the species that formed that fossil existed for only a short span of geologic time (268)

__fósil guía__ un fósil que se usa para establecer la edad de una capa de roca debido a que puede diferenciarse bien de otros, es abundante y está extendido; la especie que formó ese fósil existió sólo por un corto período de tiempo geológico (268)

*__indicate__ (IN di KAYT) to be or give a sign of; to show (261)

__indicar__ ser o dar una señal de algo; mostrar (261)

*__individual__ (IN duh VIJ oo uhl) being a single, separate entity; particular (421, 463, 493, 523)

__individual__ se dice de una entidad única e independiente; particular (421, 463, 493, 523)

*__insufficient__ (IN suh FISH uhnt) not enough (295)

__insuficiente__ que no basta (295)

__integumentary system__ (in TEG yoo MEN tuhr ee SIS tuhm) the organ system that forms a protective covering on the outside of the body (534)

__sistema integumentario__ el sistema de órganos que forma una cubierta de protección en la parte exterior del cuerpo (534)

__invertebrate__ (in VUHR tuh brit) an animal that does not have a backbone (431)

__invertebrado__ un animal que no tiene columna vertebral (431)

*__investigation__ (in VES tuh GAY shuhn) a detailed search for answers (5)

__investigación__ búsqueda cuidadosa de respuestas (5)

__iris__ (IE ris) the colored, circular part of the eye (537)

__iris__ la parte coloreada y circular del ojo (537)

J

__joint__ (JOYNT) a place where two or more bones meet (474)

__articulación__ un lugar donde se unen dos o más huesos (474)

L

*__labeled__ (LAY buhld) marked with a name or description (5)

__rotulado__ identificado con un nombre o una descripción (5)

__large intestine__ (LAHRJ in TES tuhn) the wider and shorter portion of the intestine that removes water from mostly digested food and that turns the waste into semisolid feces, or stool (447)

__intestino grueso__ la porción más ancha y más corta del intestino, que elimina el agua de los alimentos casi totalmente digeridos y convierte los desechos en heces semisólidas o excremento (447)

__larynx__ (LAR ingks) the area of the throat that contains the vocal cords and produces vocal sounds (509)

__laringe__ el área de la garganta que contiene las cuerdas vocales y que produce sonidos vocales (509)

Glossary

law (LAW) a descriptive statement or equation that reliably predicts events under certain conditions (29)

ley una ecuación o afirmación descriptiva que predice sucesos de manera confiable en determinadas condiciones (29)

law of crosscutting relationships (LAW UHV KRAWS KUHT ing ri LAY shuhn SHIPS) the principle that a fault or body of rock is younger than any other body of rock that it cuts through (243)

ley de las relaciones entrecortadas el principio que establece que una falla o cuerpo rocoso siempre es más joven que cualquier otro cuerpo rocoso que atraviese (243)

* **layer** (LAY uhr) a separate or distinct portion of matter that has thickness (231, 261)

capa una parte separada o diferenciada de materia que tiene espesor (231, 261)

lens (LENZ) a transparent object that refracts light waves such that they converge or diverge to create an image (92)

lente un objeto transparente que refracta las ondas de luz de modo que converjan o diverjan para crear una imagen (92)

lever (LEV uhr) a simple machine that consists of a bar that pivots at a fixed point called a *fulcrum* (478)

palanca una máquina simple formada por una barra que gira en un punto fijo llamado *fulcro* (478)

* **liberate** (LIB uhr AYT) to release; to set free (111, 145, 357, 393)

liberar soltar; poner en libertad (111, 145, 357, 393)

life science (LIEF SIE uhns) the study of living things (8)

ciencias biológicas el estudio de los seres vivos (8)

lipid (LIP id) a fat molecule or a molecule that has similar properties; examples include oils, waxes, and steroids (60)

lípido una molécula de grasa o una molécula que tiene propiedades similares; algunos ejemplos son los aceites, las ceras y los esteroides (60)

* **located** (LOH KAYT id) to be in a certain place (145, 171, 205)

ubicarse estar en determinado lugar (145, 171, 205)

* **logical** (LAHJ i kuhl) reasoned, well thought out (5)

lógico razonado, bien pensado (5)

lysosome (LIE suh SOHM) a cell organelle that contains digestive enzymes (126)

lisosoma un organelo celular que contiene enzimas digestivas (126)

M

* **major** (MAY juhr) of great importance or large scale (231)

principal de gran importancia o gran escala (231)

mass (MAS) a measure of the amount of matter in an object (24)

masa una medida de la cantidad de materia que tiene un objeto (24)

mechanical advantage (muh KAN i kuhl ad VANT ij) a number that tells you how many times a machine multiplies force (478)

ventaja mecánica un número que dice cuántas veces una máquina multiplica una fuerza (478)

* **mechanism** (MEK uh NIZ uhm) any system or means by which something gets done (295)

mecanismo cualquier sistema o medio que sirve para hacer algo (295)

*Academic Vocabulary

634   English and Spanish Glossary

Glossary

medium (MEE dee uhm) a substance through which something else is sent or carried (73)

   medio una sustancia a través de la cual se envía o transporta algo (73)

meiosis (mie OH sis) a process in cell division during which the number of chromosomes decreases to half the original number by two divisions of the nucleus, which results in the production of sex cells (gametes or spores) (190)

   meiosis un proceso de división celular durante el cual el número de cromosomas disminuye a la mitad del número original por medio de dos divisiones del núcleo, lo cual resulta en la producción de células sexuales (gametos o esporas) (190)

metabolism (muh TAB uh LIZ uhm) the sum of all chemical processes that occur in an organism (54)

   metabolismo la suma de todos los procesos químicos que ocurren en un organismo (54)

metamorphosis (MET uh MAWR fuh sis) a process in the life cycle of many animals during which a rapid change from the immature organism to the adult takes place; an example is the change from larva to adult in insects (442)

   metamorfosis un proceso del ciclo de vida de muchos animales durante el cual ocurre un cambio rápido de la forma inmadura del organismo a la adulta; un ejemplo es el cambio de larva a adulto en los insectos (442)

method (METH uhd) a way of doing something (357, 393, 421)

   método una forma de hacer algo (357, 393, 421)

mitochondrion (MIET oh KAHN dree uhn) in eukaryotic cells, the cell organelle that is surrounded by two membranes and that is the site of cellular respiration (124)

   mitocondria en las células eucarióticas, el organelo celular rodeado por dos membranas que es el lugar donde se lleva a cabo la respiración celular (124)

mitosis (mie TOH sis) in eukaryotic cells, a process of cell division that forms two new nuclei, each of which has the same number of chromosomes (153)

   mitosis en las células eucarióticas, un proceso de división celular que forma dos núcleos nuevos, cada uno de los cuales posee el mismo número de cromosomas (153)

model (MAHD'l) a pattern, plan, representation, or description designed to show the structure or workings of an object, system, or concept (26)

   modelo un diseño, plan, representación o descripción cuyo objetivo es mostrar la estructura o funcionamiento de un objeto, sistema o concepto (26)

muscular system (MUHS kyoo luhr SIS tuhm) the organ system whose primary function is movement and flexibility (477)

   sistema muscular el sistema de órganos cuya función principal es permitir el movimiento y la flexibilidad (477)

mutation (myoo TAY shuhn) a change in the nucleotide-base sequence of a gene or DNA molecule (216)

   mutación un cambio en la secuencia de la base de nucleótidos de un gene o de una molécula de ADN (216)

N

natural selection (NACH uhr uhl suh LEK shuhn) the process by which individuals that are better adapted to their environment survive and reproduce more successfully than less well adapted individuals do; a theory to explain the mechanism of evolution (310)

   selección natural el proceso por medio del cual los individuos que están mejor adaptados a su ambiente sobreviven y se reproducen con más éxito que los individuos menos adaptados; una teoría que explica el mecanismo de la evolución (310)

nerve (NUHRV) a collection of nerve fibers through which impulses travel between the central nervous system and other parts of the body (528)

nervio un conjunto de fibras nerviosas a través de las cuales se desplazan los impulsos entre el sistema nervioso central y otras partes del cuerpo (528)

neuron (NOO RAHN) a nerve cell that is specialized to receive and conduct electrical impulses (527)

neurona una célula nerviosa que está especializada en recibir y transmitir impulsos eléctricos (527)

nonvascular plant (nahn VAHS kyuh luhr PLANT) a plant that lacks specialized conducting tissues and true roots, stems, and leaves (362)

planta no vascular una planta que carece de tejidos transportadores y de raíces, tallos y hojas verdaderos (362)

nucleic acid (noo KLEE ik AS id) a molecule made up of subunits called *nucleotides* (61)

ácido nucleico una molécula formada por subunidades llamadas *nucleótidos* (61)

nucleotide (NOO klee oh TIED) in a nucleic-acid chain, a subunit that consists of a sugar, a phosphate, and a nitrogenous base (208)

nucleótido en una cadena de ácidos nucleicos, una subunidad formada por un azúcar, un fosfato y una base nitrogenada (208)

nucleus (NOO klee uhs) in a eukaryotic cell, a membrane-bound organelle that contains the cell's DNA and that has a role in processes such as growth, metabolism, and reproduction (117)

núcleo en una célula eucariótica, un organelo cubierto por una membrana, el cual contiene el ADN de la célula y participa en procesos tales como el crecimiento, metabolismo y reproducción (117)

O

*occur (uh KUHR) to happen (231, 295)

ocurrir pasar (231, 295)

open circulatory system (OH puhn SUHR kyuh luh TAWR ee SIS tuhm) a circulatory system in which the circulatory fluid is not contained entirely within vessels (440)

aparato circulatorio abierto un aparato circulatorio en el que el fluido circulatorio no está totalmente contenido en los vasos sanguíneos; un corazón bombea fluido por los vasos sanguíneos, los cuales se vacían en espacios llamados senos (440)

organ (AWR guhn) a collection of tissues that carry out a specialized function of the body (131, 468)

órgano un conjunto de tejidos que desempeñan una función especializada en el cuerpo (131, 468)

organelle (AWR guh NEL) one of the small bodies in a cell's cytoplasm that are specialized to perform a specific function (117)

organelo uno de los cuerpos pequeños del citoplasma de una célula que están especializados para llevar a cabo una función específica (117)

organism (AWR guh NIZ uhm) a living thing; anything that can carry out life processes independently (128)

organismo un ser vivo; cualquier cosa que pueda llevar a cabo procesos vitales independientemente (128)

organ system (AWR guhn SIS tuhm) a group of organs that work together to perform body functions (132)

aparato (o sistema) de órganos un grupo de órganos que trabajan en conjunto para desempeñar funciones corporales (132)

ovary (OH vuh ree) in flowering plants, the lower part of a pistil that produces eggs in ovules (380); in the female reproductive system of animals, an organ that produces eggs (557)

ovario en las plantas con flores, la parte inferior del pistilo que produce óvulos (380); en el aparato reproductor femenino de los animales, un órgano que produce óvulos (557)

Glossary

ovule (AHV YOOL) a structure in the ovary of a seed plant that contains an embryo sac and that develops into a seed after fertilization (380)

óvulo una estructura del ovario de una planta con semillas que contiene un saco embrionario y se desarrolla para convertirse en una semilla después de la fecundación (380)

P

paleontology (PAY lee uhn TAHL uh jee) the scientific study of fossils (237)

paleontología el estudio científico de los fósiles (237)

penis (PEE nis) the male organ that transfers sperm to a female and that carries urine out of the body (556)

pene el órgano masculino que transfiere espermatozoides a una hembra y que lleva la orina hacia el exterior del cuerpo (556)

***period** (PIR ee uhd) an interval or unit (231)

período intervalo o unidad (231)

peripheral nervous system (puh RIF uhr uhl NUHR vuhs SIS tuhm) all of the parts of the nervous system except for the brain and the spinal cord (526)

sistema nervioso periférico todas las partes del sistema nervioso, excepto el encéfalo y la médula espinal (526)

petal (PET uhl) one of the usually brightly colored, leaf-shaped parts that make up one of the rings of a flower (379)

pétalo una de las partes de una flor que normalmente tienen colores brillantes y forma de hoja, las cuales forman uno de los anillos de una flor (379)

pharynx (FAR ingks) the passage from the mouth to the larynx and esophagus (509)

faringe en los gusanos planos, el tubo muscular que va de la boca a la cavidad gastrovascular; en los animales que tienen tracto digestivo, el conducto que va de la boca a la laringe y al esófago (509)

phenotype (FEE noh TIEP) an organism's appearance or other detectable characteristic (180)

fenotipo la apariencia de un organismo u otra característica perceptible (180)

phloem (FLOH EM) the tissue that conducts food in vascular plants (374)

floema el tejido que transporta alimento en las plantas vasculares (374)

phospholipid (FAHS foh LIP id) a lipid that contains phosphorus and that is a structural component in cell membranes (60)

fosfolípido un lípido que contiene fósforo y que es un componente estructural de la membrana celular (60)

photosynthesis (FOHT oh SIN thuh sis) the process by which plants, algae, and some bacteria use sunlight, carbon dioxide, and water to make food (148, 396)

fotosíntesis el proceso por medio del cual las plantas, las algas y algunas bacterias utilizan la luz solar, el dióxido de carbono y el agua para producir alimento (148, 396)

pistil (PIS til) the female reproductive part of a flower that produces seeds and consists of an ovary, style, and stigma (380)

pistilo la parte reproductora femenina de una flor, la cual produce semillas y está formada por el ovario, estilo y estigma (380)

placenta (pluh SEN tuh) the partly fetal and partly maternal organ by which materials are exchanged between a fetus and the mother (563)

placenta el órgano parcialmente fetal y parcialmente materno por medio del cual se intercambian materiales entre el feto y la madre (563)

Plantae (PLAN tee) a kingdom made up of complex, multicellular organisms that are usually green, have cell walls made of cellulose, cannot move around, and use the sun's energy to make sugar by photosynthesis (341)

Plantae un reino formado por organismos pluricelulares complejos que normalmente son verdes, tienen una pared celular de celulosa, no tienen capacidad de movimiento y utilizan la energía del Sol para producir azúcar mediante la fotosíntesis (341)

plate tectonics (PLAYT tek TAHN iks) the theory that explains how large pieces of Earth's outermost layer, called *tectonic plates,* move and change shape (270)

tectónica de placas la teoría que explica cómo se mueven y cambian de forma las placas tectónicas, que son grandes porciones de la capa más externa de la Tierra (270)

pollen (PAHL uhn) the tiny granules that contain the male gametophyte of seed plants (368)

polen los gránulos diminutos que contienen el gametofito masculino en las plantas con semilla (368)

pollination (PAWL uh NAY shuhn) the transfer of pollen from the male reproductive structures to the female structures of seed plants (371)

polinización la transferencia de polen de las estructuras reproductoras masculinas a las estructuras femeninas de las plantas con semillas (371)

pregnancy (PREG nuhn see) in medical practice, the period of time between the first day of a woman's last menstrual period and the delivery of her baby (about 280 days, or 40 weeks); in developmental biology, the period of time in which a woman carries a developing human from fertilization until the birth of the baby (about 266 days, or 38 weeks) (563)

embarazo en medicina, el período de tiempo que transcurre entre el primer día del último período menstrual de una mujer y el nacimiento de su bebé (aproximadamente 280 días, o 40 semanas); en biología del desarrollo, el período de tiempo durante el cual una mujer lleva en su interior a un ser humano en desarrollo desde la fecundación hasta el nacimiento del bebé (aproximadamente 266 días, o 38 semanas) (563)

*principle (PRIN suh puhl) basic law, rule, or belief (463)

principio ley, regla o creencia básica (463)

probability (PRAHB uh BIL uh tee) the likelihood that a possible future event will occur in any given instance of the event (182)

probabilidad la probabilidad de que ocurra un posible suceso futuro en cualquier caso dado del suceso (182)

*process (PRAH ses) a set of steps, events, or changes (145, 231, 357, 393)

proceso una serie de pasos, sucesos o cambios (145, 231, 357, 393)

producer (proh DOOS uhr) an organism that can make its own food by using energy from its surroundings (57)

productor un organismo que puede elaborar sus propios alimentos utilizando la energía de su entorno (57)

*project (PRAH jekt) a special task done to use, explain, or add information to classroom lessons (5)

proyecto tarea especial que se realiza para aplicar o explicar las lecciones o para agregar información (5)

prokaryote (proh KAR ee oht) a single-celled organism that does not have a nucleus or membrane-bound organelles; examples are archaea and bacteria (118)

procariote un organismo unicelular que no tiene núcleo ni organelos cubiertos por una membrana, por ejemplo, las arqueas y las bacterias (118)

protein (PROH teen) a molecule that is made up of amino acids and that is needed to build and repair body structures and to regulate processes in the body (58)

proteína una molécula formada por aminoácidos que es necesaria para construir y reparar estructuras corporales y para regular procesos del cuerpo (58)

*Academic Vocabulary

Protista (proh TIST uh) a kingdom of mostly one-celled eukaryotic organisms that are different from plants, animals, archaea, bacteria, and fungi (340)

Protista un reino compuesto principalmente por organismos eucarióticos unicelulares que son diferentes de las plantas, animales, arqueas, bacterias y hongos (340)

pulmonary circulation (PUL muh NER ee SUHR kyoo LAY shuhn) the flow of blood from the heart to the lungs and back to the heart through the pulmonary arteries, capillaries, and veins (499)

circulación pulmonar el flujo de sangre del corazón a los pulmones y de vuelta al corazón a través de las arterias, los capilares y las venas pulmonares (499)

pupil (PYOO puhl) the opening that is located in the center of the iris of the eye and that controls the amount of light that enters the eye (536)

pupila la abertura que se ubica al centro del iris del ojo y que controla la cantidad de luz que entra en el ojo (536)

R

radioactive decay (RAY dee oh AK tiv dee KAY) the process in which a radioactive isotope tends to break down into a stable isotope of the same element or another element (246)

desintegración radiactiva el proceso por medio del cual un isótopo radiactivo tiende a desintegrarse y formar un isótopo estable del mismo elemento o de otro elemento (246)

radiometric dating (RAY dee oh MET rik DAYT ing) a method of determining the absolute age of an object by comparing the relative percentages of a radioactive (parent) isotope and a stable (daughter) isotope (247)

datación radiométrica un método para determinar la edad absoluta de un objeto comparando los porcentajes relativos de un isótopo radiactivo (precursor) y un isótopo estable (hijo) (247)

*react (ree AKT) to act in return; to respond (73)

reaccionar actuar en respuesta a otra cosa; responder (73)

recessive trait (ri SES iv TRAYT) a trait that reappears in the second generation after disappearing in the first generation when parents with different traits are bred (177)

carácter recesivo un carácter que vuelve a aparecer en la segunda generación después de desaparecer en la primera generación, cuando se cruzan progenitores con caracteres diferentes (177)

reflection (ri FLEK shuhn) the bouncing back of a ray of light, sound, or heat when the ray hits a surface that it does not go through (82)

reflexión el rebote de un rayo de luz, sonido o calor cuando el rayo golpea una superficie pero no la atraviesa (82)

reflex (REE FLEKS) an involuntary and almost immediate movement in response to a stimulus (535)

reflejo un movimiento involuntario y prácticamente inmediato en respuesta a un estímulo (535)

refraction (ri FRAK shuhn) the bending of a wavefront as the wavefront passes between two substances in which the speed of the wave differs (90)

refracción el curvamiento de un frente de ondas a medida que el frente pasa entre dos sustancias en las que la velocidad de las ondas difiere (90)

relative dating (REL uh tiv DAYT ing) any method of determining whether an event or object is older or younger than other events or objects (238)

datación relativa cualquier método que se utiliza para determinar si un acontecimiento u objeto es más viejo o más joven que otros acontecimientos u objetos (238)

*research (REE SUHRCH) a careful search for and study of information (5)

investigación búsqueda y análisis cuidadosos de información (5)

*resource (REE sawrs) anything that can be used to take care of a need (5)

recurso cualquier cosa que se puede usar para satisfacer una necesidad (5)

respiration (RES puh RAY shuhn) in biology, the exchange of oxygen and carbon dioxide between living cells and their environment; includes breathing and cellular respiration (508)

respiración en biología, el intercambio de oxígeno y dióxido de carbono entre células vivas y su ambiente; incluye la respiración y la respiración celular (508)

respiratory system (RES puhr uh TAWR ee SIS tuhm) a collection of organs whose primary function is to take in oxygen and expel carbon dioxide; the organs of this system include the lungs, the throat, and the passageways that lead to the lungs (508)

aparato respiratorio un conjunto de órganos cuya función principal es tomar oxígeno y expulsar dióxido de carbono; los órganos de este aparato incluyen a los pulmones, la garganta y las vías que llevan a los pulmones (508)

retina (RET 'n uh) the light-sensitive inner layer of the eye, which receives images formed by the lens and transmits them through the optic nerve to the brain (536)

retina la capa interna del ojo, sensible a la luz, que recibe imágenes formadas por el lente ocular y las transmite al cerebro por medio del nervio óptico (536)

rhizoid (RIE zoyd) a rootlike structure in nonvascular plants that holds the plants in place and helps plants get water and nutrients (364)

rizoide una estructura parecida a una raíz que se encuentra en las plantas no vasculares; mantiene a las plantas en su lugar y las ayuda a obtener agua y nutrientes (364)

rhizome (RIE zohm) a horizontal, underground stem that produces new leaves, shoots, and roots (366)

rizoma un tallo horizontal subterráneo que produce nuevas hojas, brotes y raíces (366)

ribosome (RIE buh sohm) a cell organelle composed of RNA and protein; the site of protein synthesis (123, 215)

ribosoma un organelo celular compuesto de ARN y proteína; el sitio donde ocurre la síntesis de proteínas (123, 215)

RNA (AHR EN AY) **r**ibo**n**ucleic **a**cid, a molecule that is present in all living cells and that plays a role in protein production (214)

ARN **á**cido **r**ibo**n**ucleico, una molécula que está presente en todas las células vivas y que juega un papel en la producción de proteínas (214)

S

scale (SKAYL) the relationship between the measurements on a model, map, or diagram and the actual measurement or distance (28)

escala la relación entre las medidas de un modelo, mapa o diagrama y la medida o distancia real (28)

scattering (SKAT uhr ing) an interaction of light with matter that causes light to change its energy, direction of motion, or both (85)

dispersión una interacción de la luz con la materia que hace que la luz cambie su energía, la dirección del movimiento o ambas (85)

scientific methods (SIE uhn TIF ik METH uhds) a series of steps followed to solve problems (12)

métodos científicos una serie de pasos que se siguen para solucionar problemas (12)

sedimentary rock (SED uh MEN tuhr ee RAHK) a rock that forms from compressed or cemented layers of sediment (238)

roca sedimentaria una roca que se forma a partir de capas comprimidas o cementadas de sedimento (238)

segment (SEG muhnt) any part of a larger structure, such as the body of an organism, that is set off by natural or arbitrary boundaries (439)

segmento cualquier parte de una estructura más grande, como el cuerpo de un organismo, que se determina por límites naturales o arbitrarios (439)

*Academic Vocabulary

Glossary

*select (suh LEKT) to choose; to pick out (5)

seleccionar elegir; escoger (5)

*selection (suh LEK shuhn) the process of choosing (295)

selección proceso de elegir (295)

selective breeding (suh LEK tiv BREED ing) the human practice of breeding animals or plants that have certain desired traits (308)

reproducción selectiva la práctica humana de cruzar animales o plantas que tienen ciertos caracteres deseados (308)

sepal (SEE puhl) in a flower, one of the outermost rings of modified leaves that protect the flower bud (379)

sépalo en una flor, uno de los anillos más externos de hojas modificadas que protegen el capullo de la flor (379)

*sexual (SEK shoo uhl) having to do with sex (171, 357, 393, 421, 553)

sexual relacionado con el sexo (171, 357, 393, 421, 553)

sexual reproduction (SEK shoo uhl REE pruh DUHK shuhn) reproduction in which the sex cells from two parents unite to produce offspring that share traits from both parents (54)

reproducción sexual reproducción en la que se unen las células sexuales de los dos progenitores para producir descendencia que comparte caracteres de ambos progenitores (54)

*significant (sig NIF uh kuhnt) important (261)

significativo importante (261)

*similar (SIM uh luhr) almost the same (231)

similar casi igual (231)

*similarly (SIM uh luhr lee) in almost the same way (49, 111, 205, 329)

de modo similar casi del mismo modo (49, 111, 205, 329)

skeletal system (SKEL i tuhl SIS tuhm) the organ system whose primary function is to support and protect the body and to allow the body to move (473)

sistema esquelético el sistema de órganos cuya función principal es sostener y proteger el cuerpo y permitir que se mueva (473)

small intestine (SMAWL in TES tuhn) the organ between the stomach and the large intestine where most of the breakdown of food happens and most of the nutrients from food are absorbed (447)

intestino delgado el órgano que se encuentra entre el estómago y el intestino grueso en el cual se produce la mayor parte de la descomposición de los alimentos y se absorben la mayoría de los nutrientes (447)

speciation (SPEE shee AY shuhn) the formation of new species as a result of evolution (314)

especiación la formación de especies nuevas como resultado de la evolución (314)

species (SPEE seez) a group of organisms that are closely related and can mate to produce fertile offspring (298)

especie un grupo de organismos que tienen un parentesco cercano y que pueden aparearse para producir descendencia fértil (298)

stamen (STAY muhn) the male reproductive structure of a flower that produces pollen and consists of an anther at the tip of a filament (380)

estambre la estructura reproductora masculina de una flor, que produce polen y está formada por una antera ubicada en la punta del filamento (380)

stimulus (STIM yoo luhs) anything that causes a reaction or change in an organism or any part of an organism (404)

estímulo cualquier cosa que causa una reacción o cambio en un organismo o cualquier parte de un organismo (404)

Glossary

stoma (STOH muh) one of many openings in a leaf or a stem of a plant that enable gas exchange to occur (plural, *stomata*) (398)

estoma una de las muchas aberturas de una hoja o de un tallo de una planta, la cual permite que se lleve a cabo el intercambio de gases (398)

*structural (STRUHK chuhr uhl) having to do with the arrangement of the parts of a whole (421, 463)

estructural relacionado con la distribución de las partes de un todo (421, 463)

structure (STRUHK shuhr) the arrangement of parts in an organism (130)

estructura el orden y distribución de las partes de un organismo (130)

*structure (STRUHK chuhr) the arrangement of the parts of a whole (111, 357, 393, 421, 463, 493, 523)

estructura la forma en que se distribuyen las partes de un todo (111, 357, 393, 421, 463, 493, 523)

superposition (SOO puhr puh ZISH uhn) a principle that states that younger rocks lie above older rocks if the layers have not been disturbed (240)

superposición un principio que establece que las rocas más jóvenes se encontrarán sobre las rocas más viejas si las capas no han sido alteradas (240)

*survival (suhr VIE vuhl) the continuing to live or exist (295)

supervivencia acción de continuar viviendo o existiendo (295)

systemic circulation (sis TEM ik SUHR kyoo LAY shuhn) the flow of blood from the heart to all parts of the body and back to the heart (499)

circulación sistémica el flujo de sangre del corazón a todas las partes del cuerpo y de vuelta al corazón (499)

T

taxonomy (taks AHN uh mee) the science of describing, naming, and classifying organisms (333)

taxonomía la ciencia de describir, nombrar y clasificar organismos (333)

technology (tek NAHL uh jee) the application of science for practical purposes; the use of tools, machines, materials, and processes to meet human needs (20)

tecnología la aplicación de la ciencia con fines prácticos; el uso de herramientas, máquinas, materiales y procesos para satisfacer las necesidades de los seres humanos (20)

*technology (tek NAHL uh jee) tools, including electronic products (5)

tecnología herramientas; incluye los productos electrónicos (5)

temperature (TEM puhr uh chuhr) a measure of how hot (or cold) something is; specifically, a measure of the average kinetic energy of the particles in an object (25)

temperatura una medida de qué tan caliente (o frío) está algo; específicamente, una medida de la energía cinética promedio de las partículas de un objeto (25)

testes (TES TEEZ) the primary male reproductive organs, which produce sperm and testosterone (singular, *testis*) (556)

testículos los principales órganos reproductores masculinos, los cuales producen espermatozoides y testosterona (556)

theory (THEE uh ree) a system of ideas that explains many related observations and is supported by a large body of evidence acquired through scientific investigation (29)

teoría un sistema de ideas que explica muchas observaciones relacionadas y que está respaldado por una gran cantidad de pruebas obtenidas mediante la investigación científica (29)

*Academic Vocabulary

Glossary

tissue (TISH oo) a group of similar cells that perform a common function (131, 467)

tejido un grupo de células similares que llevan a cabo una función común (131, 467)

trace fossil (TRAYS FAHS uhl) a fossilized structure, such as a footprint or coprolite, that formed in sedimentary rock by animal activity on or within soft sediment (266)

fósil traza una estructura fosilizada, como una huella o un coprolito, que se formó en una roca sedimentaria por la actividad de un animal sobre sedimento blando o dentro de éste (266)

trachea (TRAY kee uh) the tube that connects the larynx to the lungs (509)

tráquea en los insectos, miriápodos y arañas, uno de los conductos de una red de conductos de aire; en los vertebrados, el conducto que une la laringe con los pulmones (509)

trait (TRAYT) a genetically determined characteristic (308)

carácter una característica determinada genéticamente (308)

transmission (trans MISH uhn) the passing of light or other form of energy through matter (85)

transmisión el paso de la luz u otra forma de energía a través de la materia (85)

*transmit (trans MIT) to send or cause to go from one thing to another (73)

transmitir enviar o hacer que algo se mueva de un lugar a otro (73)

transpiration (TRAN spuh RAY shuhn) the process by which plants release water vapor into the air through stomata (398)

transpiración el proceso por medio del cual las plantas liberan vapor de agua al aire por medio de los estomas; *también,* la liberación de vapor de agua al aire por otros organismos (398)

tropism (TROH PIZ uhm) growth of all or part of an organism in response to an external stimulus, such as light (406)

tropismo el crecimiento de un organismo o de una parte de él en respuesta a un estímulo externo, como por ejemplo, la luz (406)

U

umbilical cord (uhm BIL i kuhl KAWRD) the rope-like structure through which blood vessels pass and by which a developing mammal is connected to the placenta (563)

cordón umbilical la estructura con forma de cuerda a través de la cual pasan vasos sanguíneos y por medio de la cual un mamífero en desarrollo está unido a la placenta (563)

unconformity (uhn kuhn FAWRM uh tee) a break in the geologic record created when rock layers are eroded or when sediment is not deposited for a long period of time (242)

disconformidad una ruptura en el registro geológico, creada cuando las capas de roca se erosionan o cuando el sedimento no se deposita durante un largo período de tiempo (242)

uniformitarianism (YOON uh FAWRM uh TER ee uhn IZ uhm) a principle that geologic processes that occurred in the past can be explained by current geologic processes (234)

uniformitarianismo un principio que establece que es posible explicar los procesos geológicos que ocurrieron en el pasado en función de los procesos geológicos actuales (234)

uterus (YOO tuhr uhs) in female placental mammals, the hollow, muscular organ in which an embryo embeds itself and develops into a fetus (557)

útero en los mamíferos placentarios hembras, el órgano hueco y muscular en el que el embrión se incrusta y se desarrolla hasta convertirse en feto (557)

V

vagina (vuh JIEN uh) the female reproductive organ that connects the outside of the body to the uterus (557)

vagina el órgano reproductivo femenino que conecta la parte exterior del cuerpo con el útero (557)

variable (VER ee uh buhl) a factor that changes in an experiment in order to test a hypothesis (16)

variable un factor que se modifica en un experimento con el fin de probar una hipótesis (16)

*variation (VER ee AY shuhn) a difference in the usual form or function (295)

variación diferencia en la forma o función habitual (295)

vascular plant (VAHS kyuh luhr PLANT) a plant that has specialized tissues that conduct materials from one part of the plant to another (362)

planta vascular una planta que tiene tejidos especializados que transportan materiales de una parte de la planta a otra (362)

vein (VAYN) in biology, a vessel that carries blood to the heart (498)

vena en biología, un vaso que lleva sangre al corazón (498)

vertebrate (VUHR tuh brit) an animal that has a backbone (434)

vertebrado un animal que tiene columna vertebral (434)

vesicle (VES i kuhl) a small cavity or sac that contains materials in a eukaryotic cell; forms when part of the cell membrane surrounds the materials to be taken into the cell or transported within the cell (125)

vesícula una cavidad o bolsa pequeña que contiene materiales en una célula eucariótica; se forma cuando parte de la membrana celular rodea los materiales que van a ser llevados al interior la célula o transportados dentro de ella (125)

*visible (VIZ uh buhl) that can be seen (73)

visible que se puede ver (73)

volume (VAHL yoom) a measure of the size of a body or region in three-dimensional space (23)

volumen una medida del tamaño de un cuerpo o región en un espacio de tres dimensiones (23)

W

weight (WAYT) a measure of the gravitational force exerted on an object; its value can change with the location of the object in the universe (24)

peso una medida de la fuerza gravitacional ejercida sobre un objeto; su valor puede cambiar en función de la ubicación del objeto en el universo (24)

X

xylem (ZIE luhm) the type of tissue in vascular plants that provides support and conducts water and nutrients from the roots (374)

xilema el tipo de tejido que se encuentra en las plantas vasculares, el cual provee soporte y transporta el agua y los nutrientes desde las raíces (374)

Index

Boldface page numbers refer to illustrative material, such as figures, tables, margin elements, photographs, and illustrations.

A

body temperature, 53, 429, 504, 535
bone-marrow transfusions, 507, **507**
bones
in human skeleton, 472–473, **472, 473**
lab on, 450–451, 474
movement and, 450–451, 477, **477**
in vertebrates, 445, **445**
bony fish, 435, **435**
booby (marine bird), 422, **422–423**
booklet instructions (FoldNote), 580, **580**
Boyle's law, 606
brain
career studying activity of, 551, **551**
central nervous system and, 530–531, **530, 531**
control areas of, **531**
feedback mechanisms in, 535
hemispheres in, 530, **530**
in invertebrates, 441, **441**
parts of, 530–531, **530, 531**
research on, 167
branching diagrams
analyzing, 301, **301,** 331
constructing, 333
of domains, 338, **338**
extinct organisms on, 336–337, **336**
fossils and, 337, 342
organization of, 333, **333**
breathing. *See also* respiratory systems
circular, 520
lab on, 512–513
process of, 510, **510**
respiration and, 508
bronchi (singular, *bronchus*), **508,** 509, **509**
bronchioles, 509, **509**
budding, 54, **54,** 427, 442, **442**
bumblebees, 433, **433**
burrs, 401
butterflies, 442, **442**

C

cactus finches, **307**
caecilians, 435
caimans, **435**
calcium, absorption of, 81, **81**
calculators, 20

California
black coral in, 352, **352**
California Institute for Quantitative Biomedical Research, 490
exotic species in, 416, **416**
forest fires in, 46, **46**
La Brea Tar Pits (Los Angeles), **262–263,** 265, 292, **292**
marine birds, **422–423**
Methuselah Tree, 390, **390**
radon in, 258, **258**
Red Rock Canyon, **240**
San Andreas fault, 271
Searles Lake, 70
Yosemite National Park, 248, **248**
California brown pelicans, **436**
California Institute for Quantitative Biomedical Research (QB3), 490
"Cambrian explosion," 280
Cambrian Period, 280
cameras, 95, **95,** 107
cancer
of the cervix, 560, **560**
definition of, 157
leukemia, 507
of the reproductive system, 560, **560**
of the skin, 157, **157**
treatment for, 166
uncontrolled cell division in, 157, **157,** 166
canine evolution, 327, **327.** *See also* dogs
canopy scientists, 419, **419**
capillaries, 446, 498–499, **498, 499**
carbohydrates, 59, **59**
carbon dioxide
in leaves, 378
need for, 56
in photosynthesis, 396–397, **397**
in respiration, 510, **510,** 512–513
cardiac muscle cells, 130–131, **130, 131,** 476, **476**
cardiovascular system, 496–507
blood transfusions, 506, **506**
blood types, 505–506, **505, 506**
blood vessels, 498, **498**
body temperature regulation by, 504
breathing and, 510, **510**
components of blood, 502–503, **502, 503**
heart, 446, 496–497, **496, 497**

in invertebrates, 440
labs on, 494, 504
major parts of, 496, **496**
modeling valves, 495
preventing backflow of blood, 495, 497
problems in, 500–501, **500, 501**
pulmonary vs. systemic circulation, 499, **499**
in vertebrates, 446, **446**
careers
astronauts, 47, **47**
biochemists, 551, **551**
canopy scientists, 417, **417**
diagnostic medical sonographers, 577, **577**
ethnobotanists, 391, **391**
evolutionary biologists, 327, **327**
finding and classifying animals, 353, **353**
flight surgeons, 47, **47**
genetic counselors, 203, **203**
genetic researchers, 227, **227**
Leader in Training (camp counselor), 521, **521**
marine biologists, 459, **459**
microscopists, 143, **143**
NASA nutritionists, 71, **71**
neuroscientists, 167, **167**
oceanographers, 107, **107**
paleontologists, 293, **293**
physical therapists, 491, **491**
cartilage, 444, 473, **473,** 474
cartilaginous fish, 435
casts, fossil, 266
catastrophic events, **232–233,** 235–236, **235**
catastrophism, **232–233,** 235–236, **235**
cats, classification of, **334–335**
cause-and-effect map instructions (Graphic Organizer), 72, 144, 584, **584**
celery, cell walls in, 361
cell biology, 112–143. *See also* cells
cell theory, 115, **115**
definition of, 114
discovery of, 114, **114**
in organization of living things, 130, **130**
cell body, in neurons, 527, **527**
cell death, 506
cell division, 152–157
cancer and, 157, **157,** 166
controls in, 156–157, **156**
cytokinesis in, 153, 154, **154**
definition of, 152
homologous chromosomes in, 153, **153,** 189, **189,** 190–191

Index

Index

D

Index

Index

Index

Index

G

Galápagos Islands, Darwin's studies on, 307, **307**, 315, **315**
gametophytes
  of gymnosperms, 371, **371**
  of nonvascular plants, **364,** 365
  in plant reproduction, 361
  of seedless vascular plants, 366, **366**
  of seed plants, 368
Garibaldi fish, 435, **435**
gelatin, pineapple enzymes and, 59
genera (singular, *genus*), 334, **335**
generations, in genetics studies, 177, **177,** 182, **182**
genes. *See also* chromosomes
  alleles of, 180–182, **181, 182,** 189, 192
  in blending inheritance, 174
  definition of, 180
  dominant, 177–178, **178,** 192, **192**
  genetic variation, 186, **186,** 312, **312**
  location of, 208
  multiple genes acting together, 185, **185**
  mutations in, 216–217, **216**
  one gene affecting many traits, 184, **184**
  recessive, 177–178, **178,** 192, **192**
  structure of, 212
genetically modified organisms, 179, **179,** 226
genetic code, 206–217. *See also* DNA
  analysis by PCR, 226, **226**
  as characteristic of life, 54
  in chromosomes, 152
  discovery of, 209, **209**
  in evolution, 304
  in nucleus of cells, 117, **117,** 122, **122**
  protein formation and, 61, 214–215, **214–215**
genetic counselors, 203, **203**
genetic disorders, 184, 196, 202
genetic engineering, 179, **179,** 226
genetic information. *See also* DNA
  on appearance, **172–173**
  in DNA, 54, 61, 117
  in fertilization, 558–559, **558**
  mutations and, 216–217, **216**
  in nucleus of cells, 117, **117,** 122, **122**
  in prokaryotes, 118, **118**

genetic instruction. *See also* genetics; traits
  environment and, 185, **185**
  gene mutations and, 216–217, **216**
  genotypes and, 181–182, **181, 182**
  phenotypes and, 180, **180**
  for protein formation, 123, 214–215, **214–215**
genetic material. *See also* DNA
  as characteristic of life, 54
  in chromosomes, 152
  discovery of, 209, **209**
  in nucleus of cells, 117, **117,** 122, **122**
genetic researchers, 227
genetics. *See also* DNA; genetic code; genetic information; genetic instruction; genetic material
  blending inheritance, 174
  as characteristic of life, 54
  characteristics in, 176
  dominant vs. recessive traits, 177–178, **178**
  environment and, 185, **185**
  evolution and, 311
  exceptions to Mendel's principles, 184–185
  in fertilization, 189, 192, **192,** 558–559, **558**
  genetic variation, 186, **186, 310,** 312, **312**
  genotype, 181–182, **181, 182,** 192, **192**
  homologous chromosomes, 153, **153,** 189, **189, 190–191**
  labs on, 177, 181, 182, 191, 194–195
  meiosis and, 192–193, **192**
  Mendel's experiments on, 175–178, **175, 176, 177, 178**
  numbers of chromosomes, 153, **153,** 188, **188,** 189
  phenotypes, 180, **180,** 186, **186, 192**
  probability and, 182–183
  protein formation and, 123, 214–215, **214–215**
genetic variation, 186, **186, 310,** 312, **312**
genital herpes, **560**
genomes, 202
genotype, 181–182, **181, 182,** 192, **192**
genus (plural, *genera*), 334, **335**
geographic connections and species distribution
  continental drift and, 272, **272**

  in Darwin's finches, 307–308, **307,** 315, **315**
  Panama Land Bridge and, 274, **274**
geologic layers
  disturbed rock layers, 241–242, **241, 242**
  law of crosscutting relationships, 243
  principle of superposition in, 240, **240**
  puzzles in, 243–244, **243, 244**
  rock cycle and, 238–239, **238**
geologic processes
  deposition, **238,** 239
  disturbed rock layers, 241–242, **241, 242**
  erosion, 238–239, **238,** 242, 242–243, **243**
  law of crosscutting relationships, 243
  rate of, 309
  rock cycle, 238–239, **238**
  unconformities, 242–243, **242, 243**
  uniformitarianism vs. catastrophism in, 234–236, **234, 235, 236**
geologic record, 239
geologic time scale, 276–277, **276, 277**
geology
  absolute dating methods, 246–249, **246, 247, 248,** 250–251
  age of Earth, 239, 249, **249,** 299, 309
  continental drift, 272–274, **272, 273, 274**
  disturbed rock layers, 241–242, **241, 242**
  early study of, 234–235, **234, 235**
  geologic record and, 239
  geologic time scale, 276–277, **276, 277**
  index fossils, 268–269, **268, 269**
  lab on, 236
  paleontology, 237, 293, **293**
  Panama Land Bridge, 270–275, **270, 271, 272, 273**
  plate tectonics, 270–275, **270, 271, 272, 273**
  principle of superposition, 240, **240**
  relative dating methods, 240–244, **240, 241, 242, 243**
  rock cycle, 238–239, **238**
  uniformitarianism vs. catastrophism in, 234–236, **234, 235, 236**

Index

Index

Index

motor nerves, 447
motor neurons, 528
mouse embryos, 427, **427**
movement
    flying, 428, **428, 445**
    methods of, 428, **428**
    by mollusks, 433, **433**
    muscles and, 477, **477**
    role of muscle and bone in,
      450–451, 477, **477**
mRNA (messenger RNA), **214,** 215
mucus, 445
multicellular organisms
    characteristics of, 128–129, **128,**
      425
    division of labor in, 129
    evolution of, 279
    lab on, 129
    levels of organization in,
      130–132, **130, 131, 132**
multiple births, 559, **559**
muscle cells, **467**
muscle fatigue, 151
muscle tissue, 131, **131, 467, 468**
muscular system, 476–481
    exercise and, 480, **480**
    injuries to, 481
    labs on, 479, 482–483
    levers and, 478–479, **478,**
      482–483
    movement and, 477, **477**
    muscle types, 476, **476**
musculoskeletal system. *See also*
    muscular system; skeletal
    system
    levers in, 478–479, **478,**
      482–483
    movement and, 450–451, 477,
      477
mutagens, 216
mutations in genes, 216–217, **216**

N

nanometers, 78
NASA nutritionist, 71, **71**
National Park Service, forest fire
    policy of, 46
naturalists, 306
natural selection
    environmental factors in, 307,
      307, 313
    extinction, 316–317, **316, 317**
    genetics and, 311
    genetic variations in populations
      and, 312, **312**
    lab on, 318–319
    in new species formation,
      314–315, **314, 315**

population changes and,
    312–313, **312**
theory of, 310–311, **310**
of lizards in white sands, 326,
    326
nautilus, **428**
nearsightedness, 537, **537**
neatness in science activities,
    importance of, 34
nectar, 379
Neohipparion, **336,** 337
nerve cells, 527, **527**
nerves
    auditory, 538, **538**
    motor, 447
    optic, 536, **536**
    sensory, 447
    structure of, 528, **528**
nervous systems
    autonomic, 529, **529**
    axons in, 527, **527,** 528, **528**
    central, 530–532, **530, 531, 532**
    in invertebrates, 441, **441**
    lab on, 532
    major parts of, 526, **526**
    peripheral, 527–529, **527, 528,**
      529
    somatic, 529
    spinal cords, 532, **532**
    in vertebrates, 447, **447**
nervous tissue, 131, **466, 468**
net force, equation for, 609
neurons
    building, 532
    motor, 528
    sensory, 528
    structure of, **467,** 527, **527**
neuroscientist, 167, **167**
newtons (units), 24
Newton's laws of motion, 605
nicotine, brain effects from, 167
night vision, 536
nitrogen, excreted from the body,
    447
nonvascular plants, 362, **362,**
    364–365, **364**
normal, in law of reflection, **82**
nose, 509
notochords, 434, **434**
nuclear-powered bacteria, 258, **258**
nucleic acids, 61
nucleolus, 122, **122**
nucleotides
    in DNA structure, 61, 212, **213**
    models of, 210, 218–219
    in protein formation, 61, 214
    types of, 208, **208**
nucleus, cell
    function of, 117, **126**
    genetic information in, 117, 122,
      122

as repository, 117
    structure of, **121,** 122, **122**
numbats, 316, **316**
nutrients, 58–60
nutritionist, 71, **71**
nymphs, 443, **443**

O

observations, 9, 13, **13**
oceanic plates, 270–271, **270, 271**
oceanographer, 107, **107**
octopuses, 433
offspring
    blending inheritance in, 174
    genotypes in, 181–182, **181, 182**
    phenotypes in, 180, **180**
    probability of traits in, 182–183
    selective breeding for, 308, **308**
    of sexual reproduction, 427
oils, 60
older adults, 567, **567**
olfactory cells, 540, **540**
On the Origin of Species (Darwin),
    310
opaque objects, 86–87, **86, 87**
open circulatory systems, 440
opossums, 436
optical illusions, 91–92, **91**
optical instruments, 95–96, **95, 96**
optic nerve, 536, **536**
oral report preparation, 18, 196
orders, 334, **335**
organelles, 117, **117,** 126. *See also*
    names of specific organelles
organisms
    cell theory and, 115, **115**
    extinct, 336, **336**
    genetically modified, 179, **179,**
      226
    geographic connections and,
      274, **274,** 307–308, 315, **315**
    levels of organization in,
      130–132, **130, 131, 132**
    multicellular, 128–129, **128,** 425
    scientific names for, 334–335,
      334–335
    unicellular, 128, 133, **133**
organization levels, 128–133, **132.**
    See also body organization
    cell level, 130, **130**
    impact of failure in one, 425,
      468
    lab on, 129
    multicellular organisms,
      128–129, **128**
    organism level, 132
    organ level, 131
    organ systems, 132, **132,** 425,
      425

Index

Index

Index

seeds
  dissecting, 369
  dormant, 402
  growing, 62–63, 402, **402**
  of gymnosperms, 371, **371**
  lab on, 369
  Mendel's experiments on, 176,
    176
  production of, 501, **501**
  seed coats, 369, **369**
  spread of, **368**, 369
  structure of, 369, **369**
segmentation, 439, **439**
segments, 439, **439**
selective breeding, 308, **308**
self-pollinating plants, 175–176,
  175
SEMs (scanning electron microscopes), 21, **21**
semen, 556, **556**
sensations, 534
sense organs, 441, **441**
sensory receptors
  central nervous system and,
    530–532, **530, 531, 532**
  feedback mechanisms, 535
  hearing, 538–539, **538**
  nerves and, 528, **528**
  peripheral nervous system and,
    526–528, **527, 528**
  reflexes and, 535, **535**
  sense organs, 441, **441**
  sensory nerves, 447
  sensory neurons, 528
  sight, 536–537, **536, 537**
  smell, 540, **540**
  somatic nervous system and,
    529, **529**
  spinal cord injuries and, 532
  taste, 540
  touch, 534, **534**
sepals, 379, **380**
separation, in speciation process,
  314, **314, 315**
severe acute respiratory syndrome
  (SARS), 511
sex cells, 189–190, **190–191,**
  192–193, **192**
sexual activity, fertilization and
  pregnancy from, 557
sexually transmitted diseases
  (STDs), 560–561, **560**
sexual reproduction. *See also*
  human reproduction
  of angiosperms, 372, **372**
  of animals, 427, **427**
  female reproductive system,
    557–558, **557**
  ferns, 366, **366**
  of flowering plants, 62–63,
    400–402, **400, 401, 402**

flowers and, 372–373, **372,**
  379–380, **380,** 382–383
of gymnosperms, 371, **371**
lab on, 62–63
male reproductive system,
  556–557, **556**
meiosis, 188–193, **189, 190–
  191, 192**
of mosses, 364, **364**
mutations and, 217
natural selection and, **310**
of vertebrates, 448–449, **448,
  449**
shared derived characteristics, 333,
  336
sharks, **425,** 435
shivering, 53
shock, 506
short-day plants, 408
shoulders, 474, **474**
shrimp, 433
shutters, in digital cameras, 95, **95**
Siccar Point (Scotland), 235
sickle cell anemia, 184
sight
  bionic eyes, 106
  colors of objects in, 86–87, **87**
  compound eyes, 94
  dissecting cow's eyes, 542–543
  eye color, 185, **185**
  glasses for correction of, 537,
    537
  in invertebrates, 441, **441**
  lenses of eyes, 93–94, **93, 94,**
    536–537, **537**
  light colors and, 79, **79,** 86–87,
    87
  night, 536
  optical illusions, 91–92, **91**
  sense of, 536–537, **536, 537**
  transmission, reflection, and
    absorption of light in, 85, **85**
SI measurement, 616
simple carbohydrates, 59
simple devices
  joint types and, 474, **474**
  levers in the body, 478–479,
    478, 482–483
simple lenses
  concave, **92,** 94, **94**
  convex, **92,** 93, **93,** 98–99
  in magnifying glasses, 93, **93,**
    98–99
  refraction of light in, 92, **92**
Sinosauropteryx, 292, **292**
SI units, 22–25, **22, 23, 24, 25**
skeletal muscle, 476, **476**
skeletal system, 472–475
  bones in, 472–473, **472, 473**
  injuries and diseases in, 475,
    475
  joints, 474, **474**

skin
  function of, 445, **445**
  sense of touch and, 534, **534**
  structure of, 534, **534**
skin cancer, 157, **157**
skin cells, **212**
SLAS-1, 70
sliding joints, 474, **474**
slime molds, 133, **133, 340**
slugs, 433
small intestines, 447
smell, sense of, 540, **540**
smoking, cardiovascular problems
  and, 500
smooth ER (endoplasmic
  reticulum), 123, **123**
smooth muscle, 476, **476**
snails, 186, 433, 440, **440**
snakes, 435, **435**
soil erosion, plants and, 365, 367
solar system, age of, 249, **249**
somatic nervous system, 529
sonographer, 577, **577**
sound, 447, 538–539, **538**
specialized functions, 129, 130, **130**
speciation, 314–315, **314, 315**
species
  changes in the fossil record,
    278, **278,** 300, **300**
  in classification system, 334, **335**
  definition of, 298, 314
  distribution by geographic
    connection, 272, **272,**
    307–308, **307,** 315, **315**
  drawing connections between,
    301, **301**
  formation of new, 314–315,
    314, 315
  observed changes in, 299
spectroscopes, 75
sperm
  in animals, 427
  chromosomes in, 189–190, 192,
    192
  delivery of, 557
  in humans, 556–557
  in plants, 361, **364,** 368, 371,
    400
SPF (sun protection factor), 80
spider map instructions (Graphic
  Organizer), 48, 260, 585, **585**
spiders, 433
spina bifida, 576, **576**
spinal cord, 532, **532**
spinal cord injuries, 532
spines, 378
sponges
  asymmetry in, 438
  characteristics of, 431
  classification of, 343, **343**
  support structures in, 439, **439**

spongy bone, 473, **473**
spores
    of gymnosperms, 371, **371**
    in mosses, **364**
    in the sporophyte stage, 361
    spread by wind, 369
sporophytes
    of ferns, **366**
    of gymnosperms, 371, **371**
    of mosses, **364**
    in plant life cycle, 361
    structure of, 369, **369**
sprains, 475
spring scales, 24, **24**
square meters, 23
squids, 433, **433**
squirrels, speciation in, 314, **314**
stamens, 380, **380**
starch, from photosynthesis, 397
STDs (sexually transmitted
        diseases), 560–561, **560**
stem cells, 142, **142,** 576, **576**
stems, **358–359,** 376–377, **376,
        377**
steroids, anabolic, 481
stigma, 380, **380,** 400, **400**
stimulus (plural, *stimuli*), 53, 404
stingrays, 435
stirrup, in the ear, 538, **538**
stomach, 131, 468, **468**
    lab on, 470
stomata (singular, *stoma*), 130,
        130, 378, **378,** 398, **398**
strains, muscle or tendon, 481
strawberry poison arrow frog, 298,
        298
strokes, 500
structural framework for movement,
        450–451, 477, **477**
structure, function and, 130, **130,**
        369, 374–380, 427, 448,
        466–467, 473–474
    labs on, 361, 369, 382–383,
        395, 441, 447, 450–451, 465,
        470, 474
sucrose, 397
sugar, from photosynthesis,
        396–397, **397**
sugar pills, 550
sunburns, 80, **80**
sundews, 378
sunlight
    plant growth toward, 406, **406**
    visible light from, 79
sunlight energy
    chemical energy from, 78, **78,**
        396, **396**
    chlorophyll and, 124, **124,** 360,
        360, 396
    leaves and, 377–378, **378**
    making sugar from, 397, **397**

in photosynthesis, 78, **78,** 148,
        396, **396**
    relationship between photosyn-
        thesis and respiration and,
        150, 151
sun protection factor (SPF), 80
sunscreens, 80
superposition, principle of, 240,
        240
surface area–to-volume ratio, 116
survival, 217, **310**
sweat glands, **534,** 535
symbols, safety, 33, **33**
symmetry in body plans
    description of, 426, **426**
    in invertebrates, 438, **438**
    in vertebrates, 444, **444**
sympathetic nervous system, 529,
        529
syphilis, **560**
systematics, 333
systemic circulation, 499, **499**
systolic pressure, 504

T

table fold instructions (FoldNote),
        582, **582**
tables of data, **38–39,** 39
tadpoles, 435
tapeworms, 432
taproot systems, 375
taste, sense of, 540
taste buds, **524–525,** 540
taste cells, 540
taxonomy, 333
technology in science, 20–21, **20,
        21**
tectonic plates, 270–271, **270, 271**
telescopes, 96, **96**
telophase, 153, **155, 158**
TEMs (transmission electron
        microscopes), 21, **21**
temperature
    body, 53, 429, 504, 535
    definition of, 25
    measuring, **22,** 25, **25**
    scales, 624
tendinitis, 481
tendons, 477, 481
tentacles, 432, **432,** 433, **433**
testes (singular, *testis*), 556, **556,**
        560
testing hypotheses, 16–17, **16, 17,**
        320
testosterone, 556
theories, scientific, 29–31
theory of evolution, 296–327
    canine, 327, **327**
    comparing organisms in, 304,
        304

Darwin's thinking on, 308–309,
        308, 309
    Darwin's voyage on the HMS
        Beagle, 306–307, **306, 307**
    definition of, 299
    drawing connections between
        species, 301, **301**
    environmental factors in, 307,
        307, 313
    evolutionary relationships,
        336–337, **336**
    extinction and, 316–317, **316,
        317,** 336
    fossil record and, 300, **300**
    humans in the Cenozoic Era,
        282, **282**
    lab on, 318–319
    natural selection in, 310–311,
        310
    new species formation,
        314–315, **314, 315**
    population changes and,
        312–313, **312**
    of whales, 301–303, **301,
        302–303**
Theory of the Earth (Hutton),
        234–235, **234**
thermometers, 25, **25**
thermoreceptors, 534, **534**
thighs, 474
third-class levers, **478,** 479
three-panel flip chart instructions
        (FoldNote), 581, **581**
thymine, 208–209, **208,** 210
tilting, 241, **241**
time scale, geologic, 276–277, **276,
        277**
tissues, 131, **131, 466–467,** 467
toads, 435
tongue, **524–525,** 540
tools
    for collecting data, 64, 544
    computers in science, 9, 20, 40
    for displaying data, 412
    for measurement, 22–25, **22, 23,
        24, 25**
    for performing tests on data,
        544
touch, sense of, 534, **534**
trace fossils, 266, **266**
tracheae, 440, **508,** 509, **509**
traits. *See also* heredity
    in blending inheritance, 174
    definition of, 176, 308
    DNA instructions for, 54
    dominant, 177–178, **178,** 192,
        192

dominant vs. recessive, 177–178, **178**
environmental influences on, 185, **185**
labs on, 173, 177, 181, 182, 194–195
meiosis and, 192–193, **192**
modeling, 173, 297, 559
multiple genes acting together, 185, **185**
mutations and, 217
ratios of, 178, **178**
recessive, 177–178, **178**, 192, **192**
selective breeding for, 308, **308**
single genes influencing multiple, 184, **184**
of survivors, 309
variations within populations, 312, **312**
transfer RNA (tRNA), 215, **215**
transform boundaries, 271, **271**
transfusions, 506, **506**
translucent objects, 86–87, **86, 87**
transmission electron microscopes (TEMs), 21, **21**
transmitted light, 85–86, **85, 86**
transparent objects, 86–87, **86, 87**
transpiration, 398, **398**
transport tissue, 131
tree, oldest, 390, **390**
tree of life, 301
trees
conifers, 281, **281**, 370–371, **370**
deciduous, 408, **408**
eucalyptus, 416, **416**
evergreen, 409
oldest, 390, **390**
trunks of, 376–377, **376, 377**
triceps muscle, 477, **477**
tri-fold instructions (FoldNote), 582, **582**
trilobites, 268, **268, 300**
triplets, 559
tropisms, 406–407, **406, 407**
Tropites, 269, **269**
true-breeding plants, 175–176, **175**
trunks, 376–377, **376, 377**
tubers, 402, **403**
tumors, treatment for, 166. *See also* cancer
tunicates, 434
turtles, 435, **446**
twins, 559, **559**
two-panel flip chart instructions (FoldNote), 582, **582**
tympanic membrane, 538–539, **538**
Tyrannosaurus rex, 335, **335**

U

ultrasound procedures, 577
ultraviolet light (UV light)
bad effects of, 80, **80**
bees and, 76, **76**
frog deformities and, 16–18, **16, 17, 18**
good effects of, 81, **81**
mutations from, 216
umbilical cord, 563, **563**
umbilicus, 563, **563**
unconformities, 242–243, **242, 243**
unicellular organisms, 128, 133, **133**
uniformitarianism, 234–236
units, SI, 22–25, **22, 23, 24, 25**
universal gravitation, law of, 606
University of California, San Francisco, 576
uracil, 214, **214**
uranium, 248, 250, 258, **258**, 259
urea, 447
urethra, 556, **556**
uterus
compared with a bird's egg, 568–569
contractions during birth, **564**
implantation in, 557, **557**
location of, 562, **562**
modeling a fetus in, **564**
UV light (ultraviolet light)
bad effects of, 80, **80**
bees and, 76, **76**
good effects of, 81, **81**
mutations from, 216

V

vacuoles, **120,** 126, **126**
vagina, 557, **557**
valves, heart, 495, 497, **497**
variable, definition of, 16
vascular plants, 362, **362**
vascular tissues
definition of, 362
in leaves, 378, **378**
in monocots and dicots, **372**
in roots, 374, **375**
in seedless plants, 365
in stems, 376–377, **376, 377**
vas deferens, 556, **556**
veins, 446, 498–499, **498, 499**
venn diagram instructions (Graphic Organizer), 356, 492, 587, **587**

ventral side, 444
ventricles, 497, **497**
Venus' flytraps, **53, 394–395**
vertebrae, 434, 445, 532, **532**
vertebrates, 434–436
amphibians, 435, **435,** 445
birds, 436, **436,** 445, **445**
body coverings, 445, **445**
body symmetry in, 444, **444**
characteristics of, 434
digestive systems in, 132, 447
endoskeletons in, 445, **445,** 450–451
excretory systems in, 447
fishes, 435, **435,** 445–448, **446, 447**
mammal characteristics, 436, **436**
nervous systems in, 447, **447**
parental care in, 449, **449**
reptiles, 435, **435,** 448, **448**
respiratory systems in, 446, **446**
vesicles, 125, **125**
vessels, blood, 498, **498**
vestibular canals, **538,** 539
Virchow, Rudolf, 115
virtual images, 93–94, **93, 94.** *See also* light
visible light, 77–79, **77, 78, 79.** *See also* light
visible spectrum, 79, **79**
vision
bionic eyes, 106
colors of objects in, 86–87, **87**
compound eyes, 94
dissecting cow's eyes, 542–543
emitted light in, 536, **536**
eye color, 185, **185**
glasses for correction of, 537, **537**
in invertebrates, 441, **441**
lenses of eyes, 93–94, **93, 94,** 536–537, **537**
light colors and, 79, **79,** 86–87, **87**
night, 536
optical illusions, 91–92, **91**
sense of sight, 536, **536**
transmission, reflection, and absorption of light in, 85, **85**
vitamin K, 339
vocal cords, 509
volcanic eruptions, catastrophic effects of, 236
volume, units of, **22,** 23
voluntary actions, 530
voluntary muscle actions, 476

Index

Acknowledgments

continued from p. ii

Advisors

Kristin L. Baker
Science Teacher
Starr King Middle School
Carmichael, California

Laura L. Bauer
Department Chair
Toby Johnson Middle School
Elk Grove, California

Jack Bettencourt
Science Department Chair
Joseph Kerr Middle School
Elk Grove, California

Rebecca Buschang
Science Partner
University of California, Los Angeles;
    Los Angeles Unified School District
Los Angeles, California

Eddyce Pope Moore
Science Teacher
Daniel Webster Middle School
Los Angeles, California

Kim O'Donnell
Science Teacher
Earle E. Williams Middle School
Tracy, California

Theresa Pearse
Science Teacher
Fremont Middle School
Stockton, California

Manuel Sanchez
Science Department Chair
Greer Middle School
Galt, California

Chuck Schindler
*Secondary Math and
    Science Coordinator*
San Bernardino City Unified
    School District
San Bernardino, California

William W. Tarr Jr., Ed.D.
Coordinator, Secondary Periodic Assessments
Los Angeles Unified School District
Los Angeles, California

Hong Tran
Science Teacher
Westlake Middle School
Oakland, California

Academic Reviewers

Jennifer Armstrong, Ph.D.
Assistant Professor of Biology
Joint Science Department
The Claremont Colleges
Claremont, California

Lisa M. Baird, Ph.D.
Professor of Biology
Department of Biology
University of San Diego
San Diego, California

Leonard Brand, Ph.D.
Professor of Biology and Paleontology
Department of Earth and Biological Sciences
Loma Linda University
Loma Linda, California

Darleen A. DeMason, Ph.D.
Professor of Botany
Department of Botany and Plant Sciences
University of California, Riverside
Riverside, California

Douglas J. Eernisse, Ph.D.
Professor
Department of Biological Sciences
California State University, Fullerton
Fullerton, California

Daniel C. Garza, M.D.
Attending Physician
Stanford University
School of Medicine
Stanford, California

Rayudu Gopalakrishna, Ph.D.
Associate Professor
Department of Cell & Neurobiology
University of Southern California
Los Angeles, California

L. Lee Grismer, Ph.D.
Professor
Department of Biology
La Sierra University
Riverside, California

H. Craig Heller, M.D.
*Professor of Biological Sciences
    and Human Biology*
Stanford University
Palo Alto, California

Jeffrey Johnson, Ph.D.
Postdoctoral Scholar
Center for Neuroscience
University of California, Davis
Davis, California

Lee B. Kats, Ph.D.
Professor of Biology
Natural Science Division
Pepperdine University
Malibu, California

Elena Levine Keeling, Ph.D.
Associate Professor
Biological Sciences Department
California Polytechnic State University
San Luis Obispo, California

Susan L. Keen, Ph.D.
Lecturer
Section of Evolution and Ecology
University of California, Davis
Davis, California

Harold Koopowitz, Ph.D.
Professor Emeritus of Biology
Department of Ecology and
    Evolutionary Biology
University of California, Irvine
Irvine, California

L. Jeanne Perry, Ph.D.
Director
Protein Expression Technology Center
    Institute for Genomics and Proteomics
University of California, Los Angeles
Los Angeles, California

Susannah M. Porter, Ph.D.
Assistant Professor
Department of Earth Science
University of California, Santa Barbara
Santa Barbara, California

Martin G. Ramirez, Ph.D.
Associate Professor of Biology
Department of Biology
Loyola Marymount University
Los Angeles, California

John J. Stachowicz, Ph.D.
Associate Professor of Evolution and Ecology
Section of Evolution and Ecology
University of California, Davis
Davis, California

Elizabeth Wenk, Ph.D.
Visiting Scholar
University Herbarium
University of California, Berkeley
Berkeley, California

Lisa D. White, Ph.D.
Professor of Geology
Department of Geosciences
San Francisco State University
San Francisco, California

Adam D. Woods, Ph.D.
Assistant Professor of Geology
Department of Geological Sciences
California State University, Fullerton
Fullerton, California

Teacher Reviewers

Karen Benitez
Science Teacher
George V. Leyva Intermediate School
San Jose, California

Joel S. Brener
Science Teacher
Daniel Webster Middle School
Los Angeles, California

Dana Carrigan
Vice Principal
Cordova High School
Rancho Cordova, California

Laskey Chatham
Science Teacher
Daniel Webster Middle School
Los Angeles, California

Ann Marie Cica
Science Teacher
Bret Harte Middle School
San Jose, California

Michelle B. Emelle
Science Teacher
Audubon Middle School
Los Angeles, California

Robin Joyce Franklin
Science Teacher
Samuel Gompers Continuation High School
Richmond, California

Catherine D. Haynes
Science Teacher
El Segundo Middle School
El Segundo, California

Treena Joi
Science Teacher
Corte Madera Elementary School
Portola Valley, California

Sushma Kashyap, MSc
Science Teacher
Alvarado Intermediate School
Rowland Heights, California

Carol Lindstrom
Science Teacher and Curriculum Specialist
Leonard Herman Intermediate School
San Jose, California

Peggy Lubchenco, MSc
Department Chair and Teacher
La Colina Junior High School
Santa Barbara, California

Heather O'Donnell
Science Teacher
Roosevelt Middle School
San Diego, California

Anne Stephens, MA
Science Teacher
Harry M. Marsh Junior High School
Co-Director, Hands-on Science Lab
College of Natural Sciences
California State University, Chico
Chico, California

Gayle Van Fossen
Science Teacher
George V. Leyva Intermediate School
San Jose, California

Lab Development

Diana Scheidle Bartos
Research Associate
Colorado School of Mines
Golden, Colorado

Carl Benson
Science Teacher
Plains High School
Plains, Montana

Charlotte Blassingame
Technology Coordinator
White Station Middle School
Memphis, Tennessee

Marsha Carver
Department Chair and Science Teacher
McLean County High School
Calhoun, Kentucky

Kenneth E. Creese
Science Teacher
White Mountain Junior High School
Rock Springs, Wyoming

Linda A. Culp
Department Chair and Science Teacher
Thorndale High School
Thorndale, Texas

James Deaver
Department Chair and Science Teacher
West Point High School
West Point, Nebraska

Michael A. DiSpezio
Professional Development Specialist
JASON Project
Cape Cod, Massachusetts

Frank McKinney, Ph.D.
Professor of Geology
Appalachian State University
Boone, North Carolina

Alyson M. Mike
Department Chair
East Valley Middle School
East Helena, Montana

C. Ford Morishita
Biology Teacher
Clackamas High School
Milwaukee, Oregon

Patricia D. Morrell, Ph.D.
Associate Professor
School of Education
University of Portland
Portland, Oregon

Hilary C. Olson, Ph.D.
Research Associate
Institute for Geophysics
The University of Texas at Austin
Austin, Texas

James B. Pulley
Science Editor and Former Science Teacher
North Kansas City, Missouri

Denice Lee Sandefur
Science Chairperson
Nucla High School
Nucla, Colorado

Patti Soderberg
Science Writer
The BioQUEST Curriculum Consortium
Biology Department
Beloit College
Beloit, Wisconsin

Phillip Vavala
Department Chair and Science Teacher
Salesianum School
Wilmington, Delaware

Albert C. Wartski, M.A.T.
Biology Teacher
Chapel Hill High School
Chapel Hill, North Carolina

Lynn Marie Wartski
Science Writer and Science Teacher
Hillsborough, North Carolina

Ivora D. Washington
Department Chair and Science Teacher
Hyattsville Middle School
Washington, D.C.

Lab Testing

Karen Benitez
Science Teacher
George V. Leyva Intermediate School
San Jose, California

Christine Erskine
Science Teacher
Brier Elementary School
Fremont, California

Rhonda DuPar
Science Teacher
La Colina Junior High School
Santa Barbara, California

Catherine D. Haynes
Science Teacher
El Segundo Middle School
El Segundo, California

Sushma Kashyap, MSc
Science Teacher
Alvarado Intermediate School
Rowland Heights, California

Carol Lindstrom
Science Teacher and Curriculum Specialist
Leonard Herman Intermediate School
San Jose, California

Peggy Lubchenco, MSc
Department Chair and Teacher
La Colina Junior High School
Santa Barbara, California

Kelly Sullivan
Science Teacher
Harry M. Marsh Junior High School
Chico, California

Gayle Van Fossen
Science Teacher
George V. Leyva Intermediate School
San Jose, California

Feature Development

Hatim Belyamani
John A. Benner
David Bradford
Jennifer Childers
Mickey Coakley
Susan Feldkamp
Jane Gardner
Erik Hahn
Christopher Hess
Abby Jones
Deena Kalai
Charlotte W. Luongo, MSc
Michael May
Persis Mehta, Ph.D.
Eileen Nehme, MPH
Catherine Podeszwa
Dennis Rathnaw
Daniel B. Sharp
John M. Stokes
April Smith West
Molly F. Wetterschneider

Staff Credits

The people who contributed to **Holt California Life Science** are listed below. They represent editorial, design, production, emedia, and permissions.

Chris Allison, Wesley M. Bain, Juan Baquera, Angela Beckmann, Ed Blake, Marc Burgamy, Rebecca Calhoun, Kimberly Cammerata, Soojinn Choi, Julie Dervin, Michelle Dike, Lydia Doty, Jen Driscoll, Diana Goetting, Angela Hemmeter, Tim Hovde, Wilonda leans, Elizabeth Ihry, Jevara Jackson, Simon Key, Jane A. Kirschman, Cathy Kuhles, Denise Mahoney, Michael Mazza, Kristen McCardel, Richard Metzger, Christina Murray, Micah Newman, Janice Noske, Dustin Ognowski, Joeleen Ornt, Laura Prescott, Bill Rader, Jim Ratcliffe, Peter Reid, Michael Rinella, Kelly Rizk, Jeff Robinson, Audrey Rozsypal, Beth Sample, Kay Selke, Chris Smith, Dawn Marie Spinozza, Sherry Sprague, Jeff Streber, Roshan Strong, Jeannie Taylor, Bob Tucek, Tam Voynick, Clay Walton, Kira J. Watkins, Ken Whiteside, Holly Whittaker, David Wisnieski, Monica Yudron

Credits

PHOTOGRAPHY

Front Cover Susumu Nishinaga/Photo Researchers, Inc.

Table of Contents iv, Peter Van Steen/HRW Photo; v (t), Visuals Unlimited/Stanley Flegler; v (b), Ted Kinsman/Photo Researchers, Inc.; vi (tl), Photodisc, Inc.; vi (b), Ed Reschke/Peter Arnold, Inc.; vii (bl), Ed Reschke/Peter Arnold, Inc.; vii (bc & br), Biology Media/Photo Researchers, Inc.; vii (t), Nancy Kedersha/Photo Researchers, Inc.; viii (b), David M. Phillips/Visuals Unlimited; viii (tl, tc & cl), Sam Dudgeon/HRW Photo; ix (tl), Sam Dudgeon/HRW Photo; ix (b),Edmond Van Hoorick/SuperStock; x (cl), James Beveridge/Visuals Unlimited; x (bl), © Gail Shumway/Getty Images/FPG International; x (t), Howard Grey/Getty Images/Stone; xi (t), SuperStock; xi (b), James L. Amos/CORBIS; xii (br), Ed Reschke/Peter Arnold, Inc.; xii (bl), Runk/Rannels/Grant Heilman Photography; xiii (tl), Courtesy of Valent BioSciences Corporation; xiii (bl), Norbert Wu; xiv (b), Bob Torrez/Getty Images/Stone; xv (b), Sam Dudgeon/HRW Photo; xvi (tl), Photo Lennart Nilsson/Albert Bonniers Forlag AB, A Child Is Born, Dell Publishing Company; xvi (cr), Digital Image copyright © 2005 PhotoDisc

Safety First! xxx, Sam Dudgeon/HRW; xxxi(t), John Langford/HRW; xxxi(bc), xxxii(br) & xxxii(tl), Sam Dudgeon/HRW xxxii(bl), Stephanie Morris/HRW; xxxiii(tl), Sam Dudgeon/HRW xxxiii(tr), Jana Birchum/HRW; xxxiii(b), Sam Dudgeon/HRW

Unit One 2 (tl), O.S.F./Animals Animals; 2 (cl), Hulton Archive/Getty Images; 2 (bl), Digital Image copyright © 2005 PhotoDisc; 2-3 (br & bl), Peter Veit/DRK Photo; 3 (cl), University of Pennsylvania/Hulton Getty; 3 (t), National Portrait Gallery, Smithsonian Institution/Art Resources; 3 (br), National Geographic Image Collection/O. Louis Mazzatenta; 3 (cr), Digital Image copyright © 2005 PhotoDisc

Chapter One 6-7 Craig Line/AP/Wide World Photos; 7 (br), John Morrison/Morrison Photography; 8 & 9 (tr), Peter Van Steen/HRW Photo; 9 (inset), International Colored Gemstone Association (ICA); 9 (b), Victoria Smith/HRW Photo; 10 (l), Hank Morgan/Photo Researchers, Inc.; 10 (b), Matt Meadows/Peter Arnold, Inc.; 11 (t), Annie Griffiths Belt/CORBIS; 11 (b), Wayne Lynch/DRK Photo; 13& 14, Sam Dudgeon/HRW Photo; 16, John Mitchell/Photo Researchers, Inc.; 18, Sam Dudgeon/HRW Photo; 20, PhotoDisc/Getty Images; 21 (tr), Pascal Goetgheluck/Photo Researchers, Inc.; 21(tl), CENCO; 21 (cl), Robert Brons/Biological Photo Service; 21 (tc), Sinclair Stammers/Science Photo Library/Photo Researchers, Inc.; 21 (c), Microworks/Phototake; 21 (cr), Visuals Unlimited/Karl Aufderheide; 22 (tl, bc & b), Victoria Smith/HRW Photo; 22 (c), Sam Dudgeon/HRW Photo; 23, Peter Van Steen/HRW Photo; 24, Victoria Smith/HRW Photo; 25 (cr), Dr. Jeremy Burgess/Science Photo Library/Photo Reseachers, Inc.; 26, Royalty-Free/CORBIS; 28 (b), John Morrison/Morrison Photography; 29, Art by Christopher Sloan/Photograph by Mark Thiessen/both National Geographic Image Collection/ © National Geographic Image Collection; 32, 33, 34 & 35, Sam Dudgeon/HRW; 36, Victoria Smith/HRW; 38, John Morrison/Morrison Photography; 41 (t), Peter Van Steen/HRW; 41 (c), Victoria Smith/HRW; 41 (bc), Art by Christopher Sloan/Photograph by Mark Thiessen/both National Geographic Image Collection/ © National Geographic Image Collection; 46, Craig Fugii/©1988 The Seattle Times; 47 (r & l), NASA

Chapter Two 50-51, Rick Friedman/Blackstar Publishing/Picture Quest; 51 (br), John Morrison/Morrison Photography; 52 (br), Visuals Unlimited/Science Visuals Unlimited; 52 (bl), William H.Mullins/Photo Researchers, Inc.; 53, David M. Dennis/Tom Stack and Associates; 54 (l), Visuals Unlimited/Stanley Flegler; 54 (tr), James M. McCann/Photo Researchers, Inc.; 56 (r), Wolfgang Bayer; 57 (t), Visuals Unlimited/Rob Simpson; 57 (b), Alex Kerstitch/Visuals Unlimited, Inc.; 58 (bl), William J. Hebert/Stone; 58 (bc), SuperStock; 58 (br), Kevin Schafer/Peter Arnold, Inc.; 59 (b), Peter Dean/Grant Heilman Photography; 59 (t), John Morrison/Morrison Photography; 63 (b), Victoria Smith/HRW; 63 (t), The Garden Picture Library/Alamy; 67, Victoria Smith/HRW; 70 (l), Sean O'Neill/Spectrum Photofile; 71 (t), Courtesy Janis Davis-Street/NASA; 71 (b), NASA

Chapter Three 74-5, Richard Herrmann/OSF/Animals Animals; 75 (br), John Morrison/Morrison Photography; 76 (c), Michael Fogden and Patricia Fogden/Corbis; 76 (bl & br), Leonard Lessin/Photo Researchers, Inc.; 78, Ted Kinsman/Photo Researchers, Inc.; 79, Cameron Davidson; 80 (t), John Morrison/Morrison Photography; 80 (b), SINCLAIR STAMMERS/SPL/Photo Researchers, Inc.; 81, Patrik Giardino/CORBIS; 83 (t), John Morrison/Morrison Photography; 84, Darwin Dale/Photo Researchers, Inc.; 85 (b), Stephanie Morris/HRW; 85 (t), Sovfoto/Eastfoto; 86, John Langford/HRW; 87 (br), ART on FILE/CORBIS; 87 (tl), Image copyright ©1998 PhotoDisc, Inc.; 87 (tr), Renee Lynn/Davis/Lynn Images; 88 (b), Index Stock Photography, Inc.; 89 (t), Rob Matheson/The Stock Market; 89 (cr), Peter Van Steen/HRW; 90, Richard Megna/Fundamental Photographs; 92 (b & c), Fundamental Photographs, New York; 92 (t), John Morrison/Morrison Photography; 93 (cl), Russell Holley; 93 (tl), Peter Van Steen/HRW; 94 (tl), Juniors Bildarchiv/Alamy; 94 (bc), Jerome Wexler/Photo Researchers, Inc.; 99 (br), Sam Dudgeon/HRW; 100 (b), Robert Brons/Biological Photo Service; 101 (t), SINCLAIRSTAMMERS/SPL/Photo Researchers, Inc.; 102 (cr), Ken Kay/Fundamental Photographs; 103 (t), Charles D. Winters/Photo Researchers, Inc.; 103 (c), Mark E. Gibson; 103 (b), Richard Megna/Fundamental Photographs; 106 (r), M. Spencer Green/AP/Wide World Photos; 106 (tl), Dr. E. R. Degginger; 107 (b), E. Widder/HBOI/Visuals Unlimited;107 (t), Tom Smoyer/HBO!

Unit Two 108 (c), The National Archives/Corbis; 108 (b), Cold Spring Harbor Laboratory; 108 (t), Burstein Collection/CORBIS; 109 (t & bcl), Ed Reschke/Peter Arnold, Inc; 109 (tcr), Keith Porter/Photo Researchers, Inc.; 109 (br), Dr. Ian Wilmut/Liaison/Getty News Images; 109 (bl), Dan McCoy/Rainbow; 109 (bcr), Glen Allison/Getty Images/Stone; 109 (tcl), Bettmann/CORBIS

Chapter Four 112-113, Dennis Kunkel/Phototake; 113 (br), John Morrison/Morrison Photography; 114 (bl), Visuals Unlimited/Kevin Collins; 114 (br), Leonard Lessin/Peter Arnold, Inc.; 115 (tl), Eric Grave/Phototake; 115 (tr), Biodisc/Visuals Unlimited; 115 (tcr), Michael Abbey/Visuals Unlimited; 115 (tcl), Steve Allen/Photo Researchers, Inc.; 115 (br), CENCO; 117 (t), William Dentler/Biological Photo Service; 117 (b), Dr. Gopal Murti/Science Photo Library/Photo Researchers, Inc.; 122 (br), Don Fawcett/Visuals Unlimited; 123 (br), R. Bolender-D. Fawcett/Visuals Unlimited; 124 (cl), Don Fawcett/Visuals Unlimited; 124 (br), Newcomb & Wergin/Biological Photo Service; 125 (tr), Garry T Cole/Biological Photo Service; 126 (cl), Dr. Jeremy Burgess/Science PhotoLibrary/Science Source/Photo Researchers, Inc.; 126 (tl), DR GOPAL MURTI/SCIENCE PHOTO LIBRARY; 128 (l, bl & br), Dr. Yorgos Nikas/Science Photo Library/Photo Researchers, Inc.; 128 (br), Lennert Nilsson/Albert Bonniers Forlag AB, A CHILD IS BORN; 129, John Morrison/Morrison Photography; 130 (t), Quest/Science Photo Library/Photo Researchers, Inc.; 130 (b), Ed Reschke/Peter Arnold, Inc.; 131, Manfred Kage/Peter Arnold, Inc.; 133 (t), David M. Dennis/Tom Stack & Associates; 134 (c & cl), Runk/Schoenberger/Grant Heilman; 134 (cr), Michael Abbey/Photo Researchers, Inc.; 134 (b), Sam Dudgeon/HRW Photo; 135, Runk/Schoenberger/Grant Heilman; 136 (br), Eric Grave/Phototake; 136 (b), Steve Allen/Photo Researchers, Inc.; 136 (l), Michael Abbey/Visuals Unlimited; 142 (r), Photo Researchers, Inc.; 142 (l), Science Photo Library/Photo Researchers, Inc.; 143 (l), Digital Image copyright © 2005 Artville; 143 (r), Courtesy Caroline Schooley

Chapter Five 146-7, Grant Heilman Photography; 147 (br), John Morrison/Morrison Photography; 148 (bl), Runk/Schoenberger/Grant Heilman Photography; 149 (br), John Langford/HRW; 152, CNRI/Science Photo Library/Photo Researchers, Inc.; 153 (b), L. Willatt, East Anglian Regional Genetics Service/Science Photo Library/Photo Researchers, Inc.; 153 (t), Biophoto Associates/Photo Researchers, Inc.; 154 (b), Visuals Unlimited/R. Calentine; 154 (t) & 155 (tl), Ed Reschke/Peter Arnold, Inc.; 155 (tc & tr) Biology Media/Photo Researchers, Inc.; 155 (br), John Morrison/Morrison Photography; 157, Nancy Kedersha/Photo Researchers, Inc.; 158 (l), Authors Image/Alamy; 158, Peter Arnold, Inc./Alamy; 159, Sam Dudgeon/HRW; 161 (bc), Biology Media/Photo Researchers, Inc.; 166, SIU BioMed/Custom Medical Stock Photo; 167 (tr), Courtesy Dr. Jarrel Yakel; 167 (c), David McCarthy/SPL/Photo Researchers, Inc

Unit Three 168 (bc), Ted Thai/Time Magazine; 168 (t), David L. Brown/Tom Stack; 169 (cl), MBL/WHOI Library; 169 (cr), Ken Eward/Bio Grafx/Photo Researchers, Inc.; 169 tr), John Conrad/CORBIS; 169 (bl), Dr. Tony Brain/Science Photo Library/Photo Researchers, Inc.

Chapter Fourteen 422-3, Michele Westmorland/The Image Bank/Getty Images; 423 (br), John Morrison/Morrison Photography; 424, David B. Fleetham/Getty Images/FPG International; 426 (bl), Keren Su/Getty Images/Stone; 427 (l), Visuals Unlimited/Fred Hossler; 427 (r), CENCO; 428(bcl), Nuridsany et Perennou/Photo Researchers, Inc.; 428 (bcr), Stephen Dalton/Photo Researchers, Inc.; 428 (cl), Neil G. McDaniel/Photo Researchers, Inc.; 428 (cr), Steve Allen/PictureQuest; 428 (bl), JEF MEUL/FOTO NATURA/Minden Pictures; 428 (br), Holger Ehlers/Alamy; 428 (c), AA/Rudie Kuiter/OSF; 431 (cr), John Morrison/Morrison Photography; 432 (t), Lee Foster/Getty Images/FPG International; 432 (b), Visuals Unlimited/T. E. Adams; 433 (t), Brandon Cole/Brandon Cole Marine Photography; 433 (c), Milton Rand/Tom Stack & Associates; 433 (b), Stephen Dalton/NHPA; 434 (tl), Norbert Wu/ Peter Arnold, Inc.; 434 (bl), G.I. Bernard OSF/Animals Animals; 435 (tr), Royalty-Free/ Corbis; 435 (cr), Joe McDonald/CORBIS; 435 (b), MARTIN WENDLER/NHPA; 436 (t), Tom Vezo/Minden Pictures; 436 (bl), Norbert Wu; 436 (bc), David Austen/TSI; 436 (br), Pavel German/NHPA; 438 (b), S.J. Krasemann/PA; 439 (tr), Creatas/ PictureQuest; 439 (bl), Digital imagery® copyright 2002 PhotoDisc, Inc.; 439 (br), Visuals Unlimited/A. M. Siegelman; 439 (tl), Milton Rand/Tom Stack & Associates; 439 (bc), Daniel Gotshall/Visuals Unlimited; 441 (br), Dr. Jeremy Burgess/SPL/Photo Researchers, Inc.; 442 (t), Biophoto Associates/Science Source/Photo Researchers, Inc.; 444, Dan Suzio/Suzio Photography; 445 (tl), Visuals Unlimited/Rob & Ann Simpson; 445 (tcl), Arthur Morris/Visuals Unlimited; 445 (tcr), Frans Lanting/Minden Pictures; 445 (tr), Michio Hoshino/Minden Pictures; 447 (tr), John Morrison/Morrison Photography; 449 (t), Fred Bavendam; 451, Victoria Smith/HRW; 453 (t), Keren Su/ Getty Images/Stone; 453 (bc), Daniel Gotshall/Visuals Unlimited; 453 (tc), Norbert Wu; 454, Leroy Simon/Visuals Unlimited; 458 (l), Bill Beatty/Visuals Unlimited; 458 (r), Dave Watts/Nature Picture Library; 459 (l), Norbert Wu; 459 (r), Ed Seibel © 2000 MBARI

Unit Six 460 (t), Geoffrey Clifford/Woodfin Camp; 460 (c), J & L Weber/Peter Arnold, Inc.; 460 (b), AP/Wide World Photos; 461 (cl), Brown Brothers; 461 (cr), SuperStock; 461 (bl), Enrico Ferorelli; 461 (br), CORBIS; 461 (tl), Reuters/CORBIS

Chapter Fifteen 464-5, AFP/CORBIS; 465 (br), John Morrison/Morrison Photography; 466-7 (b), David Madison/Getty Images/Stone; 467 (tl), SPL/Photo Researchers, Inc.; 467 (tcl), David McCarthy/Photo Researchers, Inc.; 467 (tcr), David M. Phillips/Photo Researchers, Inc.; 467 (tr), SPL/Photo Researchers, Inc.; 469, Sam Dudgeon/HRW; 470 (b), John Morrison/Morrison Photography; 472, Sam Dudgeon/HRW; 474 (tc & tr), HRW Photo by Sergio Purtell/FOCA; 474(tl), SP/FOCA/ HRW Photo; 474 (bl), John Morrison/Morrison Photography; 475 (tr), Scott Camazine/Photo Researchers, Inc.; 475 (b), John Morrison/Morrison Photography; 476 (tl), Gladden WIllis, M.D./Visuals Unlimited; 476 (b), Bob Torrez/Getty Images/ Stone; 476 (bc), Dr. E.R. Degginger; 476 (br), Manfred Kage/Peter Arnold, Inc.; 478, Les Walker/NewSport/Corbis; 479, John Morrison/Morrison Photography; 480 (tr), Sam Dudgeon/HRW; 480 (tl), Chris Hamilton; 481, Franck Seguin/CORBIS; 483, Sam Dudgeon/HRW; 486, Sam Dudgeon/HRW Photo; 487, Michael Cole/Corbis; 490 (tr), Reuters/David Gray/NewsCom; 490 (l), blickwinkel/Alamy; 491 (tr), Photo courtesy of Dr. Zahra Beheshti; 491 (bl), Creatas/PictureQuest

Chapter Sixteen 494-5, Nih/Science Source/Photo Researchers, Inc.; 495 (br), John Morrison/Morrison Photography; 502, SUSUMU NISHINAGA/SCIENCE PHOTO LIBRARY/Photo Researchers, Inc.; 503 (br), Don Fawcett/Photo Researchers, Inc.; 504, John Morrison/Morrison Photography; 505 (tl), ISM/Phototake; 505 (tr), ISM/ Phototake; 506, Michael Prince/CORBIS; 507, Oliver Meckes/Nicole Ottawa/Photo Researchers, Inc.; 510 (bl), John Morrison/Morrison Photography; 511 (tr), Matt Meadows/Peter Arnold, Inc.; 511(cr), Matt Meadows/Peter Arnold, Inc.; 512 & 513, Sam Dudgeon/HRW; 517 (bl), Richard Levine/Alamy; 520 (tr), Paul A. Souders/ CORBIS; 520 (tl), Joseph Sohm; ChromoSohm Inc./CORBIS; 521, Courtesy of Camp Boggy Creek

Chapter Seventeen 524-5, Omikron/Photo Researchers, Inc.; 525 (br), John Morrison/Morrison Photography; 531 (cr), Sam Dudgeon/HRW; 532 (b), John Morrison/Morrison Photography; 535, Sam Dudgeon/HRW Photo; 539, John Morrison/Morrison Photography; 543, Victoria Smith/HRW; 550 (r), Mike Derer/AP/ Wide World Photos; 550 (l), Richard T. Nowitz/Phototake; 551 (r), Photo courtesy of Dr. Bertha Madras; 551 (l), SPL/Photo Researchers, Inc.

Chapter Eighteen 554-5, Photo Lennart Nilsson/Albert Bonniers Forlag AB, A Child Is Born, Dell Publishing Company; 559, Chip Henderson; 560, Stone/Getty Images; 561, Stock Image/SuperStock; 565 (cl), Petit Format/Nestle/Science Source/Photo Researchers, Inc.; 565 (c & cr), Photo Lennart Nilsson/Albert Bonniers Forlag AB, A Child Is Born, Dell Publishing Company; 565 (b), Keith/Custom Medical Stock Photo; 565 (tr), David M. Phillips/Photo Researchers, Inc.; 566, Peter Van Steen/HRW; 567 (tr), Mark Harmel/Getty Images/FPG International; 569, Digital Image copyright © 2005 PhotoDisc; 573, Dr. G. Moscoso/Photo Researchers, Inc.; 576 (tr), Michael Clancy; 576 (l), PROFESSOR MIODRAG STOJKOVIC/SCIENCE PHOTO LIBRARY; 577 (l), ZEPHYR/Science Photo Library/Photo Researchers, Inc.; 577 (r), Salem Community College

Appendix 578, Sam Dudgeon/HRW; 580, Sam Dudgeon/HRW; 605(b), John Langford/HRW; 606(l), Michelle Bridwell/Frontera Fotos; 606(r), Images © 1996 Photodisc, Inc.; 608, Steve Coleman/AP/Wide World Photos; 609, Daniel Schaefer/ HRW; 610, Sam Dudgeon/HRW; 611, AP Photo/Joe Giblin; 613, Victoria Smith/HRW; 614, Andy Christiansen/HRW; 617(t), Peter Van Steen/HRW; 617b(tc), Sam Dudgeon/ HRW; 618, CENCO; 658, Dr. Tony Brian & David Parker/Science Photo Library/Photo Researchers; 659, Alex Kerstitch/Visuals Unlimited, Inc.

TEACHERS EDITION CREDITS

143E Runk/Schoenberger/Grant Heilman; 143F Biophoto Associates/Photo Researchers; 229F (l), Sam Dudgeon/HRW Photo; 229F (r), Edmond Van Hoorick/ SuperStock; 259E BIOS/Peter Arnold, Inc.; 355F Runk/Rannels/Grant Heilman Photography; 419E Visuals Unlimited/Fred Hossler; 461E (bl), SPL/Photo Researchers, Inc.; 461E (bcl), David McCarthy/Photo Researchers, Inc.; 461E (bcr), David M. Phillips/Photo Researchers, Inc.; 461E (br), SPL/Photo Researchers, Inc.; 461F (tc), HRW Photo by Sergio Purtell/FOCA; 461F (tr), HRW Photo by Sergio Purtell/FOCA; 461F (tl), SP/FOCA/HRW Photo; 47E James M. McCann/Photo Researchers, Inc.; 491F SUSUMU NISHINAGA/SCIENCE PHOTO LIBRARY/Photo Researchers, Inc.

Answers to Concept Mapping Questions

The following pages contain sample answers to all of the concept mapping questions that appear in the Chapter Reviews. Because there is more than one way to do a concept map, your students' answers may vary.

CHAPTER The Nature of Life Science

16.

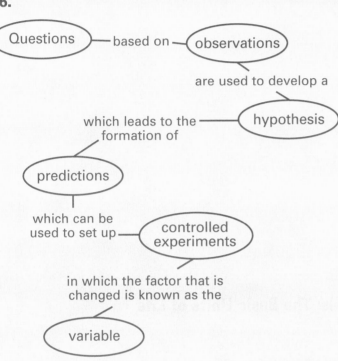

CHAPTER 2 It's Alive!! Or Is It?

18.

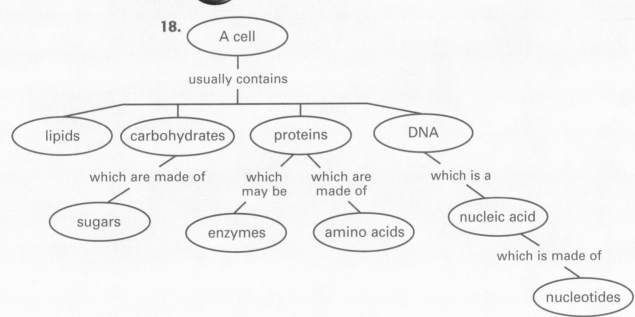

CHAPTER ③ Light and Living Things

19.

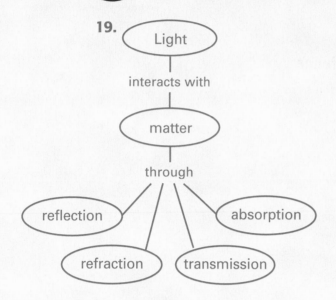

CHAPTER ④ Cells: The Basic Units of Life

16.

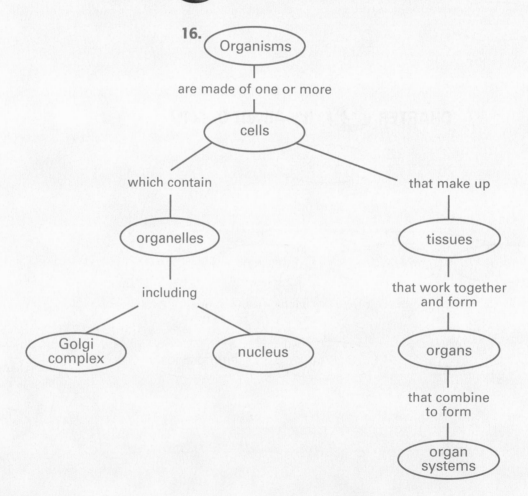

CHAPTER **5** The Cell in Action

15.

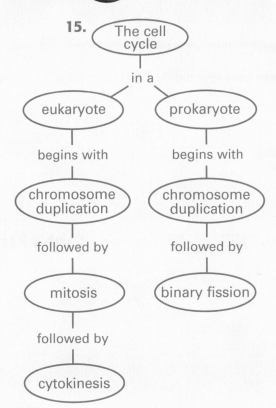

The cell cycle

in a

eukaryote — prokaryote

begins with — begins with

chromosome duplication — chromosome duplication

followed by — followed by

mitosis — binary fission

followed by

cytokinesis

CHAPTER **6** Heredity

15.

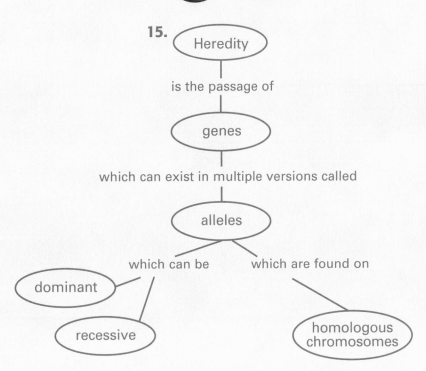

Heredity

is the passage of

genes

which can exist in multiple versions called

alleles

which can be — which are found on

dominant

recessive — homologous chromosomes

CHAPTER **7** **Genes and DNA**

13.

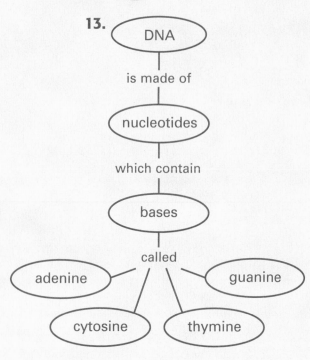

DNA

is made of

nucleotides

which contain

bases

called

adenine

guanine

cytosine

thymine

CHAPTER **8** **Studying Earth's Past**

18.

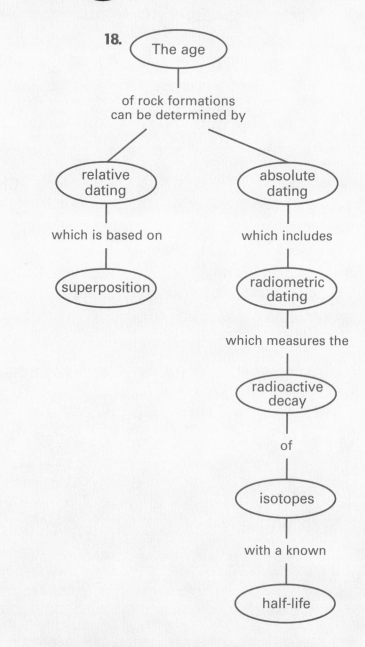

The age

of rock formations
can be determined by

relative
dating

absolute
dating

which is based on

which includes

superposition

radiometric
dating

which measures the

radioactive
decay

of

isotopes

with a known

half-life

CHAPTER ⑨ The History of Life on Earth

18.

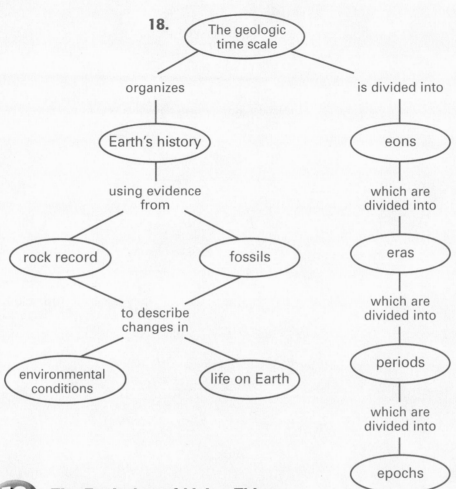

CHAPTER ⑩ The Evolution of Living Things

14.

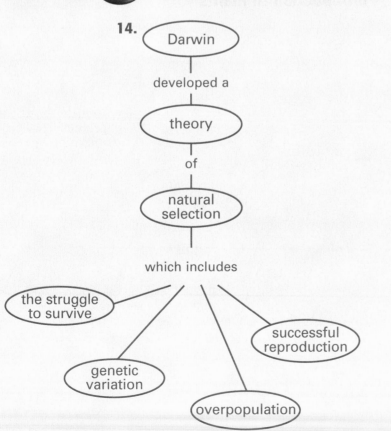

14.

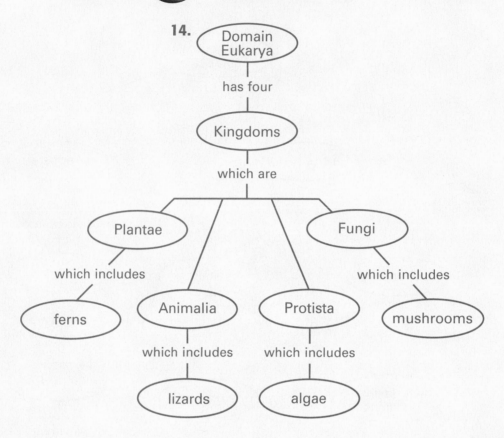

23.

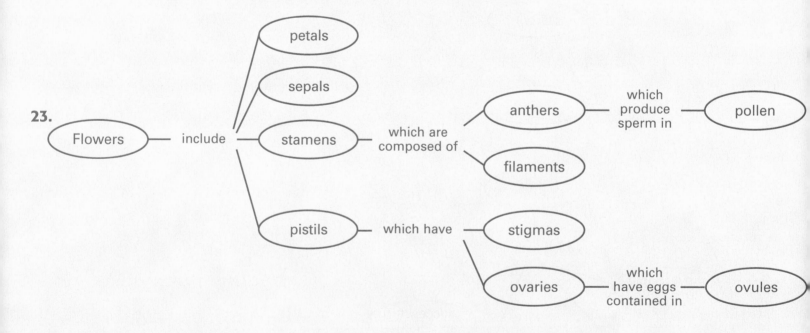

CHAPTER 13 Plant Processes

20.

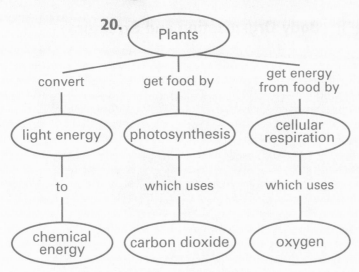

CHAPTER 14 Introduction to Animals

17.

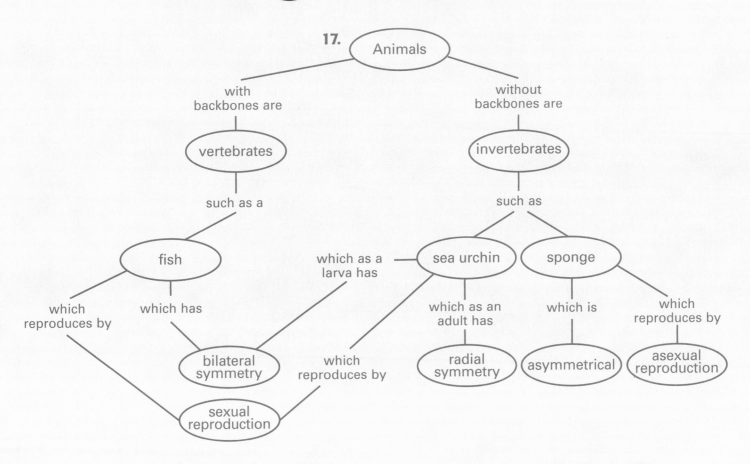

CHAPTER ⑮ Body Organization and Structure

17.

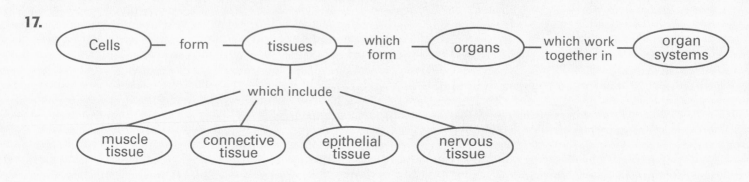

CHAPTER ⑯ Circulation and Respiration

17.

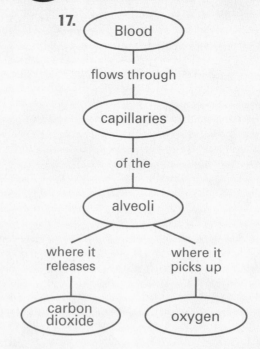

CHAPTER **17** Communication and Control

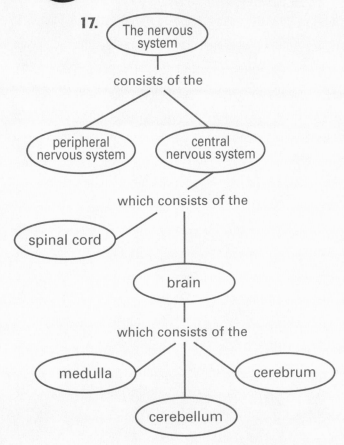

17.

The nervous system

consists of the

peripheral nervous system

central nervous system

which consists of the

spinal cord

brain

which consists of the

medulla

cerebrum

cerebellum

CHAPTER **18** Reproduction and Development

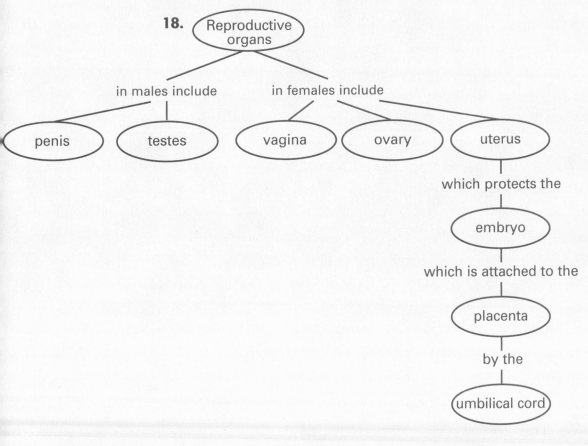

18.

Reproductive organs

in males include

in females include

penis

testes

vagina

ovary

uterus

which protects the

embryo

which is attached to the

placenta

by the

umbilical cord

Periodic Table of the Elements

Each square on the table includes an element's name, chemical symbol, atomic number, and atomic mass.

The color of the chemical symbol indicates the physical state at room temperature. Carbon is a solid.

6
C
Carbon
12.0

— Atomic number
— Chemical symbol
— Element name
— Atomic mass

The background color indicates the type of element. Carbon is a nonmetal.

Period 1

1
H
Hydrogen
1.0

Background

Metals	
Metalloids	
Nonmetals	

Chemical symbol

Solid	
Liquid	
Gas	

	Group 1	Group 2	Group 3	Group 4	Group 5	Group 6	Group 7	Group 8	Group 9
Period 2	3 **Li** Lithium 6.9	4 **Be** Beryllium 9.0							
Period 3	11 **Na** Sodium 23.0	12 **Mg** Magnesium 24.3							
Period 4	19 **K** Potassium 39.1	20 **Ca** Calcium 40.1	21 **Sc** Scandium 45.0	22 **Ti** Titanium 47.9	23 **V** Vanadium 50.9	24 **Cr** Chromium 52.0	25 **Mn** Manganese 54.9	26 **Fe** Iron 55.8	27 **Co** Cobalt 58.9
Period 5	37 **Rb** Rubidium 85.5	38 **Sr** Strontium 87.6	39 **Y** Yttrium 88.9	40 **Zr** Zirconium 91.2	41 **Nb** Niobium 92.9	42 **Mo** Molybdenum 95.9	43 **Tc** Technetium (98)	44 **Ru** Ruthenium 101.1	45 **Rh** Rhodium 102.9
Period 6	55 **Cs** Cesium 132.9	56 **Ba** Barium 137.3	57 **La** Lanthanum 138.9	72 **Hf** Hafnium 178.5	73 **Ta** Tantalum 180.9	74 **W** Tungsten 183.8	75 **Re** Rhenium 186.2	76 **Os** Osmium 190.2	77 **Ir** Iridium 192.2
Period 7	87 **Fr** Francium (223)	88 **Ra** Radium (226)	89 **Ac** Actinium (227)	104 **Rf** Rutherfordium (261)	105 **Db** Dubnium (262)	106 **Sg** Seaborgium (266)	107 **Bh** Bohrium (264)	108 **Hs** Hassium (277)	109 **Mt** Meitnerium (268)

A row of elements is called a *period*.

A column of elements is called a *group* or *family*.

Values in parentheses are the mass numbers of those radioactive elements' most stable or most common isotopes.

These elements are placed below the table to allow the table to be narrower.

Lanthanides

58 **Ce** Cerium 140.1	59 **Pr** Praseodymium 140.9	60 **Nd** Neodymium 144.2	61 **Pm** Promethium (145)	62 **Sm** Samarium 150.4

Actinides

90 **Th** Thorium 232.0	91 **Pa** Protactinium 231.0	92 **U** Uranium 238.0	93 **Np** Neptunium (237)	94 **Pu** Plutonium (244)